WebAssign.

WebAssign Student Quick Start Guide

You can use WebAssign to access your homework, quizzes, and tests — whatever your instructor chooses — at any time of day or night, from any computer with a connection to the Internet and a Web browser. Your instructor creates your assignments, schedules them, and decides how many submissions you get. Your instructor also determines if you can have an extension, if you can save your work without submitting it at the time, and how much feedback you get after you submit an assignment.

The WebAssign support staff cannot change your username or password, give extensions, change your score, give you extra submissions, or help you with the content of your assignments.

Logging In
You can log in to WebAssign using any Web browser connected to the Internet. There are two different ways to log in to WebAssign. Each requires information from your teacher. If you are unsure about how to log in, please check with your teacher or another student in your class.

Go to the login page at http://webassign.net/login.html or the web address provided by your teacher. The way you log in depends on how your instructor set up the class:

- If your teacher created a WebAssign account for you, they will provide you with a **Username**, an **Institution** code and a **Password**. Simply enter this information in the boxes provided and click the **Log In** button.

Math 1130 / College Algebra

California State University, East Bay

4th Edition

Stewart | Redlin | Watson

CENGAGE
Learning·

Australia • Brazil • Japan • Korea • Mexico • Singapore • Spain • United Kingdom • United States

Math 1130 / College Algebra: California State University, East Bay, 4th Edition

Algebra and Trigonometry, 4th Edition
James Stewart | Lothar Redlin | Saleem Watson

© 2016 Cengage Learning. All rights reserved.

For product information and technology assistance, contact us at
Cengage Learning Customer & Sales Support, 1-800-354-9706

For permission to use material from this text or product,
submit all requests online at **cengage.com/permissions**
Further permissions questions can be emailed to
permissionrequest@cengage.com

This book contains select works from existing Cengage Learning resources and was produced by Cengage Learning Custom Solutions for collegiate use. As such, those adopting and/or contributing to this work are responsible for editorial content accuracy, continuity and completeness.

Compilation © 2015 Cengage Learning

ISBN: 978-1-305-75136-1

WCN: 01-100-101

Cengage Learning
20 Channel Center Street
Boston, MA 02210
USA

Cengage Learning is a leading provider of customized learning solutions with office locations around the globe, including Singapore, the United Kingdom, Australia, Mexico, Brazil, and Japan. Locate your local office at:
www.international.cengage.com/region.

Cengage Learning products are represented in Canada by Nelson Education, Ltd.

For your lifelong learning solutions, visit **www.cengage.com/custom.**

Visit our corporate website at **www.cengage.com.**

CONTENTS

P

Prerequisites

In this chapter we begin by taking a look at the central reason for studying algebra: its usefulness in describing (or modeling) real-world situations.

In algebra we use letters to stand for numbers. This allows us to write equations and solve problems. Of course, the letters in our equations must obey the same rules that numbers do. So in this chapter we review properties of numbers and algebraic expressions. You are probably already familiar with many of these properties, but it is helpful to get a fresh look at how these properties work together to solve real-world problems.

In the *Focus on Modeling* at the end of the chapter we see how equations can help us make the best decisions in some everyday situations. This theme of using algebra to model real-world situations is further developed throughout the textbook.

P.1 MODELING THE REAL WORLD WITH ALGEBRA

■ Using Algebra Models ■ Making Algebra Models

In algebra we use letters to stand for numbers. This allows us to describe patterns that we see in the real world.

For example, if we let N stand for the number of hours you work and let W stand for your hourly wage, then the formula

$$P = NW$$

gives your pay P. The formula $P = NW$ is a description or *model* for pay. We can also call this formula an *algebra model*. We summarize the situation as follows:

Real World
You work for an hourly *wage*. You would like to know your *pay* for any *number* of hours worked.

Algebra Model
$$P = NW$$

The model $P = NW$ gives the pattern for finding the pay for *any* worker, with *any* hourly wage, working *any* number of hours. That's the power of algebra: By using letters to stand for numbers, we can write a single formula that describes many different situations.

We can now use the model $P = NW$ to answer questions such as "I make $10 an hour, and I worked 35 hours; how much do I get paid?" or "I make $8 an hour; how many hours do I need to work to get paid $1000?"

In general, a **model** is a mathematical representation (such as a formula) of a real-world situation. **Modeling** is the process of making mathematical models. Once a model has been made, it can be used to answer questions about the thing being modeled.

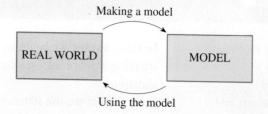

The examples we study in this section are simple, but the methods are far reaching. This will become more apparent as we explore the applications of algebra in subsequent *Focus on Modeling* sections that follow each chapter.

■ Using Algebra Models

We begin our study of modeling by using models that are given to us. In the next subsection we learn how to make our own models.

EXAMPLE 1 ■ Using a Model for Pay

Aaron makes $9 an hour at his part-time job. Use the model $P = NW$ to answer the following questions:

(a) Aaron worked 35 hours last week. How much did he get paid?

(b) Aaron wants to earn enough money to buy a calculus text that costs $126. How many hours does he need to work to earn this amount?

SOLUTION

(a) We know that $N = 35$ h and $W = \$9$. To find P, we substitute these values into the model.

$$P = NW \qquad \text{Model}$$
$$= 35 \times 9 \qquad \text{Substitute } N = 35, W = 9$$
$$= 315 \qquad \text{Calculate}$$

So Aaron was paid $315.

(b) Aaron's hourly wage is $W = \$9$, and the amount of pay he needs to buy the book is $P = \$126$. To find N, we substitute these values into the model.

$$P = NW \qquad \text{Model}$$
$$126 = 9N \qquad \text{Substitute } P = 126, W = 9$$
$$\frac{126}{9} = N \qquad \text{Divide by 9}$$
$$N = 14 \qquad \text{Calculate}$$

So Aaron must work 14 hours to buy this book.

 Now Try Exercises 3 and 7

EXAMPLE 2 ■ Using an Elevation-Temperature Model

A mountain climber uses the model

$$T = 20 - 10h$$

to estimate the temperature T (in °C) at elevation h (in kilometers, km).

(a) Make a table that gives the temperature for each 1-km change in elevation, from elevation 0 km to elevation 5 km. How does temperature change as elevation increases?

(b) If the temperature is 5°C, what is the elevation?

SOLUTION

(a) Let's use the model to find the temperature at elevation $h = 3$ km.

$$T = 20 - 10h \qquad \text{Model}$$
$$= 20 - 10(3) \qquad \text{Substitute } h = 3$$
$$= -10 \qquad \text{Calculate}$$

So at an elevation of 3 km the temperature is $-10°$C. The other entries in the following table are calculated similarly.

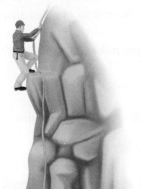

Elevation (km)	Temperature (°C)
0	20°
1	10°
2	0°
3	−10°
4	−20°
5	−30°

We see that temperature decreases as elevation increases.

(b) We substitute $T = 5°C$ in the model and solve for h.

$$T = 20 - 10h \qquad \text{Model}$$
$$5 = 20 - 10h \qquad \text{Substitute } T = 5$$
$$-15 = -10h \qquad \text{Subtract 20}$$
$$\frac{-15}{-10} = h \qquad \text{Divide by } -10$$
$$1.5 = h \qquad \text{Calculator}$$

The elevation is 1.5 km.

✎. **Now Try Exercise 11**

■

■ Making Algebra Models

In the next example we explore the process of making an algebra model for a real-life situation.

12 mi/gal   40 mi/gal

EXAMPLE 3 ■ Making a Model for Gas Mileage

The gas mileage of a car is the number of miles it can travel on one gallon of gas.

(a) Find a formula that models gas mileage in terms of the number of miles driven and the number of gallons of gasoline used.

(b) Henry's car used 10.5 gal to drive 230 mi. Find its gas mileage.

THINKING ABOUT THE PROBLEM

Let's try a simple case. If a car uses 2 gal to drive 100 mi, we easily see that

$$\text{gas mileage} = \frac{100}{2} = 50 \text{ mi/gal}$$

So gas mileage is the number of miles driven divided by the number of gallons used.

SOLUTION

(a) To find the formula we want, we need to assign symbols to the quantities involved.

In Words	In Algebra
Number of miles driven	N
Number of gallons used	G
Gas mileage (mi/gal)	M

We can express the model as follows:

$$\text{gas mileage} = \frac{\text{number of miles driven}}{\text{number of gallons used}}$$

$$M = \frac{N}{G} \qquad \text{Model}$$

(b) To get the gas mileage, we substitute $N = 230$ and $G = 10.5$ in the formula.

$$M = \frac{N}{G} \qquad \text{Model}$$

$$= \frac{230}{10.5} \qquad \text{Substitute } N = 230, G = 10.5$$

$$\approx 21.9 \qquad \text{Calculator}$$

The gas mileage for Henry's car is about 21.9 mi/gal.

Now Try Exercise 19

P.1 EXERCISES

CONCEPTS

1. The model $L = 4S$ gives the total number of legs that S sheep have. Using this model, we find that 12 sheep have

$L =$ _____ legs.

2. Suppose gas costs $3.50 a gallon. We make a model for the cost C of buying x gallons of gas by writing the formula

$C =$ _____.

SKILLS

3–12 ■ Using Models Use the model given to answer the questions about the object or process being modeled.

3. The sales tax T in a certain county is modeled by the formula $T = 0.06x$. Find the sales tax on an item whose price is $120.

4. Mintonville School District residents pay a wage tax T that is modeled by the formula $T = 0.005x$. Find the wage tax paid by a resident who earns $62,000 per year.

5. The distance d (in mi) driven by a car traveling at a speed of v miles per hour for t hours is given by

$$d = vt$$

If the car is driven at 70 mi/h for 3.5 h, how far has it traveled?

6. The volume V of a cylindrical can is modeled by the formula

$$V = \pi r^2 h$$

where r is the radius and h is the height of the can. Find the volume of a can with radius 3 in. and height 5 in.

7. The gas mileage M (in mi/gal) of a car is modeled by $M = N/G$, where N is the number of miles driven and G is the number of gallons of gas used.

(a) Find the gas mileage M for a car that drove 240 mi on 8 gal of gas.

(b) A car with a gas mileage $M = 25$ mi/gal is driven 175 mi. How many gallons of gas are used?

8. A mountain climber models the temperature T (in °F) at elevation h (in ft) by

$$T = 70 - 0.003h$$

(a) Find the temperature T at an elevation of 1500 ft.

(b) If the temperature is 64°F, what is the elevation?

9. The portion of a floating iceberg that is below the water surface is much larger than the portion above the surface. The total volume V of an iceberg is modeled by

$$V = 9.5S$$

where S is the volume showing above the surface.

(a) Find the total volume of an iceberg if the volume showing above the surface is 4 km³.

(b) Find the volume showing above the surface for an iceberg with total volume 19 km³.

10. The power P measured in horsepower (hp) needed to drive a certain ship at a speed of s knots is modeled by

$$P = 0.06s^3$$

(a) Find the power needed to drive the ship at 12 knots.

(b) At what speed will a 7.5-hp engine drive the ship?

11. An ocean diver models the pressure P (in lb/in²) at depth d (in ft) by

$$P = 14.7 + 0.45d$$

(a) Make a table that gives the pressure for each 10-ft change in depth, from a depth of 0 ft to 60 ft.

(b) If the pressure is 30 lb/in², what is the depth?

12. Arizonans use an average of 40 gal of water per person each day. The number of gallons W of water used by x Arizonans each day is modeled by $W = 40x$.

(a) Make a table that gives the number of gallons of water used for each 1000-person change in population, from 0 to 5000.

(b) What is the population of an Arizona town whose water usage is 120,000 gal per day?

13–18 ■ **Making Models** Write an algebraic formula that models the given quantity.

13. The number N of cents in q quarters

14. The average A of two numbers a and b

15. The cost C of purchasing x gallons of gas at $3.50 a gallon

16. The amount T of a 15% tip on a restaurant bill of x dollars

17. The distance d in miles that a car travels in t hours at 60 mi/h

18. The speed r of a boat that travels d miles in 3 h

APPLICATIONS

19. Cost of a Pizza A pizza parlor charges $12 for a cheese pizza and $1 for each topping.

(a) How much does a 3-topping pizza cost?

(b) Find a formula that models the cost C of a pizza with n toppings.

(c) If a pizza costs $16, how many toppings does it have?

 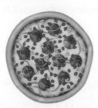

$n = 1$ $\qquad\qquad$ $n = 4$

20. Renting a Car At a certain car rental agency a compact car rents for $30 a day and 10¢ a mile.

(a) How much does it cost to rent a car for 3 days if the car is driven 280 mi?

(b) Find a formula that models the cost C of renting this car for n days if it is driven m miles.

(c) If the cost for a 3-day rental was $140, how many miles was the car driven?

21. Energy Cost for a Car The cost of the electricity needed to drive an all-electric car is about 4 cents per mile. The cost of the gasoline needed to drive the average gasoline-powered car is about 12 cents per mile.

(a) Find a formula that models the energy cost C of driving x miles for (i) the all-electric car and (ii) the average gasoline-powered car.

(b) Find the cost of driving 10,000 mi with each type of car.

22. Volume of Fruit Crate A fruit crate has square ends and is twice as long as it is wide.

(a) Find the volume of the crate if its width is 20 in.

(b) Find a formula for the volume V of the crate in terms of its width x.

23. Grade Point Average In many universities students are given grade points for each credit unit according to the following scale:

A	4 points
B	3 points
C	2 points
D	1 point
F	0 point

For example, a grade of A in a 3-unit course earns $4 \times 3 = 12$ grade points and a grade of B in a 5-unit course earns $3 \times 5 = 15$ grade points. A student's grade point average (GPA) for these two courses is the total number of grade points earned divided by the number of units; in this case the GPA is $(12 + 15)/8 = 3.375$.

(a) Find a formula for the GPA of a student who earns a grade of A in a units of course work, B in b units, C in c units, D in d units, and F in f units.

(b) Find the GPA of a student who has earned a grade of A in two 3-unit courses, B in one 4-unit course, and C in three 3-unit courses.

P.2 REAL NUMBERS

■ **Real Numbers** ■ **Properties of Real Numbers** ■ **Addition and Subtraction** ■ **Multiplication and Division** ■ **The Real Line** ■ **Sets and Intervals** ■ **Absolute Value and Distance**

In the real world we use numbers to measure and compare different quantities. For example, we measure temperature, length, height, weight, blood pressure, distance, speed, acceleration, energy, force, angles, age, cost, and so on. Figure 1 illustrates some situations in which numbers are used. Numbers also allow us to express relationships between different quantities—for example, relationships between the radius and volume of a ball, between miles driven and gas used, or between education level and starting salary.

Count   Length   Speed   Weight

FIGURE 1 Measuring with real numbers

Real Numbers

Let's review the types of numbers that make up the real number system. We start with the **natural numbers**:

$$1, 2, 3, 4, \ldots$$

The **integers** consist of the natural numbers together with their negatives and 0:

$$\ldots, -3, -2, -1, 0, 1, 2, 3, 4, \ldots$$

We construct the **rational numbers** by taking ratios of integers. Thus any rational number r can be expressed as

$$r = \frac{m}{n}$$

The different types of real numbers were invented to meet specific needs. For example, natural numbers are needed for counting, negative numbers for describing debt or below-zero temperatures, rational numbers for concepts like "half a gallon of milk," and irrational numbers for measuring certain distances, like the diagonal of a square.

where m and n are integers and $n \neq 0$. Examples are

$$\frac{1}{2} \qquad -\frac{3}{7} \qquad 46 = \frac{46}{1} \qquad 0.17 = \frac{17}{100}$$

(Recall that division by 0 is always ruled out, so expressions like $\frac{3}{0}$ and $\frac{0}{0}$ are undefined.) There are also real numbers, such as $\sqrt{2}$, that cannot be expressed as a ratio of integers and are therefore called **irrational numbers**. It can be shown, with varying degrees of difficulty, that these numbers are also irrational:

$$\sqrt{3} \qquad \sqrt{5} \qquad \sqrt[3]{2} \qquad \pi \qquad \frac{3}{\pi^2}$$

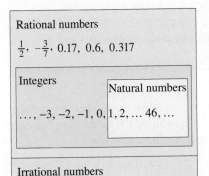

Rational numbers

$\frac{1}{2}$, $-\frac{3}{7}$, 0.17, 0.6, 0.317

Integers

Natural numbers

$\ldots, -3, -2, -1, 0,$ 1, 2, $\ldots$ 46, $\ldots$

Irrational numbers

$\sqrt{3}$, $\sqrt{5}$, $\sqrt[3]{2}$, π, $\frac{3}{\pi^2}$

FIGURE 2 The real number system

The set of all real numbers is usually denoted by the symbol $\mathbb{R}$. When we use the word *number* without qualification, we will mean "real number." Figure 2 is a diagram of the types of real numbers that we work with in this book.

Every real number has a decimal representation. If the number is rational, then its corresponding decimal is repeating. For example,

$$\frac{1}{2} = 0.5000\ldots = 0.5\overline{0} \qquad \frac{2}{3} = 0.66666\ldots = 0.\overline{6}$$
$$\frac{157}{495} = 0.3171717\ldots = 0.3\overline{17} \qquad \frac{9}{7} = 1.285714285714\ldots = 1.\overline{285714}$$

A repeating decimal such as

$$x = 3.5474747\ldots$$

is a rational number. To convert it to a ratio of two integers, we write

$$1000x = 3547.47474747\ldots$$
$$\underline{10x = \quad 35.47474747\ldots}$$
$$990x = 3512.0$$

Thus $x = \frac{3512}{990}$. (The idea is to multiply x by appropriate powers of 10 and then subtract to eliminate the repeating part.)

(The bar indicates that the sequence of digits repeats forever.) If the number is irrational, the decimal representation is nonrepeating:

$$\sqrt{2} = 1.414213562373095\ldots \qquad \pi = 3.141592653589793\ldots$$

If we stop the decimal expansion of any number at a certain place, we get an approximation to the number. For instance, we can write

$$\pi \approx 3.14159265$$

where the symbol $\approx$ is read "is approximately equal to." The more decimal places we retain, the better our approximation.

■ Properties of Real Numbers

We all know that $2 + 3 = 3 + 2$, and $5 + 7 = 7 + 5$, and $513 + 87 = 87 + 513$, and so on. In algebra we express all these (infinitely many) facts by writing

$$a + b = b + a$$

where a and b stand for any two numbers. In other words, "$a + b = b + a$" is a concise way of saying that "when we add two numbers, the order of addition doesn't matter." This fact is called the *Commutative Property* of addition. From our experience with numbers we know that the properties in the following box are also valid.

PROPERTIES OF REAL NUMBERS

Property	Example	Description
Commutative Properties		
$a + b = b + a$	$7 + 3 = 3 + 7$	When we add two numbers, order doesn't matter.
$ab = ba$	$3 \cdot 5 = 5 \cdot 3$	When we multiply two numbers, order doesn't matter.
Associative Properties		
$(a + b) + c = a + (b + c)$	$(2 + 4) + 7 = 2 + (4 + 7)$	When we add three numbers, it doesn't matter which two we add first.
$(ab)c = a(bc)$	$(3 \cdot 7) \cdot 5 = 3 \cdot (7 \cdot 5)$	When we multiply three numbers, it doesn't matter which two we multiply first.
Distributive Property		
$a(b + c) = ab + ac$	$2 \cdot (3 + 5) = 2 \cdot 3 + 2 \cdot 5$	When we multiply a number by a sum of two numbers, we get the same result as we get if we multiply the number by each of the terms and then add the results.
$(b + c)a = ab + ac$	$(3 + 5) \cdot 2 = 2 \cdot 3 + 2 \cdot 5$	

The Distributive Property applies whenever we multiply a number by a sum. Figure 3 explains why this property works for the case in which all the numbers are positive integers, but the property is true for any real numbers a, b, and c.

The Distributive Property is crucial because it describes the way addition and multiplication interact with each other.

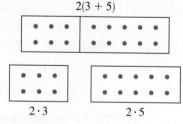

FIGURE 3 The Distributive Property

EXAMPLE 1 ■ Using the Distributive Property

(a) $2(x + 3) = 2 \cdot x + 2 \cdot 3$ Distributive Property

$\qquad\qquad = 2x + 6$ Simplify

(b) $\overbrace{(a + b)}(x + y) = (a + b)x + (a + b)y$ Distributive Property

$$= (ax + bx) + (ay + by) \quad \text{Distributive Property}$$

$$= ax + bx + ay + by \quad \text{Associative Property of Addition}$$

In the last step we removed the parentheses because, according to the Associative Property, the order of addition doesn't matter.

✎ **Now Try Exercise 15**

▪

Addition and Subtraction

The number 0 is special for addition; it is called the **additive identity** because $a + 0 = a$ for any real number a. Every real number a has a **negative**, $-a$, that satisfies $a + (-a) = 0$. **Subtraction** is the operation that undoes addition; to subtract a number from another, we simply add the negative of that number. By definition

$$a - b = a + (-b)$$

To combine real numbers involving negatives, we use the following properties.

⊘ Don't assume that $-a$ is a negative number. Whether $-a$ is negative or positive depends on the value of a. For example, if $a = 5$, then $-a = -5$, a negative number, but if $a = -5$, then $-a = -(-5) = 5$ (Property 2), a positive number.

PROPERTIES OF NEGATIVES

Property	Example
1. $(-1)a = -a$	$(-1)5 = -5$
2. $-(-a) = a$	$-(-5) = 5$
3. $(-a)b = a(-b) = -(ab)$	$(-5)7 = 5(-7) = -(5 \cdot 7)$
4. $(-a)(-b) = ab$	$(-4)(-3) = 4 \cdot 3$
5. $-(a + b) = -a - b$	$-(3 + 5) = -3 - 5$
6. $-(a - b) = b - a$	$-(5 - 8) = 8 - 5$

Property 6 states the intuitive fact that $a - b$ and $b - a$ are negatives of each other. Property 5 is often used with more than two terms:

$$-(a + b + c) = -a - b - c$$

EXAMPLE 2 ▪ Using Properties of Negatives

Let x, y, and z be real numbers.

(a) $-(x + 2) = -x - 2$ Property 5: $-(a + b) = -a - b$

(b) $-(x + y - z) = -x - y - (-z)$ Property 5: $-(a + b) = -a - b$

$$= -x - y + z \quad \text{Property 2: } -(-a) = a$$

✎ **Now Try Exercise 27**

▪

Multiplication and Division

The number 1 is special for multiplication; it is called the **multiplicative identity** because $a \cdot 1 = a$ for any real number a. Every nonzero real number a has an **inverse**, $1/a$, that satisfies $a \cdot (1/a) = 1$. **Division** is the operation that undoes multiplication;

to divide by a number, we multiply by the inverse of that number. If $b \neq 0$, then, by definition,

$$a \div b = a \cdot \frac{1}{b}$$

We write $a \cdot (1/b)$ as simply a/b. We refer to a/b as the **quotient** of a and b or as the **fraction** a over b; a is the **numerator** and b is the **denominator** (or **divisor**). To combine real numbers using the operation of division, we use the following properties.

PROPERTIES OF FRACTIONS

Property	Example	Description
1. $\dfrac{a}{b} \cdot \dfrac{c}{d} = \dfrac{ac}{bd}$	$\dfrac{2}{3} \cdot \dfrac{5}{7} = \dfrac{2 \cdot 5}{3 \cdot 7} = \dfrac{10}{21}$	When **multiplying fractions**, multiply numerators and denominators.
2. $\dfrac{a}{b} \div \dfrac{c}{d} = \dfrac{a}{b} \cdot \dfrac{d}{c}$	$\dfrac{2}{3} \div \dfrac{5}{7} = \dfrac{2}{3} \cdot \dfrac{7}{5} = \dfrac{14}{15}$	When **dividing fractions**, invert the divisor and multiply.
3. $\dfrac{a}{c} + \dfrac{b}{c} = \dfrac{a+b}{c}$	$\dfrac{2}{5} + \dfrac{7}{5} = \dfrac{2+7}{5} = \dfrac{9}{5}$	When **adding fractions** with the **same denominator**, add the numerators.
4. $\dfrac{a}{b} + \dfrac{c}{d} = \dfrac{ad+bc}{bd}$	$\dfrac{2}{5} + \dfrac{3}{7} = \dfrac{2 \cdot 7 + 3 \cdot 5}{35} = \dfrac{29}{35}$	When **adding fractions** with **different denominators**, find a common denominator. Then add the numerators.
5. $\dfrac{ac}{bc} = \dfrac{a}{b}$	$\dfrac{2 \cdot 5}{3 \cdot 5} = \dfrac{2}{3}$	**Cancel** numbers that are **common factors** in numerator and denominator.
6. If $\dfrac{a}{b} = \dfrac{c}{d}$, then $ad = bc$	$\dfrac{2}{3} = \dfrac{6}{9}$, so $2 \cdot 9 = 3 \cdot 6$	**Cross-multiply**.

When adding fractions with different denominators, we don't usually use Property 4. Instead we rewrite the fractions so that they have the smallest possible common denominator (often smaller than the product of the denominators), and then we use Property 3. This denominator is the **Least Common Denominator** (LCD) described in the next example.

EXAMPLE 3 ■ Using the LCD to Add Fractions

Evaluate: $\dfrac{5}{36} + \dfrac{7}{120}$

SOLUTION Factoring each denominator into prime factors gives

$$36 = 2^2 \cdot 3^2 \quad \text{and} \quad 120 = 2^3 \cdot 3 \cdot 5$$

We find the least common denominator (LCD) by forming the product of all the prime factors that occur in these factorizations, using the highest power of each prime factor. Thus the LCD is $2^3 \cdot 3^2 \cdot 5 = 360$. So

$$\frac{5}{36} + \frac{7}{120} = \frac{5 \cdot 10}{36 \cdot 10} + \frac{7 \cdot 3}{120 \cdot 3} \qquad \text{Use common denominator}$$

$$= \frac{50}{360} + \frac{21}{360} = \frac{71}{360} \qquad \text{Property 3: Adding fractions with the same denominator}$$

✎ **Now Try Exercise 29** ■

■ The Real Line

The real numbers can be represented by points on a line, as shown in Figure 4. The positive direction (toward the right) is indicated by an arrow. We choose an arbitrary reference point O, called the **origin**, which corresponds to the real number 0. Given any convenient unit of measurement, each positive number x is represented by the point on the line a distance of x units to the right of the origin, and each negative number $-x$ is represented by the point x units to the left of the origin. The number associated with the point P is called the coordinate of P, and the line is then called a **coordinate line**, or a **real number line**, or simply a **real line**. Often we identify the point with its coordinate and think of a number as being a point on the real line.

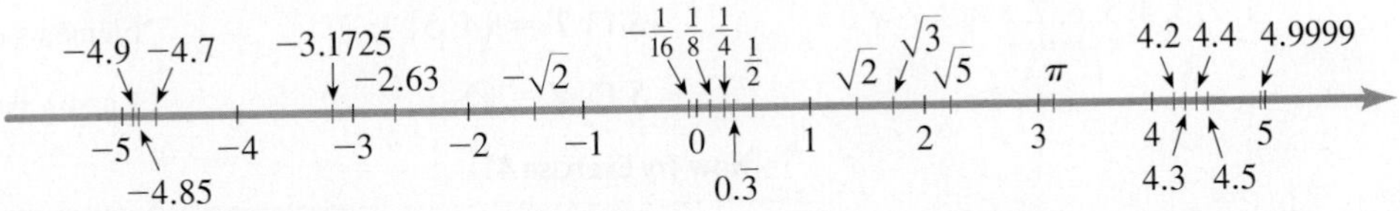

FIGURE 4 The real line

The real numbers are *ordered*. We say that **a is less than b** and write $a < b$ if $b - a$ is a positive number. Geometrically, this means that a lies to the left of b on the number line. Equivalently, we can say that **b is greater than a** and write $b > a$. The symbol $a \le b$ (or $b \ge a$) means that either $a < b$ or $a = b$ and is read "a is less than or equal to b." For instance, the following are true inequalities (see Figure 5):

$$7 < 7.4 < 7.5 \qquad -\pi < -3 \qquad \sqrt{2} < 2 \qquad 2 \le 2$$

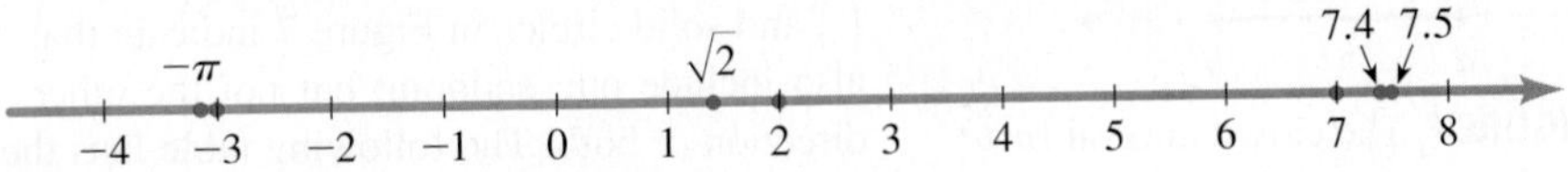

FIGURE 5

■ Sets and Intervals

A **set** is a collection of objects, and these objects are called the **elements** of the set. If S is a set, the notation $a \in S$ means that a is an element of S, and $b \notin S$ means that b is not an element of S. For example, if Z represents the set of integers, then $-3 \in Z$ but $\pi \notin Z$.

Some sets can be described by listing their elements within braces. For instance, the set A that consists of all positive integers less than 7 can be written as

$$A = \{1, 2, 3, 4, 5, 6\}$$

We could also write A in **set-builder notation** as

$$A = \{x \mid x \text{ is an integer and } 0 < x < 7\}$$

which is read "A is the set of all x such that x is an integer and $0 < x < 7$."

DISCOVERY PROJECT

Real Numbers in the Real World

Real-world measurements always involve units. For example, we usually measure distance in feet, miles, centimeters, or kilometers. Some measurements involve different types of units. For example, speed is measured in miles per hour or meters per second. We often need to convert a measurement from one type of unit to another. In this project we explore different types of units used for different purposes and how to convert from one type of unit to another. You can find the project at **www.stewartmath.com**.

If S and T are sets, then their **union** $S \cup T$ is the set that consists of all elements that are in S *or* T (or in both). The **intersection** of S and T is the set $S \cap T$ consisting of all elements that are in both S *and* T. In other words, $S \cap T$ is the common part of S and T. The **empty set**, denoted by $\varnothing$, is the set that contains no element.

EXAMPLE 4 ■ Union and Intersection of Sets

If $S = \{1, 2, 3, 4, 5\}$, $T = \{4, 5, 6, 7\}$, and $V = \{6, 7, 8\}$, find the sets $S \cup T$, $S \cap T$, and $S \cap V$.

SOLUTION

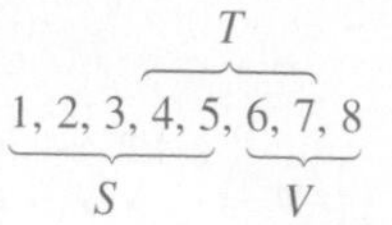

$$S \cup T = \{1, 2, 3, 4, 5, 6, 7\} \qquad \text{All elements in } S \text{ or } T$$

$$S \cap T = \{4, 5\} \qquad \text{Elements common to both } S \text{ and } T$$

$$S \cap V = \varnothing \qquad \text{S and V have no element in common}$$

■✎ **Now Try Exercise 41**

Certain sets of real numbers, called **intervals**, occur frequently in calculus and correspond geometrically to line segments. If $a < b$, then the **open interval** from a to b consists of all numbers between a and b and is denoted (a, b). The **closed interval** from a to b includes the endpoints and is denoted $[a, b]$. Using set-builder notation, we can write

$$(a, b) = \{x \mid a < x < b\} \qquad [a, b] = \{x \mid a \le x \le b\}$$

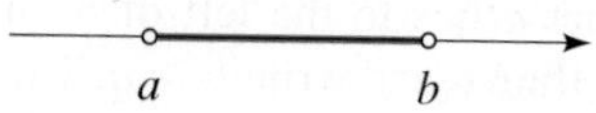

Note that parentheses ( ) in the interval notation and open circles on the graph in Figure 6 indicate that endpoints are *excluded* from the interval, whereas square brackets [ ] and solid circles in Figure 7 indicate that the endpoints are *included*. Intervals may also include one endpoint but not the other, or they may extend infinitely far in one direction or both. The following table lists the possible types of intervals.

FIGURE 6 The open interval (a, b)

FIGURE 7 The closed interval $[a, b]$

The symbol ∞ ("infinity") does not stand for a number. The notation (a, ∞), for instance, simply indicates that the interval has no endpoint on the right but extends infinitely far in the positive direction.

Notation	Set description	Graph
(a, b)	$\{x \mid a < x < b\}$	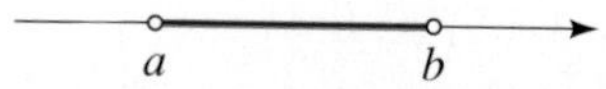
$[a, b]$	$\{x \mid a \le x \le b\}$	
$[a, b)$	$\{x \mid a \le x < b\}$	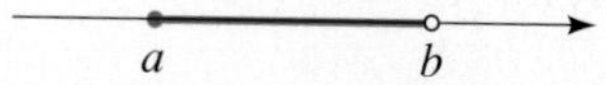
$(a, b]$	$\{x \mid a < x \le b\}$	
(a, ∞)	$\{x \mid a < x\}$	
$[a, \infty)$	$\{x \mid a \le x\}$	
$(-\infty, b)$	$\{x \mid x < b\}$	
$(-\infty, b]$	$\{x \mid x \le b\}$	
$(-\infty, \infty)$	$\mathbb{R}$ (set of all real numbers)	

EXAMPLE 5 ■ Graphing Intervals

Express each interval in terms of inequalities, and then graph the interval.

(a) $[-1, 2) = \{x \mid -1 \le x < 2\}$

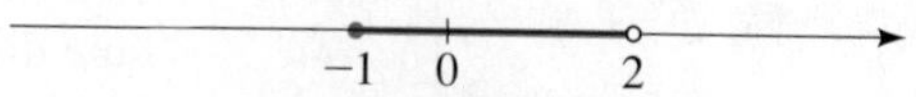

(b) $[1.5, 4] = \{x \mid 1.5 \le x \le 4\}$

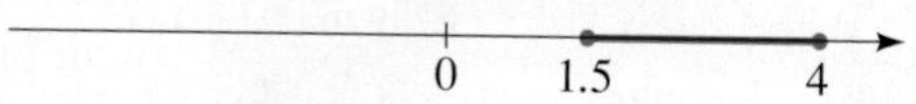

(c) $(-3, \infty) = \{x \mid -3 < x\}$

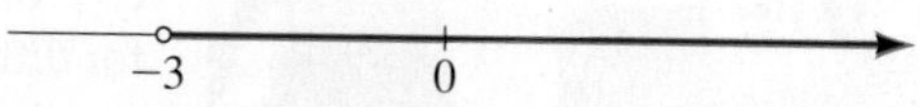

■✎ **Now Try Exercise 47**

EXAMPLE 6 ■ Finding Unions and Intersections of Intervals

Graph each set.

(a) $(1, 3) \cap [2, 7]$ **(b)** $(1, 3) \cup [2, 7]$

SOLUTION

(a) The intersection of two intervals consists of the numbers that are in both intervals. Therefore

$$(1, 3) \cap [2, 7] = \{x \mid 1 < x < 3 \text{ and } 2 \leq x \leq 7\}$$
$$= \{x \mid 2 \leq x < 3\} = [2, 3)$$

This set is illustrated in Figure 8.

(b) The union of two intervals consists of the numbers that are in either one interval or the other (or both). Therefore

$$(1, 3) \cup [2, 7] = \{x \mid 1 < x < 3 \text{ or } 2 \leq x \leq 7\}$$
$$= \{x \mid 1 < x \leq 7\} = (1, 7]$$

This set is illustrated in Figure 9.

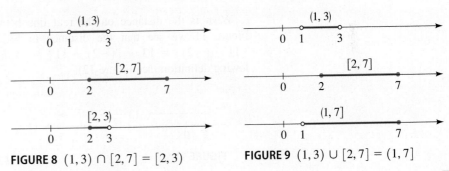

FIGURE 8 $(1, 3) \cap [2, 7] = [2, 3)$ **FIGURE 9** $(1, 3) \cup [2, 7] = (1, 7]$

✎ **Now Try Exercise 61**

Sidebar

No Smallest or Largest Number in an Open Interval

Any interval contains infinitely many numbers—every point on the graph of an interval corresponds to a real number. In the closed interval $[0, 1]$, the smallest number is 0 and the largest is 1, but the open interval $(0, 1)$ contains no smallest or largest number. To see this, note that 0.01 is close to zero, but 0.001 is closer, 0.0001 is closer yet, and so on. We can always find a number in the interval $(0, 1)$ closer to zero than any given number. Since 0 itself is not in the interval, the interval contains no smallest number. Similarly, 0.99 is close to 1, but 0.999 is closer, 0.9999 closer yet, and so on. Since 1 itself is not in the interval, the interval has no largest number.

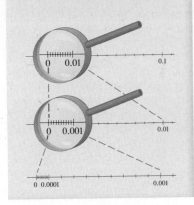

■ Absolute Value and Distance

The **absolute value** of a number a, denoted by $|a|$, is the distance from a to 0 on the real number line (see Figure 10). Distance is always positive or zero, so we have $|a| \geq 0$ for every number a. Remembering that $-a$ is positive when a is negative, we have the following definition.

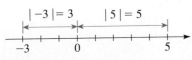

FIGURE 10

DEFINITION OF ABSOLUTE VALUE

If a is a real number, then the **absolute value** of a is

$$|a| = \begin{cases} a & \text{if } a \geq 0 \\ -a & \text{if } a < 0 \end{cases}$$

EXAMPLE 7 ■ Evaluating Absolute Values of Numbers

(a) $|3| = 3$

(b) $|-3| = -(-3) = 3$

(c) $|0| = 0$

(d) $|3 - \pi| = -(3 - \pi) = \pi - 3$ (since $3 < \pi \Rightarrow 3 - \pi < 0$)

✎ **Now Try Exercise 67**

When working with absolute values, we use the following properties.

PROPERTIES OF ABSOLUTE VALUE

Property	Example	Description
1. $\lvert a \rvert \geq 0$	$\lvert -3 \rvert = 3 \geq 0$	The absolute value of a number is always positive or zero.
2. $\lvert a \rvert = \lvert -a \rvert$	$\lvert 5 \rvert = \lvert -5 \rvert$	A number and its negative have the same absolute value.
3. $\lvert ab \rvert = \lvert a \rvert \lvert b \rvert$	$\lvert -2 \cdot 5 \rvert = \lvert -2 \rvert \lvert 5 \rvert$	The absolute value of a product is the product of the absolute values.
4. $\left\lvert \dfrac{a}{b} \right\rvert = \dfrac{\lvert a \rvert}{\lvert b \rvert}$	$\left\lvert \dfrac{12}{-3} \right\rvert = \dfrac{\lvert 12 \rvert}{\lvert -3 \rvert}$	The absolute value of a quotient is the quotient of the absolute values.
5. $\lvert a + b \rvert \leq \lvert a \rvert + \lvert b \rvert$	$\lvert -3 + 5 \rvert \leq \lvert -3 \rvert + \lvert 5 \rvert$	Triangle Inequality

---

What is the distance on the real line between the numbers -2 and 11? From Figure 11 we see that the distance is 13. We arrive at this by finding either $\lvert 11 - (-2) \rvert = 13$ or $\lvert (-2) - 11 \rvert = 13$. From this observation we make the following definition (see Figure 12).

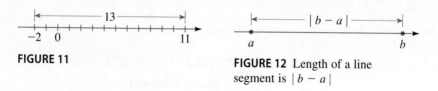

FIGURE 11

FIGURE 12 Length of a line segment is $\lvert b - a \rvert$

DISTANCE BETWEEN POINTS ON THE REAL LINE

If a and b are real numbers, then the **distance** between the points a and b on the real line is

$$d(a, b) = \lvert b - a \rvert$$

From Property 6 of negatives it follows that

$$\lvert b - a \rvert = \lvert a - b \rvert$$

This confirms that, as we would expect, the distance from a to b is the same as the distance from b to a.

EXAMPLE 8 ■ Distance Between Points on the Real Line

The distance between the numbers -8 and 2 is

$$d(a, b) = \lvert 2 - (-8) \rvert = \lvert -10 \rvert = 10$$

We can check this calculation geometrically, as shown in Figure 13.

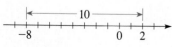

FIGURE 13

✎ **Now Try Exercise 75** ■

P.2 EXERCISES

CONCEPTS

1. Give an example of each of the following:

(a) A natural number

(b) An integer that is not a natural number

(c) A rational number that is not an integer

(d) An irrational number

2. Complete each statement and name the property of real numbers you have used.

(a) $ab =$ _____; _____ Property

(b) $a + (b + c) =$ _____; _____ Property

(c) $a(b + c) =$ _____; _____ Property

3. Express the set of real numbers between but not including 2 and 7 as follows.

(a) In set-builder notation: _____

(b) In interval notation: _____

4. The symbol $|x|$ stands for the _____ of the number x. If x is not 0, then the sign of $|x|$ is always _____.

5. The distance between a and b on the real line is $d(a, b) =$ _____. So the distance between -5 and 2 is _____.

6–8 ■ *Yes or No?* If *No*, give a reason. Assume that a and b are nonzero real numbers.

6. (a) Is the sum of two rational numbers always a rational number?

(b) Is the sum of two irrational numbers always an irrational number?

7. (a) Is $a - b$ equal to $b - a$?

(b) Is $-2(a - 5)$ equal to $-2a - 10$?

8. (a) Is the distance between any two different real numbers always positive?

(b) Is the distance between a and b the same as the distance between b and a?

SKILLS

9–10 ■ **Real Numbers** List the elements of the given set that are

(a) natural numbers

(b) integers

(c) rational numbers

(d) irrational numbers

9. $\left\{-1.5, 0, \frac{5}{2}, \sqrt{7}, 2.71, -\pi, 3.1\overline{4}, 100, -8\right\}$

10. $\left\{1.3, 1.3333\ldots, \sqrt{5}, 5.34, -500, 1\frac{2}{3}, \sqrt{16}, \frac{246}{579}, -\frac{20}{5}\right\}$

11–18 ■ **Properties of Real Numbers** State the property of real numbers being used.

11. $3 + 7 = 7 + 3$

12. $4(2 + 3) = (2 + 3)4$

13. $(x + 2y) + 3z = x + (2y + 3z)$

14. $2(A + B) = 2A + 2B$

15. $(5x + 1)3 = 15x + 3$

16. $(x + a)(x + b) = (x + a)x + (x + a)b$

17. $2x(3 + y) = (3 + y)2x$

18. $7(a + b + c) = 7(a + b) + 7c$

19–22 ■ **Properties of Real Numbers** Rewrite the expression using the given property of real numbers.

19. Commutative Property of Addition, $x + 3 =$

20. Associative Property of Multiplication, $7(3x) =$

21. Distributive Property, $4(A + B) =$

22. Distributive Property, $5x + 5y =$

23–28 ■ **Properties of Real Numbers** Use properties of real numbers to write the expression without parentheses.

23. $3(x + y)$

24. $(a - b)8$

25. $4(2m)$

26. $\frac{4}{3}(-6y)$

27. $-\frac{5}{2}(2x - 4y)$

28. $(3a)(b + c - 2d)$

29–32 ■ **Arithmetic Operations** Perform the indicated operations.

29. (a) $\frac{3}{10} + \frac{4}{15}$ (b) $\frac{1}{4} + \frac{1}{5}$

30. (a) $\frac{2}{3} - \frac{3}{5}$ (b) $1 + \frac{5}{8} - \frac{1}{6}$

31. (a) $\frac{2}{3}\left(6 - \frac{3}{2}\right)$ (b) $\left(3 + \frac{1}{4}\right)\left(1 - \frac{4}{5}\right)$

32. (a) $\dfrac{\frac{2}{3} - \frac{2}{3}}{2}$ (b) $\dfrac{\frac{2}{5} + \frac{1}{2}}{\frac{1}{10} + \frac{3}{15}}$

33–34 ■ **Inequalities** Place the correct symbol ($<$, $>$, or $=$) in the space.

33. (a) 3 ▢ $\frac{7}{2}$ (b) -3 ▢ $-\frac{7}{2}$ (c) 3.5 ▢ $\frac{7}{2}$

34. (a) $\frac{2}{3}$ ▢ 0.67 (b) $\frac{2}{3}$ ▢ -0.67

(c) $|0.67|$ ▢ $|-0.67|$

35–38 ■ **Inequalities** State whether each inequality is true or false.

35. (a) $-3 < -4$ (b) $3 < 4$

36. (a) $\sqrt{3} > 1.7325$ (b) $1.732 \geq \sqrt{3}$

37. (a) $\frac{10}{2} \geq 5$ (b) $\frac{6}{10} \geq \frac{5}{6}$

38. (a) $\frac{7}{11} \geq \frac{8}{13}$ (b) $-\frac{3}{5} > -\frac{3}{4}$

39–40 ■ **Inequalities** Write each statement in terms of inequalities.

39. (a) x is positive.

(b) t is less than 4.

(c) a is greater than or equal to π.

(d) x is less than $\frac{1}{3}$ and is greater than -5.

(e) The distance from p to 3 is at most 5.

40. (a) y is negative.

(b) z is greater than 1.

(c) b is at most 8.

(d) w is positive and is less than or equal to 17.

(e) y is at least 2 units from π.

41–44 ■ Sets Find the indicated set if

$$A = \{1, 2, 3, 4, 5, 6, 7\} \qquad B = \{2, 4, 6, 8\}$$
$$C = \{7, 8, 9, 10\}$$

41. (a) $A \cup B$ (b) $A \cap B$

42. (a) $B \cup C$ (b) $B \cap C$

43. (a) $A \cup C$ (b) $A \cap C$

44. (a) $A \cup B \cup C$ (b) $A \cap B \cap C$

45–46 ■ Sets Find the indicated set if

$$A = \{x \mid x \geq -2\} \qquad B = \{x \mid x < 4\}$$
$$C = \{x \mid -1 < x \leq 5\}$$

45. (a) $B \cup C$ (b) $B \cap C$

46. (a) $A \cap C$ (b) $A \cap B$

47–52 ■ Intervals Express the interval in terms of inequalities, and then graph the interval.

47. $(-3, 0)$ **48.** $(2, 8]$

49. $[2, 8)$ **50.** $\left[-6, -\frac{1}{2}\right]$

51. $[2, \infty)$ **52.** $(-\infty, 1)$

53–58 ■ Intervals Express the inequality in interval notation, and then graph the corresponding interval.

53. $x \leq 1$ **54.** $1 \leq x \leq 2$

55. $-2 < x \leq 1$ **56.** $x \geq -5$

57. $x > -1$ **58.** $-5 < x < 2$

59–60 ■ Intervals Express each set in interval notation.

59. (a)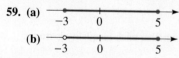

(b)

60. (a)

(b)

61–66 ■ Intervals Graph the set.

61. $(-2, 0) \cup (-1, 1)$ **62.** $(-2, 0) \cap (-1, 1)$

63. $[-4, 6] \cap [0, 8)$ **64.** $[-4, 6) \cup [0, 8)$

65. $(-\infty, -4) \cup (4, \infty)$ **66.** $(-\infty, 6] \cap (2, 10)$

67–72 ■ Absolute Value Evaluate each expression.

67. (a) $|100|$ (b) $|-73|$

68. (a) $|\sqrt{5} - 5|$ (b) $|10 - \pi|$

69. (a) $\big||-6| - |-4|\big|$ (b) $\dfrac{-1}{|-1|}$

70. (a) $\big|2 - |-12|\big|$ (b) $-1 - \big|1 - |-1|\big|$

71. (a) $|(-2) \cdot 6|$ (b) $\left|\left(-\frac{1}{3}\right)(-15)\right|$

72. (a) $\left|\dfrac{-6}{24}\right|$ (b) $\left|\dfrac{7 - 12}{12 - 7}\right|$

73–76 ■ Distance Find the distance between the given numbers.

73.

74.

75. (a) 2 and 17   (b) -3 and 21   (c) $\frac{11}{8}$ and $-\frac{3}{10}$

76. (a) $\frac{7}{15}$ and $-\frac{1}{21}$ (b) -38 and -57 (c) -2.6 and -1.8

SKILLS Plus

77–78 ■ Repeating Decimal Express each repeating decimal as a fraction. (See the margin note on page 7.)

77. (a) $0.\overline{7}$ (b) $0.2\overline{8}$ (c) $0.\overline{57}$

78. (a) $5.\overline{23}$ (b) $1.3\overline{7}$ (c) $2.1\overline{35}$

79–82 ■ Simplifying Absolute Value Express the quantity without using absolute value.

79. $|\pi - 3|$ **80.** $|1 - \sqrt{2}|$

81. $|a - b|$, where $a < b$

82. $a + b + |a - b|$, where $a < b$

83–84 ■ Signs of Numbers Let a, b, and c be real numbers such that $a > 0$, $b < 0$, and $c < 0$. Find the sign of each expression.

83. (a) $-a$ (b) bc (c) $a - b$ (d) $ab + ac$

84. (a) $-b$ (b) $a + bc$ (c) $c - a$ (d) ab^2

APPLICATIONS

85. Area of a Garden Mary's backyard vegetable garden measures 20 ft by 30 ft, so its area is $20 \times 30 = 600$ ft^2. She decides to make it longer, as shown in the figure, so that the area increases to $A = 20(30 + x)$. Which property of real numbers tells us that the new area can also be written $A = 600 + 20x$?

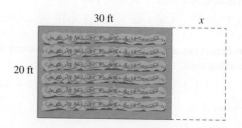

86. Temperature Variation The bar graph shows the daily high temperatures for Omak, Washington, and Geneseo, New York, during a certain week in June. Let T_O represent the temperature in Omak and T_G the temperature in Geneseo. Calculate $T_O - T_G$ and $|T_O - T_G|$ for each day shown. Which of these two values gives more information?

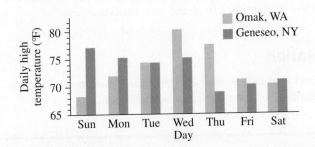

87. Mailing a Package The post office will accept only packages for which the length plus the "girth" (distance around) is no more than 108 in. Thus for the package in the figure, we must have

$$L + 2(x + y) \le 108$$

(a) Will the post office accept a package that is 6 in. wide, 8 in. deep, and 5 ft long? What about a package that measures 2 ft by 2 ft by 4 ft?

(b) What is the greatest acceptable length for a package that has a square base measuring 9 in. by 9 in.?

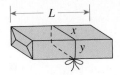 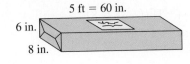

DISCUSS ■ DISCOVER ■ PROVE ■ WRITE

88. DISCUSS: Sums and Products of Rational and Irrational Numbers Explain why the sum, the difference, and the product of two rational numbers are rational numbers. Is the product of two irrational numbers necessarily irrational? What about the sum?

89. DISCOVER ■ PROVE: Combining Rational and Irrational Numbers Is $\frac{1}{2} + \sqrt{2}$ rational or irrational? Is $\frac{1}{2} \cdot \sqrt{2}$ rational or irrational? Experiment with sums and products of other rational and irrational numbers. Prove the following.

(a) The sum of a rational number r and an irrational number t is irrational.

(b) The product of a nonzero rational number r and an irrational number t is irrational.

[*Hint:* For part (a), suppose that $r + t$ is a rational number q, that is, $r + t = q$. Show that this leads to a contradiction. Use similar reasoning for part (b).]

90. DISCOVER: Limiting Behavior of Reciprocals Complete the tables. What happens to the size of the fraction $1/x$ as x gets large? As x gets small?

x	$1/x$
1	
2	
10	
100	
1000	

x	$1/x$
1.0	
0.5	
0.1	
0.01	
0.001	

91. DISCOVER: Irrational Numbers and Geometry Using the following figure, explain how to locate the point $\sqrt{2}$ on a number line. Can you locate $\sqrt{5}$ by a similar method? What about $\sqrt{6}$? List some other irrational numbers that can be located this way.

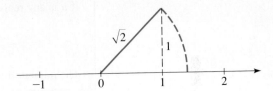

92. DISCUSS: Commutative and Noncommutative Operations We have seen that addition and multiplication are both commutative operations.

(a) Is subtraction commutative?

(b) Is division of nonzero real numbers commutative?

(c) Are the actions of putting on your socks and putting on your shoes commutative?

(d) Are the actions of putting on your hat and putting on your coat commutative?

(e) Are the actions of washing laundry and drying it commutative?

(f) Give an example of a pair of actions that are commutative.

(g) Give an example of a pair of actions that are not commutative.

93. WRITE: Real Numbers in the Real World Write a paragraph describing different real-world situations in which you would use natural numbers, integers, rational numbers, and irrational numbers. Give examples for each type of situation.

94. PROVE: Triangle Inequality We prove Property 5 of absolute values, the Triangle Inequality:

$$|x + y| \le |x| + |y|$$

(a) Verify that the Triangle Inequality holds for $x = 2$ and $y = 3$, for $x = -2$ and $y = -3$, and for $x = -2$ and $y = 3$.

(b) Prove that the Triangle Inequality is true for all real numbers x and y. [*Hint:* Take cases.]

P.3 INTEGER EXPONENTS AND SCIENTIFIC NOTATION

■ Exponential Notation ■ Rules for Working with Exponents ■ Scientific Notation

In this section we review the rules for working with exponential notation. We also see how exponents can be used to represent very large and very small numbers.

■ Exponential Notation

A product of identical numbers is usually written in exponential notation. For example, $5 \cdot 5 \cdot 5$ is written as 5^3. In general, we have the following definition.

EXPONENTIAL NOTATION

If a is any real number and n is a positive integer, then the **nth power** of a is

$$a^n = \underbrace{a \cdot a \cdots \cdot a}_{n \text{ factors}}$$

The number a is called the **base**, and n is called the **exponent**.

EXAMPLE 1 ■ Exponential Notation

(a) $\left(\dfrac{1}{2}\right)^5 = \left(\dfrac{1}{2}\right)\left(\dfrac{1}{2}\right)\left(\dfrac{1}{2}\right)\left(\dfrac{1}{2}\right)\left(\dfrac{1}{2}\right) = \dfrac{1}{32}$

(b) $(-3)^4 = (-3) \cdot (-3) \cdot (-3) \cdot (-3) = 81$

(c) $-3^4 = -(3 \cdot 3 \cdot 3 \cdot 3) = -81$

⬛ **Now Try Exercise 11**

⊘ Note the distinction between $(-3)^4$ and -3^4. In $(-3)^4$ the exponent applies to -3, but in -3^4 the exponent applies only to 3.

We can state several useful rules for working with exponential notation. To discover the rule for multiplication, we multiply 5^4 by 5^2:

$$5^4 \cdot 5^2 = \underbrace{(5 \cdot 5 \cdot 5 \cdot 5)}_{4 \text{ factors}}\underbrace{(5 \cdot 5)}_{2 \text{ factors}} = \underbrace{5 \cdot 5 \cdot 5 \cdot 5 \cdot 5 \cdot 5}_{6 \text{ factors}} = 5^6 = 5^{4+2}$$

It appears that *to multiply two powers of the same base, we add their exponents.* In general, for any real number a and any positive integers m and n, we have

$$a^m a^n = \underbrace{(a \cdot a \cdots \cdot a)}_{m \text{ factors}}\underbrace{(a \cdot a \cdots \cdot a)}_{n \text{ factors}} = \underbrace{a \cdot a \cdot a \cdots \cdot a}_{m + n \text{ factors}} = a^{m+n}$$

Thus $a^m a^n = a^{m+n}$.

We would like this rule to be true even when m and n are 0 or negative integers. For instance, we must have

$$2^0 \cdot 2^3 = 2^{0+3} = 2^3$$

But this can happen only if $2^0 = 1$. Likewise, we want to have

$$5^4 \cdot 5^{-4} = 5^{4+(-4)} = 5^{4-4} = 5^0 = 1$$

and this will be true if $5^{-4} = 1/5^4$. These observations lead to the following definition.

ZERO AND NEGATIVE EXPONENTS

If $a \neq 0$ is a real number and n is a positive integer, then

$$a^0 = 1 \qquad \text{and} \qquad a^{-n} = \frac{1}{a^n}$$

EXAMPLE 2 ■ Zero and Negative Exponents

(a) $\left(\frac{4}{7}\right)^0 = 1$

(b) $x^{-1} = \frac{1}{x^1} = \frac{1}{x}$

(c) $(-2)^{-3} = \frac{1}{(-2)^3} = \frac{1}{-8} = -\frac{1}{8}$

✎ Now Try Exercise 13   ■

■ Rules for Working with Exponents

Familiarity with the following rules is essential for our work with exponents and bases. In the table the bases a and b are real numbers, and the exponents m and n are integers.

LAWS OF EXPONENTS

Law	Example	Description
1. $a^m a^n = a^{m+n}$	$3^2 \cdot 3^5 = 3^{2+5} = 3^7$	To multiply two powers of the same number, add the exponents.
2. $\dfrac{a^m}{a^n} = a^{m-n}$	$\dfrac{3^5}{3^2} = 3^{5-2} = 3^3$	To divide two powers of the same number, subtract the exponents.
3. $(a^m)^n = a^{mn}$	$(3^2)^5 = 3^{2\cdot5} = 3^{10}$	To raise a power to a new power, multiply the exponents.
4. $(ab)^n = a^n b^n$	$(3 \cdot 4)^2 = 3^2 \cdot 4^2$	To raise a product to a power, raise each factor to the power.
5. $\left(\dfrac{a}{b}\right)^n = \dfrac{a^n}{b^n}$	$\left(\dfrac{3}{4}\right)^2 = \dfrac{3^2}{4^2}$	To raise a quotient to a power, raise both numerator and denominator to the power.
6. $\left(\dfrac{a}{b}\right)^{-n} = \left(\dfrac{b}{a}\right)^n$	$\left(\dfrac{3}{4}\right)^{-2} = \left(\dfrac{4}{3}\right)^2$	To raise a fraction to a negative power, invert the fraction and change the sign of the exponent.
7. $\dfrac{a^{-n}}{b^{-m}} = \dfrac{b^m}{a^n}$	$\dfrac{3^{-2}}{4^{-5}} = \dfrac{4^5}{3^2}$	To move a number raised to a power from numerator to denominator or from denominator to numerator, change the sign of the exponent.

Proof of Law 3   If m and n are positive integers, we have

$$(a^m)^n = \underbrace{(a \cdot a \cdots \cdots a)}_{m \text{ factors}}{}^n$$

$$= \underbrace{\underbrace{(a \cdot a \cdots \cdots a)}_{m \text{ factors}}\underbrace{(a \cdot a \cdots \cdots a)}_{m \text{ factors}} \cdots \underbrace{(a \cdot a \cdots \cdots a)}_{m \text{ factors}}}_{n \text{ groups of factors}}$$

$$= \underbrace{a \cdot a \cdots \cdots a}_{mn \text{ factors}} = a^{mn}$$

The cases for which $m \leq 0$ or $n \leq 0$ can be proved by using the definition of negative exponents.   ■

Proof of Law 4 If n is a positive integer, we have

$$(ab)^n = \underbrace{(ab)(ab) \cdots (ab)}_{n \text{ factors}} = \underbrace{(a \cdot a \cdots \cdots a)}_{n \text{ factors}} \cdot \underbrace{(b \cdot b \cdots \cdots b)}_{n \text{ factors}} = a^n b^n$$

Here we have used the Commutative and Associative Properties repeatedly. If $n \leq 0$, Law 4 can be proved by using the definition of negative exponents. ■

You are asked to prove Laws 2, 5, 6, and 7 in Exercises 58 and 59.

EXAMPLE 3 ■ Using Laws of Exponents

(a) $x^4 x^7 = x^{4+7} = x^{11}$ Law 1: $a^m a^n = a^{m+n}$

(b) $y^4 y^{-7} = y^{4-7} = y^{-3} = \dfrac{1}{y^3}$ Law 1: $a^m a^n = a^{m+n}$

(c) $\dfrac{c^9}{c^5} = c^{9-5} = c^4$ Law 2: $\dfrac{a^m}{a^n} = a^{m-n}$

(d) $(b^4)^5 = b^{4 \cdot 5} = b^{20}$ Law 3: $(a^m)^n = a^{mn}$

(e) $(3x)^3 = 3^3 x^3 = 27x^3$ Law 4: $(ab)^n = a^n b^n$

(f) $\left(\dfrac{x}{2}\right)^5 = \dfrac{x^5}{2^5} = \dfrac{x^5}{32}$ Law 5: $\left(\dfrac{a}{b}\right)^n = \dfrac{a^n}{b^n}$

✎ **Now Try Exercises 19 and 21** ■

EXAMPLE 4 ■ Simplifying Expressions with Exponents

Simplify:

(a) $(2a^3 b^2)(3ab^4)^3$ **(b)** $\left(\dfrac{x}{y}\right)^3 \left(\dfrac{y^2 x}{z}\right)^4$

SOLUTION

(a) $(2a^3 b^2)(3ab^4)^3 = (2a^3 b^2)[3^3 a^3 (b^4)^3]$ Law 4: $(ab)^n = a^n b^n$

$ = (2a^3 b^2)(27a^3 b^{12})$ Law 3: $(a^m)^n = a^{mn}$

$ = (2)(27)a^3 a^3 b^2 b^{12}$ Group factors with the same base

$ = 54a^6 b^{14}$ Law 1: $a^m a^n = a^{m+n}$

(b) $\left(\dfrac{x}{y}\right)^3 \left(\dfrac{y^2 x}{z}\right)^4 = \dfrac{x^3}{y^3} \dfrac{(y^2)^4 x^4}{z^4}$ Laws 5 and 4

$\phantom{\left(\dfrac{x}{y}\right)^3 \left(\dfrac{y^2 x}{z}\right)^4} = \dfrac{x^3}{y^3} \dfrac{y^8 x^4}{z^4}$ Law 3

$\phantom{\left(\dfrac{x}{y}\right)^3 \left(\dfrac{y^2 x}{z}\right)^4} = (x^3 x^4)\left(\dfrac{y^8}{y^3}\right)\dfrac{1}{z^4}$ Group factors with the same base

$\phantom{\left(\dfrac{x}{y}\right)^3 \left(\dfrac{y^2 x}{z}\right)^4} = \dfrac{x^7 y^5}{z^4}$ Laws 1 and 2

✎ **Now Try Exercises 25 and 29** ■

When simplifying an expression, you will find that many different methods will lead to the same result; you should feel free to use any of the rules of exponents to arrive at your own method. In the next example we see how to simplify expressions with negative exponents.

EXAMPLE 5 ■ Simplifying Expressions with Negative Exponents

Eliminate negative exponents, and simplify each expression.

(a) $\dfrac{6st^{-4}}{2s^{-2}t^2}$ **(b)** $\left(\dfrac{y}{3z^3}\right)^{-2}$

SOLUTION

(a) We use Law 7, which allows us to move a number raised to a power from the numerator to the denominator (or vice versa) by changing the sign of the exponent.

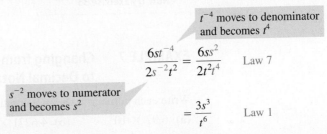

t^{-4} moves to denominator and becomes t^4

s^{-2} moves to numerator and becomes s^2

$$\frac{6st^{-4}}{2s^{-2}t^2} = \frac{6ss^2}{2t^2t^4} \quad \text{Law 7}$$

$$= \frac{3s^3}{t^6} \quad \text{Law 1}$$

(b) We use Law 6, which allows us to change the sign of the exponent of a fraction by inverting the fraction.

$$\left(\frac{y}{3z^3}\right)^{-2} = \left(\frac{3z^3}{y}\right)^2 \quad \text{Law 6}$$

$$= \frac{9z^6}{y^2} \quad \text{Laws 5 and 4}$$

✎ **Now Try Exercise 31** ■

■ Scientific Notation

Exponential notation is used by scientists as a compact way of writing very large numbers and very small numbers. For example, the nearest star beyond the sun, Proxima Centauri, is approximately 40,000,000,000,000 km away. The mass of a hydrogen atom is about 0.00000000000000000000000166 g. Such numbers are difficult to read and to write, so scientists usually express them in *scientific notation*.

> **SCIENTIFIC NOTATION**
>
> A positive number x is said to be written in **scientific notation** if it is expressed as follows:
>
> $$x = a \times 10^n \quad \text{where } 1 \le a < 10 \text{ and } n \text{ is an integer}$$

For instance, when we state that the distance to the star Proxima Centauri is 4×10^{13} km, the positive exponent 13 indicates that the decimal point should be moved 13 places to the *right*:

$$4 \times 10^{13} = 40,000,000,000,000$$

Move decimal point 13 places to the right

When we state that the mass of a hydrogen atom is 1.66×10^{-24} g, the exponent -24 indicates that the decimal point should be moved 24 places to the *left*:

$$1.66 \times 10^{-24} = 0.00000000000000000000000166$$

Move decimal point 24 places to the left

EXAMPLE 6 ■ Changing from Decimal Notation to Scientific Notation

Write each number in scientific notation.

(a) 56,920   **(b)** 0.000093

SOLUTION

(a) $56{,}920 = 5.692 \times 10^4$
$\underbrace{\qquad}_{\text{4 places}}$

(b) $0.000093 = 9.3 \times 10^{-5}$
$\underbrace{\qquad}_{\text{5 places}}$

✎ **Now Try Exercise 35** ■

EXAMPLE 7 ■ Changing from Scientific Notation to Decimal Notation

Write each number in decimal notation.

(a) 6.97×10^9 **(b)** 4.6271×10^{-6}

SOLUTION

(a) $6.97 \times 10^9 = 6{,}970{,}000{,}000$ Move decimal 9 places to the right
$\phantom{6.97 \times 10^9 = 6{,}9}\underbrace{\qquad\quad}_{\text{9 places}}$

(b) $4.6271 \times 10^{-6} = 0.0000046271$ Move decimal 6 places to the left
$\phantom{4.6271 \times 10^{-6} = 0.}\underbrace{\qquad\quad}_{\text{6 places}}$

✎ **Now Try Exercise 37** ■

To use scientific notation on a calculator, press the key labeled EE or EXP or EEX to enter the exponent. For example, to enter the number 3.629×10^{15} on a TI-83 or TI-84 calculator, we enter

3.629 2ND EE 15

and the display reads

3.629E15

Scientific notation is often used on a calculator to display a very large or very small number. For instance, if we use a calculator to square the number 1,111,111, the display panel may show (depending on the calculator model) the approximation

1.234568 12   or   1.234568 E12

Here the final digits indicate the power of 10, and we interpret the result as

$$1.234568 \times 10^{12}$$

EXAMPLE 8 ■ Calculating with Scientific Notation

If $a \approx 0.00046$, $b \approx 1.697 \times 10^{22}$, and $c \approx 2.91 \times 10^{-18}$, use a calculator to approximate the quotient ab/c.

SOLUTION We could enter the data using scientific notation, or we could use laws of exponents as follows:

$$\frac{ab}{c} \approx \frac{(4.6 \times 10^{-4})(1.697 \times 10^{22})}{2.91 \times 10^{-18}}$$

$$= \frac{(4.6)(1.697)}{2.91} \times 10^{-4+22+18}$$

$$\approx 2.7 \times 10^{36}$$

For guidelines on working with significant figures, see Appendix B, *Calculations and Significant Figures*.

We state the answer rounded to two significant figures because the least accurate of the given numbers is stated to two significant figures.

✎ **Now Try Exercise 41** ■

P.3 EXERCISES

CONCEPTS

1. Using exponential notation, we can write the product
$5 \cdot 5 \cdot 5 \cdot 5 \cdot 5 \cdot 5$ as _____.

2. Is there a difference between $(-5)^4$ and -5^4?

3. In the expression 3^4 the number 3 is called the _____,
and the number 4 is called the _____.

4. When we multiply two powers with the same base, we
_____ the exponents. So $3^4 \cdot 3^5 =$ _____.

5. When we divide two powers with the same base, we _____
the exponents. So $\dfrac{3^5}{3^2} =$ _____.

6. When we raise a power to a new power, we _____ the
exponents. So $(3^4)^2 =$ _____.

7. Express the following numbers without using exponents.

   (a) $2^{-1} =$ _____   (b) $2^{-3} =$ _____

   (c) $\left(\tfrac{1}{2}\right)^{-1} =$ _____   (d) $\dfrac{1}{2^{-3}} =$ _____

8. Scientists express very large or very small numbers using
_____ notation. In scientific notation 8,300,000 is
_____, and 0.0000327 is _____.

9–10 ■ *Yes or No?* If *No*, give a reason.

9. (a) Is the expression $\left(\tfrac{2}{3}\right)^{-2}$ equal to $\tfrac{3}{4}$?
   (b) Is there a difference between $(-5)^4$ and -5^4?

10. (a) Is the expression $(x^2)^3$ equal to x^5?
    (b) Is the expression $(2x^4)^3$ equal to $2x^{12}$?

SKILLS

11–18 ■ Exponential Notation   Evaluate each expression.

11. (a) -2^6 (b) $(-2)^6$ (c) $\left(\tfrac{1}{5}\right)^2 \cdot (-3)^3$

12. (a) $(-5)^3$ (b) -5^3 (c) $(-5)^2 \cdot \left(\tfrac{2}{5}\right)^2$

13. (a) $\left(\tfrac{5}{3}\right)^0 \cdot 2^{-1}$ (b) $\dfrac{2^{-3}}{3^0}$ (c) $\left(\tfrac{1}{4}\right)^{-2}$

14. (a) $-2^{-3} \cdot (-2)^0$ (b) $-2^3 \cdot (-2)^0$ (c) $\left(\tfrac{-2}{3}\right)^{-3}$

15. (a) $5^3 \cdot 5$ (b) $3^2 \cdot 3^0$ (c) $(2^2)^3$

16. (a) $3^8 \cdot 3^5$ (b) $6^0 \cdot 6$ (c) $(5^4)^2$

17. (a) $5^4 \cdot 5^{-2}$ (b) $\dfrac{10^7}{10^4}$ (c) $\dfrac{3^2}{3^4}$

18. (a) $3^{-3} \cdot 3^{-1}$ (b) $\dfrac{5^4}{5}$ (c) $\dfrac{7^2}{7^5}$

19–24 ■ Expressions with Exponents   Simplify each expression.

19. (a) $x^2 x^3$ (b) $(-x^2)^3$ (c) $t^{-3}t^5$

20. (a) $y^5 \cdot y^2$ (b) $(8x)^2$ (c) $x^4 x^{-3}$

21. (a) $x^{-5} \cdot x^3$ (b) $w^{-2}w^{-4}w^5$ (c) $\dfrac{y^{10}y^0}{y^7}$

22. (a) $y^2 \cdot y^{-5}$ (b) $z^5 z^{-3} z^{-4}$ (c) $\dfrac{x^6}{x^{10}}$

23. (a) $\dfrac{a^9 a^{-2}}{a}$ (b) $(a^2 a^4)^3$ (c) $(2x)^2(5x^6)$

24. (a) $\dfrac{z^2 z^4}{z^3 z^{-1}}$ (b) $(2a^3 a^2)^4$ (c) $(-3z^2)^3(2z^3)$

25–34 ■ Simplifying Expressions with Exponents   Simplify each expression, and eliminate any negative exponent(s).

25. (a) $(3x^2 y)(2x^3)$ (b) $(2a^2 b^{-1})(3a^{-2}b^2)$
    (c) $(4y^2)(x^4 y)^2$

26. (a) $(4x^3 y^2)(7y^5)$ (b) $(9y^{-2}z^2)(3y^3 z)$
    (c) $(8x^7 y^2)(\tfrac{1}{2}x^3 y)^{-2}$

27. (a) $(2x^2 y^3)^2(3y)$ (b) $\dfrac{x^2 y^{-1}}{x^{-5}}$

    (c) $\left(\dfrac{x^2 y}{3}\right)^3$

28. (a) $(5x^{-4}y^3)(8x^3)^2$ (b) $\dfrac{y^{-2}z^{-3}}{y^{-1}}$

    (c) $\left(\dfrac{a^3 b^{-2}}{b^3}\right)^2$

29. (a) $(x^3 y^3)^{-1}$ (b) $(a^2 b^{-2})^{-3}(a^3)^{-2}$
    (c) $\left(\dfrac{x^2}{y^{-2}}\right)^{-2}\left(\dfrac{2y^{-3}}{x^2}\right)^3$

30. (a) $(x^{-2}y^4)^{-3}$ (b) $(y^2)^{-1}(2x^{-3}y^4)^{-3}$
    (c) $\left(\dfrac{2a^{-1}}{b^{-2}}\right)^{-3}\left(\dfrac{b^{-1}}{2a^2}\right)^2$

31. (a) $\dfrac{3x^{-2}y^5}{9x^{-3}y^2}$ (b) $\left(\dfrac{2x^3 y^{-1}}{y^2}\right)^{-2}$

    (c) $\left(\dfrac{y^{-1}}{x^{-2}}\right)^{-1}\left(\dfrac{3x^{-3}}{y^2}\right)^{-2}$

32. (a) $\dfrac{\tfrac{1}{2}a^{-3}b^{-4}}{2a^{-5}b^{-1}}$ (b) $\left(\dfrac{x^2 y}{5x^4}\right)^{-2}$

    (c) $\left(\dfrac{2y^{-1}z}{z^2}\right)^{-1}\left(\dfrac{y}{3z^2}\right)^2$

33. (a) $\left(\dfrac{3a}{b^3}\right)^{-1}$ (b) $\left(\dfrac{q^{-1}r^{-1}s^{-2}}{r^{-5}sq^{-8}}\right)^{-1}$

34. (a) $\left(\dfrac{s^2 t^{-4}}{5s^{-1}t}\right)^{-2}$ (b) $\left(\dfrac{xy^{-2}z^{-3}}{x^2 y^3 z^{-4}}\right)^{-3}$

35–36 ▪ Scientific Notation   Write each number in scientific notation.

35. (a) 69,300,000
     (c) 0.000028536
     (b) 7,200,000,000,000
     (d) 0.0001213

36. (a) 129,540,000
     (c) 0.0000000014
     (b) 7,259,000,000
     (d) 0.0007029

37–38 ▪ Decimal Notation   Write each number in decimal notation.

37. (a) 3.19×10^5
     (c) 2.670×10^{-8}
     (b) 2.721×10^8
     (d) 9.999×10^{-9}

38. (a) 7.1×10^{14}
     (c) 8.55×10^{-3}
     (b) 6×10^{12}
     (d) 6.257×10^{-10}

39–40 ▪ Scientific Notation   Write the number indicated in each statement in scientific notation.

39. (a) A light-year, the distance that light travels in one year, is about 5,900,000,000,000 mi.

   (b) The diameter of an electron is about 0.0000000000004 cm.

   (c) A drop of water contains more than 33 billion billion molecules.

40. (a) The distance from the earth to the sun is about 93 million miles.

   (b) The mass of an oxygen molecule is about 0.0000000000000000000000053 g.

   (c) The mass of the earth is about 5,970,000,000,000,000,000,000,000 kg.

41–46 ▪ Scientific Notation   Use scientific notation, the Laws of Exponents, and a calculator to perform the indicated operations. State your answer rounded to the number of significant digits indicated by the given data.

41. $(7.2 \times 10^{-9})(1.806 \times 10^{-12})$

42. $(1.062 \times 10^{24})(8.61 \times 10^{19})$

43. $\dfrac{1.295643 \times 10^9}{(3.610 \times 10^{-17})(2.511 \times 10^6)}$

44. $\dfrac{(73.1)(1.6341 \times 10^{28})}{0.0000000019}$

45. $\dfrac{(0.0000162)(0.01582)}{(594,621,000)(0.0058)}$

46. $\dfrac{(3.542 \times 10^{-6})^9}{(5.05 \times 10^4)^{12}}$

SKILLS Plus

47. Distances Between Powers   Which pair of numbers is closer together?

$$10^{10} \text{ and } 10^{50} \quad \text{ or } \quad 10^{100} \text{ and } 10^{101}$$

48. Signs of Numbers   Let a, b, and c be real numbers with $a > 0$, $b < 0$, and $c < 0$. Determine the sign of each expression.

   (a) b^5 **(b)** b^{10} **(c)** ab^2c^3

   (d) $(b - a)^3$ **(e)** $(b - a)^4$ **(f)** $\dfrac{a^3c^3}{b^6c^6}$

APPLICATIONS

49. Distance to the Nearest Star   Proxima Centauri, the star nearest to our solar system, is 4.3 light-years away. Use the information in Exercise 39(a) to express this distance in miles.

50. Speed of Light   The speed of light is about 186,000 mi/s. Use the information in Exercise 40(a) to find how long it takes for a light ray from the sun to reach the earth.

51. Volume of the Oceans   The average ocean depth is 3.7×10^3 m, and the area of the oceans is 3.6×10^{14} m^2. What is the total volume of the ocean in liters? (One cubic meter contains 1000 liters.)

52. National Debt   As of July 2013, the population of the United States was 3.164×10^8, and the national debt was 1.674×10^{13} dollars. How much was each person's share of the debt?
[*Source:* U.S. Census Bureau and U.S. Department of Treasury]

53. Number of Molecules   A sealed room in a hospital, measuring 5 m wide, 10 m long, and 3 m high, is filled with pure oxygen. One cubic meter contains 1000 L, and 22.4 L of any gas contains 6.02×10^{23} molecules (Avogadro's number). How many molecules of oxygen are there in the room?

54. Body-Mass Index   The body-mass index is a measure that medical researchers use to determine whether a person is overweight, underweight, or of normal weight. For a person who weighs W pounds and who is H inches tall, the body-mass index B is given by

$$B = 703 \frac{W}{H^2}$$

A body-mass index is considered "normal" if it satisfies $18.5 \le B \le 24.9$, while a person with body-mass index $B \ge 30$ is considered obese.

   (a) Calculate the body-mass index for each person listed in the table, then determine whether he or she is of normal weight, underweight, overweight, or obese.

Person	Weight	Height
Brian	295 lb	5 ft 10 in.
Linda	105 lb	5 ft 6 in.
Larry	220 lb	6 ft 4 in.
Helen	110 lb	5 ft 2 in.

   (b) Determine your own body-mass index.

55. Interest on a CD A sum of $5000 is invested in a 5-year certificate of deposit paying 3% interest per year, compounded monthly. After n years the amount of interest I that has accumulated is given by

$$I = 5000[(1.0025)^{12n} - 1]$$

Complete the following table, which gives the amount of interest accumulated after the given number of years.

Year	Total interest
1	$152.08
2	308.79
3	
4	
5	

DISCUSS ■ **DISCOVER** ■ **PROVE** ■ **WRITE**

56. DISCUSS: How Big Is a Billion? If you had a million (10^6) dollars in a suitcase and you spent a thousand (10^3) dollars each day, how many years would it take you to use all the money? If you spent at the same rate, how many years would it take you to empty a suitcase filled with a *billion* (10^9) dollars?

57. DISCUSS: Easy Powers That Look Hard Calculate these expressions in your head. Use the Laws of Exponents to help you.

(a) $\dfrac{18^5}{9^5}$ (b) $20^6 \cdot (0.5)^6$

58. PROVE: Laws of Exponents Prove the following laws of exponents for the case in which m and n are positive integers and $m > n$.

(a) Law 2: $\dfrac{a^m}{a^n} = a^{m-n}$ (b) Law 5: $\left(\dfrac{a}{b}\right)^n = \dfrac{a^n}{b^n}$

59. PROVE: Laws of Exponents Prove the following laws of exponents.

(a) Law 6: $\left(\dfrac{a}{b}\right)^{-n} = \dfrac{b^n}{a^n}$ (b) Law 7: $\dfrac{a^{-n}}{b^{-m}} = \dfrac{b^m}{a^n}$

P.4 RATIONAL EXPONENTS AND RADICALS

■ **Radicals** ■ **Rational Exponents** ■ **Rationalizing the Denominator; Standard Form**

In this section we learn to work with expressions that contain radicals or rational exponents.

■ Radicals

We know what 2^n means whenever n is an integer. To give meaning to a power, such as $2^{4/5}$, whose exponent is a rational number, we need to discuss radicals.

The symbol $\sqrt{}$ means "the positive square root of." Thus

$$\sqrt{a} = b \quad \text{means} \quad b^2 = a \quad \text{and} \quad b \geq 0$$

Since $a = b^2 \geq 0$, the symbol $\sqrt{a}$ makes sense only when $a \geq 0$. For instance,

$$\sqrt{9} = 3 \quad \text{because} \quad 3^2 = 9 \quad \text{and} \quad 3 \geq 0$$

Square roots are special cases of nth roots. The nth root of x is the number that, when raised to the nth power, gives x.

It is true that the number 9 has two square roots, 3 and -3, but the notation $\sqrt{9}$ is reserved for the *positive* square root of 9 (sometimes called the *principal square root* of 9). If we want the negative root, we must write $-\sqrt{9}$, which is -3.

DEFINITION OF nth ROOT

If n is any positive integer, then the **principal nth root** of a is defined as follows:

$$\sqrt[n]{a} = b \quad \text{means} \quad b^n = a$$

If n is even, we must have $a \geq 0$ and $b \geq 0$.

For example,

$$\sqrt[4]{81} = 3 \qquad \text{because} \qquad 3^4 = 81 \qquad \text{and} \qquad 3 \geq 0$$

$$\sqrt[3]{-8} = -2 \qquad \text{because} \qquad (-2)^3 = -8$$

But $\sqrt{-8}$, $\sqrt[4]{-8}$, and $\sqrt[6]{-8}$ are not defined. (For instance, $\sqrt{-8}$ is not defined because the square of every real number is nonnegative.)

Notice that

$$\sqrt{4^2} = \sqrt{16} = 4 \qquad \text{but} \qquad \sqrt{(-4)^2} = \sqrt{16} = 4 = |-4|$$

So the equation $\sqrt{a^2} = a$ is not always true; it is true only when $a \geq 0$. However, we can always write $\sqrt{a^2} = |a|$. This last equation is true not only for square roots, but for any even root. This and other rules used in working with nth roots are listed in the following box. In each property we assume that all the given roots exist.

PROPERTIES OF nth ROOTS

Property	Example
1. $\sqrt[n]{ab} = \sqrt[n]{a}\,\sqrt[n]{b}$	$\sqrt[3]{-8 \cdot 27} = \sqrt[3]{-8}\,\sqrt[3]{27} = (-2)(3) = -6$
2. $\sqrt[n]{\dfrac{a}{b}} = \dfrac{\sqrt[n]{a}}{\sqrt[n]{b}}$	$\sqrt[4]{\dfrac{16}{81}} = \dfrac{\sqrt[4]{16}}{\sqrt[4]{81}} = \dfrac{2}{3}$
3. $\sqrt[m]{\sqrt[n]{a}} = \sqrt[mn]{a}$	$\sqrt{\sqrt[3]{729}} = \sqrt[6]{729} = 3$
4. $\sqrt[n]{a^n} = a$ if n is odd	$\sqrt[3]{(-5)^3} = -5, \quad \sqrt[5]{2^5} = 2$
5. $\sqrt[n]{a^n} = |a|$ if n is even	$\sqrt[4]{(-3)^4} = |-3| = 3$

EXAMPLE 1 ■ Simplifying Expressions Involving nth Roots

(a) $\sqrt[3]{x^4} = \sqrt[3]{x^3 x}$ Factor out the largest cube

$\phantom{\sqrt[3]{x^4}} = \sqrt[3]{x^3}\,\sqrt[3]{x}$ Property 1: $\sqrt[3]{ab} = \sqrt[3]{a}\,\sqrt[3]{b}$

$\phantom{\sqrt[3]{x^4}} = x\sqrt[3]{x}$ Property 4: $\sqrt[3]{a^3} = a$

(b) $\sqrt[4]{81x^8y^4} = \sqrt[4]{81}\,\sqrt[4]{x^8}\,\sqrt[4]{y^4}$ Property 1: $\sqrt[4]{abc} = \sqrt[4]{a}\,\sqrt[4]{b}\,\sqrt[4]{c}$

$\phantom{\sqrt[4]{81x^8y^4}} = 3\sqrt[4]{(x^2)^4}\,|y|$ Property 5: $\sqrt[4]{a^4} = |a|$

$\phantom{\sqrt[4]{81x^8y^4}} = 3x^2|y|$ Property 5: $\sqrt[4]{a^4} = |a|, |x^2| = x^2$

✎ **Now Try Exercises 27 and 35**

It is frequently useful to combine like radicals in an expression such as $2\sqrt{3} + 5\sqrt{3}$. This can be done by using the Distributive Property. For example,

$$2\sqrt{3} + 5\sqrt{3} = (2 + 5)\sqrt{3} = 7\sqrt{3}$$

The next example further illustrates this process.

 Avoid making the following error:

$$\sqrt{a + b} \quad \text{✗} \quad \sqrt{a} + \sqrt{b}$$

For instance, if we let $a = 9$ and $b = 16$, then we see the error:

$$\sqrt{9 + 16} \stackrel{?}{=} \sqrt{9} + \sqrt{16}$$

$$\sqrt{25} \stackrel{?}{=} 3 + 4$$

$$5 \stackrel{?}{=} 7 \quad \text{Wrong!}$$

EXAMPLE 2 ■ Combining Radicals

(a) $\sqrt{32} + \sqrt{200} = \sqrt{16 \cdot 2} + \sqrt{100 \cdot 2}$ Factor out the largest squares

$\phantom{\sqrt{32} + \sqrt{200}} = \sqrt{16}\sqrt{2} + \sqrt{100}\sqrt{2}$ Property 1

$\phantom{\sqrt{32} + \sqrt{200}} = 4\sqrt{2} + 10\sqrt{2} = 14\sqrt{2}$ Distributive Property

(b) If $b > 0$, then

$$\sqrt{25b} - \sqrt{b^3} = \sqrt{25}\sqrt{b} - \sqrt{b^2}\sqrt{b} \qquad \text{Property 1: } \sqrt{xy} = \sqrt{x}\sqrt{y}$$
$$= 5\sqrt{b} - b\sqrt{b} \qquad \text{Property 5, } b > 0$$
$$= (5 - b)\sqrt{b} \qquad \text{Distributive Property}$$

(c) $\sqrt{49x^2 + 49} = \sqrt{49(x^2 + 1)} \qquad \text{Factor out 49}$
$$= 7\sqrt{x^2 + 1} \qquad \text{Property 1: } \sqrt{ab} = \sqrt{a}\sqrt{b}$$

✎ **Now Try Exercises 39, 43, and 47** ■

■ Rational Exponents

To define what is meant by a *rational exponent* or, equivalently, a *fractional exponent* such as $a^{1/3}$, we need to use radicals. To give meaning to the symbol $a^{1/n}$ in a way that is consistent with the Laws of Exponents, we would have to have

$$(a^{1/n})^n = a^{(1/n)n} = a^1 = a$$

So by the definition of nth root,

$$\boxed{a^{1/n} = \sqrt[n]{a}}$$

In general, we define rational exponents as follows.

> **DEFINITION OF RATIONAL EXPONENTS**
>
> For any rational exponent m/n in lowest terms, where m and n are integers and $n > 0$, we define
>
> $$a^{m/n} = (\sqrt[n]{a})^m \qquad \text{or equivalently} \qquad a^{m/n} = \sqrt[n]{a^m}$$
>
> If n is even, then we require that $a \geq 0$.

With this definition it can be proved that *the Laws of Exponents also hold for rational exponents* (see page 19).

EXAMPLE 3 ■ Using the Definition of Rational Exponents

(a) $4^{1/2} = \sqrt{4} = 2$
(b) $8^{2/3} = (\sqrt[3]{8})^2 = 2^2 = 4 \qquad$ Alternative solution: $8^{2/3} = \sqrt[3]{8^2} = \sqrt[3]{64} = 4$
(c) $125^{-1/3} = \dfrac{1}{125^{1/3}} = \dfrac{1}{\sqrt[3]{125}} = \dfrac{1}{5}$

✎ **Now Try Exercises 49 and 51** ■

EXAMPLE 4 ■ Using the Laws of Exponents with Rational Exponents

(a) $a^{1/3}a^{7/3} = a^{8/3} \qquad \text{Law 1: } a^m a^n = a^{m+n}$
(b) $\dfrac{a^{2/5}a^{7/5}}{a^{3/5}} = a^{2/5 + 7/5 - 3/5} = a^{6/5} \qquad \text{Law 1, Law 2: } \dfrac{a^m}{a^n} = a^{m-n}$

(c) $(2a^3b^4)^{3/2} = 2^{3/2}(a^3)^{3/2}(b^4)^{3/2}$ Law 4: $(abc)^n = a^nb^nc^n$

$\quad\quad = (\sqrt{2})^3a^{3(3/2)}b^{4(3/2)}$ Law 3: $(a^m)^n = a^{mn}$

$\quad\quad = 2\sqrt{2}a^{9/2}b^6$

(d) $\left(\dfrac{2x^{3/4}}{y^{1/3}}\right)^3\left(\dfrac{y^4}{x^{-1/2}}\right) = \dfrac{2^3(x^{3/4})^3}{(y^{1/3})^3}\cdot(y^4x^{1/2})$ Laws 5, 4, and 7

$\quad\quad = \dfrac{8x^{9/4}}{y}\cdot y^4x^{1/2}$ Law 3

$\quad\quad = 8x^{11/4}y^3$ Laws 1 and 2

✎ **Now Try Exercises 59, 61, 63, and 67**   ■

EXAMPLE 5 ■ Simplifying by Writing Radicals as Rational Exponents

(a) $\dfrac{1}{\sqrt[3]{x^4}} = \dfrac{1}{x^{4/3}} = x^{-4/3}$ Definition of rational and negative exponents

(b) $(2\sqrt{x})(3\sqrt[3]{x}) = (2x^{1/2})(3x^{1/3})$ Definition of rational exponents

$\quad\quad = 6x^{1/2+1/3} = 6x^{5/6}$ Law 1

(c) $\sqrt{x\sqrt{x}} = (xx^{1/2})^{1/2}$ Definition of rational exponents

$\quad\quad = (x^{3/2})^{1/2}$ Law 1

$\quad\quad = x^{3/4}$ Law 3

✎ **Now Try Exercises 71, 75, and 83**   ■

■ Rationalizing the Denominator; Standard Form

It is often useful to eliminate the radical in a denominator by multiplying both numerator and denominator by an appropriate expression. This procedure is called **rationalizing the denominator**. If the denominator is of the form $\sqrt{a}$, we multiply numerator and denominator by $\sqrt{a}$. In doing this we multiply the given quantity by 1, so we do not change its value. For instance,

$$\frac{1}{\sqrt{a}} = \frac{1}{\sqrt{a}}\cdot 1 = \frac{1}{\sqrt{a}}\cdot\frac{\sqrt{a}}{\sqrt{a}} = \frac{\sqrt{a}}{a}$$

Note that the denominator in the last fraction contains no radical. In general, if the denominator is of the form $\sqrt[n]{a^m}$ with $m < n$, then multiplying the numerator and denominator by $\sqrt[n]{a^{n-m}}$ will rationalize the denominator, because (for $a > 0$)

$$\sqrt[n]{a^m}\sqrt[n]{a^{n-m}} = \sqrt[n]{a^{m+n-m}} = \sqrt[n]{a^n} = a$$

A fractional expression whose denominator contains no radicals is said to be in **standard form**.

EXAMPLE 6 ■ Rationalizing Denominators

Put each fractional expression into standard form by rationalizing the denominator.

(a) $\dfrac{2}{\sqrt{3}}$ **(b)** $\dfrac{1}{\sqrt[3]{5}}$ **(c)** $\sqrt[7]{\dfrac{1}{a^2}}$

SOLUTION

$\boxed{\text{This equals 1}}$

(a) $\dfrac{2}{\sqrt{3}} = \dfrac{2}{\sqrt{3}}\cdot\dfrac{\sqrt{3}}{\sqrt{3}}$ Multiply by $\dfrac{\sqrt{3}}{\sqrt{3}}$

$\quad\quad = \dfrac{2\sqrt{3}}{3}$ $\sqrt{3}\cdot\sqrt{3} = 3$

(b) $\dfrac{1}{\sqrt[3]{5}} = \dfrac{1}{\sqrt[3]{5}} \cdot \dfrac{\sqrt[3]{5^2}}{\sqrt[3]{5^2}}$ Multiply by $\dfrac{\sqrt[3]{5^2}}{\sqrt[3]{5^2}}$

$= \dfrac{\sqrt[3]{25}}{5}$ $\sqrt[3]{5} \cdot \sqrt[3]{5^2} = \sqrt[3]{5^3} = 5$

(c) $\sqrt[7]{\dfrac{1}{a^2}} = \dfrac{1}{\sqrt[7]{a^2}}$ Property 2: $\sqrt[n]{\dfrac{a}{b}} = \dfrac{\sqrt[n]{a}}{\sqrt[n]{b}}$

$= \dfrac{1}{\sqrt[7]{a^2}} \cdot \dfrac{\sqrt[7]{a^5}}{\sqrt[7]{a^5}}$ Multiply by $\dfrac{\sqrt[7]{a^5}}{\sqrt[7]{a^5}}$

$= \dfrac{\sqrt[7]{a^5}}{a}$ $\sqrt[7]{a^2} \cdot \sqrt[7]{a^5} = a$

✎ **Now Try Exercises 85, 87, and 89** ■

P.4 EXERCISES

CONCEPTS

1. Using exponential notation, we can write $\sqrt[3]{5}$ as _____.

2. Using radicals, we can write $5^{1/2}$ as _____.

3. Is there a difference between $\sqrt{5^2}$ and $(\sqrt{5})^2$? Explain.

4. Explain what $4^{3/2}$ means, then calculate $4^{3/2}$ in two different ways:

   $(4^{1/2})^{\boxed{}} =$ _____   or $(4^3)^{\boxed{}} =$ _____

5. Explain how we rationalize a denominator, then complete the following steps to rationalize $\dfrac{1}{\sqrt{3}}$:

   $\dfrac{1}{\sqrt{3}} = \dfrac{1}{\sqrt{3}} \cdot \dfrac{\boxed{}}{\boxed{}} = \dfrac{\boxed{}}{\boxed{}}$

6. Find the missing power in the following calculation:
   $5^{1/3} \cdot 5^{\boxed{}} = 5$.

7–8 ■ *Yes or No?* If *No*, give a reason.

7. Is the expression $\sqrt{4a^2}$ necessarily equal to $2a$?

8. Is the expression $\sqrt{a^2 + 4}$ necessarily equal to $a + 2$?

SKILLS

9–18 ■ **Radicals and Exponents** Write each radical expression using exponents and each exponential expression using radicals.

Radical expression	Exponential expression
9. $\dfrac{1}{\sqrt{3}}$	
10. $\sqrt[3]{7^2}$	
11.	$4^{2/3}$
12.	$10^{-3/2}$

13. $\sqrt[5]{5^3}$	
14.	$2^{-1.5}$
15.	$a^{2/5}$
16. $\dfrac{1}{\sqrt{x^5}}$	
17. $\sqrt[3]{y^4}$	
18.	$y^{-5/3}$

19–26 ■ **Evaluating Radicals** Evaluate each expression.

19. (a) $\sqrt{16}$ (b) $\sqrt[4]{16}$ (c) $\sqrt[4]{\tfrac{1}{16}}$

20. (a) $\sqrt{64}$ (b) $\sqrt[3]{-64}$ (c) $\sqrt[5]{-32}$

21. (a) $3\sqrt[3]{16}$ (b) $\dfrac{\sqrt{18}}{\sqrt{81}}$ (c) $\sqrt{\tfrac{27}{4}}$

22. (a) $2\sqrt[3]{81}$ (b) $\dfrac{\sqrt{12}}{\sqrt{25}}$ (c) $\sqrt{\tfrac{18}{49}}$

23. (a) $\sqrt{7}\sqrt{28}$ (b) $\dfrac{\sqrt{48}}{\sqrt{3}}$ (c) $\sqrt[4]{24}\sqrt[4]{54}$

24. (a) $\sqrt{12}\sqrt{24}$ (b) $\dfrac{\sqrt{54}}{\sqrt{6}}$ (c) $\sqrt[3]{15}\sqrt[3]{75}$

25. (a) $\dfrac{\sqrt{216}}{\sqrt{6}}$ (b) $\sqrt[3]{2}\sqrt[3]{32}$ (c) $\sqrt[4]{\tfrac{1}{4}}\sqrt[4]{\tfrac{1}{64}}$

26. (a) $\sqrt[5]{\tfrac{1}{8}}\sqrt[5]{\tfrac{1}{4}}$ (b) $\sqrt[6]{\tfrac{1}{2}}\sqrt[6]{128}$ (c) $\dfrac{\sqrt[3]{4}}{\sqrt[3]{108}}$

27–38 ■ **Simplifying Radicals** Simplify the expression. Assume that the letters denote any real numbers.

27. $\sqrt[4]{x^4}$ 28. $\sqrt[5]{x^{10}}$

29. $\sqrt[5]{32y^6}$ 30. $\sqrt[3]{8a^5}$

31. $\sqrt[4]{16x^8}$ 32. $\sqrt[3]{x^3y^6}$

33. $\sqrt[3]{x^3 y}$

34. $\sqrt{x^4 y^4}$

35. $\sqrt{36r^2 t^4}$

36. $\sqrt[4]{48a^7 b^4}$

37. $\sqrt[3]{\sqrt{64x^6}}$

38. $\sqrt[4]{x^4 y^2 z^2}$

39–48 ■ **Combining Radicals** Simplify the expression. Assume that all letters denote positive numbers.

39. $\sqrt{32} + \sqrt{18}$

40. $\sqrt{75} + \sqrt{48}$

41. $\sqrt{125} - \sqrt{45}$

42. $\sqrt[3]{54} - \sqrt[3]{16}$

43. $\sqrt{9a^3} - \sqrt{a}$

44. $\sqrt{16x} + \sqrt{x^5}$

45. $\sqrt[3]{x^4} + \sqrt[3]{8x}$

46. $\sqrt[3]{2y^4} - \sqrt[3]{2y}$

47. $\sqrt{81x^2 + 81}$

48. $\sqrt{36x^2 + 36y^2}$

49–54 ■ **Rational Exponents** Evaluate each expression.

49. (a) $16^{1/4}$ (b) $-125^{1/3}$ (c) $9^{-1/2}$

50. (a) $27^{1/3}$ (b) $(-8)^{1/3}$ (c) $-\left(\frac{1}{8}\right)^{1/3}$

51. (a) $32^{2/5}$ (b) $\left(\frac{4}{9}\right)^{-1/2}$ (c) $\left(\frac{16}{81}\right)^{3/4}$

52. (a) $125^{2/3}$ (b) $\left(\frac{25}{64}\right)^{3/2}$ (c) $27^{-4/3}$

53. (a) $5^{2/3} \cdot 5^{1/3}$ (b) $\dfrac{3^{3/5}}{3^{2/5}}$ (c) $(\sqrt[3]{4})^3$

54. (a) $3^{2/7} \cdot 3^{12/7}$ (b) $\dfrac{7^{2/3}}{7^{5/3}}$ (c) $(\sqrt[5]{6})^{-10}$

55–58 ■ **Evaluating for Given Values** Evaluate the expression using $x = 3$, $y = 4$, and $z = -1$.

55. $\sqrt{x^2 + y^2}$

56. $\sqrt[4]{x^3 + 14y + 2z}$

57. $(9x)^{2/3} + (2y)^{2/3} + z^{2/3}$

58. $(xy)^{2z}$

59–68 ■ **Simplifying Expressions Involving Rational Exponents** Simplify the expression and eliminate any negative exponent(s). Assume that all letters denote positive numbers.

59. (a) $x^{3/4} x^{5/4}$ (b) $y^{2/3} y^{4/3}$

60. (a) $r^{1/6} r^{5/6}$ (b) $a^{3/5} a^{3/10}$

61. (a) $\dfrac{w^{4/3} w^{2/3}}{w^{1/3}}$ (b) $\dfrac{a^{5/4}(2a^{3/4})^3}{a^{1/4}}$

62. (a) $\dfrac{x^{3/4} x^{7/4}}{x^{5/4}}$ (b) $\dfrac{(2y^{4/3})^2 y^{-2/3}}{y^{7/3}}$

63. (a) $(8a^6 b^{3/2})^{2/3}$ (b) $(4a^6 b^8)^{3/2}$

64. (a) $(64a^6 b^3)^{2/3}$ (b) $(16w^8 z^3)^{3/4}$

65. (a) $(8y^3)^{-2/3}$ (b) $(u^4 v^6)^{-1/3}$

66. (a) $(x^{-5} y^{1/3})^{-3/5}$ (b) $(4r^8 t^{-1/2})^{1/2}(32t^{-5/4})^{-1/5}$

67. (a) $\left(\dfrac{x^{-2/3}}{y^{1/2}}\right)\left(\dfrac{x^{-2}}{y^{-3}}\right)^{1/6}$ (b) $\left(\dfrac{x^{1/2} y^2}{2y^{1/4}}\right)^4 \left(\dfrac{4x^{-2} y^{-4}}{y^2}\right)^{1/2}$

68. (a) $\left(\dfrac{x^8 y^{-4}}{16y^{4/3}}\right)^{-1/4}$ (b) $\left(\dfrac{-8y^{3/4}}{y^3 z^6}\right)^{-1/3}$

69–84 ■ **Simplifying Expressions Involving Radicals** Simplify the expression and express the answer using rational exponents. Assume that all letters denote positive numbers.

69. (a) $\sqrt{x^3}$

70. $\sqrt{x^5}$

71. $\sqrt[9]{x^5}$

72. $\dfrac{1}{\sqrt[5]{x^3}}$

73. $(\sqrt[6]{y^5})(\sqrt[3]{y^2})$

74. $\sqrt[4]{b^3} \sqrt{b}$

75. $(5\sqrt[3]{x})(2\sqrt[4]{x})$

76. $(2\sqrt{a})(\sqrt[3]{a^2})$

77. $\dfrac{\sqrt[4]{x^7}}{\sqrt[4]{x^3}}$

78. $\dfrac{\sqrt[3]{8x^2}}{\sqrt{x}}$

79. $\sqrt{\dfrac{16u^3 v}{uv^5}}$

80. $\sqrt[3]{\dfrac{54x^2 y^4}{2x^5 y}}$

81. $\dfrac{\sqrt{xy}}{\sqrt[4]{16xy}}$

82. $\dfrac{\sqrt{a^3 b}}{\sqrt[4]{a^3 b^2}}$

83. $\sqrt[3]{y\sqrt{y}}$

84. $\sqrt{s\sqrt{s^3}}$

85–90 ■ **Rationalizing the Denominator** Put each fractional expression into standard form by rationalizing the denominator.

85. (a) $\dfrac{1}{\sqrt{6}}$ (b) $\sqrt{\dfrac{3}{2}}$ (c) $\dfrac{9}{\sqrt[4]{2}}$

86. (a) $\dfrac{12}{\sqrt{3}}$ (b) $\sqrt{\dfrac{12}{5}}$ (c) $\dfrac{8}{\sqrt[3]{5^2}}$

87. (a) $\dfrac{1}{\sqrt{5x}}$ (b) $\sqrt{\dfrac{x}{5}}$ (c) $\sqrt[5]{\dfrac{1}{x^3}}$

88. (a) $\sqrt{\dfrac{s}{3t}}$ (b) $\dfrac{a}{\sqrt[6]{b^2}}$ (c) $\dfrac{1}{c^{3/5}}$

89. (a) $\dfrac{1}{\sqrt[3]{x}}$ (b) $\dfrac{1}{\sqrt[6]{x^5}}$ (c) $\dfrac{1}{\sqrt[7]{x^3}}$

90. (a) $\dfrac{1}{\sqrt[3]{x^2}}$ (b) $\dfrac{1}{\sqrt[4]{x^3}}$ (c) $\dfrac{1}{\sqrt[3]{x^4}}$

SKILLS Plus

91–92 ■ **Comparing Roots** Without using a calculator, determine which number is larger in each pair.

91. (a) $2^{1/2}$ or $2^{1/3}$ (b) $\left(\frac{1}{2}\right)^{1/2}$ or $\left(\frac{1}{2}\right)^{1/3}$

92. (a) $7^{1/4}$ or $4^{1/3}$ (b) $\sqrt[3]{5}$ or $\sqrt{3}$

APPLICATIONS

93. How Far Can You See? Because of the curvature of the earth, the maximum distance D that you can see from the top of a tall building of height h is estimated by the formula

$$D = \sqrt{2rh + h^2}$$

where $r = 3960$ mi is the radius of the earth and D and h are also measured in miles. How far can you see from the observation deck of the Toronto CN Tower, 1135 ft above the ground?

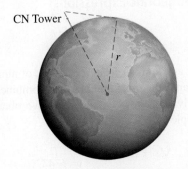

CN Tower

r

94. Speed of a Skidding Car Police use the formula

$$s = \sqrt{30fd}$$

to estimate the speed s (in mi/h) at which a car is traveling if it skids d feet after the brakes are applied suddenly. The number f is the coefficient of friction of the road, which is a measure of the "slipperiness" of the road. The table gives some typical estimates for f.

	Tar	**Concrete**	**Gravel**
Dry	1.0	0.8	0.2
Wet	0.5	0.4	0.1

(a) If a car skids 65 ft on wet concrete, how fast was it moving when the brakes were applied?

(b) If a car is traveling at 50 mi/h, how far will it skid on wet tar?

95. Sailboat Races The speed that a sailboat is capable of sailing is determined by three factors: its total length L, the surface area A of its sails, and its displacement V (the volume of water it displaces).

In general, a sailboat is capable of greater speed if it is longer, has a larger sail area, or displaces less water. To make sailing races fair, only boats in the same "class" can qualify to race together. For a certain race, a boat is considered to qualify if

$$0.30L + 0.38A^{1/2} - 3V^{1/3} \le 16$$

where L is measured in feet, A in square feet, and V in cubic feet. Use this inequality to answer the following questions.

(a) A sailboat has length 60 ft, sail area 3400 ft^2, and displacement 650 ft^3. Does this boat qualify for the race?

(b) A sailboat has length 65 ft and displaces 600 ft^3. What is the largest possible sail area that could be used and still allow the boat to qualify for this race?

96. Flow Speed in a Channel The speed of water flowing in a channel, such as a canal or river bed, is governed by the Manning Equation,

$$V = 1.486\frac{A^{2/3}S^{1/2}}{p^{2/3}n}$$

Here V is the velocity of the flow in ft/s; A is the cross-sectional area of the channel in square feet; S is the downward slope of the channel; p is the wetted perimeter in feet (the distance from the top of one bank, down the side of the channel, across the bottom, and up to the top of the other bank); and n is the roughness coefficient (a measure of the roughness of the channel bottom). This equation is used to predict the capacity of flood channels to handle runoff from heavy rainfalls. For the canal shown in the figure, $A = 75$ ft^2, $S = 0.050$, $p = 24.1$ ft, and $n = 0.040$.

(a) Find the speed at which water flows through the canal.

(b) How many cubic feet of water can the canal discharge per second? [*Hint:* Multiply V by A to get the volume of the flow per second.]

20 ft

5 ft

10 ft

DISCUSS ■ DISCOVER ■ PROVE ■ WRITE

97. DISCOVER: Limiting Behavior of Powers Complete the following tables. What happens to the nth root of 2 as n gets large? What about the nth root of $\frac{1}{2}$?

n	$2^{1/n}$		n	$\left(\frac{1}{2}\right)^{1/n}$
1			1	
2			2	
5			5	
10			10	
100			100	

Construct a similar table for $n^{1/n}$. What happens to the nth root of n as n gets large?

P.5 ALGEBRAIC EXPRESSIONS

■ **Adding and Subtracting Polynomials** ■ **Multiplying Algebraic Expressions**
■ **Special Product Formulas**

A **variable** is a letter that can represent any number from a given set of numbers. If we start with variables, such as x, y, and z, and some real numbers and combine them using addition, subtraction, multiplication, division, powers, and roots, we obtain an **algebraic expression**. Here are some examples:

$$2x^2 - 3x + 4 \qquad \sqrt{x} + 10 \qquad \frac{y - 2z}{y^2 + 4}$$

A **monomial** is an expression of the form ax^k, where a is a real number and k is a nonnegative integer. A **binomial** is a sum of two monomials and a **trinomial** is a sum of three monomials. In general, a sum of monomials is called a *polynomial*. For example, the first expression listed above is a polynomial, but the other two are not.

POLYNOMIALS

A **polynomial** in the variable x is an expression of the form

$$a_n x^n + a_{n-1} x^{n-1} + \cdots + a_1 x + a_0$$

where $a_0, a_1, \ldots, a_n$ are real numbers, and n is a nonnegative integer. If $a_n \neq 0$, then the polynomial has **degree n**. The monomials $a_k x^k$ that make up the polynomial are called the **terms** of the polynomial.

Note that the degree of a polynomial is the highest power of the variable that appears in the polynomial.

Polynomial	Type	Terms	Degree
$2x^2 - 3x + 4$	trinomial	$2x^2, -3x, 4$	2
$x^8 + 5x$	binomial	$x^8, 5x$	8
$8 - x + x^2 - \frac{1}{2}x^3$	four terms	$-\frac{1}{2}x^3, x^2, -x, 8$	3
$5x + 1$	binomial	$5x, 1$	1
$9x^5$	monomial	$9x^5$	5
6	monomial	6	0

■ Adding and Subtracting Polynomials

We **add** and **subtract** polynomials using the properties of real numbers that were discussed in Section P.2. The idea is to combine **like terms** (that is, terms with the same variables raised to the same powers) using the Distributive Property. For instance,

$$5x^7 + 3x^7 = (5 + 3)x^7 = 8x^7$$

Distributive Property

$$ac + bc = (a + b)c$$

 In subtracting polynomials, we have to remember that if a minus sign precedes an expression in parentheses, then the sign of every term within the parentheses is changed when we remove the parentheses:

$$-(b + c) = -b - c$$

[This is simply a case of the Distributive Property, $a(b + c) = ab + ac$, with $a = -1$.]

EXAMPLE 1 ■ Adding and Subtracting Polynomials

(a) Find the sum $(x^3 - 6x^2 + 2x + 4) + (x^3 + 5x^2 - 7x)$.

(b) Find the difference $(x^3 - 6x^2 + 2x + 4) - (x^3 + 5x^2 - 7x)$.

SOLUTION

(a) $(x^3 - 6x^2 + 2x + 4) + (x^3 + 5x^2 - 7x)$

$$= (x^3 + x^3) + (-6x^2 + 5x^2) + (2x - 7x) + 4 \qquad \text{Group like terms}$$

$$= 2x^3 - x^2 - 5x + 4 \qquad \text{Combine like terms}$$

(b) $(x^3 - 6x^2 + 2x + 4) - (x^3 + 5x^2 - 7x)$

$$= x^3 - 6x^2 + 2x + 4 - x^3 - 5x^2 + 7x \qquad \text{Distributive Property}$$

$$= (x^3 - x^3) + (-6x^2 - 5x^2) + (2x + 7x) + 4 \qquad \text{Group like terms}$$

$$= -11x^2 + 9x + 4 \qquad \text{Combine like terms}$$

✎ **Now Try Exercises 17 and 21** ∎

■ Multiplying Algebraic Expressions

To find the **product** of polynomials or other algebraic expressions, we need to use the Distributive Property repeatedly. In particular, using it three times on the product of two binomials, we get

$$(a + b)(c + d) = a(c + d) + b(c + d) = ac + ad + bc + bd$$

This says that we multiply the two factors by multiplying each term in one factor by each term in the other factor and adding these products. Schematically, we have

The acronym **FOIL** helps us remember that the product of two binomials is the sum of the products of the **F**irst terms, the **O**uter terms, the **I**nner terms, and the **L**ast terms.

$$(a + b)(c + d) = ac + ad + bc + bd$$
$$\qquad\qquad\quad\; \uparrow \quad\; \uparrow \quad\; \uparrow \quad\; \uparrow$$
$$\qquad\qquad\quad\; \text{F} \quad\; \text{O} \quad\; \text{I} \quad\; \text{L}$$

In general, we can multiply two algebraic expressions by using the Distributive Property and the Laws of Exponents.

EXAMPLE 2 ■ Multiplying Binomials Using FOIL

$$(2x + 1)(3x - 5) = 6x^2 - 10x + 3x - 5 \qquad \text{Distributive Property}$$
$$\qquad\qquad\qquad\quad\; \uparrow \qquad \uparrow \qquad \uparrow \qquad \uparrow$$
$$\qquad\qquad\qquad\quad\; \text{F} \qquad \text{O} \qquad \text{I} \qquad \text{L}$$

$$= 6x^2 - 7x - 5 \qquad \text{Combine like terms}$$

✎ **Now Try Exercise 37** ∎

When we multiply trinomials or other polynomials with more terms, we use the Distributive Property. It is also helpful to arrange our work in table form. The next example illustrates both methods.

EXAMPLE 3 ■ Multiplying Polynomials

Find the product: $(2x + 3)(x^2 - 5x + 4)$

SOLUTION 1: Using the Distributive Property

$$(2x + 3)(x^2 - 5x + 4) = 2x(x^2 - 5x + 4) + 3(x^2 - 5x + 4) \qquad \text{Distributive Property}$$

$$= (2x \cdot x^2 - 2x \cdot 5x + 2x \cdot 4) + (3 \cdot x^2 - 3 \cdot 5x + 3 \cdot 4) \qquad \text{Distributive Property}$$

$$= (2x^3 - 10x^2 + 8x) + (3x^2 - 15x + 12) \qquad \text{Laws of Exponents}$$

$$= 2x^3 - 7x^2 - 7x + 12 \qquad \text{Combine like terms}$$

SOLUTION 2: Using Table Form

$$
\begin{array}{r}
x^2 - 5x + 4 \\
2x + 3 \\
\hline
3x^2 - 15x + 12 \\
2x^3 - 10x^2 + 8x \\
\hline
2x^3 - 7x^2 - 7x + 12
\end{array}
$$

Multiply $x^2 - 5x + 4$ by 3

Multiply $x^2 - 5x + 4$ by $2x$

Add like terms

✎ Now Try Exercise 67 ■

■ Special Product Formulas

Certain types of products occur so frequently that you should memorize them. You can verify the following formulas by performing the multiplications.

SPECIAL PRODUCT FORMULAS

If A and B are any real numbers or algebraic expressions, then

1. $(A + B)(A - B) = A^2 - B^2$ Sum and difference of same terms

2. $(A + B)^2 = A^2 + 2AB + B^2$ Square of a sum

3. $(A - B)^2 = A^2 - 2AB + B^2$ Square of a difference

4. $(A + B)^3 = A^3 + 3A^2B + 3AB^2 + B^3$ Cube of a sum

5. $(A - B)^3 = A^3 - 3A^2B + 3AB^2 - B^3$ Cube of a difference

---

The key idea in using these formulas (or any other formula in algebra) is the **Principle of Substitution**: We may substitute any algebraic expression for any letter in a formula. For example, to find $(x^2 + y^3)^2$ we use Product Formula 2, substituting x^2 for A and y^3 for B, to get

$$(x^2 + y^3)^2 = (x^2)^2 + 2(x^2)(y^3) + (y^3)^2$$

$$(A + B)^2 = A^2 + 2AB + B^2$$

EXAMPLE 4 ■ Using the Special Product Formulas

Use the Special Product Formulas to find each product.

(a) $(3x + 5)^2$ **(b)** $(x^2 - 2)^3$

SOLUTION

(a) Substituting $A = 3x$ and $B = 5$ in Product Formula 2, we get

$$(3x + 5)^2 = (3x)^2 + 2(3x)(5) + 5^2 = 9x^2 + 30x + 25$$

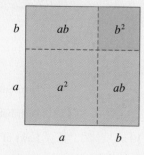

DISCOVERY PROJECT

Visualizing a Formula

Many of the Special Product Formulas in this section can be "seen" as geometrical facts about length, area, and volume. For example, the formula about the square of a sum can be interpreted to be about areas of squares and rectangles. The ancient Greeks always interpreted algebraic formulas in terms of geometric figures. Such figures give us special insight into how these formulas work. You can find the project at **www.stewartmath.com**.

(b) Substituting $A = x^2$ and $B = 2$ in Product Formula 5, we get

$$(x^2 - 2)^3 = (x^2)^3 - 3(x^2)^2(2) + 3(x^2)(2)^2 - 2^3$$
$$= x^6 - 6x^4 + 12x^2 - 8$$

✎ Now Try Exercises 45 and 63 ∎

EXAMPLE 5 ■ Using the Special Product Formulas

Find each product.

(a) $(2x - \sqrt{y})(2x + \sqrt{y})$ **(b)** $(x + y - 1)(x + y + 1)$

SOLUTION

(a) Substituting $A = 2x$ and $B = \sqrt{y}$ in Product Formula 1, we get

$$(2x - \sqrt{y})(2x + \sqrt{y}) = (2x)^2 - (\sqrt{y})^2 = 4x^2 - y$$

(b) If we group $x + y$ together and think of this as one algebraic expression, we can use Product Formula 1 with $A = x + y$ and $B = 1$.

$$(x + y - 1)(x + y + 1) = [(x + y) - 1][(x + y) + 1]$$
$$= (x + y)^2 - 1^2 \qquad \text{Product Formula 1}$$
$$= x^2 + 2xy + y^2 - 1 \qquad \text{Product Formula 2}$$

✎ Now Try Exercises 61 and 85 ∎

P.5 EXERCISES

CONCEPTS

1. Which of the following expressions are polynomials?

(a) $2x^3 - \frac{1}{2}x + \sqrt{3}$ **(b)** $x^2 - \frac{1}{2} - 3\sqrt{x}$

(c) $\dfrac{1}{x^2 + 4x + 7}$ **(d)** $x^5 + 7x^2 - x + 100$

(e) $\sqrt[3]{8x^6 - 5x^3 + 7x - 3}$ **(f)** $\sqrt{3}x^4 + \sqrt{5}x^2 - 15x$

2. To add polynomials, we add _____ terms. So

$(3x^2 + 2x + 4) + (8x^2 - x + 1) =$ _____.

3. To subtract polynomials, we subtract _____ terms. So

$(2x^3 + 9x^2 + x + 10) - (x^3 + x^2 + 6x + 8) =$ _____.

4. Explain how we multiply two polynomials, then perform the following multiplication: $(x + 2)(x + 3) =$ _____.

5. The Special Product Formula for the "square of a sum" is

$(A + B)^2 =$ _____. So $(2x + 3)^2 =$ _____.

6. The Special Product Formula for the "product of the sum and difference of terms" is $(A + B)(A - B) =$ _____.

So $(5 + x)(5 - x) =$ _____.

7–8 ■ *Yes* or *No*? If *No*, give a reason.

7. **(a)** Is the expression $(x + 5)^2$ equal to $x^2 + 25$?

(b) When you expand $(x + a)^2$, where $a \neq 0$, do you get three terms?

8. **(a)** Is the expression $(x + 5)(x - 5)$ equal to $x^2 - 25$?

(b) When you expand $(x + a)(x - a)$, where $a \neq 0$, do you get two terms?

SKILLS

9–14 ■ **Polynomials** Complete the following table by stating whether the polynomial is a monomial, binomial, or trinomial; then list its terms and state its degree.

Polynomial	Type	Terms	Degree
9. $5x^3 + 6$			
10. $-2x^2 + 5x - 3$			
11. -8			
12. $\frac{1}{2}x^7$			
13. $x - x^2 + x^3 - x^4$			
14. $\sqrt{2}x - \sqrt{3}$			

15–32 ■ **Adding and Subtracting Polynomials** Find the sum, difference, or product.

15. $(6x - 3) + (3x + 7)$ **16.** $(3 - 7x) - (11 + 4x)$

✎ **17.** $(2x^2 - 5x) - (x^2 - 8x + 3)$

18. $(-2x^2 - 3x + 1) + (3x^2 + 5x - 4)$

19. $3(x - 1) + 4(x + 2)$

20. $8(2x + 5) - 7(x - 9)$

21. $(5x^3 + 4x^2 - 3x) - (x^2 + 7x + 2)$

22. $4(x^2 - 3x + 5) - 3(x^2 - 2x + 1)$

23. $2x(x - 1)$ **24.** $3y(2y + 5)$

25. $x^2(x + 3)$ **26.** $-y(y^2 - 2)$

27. $2(2 - 5t) + t(t + 10)$ **28.** $5(3t - 4) - 2t(t - 3)$

29. $r(r^2 - 9) + 3r^2(2r - 1)$ **30.** $v^3(v - 9) - 2v^2(2 - 2v)$

31. $x^2(2x^2 - x + 1)$ **32.** $3x^3(x^4 - 4x^2 + 5)$

33–44 ■ **Using FOIL** Multiply the algebraic expressions using the FOIL method, and simplify.

33. $(x - 3)(x + 5)$ **34.** $(4 + x)(2 + x)$

35. $(s + 6)(2s + 3)$ **36.** $(2t + 3)(t - 1)$

37. $(3t - 2)(7t - 4)$ **38.** $(4s - 1)(2s + 5)$

39. $(3x + 5)(2x - 1)$ **40.** $(7y - 3)(2y - 1)$

41. $(x + 3y)(2x - y)$ **42.** $(4x - 5y)(3x - y)$

43. $(2r - 5s)(3r - 2s)$ **44.** $(6u + 5v)(u - 2v)$

45–66 ■ **Using Special Product Formulas** Multiply the algebraic expressions using a Special Product Formula, and simplify.

45. $(5x + 1)^2$ **46.** $(2 - 7y)^2$

47. $(3y - 1)^2$ **48.** $(2y + 5)^2$

49. $(2u + v)^2$ **50.** $(x - 3y)^2$

51. $(2x + 3y)^2$ **52.** $(r - 2s)^2$

53. $(x^2 + 1)^2$ **54.** $(2 + y^3)^2$

55. $(x + 6)(x - 6)$ **56.** $(5 - y)(5 + y)$

57. $(3x - 4)(3x + 4)$ **58.** $(2y + 5)(2y - 5)$

59. $(x + 3y)(x - 3y)$ **60.** $(2u + v)(2u - v)$

61. $(\sqrt{x} + 2)(\sqrt{x} - 2)$ **62.** $(\sqrt{y} + \sqrt{2})(\sqrt{y} - \sqrt{2})$

63. $(y + 2)^3$ **64.** $(x - 3)^3$

65. $(1 - 2r)^3$ **66.** $(3 + 2y)^3$

67–86 ■ **Multiplying Algebraic Expressions** Perform the indicated operations, and simplify.

67. $(x + 2)(x^2 + 2x + 3)$ **68.** $(x + 1)(2x^2 - x + 1)$

69. $(2x - 5)(x^2 - x + 1)$ **70.** $(1 + 2x)(x^2 - 3x + 1)$

71. $\sqrt{x}(x - \sqrt{x})$ **72.** $x^{3/2}(\sqrt{x} - 1/\sqrt{x})$

73. $y^{1/3}(y^{2/3} + y^{5/3})$ **74.** $x^{1/4}(2x^{3/4} - x^{1/4})$

75. $(x^2 + y^2)^2$ **76.** $\left(c + \dfrac{1}{c}\right)^2$

77. $(x^2 - a^2)(x^2 + a^2)$ **78.** $(x^{1/2} + y^{1/2})(x^{1/2} - y^{1/2})$

79. $(\sqrt{a} - b)(\sqrt{a} + b)$

80. $(\sqrt{h^2 + 1} + 1)(\sqrt{h^2 + 1} - 1)$

81. $(1 + x^{2/3})(1 - x^{2/3})$ **82.** $(1 - b)^2(1 + b)^2$

83. $((x - 1) + x^2)((x - 1) - x^2)$

84. $(x + (2 + x^2))(x - (2 + x^2))$

85. $(2x + y - 3)(2x + y + 3)$ **86.** $(x + y + z)(x - y - z)$

SKILLS Plus

87–88 ■ **Verifying Identities** Show that the following identities hold.

87. (a) $ab = \frac{1}{2}[(a + b)^2 - (a^2 + b^2)]$

    (b) $(a^2 + b^2)^2 - (a^2 - b^2)^2 = 4a^2b^2$

88. $(a^2 + b^2)(c^2 + d^2) = (ac + bd)^2 + (ad - bc)^2$

APPLICATIONS

89. Volume of a Box An open box is constructed from a 6 in. by 10 in. sheet of cardboard by cutting a square piece from each corner and then folding up the sides, as shown in the figure. The volume of the box is

$$V = x(6 - 2x)(10 - 2x)$$

(a) Explain how the expression for V is obtained.

(b) Expand the expression for V. What is the degree of the resulting polynomial?

(c) Find the volume when $x = 1$ and when $x = 2$.

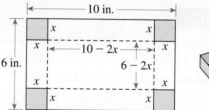 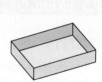

90. Building Envelope The building code in a certain town requires that a house be at least 10 ft from the boundaries of the lot. The buildable area (or *building envelope*) for the rectangular lot shown in the following figure is given by

$$A = (x - 20)(y - 20)$$

(a) Explain how the expression for A is obtained.

(b) Expand to express A as a polynomial in x and y.

(c) A contractor has a choice of purchasing one of two rectangular lots, each having the same area. One lot measures 100 ft by 400 ft; the other measures 200 ft by 200 ft. Which lot has the larger building envelope?

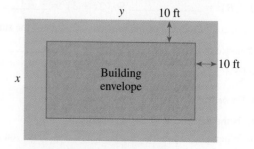

91. Interest on an Investment A 3-year certificate of deposit pays interest at a rate r compounded annually. If $2000 is invested, then the amount at maturity is

$$A = 2000(1 + r)^3$$

(a) Expand the expression for A. What is the degree of the resulting polynomial?

(b) Find the amounts A for the values of r in the table.

Interest rate r	2%	3%	4.5%	6%	10%
Amount A					

92. Profit A wholesaler sells graphing calculators. For an order of x calculators his total cost in dollars is

$$C = 50 + 30x - 0.1x^2$$

and his total revenue is

$$R = 50x - 0.05x^2$$

(a) Find the profit P on an order of x calculators.

(b) Find the profit on an order of 10 calculators and on an order of 20 calculators.

■ **DISCUSS** ■ **DISCOVER** ■ **PROVE** ■ **WRITE**

93. DISCUSS: An Algebra Error Beginning algebra students sometimes make the following error when squaring a binomial:

$$(x + 5)^2 \ \cancel{=}\ x^2 + 25$$

(a) Substitute a value for x to verify that this is an error.

(b) What is the correct expansion for $(x + 5)^2$?

94. DISCUSS: Degrees of Sums and Products of Polynomials Make up several pairs of polynomials, then calculate the sum and product of each pair. On the basis of your experiments and observations, answer the following questions.

(a) How is the degree of the product related to the degrees of the original polynomials?

(b) How is the degree of the sum related to the degrees of the original polynomials?

(c) Test your conclusions by finding the sum and product of the following polynomials:

$$2x^3 + x - 3 \quad \text{and} \quad -2x^3 - x + 7$$

P.6 FACTORING

■ **Common Factors** ■ **Factoring Trinomials** ■ **Special Factoring Formulas** ■ **Factoring an Expression Completely** ■ **Factoring by Grouping Terms**

We use the Distributive Property to expand algebraic expressions. We sometimes need to reverse this process (again using the Distributive Property) by **factoring** an expression as a product of simpler ones. For example, we can write

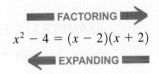

$$x^2 - 4 = (x - 2)(x + 2)$$

We say that $x - 2$ and $x + 2$ are **factors** of $x^2 - 4$.

■ Common Factors

The easiest type of factoring occurs when the terms have a common factor.

EXAMPLE 1 ■ Factoring Out Common Factors

Factor each expression.

(a) $3x^2 - 6x$ **(b)** $8x^4y^2 + 6x^3y^3 - 2xy^4$

SOLUTION

(a) The greatest common factor of the terms $3x^2$ and $-6x$ is $3x$, so we have

$$3x^2 - 6x = 3x(x - 2)$$

Terms and Factors

When we multiply two numbers together, each of the numbers is called a **factor** of the product. When we add two numbers together, each number is called a **term** of the sum.

$$2 \times 3 \qquad 2 + 3$$

If a factor is common to each term of an expression we can factor it out. The following expression has two terms.

$$ax + 2ay$$

a is a factor
of each term

Each term contains the factor *a*, so we can factor *a* out and write the expression as

$$ax + 2ay = a(x + 2y)$$

(b) We note that

$$8, 6, \text{ and } -2 \text{ have the greatest common factor } 2$$

$$x^4, x^3, \text{ and } x \text{ have the greatest common factor } x$$

$$y^2, y^3, \text{ and } y^4 \text{ have the greatest common factor } y^2$$

So the greatest common factor of the three terms in the polynomial is $2xy^2$, and we have

$$8x^4y^2 + 6x^3y^3 - 2xy^4 = (2xy^2)(4x^3) + (2xy^2)(3x^2y) + (2xy^2)(-y^2)$$
$$= 2xy^2(4x^3 + 3x^2y - y^2)$$

CHECK YOUR ANSWERS

(a) Multiplying gives

$$3x(x - 2) = 3x^2 - 6x \quad \checkmark$$

(b) Multiplying gives

$$2xy^2(4x^3 + 3x^2y - y^2)$$
$$= 8x^4y^2 + 6x^3y^3 - 2xy^4 \quad \checkmark$$

✎ **Now Try Exercises 9 and 11**   ■

EXAMPLE 2   ■   Factoring Out a Common Factor

Factor: $(2x + 4)(x - 3) - 5(x - 3)$

SOLUTION   The two terms have the common factor $x - 3$.

$$(2x + 4)(x - 3) - 5(x - 3) = [(2x + 4) - 5](x - 3) \qquad \text{Distributive Property}$$
$$= (2x - 1)(x - 3) \qquad \text{Simplify}$$

✎ **Now Try Exercise 13**   ■

■ Factoring Trinomials

To factor a trinomial of the form $x^2 + bx + c$, we note that

$$(x + r)(x + s) = x^2 + (r + s)x + rs$$

so we need to choose numbers r and s so that $r + s = b$ and $rs = c$.

EXAMPLE 3   ■   Factoring $x^2 + bx + c$ by Trial and Error

Factor: $x^2 + 7x + 12$

SOLUTION   We need to find two integers whose product is 12 and whose sum is 7. By trial and error we find that the two integers are 3 and 4. Thus the factorization is

$$x^2 + 7x + 12 = (x + 3)(x + 4)$$

factors of 12

CHECK YOUR ANSWER

Multiplying gives

$$(x + 3)(x + 4) = x^2 + 7x + 12 \quad \checkmark$$

✎ **Now Try Exercise 15**   ■

To factor a trinomial of the form $ax^2 + bx + c$ with $a \neq 1$, we look for factors of the form $px + r$ and $qx + s$:

$$ax^2 + bx + c = (px + r)(qx + s) = pqx^2 + (ps + qr)x + rs$$

factors of *a*

$$ax^2 + bx + c = (px + r)(qx + s)$$

factors of *c*

Therefore we try to find numbers p, q, r, and s such that $pq = a$, $rs = c$, $ps + qr = b$. If these numbers are all integers, then we will have a limited number of possibilities to try for p, q, r, and s.

EXAMPLE 4 ■ Factoring $ax^2 + bx + c$ by Trial and Error

Factor: $6x^2 + 7x - 5$

SOLUTION We can factor 6 as $6 \cdot 1$ or $3 \cdot 2$ and can factor -5 as $-5 \cdot 1$ or $5 \cdot (-1)$. By trying these possibilities, we arrive at the factorization

Multiplying gives

$(3x + 5)(2x - 1) = 6x^2 + 7x - 5$ ✓

factors of 6

$$6x^2 + 7x - 5 = (3x + 5)(2x - 1)$$

factors of -5

✎ **Now Try Exercise 19** ■

EXAMPLE 5 ■ Recognizing the Form of an Expression

Factor each expression.

(a) $x^2 - 2x - 3$ **(b)** $(5a + 1)^2 - 2(5a + 1) - 3$

SOLUTION

(a) $x^2 - 2x - 3 = (x - 3)(x + 1)$ Trial and error

(b) This expression is of the form

$$\blacksquare^2 - 2\,\blacksquare - 3$$

where $\blacksquare$ represents $5a + 1$. This is the same form as the expression in part (a), so it will factor as $(\blacksquare - 3)(\blacksquare + 1)$:

$$(5a + 1)^2 - 2(5a + 1) - 3 = [(5a + 1) - 3][(5a + 1) + 1]$$
$$= (5a - 2)(5a + 2)$$

✎ **Now Try Exercise 21** ■

■ Special Factoring Formulas

Some special algebraic expressions can be factored by using the following formulas. The first three are simply Special Product Formulas written backward.

FACTORING FORMULAS

Formula	Name
1. $A^2 - B^2 = (A - B)(A + B)$	Difference of squares
2. $A^2 + 2AB + B^2 = (A + B)^2$	Perfect square
3. $A^2 - 2AB + B^2 = (A - B)^2$	Perfect square
4. $A^3 - B^3 = (A - B)(A^2 + AB + B^2)$	Difference of cubes
5. $A^3 + B^3 = (A + B)(A^2 - AB + B^2)$	Sum of cubes

EXAMPLE 6 ■ Factoring Differences of Squares

Factor each expression.

(a) $4x^2 - 25$ **(b)** $(x + y)^2 - z^2$

SOLUTION

(a) Using the Difference of Squares Formula with $A = 2x$ and $B = 5$, we have

$$4x^2 - 25 = (2x)^2 - 5^2 = (2x - 5)(2x + 5)$$

$$A^2 - B^2 = (A - B)(A + B)$$

(b) We use the Difference of Squares Formula with $A = x + y$ and $B = z$.

$$(x + y)^2 - z^2 = (x + y - z)(x + y + z)$$

✎ **Now Try Exercises 25 and 29**

A trinomial is a perfect square if it is of the form

$$A^2 + 2AB + B^2 \quad \text{or} \quad A^2 - 2AB + B^2$$

So we **recognize a perfect square** if the middle term ($2AB$ or $-2AB$) is plus or minus twice the product of the square roots of the outer two terms.

EXAMPLE 7 ■ Recognizing Perfect Squares

Factor each trinomial.

(a) $x^2 + 6x + 9$ **(b)** $4x^2 - 4xy + y^2$

SOLUTION

(a) Here $A = x$ and $B = 3$, so $2AB = 2 \cdot x \cdot 3 = 6x$. Since the middle term is $6x$, the trinomial is a perfect square. By the Perfect Square Formula we have

$$x^2 + 6x + 9 = (x + 3)^2$$

(b) Here $A = 2x$ and $B = y$, so $2AB = 2 \cdot 2x \cdot y = 4xy$. Since the middle term is $-4xy$, the trinomial is a perfect square. By the Perfect Square Formula we have

$$4x^2 - 4xy + y^2 = (2x - y)^2$$

✎ **Now Try Exercises 31 and 37**

EXAMPLE 8 ■ Factoring Differences and Sums of Cubes

Factor each polynomial.

(a) $27x^3 - 1$ **(b)** $x^6 + 8$

SOLUTION

(a) Using the Difference of Cubes Formula with $A = 3x$ and $B = 1$, we get

$$27x^3 - 1 = (3x)^3 - 1^3 = (3x - 1)[(3x)^2 + (3x)(1) + 1^2]$$
$$= (3x - 1)(9x^2 + 3x + 1)$$

(b) Using the Sum of Cubes Formula with $A = x^2$ and $B = 2$, we have

$$x^6 + 8 = (x^2)^3 + 2^3 = (x^2 + 2)(x^4 - 2x^2 + 4)$$

✎ **Now Try Exercises 41 and 43**

■ **Factoring an Expression Completely**

When we factor an expression, the result can sometimes be factored further. In general, we first factor out common factors, then inspect the result to see whether it can be factored by any of the other methods of this section. We repeat this process until we have factored the expression completely.

EXAMPLE 9 ■ Factoring an Expression Completely

Factor each expression completely.

(a) $2x^4 - 8x^2$ **(b)** $x^5y^2 - xy^6$

SOLUTION

(a) We first factor out the power of x with the smallest exponent.

$$2x^4 - 8x^2 = 2x^2(x^2 - 4) \qquad \text{Common factor is } 2x^2$$
$$= 2x^2(x - 2)(x + 2) \qquad \text{Factor } x^2 - 4 \text{ as a difference of squares}$$

(b) We first factor out the powers of x and y with the smallest exponents.

$$x^5y^2 - xy^6 = xy^2(x^4 - y^4) \qquad \text{Common factor is } xy^2$$
$$= xy^2(x^2 + y^2)(x^2 - y^2) \qquad \text{Factor } x^4 - y^4 \text{ as a difference of squares}$$
$$= xy^2(x^2 + y^2)(x + y)(x - y) \qquad \text{Factor } x^2 - y^2 \text{ as a difference of squares}$$

▶ **Now Try Exercises 87 and 91**

In the next example we factor out variables with fractional exponents. This type of factoring occurs in calculus.

EXAMPLE 10 ■ Factoring Expressions with Fractional Exponents

Factor each expression.

(a) $3x^{3/2} - 9x^{1/2} + 6x^{-1/2}$ **(b)** $(2 + x)^{-2/3}x + (2 + x)^{1/3}$

SOLUTION

(a) Factor out the power of x with the *smallest exponent*, that is, $x^{-1/2}$.

$$3x^{3/2} - 9x^{1/2} + 6x^{-1/2} = 3x^{-1/2}(x^2 - 3x + 2) \qquad \text{Factor out } 3x^{-1/2}$$
$$= 3x^{-1/2}(x - 1)(x - 2) \qquad \text{Factor the quadratic } x^2 - 3x + 2$$

(b) Factor out the power of $2 + x$ with the *smallest exponent*, that is, $(2 + x)^{-2/3}$.

$$(2 + x)^{-2/3}x + (2 + x)^{1/3} = (2 + x)^{-2/3}[x + (2 + x)] \qquad \text{Factor out } (2 + x)^{-2/3}$$
$$= (2 + x)^{-2/3}(2 + 2x) \qquad \text{Simplify}$$
$$= 2(2 + x)^{-2/3}(1 + x) \qquad \text{Factor out } 2$$

To factor out $x^{-1/2}$ from $x^{3/2}$, we *subtract* exponents:

$$x^{3/2} = x^{-1/2}(x^{3/2 - (-1/2)})$$
$$= x^{-1/2}(x^{3/2 + 1/2})$$
$$= x^{-1/2}(x^2)$$

CHECK YOUR ANSWERS

To see that you have factored correctly, multiply using the Laws of Exponents.

(a) $3x^{-1/2}(x^2 - 3x + 2)$
$= 3x^{3/2} - 9x^{1/2} + 6x^{-1/2}$ ✓

(b) $(2 + x)^{-2/3}[x + (2 + x)]$
$= (2 + x)^{-2/3}x + (2 + x)^{1/3}$ ✓

▶ **Now Try Exercises 55 and 57**

■ Factoring by Grouping Terms

Polynomials with at least four terms can sometimes be factored by grouping terms. The following example illustrates the idea.

EXAMPLE 11 ■ Factoring by Grouping

Factor each polynomial.

(a) $x^3 + x^2 + 4x + 4$ **(b)** $x^3 - 2x^2 - 9x + 18$

SOLUTION

(a) $x^3 + x^2 + 4x + 4 = (x^3 + x^2) + (4x + 4)$ Group terms

$\qquad\qquad\qquad\qquad = x^2(x + 1) + 4(x + 1)$ Factor out common factors

$\qquad\qquad\qquad\qquad = (x^2 + 4)(x + 1)$ Factor $x + 1$ from each term

(b) $x^3 - 2x^2 - 9x + 18 = (x^3 - 2x^2) - (9x - 18)$ Group terms

$\qquad\qquad\qquad\qquad\quad = x^2(x - 2) - 9(x - 2)$ Factor common factors

$\qquad\qquad\qquad\qquad\quad = (x^2 - 9)(x - 2)$ Factor $(x - 2)$ from each term

$\qquad\qquad\qquad\qquad\quad = (x - 3)(x + 3)(x - 2)$ Factor completely

Now Try Exercises 47 and 95

P.6 EXERCISES

CONCEPTS

1–2 ■ Consider the polynomial $2x^5 + 6x^4 + 4x^3$.

1. How many terms does this polynomial have? _____
List the terms: _____

2. What factor is common to each term? _____
Factor the polynomial: $2x^5 + 6x^4 + 4x^3 =$ _____.

3. To factor the trinomial $x^2 + 7x + 10$, we look for two integers whose product is _____ and whose sum is _____.
These integers are _____ and _____, so the trinomial factors as _____.

4. The greatest common factor in the expression
$4(x + 1)^2 - x(x + 1)^2$ is _____, and the expression factors as _____ (_____ − _____).

5. The Special Factoring Formula for the "difference of squares" is $A^2 - B^2 =$ _____. So $4x^2 - 25$ factors as _____.

6. The Special Factoring Formula for a "perfect square" is
$A^2 + 2AB + B^2 =$ _____. So $x^2 + 10x + 25$ factors as _____.

SKILLS

7–14 ■ **Factoring Common Factors**   Factor out the common factor.

7. $5a - 20$

8. $-3b + 12$

9. $-2x^3 + x$

10. $3x^4 - 6x^3 - x^2$

11. $2x^2y - 6xy^2 + 3xy$

12. $-7x^4y^2 + 14xy^3 + 21xy^4$

13. $y(y - 6) + 9(y - 6)$

14. $(z + 2)^2 - 5(z + 2)$

15–22 ■ **Factoring Trinomials**   Factor the trinomial.

15. $x^2 + 8x + 7$

16. $x^2 + 4x - 5$

17. $x^2 + 2x - 15$

18. $2x^2 - 5x - 7$

19. $3x^2 - 16x + 5$

20. $5x^2 - 7x - 6$

21. $(3x + 2)^2 + 8(3x + 2) + 12$

22. $2(a + b)^2 + 5(a + b) - 3$

23–30 ■ **Difference of Squares**   Factor the difference of squares.

23. $x^2 - 25$

24. $9 - y^2$

25. $49 - 4z^2$

26. $9a^2 - 16$

27. $16y^2 - z^2$

28. $a^2 - 36b^2$

29. $(x + 3)^2 - y^2$

30. $x^2 - (y + 5)^2$

31–38 ■ **Perfect Squares**   Factor the perfect square.

31. $x^2 + 10x + 25$

32. $9 + 6y + y^2$

33. $z^2 - 12z + 36$

34. $w^2 - 16w + 64$

35. $4t^2 - 20t + 25$

36. $16a^2 + 24a + 9$

37. $9u^2 - 6uv + v^2$

38. $x^2 + 10xy + 25y^2$

39–46 ■ **Sum or Difference of Cubes**   Factor the sum or difference of cubes.

39. $x^3 + 27$

40. $y^3 - 64$

41. $8a^3 - 1$

42. $8 + 27w^3$

43. $27x^3 + y^3$

44. $1 + 1000y^3$

45. $u^3 - v^6$

46. $8r^3 - 64t^6$

47–52 ■ **Factoring by Grouping**   Factor the expression by grouping terms.

47. $x^3 + 4x^2 + x + 4$

48. $3x^3 - x^2 + 6x - 2$

49. $5x^3 + x^2 + 5x + 1$

50. $18x^3 + 9x^2 + 2x + 1$

51. $x^3 + x^2 + x + 1$

52. $x^5 + x^4 + x + 1$

53–60 ■ **Fractional Exponents**   Factor the expression completely. Begin by factoring out the lowest power of each common factor.

53. $x^{5/2} - x^{1/2}$

54. $3x^{-1/2} + 4x^{1/2} + x^{3/2}$

55. $x^{-3/2} + 2x^{-1/2} + x^{1/2}$

56. $(x - 1)^{7/2} - (x - 1)^{3/2}$

57. $(x^2 + 1)^{1/2} + 2(x^2 + 1)^{-1/2}$

58. $x^{-1/2}(x + 1)^{1/2} + x^{1/2}(x + 1)^{-1/2}$

59. $2x^{1/3}(x - 2)^{2/3} - 5x^{4/3}(x - 2)^{-1/3}$

60. $3x^{-1/2}(x^2 + 1)^{5/4} - x^{3/2}(x^2 + 1)^{1/4}$

61–86 ■ Factoring Completely   Factor the expression completely.

61. $12x^3 + 18x$ **62.** $30x^3 + 15x^4$

63. $6y^4 - 15y^3$ **64.** $5ab - 8abc$

65. $x^2 - 2x - 8$ **66.** $x^2 - 14x + 48$

67. $y^2 - 8y + 15$ **68.** $z^2 + 6z - 16$

69. $2x^2 + 5x + 3$ **70.** $2x^2 + 7x - 4$

71. $9x^2 - 36x - 45$ **72.** $8x^2 + 10x + 3$

73. $6x^2 - 5x - 6$ **74.** $6 + 5t - 6t^2$

75. $x^2 - 36$ **76.** $4x^2 - 25$

77. $49 - 4y^2$ **78.** $4t^2 - 9s^2$

79. $t^2 - 6t + 9$ **80.** $x^2 + 10x + 25$

81. $4x^2 + 4xy + y^2$ **82.** $r^2 - 6rs + 9s^2$

83. $t^3 + 1$ **84.** $x^3 - 27$

85. $8x^3 - 125$ **86.** $125 + 27y^3$

87–98 ■ Factoring Completely   Factor the expression completely.

87. $x^3 + 2x^2 + x$ **88.** $3x^3 - 27x$

89. $x^4 + 2x^3 - 3x^2$ **90.** $3w^3 - 5w^4 - 2w^3$

91. $x^4y^3 - x^2y^5$ **92.** $18y^3x^2 - 2xy^4$

93. $x^6 - 8y^3$ **94.** $27a^3 + b^6$

95. $y^3 - 3y^2 - 4y + 12$ **96.** $y^3 - y^2 + y - 1$

97. $3x^3 - x^2 - 12x + 4$ **98.** $9x^3 + 18x^2 - x - 2$

99–108 ■ Factoring Completely   Factor the expression and simplify.

99. $(a + b)^2 - (a - b)^2$

100. $\left(1 + \dfrac{1}{x}\right)^2 - \left(1 - \dfrac{1}{x}\right)^2$

101. $x^2(x^2 - 1) - 9(x^2 - 1)$

102. $(a^2 - 1)b^2 - 4(a^2 - 1)$

103. $(x - 1)(x + 2)^2 - (x - 1)^2(x + 2)$

104. $(x + 1)^3 x - 2(x + 1)^2 x^2 + x^3(x + 1)$

105. $y^4(y + 2)^3 + y^5(y + 2)^4$

106. $n(x - y) + (n - 1)(y - x)$

107. $(a^2 + 1)^2 - 7(a^2 + 1) + 10$

108. $(a^2 + 2a)^2 - 2(a^2 + 2a) - 3$

109–114 ■ Factoring Completely   Factor the expression completely. (This type of expression arises in calculus in using the "product rule.")

109. $3x^2(4x - 12)^2 + x^3(2)(4x - 12)(4)$

110. $5(x^2 + 4)^4(2x)(x - 2)^4 + (x^2 + 4)^5(4)(x - 2)^3$

111. $3(2x - 1)^2(2)(x + 3)^{1/2} + (2x - 1)^3(\frac{1}{2})(x + 3)^{-1/2}$

112. $\frac{1}{3}(x + 6)^{-2/3}(2x - 3)^2 + (x + 6)^{1/3}(2)(2x - 3)(2)$

113. $(x^2 + 3)^{-1/3} - \frac{2}{3}x^2(x^2 + 3)^{-4/3}$

114. $\frac{1}{2}x^{-1/2}(3x + 4)^{1/2} + \frac{3}{2}x^{1/2}(3x + 4)^{-1/2}$

APPLICATIONS

115. Volume of Concrete   A culvert is constructed out of large cylindrical shells cast in concrete, as shown in the figure. Using the formula for the volume of a cylinder given on the inside front cover of this book, explain why the volume of the cylindrical shell is

$$V = \pi R^2 h - \pi r^2 h$$

Factor to show that

$$V = 2\pi \cdot \text{average radius} \cdot \text{height} \cdot \text{thickness}$$

Use the "unrolled" diagram to explain why this makes sense geometrically.

116. Mowing a Field   A square field in a certain state park is mowed around the edges every week. The rest of the field is kept unmowed to serve as a habitat for birds and small animals (see the figure). The field measures b feet by b feet, and the mowed strip is x feet wide.

(a) Explain why the area of the mowed portion is $b^2 - (b - 2x)^2$.

(b) Factor the expression in part (a) to show that the area of the mowed portion is also $4x(b - x)$.

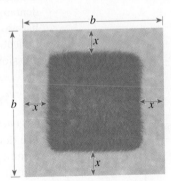

DISCUSS ■ DISCOVER ■ PROVE ■ WRITE

117. DISCUSS: The Power of Algebraic Formulas   Use the Difference of Squares Formula $A^2 - B^2 = (A + B)(A - B)$ to evaluate the following differences of squares in your head. Make up more such expressions that you can do in your head.

(a) $528^2 - 527^2$

(b) $122^2 - 120^2$

(c) $1020^2 - 1010^2$

118. DISCUSS: The Power of Algebraic Formulas Use the Special Product Formula $(A + B)(A - B) = A^2 - B^2$ to evaluate the following products of numbers in your head. Make up more such products that you can do in your head.

(a) $501 \cdot 499$

(b) $79 \cdot 61$

(c) $2007 \cdot 1993$

119. DISCOVER: Differences of Even Powers

(a) Factor the expressions completely: $A^4 - B^4$ and $A^6 - B^6$.

(b) Verify that $18{,}335 = 12^4 - 7^4$ and that $2{,}868{,}335 = 12^6 - 7^6$.

(c) Use the results of parts (a) and (b) to factor the integers $18{,}335$ and $2{,}868{,}335$. Then show that in both of these factorizations, all the factors are prime numbers.

120. DISCOVER: Factoring $A^n - 1$

(a) Verify the following formulas by expanding and simplifying the right-hand side.

$$A^2 - 1 = (A - 1)(A + 1)$$
$$A^3 - 1 = (A - 1)(A^2 + A + 1)$$
$$A^4 - 1 = (A - 1)(A^3 + A^2 + A + 1)$$

(b) On the basis of the pattern displayed in this list, how do you think $A^5 - 1$ would factor? Verify your conjecture. Now generalize the pattern you have observed to obtain a factoring formula for $A^n - 1$, where n is a positive integer.

121. PROVE: Special Factoring Formulas Prove the following formulas by expanding the right-hand side.

(a) Difference of Cubes:
$$A^3 - B^3 = (A - B)(A^2 + AB + B^2)$$

(b) Sum of Cubes:
$$A^3 + B^3 = (A + B)(A^2 - AB + B^2)$$

P.7 RATIONAL EXPRESSIONS

■ The Domain of an Algebraic Expression ■ Simplifying Rational Expressions ■ Multiplying and Dividing Rational Expressions ■ Adding and Subtracting Rational Expressions ■ Compound Fractions ■ Rationalizing the Denominator or the Numerator ■ Avoiding Common Errors

A quotient of two algebraic expressions is called a **fractional expression**. Here are some examples:

$$\frac{2x}{x - 1} \qquad \frac{y - 2}{y^2 + 4} \qquad \frac{x^3 - x}{x^2 - 5x + 6} \qquad \frac{x}{\sqrt{x^2 + 1}}$$

A **rational expression** is a fractional expression in which both the numerator and the denominator are polynomials. For example, the first three expressions in the above list are rational expressions, but the fourth is not, since its denominator contains a radical. In this section we learn how to perform algebraic operations on rational expressions.

■ The Domain of an Algebraic Expression

In general, an algebraic expression may not be defined for all values of the variable. The **domain** of an algebraic expression is the set of real numbers that the variable is permitted to have. The table in the margin gives some basic expressions and their domains.

Expression	Domain
$\dfrac{1}{x}$	$\{x \mid x \neq 0\}$
$\sqrt{x}$	$\{x \mid x \geq 0\}$
$\dfrac{1}{\sqrt{x}}$	$\{x \mid x > 0\}$

EXAMPLE 1 ■ Finding the Domain of an Expression

Find the domains of the following expressions.

(a) $2x^2 + 3x - 1$ 　　(b) $\dfrac{x}{x^2 - 5x + 6}$ 　　(c) $\dfrac{\sqrt{x}}{x - 5}$

SOLUTION

(a) This polynomial is defined for every x. Thus the domain is the set $\mathbb{R}$ of real numbers.

(b) We first factor the denominator.

$$\frac{x}{x^2 - 5x + 6} = \frac{x}{(x - 2)(x - 3)}$$

> Denominator would be 0 if $x = 2$ or $x = 3$

Since the denominator is zero when $x = 2$ or 3, the expression is not defined for these numbers. The domain is $\{x \mid x \neq 2 \text{ and } x \neq 3\}$.

(c) For the numerator to be defined, we must have $x \geq 0$. Also, we cannot divide by zero, so $x \neq 5$.

> Must have $x \geq 0$ to take square root

$$\frac{\sqrt{x}}{x - 5}$$

> Denominator would be 0 if $x = 5$

Thus the domain is $\{x \mid x \geq 0 \text{ and } x \neq 5\}$.

✎ Now Try Exercise 13 ■

Simplifying Rational Expressions

To **simplify rational expressions**, we factor both numerator and denominator and use the following property of fractions:

$$\frac{AC}{BC} = \frac{A}{B}$$

This allows us to **cancel** common factors from the numerator and denominator.

EXAMPLE 2 ■ Simplifying Rational Expressions by Cancellation

Simplify: $\dfrac{x^2 - 1}{x^2 + x - 2}$

SOLUTION

⊘ We can't cancel the x^2's in $\dfrac{x^2 - 1}{x^2 + x - 2}$ because x^2 is not a factor.

$$\frac{x^2 - 1}{x^2 + x - 2} = \frac{(x - 1)(x + 1)}{(x - 1)(x + 2)} \qquad \text{Factor}$$

$$= \frac{x + 1}{x + 2} \qquad \text{Cancel common factors}$$

✎ Now Try Exercise 19 ■

Multiplying and Dividing Rational Expressions

To **multiply rational expressions**, we use the following property of fractions:

$$\frac{A}{B} \cdot \frac{C}{D} = \frac{AC}{BD}$$

This says that to multiply two fractions, we multiply their numerators and multiply their denominators.

EXAMPLE 3 ■ Multiplying Rational Expressions

Perform the indicated multiplication and simplify: $\dfrac{x^2 + 2x - 3}{x^2 + 8x + 16} \cdot \dfrac{3x + 12}{x - 1}$

SOLUTION   We first factor.

$$\frac{x^2 + 2x - 3}{x^2 + 8x + 16} \cdot \frac{3x + 12}{x - 1} = \frac{(x - 1)(x + 3)}{(x + 4)^2} \cdot \frac{3(x + 4)}{x - 1} \qquad \text{Factor}$$

$$= \frac{3(x - 1)(x + 3)(x + 4)}{(x - 1)(x + 4)^2} \qquad \text{Property of fractions}$$

$$= \frac{3(x + 3)}{x + 4} \qquad \text{Cancel common factors}$$

✎ **Now Try Exercise 27**   ■

To **divide rational expressions**, we use the following property of fractions:

$$\frac{A}{B} \div \frac{C}{D} = \frac{A}{B} \cdot \frac{D}{C}$$

This says that to divide a fraction by another fraction, we invert the divisor and multiply.

EXAMPLE 4 ■ Dividing Rational Expressions

Perform the indicated division and simplify: $\dfrac{x - 4}{x^2 - 4} \div \dfrac{x^2 - 3x - 4}{x^2 + 5x + 6}$

SOLUTION

$$\frac{x - 4}{x^2 - 4} \div \frac{x^2 - 3x - 4}{x^2 + 5x + 6} = \frac{x - 4}{x^2 - 4} \cdot \frac{x^2 + 5x + 6}{x^2 - 3x - 4} \qquad \text{Invert and multiply}$$

$$= \frac{(x - 4)(x + 2)(x + 3)}{(x - 2)(x + 2)(x - 4)(x + 1)} \qquad \text{Factor}$$

$$= \frac{x + 3}{(x - 2)(x + 1)} \qquad \text{Cancel common factors}$$

✎ **Now Try Exercise 33**   ■

■ Adding and Subtracting Rational Expressions

To **add or subtract rational expressions**, we first find a common denominator and then use the following property of fractions:

$$\frac{A}{C} + \frac{B}{C} = \frac{A + B}{C}$$

⊘ Avoid making the following error:

$$\frac{A}{B + C} \quad ✗ \quad \frac{A}{B} + \frac{A}{C}$$

For instance, if we let $A = 2$, $B = 1$, and $C = 1$, then we see the error:

$$\frac{2}{1 + 1} \overset{?}{=} \frac{2}{1} + \frac{2}{1}$$

$$\frac{2}{2} \overset{?}{=} 2 + 2$$

$$1 \overset{?}{=} 4 \quad \text{Wrong!}$$

Although any common denominator will work, it is best to use the **least common denominator** (LCD) as explained in Section P.2. The LCD is found by factoring each denominator and taking the product of the distinct factors, using the highest power that appears in any of the factors.

EXAMPLE 5 ■ Adding and Subtracting Rational Expressions

Perform the indicated operations and simplify.

(a) $\dfrac{3}{x-1} + \dfrac{x}{x+2}$

(b) $\dfrac{1}{x^2-1} - \dfrac{2}{(x+1)^2}$

SOLUTION

(a) Here the LCD is simply the product $(x-1)(x+2)$.

$$\dfrac{3}{x-1} + \dfrac{x}{x+2} = \dfrac{3(x+2)}{(x-1)(x+2)} + \dfrac{x(x-1)}{(x-1)(x+2)} \qquad \text{Write fractions using LCD}$$

$$= \dfrac{3x+6+x^2-x}{(x-1)(x+2)} \qquad \text{Add fractions}$$

$$= \dfrac{x^2+2x+6}{(x-1)(x+2)} \qquad \text{Combine terms in numerator}$$

(b) The LCD of $x^2 - 1 = (x-1)(x+1)$ and $(x+1)^2$ is $(x-1)(x+1)^2$.

$$\dfrac{1}{x^2-1} - \dfrac{2}{(x+1)^2} = \dfrac{1}{(x-1)(x+1)} - \dfrac{2}{(x+1)^2} \qquad \text{Factor}$$

$$= \dfrac{(x+1) - 2(x-1)}{(x-1)(x+1)^2} \qquad \text{Combine fractions using LCD}$$

$$= \dfrac{x+1-2x+2}{(x-1)(x+1)^2} \qquad \text{Distributive Property}$$

$$= \dfrac{3-x}{(x-1)(x+1)^2} \qquad \text{Combine terms in numerator}$$

✎ Now Try Exercises 43 and 45 ■

■ Compound Fractions

A **compound fraction** is a fraction in which the numerator, the denominator, or both, are themselves fractional expressions.

EXAMPLE 6 ■ Simplifying a Compound Fraction

Simplify: $\dfrac{\dfrac{x}{y} + 1}{1 - \dfrac{y}{x}}$

SOLUTION 1 We combine the terms in the numerator into a single fraction. We do the same in the denominator. Then we invert and multiply.

$$\dfrac{\dfrac{x}{y} + 1}{1 - \dfrac{y}{x}} = \dfrac{\dfrac{x+y}{y}}{\dfrac{x-y}{x}} = \dfrac{x+y}{y} \cdot \dfrac{x}{x-y}$$

$$= \dfrac{x(x+y)}{y(x-y)}$$

SOLUTION 2 We find the LCD of all the fractions in the expression, then multiply numerator and denominator by it. In this example the LCD of all the fractions is xy. Thus

$$\frac{\dfrac{x}{y}+1}{1-\dfrac{y}{x}}=\frac{\dfrac{x}{y}+1}{1-\dfrac{y}{x}}\cdot\frac{xy}{xy} \qquad \text{Multiply numerator and denominator by } xy$$

$$=\frac{x^2+xy}{xy-y^2} \qquad \text{Simplify}$$

$$=\frac{x(x+y)}{y(x-y)} \qquad \text{Factor}$$

✎ **Now Try Exercises 59 and 65** ■

The next two examples show situations in calculus that require the ability to work with fractional expressions.

EXAMPLE 7 ■ Simplifying a Compound Fraction

Simplify: $\dfrac{\dfrac{1}{a+h}-\dfrac{1}{a}}{h}$

SOLUTION We begin by combining the fractions in the numerator using a common denominator.

We can also simplify by multiplying the numerator and the denominator by $a(a+h)$.

$$\frac{\dfrac{1}{a+h}-\dfrac{1}{a}}{h}=\frac{\dfrac{a-(a+h)}{a(a+h)}}{h} \qquad \text{Combine fractions in the numerator}$$

$$=\frac{a-(a+h)}{a(a+h)}\cdot\frac{1}{h} \qquad \text{Property 2 of fractions (invert divisor and multiply)}$$

$$=\frac{a-a-h}{a(a+h)}\cdot\frac{1}{h} \qquad \text{Distributive Property}$$

$$=\frac{-h}{a(a+h)}\cdot\frac{1}{h} \qquad \text{Simplify}$$

$$=\frac{-1}{a(a+h)} \qquad \text{Property 5 of fractions (cancel common factors)}$$

✎ **Now Try Exercise 73** ■

EXAMPLE 8 ■ Simplifying a Compound Fraction

Simplify: $\dfrac{(1+x^2)^{1/2}-x^2(1+x^2)^{-1/2}}{1+x^2}$

SOLUTION 1 Factor $(1+x^2)^{-1/2}$ from the numerator.

Factor out the power of $1+x^2$ with the *smallest* exponent, in this case $(1+x^2)^{-1/2}$.

$$\frac{(1+x^2)^{1/2}-x^2(1+x^2)^{-1/2}}{1+x^2}=\frac{(1+x^2)^{-1/2}[(1+x^2)-x^2]}{1+x^2}$$

$$=\frac{(1+x^2)^{-1/2}}{1+x^2}=\frac{1}{(1+x^2)^{3/2}}$$

SOLUTION 2 Since $(1 + x^2)^{-1/2} = 1/(1 + x^2)^{1/2}$ is a fraction, we can clear all fractions by multiplying numerator and denominator by $(1 + x^2)^{1/2}$.

$$\frac{(1 + x^2)^{1/2} - x^2(1 + x^2)^{-1/2}}{1 + x^2} = \frac{(1 + x^2)^{1/2} - x^2(1 + x^2)^{-1/2}}{1 + x^2} \cdot \frac{(1 + x^2)^{1/2}}{(1 + x^2)^{1/2}}$$

$$= \frac{(1 + x^2) - x^2}{(1 + x^2)^{3/2}} = \frac{1}{(1 + x^2)^{3/2}}$$

✎ Now Try Exercise 81 ■

■ Rationalizing the Denominator or the Numerator

If a fraction has a denominator of the form $A + B\sqrt{C}$, we can rationalize the denominator by multiplying numerator and denominator by the **conjugate radical** $A - B\sqrt{C}$. This works because, by Special Product Formula 1 in Section P.5, the product of the denominator and its conjugate radical does not contain a radical:

$$(A + B\sqrt{C})(A - B\sqrt{C}) = A^2 - B^2C$$

EXAMPLE 9 ■ Rationalizing the Denominator

Rationalize the denominator: $\dfrac{1}{1 + \sqrt{2}}$

SOLUTION We multiply both the numerator and the denominator by the conjugate radical of $1 + \sqrt{2}$, which is $1 - \sqrt{2}$.

Special Product Formula 1
$(A + B)(A - B) = A^2 - B^2$

$$\frac{1}{1 + \sqrt{2}} = \frac{1}{1 + \sqrt{2}} \cdot \frac{1 - \sqrt{2}}{1 - \sqrt{2}} \qquad \begin{array}{l}\text{Multiply numerator and} \\ \text{denominator by the} \\ \text{conjugate radical}\end{array}$$

$$= \frac{1 - \sqrt{2}}{1^2 - (\sqrt{2})^2} \qquad \text{Special Product Formula 1}$$

$$= \frac{1 - \sqrt{2}}{1 - 2} = \frac{1 - \sqrt{2}}{-1} = \sqrt{2} - 1$$

✎ Now Try Exercise 85 ■

EXAMPLE 10 ■ Rationalizing the Numerator

Rationalize the numerator: $\dfrac{\sqrt{4 + h} - 2}{h}$

SOLUTION We multiply numerator and denominator by the conjugate radical $\sqrt{4 + h} + 2$.

Special Product Formula 1
$(A + B)(A - B) = A^2 - B^2$

$$\frac{\sqrt{4 + h} - 2}{h} = \frac{\sqrt{4 + h} - 2}{h} \cdot \frac{\sqrt{4 + h} + 2}{\sqrt{4 + h} + 2} \qquad \begin{array}{l}\text{Multiply numerator and} \\ \text{denominator by the} \\ \text{conjugate radical}\end{array}$$

$$= \frac{(\sqrt{4 + h})^2 - 2^2}{h(\sqrt{4 + h} + 2)} \qquad \text{Special Product Formula 1}$$

$$= \frac{4 + h - 4}{h(\sqrt{4 + h} + 2)}$$

$$= \frac{h}{h(\sqrt{4 + h} + 2)} = \frac{1}{\sqrt{4 + h} + 2} \qquad \begin{array}{l}\text{Property 5 of fractions} \\ \text{(cancel common factors)}\end{array}$$

✎ Now Try Exercise 91 ■

■ Avoiding Common Errors

 Don't make the mistake of applying properties of multiplication to the operation of addition. Many of the common errors in algebra involve doing just that. The following table states several properties of multiplication and illustrates the error in applying them to addition.

Correct multiplication property	Common error with addition
$(a \cdot b)^2 = a^2 \cdot b^2$	$(a + b)^2 \neq a^2 + b^2$
$\sqrt{a \cdot b} = \sqrt{a}\sqrt{b} \quad (a, b \geq 0)$	$\sqrt{a + b} \neq \sqrt{a} + \sqrt{b}$
$\sqrt{a^2 \cdot b^2} = a \cdot b \quad (a, b \geq 0)$	$\sqrt{a^2 + b^2} \neq a + b$
$\dfrac{1}{a} \cdot \dfrac{1}{b} = \dfrac{1}{a \cdot b}$	$\dfrac{1}{a} + \dfrac{1}{b} \neq \dfrac{1}{a + b}$
$\dfrac{ab}{a} = b$	$\dfrac{a + b}{a} \neq b$
$a^{-1} \cdot b^{-1} = (a \cdot b)^{-1}$	$a^{-1} + b^{-1} \neq (a + b)^{-1}$

To verify that the equations in the right-hand column are wrong, simply substitute numbers for a and b and calculate each side. For example, if we take $a = 2$ and $b = 2$ in the fourth error, we get different values for the left- and right-hand sides:

$$\underset{\text{Left-hand side}}{\frac{1}{a} + \frac{1}{b} = \frac{1}{2} + \frac{1}{2} = 1} \qquad \underset{\text{Right-hand side}}{\frac{1}{a + b} = \frac{1}{2 + 2} = \frac{1}{4}}$$

Since $1 \neq \frac{1}{4}$, the stated equation is wrong. You should similarly convince yourself of the error in each of the other equations. (See Exercises 101 and 102.)

P.7 EXERCISES

CONCEPTS

1. Which of the following are rational expressions?

(a) $\dfrac{3x}{x^2 - 1}$ (b) $\dfrac{\sqrt{x + 1}}{2x + 3}$ (c) $\dfrac{x(x^2 - 1)}{x + 3}$

2. To simplify a rational expression, we cancel *factors* that are common to the _____ and _____. So the expression

$$\frac{(x + 1)(x + 2)}{(x + 3)(x + 2)}$$

simplifies to _____.

3. To multiply two rational expressions, we multiply their

_____ together and multiply their _____ together.

So $\dfrac{2}{x + 1} \cdot \dfrac{x}{x + 3}$ is the same as _____.

4. Consider the expression $\dfrac{1}{x} - \dfrac{2}{x + 1} - \dfrac{x}{(x + 1)^2}$.

(a) How many terms does this expression have?

(b) Find the least common denominator of all the terms.

(c) Perform the addition and simplify.

5–6 ■ *Yes or No?* If *No*, give a reason. (Disregard any value that makes a denominator zero.)

5. (a) Is the expression $\dfrac{x(x + 1)}{(x + 1)^2}$ equal to $\dfrac{x}{x + 1}$?

(b) Is the expression $\sqrt{x^2 + 25}$ equal to $x + 5$?

6. (a) Is the expression $\dfrac{3 + a}{3}$ equal to $1 + \dfrac{a}{3}$?

(b) Is the expression $\dfrac{2}{4 + x}$ equal to $\dfrac{1}{2} + \dfrac{2}{x}$?

SKILLS

7–14 ■ **Domain** Find the domain of the expression.

7. $4x^2 - 10x + 3$

8. $-x^4 + x^3 + 9x$

9. $\dfrac{x^2 - 1}{x - 3}$

10. $\dfrac{2t^2 - 5}{3t + 6}$

11. $\sqrt{x + 3}$

12. $\dfrac{1}{\sqrt{x - 1}}$

13. $\dfrac{x^2 + 1}{x^2 - x - 2}$

14. $\dfrac{\sqrt{2x}}{x + 1}$

15–24 ■ Simplify   Simplify the rational expression.

15. $\dfrac{5(x-3)(2x+1)}{10(x-3)^2}$

16. $\dfrac{4(x^2-1)}{12(x+2)(x-1)}$

17. $\dfrac{x-2}{x^2-4}$

18. $\dfrac{x^2-x-2}{x^2-1}$

19. $\dfrac{x^2+5x+6}{x^2+8x+15}$

20. $\dfrac{x^2-x-12}{x^2+5x+6}$

21. $\dfrac{y^2+y}{y^2-1}$

22. $\dfrac{y^2-3y-18}{2y^2+7y+3}$

23. $\dfrac{2x^3-x^2-6x}{2x^2-7x+6}$

24. $\dfrac{1-x^2}{x^3-1}$

25–38 ■ Multiply or Divide   Perform the multiplication or division and simplify.

25. $\dfrac{4x}{x^2-4}\cdot\dfrac{x+2}{16x}$

26. $\dfrac{x^2-25}{x^2-16}\cdot\dfrac{x+4}{x+5}$

27. $\dfrac{x^2+2x-15}{x^2-25}\cdot\dfrac{x-5}{x+2}$

28. $\dfrac{x^2+2x-3}{x^2-2x-3}\cdot\dfrac{3-x}{3+x}$

29. $\dfrac{t-3}{t^2+9}\cdot\dfrac{t+3}{t^2-9}$

30. $\dfrac{x^2-x-6}{x^2+2x}\cdot\dfrac{x^3+x^2}{x^2-2x-3}$

31. $\dfrac{x^2+7x+12}{x^2+3x+2}\cdot\dfrac{x^2+5x+6}{x^2+6x+9}$

32. $\dfrac{x^2+2xy+y^2}{x^2-y^2}\cdot\dfrac{2x^2-xy-y^2}{x^2-xy-2y^2}$

33. $\dfrac{x+3}{4x^2-9}\div\dfrac{x^2+7x+12}{2x^2+7x-15}$

34. $\dfrac{2x+1}{2x^2+x-15}\div\dfrac{6x^2-x-2}{x+3}$

35. $\dfrac{\dfrac{x^3}{x+1}}{\dfrac{x}{x^2+2x+1}}$

36. $\dfrac{\dfrac{2x^2-3x-2}{x^2-1}}{\dfrac{2x^2+5x+2}{x^2+x-2}}$

37. $\dfrac{x/y}{z}$

38. $\dfrac{x}{y/z}$

39–58 ■ Add or Subtract   Perform the addition or subtraction and simplify.

39. $1+\dfrac{1}{x+3}$

40. $\dfrac{3x-2}{x+1}-2$

41. $\dfrac{1}{x+5}+\dfrac{2}{x-3}$

42. $\dfrac{1}{x+1}+\dfrac{1}{x-1}$

43. $\dfrac{3}{x+1}-\dfrac{1}{x+2}$

44. $\dfrac{x}{x-4}-\dfrac{3}{x+6}$

45. $\dfrac{5}{2x-3}-\dfrac{3}{(2x-3)^2}$

46. $\dfrac{x}{(x+1)^2}+\dfrac{2}{x+1}$

47. $u+1+\dfrac{u}{u+1}$

48. $\dfrac{2}{a^2}-\dfrac{3}{ab}+\dfrac{4}{b^2}$

49. $\dfrac{1}{x^2}+\dfrac{1}{x^2+x}$

50. $\dfrac{1}{x}+\dfrac{1}{x^2}+\dfrac{1}{x^3}$

51. $\dfrac{2}{x+3}-\dfrac{1}{x^2+7x+12}$

52. $\dfrac{x}{x^2-4}+\dfrac{1}{x-2}$

53. $\dfrac{1}{x+3}+\dfrac{1}{x^2-9}$

54. $\dfrac{x}{x^2+x-2}-\dfrac{2}{x^2-5x+4}$

55. $\dfrac{2}{x}+\dfrac{3}{x-1}-\dfrac{4}{x^2-x}$

56. $\dfrac{x}{x^2-x-6}-\dfrac{1}{x+2}-\dfrac{2}{x-3}$

57. $\dfrac{1}{x^2+3x+2}-\dfrac{1}{x^2-2x-3}$

58. $\dfrac{1}{x+1}-\dfrac{2}{(x+1)^2}+\dfrac{3}{x^2-1}$

59–72 ■ Compound Fractions   Simplify the compound fractional expression.

59. $\dfrac{1+\dfrac{1}{x}}{\dfrac{1}{x}-2}$

60. $\dfrac{1-\dfrac{2}{y}}{\dfrac{3}{y}-1}$

61. $\dfrac{1+\dfrac{1}{x+2}}{1-\dfrac{1}{x+2}}$

62. $\dfrac{1+\dfrac{1}{c-1}}{1-\dfrac{1}{c-1}}$

63. $\dfrac{\dfrac{1}{x-1}+\dfrac{1}{x+3}}{x+1}$

64. $\dfrac{\dfrac{x-3}{x-4}-\dfrac{x+2}{x+1}}{x+3}$

65. $\dfrac{x-\dfrac{x}{y}}{y-\dfrac{y}{x}}$

66. $\dfrac{x+\dfrac{y}{x}}{y+\dfrac{x}{y}}$

67. $\dfrac{\dfrac{x}{y}-\dfrac{y}{x}}{\dfrac{1}{x^2}-\dfrac{1}{y^2}}$

68. $x-\dfrac{y}{\dfrac{x}{y}+\dfrac{y}{x}}$

69. $\dfrac{x^{-2}-y^{-2}}{x^{-1}+y^{-1}}$

70. $\dfrac{x^{-1}+y^{-1}}{(x+y)^{-1}}$

71. $1-\dfrac{1}{1-\dfrac{1}{x}}$

72. $1+\dfrac{1}{1+\dfrac{1}{1+x}}$

73–78 ■ Expressions Found in Calculus   Simplify the fractional expression. (Expressions like these arise in calculus.)

73. $\dfrac{\dfrac{1}{1+x+h}-\dfrac{1}{1+x}}{h}$

74. $\dfrac{\dfrac{1}{\sqrt{x+h}}-\dfrac{1}{\sqrt{x}}}{h}$

75. $\dfrac{\dfrac{1}{(x+h)^2} - \dfrac{1}{x^2}}{h}$

76. $\dfrac{(x+h)^3 - 7(x+h) - (x^3 - 7x)}{h}$

77. $\sqrt{1 + \left(\dfrac{x}{\sqrt{1-x^2}}\right)^2}$ **78.** $\sqrt{1 + \left(x^3 - \dfrac{1}{4x^3}\right)^2}$

79–84 ■ Expressions Found in Calculus Simplify the expression. (This type of expression arises in calculus when using the "quotient rule.")

79. $\dfrac{3(x+2)^2(x-3)^2 - (x+2)^3(2)(x-3)}{(x-3)^4}$

80. $\dfrac{2x(x+6)^4 - x^2(4)(x+6)^3}{(x+6)^8}$

81. $\dfrac{2(1+x)^{1/2} - x(1+x)^{-1/2}}{x+1}$

82. $\dfrac{(1-x^2)^{1/2} + x^2(1-x^2)^{-1/2}}{1-x^2}$

83. $\dfrac{3(1+x)^{1/3} - x(1+x)^{-2/3}}{(1+x)^{2/3}}$

84. $\dfrac{(7-3x)^{1/2} + \frac{3}{2}x(7-3x)^{-1/2}}{7-3x}$

85–90 ■ Rationalize Denominator Rationalize the denominator.

85. $\dfrac{1}{5 - \sqrt{3}}$ **86.** $\dfrac{3}{2 - \sqrt{5}}$

87. $\dfrac{2}{\sqrt{2} + \sqrt{7}}$ **88.** $\dfrac{1}{\sqrt{x} + 1}$

89. $\dfrac{y}{\sqrt{3} + \sqrt{y}}$ **90.** $\dfrac{2(x-y)}{\sqrt{x} - \sqrt{y}}$

91–96 ■ Rationalize Numerator Rationalize the numerator.

91. $\dfrac{1 - \sqrt{5}}{3}$ **92.** $\dfrac{\sqrt{3} + \sqrt{5}}{2}$

93. $\dfrac{\sqrt{r} + \sqrt{2}}{5}$ **94.** $\dfrac{\sqrt{x} - \sqrt{x+h}}{h\sqrt{x}\sqrt{x+h}}$

95. $\sqrt{x^2 + 1} - x$ **96.** $\sqrt{x+1} - \sqrt{x}$

APPLICATIONS

97. Electrical Resistance If two electrical resistors with resistances R_1 and R_2 are connected in parallel (see the figure), then the total resistance R is given by

$$R = \dfrac{1}{\dfrac{1}{R_1} + \dfrac{1}{R_2}}$$

(a) Simplify the expression for R.

(b) If $R_1 = 10$ ohms and $R_2 = 20$ ohms, what is the total resistance R?

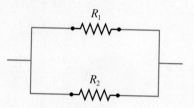

98. Average Cost A clothing manufacturer finds that the cost of producing x shirts is $500 + 6x + 0.01x^2$ dollars.

(a) Explain why the average cost per shirt is given by the rational expression

$$A = \dfrac{500 + 6x + 0.01x^2}{x}$$

(b) Complete the table by calculating the average cost per shirt for the given values of x.

x	Average cost
10	
20	
50	
100	
200	
500	
1000	

DISCUSS ■ DISCOVER ■ PROVE ■ WRITE

99. DISCOVER: Limiting Behavior of a Rational Expression The rational expression

$$\dfrac{x^2 - 9}{x - 3}$$

is not defined for $x = 3$. Complete the tables, and determine what value the expression approaches as x gets closer and closer to 3. Why is this reasonable? Factor the numerator of the expression and simplify to see why.

x	$\dfrac{x^2-9}{x-3}$
2.80	
2.90	
2.95	
2.99	
2.999	

x	$\dfrac{x^2-9}{x-3}$
3.20	
3.10	
3.05	
3.01	
3.001	

100. DISCUSS ■ WRITE: Is This Rationalization? In the expression $2/\sqrt{x}$ we would eliminate the radical if we were to square both numerator and denominator. Is this the same thing as rationalizing the denominator? Explain.

101. DISCUSS: Algebraic Errors The left-hand column of the table lists some common algebraic errors. In each case, give an example using numbers that shows that the formula is not valid. An example of this type, which shows that a statement is false, is called a *counterexample*.

Algebraic errors	Counterexample
$\dfrac{1}{a} + \dfrac{1}{b} \not= \dfrac{1}{a+b}$	$\dfrac{1}{2} + \dfrac{1}{2} \neq \dfrac{1}{2+2}$
$(a+b)^2 \not= a^2 + b^2$	
$\sqrt{a^2 + b^2} \not= a + b$	
$\dfrac{a+b}{a} \not= b$	
$\dfrac{a}{a+b} \not= \dfrac{1}{b}$	
$\dfrac{a^m}{a^n} \not= a^{m/n}$	

102. DISCUSS: Algebraic Errors Determine whether the given equation is true for all values of the variables. If not, give a counterexample. (Disregard any value that makes a denominator zero.)

(a) $\dfrac{5+a}{5} = 1 + \dfrac{a}{5}$ **(b)** $\dfrac{x+1}{y+1} = \dfrac{x}{y}$

(c) $\dfrac{x}{x+y} = \dfrac{1}{1+y}$ **(d)** $2\left(\dfrac{a}{b}\right) = \dfrac{2a}{2b}$

(e) $\dfrac{-a}{b} = -\dfrac{a}{b}$ **(f)** $\dfrac{1+x+x^2}{x} = \dfrac{1}{x} + 1 + x$

103. DISCOVER ■ PROVE: Values of a Rational Expression Consider the expression

$$x + \frac{1}{x}$$

for $x > 0$.

(a) Fill in the table, and try other values for x. What do you think is the smallest possible value for this expression?

x	1	3	$\frac{1}{2}$	$\frac{9}{10}$	$\frac{99}{100}$	
$x + \dfrac{1}{x}$						

(b) Prove that for $x > 0$,

$$x + \frac{1}{x} \geq 2$$

[*Hint:* Multiply by x, move terms to one side, and then factor to arrive at a true statement. Note that each step you made is reversible.]

P.8 SOLVING BASIC EQUATIONS

■ Solving Linear Equations   ■ Solving Power Equations   ■ Solving for One Variable in Terms of Others

Equations are the basic mathematical tool for solving real-world problems. In this section we learn how to solve equations.

An equation is a statement that two mathematical expressions are equal. For example,

$$3 + 5 = 8$$

is an equation. Most equations that we study in algebra contain variables, which are symbols (usually letters) that stand for numbers. In the equation

$$4x + 7 = 19$$

the letter x is the variable. We think of x as the "unknown" in the equation, and our goal is to find the value of x that makes the equation true. The values of the unknown that make the equation true are called the **solutions** or **roots** of the equation, and the process of finding the solutions is called **solving the equation**.

Two equations with exactly the same solutions are called **equivalent equations**. To solve an equation, we try to find a simpler, equivalent equation in which the variable stands alone on one side of the equal sign. Here are the properties that we use to solve an equation. (In these properties, A, B, and C stand for any algebraic expressions, and the symbol $\Leftrightarrow$ means "is equivalent to.")

$x = 3$ is a solution of the equation $4x + 7 = 19$, because substituting $x = 3$ makes the equation true:

$x = 3$

$4(3) + 7 = 19$ ✓

PROPERTIES OF EQUALITY

Property	Description
1. $A = B \iff A + C = B + C$	Adding the same quantity to both sides of an equation gives an equivalent equation.
2. $A = B \iff CA = CB \quad (C \neq 0)$	Multiplying both sides of an equation by the same nonzero quantity gives an equivalent equation.

These properties require that you *perform the same operation on both sides of an equation* when solving it. Thus if we say "*add* 4" when solving an equation, that is just a short way of saying "*add* 4 to each side of the equation."

■ Solving Linear Equations

The simplest type of equation is a *linear equation*, or first-degree equation, which is an equation in which each term is either a constant or a nonzero multiple of the variable.

LINEAR EQUATIONS

A **linear equation** in one variable is an equation equivalent to one of the form

$$ax + b = 0$$

where a and b are real numbers and x is the variable.

Here are some examples that illustrate the difference between linear and nonlinear equations.

Linear equations	Nonlinear equations	
$4x - 5 = 3$	$x^2 + 2x = 8$	Not linear; contains the square of the variable
$2x = \frac{1}{2}x - 7$	$\sqrt{x} - 6x = 0$	Not linear; contains the square root of the variable
$x - 6 = \dfrac{x}{3}$	$\dfrac{3}{x} - 2x = 1$	Not linear; contains the reciprocal of the variable

EXAMPLE 1 ■ Solving a Linear Equation

Solve the equation $7x - 4 = 3x + 8$.

SOLUTION We solve this by changing it to an equivalent equation with all terms that have the variable x on one side and all constant terms on the other.

$7x - 4 = 3x + 8$	Given equation
$(7x - 4) + 4 = (3x + 8) + 4$	Add 4
$7x = 3x + 12$	Simplify
$7x - 3x = (3x + 12) - 3x$	Subtract $3x$
$4x = 12$	Simplify
$\frac{1}{4} \cdot 4x = \frac{1}{4} \cdot 12$	Multiply by $\frac{1}{4}$
$x = 3$	Simplify

Because it is important to CHECK YOUR ANSWER, we do this in many of our examples. In these checks, LHS stands for "left-hand side" and RHS stands for "right-hand side" of the original equation.

$x = 3$:

$x = 3$
LHS $= 7(3) - 4$
$= 17$

$x = 3$
RHS $= 3(3) + 8$
$= 17$

LHS = RHS ✓

✎ Now Try Exercises 15 and 21

When a linear equation involves fractions, solving the equation is usually easier if we first multiply each side by the lowest common denominator (LCD) of the fractions, as we see in the following examples.

EXAMPLE 2 ■ Solving an Equation That Involves Fractions

Solve the equation $\dfrac{x}{6} + \dfrac{2}{3} = \dfrac{3}{4}x$.

SOLUTION The LCD of the denominators 6, 3, and 4 is 12, so we first multiply each side of the equation by 12 to clear the denominators.

$$12 \cdot \left(\frac{x}{6} + \frac{2}{3} \right) = 12 \cdot \frac{3}{4}x \qquad \text{Multiply by LCD}$$

$$2x + 8 = 9x \qquad \text{Distributive Property}$$

$$8 = 7x \qquad \text{Subtract } 2x$$

$$\frac{8}{7} = x \qquad \text{Divide by 7}$$

The solution is $x = \frac{8}{7}$.

✎ Now Try Exercise 27

In the next example we solve an equation that doesn't look like a linear equation, but it simplifies to one when we multiply by the LCD.

EXAMPLE 3 ■ An Equation Involving Fractional Expressions

Solve the equation $\dfrac{1}{x + 1} + \dfrac{1}{x - 2} = \dfrac{x + 3}{x^2 - x - 2}$.

SOLUTION The LCD of the fractional expressions is $(x + 1)(x - 2) = x^2 - x - 2$. So as long as $x \neq -1$ and $x \neq 2$, we can multiply both sides of the equation by the LCD to get

$$(x + 1)(x - 2)\left(\frac{1}{x + 1} + \frac{1}{x - 2} \right) = (x + 1)(x - 2)\left(\frac{x + 3}{x^2 - x - 2} \right) \quad \begin{array}{l}\text{Multiply}\\\text{by LCD}\end{array}$$

$$(x - 2) + (x + 1) = x + 3 \qquad \text{Expand}$$

$$2x - 1 = x + 3 \qquad \text{Simplify}$$

$$x = 4 \qquad \text{Solve}$$

The solution is $x = 4$.

✎ Now Try Exercise 49

$x = 4$:

LHS $= \dfrac{1}{4 + 1} + \dfrac{1}{4 - 2}$

$= \dfrac{1}{5} + \dfrac{1}{2} = \dfrac{7}{10}$

RHS $= \dfrac{4 + 3}{4^2 - 4 - 2} = \dfrac{7}{10}$

LHS = RHS ✓

⊘ It is always important to check your answer, even if you never make a mistake in your calculations. This is because you sometimes end up with **extraneous solutions**, which are potential solutions that do not satisfy the original equation. The next example shows how this can happen.

EXAMPLE 4 ■ An Equation with No Solution

Solve the equation $2 + \dfrac{5}{x - 4} = \dfrac{x + 1}{x - 4}$.

SOLUTION First, we multiply each side by the common denominator, which is $x - 4$.

$$(x - 4)\left(2 + \frac{5}{x - 4}\right) = (x - 4)\left(\frac{x + 1}{x - 4}\right) \qquad \text{Multiply by } x - 4$$

$$2(x - 4) + 5 = x + 1 \qquad \text{Expand}$$

$$2x - 8 + 5 = x + 1 \qquad \text{Distributive Property}$$

$$2x - 3 = x + 1 \qquad \text{Simplify}$$

$$2x = x + 4 \qquad \text{Add 3}$$

$$x = 4 \qquad \text{Subtract } x$$

But now if we try to substitute $x = 4$ back into the original equation, we would be dividing by 0, which is impossible. So this equation has *no solution*.

CHECK YOUR ANSWER

$x = 4$:

$$\text{LHS} = 2 + \frac{5}{4 - 4} = 2 + \frac{5}{0} \qquad \text{RHS} = \frac{4 + 1}{4 - 4} = \frac{5}{0}$$

Impossible—can't divide by 0. LHS and RHS are undefined, so $x = 4$ is not a solution. ✗

✎ Now Try Exercise 51 ■

⊘ The first step in the preceding solution, multiplying by $x - 4$, had the effect of multiplying by 0. (Do you see why?) Multiplying each side of an equation by an expression that contains the variable may introduce extraneous solutions. That is why it is important to check every answer.

■ Solving Power Equations

Linear equations have variables only to the first power. Now let's consider some equations that involve squares, cubes, and other powers of the variable. Such equations will be studied more extensively in Sections 1.4 and 1.6. Here we just consider basic equations that can be simplified into the form $X^n = a$. Equations of this form are called **power equations** and can be solved by taking radicals of both sides of the equation.

SOLVING A POWER EQUATION

The power equation $X^n = a$ has the solution

$$X = \sqrt[n]{a} \qquad \text{if } n \text{ is odd}$$

$$X = \pm\sqrt[n]{a} \qquad \text{if } n \text{ is even and } a \geq 0$$

If n is even and $a < 0$, the equation has no real solution.

Here are some examples of solving power equations:

The equation $x^5 = 32$ has only one real solution: $x = \sqrt[5]{32} = 2$.

The equation $x^4 = 16$ has two real solutions: $x = \pm\sqrt[4]{16} = \pm 2$.

The equation $x^5 = -32$ has only one real solution: $x = \sqrt[5]{-32} = -2$.

The equation $x^4 = -16$ has no real solutions because $\sqrt[4]{-16}$ does not exist.

EXAMPLE 5 ■ Solving Power Equations

Solve each equation.

(a) $x^2 - 5 = 0$

(b) $(x - 4)^2 = 5$

SOLUTION

(a) $x^2 - 5 = 0$

$$x^2 = 5 \qquad \text{Add 5}$$

$$x = \pm\sqrt{5} \qquad \text{Take the square root}$$

The solutions are $x = \sqrt{5}$ and $x = -\sqrt{5}$.

(b) We can take the square root of each side of this equation as well.

$$(x - 4)^2 = 5$$

$$x - 4 = \pm\sqrt{5} \qquad \text{Take the square root}$$

$$x = 4 \pm \sqrt{5} \qquad \text{Add 4}$$

The solutions are $x = 4 + \sqrt{5}$ and $x = 4 - \sqrt{5}$.

Be sure to check that each answer satisfies the original equation.

✎ **Now Try Exercises 55 and 63** ■

We will revisit equations like the ones in Example 5 in Section 1.6.

EXAMPLE 6 ■ Solving Power Equations

Find all real solutions for each equation.

(a) $x^3 = -8$

(b) $16x^4 = 81$

SOLUTION

(a) Since every real number has exactly one real cube root, we can solve this equation by taking the cube root of each side:

$$(x^3)^{1/3} = (-8)^{1/3}$$

$$x = -2$$

(b) Here we must remember that if n is even, then every positive real number has *two* real nth roots, a positive one and a negative one.

$$x^4 = \tfrac{81}{16} \qquad \text{Divide by 16}$$

$$(x^4)^{1/4} = \pm\left(\tfrac{81}{16}\right)^{1/4} \qquad \text{Take the fourth root}$$

$$x = \pm\tfrac{3}{2}$$

✎ **Now Try Exercises 65 and 67** ■

The next example shows how to solve an equation that involves a fractional power of the variable.

EUCLID (circa 300 B.C.) taught in Alexandria, Egypt. His *Elements* is the most widely influential scientific book in history. For 2000 years it was the standard introduction to geometry in the schools, and for many generations it was considered the best way to develop logical reasoning. Abraham Lincoln, for instance, studied the Elements as a way to sharpen his mind. The story is told that King Ptolemy once asked Euclid whether there was a faster way to learn geometry than through the *Elements*. Euclid replied that there is "no royal road to geometry"—meaning by this that mathematics does not respect wealth or social status. Euclid was revered in his own time and was referred to by the title "The Geometer" or "The Writer of the *Elements*." The greatness of the *Elements* stems from its precise, logical, and systematic treatment of geometry. For dealing with equality, Euclid lists the following rules, which he calls "common notions."

1. Things that are equal to the same thing are equal to each other.

2. If equals are added to equals, the sums are equal.

3. If equals are subtracted from equals, the remainders are equal.

4. Things that coincide with one another are equal.

5. The whole is greater than the part.

⊘ If n is even, the equation $x^n = c$ ($c > 0$) has two solutions, $x = c^{1/n}$ and $x = -c^{1/n}$.

EXAMPLE 7 ■ **Solving an Equation with a Fractional Power**

Solve the equation $5x^{2/3} - 2 = 43$.

SOLUTION The idea is to first isolate the term with the fractional exponent, then raise both sides of the equation to the *reciprocal* of that exponent.

$$5x^{2/3} - 2 = 43$$

$$5x^{2/3} = 45 \qquad \text{Add 2}$$

$$x^{2/3} = 9 \qquad \text{Divide by 5}$$

$$x = \pm 9^{3/2} \qquad \text{Raise both sides to } \tfrac{3}{2} \text{ power}$$

$$x = \pm 27 \qquad \text{Simplify}$$

⊘ If n is even, the equation $x^{n/m} = c$ has two solutions, $x = c^{m/n}$ and $x = -c^{m/n}$.

The solutions are $x = 27$ and $x = -27$.

CHECK YOUR ANSWER

$x = 27$:

$$\begin{aligned} \text{LHS} &= 5(27)^{2/3} - 2 \\ &= 5(9) - 2 \\ &= 43 \\ \text{RHS} &= 43 \\ \text{LHS} &= \text{RHS} \quad \checkmark \end{aligned}$$

$x = -27$:

$$\begin{aligned} \text{LHS} &= 5(-27)^{2/3} - 2 \\ &= 5(9) - 2 \\ &= 43 \\ \text{RHS} &= 43 \\ \text{LHS} &= \text{RHS} \quad \checkmark \end{aligned}$$

✎ Now Try Exercise 77

■ Solving for One Variable in Terms of Others

Many formulas in the sciences involve several variables, and it is often necessary to express one of the variables in terms of the others. In the next example we solve for a variable in Newton's Law of Gravity.

EXAMPLE 8 ■ **Solving for One Variable in Terms of Others**

This is Newton's Law of Gravity. It gives the gravitational force F between two masses m and M that are a distance r apart. The constant G is the universal gravitational constant.

Solve for the variable M in the equation

$$F = G\frac{mM}{r^2}$$

SOLUTION Although this equation involves more than one variable, we solve it as usual by isolating M on one side and treating the other variables as we would numbers:

$$F = \left(\frac{Gm}{r^2}\right)M \qquad \text{Factor } M \text{ from RHS}$$

$$\left(\frac{r^2}{Gm}\right)F = \left(\frac{r^2}{Gm}\right)\left(\frac{Gm}{r^2}\right)M \qquad \text{Multiply by reciprocal of } \frac{Gm}{r^2}$$

$$\frac{r^2F}{Gm} = M \qquad \text{Simplify}$$

The solution is $M = \dfrac{r^2F}{Gm}$.

✎ Now Try Exercise 89

EXAMPLE 9 ■ Solving for One Variable in Terms of Others

The surface area A of the closed rectangular box shown in Figure 1 can be calculated from the length l, the width w, and the height h according to the formula

$$A = 2lw + 2wh + 2lh$$

Solve for w in terms of the other variables in this equation.

SOLUTION   Although this equation involves more than one variable, we solve it as usual by isolating w on one side, treating the other variables as we would numbers:

$$A = (2lw + 2wh) + 2lh \qquad \text{Collect terms involving } w$$

$$A - 2lh = 2lw + 2wh \qquad \text{Subtract } 2lh$$

$$A - 2lh = (2l + 2h)w \qquad \text{Factor } w \text{ from RHS}$$

$$\frac{A - 2lh}{2l + 2h} = w \qquad \text{Divide by } 2l + 2h$$

The solution is $w = \dfrac{A - 2lh}{2l + 2h}$.

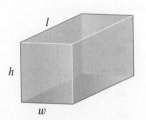

FIGURE 1 A closed rectangular box

✎. **Now Try Exercise 91**

P.8 EXERCISES

CONCEPTS

1. Substituting $x = 3$ in the equation $4x - 2 = 10$ makes the equation true, so the number 3 is a _____ of the equation.

2. To solve an equation, we use the rules of algebra to put the variable alone on one side. Solve the equation $3x + 4 = 10$ by using the following steps:

$$3x + 4 = 10 \qquad \text{Given equation}$$

_____   Subtract 4

_____   Multiply by $\frac{1}{3}$

So the solution is $x =$ _____.

3. Which of the following equations are linear?

(a) $\dfrac{x}{2} + 2x = 10$ (b) $\dfrac{2}{x} - 2x = 1$

(c) $x + 7 = 5 - 3x$

4. Explain why each of the following equations is not linear.

(a) $x(x + 1) = 6$ (b) $\sqrt{x + 2} = x$

(c) $3x^2 - 2x - 1 = 0$

5. *True or False?*

(a) Adding the same number to each side of an equation always gives an equivalent equation.

(b) Multiplying each side of an equation by the same number always gives an equivalent equation.

(c) Squaring each side of an equation always gives an equivalent equation.

6. To solve the equation $x^3 = 125$, we take the _____ root of each side. So the solution is $x =$ _____.

SKILLS

7–14 ■ **Solution?**   Determine whether the given value is a solution of the equation.

7. $4x + 7 = 9x - 3$

(a) $x = -2$ (b) $x = 2$

8. $2 - 5x = 8 + x$

(a) $x = -1$ (b) $x = 1$

9. $1 - [2 - (3 - x)] = 4x - (6 + x)$

(a) $x = 2$ (b) $x = 4$

10. $\dfrac{1}{x} - \dfrac{1}{x - 4} = 1$

(a) $x = 2$ (b) $x = 4$

11. $2x^{1/3} - 3 = 1$

(a) $x = -1$ (b) $x = 8$

12. $\dfrac{x^{3/2}}{x - 6} = x - 8$

(a) $x = 4$ (b) $x = 8$

13. $\dfrac{x - a}{x - b} = \dfrac{a}{b}$ $(b \neq 0)$

(a) $x = 0$ (b) $x = b$

14. $x^2 - bx + \dfrac{1}{4}b^2 = 0$

(a) $x = \dfrac{b}{2}$ (b) $x = \dfrac{1}{b}$

15–28 ■ Linear Equations Solve the given linear equation.

15. $5x - 6 = 14$

16. $3x + 4 = 7$

17. $7 - 2x = 15$

18. $4x - 95 = 1$

19. $\frac{1}{2}x + 7 = 3$

20. $2 + \frac{1}{3}x = -4$

21. $-3x - 3 = 5x - 3$

22. $2x + 3 = 5 - 2x$

23. $7x + 1 = 4 - 2x$

24. $1 - x = x + 4$

25. $-x + 3 = 4x$

26. $2x + 3 = 7 - 3x$

27. $\frac{x}{3} - 1 = \frac{5}{3}x + 7$

28. $\frac{2}{5}x - 1 = \frac{3}{10}x + 3$

29–40 ■ Linear Equations The given equation is either linear or equivalent to a linear equation. Solve the equation.

29. $2(1 - x) = 3(1 + 2x) + 5$

30. $5(x + 3) + 9 = -2(x - 2) - 1$

31. $4\left(y - \frac{1}{2}\right) - y = 6(5 - y)$

32. $r - 2[1 - 3(2r + 4)] = 61$

33. $x - \frac{1}{3}x - \frac{1}{2}x - 5 = 0$ **34.** $\frac{2}{3}y + \frac{1}{2}(y - 3) = \frac{y + 1}{4}$

35. $2x - \frac{x}{2} + \frac{x + 1}{4} = 6x$ **36.** $3x - \frac{5x}{2} = \frac{x + 1}{3} - \frac{1}{6}$

37. $(x - 1)(x + 2) = (x - 2)(x - 3)$

38. $x(x + 1) = (x + 3)^2$

39. $(x - 1)(4x + 5) = (2x - 3)^2$

40. $(t - 4)^2 = (t + 4)^2 + 32$

41–54 ■ Equations Involving Fractional Expressions The given equation is either linear or equivalent to a linear equation. Solve the equation.

41. $\frac{1}{x} = \frac{4}{3x} + 1$ **42.** $\frac{2}{x} - 5 = \frac{6}{x} + 4$

43. $\frac{2x - 1}{x + 2} = \frac{4}{5}$ **44.** $\frac{2x - 7}{2x + 4} = \frac{2}{3}$

45. $\frac{2}{t + 6} = \frac{3}{t - 1}$ **46.** $\frac{6}{x - 3} = \frac{5}{x + 4}$

47. $\frac{3}{x + 1} - \frac{1}{2} = \frac{1}{3x + 3}$ **48.** $\frac{12x - 5}{6x + 3} = 2 - \frac{5}{x}$

49. $\frac{1}{z} - \frac{1}{2z} - \frac{1}{5z} = \frac{10}{z + 1}$

50. $\frac{1}{3 - t} + \frac{4}{3 + t} + \frac{15}{9 - t^2} = 0$

51. $\frac{x}{2x - 4} - 2 = \frac{1}{x - 2}$

52. $\frac{1}{x + 3} + \frac{5}{x^2 - 9} = \frac{2}{x - 3}$

53. $\frac{3}{x + 4} = \frac{1}{x} + \frac{6x + 12}{x^2 + 4x}$ **54.** $\frac{1}{x} - \frac{2}{2x + 1} = \frac{1}{2x^2 + x}$

55–78 ■ Power Equations The given equation involves a power of the variable. Find all real solutions of the equation.

55. $x^2 = 25$

56. $3x^2 = 48$

57. $5x^2 = 15$

58. $x^2 = 1000$

59. $8x^2 - 64 = 0$

60. $5x^2 - 125 = 0$

61. $x^2 + 16 = 0$

62. $6x^2 + 100 = 0$

63. $(x - 3)^2 = 5$

64. $(3x - 4)^2 = 7$

65. $x^3 = 27$

66. $x^5 + 32 = 0$

67. $x^4 - 16 = 0$

68. $64x^6 = 27$

69. $x^4 + 64 = 0$

70. $(x - 1)^3 + 8 = 0$

71. $(x + 2)^4 - 81 = 0$

72. $(x + 1)^4 + 16 = 0$

73. $3(x - 3)^3 = 375$

74. $4(x + 2)^5 = 1$

75. $\sqrt[3]{x} = 5$

76. $x^{4/3} - 16 = 0$

77. $2x^{5/3} + 64 = 0$

78. $6x^{2/3} - 216 = 0$

79–86 ■ Linear Equations Find the solution of the equation rounded to two decimals.

79. $3.02x + 1.48 = 10.92$ **80.** $8.36 - 0.95x = 9.97$

81. $2.15x - 4.63 = x + 1.19$

82. $3.95 - x = 2.32x + 2.00$

83. $3.16(x + 4.63) = 4.19(x - 7.24)$

84. $2.14(x - 4.06) = 2.27 - 0.11x$

85. $\frac{0.26x - 1.94}{3.03 - 2.44x} = 1.76$

86. $\frac{1.73x}{2.12 + x} = 1.51$

87–100 ■ Solving for a Variable Solve the equation for the indicated variable.

87. $r = \frac{12}{M}$;   for M **88.** $wd = rTH$;   for T

89. $PV = nRT$;   for R **90.** $F = G\frac{mM}{r^2}$;   for m

91. $P = 2l + 2w$;   for w **92.** $\frac{1}{R} = \frac{1}{R_1} + \frac{1}{R_2}$;   for R_1

93. $V = \frac{1}{3}\pi r^2 h$;   for r **94.** $F = G\frac{mM}{r^2}$;   for r

95. $V = \frac{4}{3}\pi r^3$;   for r

96. $a^2 + b^2 = c^2$;   for b

97. $A = P\left(1 + \frac{i}{100}\right)^2$;   for i

98. $a^2 x + (a - 1) = (a + 1)x$;   for x

99. $\frac{ax + b}{cx + d} = 2$;   for x

100. $\frac{a + 1}{b} = \frac{a - 1}{b} + \frac{b + 1}{a}$;   for a

APPLICATIONS

101. Shrinkage in Concrete Beams   As concrete dries, it shrinks; the higher the water content, the greater the shrinkage. If a concrete beam has a water content of w kg/m^3, then it will shrink by a factor

$$S = \frac{0.032w - 2.5}{10,000}$$

where S is the fraction of the original beam length that disappears owing to shrinkage.

(a) A beam 12.025 m long is cast in concrete that contains 250 kg/m^3 water. What is the shrinkage factor S? How long will the beam be when it has dried?

(b) A beam is 10.014 m long when wet. The manufacturer wants it to shrink to 10.009 m, so the shrinkage factor should be $S = 0.00050$. What water content will provide this amount of shrinkage?

102. Manufacturing Cost   A toy maker finds that it costs $C = 450 + 3.75x$ dollars to manufacture x toy trucks. If the budget allows \$3600 in costs, how many trucks can be made?

103. Power Produced by a Windmill   When the wind blows with speed v km/h, a windmill with blade length 150 cm generates P watts (W) of power according to the formula $P = 15.6\,v^3$.

(a) How fast would the wind have to blow to generate 10,000 W of power?

(b) How fast would the wind have to blow to generate 50,000 W of power?

104. Food Consumption   The average daily food consumption F of a herbivorous mammal with body weight x, where both F and x are measured in pounds, is given approximately by the equation $F = 0.3x^{3/4}$. Find the weight x of an elephant that consumes 300 lb of food per day.

DISCUSS ■ DISCOVER ■ PROVE ■ WRITE

105. DISCUSS: A Family of Equations   The equation

$$3x + k - 5 = kx - k + 1$$

is really a **family of equations**, because for each value of k, we get a different equation with the unknown x. The letter k is called a **parameter** for this family. What value should we pick for k to make the given value of x a solution of the resulting equation?

(a) $x = 0$ (b) $x = 1$ (c) $x = 2$

106. DISCUSS: Proof That 0 = 1?   The following steps appear to give equivalent equations, which seem to prove that $1 = 0$. Find the error.

$x = 1$	Given
$x^2 = x$	Multiply by x
$x^2 - x = 0$	Subtract x
$x(x - 1) = 0$	Factor
$x = 0$	Divide by $x - 1$
$1 = 0$	Given $x = 1$

P.9   MODELING WITH EQUATIONS

■ Making and Using Models ■ Problems About Interest ■ Problems About Area or Length ■ Problems About Mixtures ■ Problems About the Time Needed to Do a Job ■ Problems About Distance, Rate, and Time

Many problems in the sciences, economics, finance, medicine, and numerous other fields can be translated into algebra problems; this is one reason that algebra is so useful. In this section we use equations as mathematical models to solve real-life problems.

■ Making and Using Models

We will use the following guidelines to help us set up equations that model situations described in words. To show how the guidelines can help you to set up equations, we note them as we work each example in this section.

GUIDELINES FOR MODELING WITH EQUATIONS

1. **Identify the Variable.**   Identify the quantity that the problem asks you to find. This quantity can usually be determined by a careful reading of the question that is posed at the end of the problem. Then **introduce notation** for the variable (call it x or some other letter).

2. **Translate from Words to Algebra.**   Read each sentence in the problem again, and express all the quantities mentioned in the problem in terms of the variable you defined in Step 1. To organize this information, it is sometimes helpful to **draw a diagram** or **make a table**.

3. **Set Up the Model.**   Find the crucial fact in the problem that gives a relationship between the expressions you listed in Step 2. **Set up an equation** (or **model**) that expresses this relationship.

4. **Solve the Equation and Check Your Answer.**   Solve the equation, check your answer, and express it as a sentence that answers the question posed in the problem.

The following example illustrates how these guidelines are used to translate a "word problem" into the language of algebra.

EXAMPLE 1 ▪ Renting a Car

A car rental company charges \$30 a day and 15¢ a mile for renting a car. Helen rents a car for two days, and her bill comes to \$108. How many miles did she drive?

SOLUTION Identify the variable.   We are asked to find the number of miles Helen has driven. So we let

$$x = \text{number of miles driven}$$

Translate from words to algebra.   Now we translate all the information given in the problem into the language of algebra.

In Words	In Algebra
Number of miles driven	x
Mileage cost (at \$0.15 per mile)	$0.15x$
Daily cost (at \$30 per day)	$2(30)$

Set up the model.   Now we set up the model.

$$\boxed{\text{mileage cost}} + \boxed{\text{daily cost}} = \boxed{\text{total cost}}$$

$$0.15x + 2(30) = 108$$

Solve.   Now we solve for x.

$$0.15x = 48 \qquad \text{Subtract 60}$$

$$x = \frac{48}{0.15} \qquad \text{Divide by 0.15}$$

$$x = 320 \qquad \text{Calculator}$$

Helen drove her rental car 320 mi.

🔊 Now Try Exercise 21

CHECK YOUR ANSWER

total cost = mileage cost + daily cost

$= 0.15(320) + 2(30)$

$= 108$ ✓

In the examples and exercises that follow, we construct equations that model problems in many different real-life situations. Pay special attention to the process of translating a word problem into the language of algebra.

■ Problems About Interest

When you borrow money from a bank or when a bank "borrows" your money by keeping it for you in a savings account, the borrower in each case must pay for the privilege of using the money. The fee that is paid is called **interest**. The most basic type of interest is **simple interest**, which is just an annual percentage of the total amount borrowed or deposited. The amount of a loan or deposit is called the **principal** P. The annual percentage paid for the use of this money is the **interest rate** r. We will use the variable t to stand for the number of years that the money is on deposit and the variable I to stand for the total interest earned. The following **simple interest formula** gives the amount of interest I earned when a principal P is deposited for t years at an interest rate r.

$$I = Prt$$

 When using this formula, remember to convert r from a percentage to a decimal. For example, in decimal form, 5% is 0.05. So at an interest rate of 5%, the interest paid on a $1000 deposit over a 3-year period is

$$I = Prt = 1000(0.05)(3) = \$150$$

EXAMPLE 2 ■ Interest on an Investment

Mary inherits $100,000 and invests it in two certificates of deposit. One certificate pays 6% and the other pays $4\frac{1}{2}\%$ simple interest annually. If Mary's total interest is $5025 per year, how much money is invested at each rate?

SOLUTION Identify the variable. The problem asks for the amount she has invested at each rate. So we let

$$x = \text{the amount invested at } 6\%$$

DISCOVERY PROJECT

Equations Through the Ages

Equations have always been important in solving real-world problems. Very old manuscripts from Babylon, Egypt, India, and China show that ancient peoples used equations to solve real-world problems that they encountered. In this project we discover that they also solved equations just for fun or for practice. You can find the project at **www.stewartmath.com**.

Translate from words to algebra. Since Mary's total inheritance is $100,000, it follows that she invested $100,000 - x$ at $4\frac{1}{2}\%$. We translate all the information given into the language of algebra.

In Words	In Algebra
Amount invested at 6%	x
Amount invested at $4\frac{1}{2}\%$	$100,000 - x$
Interest earned at 6%	$0.06x$
Interest earned at $4\frac{1}{2}\%$	$0.045(100,000 - x)$

Set up the model. We use the fact that Mary's total interest is $5025 to set up the model.

$$\boxed{\text{interest at 6\%}} + \boxed{\text{interest at } 4\frac{1}{2}\%} = \boxed{\text{total interest}}$$

$$0.06x + 0.045(100,000 - x) = 5025$$

Solve. Now we solve for x.

$$0.06x + 4500 - 0.045x = 5025 \qquad \text{Multiply}$$
$$0.015x + 4500 = 5025 \qquad \text{Combine the } x\text{-terms}$$
$$0.015x = 525 \qquad \text{Subtract 4500}$$
$$x = \frac{525}{0.015} \qquad \text{Divide by 0.015}$$
$$= 35,000$$

So Mary has invested $35,000 at 6% and the remaining $65,000 at $4\frac{1}{2}\%$.

CHECK YOUR ANSWER

$$\text{total interest} = 6\% \text{ of } \$35,000 + 4\frac{1}{2}\% \text{ of } \$65,000$$
$$= 0.06(\$35,000) + 0.045(\$65,000)$$
$$= \$2100 + \$2925 = \$5025 \quad \checkmark$$

✎ Now Try Exercise 25

■ Problems About Area or Length

When we use algebra to model a physical situation, we must sometimes use basic formulas from geometry. For example, we may need a formula for an area or a perimeter, or the formula that relates the sides of similar triangles, or the Pythagorean Theorem. Most of these formulas are listed on the inside front cover of this book. The next two examples use these geometric formulas to solve some real-world problems.

EXAMPLE 3 ■ Dimensions of a Garden

A square garden has a walkway 3 ft wide around its outer edge, as shown in Figure 2 on following page. If the area of the entire garden, including the walkway, is 18,000 ft^2, what are the dimensions of the planted area?

SOLUTION **Identify the variable.** We are asked to find the length and width of the planted area. So we let

$$x = \text{the length of the planted area}$$

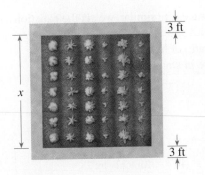

FIGURE 1

Translate from words to algebra. Next, translate the information from Figure 1 into the language of algebra.

In Words	In Algebra
Length of planted area	x
Length of entire garden	$x + 6$
Area of entire garden	$(x + 6)^2$

Set up the model. We now set up the model.

$$\text{area of entire garden} = 18{,}000 \text{ ft}^2$$
$$(x + 6)^2 = 18{,}000$$

Solve. Now we solve for x.

$$x + 6 = \sqrt{18{,}000} \qquad \text{Take square roots}$$
$$x = \sqrt{18{,}000} - 6 \qquad \text{Subtract 6}$$
$$x \approx 128$$

The planted area of the garden is about 128 ft by 128 ft.

✎ **Now Try Exercise 43**

EXAMPLE 4 ■ Determining the Height of a Building Using Similar Triangles

A man who is 6 ft tall wishes to find the height of a certain four-story building. He measures its shadow and finds it to be 28 ft long, while his own shadow is $3\frac{1}{2}$ ft long. How tall is the building?

SOLUTION **Identify the variable.** The problem asks for the height of the building. So let

$$h = \text{the height of the building}$$

Translate from words to algebra. We use the fact that the triangles in Figure 2 are similar. Recall that for any pair of similar triangles the ratios of corresponding sides are equal. Now we translate these observations into the language of algebra.

In Words	In Algebra
Height of building	h
Ratio of height to base in large triangle	$\frac{h}{28}$
Ratio of height to base in small triangle	$\frac{6}{3.5}$

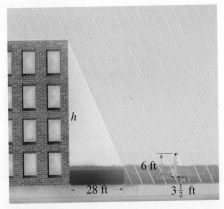

FIGURE 2

Set up the model.   Since the large and small triangles are similar, we get the equation

$$\boxed{\begin{array}{c}\text{ratio of height to}\\\text{base in large triangle}\end{array}} = \boxed{\begin{array}{c}\text{ratio of height to}\\\text{base in small triangle}\end{array}}$$

$$\frac{h}{28} = \frac{6}{3.5}$$

Solve.   Now we solve for h.

$$h = \frac{6 \cdot 28}{3.5} = 48 \qquad \text{Multiply by 28}$$

So the building is 48 ft tall.

✎ **Now Try Exercise 45**   ∎

■ Problems About Mixtures

Many real-world problems involve mixing different types of substances. For example, construction workers may mix cement, gravel, and sand; fruit juice from concentrate may involve mixing different types of juices. Problems involving mixtures and concentrations make use of the fact that if an amount x of a substance is dissolved in a solution with volume V, then the concentration C of the substance is given by

$$C = \frac{x}{V}$$

So if 10 g of sugar is dissolved in 5 L of water, then the sugar concentration is $C = 10/5 = 2$ g/L. Solving a mixture problem usually requires us to analyze the amount x of the substance that is in the solution. When we solve for x in this equation, we see that $x = CV$. Note that in many mixture problems the concentration C is expressed as a percentage, as in the next example.

EXAMPLE 5   ■   Mixtures and Concentration

A manufacturer of soft drinks advertises their orange soda as "naturally flavored," although it contains only 5% orange juice. A new federal regulation stipulates that to be called "natural," a drink must contain at least 10% fruit juice. How much pure orange juice must this manufacturer add to 900 gal of orange soda to conform to the new regulation?

SOLUTION **Identify the variable.**   The problem asks for the amount of pure orange juice to be added. So let

x = the amount (in gallons) of pure orange juice to be added

Translate from words to algebra.   In any problem of this type—in which two different substances are to be mixed—drawing a diagram helps us to organize the given information (see Figure 3).

We now translate the information in the figure into the language of algebra.

In Words	In Algebra
Amount of orange juice to be added	x
Amount of the mixture	$900 + x$
Amount of orange juice in the first vat	$0.05(900) = 45$
Amount of orange juice in the second vat	$1 \cdot x = x$
Amount of orange juice in the mixture	$0.10(900 + x)$

FIGURE 3

Set up the model. To set up the model, we use the fact that the total amount of orange juice in the mixture is equal to the orange juice in the first two vats.

$$\boxed{\begin{array}{c}\text{amount of}\\\text{orange juice}\\\text{in first vat}\end{array}} + \boxed{\begin{array}{c}\text{amount of}\\\text{orange juice}\\\text{in second vat}\end{array}} = \boxed{\begin{array}{c}\text{amount of}\\\text{orange juice}\\\text{in mixture}\end{array}}$$

$$45 + x = 0.1(900 + x) \qquad \text{From Figure 3}$$

Solve. Now we solve for x.

$$45 + x = 90 + 0.1x \qquad \text{Distributive Property}$$
$$0.9x = 45 \qquad \text{Subtract } 0.1x \text{ and } 45$$
$$x = \frac{45}{0.9} = 50 \qquad \text{Divide by } 0.9$$

The manufacturer should add 50 gal of pure orange juice to the soda.

CHECK YOUR ANSWER

$$\text{amount of juice before mixing} = 5\% \text{ of } 900 \text{ gal} + 50 \text{ gal pure juice}$$
$$= 45 \text{ gal} + 50 \text{ gal} = 95 \text{ gal}$$
$$\text{amount of juice after mixing} = 10\% \text{ of } 950 \text{ gal} = 95 \text{ gal}$$

Amounts are equal. ✓

✎ Now Try Exercise 47

■ Problems About the Time Needed to Do a Job

When solving a problem that involves determining how long it takes several workers to complete a job, we use the fact that if a person or machine takes H time units to complete the task, then in one time unit the fraction of the task that has been completed is $1/H$. For example, if a worker takes 5 hours to mow a lawn, then in 1 hour the worker will mow 1/5 of the lawn.

EXAMPLE 6 ■ Time Needed to Do a Job

Because of an anticipated heavy rainstorm, the water level in a reservoir must be lowered by 1 ft. Opening spillway A lowers the level by this amount in 4 hours, whereas opening the smaller spillway B does the job in 6 hours. How long will it take to lower the water level by 1 ft if both spillways are opened?

SOLUTION **Identify the variable.** We are asked to find the time needed to lower the level by 1 ft if both spillways are open. So let

$$x = \text{the time (in hours) it takes to lower the water level}$$
$$\text{by 1 ft if both spillways are open}$$

Translate from words to algebra. Finding an equation relating x to the other quantities in this problem is not easy. Certainly x is not simply $4 + 6$, because that would mean that together the two spillways require longer to lower the water level than either spillway alone. Instead, *we look at the fraction of the job that can be done in 1 hour by each spillway.*

In Words	In Algebra
Time it takes to lower level 1 ft with A and B together	x h
Distance A lowers level in 1 h	$\frac{1}{4}$ ft
Distance B lowers level in 1 h	$\frac{1}{6}$ ft
Distance A and B together lower levels in 1 h	$\frac{1}{x}$ ft

Set up the model. Now we set up the model.

fraction done by A	+	fraction done by B	=	fraction done by both

$$\frac{1}{4} + \frac{1}{6} = \frac{1}{x}$$

Solve. Now we solve for x.

$$3x + 2x = 12 \qquad \text{Multiply by the LCD, } 12x$$
$$5x = 12 \qquad \text{Add}$$
$$x = \frac{12}{5} \qquad \text{Divide by 5}$$

It will take $2\frac{2}{5}$ hours, or 2 h 24 min, to lower the water level by 1 ft if both spillways are open.

✎ **Now Try Exercise 55** ■

■ Problems About Distance, Rate, and Time

The next example deals with distance, rate (speed), and time. The formula to keep in mind here is

$$\boxed{\text{distance} = \text{rate} \times \text{time}}$$

where the rate is either the constant speed or average speed of a moving object. For example, driving at 60 mi/h for 4 hours takes you a distance of $60 \cdot 4 = 240$ mi.

EXAMPLE 7 ■ Distance, Speed, and Time

Bill left his house at 2:00 P.M. and rode his bicycle down Main Street at a speed of 12 mi/h. When his friend Mary arrived at his house at 2:10 P.M., Bill's mother told her the direction in which Bill had gone, and Mary cycled after him at a speed of 16 mi/h. At what time did Mary catch up with Bill?

SOLUTION Identify the variable.   We are asked to find the time that it took Mary to catch up with Bill. Let

$$t = \text{the time (in hours) it took Mary to catch up with Bill}$$

Translate from words to algebra.   In problems involving motion, it is often helpful to organize the information in a table, using the formula distance = rate × time. First we fill in the "Speed" column in the table, since we are told the speeds at which Mary and Bill cycled. Then we fill in the "Time" column. (Because Bill had a 10-minute, or $\frac{1}{6}$-hour head start, he cycled for $t + \frac{1}{6}$ hours.) Finally, we multiply these columns to calculate the entries in the "Distance" column.

	Distance (mi)	Speed (mi/h)	Time (h)
Mary	$16t$	16	t
Bill	$12\left(t + \frac{1}{6}\right)$	12	$t + \frac{1}{6}$

Set up the model.   At the instant when Mary caught up with Bill, they had both cycled the same distance. We use this fact to set up the model for this problem.

$$\boxed{\text{distance traveled by Mary}} = \boxed{\text{distance traveled by Bill}}$$

$$16t = 12\left(t + \tfrac{1}{6}\right) \qquad \text{From table}$$

Solve.   Now we solve for t.

$$16t = 12t + 2 \qquad \text{Distributive Property}$$

$$4t = 2 \qquad \text{Subtract } 12t$$

$$t = \tfrac{1}{2} \qquad \text{Divide by 4}$$

Mary caught up with Bill after cycling for half an hour, that is, at 2:40 P.M.

CHECK YOUR ANSWER

Bill traveled for $\frac{1}{2} + \frac{1}{6} = \frac{2}{3}$ h, so

$$\text{distance Bill traveled} = 12 \text{ mi/h} \times \tfrac{2}{3} \text{ h} = 8 \text{ mi}$$

$$\text{distance Mary traveled} = 16 \text{ mi/h} \times \tfrac{1}{2} \text{ h} = 8 \text{ mi}$$

Distances are equal. ✓

✎ **Now Try Exercise 59**

P.9 EXERCISES

CONCEPTS

1. Explain in your own words what it means for an equation to model a real-world situation, and give an example.

2. In the formula $I = Prt$ for simple interest, P stands for _____, r for _____, and t for _____.

3. Give a formula for the area of the geometric figure.

   (a) A square of side x: $A =$ _____.

   (b) A rectangle of length l and width w: $A =$ _____.

   (c) A circle of radius r: $A =$ _____.

4. Balsamic vinegar contains 5% acetic acid, so a 32-oz bottle of balsamic vinegar contains _____ ounces of acetic acid.

5. A painter paints a wall in x hours, so the fraction of the wall that she paints in 1 hour is _____.

6. The formula $d = rt$ models the distance d traveled by an object moving at the constant rate r in time t. Find formulas for the following quantities.

   $$r = \underline{\hspace{2cm}} \qquad t = \underline{\hspace{2cm}}$$

SKILLS

7–20 ■ Using Variables   Express the given quantity in terms of the indicated variable.

7. The sum of three consecutive integers; $n =$ first integer of the three

8. The sum of three consecutive integers; $n =$ middle integer of the three

9. The sum of three consecutive even integers; $n =$ first integer of the three

10. The sum of the squares of two consecutive integers; $n =$ first integer of the two

11. The average of three test scores if the first two scores are 78 and 82; $s =$ third test score

12. The average of four quiz scores if each of the first three scores is 8; $q =$ fourth quiz score

13. The interest obtained after one year on an investment at $2\frac{1}{2}\%$ simple interest per year; $x =$ number of dollars invested

14. The total rent paid for an apartment if the rent is $795 a month; $n =$ number of months

15. The area (in ft^2) of a rectangle that is four times as long as it is wide; $w =$ width of the rectangle (in ft)

16. The perimeter (in cm) of a rectangle that is 4 cm longer than it is wide; $w =$ width of the rectangle (in cm)

17. The time (in hours) it takes to travel a given distance at 55 mi/h; $d =$ given distance (in mi)

18. The distance (in mi) that a car travels in 45 min; $s =$ speed of the car (in mi/h)

19. The concentration (in oz/gal) of salt in a mixture of 3 gal of brine containing 25 oz of salt to which some pure water has been added; $x =$ volume of pure water added (in gal)

20. The value (in cents) of the change in a purse that contains twice as many nickels as pennies, four more dimes than nickels, and as many quarters as dimes and nickels combined; $p =$ number of pennies

APPLICATIONS

21. **Renting a Truck**   A rental company charges $65 a day and 20 cents a mile for renting a truck. Michael rents a truck for 3 days, and his bill comes to $275. How many miles did he drive?

22. **Cell Phone Costs**   A cell phone company charges a monthly fee of $10 for the first 1000 text messages and 10 cents for each additional text message. Miriam's bill for text messages for the month of June is $38.50. How many text messages did she send that month?

23. **Average**   Linh has obtained scores of 82, 75, and 71 on her midterm algebra exams. If the final exam counts twice as much as a midterm, what score must she make on her final exam to get an average score of 80? (Assume that the maximum possible score on each test is 100.)

24. **Average**   In a class of 25 students, the average score is 84. Six students in the class each received a maximum score of 100, and three students each received a score of 60. What is the average score of the remaining students?

25. **Investments**   Phyllis invested $12,000, a portion earning a simple interest rate of $4\frac{1}{2}\%$ per year and the rest earning a rate of 4% per year. After 1 year the total interest earned on these investments was $525. How much money did she invest at each rate?

26. **Investments**   If Ben invests $4000 at 4% interest per year, how much additional money must he invest at $5\frac{1}{2}\%$ annual interest to ensure that the interest he receives each year is $4\frac{1}{2}\%$ of the total amount invested?

27. **Investments**   What annual rate of interest would you have to earn on an investment of $3500 to ensure receiving $262.50 interest after 1 year?

28. **Investments**   Jack invests $1000 at a certain annual interest rate, and he invests another $2000 at an annual rate that is one-half percent higher. If he receives a total of $190 interest in 1 year, at what rate is the $1000 invested?

29. **Salaries**   An executive in an engineering firm earns a monthly salary plus a Christmas bonus of $8500. If she earns a total of $97,300 per year, what is her monthly salary?

30. **Salaries**   A woman earns 15% more than her husband. Together they make $69,875 per year. What is the husband's annual salary?

31. **Overtime Pay**   Helen earns $7.50 an hour at her job, but if she works more than 35 hours in a week, she is paid $1\frac{1}{2}$ times her regular salary for the overtime hours worked. One week her gross pay was $352.50. How many overtime hours did she work that week?

32. **Labor Costs**   A plumber and his assistant work together to replace the pipes in an old house. The plumber charges $45 an hour for his own labor and $25 an hour for his assistant's labor. The plumber works twice as long as his assistant on this job, and the labor charge on the final bill is $4025. How long did the plumber and his assistant work on this job?

33. **A Riddle**   A movie star, unwilling to give his age, posed the following riddle to a gossip columnist: "Seven years ago, I was eleven times as old as my daughter. Now I am four times as old as she is." How old is the movie star?

34. Career Home Runs During his major league career, Hank Aaron hit 41 more home runs than Babe Ruth hit during his career. Together they hit 1469 home runs. How many home runs did Babe Ruth hit?

35. Value of Coins A change purse contains an equal number of pennies, nickels, and dimes. The total value of the coins is $1.44. How many coins of each type does the purse contain?

36. Value of Coins Mary has $3.00 in nickels, dimes, and quarters. If she has twice as many dimes as quarters and five more nickels than dimes, how many coins of each type does she have?

37. Length of a Garden A rectangular garden is 25 ft wide. If its area is 1125 ft², what is the length of the garden?

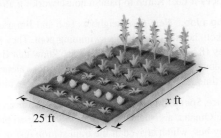

25 ft   x ft

38. Width of a Pasture A pasture is twice as long as it is wide. Its area is 115,200 ft². How wide is the pasture?

39. Dimensions of a Lot A square plot of land has a building 60 ft long and 40 ft wide at one corner. The rest of the land outside the building forms a parking lot. If the parking lot has area 12,000 ft², what are the dimensions of the entire plot of land?

40. Dimensions of a Lot A half-acre building lot is five times as long as it is wide. What are its dimensions?
[*Note:* 1 acre = 43,560 ft².]

41. Geometry Find the length y in the figure if the shaded area is 120 in².

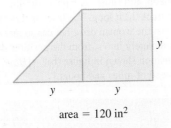

area = 120 in²

42. Geometry Find the length x in the figure if the shaded area is 144 cm².

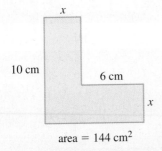

10 cm   6 cm

area = 144 cm²

43. Framing a Painting Ali paints with watercolors on a sheet of paper 20 in. wide by 15 in. high. He then places this sheet on a mat so that a uniformly wide strip of the mat shows all around the picture. The perimeter of the mat is 102 in. How wide is the strip of the mat showing around the picture?

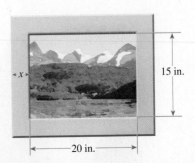

15 in.

20 in.

44. Dimensions of a Poster A poster has a rectangular printed area 100 cm by 140 cm and a blank strip of uniform width around the edges. The perimeter of the poster is $1\frac{1}{2}$ times the perimeter of the printed area. What is the width of the blank strip?

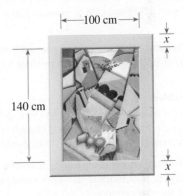

100 cm

140 cm

x

x

45. Length of a Shadow A man is walking away from a lamppost with a light source 6 m above the ground. The man is 2 m tall. How long is the man's shadow when he is 10 m from the lamppost? [*Hint:* Use similar triangles.]

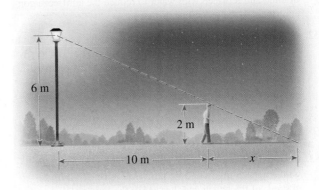

6 m

2 m

10 m x

46. Height of a Tree A woodcutter determines the height of a tall tree by first measuring a smaller one 125 ft away, then moving so that his eyes are in the line of sight along the tops of the trees and measuring how far he is standing from the small tree (see the figure). Suppose the small tree is 20 ft tall, the man is 25 ft from the small tree, and his eye level is 5 ft above the ground. How tall is the taller tree?

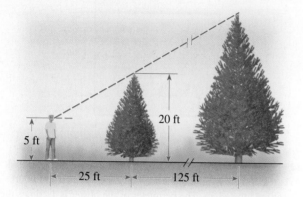

47. Mixture Problem What amount of a 60% acid solution must be mixed with a 30% solution to produce 300 mL of a 50% solution?

48. Mixture Problem What amount of pure acid must be added to 300 mL of a 50% acid solution to produce a 60% acid solution?

49. Mixture Problem A jeweler has five rings, each weighing 18 g, made of an alloy of 10% silver and 90% gold. She decides to melt down the rings and add enough silver to reduce the gold content to 75%. How much silver should she add?

50. Mixture Problem A pot contains 6 L of brine at a concentration of 120 g/L. How much of the water should be boiled off to increase the concentration to 200 g/L?

51. Mixture Problem The radiator in a car is filled with a solution of 60% antifreeze and 40% water. The manufacturer of the antifreeze suggests that for summer driving, optimal cooling of the engine is obtained with only 50% antifreeze. If the capacity of the radiator is 3.6 L, how much coolant should be drained and replaced with water to reduce the antifreeze concentration to the recommended level?

52. Mixture Problem A health clinic uses a solution of bleach to sterilize petri dishes in which cultures are grown. The sterilization tank contains 100 gal of a solution of 2% ordinary household bleach mixed with pure distilled water. New research indicates that the concentration of bleach should be 5% for complete sterilization. How much of the solution should be drained and replaced with bleach to increase the bleach content to the recommended level?

53. Mixture Problem A bottle contains 750 mL of fruit punch with a concentration of 50% pure fruit juice. Jill drinks 100 mL of the punch and then refills the bottle with an equal amount of a cheaper brand of punch. If the concentration of juice in the bottle is now reduced to 48%, what was the concentration in the punch that Jill added?

54. Mixture Problem A merchant blends tea that sells for $3.00 an ounce with tea that sells for $2.75 an ounce to produce 80 oz of a mixture that sells for $2.90 an ounce. How many ounces of each type of tea does the merchant use in the blend?

55. Sharing a Job Candy and Tim share a paper route. It takes Candy 70 min to deliver all the papers, and it takes Tim 80 min. How long does it take the two when they work together?

56. Sharing a Job Stan and Hilda can mow the lawn in 40 min if they work together. If Hilda works twice as fast as Stan, how long does it take Stan to mow the lawn alone?

57. Sharing a Job Betty and Karen have been hired to paint the houses in a new development. Working together, the women can paint a house in two-thirds the time that it takes Karen working alone. Betty takes 6 h to paint a house alone. How long does it take Karen to paint a house working alone?

58. Sharing a Job Next-door neighbors Bob and Jim use hoses from both houses to fill Bob's swimming pool. They know that it takes 18 h using both hoses. They also know that Bob's hose, used alone, takes 20% less time than Jim's hose alone. How much time is required to fill the pool by each hose alone?

59. Distance, Speed, and Time Wendy took a trip from Davenport to Omaha, a distance of 300 mi. She traveled part of the way by bus, which arrived at the train station just in time for Wendy to complete her journey by train. The bus averaged 40 mi/h, and the train averaged 60 mi/h. The entire trip took $5\frac{1}{2}$ h. How long did Wendy spend on the train?

60. Distance, Speed, and Time Two cyclists, 90 mi apart, start riding toward each other at the same time. One cycles twice as fast as the other. If they meet 2 h later, at what average speed is each cyclist traveling?

61. Distance, Speed, and Time A pilot flew a jet from Montreal to Los Angeles, a distance of 2500 mi. On the return trip, the average speed was 20% faster than the outbound speed. The round-trip took 9 h 10 min. What was the speed from Montreal to Los Angeles?

62. Distance, Speed, and Time A woman driving a car 14 ft long is passing a truck 30 ft long. The truck is traveling at 50 mi/h. How fast must the woman drive her car so that she can pass the truck completely in 6 s, from the position shown in figure (a) to the position shown in figure (b)? [*Hint:* Use feet and seconds instead of miles and hours.]

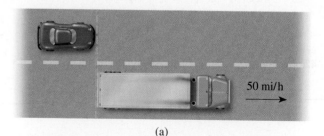

(a)

(b)

63. Law of the Lever The figure shows a lever system, similar to a seesaw that you might find in a children's playground. For the system to balance, the product of the weight and its distance from the fulcrum must be the same on each side; that is,

$$w_1 x_1 = w_2 x_2$$

This equation is called the **law of the lever** and was first discovered by Archimedes (see page 831).

A woman and her son are playing on a seesaw. The boy is at one end, 8 ft from the fulcrum. If the son weighs 100 lb and the mother weighs 125 lb, where should the woman sit so that the seesaw is balanced?

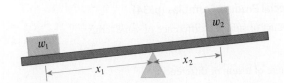

64. Law of the Lever A plank 30 ft long rests on top of a flat-roofed building, with 5 ft of the plank projecting over the edge, as shown in the figure. A worker weighing 240 lb sits on one end of the plank. What is the largest weight that can be hung on the projecting end of the plank if it is to remain in balance? (Use the law of the lever stated in Exercise 63.)

65. Dimensions of a Lot A rectangular parcel of land is 50 ft wide. The length of a diagonal between opposite corners is 10 ft more than the length of the parcel. What is the length of the parcel?

66. Dimensions of a Track A running track has the shape shown in the figure, with straight sides and semicircular ends. If the length of the track is 440 yd and the two straight parts are each 110 yd long, what is the radius of the semicircular parts (to the nearest yard)?

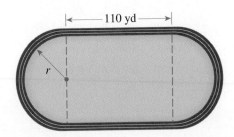

67. Dimensions of a Structure A storage bin for corn consists of a cylindrical section made of wire mesh, surmounted by a conical tin roof, as shown in the figure. The height of the roof is one-third the height of the entire structure. If the total volume of the structure is 1400π ft^3 and its radius is 10 ft, what is its height? [*Hint:* Use the volume formulas listed on the inside front cover of this book.]

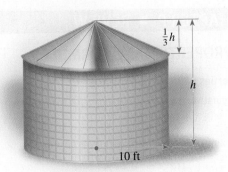

68. An Ancient Chinese Problem This problem is taken from a Chinese mathematics textbook called *Chui-chang suan-shu*, or *Nine Chapters on the Mathematical Art*, which was written about 250 B.C.

A 10-ft-long stem of bamboo is broken in such a way that its tip touches the ground 3 ft from the base of the stem, as shown in the figure. What is the height of the break?

[*Hint:* Use the Pythagorean Theorem.]

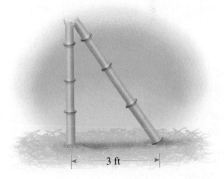

DISCUSS ■ **DISCOVER** ■ **PROVE** ■ **WRITE**

69. WRITE: Historical Research Read the biographical notes on Pythagoras (page 277), Euclid (page 57), and Archimedes (page 831). Choose one of these mathematicians, and find out more about him from the library or on the Internet. Write a short essay on your findings. Include both biographical information and a description of the mathematics for which he is famous.

70. WRITE: Real-world Equations   In this section we learned how to translate words into algebra. In this exercise we try to find real-world situations that could correspond to an algebraic equation. For instance, the equation $A = (x + y)/2$ could model the average amount of money in two bank accounts, where x represents the amount in one account and y the amount in the other. Write a story that could correspond to the given equation, stating what the variables represent.

(a) $C = 20{,}000 + 4.50x$

(b) $A = w(w + 10)$

(c) $C = 10.50x + 11.75y$

CHAPTER P ■ REVIEW

■ PROPERTIES AND FORMULAS

Properties of Real Numbers (p. 8)

Commutative: $a + b = b + a$

$ab = ba$

Associative: $(a + b) + c = a + (b + c)$

$(ab)c = a(bc)$

Distributive: $a(b + c) = ab + ac$

Absolute Value (pp. 13–14)

$$|a| = \begin{cases} a & \text{if } a \geq 0 \\ -a & \text{if } a < 0 \end{cases}$$

$$|ab| = |a||b|$$

$$\left|\frac{a}{b}\right| = \frac{|a|}{|b|}$$

Distance between a and b:

$$d(a, b) = |b - a|$$

Exponents (p. 19)

$$a^m a^n = a^{m+n}$$

$$\frac{a^m}{a^n} = a^{m-n}$$

$$(a^m)^n = a^{mn}$$

$$(ab)^n = a^n b^n$$

$$\left(\frac{a}{b}\right)^n = \frac{a^n}{b^n}$$

Radicals (pp. 25–27)

$\sqrt[n]{a} = b$ means $b^n = a$

$$\sqrt[n]{ab} = \sqrt[n]{a}\sqrt[n]{b}$$

$$\sqrt[n]{\frac{a}{b}} = \frac{\sqrt[n]{a}}{\sqrt[n]{b}}$$

$$\sqrt[m]{\sqrt[n]{a}} = \sqrt[mn]{a}$$

$$a^{m/n} = \sqrt[n]{a^m}$$

If n is odd, then $\sqrt[n]{a^n} = a$.

If n is even, then $\sqrt[n]{a^n} = |a|$.

Special Product Formulas (p. 34)

Product of sum and difference of same terms:

$$(A + B)(A - B) = A^2 - B^2$$

Square of a sum or difference:

$$(A + B)^2 = A^2 + 2AB + B^2$$

$$(A - B)^2 = A^2 - 2AB + B^2$$

Cube of a sum or difference:

$$(A + B)^3 = A^3 + 3A^2B + 3AB^2 + B^3$$

$$(A - B)^3 = A^3 - 3A^2B + 3AB^2 - B^3$$

Special Factoring Formulas (p. 39)

Difference of squares:

$$A^2 - B^2 = (A + B)(A - B)$$

Perfect squares:

$$A^2 + 2AB + B^2 = (A + B)^2$$

$$A^2 - 2AB + B^2 = (A - B)^2$$

Sum or difference of cubes:

$$A^3 - B^3 = (A - B)(A^2 + AB + B^2)$$

$$A^3 + B^3 = (A + B)(A^2 - AB + B^2)$$

Rational Expressions (pp. 45–46)

We can cancel common factors:

$$\frac{AC}{BC} = \frac{A}{B}$$

To multiply two fractions, we multiply their numerators together and their denominators together:

$$\frac{A}{B} \times \frac{C}{D} = \frac{AC}{BD}$$

To divide fractions, we invert the divisor and multiply:

$$\frac{A}{B} \div \frac{C}{D} = \frac{A}{B} \times \frac{D}{C}$$

To add fractions, we find a common denominator:

$$\frac{A}{C} + \frac{B}{C} = \frac{A + B}{C}$$

Properties of Equality (p. 54)

$A = B \quad \Leftrightarrow \quad A + C = B + C$

$A = B \quad \Leftrightarrow \quad CA = CB \quad (C \neq 0)$

Linear Equations (p. 54)

A **linear equation** is an equation of the form $ax + b = 0$

Power Equations (p. 56)

The **power equation** $X^n = a$ has the solution $X = \sqrt[n]{a}$ if n is odd and $X = \pm\sqrt[n]{a}$ if n is even and $a \geq 0$.

■ CONCEPT CHECK

1. What is an algebra model for a real-world situation? If Shellie's wages are $12 an hour, find a model for the amount W that Shellie earns after working x hours.

2. (a) What does the set of natural numbers consist of? What does the set of integers consist of? Give an example of an integer that is not a natural number.

   (b) What does the set of rational numbers consist of? Give an example of a rational number that is not an integer.

   (c) What does the set of irrational numbers consist of? Give an example of an irrational number.

   (d) What does the set of real numbers consist of?

3. A property of real numbers is given. State the property and give an example in which the property is used.

   (i) Commutative Property

   (ii) Associative Property

   (iii) Distributive Property

4. Explain the difference between the open interval (a, b) and the closed interval $[a, b]$. Give an example of an interval that is neither open nor closed.

5. Give the formula for finding the distance between two real numbers a and b. Use the formula to find the distance between 103 and -52.

6. Suppose $a \neq 0$ is any real number.

   (a) In the expression a^n, which is the base and which is the exponent?

   (b) What does a^n mean if n is a positive integer? What does 6^5 mean?

   (c) What does a^{-n} mean if n is a positive integer? What does 3^{-2} mean?

   (d) What does a^n mean if n is zero?

   (e) If m and n are positive integers, what does $a^{m/n}$ mean? What does $4^{3/2}$ mean?

7. State the first five Laws of Exponents. Give examples in which you would use each law.

8. When you multiply two powers of the same number, what should you do with the exponents? When you raise a power to a new power, what should you do with the exponents?

9. (a) What does $\sqrt[n]{a} = b$ mean?

   (b) Is it true that $\sqrt{a^2}$ is equal to $|a|$? Try values for a that are positive and negative.

   (c) How many real nth roots does a positive real number have if n is even? If n is odd?

   (d) Is $\sqrt[4]{-2}$ a real number? Is $\sqrt[3]{-2}$ a real number? Explain why or why not.

10. Explain the steps involved in rationalizing a denominator. What is the logical first step in rationalizing the denominator of the expression $\dfrac{5}{\sqrt{3}}$?

11. Explain the difference between expanding an expression and factoring an expression.

12. State the Special Product Formulas used for expanding the given expression.

    (i) $(a + b)^2$ (ii) $(a - b)^2$ (iii) $(a + b)^3$

    (iv) $(a - b)^3$ (v) $(a + b)(a - b)$

    Use the appropriate formula to expand $(x + 5)^2$ and $(x + 5)(x - 5)$.

13. State the following Special Factoring Formulas.

    (i) Difference of Squares

    (ii) Perfect Square

    (iii) Sum of Cubes

    Use the appropriate formula to factor $x^2 - 9$.

14. If the numerator and the denominator of a rational expression have a common factor, how would you simplify the expression? Simplify the expression $\dfrac{x^2 + x}{x + 1}$.

15. Explain the following.

    (a) How to multiply and divide rational expressions.

    (b) How to add and subtract rational expressions.

    (c) What LCD do we use to perform the addition in the expression $\dfrac{3}{x - 1} + \dfrac{5}{x + 2}$?

16. What is the logical first step in rationalizing the denominator of $\dfrac{3}{1 + \sqrt{x}}$?

17. What is the difference between an algebraic expression and an equation? Give examples.

18. Consider the equation $5x + 7 = 10 - 3x$.

    (a) Determine whether $x = -1$ is a solution to the equation.

    (b) Show how to use the rules of algebra to solve the equation.

19. (a) Give some examples of power equations.

    (b) Find all real solutions to the power equation $x^2 = 15$.

    (c) Find all real solutions to the power equation $x^3 = 15$.

ANSWERS TO THE CONCEPT CHECK CAN BE FOUND AT THE BACK OF THE BOOK.

▪ EXERCISES

1–2 ▪ Making and Using a Model   Make and use an algebra model to solve the problem.

1. Elena regularly takes a multivitamin and mineral supplement. She purchases a bottle of 250 tablets and takes two tablets every day.

 (a) Find a formula for the number of tablets T that are left in the bottle after she has been taking the tablets for x days.

 (b) How many tablets are left after 30 days?

 (c) How many days will it take for her to run out of tablets?

2. Alonzo's Delivery is having a sale on calzones. Each calzone costs $2, and there is a $3 delivery charge for phone-in orders.

 (a) Find a formula for the total cost C of ordering x calzones for delivery.

 (b) How much would it cost to have 4 calzones delivered?

 (c) If you have $15, how many calzones can you order?

3–4 ▪ Rational or Irrational?   Determine whether each number is rational or irrational. If it is rational, determine whether it is a natural number, an integer, or neither.

3. (a) 16   **(b)** -16 **(c)** $\sqrt{16}$ **(d)** $\sqrt{2}$

 (e) $\frac{8}{3}$ **(f)** $-\frac{8}{2}$

4. (a) -5 **(b)** $-\frac{25}{6}$ **(c)** $\sqrt{25}$ **(d)** 3π

 (e) $\frac{24}{16}$ **(f)** 10^{20}

5–8 ▪ Properties of Real Numbers   State the property of real numbers being used.

5. $3 + 2x = 2x + 3$

6. $(a + b)(a - b) = (a - b)(a + b)$

7. $4(a + b) = 4a + 4b$

8. $(A + 1)(x + y) = (A + 1)x + (A + 1)y$

9–12 ▪ Evaluate   Evaluate each expression. Express your answer as a fraction in lowest terms.

9. (a) $\dfrac{5}{6} + \dfrac{2}{3}$ **(b)** $\dfrac{5}{6} - \dfrac{2}{3}$

10. (a) $\dfrac{7}{10} - \dfrac{11}{15}$ **(b)** $\dfrac{7}{10} + \dfrac{11}{15}$

11. (a) $\dfrac{15}{8} \cdot \dfrac{12}{5}$ **(b)** $\dfrac{15}{8} \div \dfrac{12}{5}$

12. (a) $\dfrac{30}{7} \div \dfrac{12}{35}$ **(b)** $\dfrac{30}{7} \cdot \dfrac{12}{35}$

13–16 ▪ Intervals   Express the interval in terms of inequalities, and then graph the interval.

13. $[-2, 6)$ **14.** $(0, 10]$

15. $(-\infty, 4]$ **16.** $[-2, \infty)$

17–20 ▪ Intervals   Express the inequality in interval notation, and then graph the corresponding interval.

17. $x \geq 5$ **18.** $x < -3$

19. $-1 < x \leq 5$ **20.** $0 \leq x \leq \frac{1}{2}$

21–24 ▪ Unions and Intersections   The sets A, B, C, and D are defined as follows:

$$A = \{-1, 0, 1, 2, 3\} \qquad B = \{\tfrac{1}{2}, 1, 4\}$$
$$C = \{x \mid 0 < x \leq 2\} \qquad D = (-1, 1]$$

Find each of the following sets.

21. (a) $A \cup B$ **(b)** $A \cap B$

22. (a) $C \cup D$ **(b)** $C \cap D$

23. (a) $A \cap C$ **(b)** $B \cap D$

24. (a) $A \cap D$ **(b)** $B \cap C$

25–32 ▪ Evaluate   Evaluate the expression.

25. $|7 - 10|$ **26.** $\big|3 - |-9|\big|$

27. $2^{1/2} 8^{1/2}$ **28.** $2^{-3} - 3^{-2}$

29. $216^{-1/3}$ **30.** $64^{2/3}$

31. $\dfrac{\sqrt{242}}{\sqrt{2}}$ **32.** $\sqrt{2}\,\sqrt{50}$

33–34 ▪ Distance on the Real Line   Express the distance between the given numbers on the real line using an absolute value. Then evaluate this distance.

33. (a) 3 and 5   **(b)** 3 and -5

34. (a) 0 and -4 **(b)** 4 and -4

35–38 ▪ Rational Exponents   Express the radical as a power with a rational exponent.

35. (a) $\sqrt[3]{7}$ **(b)** $\sqrt[5]{7^4}$ **36. (a)** $\sqrt[3]{5^7}$ **(b)** $\left(\sqrt[4]{5}\right)^3$

37. (a) $\sqrt[6]{x^5}$ **(b)** $\left(\sqrt{x}\right)^9$ **38. (a)** $\sqrt{y^3}$ **(b)** $\left(\sqrt[8]{y}\right)^2$

39–46 ▪ Radicals and Exponents   Simplify the expression.

39. $(2x^3 y)^2(3x^{-1}y^2)$ **40.** $(a^2)^{-3}(a^3 b)^2(b^3)^4$

41. $\dfrac{x^4(3x)^2}{x^3}$ **42.** $\left(\dfrac{r^2 s^{4/3}}{r^{1/3}s}\right)^6$

43. $\sqrt[3]{(x^3 y)^2 y^4}$ **44.** $\sqrt{x^2 y^4}$

45. $\dfrac{8r^{1/2}s^{-3}}{2r^{-2}s^4}$ **46.** $\left(\dfrac{ab^2 c^{-3}}{2a^2 b^{-4}}\right)^{-2}$

47–50 ▪ Scientific Notation   These exercises involve scientific notation.

47. Write the number 78,250,000,000 in scientific notation.

48. Write the number 2.08×10^{-8} in decimal notation.

49. If $a \approx 0.00000293$, $b \approx 1.582 \times 10^{-14}$, and $c \approx 2.8064 \times 10^{12}$, use a calculator to approximate the number ab/c.

50. If your heart beats 80 times per minute and you live to be 90 years old, estimate the number of times your heart beats during your lifetime. State your answer in scientific notation.

51–68 ■ Factoring Factor the expression completely.

51. $2x^2y - 6xy^2$

52. $12x^2y^4 - 3xy^5 + 9x^3y^2$

53. $x^2 + 5x - 14$

54. $x^4 + x^2 - 2$

55. $3x^2 - 2x - 1$

56. $6x^2 + x - 12$

57. $4t^2 - 13t - 12$

58. $x^4 - 2x^2 + 1$

59. $16 - 4t^2$

60. $2y^6 - 32y^2$

61. $x^6 - 1$

62. $a^4b^2 + ab^5$

63. $x^3 - 27$

64. $3y^3 - 81x^3$

65. $4x^3 - 8x^2 + 3x - 6$

66. $3x^3 - 2x^2 + 18x - 12$

67. $(x + y)^2 - 7(x + y) + 6$

68. $(a + b)^2 - 3(a + b) - 10$

69–86 ■ Operations with Algebraic Expressions Perform the indicated operations.

69. $(2y - 7)(2y + 7)$

70. $(1 + x)(2 - x) - (3 - x)(3 + x)$

71. $x^2(x - 2) + x(x - 2)^2$

72. $\dfrac{x^3 + 2x^2 + 3x}{x}$

73. $\sqrt{x}(\sqrt{x} + 1)(2\sqrt{x} - 1)$

74. $(2x + 1)^3$

75. $\dfrac{x^2 - 2x - 3}{2x^2 + 5x + 3}$

76. $\dfrac{t^3 - 1}{t^2 - 1}$

77. $\dfrac{x^2 + 2x - 3}{x^2 + 8x + 16} \cdot \dfrac{3x + 12}{x - 1}$

78. $\dfrac{x^2 - 2x - 15}{x^2 - 6x + 5} \div \dfrac{x^2 - x - 12}{x^2 - 1}$

79. $x - \dfrac{1}{x + 1}$

80. $\dfrac{1}{x - 1} - \dfrac{x}{x^2 + 1}$

81. $\dfrac{2}{x} + \dfrac{1}{x - 2} + \dfrac{3}{(x - 2)^2}$

82. $\dfrac{1}{x + 2} + \dfrac{1}{x^2 - 4} - \dfrac{2}{x^2 - x - 2}$

83. $\dfrac{\dfrac{1}{x} - \dfrac{1}{2}}{x - 2}$

84. $\dfrac{\dfrac{1}{x} - \dfrac{1}{x + 1}}{\dfrac{1}{x} + \dfrac{1}{x + 1}}$

85. $\dfrac{3(x + h)^2 - 5(x + h) - (3x^2 - 5x)}{h}$

86. $\dfrac{\sqrt{x + h} - \sqrt{x}}{h}$ (rationalize the numerator)

87–92 ■ Rationalizing Rationalize the denominator, and simplify.

87. $\dfrac{1}{\sqrt{11}}$

88. $\dfrac{3}{\sqrt{6}}$

89. $\dfrac{10}{\sqrt{2} - 1}$

90. $\dfrac{14}{3 - \sqrt{2}}$

91. $\dfrac{x}{2 + \sqrt{x}}$

92. $\dfrac{\sqrt{x} - 2}{\sqrt{x} + 2}$

93–96 ■ Domain Find the domain of the algebraic expression.

93. $\dfrac{x + 5}{x + 10}$

94. $\dfrac{2x}{x^2 - 9}$

95. $\dfrac{\sqrt{x}}{x^2 - 3x - 4}$

96. $\dfrac{\sqrt{x - 3}}{x^2 - 4x + 4}$

97–102 ■ Is the Equation True? State whether the given equation is true for all values of the variables. (Disregard any value that makes a denominator 0.)

97. $(x + y)^3 = x^3 + y^3$

98. $\dfrac{1 + \sqrt{a}}{1 - a} = \dfrac{1}{1 - \sqrt{a}}$

99. $\dfrac{12 + y}{y} = \dfrac{12}{y} + 1$

100. $\sqrt[3]{a + b} = \sqrt[3]{a} + \sqrt[3]{b}$

101. $\sqrt{a^2} = a$

102. $\dfrac{1}{x + 4} = \dfrac{1}{x} + \dfrac{1}{4}$

103–124 ■ Solving Basic Equations Find all real solutions of the equation.

103. $3x + 12 = 24$

104. $5x - 7 = 42$

105. $7x - 6 = 4x + 9$

106. $8 - 2x = 14 + x$

107. $\frac{1}{3}x - \frac{1}{2} = 2$

108. $\frac{2}{3}x + \frac{3}{5} = \frac{1}{5} - 2x$

109. $2(x + 3) - 4(x - 5) = 8 - 5x$

110. $\dfrac{x - 5}{2} - \dfrac{2x + 5}{3} = \dfrac{5}{6}$

111. $\dfrac{x + 1}{x - 1} = \dfrac{2x - 1}{2x + 1}$

112. $\dfrac{x}{x + 2} - 3 = \dfrac{1}{x + 2}$

113. $\dfrac{x + 1}{x - 1} = \dfrac{3x}{3x - 6}$

114. $(x + 2)^2 = (x - 4)^2$

115. $x^2 = 144$

116. $4x^2 = 49$

117. $x^3 - 27 = 0$

118. $6x^4 + 15 = 0$

119. $(x + 1)^3 = -64$

120. $(x + 2)^2 - 2 = 0$

121. $\sqrt[3]{x} = -3$

122. $x^{2/3} - 4 = 0$

123. $4x^{3/4} - 500 = 0$

124. $(x - 2)^{1/5} = 2$

125–128 ■ Solving for a Variable Solve the equation for the indicated variable.

125. $A = \dfrac{x + y}{2}$; solve for x

126. $V = xy + yz + xz$; solve for y

127. $J = \dfrac{1}{t} + \dfrac{1}{2t} + \dfrac{1}{3t}$; solve for t

128. $F = k\dfrac{q_1 q_2}{r^2}$; solve for r

129. Mixtures The owner of a store sells raisins for $3.20 per pound and nuts for $2.40 per pound. He decides to mix the raisins and nuts and sell 50 lb of the mixture for $2.72 per pound. What quantities of raisins and nuts should he use?

130. Distance and Time Anthony leaves Kingstown at 2:00 P.M. and drives to Queensville, 160 mi distant, at 45 mi/h. At 2:15 P.M. Helen leaves Queensville and drives to Kingstown at 40 mi/h. At what time do they pass each other on the road?

131. Investment Luc invests $7000 in two bank accounts. One earns 1.5% simple interest per year, and the other earns 2.5% simple interest per year. After one year the total interest earned on these investments is $120.25. How much money did he invest in each account?

132. Investment Shania invests $6000 at 3% simple interest per year. How much additional money must she invest at 1.25% simple interest per year to ensure that the interest she receives each year is $300?

133. Doing the Job Abbie paints twice as fast as Beth and three times as fast as Cathie. If it takes them 60 min to paint a living room with all three working together, how long would it take Abbie if she worked alone?

134. Dimensions of a Swimming Pool A rectangular swimming pool is 8 ft deep everywhere and twice as long as it is wide. If the pool holds 8464 ft^3 of water, what are its dimensions?

1. A pizzeria charges $9 for a medium plain cheese pizza plus $1.50 for each extra topping.

   (a) Find a formula that models the cost C of a medium pizza with x toppings.

   (b) Use your model from part (a) to find the cost of a medium pizza with the following extra toppings: anchovies, ham, sausage, and pineapple.

2. Determine whether each number is rational or irrational. If it is rational, determine whether it is a natural number, an integer, or neither.

   (a) 5   (b) $\sqrt{5}$ (c) $-\frac{9}{3}$ (d) $-1{,}000{,}000$

3. Let $A = \{-2, 0, 1, 3, 5\}$ and $B = \{0, \frac{1}{2}, 1, 5, 7\}$. Find each of the following sets.

   (a) $A \cap B$ (b) $A \cup B$

4. (a) Graph the intervals $[-4, 2)$ and $[0, 3]$ on a real line.

   (b) Find the intersection and the union of the intervals in part (a), and graph each of them on a real line.

   (c) Use an absolute value to express the distance between -4 and 2 on the real line, and then evaluate this distance.

5. Evaluate each expression.

   (a) -2^6 (b) $(-2)^6$ (c) 2^{-6} (d) $\dfrac{7^{10}}{7^{12}}$

   (e) $\left(\dfrac{3}{2}\right)^{-2}$ (f) $\dfrac{\sqrt[5]{32}}{\sqrt{16}}$ (g) $\sqrt[4]{\dfrac{3^8}{2^{16}}}$ (h) $81^{-3/4}$

6. Write each number in scientific notation.

   (a) 186,000,000,000   (b) 0.0000003965

7. Simplify each expression. Write your final answer without negative exponents.

   (a) $\dfrac{a^3 b^2}{ab^3}$ (b) $(2x^3 y^{-2})^{-2}$ (c) $(2x^{1/2} y^2)(3x^{1/4} y^{-1})^2$

   (d) $\sqrt{20} - \sqrt{125}$ (e) $\sqrt{18x^3 y^4}$ (f) $\left(\dfrac{2x^2 y}{x^{-3} y^{1/2}}\right)^{-2}$

8. Perform the indicated operations, and simplify.

   (a) $3(x + 6) + 4(2x - 5)$ (b) $(x + 3)(4x - 5)$ (c) $(\sqrt{a} + \sqrt{b})(\sqrt{a} - \sqrt{b})$
   (d) $(2x + 3)^2$ (e) $(x + 2)^3$ (f) $x^2(x - 3)(x + 3)$

9. Factor each expression completely.

   (a) $4x^2 - 25$ (b) $2x^2 + 5x - 12$ (c) $x^3 - 3x^2 - 4x + 12$
   (d) $x^4 + 27x$ (e) $(2x - y)^2 - 10(2x - y) + 25$ (f) $x^3 y - 4xy$

10. Simplify the rational expression.

    (a) $\dfrac{x^2 + 3x + 2}{x^2 - x - 2}$ (b) $\dfrac{2x^2 - x - 1}{x^2 - 9} \cdot \dfrac{x + 3}{2x + 1}$

    (c) $\dfrac{x^2}{x^2 - 4} - \dfrac{x + 1}{x + 2}$ (d) $\dfrac{\dfrac{y}{x} - \dfrac{x}{y}}{\dfrac{1}{y} - \dfrac{1}{x}}$

11. Rationalize the denominator, and simplify.

    (a) $\dfrac{6}{\sqrt[3]{4}}$ (b) $\dfrac{\sqrt{10}}{\sqrt{5} - 2}$ (c) $\dfrac{1}{1 + \sqrt{x}}$

12. Find all real solutions of each equation.

(a) $4x - 3 = 2x + 7$

(b) $8x^3 = -125$

(c) $x^{2/3} - 64 = 0$

(d) $\dfrac{x}{2x - 5} = \dfrac{x + 3}{2x - 1}$

(e) $3(x + 1)^2 - 18 = 0$

13. Einstein's famous equation $E = mc^2$ gives the relationship between energy E and mass m. In this equation c represents the speed of light. Solve the equation to express c in terms of E and m.

14. Natasha drove from Bedingfield to Portsmouth at an average speed of 100 km/h to attend a job interview. On the way back she decided to slow down to enjoy the scenery, so she drove at just 75 km/h. Her trip involved a total of 3.5 h of driving time. What is the distance between Bedingfield and Portsmouth?

When you buy a car, subscribe to a cell phone plan, or put an addition on your house, you need to make decisions. Such decisions are usually difficult because they require you to choose between several good alternatives. For example, there are many good car models, but which one has the optimal combination of features for the amount of money you want to spend? In this *Focus on Modeling* we explore how to construct and use algebraic models of real-life situations to help make the best (or optimal) decisions.

EXAMPLE 1 ■ Buying a Car

Ben wants to buy a car, and he has narrowed his choices to two models.

  Model A sells for $12,500, gets 25 mi/gal, and costs $350 a year for insurance.

  Model B sells for $21,000, gets 48 mi/gal, and costs $425 a year for insurance.

Ben drives about 36,000 miles a year, and gas costs about $4.00 a gallon.

(a) Find a formula for the total cost of owning Model A for any number of years.

(b) Find a formula for the total cost of owning Model B for any number of years.

(c) Make a table of the total cost of owning each model from 1 year to 6 years, in 1-year increments.

(d) If Ben expects to keep the car for 3 years, which model is more economical? What if he expects to keep it for 5 years?

THINKING ABOUT THE PROBLEM

Model A has a smaller initial price and costs less in insurance per year but is more costly to operate (uses more gas) than Model B. Model B has a larger initial price and costs more to insure but is cheaper to operate (uses less gas) than Model A. If Ben drives a lot, then what he will save in gas with Model B could make up for the initial cost of buying the car and the higher yearly insurance premiums. So how many years of driving does it take before the gas savings make up for the initial higher price? To find out, we must write formulas for the total cost for each car:

$$\text{cost} = \text{purchase price} + \text{insurance cost} + \text{gas cost}$$

The insurance costs and gas costs depend on the number of years Ben drives the car.

SOLUTION The cost of operating each model depends on the number of years of ownership. So let

$$n = \text{number of years Ben expects to own the car}$$

(a) For Model A we have the following:

In Words	In Algebra
Price of car	12,500
Insurance cost for n years	$350n$
Cost of gas per year	$(36,000/25) \times \$4.00 = \$5760$
Cost of gas for n years	$5760n$

Let C represent the cost of owning model A for n years. Then

$$\boxed{\text{cost of ownership}} = \boxed{\text{initial cost}} + \boxed{\text{insurance cost}} + \boxed{\text{gas cost}}$$

$$C = 12,500 + 350n + 5760n$$

$$C = 12,500 + 6110n$$

81

(b) For Model B we have the following:

In Words	In Algebra
Price of car	21,000
Insurance cost for n years	$425n$
Cost of gas per year	$(36,000/48) \times \$4.00 = \$3000$
Cost of gas for n years	$3000n$

Let C represent the cost of owning model B for n years. Then

$$\boxed{\text{cost of ownership}} = \boxed{\text{initial cost}} + \boxed{\text{insurance cost}} + \boxed{\text{gas cost}}$$

$$C = 21{,}000 + 425n + 3000n$$

$$C = 21{,}000 + 3425n$$

(c) If Ben keeps the car for 2 years, the cost of ownership can be calculated from the formulas we found by substituting 2 for n.

$$\text{For Model A:} \quad C = 12{,}500 + 6110(2) = 24{,}720$$

$$\text{For Model B:} \quad C = 21{,}000 + 3425(2) = 27{,}850$$

The other entries in the table are calculated similarly.

Years	Cost of ownership Model A	Cost of ownership Model B
1	18,610	24,425
2	24,720	27,850
3	30,830	31,275
4	36,940	34,700
5	43,050	38,125
6	49,160	41,550

(d) If Ben intends to keep the car 3 years, then Model A is a better buy (see the table), but if he intends to keep the car 5 years, Model B is the better buy. ∎

EXAMPLE 2 ■ Equal Ownership Cost

Find the number of years of ownership for which the cost to Ben (from Example 1) of owning Model A equals the cost of owning Model B.

THINKING ABOUT THE PROBLEM

We see from the table that the cost of owning Model A starts lower but then exceeds that for Model B. We want to find the value of n for which the two costs are equal.

SOLUTION   We equate the cost of owning Model A to that of Model B and solve for n.

$$12{,}500 + 6110n = 21{,}000 + 3425n \qquad \text{Set the two costs equal}$$

$$2685n = 8500 \qquad \text{Subtract 12,500 and } 3425n$$

$$n \approx 3.17 \qquad \text{Divide by 2685}$$

If Ben keeps the car for about 3.17 years, the cost of owning *either model* would be the same. ∎

EXAMPLE 3 ■ Dividing Assets Fairly

When high-tech Company A goes bankrupt, it owes $120 million to Company B and $480 million to Company C. Unfortunately, Company A has only $300 million in assets. How should the court divide these assets between Companies B and C? Explore the following methods, and determine which are fair.

(a) Companies B and C divide the assets equally.

(b) The two companies share the losses equally.

(c) The two companies get an amount that is proportional to the amount they are owed.

THINKING ABOUT THE PROBLEM

It might seem fair for Companies B and C to divide the assets equally between them. Or it might seem fair that they share the loss equally between them. To be certain of the fairness of each plan, we should calculate how much each company loses under each plan.

SOLUTION

(a) Under this method, Company B gets $150 million and Company C gets $150 million. Because B is owed only $120 million, it will get $30 million more than it is owed. This doesn't seem fair to C, which will still lose $330 million.

(b) We want Companies B and C to each lose the same amount. Let x be the amount of money Company B gets. Then Company C would get the rest $(300 - x)$. We can organize the information as follows.

In Words	In Algebra
Amount B gets	x
Amount C gets	$300 - x$
Amount B loses	$120 - x$
Amount C loses	$480 - (300 - x) = 180 + x$

Because we want Companies B and C to lose equal amounts, we must have

$$180 + x = 120 - x \qquad \text{Amounts B and C lose are equal}$$
$$2x = -60 \qquad \text{Add } x, \text{ subtract } 180$$
$$x = -30 \qquad \text{Divide by 2}$$

Thus Company B gets -30 million dollars. The negative sign means that B must give up an additional $30 million and pay it to C. So Company C gets all of the $300 million plus $30 million from B for a total of $330 million. Doing this would ensure that the two companies lose the same amount (see *Check Your Answer*). This method is clearly not fair.

(c) The claims total $120 million + $480 million = $600 million. The assets total $300 million. Because Company B is owed $120 million out of the total claim of $600 million, it would get

$$\frac{120 \text{ million}}{600 \text{ million}} \times 300 \text{ million} = \$60 \text{ million}$$

Because Company C is owed 480 million, it would get

$$\frac{480 \text{ million}}{600 \text{ million}} \times 300 \text{ million} = \$240 \text{ million}$$

This seems like the fairest alternative.   ∎

CHECK YOUR ANSWER

B loses $120 + 30 = 150$ million

C loses $480 - 330 = 150$ million

They lose equal amounts. ✓

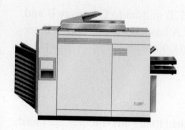

PROBLEMS

1. **Renting Versus Buying a Photocopier**   A certain office can purchase a photocopier for $5800 with a maintenance fee of $25 a month. On the other hand, they can rent the photocopier for $95 a month (including maintenance). If they purchase the photocopier, each copy would cost 3¢; if they rent, the cost is 6¢ per copy. The office estimates that they make 8000 copies a month.

   (a) Find a formula for the cost C of purchasing and using the copier for n months.

   (b) Find a formula for the cost C of renting and using the copier for n months.

   (c) Make a table of the cost of each method for 1 year to 6 years of use, in 1-year increments.

   (d) After how many months of use would the cost be the same for each method?

2. **Car Rental**   A businessman intends to rent a car for a 3-day business trip. The rental is $65 a day and 15¢ per mile (Plan 1) or $90 a day with unlimited mileage (Plan 2). He is not sure how many miles he will drive but estimates that it will be between 400 and 800 mi.

   (a) For each plan, find a formula for the cost C in terms of the number x of miles driven.

   (b) Which rental plan is cheaper if the businessman drives 400 miles? 800 miles?

   (c) At what mileage do the two plans cost the same?

3. **Cost and Revenue**   A tire company determines that to manufacture a certain type of tire, it costs $8000 to set up the production process. Each tire that is produced costs $22 in material and labor. The company sells this tire to wholesale distributors for $49 each.

   (a) Find a formula for the total cost C of producing x tires.

   (b) Find a formula for the revenue R from selling x tires.

profit = revenue − cost

   (c) Find a formula for the profit P from selling x tires.

   (d) How many tires must the company sell to break even?

4. **Enlarging a Field**   A farmer has a rectangular cow pasture with width 100 ft and length 180 ft. An increase in the number of cows requires the farmer to increase the area of her pasture. She has two options:

   Option 1: Increase the length of the field.

   Option 2: Increase the width of the field.

Cost	Area gain (Option 1)	Area gain (Option 2)
$1100	2500 ft²	180 ft²
$1200		
$1500		
$2000		
$2500		
$3000		

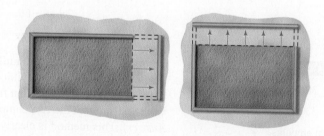

It costs $10 per foot to install new fence. Moving the old fence costs $6 per linear foot of fence to be moved.

   (a) For each option, find a formula for A, the area gained, in terms of the cost C.

   (b) Complete the table for the area gained in terms of the cost for each option.

   (c) If the farmer has $1200 for this project, which option gives her the greatest gain in area for her money? What if she had $2000 for the project?

5. Edging a Planter A woman wants to make a small planter and surround it with edging material. She is deciding between two designs.

> Design 1: A square planter
>
> Design 2: A circular planter

Edging material costs $3 a foot for the straight variety, which she would use for Design 1, and $4 a foot for the flexible variety, which she would use for Design 2.

(a) If she decides on a perimeter of 24 ft, which design would give her the larger planting area?

(b) If she decides to spend $120 on edging material, which design would give her the larger planting area?

6. Planting Crops A farmer is considering two plans of crop rotation on his 100-acre farm.

> Plan A: Plant tomatoes every season.
>
> Plan B: Alternate between soybeans and tomatoes each season.

The revenue from tomatoes is $1600 an acre, and the revenue from soybeans is $1200 an acre. Tomatoes require fertilizing the land, which costs about $300 an acre. Soybeans do not require fertilizer; moreover, they add nitrogen to the soil so tomatoes can be planted the following season without fertilizing.

profit = revenue − cost

(a) Find a formula for the profit if Plan A is used for n years.

(b) Find a formula for the profit if Plan B is used for $2n$ years (starting with soybeans).

(c) If the farmer intends to plant these crops for 10 years, which plan is more profitable?

7. Cell Phone Plans Gwendolyn is mulling over the three cell phone plans shown in the table.

	Gigabytes (GB) of data included	Monthly cost	Each additional 100 megabytes (MB)
Plan A	1	$25.00	$2.00
Plan B	1	$40.00	$1.50
Plan C	1	$60.00	$1.00

From past experience, Gwendolyn knows that she will always use more than 1 GB of cell phone data every month.

(a) Make a table of values that shows the cost of each plan for 1 GB to 4 GB, in 500 MB increments.

(b) Find formulas that give Gwendolyn's monthly cost for each plan, assuming that she uses x gigabytes of data per month (where $x \geq 1$).

(c) What is the charge from each plan when Gwendolyn uses 2.2 GB? 3.7 GB? 4.9 GB?

(d) Use your formulas from part (b) to determine the number of gigabytes of data usage for which:
   (i) Plan A and Plan B give the same cost.
   (ii) Plan A and Plan C give the same cost.
   (iii) Plan B and Plan C give the same cost.

8. Profit Sharing To form a new enterprise, Company A invests $1.4 million and Company B invests $2.6 million. The enterprise is sold a year later for $6.4 million. Explore the following methods of dividing the $6.4 million, and comment on their fairness.

(a) Companies A and B divide the $6.4 million equally.

(b) Companies A and B get their original investment back and share the profit equally.

(c) Each company gets a fraction of the $6.4 million proportional to the amount it invested.

© Anton Ivanov/Shutterstock.com

1   Equations and Graphs

In this chapter we study the coordinate plane and how to graph two-variable equations in the coordinate plane. We also study how to solve quadratic and other types of equations and how the solutions of equations relate to their graphs.

Many real-world situations can be modeled with equations. These models can help us predict how such situations will change. Governments and businesses are continually planning for the future. Will our freeways be able to handle the traffic ten years from now? How many air-conditioning units should a manufacturer produce for next summer? What will the average global temperature be two or three decades from now? In each case, a graph of the relevant data may reveal long-term trends that can be modeled by equations. We can then use the models to predict future conditions. For example, available data show a warming trend in global temperature. A significant increase in global temperature could have drastic consequences for the survival of many species, including the penguins pictured here. In the *Focus on Modeling* at the end of the chapter, we learn how to find linear equations that model trends in data and how these trends allow us to make reasonable predictions about the future.

1.1   THE COORDINATE PLANE

■ The Coordinate Plane   ■ The Distance Formula   ■ The Midpoint Formula

The *coordinate plane* is the link between algebra and geometry. In the coordinate plane we can draw graphs of algebraic equations. The graphs, in turn, allow us to "see" the relationship between the variables in the equation. In this section we study the coordinate plane.

■ The Coordinate Plane

The Cartesian plane is named in honor of the French mathematician René Descartes (1596–1650), although another Frenchman, Pierre Fermat (1601–1665), also invented the principles of coordinate geometry at the same time. (See their biographies on pages 237 and 154.)

Just as points on a line can be identified with real numbers to form the coordinate line, points in a plane can be identified with ordered pairs of numbers to form the **coordinate plane** or **Cartesian plane**. To do this, we draw two perpendicular real lines that intersect at 0 on each line. Usually, one line is horizontal with positive direction to the right and is called the **x-axis**; the other line is vertical with positive direction upward and is called the **y-axis**. The point of intersection of the x-axis and the y-axis is the **origin O**, and the two axes divide the plane into four **quadrants**, labeled I, II, III, and IV in Figure 1. (The points *on* the coordinate axes are not assigned to any quadrant.)

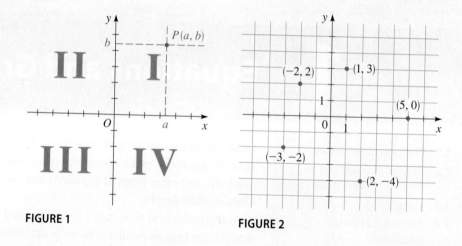

FIGURE 1   **FIGURE 2**

Although the notation for a point (a, b) is the same as the notation for an open interval (a, b), the context should make clear which meaning is intended.

Any point P in the coordinate plane can be located by a unique **ordered pair** of numbers (a, b), as shown in Figure 1. The first number a is called the **x-coordinate** of P; the second number b is called the **y-coordinate** of P. We can think of the coordinates of P as its "address," because they specify its location in the plane. Several points are labeled with their coordinates in Figure 2.

EXAMPLE 1   ■   Graphing Regions in the Coordinate Plane

Describe and sketch the regions given by each set.

(a) $\{(x, y) \mid x \geq 0\}$ (b) $\{(x, y) \mid y = 1\}$ (c) $\{(x, y) \mid -1 < y < 1\}$

SOLUTION

(a) The points whose x-coordinates are 0 or positive lie on the y-axis or to the right of it, as shown in Figure 3(a).

(b) The set of all points with y-coordinate 1 is a horizontal line one unit above the x-axis, as shown in Figure 3(b).

(c) The given region consists of those points in the plane whose y-coordinates lie
between -1 and 1. Thus the region consists of all points that lie between (but not
on) the horizontal lines $y = 1$ and $y = -1$. These lines are shown as broken lines in
Figure 3(c) to indicate that the points on these lines are not in the set.

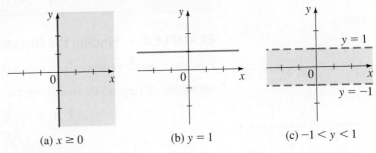

(a) $x \geq 0$ (b) $y = 1$ (c) $-1 < y < 1$

FIGURE 3

✎ Now Try Exercises 9, 11, and 13

▪ The Distance Formula

We now find a formula for the distance $d(A, B)$ between two points $A(x_1, y_1)$ and
$B(x_2, y_2)$ in the plane. Recall from Section P.2 that the distance between points a
and b on a number line is $d(a, b) = |b - a|$. So from Figure 4 we see that the
distance between the points $A(x_1, y_1)$ and $C(x_2, y_1)$ on a horizontal line must be
$|x_2 - x_1|$, and the distance between $B(x_2, y_2)$ and $C(x_2, y_1)$ on a vertical line must
be $|y_2 - y_1|$.

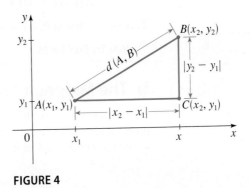

FIGURE 4

Since triangle ABC is a right triangle, the Pythagorean Theorem gives

$$d(A, B) = \sqrt{|x_2 - x_1|^2 + |y_2 - y_1|^2} = \sqrt{(x_2 - x_1)^2 + (y_2 - y_1)^2}$$

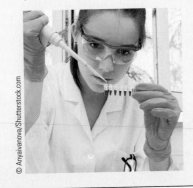

© Anyaivanova/Shutterstock.com

DISCOVERY PROJECT

Visualizing Data

When scientists analyze data, they look for a trend or pattern from which they
can draw a conclusion about the process they are studying. It is difficult to find
hidden patterns in lists of numbers. But a graph of the data can efficiently reveal
any hidden pattern. In this project we examine data obtained by a biologist on
the levels of three different enzymes in blood samples taken from expectant
mothers. You can find the project at **www.stewartmath.com**.

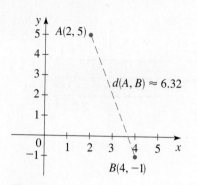

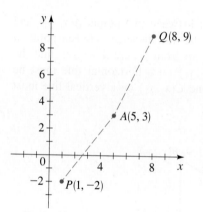

FIGURE 5

FIGURE 6

DISTANCE FORMULA

The distance between the points $A(x_1, y_1)$ and $B(x_2, y_2)$ in the plane is

$$d(A, B) = \sqrt{(x_2 - x_1)^2 + (y_2 - y_1)^2}$$

EXAMPLE 2 ■ Finding the Distance Between Two Points

Find the distance between the points $A(2, 5)$ and $B(4, -1)$.

SOLUTION Using the Distance Formula, we have

$$d(A, B) = \sqrt{(4 - 2)^2 + (-1 - 5)^2}$$
$$= \sqrt{2^2 + (-6)^2}$$
$$= \sqrt{4 + 36} = \sqrt{40} \approx 6.32$$

See Figure 5.

✎ **Now Try Exercise 25(b)**

EXAMPLE 3 ■ Applying the Distance Formula

Which of the points $P(1, -2)$ or $Q(8, 9)$ is closer to the point $A(5, 3)$?

SOLUTION By the Distance Formula we have

$$d(P, A) = \sqrt{(5 - 1)^2 + [3 - (-2)]^2} = \sqrt{4^2 + 5^2} = \sqrt{41}$$
$$d(Q, A) = \sqrt{(5 - 8)^2 + (3 - 9)^2} = \sqrt{(-3)^2 + (-6)^2} = \sqrt{45}$$

This shows that $d(P, A) < d(Q, A)$, so P is closer to A (see Figure 6).

✎ **Now Try Exercise 35**

■ The Midpoint Formula

Now let's find the coordinates (x, y) of the midpoint M of the line segment that joins the point $A(x_1, y_1)$ to the point $B(x_2, y_2)$. In Figure 7, notice that triangles APM and MQB are congruent because $d(A, M) = d(M, B)$ and the corresponding angles are equal.

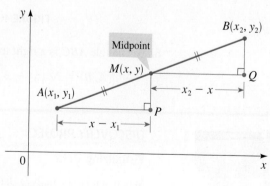

FIGURE 7

It follows that $d(A, P) = d(M, Q)$, so

$$x - x_1 = x_2 - x$$

Solving this equation for x, we get $2x = x_1 + x_2$, so $x = \dfrac{x_1 + x_2}{2}$. Similarly, $y = \dfrac{y_1 + y_2}{2}$.

> **MIDPOINT FORMULA**
>
> The midpoint of the line segment from $A(x_1, y_1)$ to $B(x_2, y_2)$ is
>
> $$\left(\frac{x_1 + x_2}{2}, \frac{y_1 + y_2}{2} \right)$$

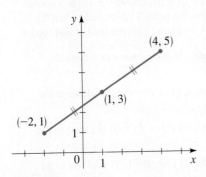

FIGURE 8

EXAMPLE 4 ■ Finding the Midpoint

Find the midpoint of the line segment that joins $(-2, 1)$ and $(4, 5)$.

SOLUTION By the Midpoint Formula, the midpoint (see Figure 8) is

$$\left(\frac{-2 + 4}{2}, \frac{1 + 5}{2} \right) = (1, 3)$$

✎ Now Try Exercise 25(c)   ■

EXAMPLE 5 ■ Applying the Midpoint Formula

Show that the quadrilateral with vertices $P(1, 2)$, $Q(4, 4)$, $R(5, 9)$, and $S(2, 7)$ is a parallelogram by proving that its two diagonals bisect each other.

SOLUTION If the two diagonals have the same midpoint, then they must bisect each other. The midpoint of the diagonal PR is

$$\left(\frac{1 + 5}{2}, \frac{2 + 9}{2} \right) = \left(3, \frac{11}{2} \right)$$

and the midpoint of the diagonal QS is

$$\left(\frac{4 + 2}{2}, \frac{4 + 7}{2} \right) = \left(3, \frac{11}{2} \right)$$

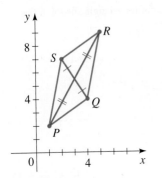

FIGURE 9

so each diagonal bisects the other, as shown in Figure 9. (A theorem from elementary geometry states that the quadrilateral is therefore a parallelogram.)

✎ Now Try Exercise 49   ■

1.1 EXERCISES

CONCEPTS

1. The point that is 2 units to the left of the y-axis and

   4 units above the x-axis has coordinates (_____, _____).

2. If x is positive and y is negative, then the point (x, y) is

   in Quadrant _____.

3. The distance between the points (a, b) and (c, d) is

   _____. So the distance between $(1, 2)$

   and $(7, 10)$ is _____.

4. The point midway between (a, b) and (c, d)

   is _____.

   So the point midway between $(1, 2)$ and $(7, 10)$

   is _____.

SKILLS

5–6 ■ Points in a Coordinate Plane Refer to the following figure.

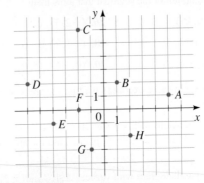

5. Find the coordinates of the points shown.

6. List the points that lie in Quadrants I and III.

7–8 ■ Points in a Coordinate Plane Plot the given points in a coordinate plane.

7. $(0, 5), (-1, 0), (-1, -2), \left(\frac{1}{2}, \frac{2}{3}\right)$

8. $(-5, 0), (2, 0), (2.6, -1.3), (-2.5, 3.5)$

9–20 ■ Regions in a Coordinate Plane Sketch the region given by the set.

9. $\{(x, y) \mid x \geq 2\}$
10. $\{(x, y) \mid y = 2\}$

11. $\{(x, y) \mid x = -4\}$
12. $\{(x, y) \mid y < 3\}$

13. $\{(x, y) \mid -3 < x < 3\}$
14. $\{(x, y) \mid 0 \leq y \leq 2\}$

15. $\{(x, y) \mid xy < 0\}$
16. $\{(x, y) \mid xy > 0\}$

17. $\{(x, y) \mid x \geq 1 \text{ and } y < 3\}$

18. $\{(x, y) \mid x < 2 \text{ and } y \geq 1\}$

19. $\{(x, y) \mid -1 < x < 1 \text{ and } -2 < y < 2\}$

20. $\{(x, y) \mid -3 \leq x \leq 3 \text{ and } -1 \leq y \leq 1\}$

21–24 ■ Distance and Midpoint A pair of points is graphed. **(a)** Find the distance between them. **(b)** Find the midpoint of the segment that joins them.

21.

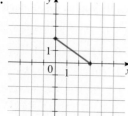

22.

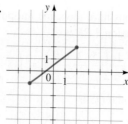

23.

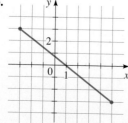

24.

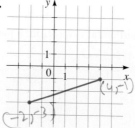

25–30 ■ Distance and Midpoint A pair of points is given. **(a)** Plot the points in a coordinate plane. **(b)** Find the distance between them. **(c)** Find the midpoint of the segment that joins them.

25. $(0, 8), (6, 16)$
26. $(-2, 5), (10, 0)$

27. $(3, -2), (-4, 5)$
28. $(-1, 1), (-6, -3)$

29. $(6, -2), (-6, 2)$
30. $(0, -6), (5, 0)$

31–34 ■ Area In these exercises we find the areas of plane figures.

31. Draw the rectangle with vertices $A(1, 3)$, $B(5, 3)$, $C(1, -3)$, and $D(5, -3)$ on a coordinate plane. Find the area of the rectangle.

32. Draw the parallelogram with vertices $A(1, 2)$, $B(5, 2)$, $C(3, 6)$, and $D(7, 6)$ on a coordinate plane. Find the area of the parallelogram.

33. Plot the points $A(1, 0)$, $B(5, 0)$, $C(4, 3)$, and $D(2, 3)$ on a coordinate plane. Draw the segments AB, BC, CD, and DA. What kind of quadrilateral is $ABCD$, and what is its area?

34. Plot the points $P(5, 1)$, $Q(0, 6)$, and $R(-5, 1)$ on a coordinate plane. Where must the point S be located so that the quadrilateral $PQRS$ is a square? Find the area of this square.

35–39 ■ Distance Formula In these exercises we use the Distance Formula.

35. Which of the points $A(6, 7)$ or $B(-5, 8)$ is closer to the origin?

36. Which of the points $C(-6, 3)$ or $D(3, 0)$ is closer to the point $E(-2, 1)$?

37. Which of the points $P(3, 1)$ or $Q(-1, 3)$ is closer to the point $R(-1, -1)$?

38. (a) Show that the points $(7, 3)$ and $(3, 7)$ are the same distance from the origin.

(b) Show that the points (a, b) and (b, a) are the same distance from the origin.

39. Show that the triangle with vertices $A(0, 2)$, $B(-3, -1)$, and $C(-4, 3)$ is isosceles.

40. Area of Triangle Find the area of the triangle shown in the figure.

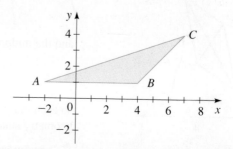

41–42 ■ Pythagorean Theorem In these exercises we use the converse of the Pythagorean Theorem (see page 277) to show that the given triangle is a right triangle.

41. Refer to triangle ABC in the figure below.

(a) Show that triangle ABC is a right triangle by using the converse of the Pythagorean Theorem.

(b) Find the area of triangle ABC.

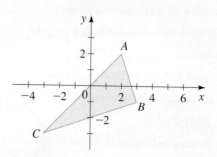

42. Show that the triangle with vertices $A(6, -7)$, $B(11, -3)$, and $C(2, -2)$ is a right triangle by using the converse of the Pythagorean Theorem. Find the area of the triangle.

43–45 ■ Distance Formula In these exercises we use the Distance Formula.

43. Show that the points $A(-2,9)$, $B(4,6)$, $C(1,0)$, and $D(-5,3)$ are the vertices of a square.

44. Show that the points $A(-1,3)$, $B(3,11)$, and $C(5,15)$ are collinear by showing that $d(A,B) + d(B,C) = d(A,C)$.

45. Find a point on the y-axis that is equidistant from the points $(5,-5)$ and $(1,1)$.

46–50 ■ Distance and Midpoint Formulas In these exercises we use the Distance Formula and the Midpoint Formula.

46. Find the lengths of the medians of the triangle with vertices $A(1,0)$, $B(3,6)$, and $C(8,2)$. (A *median* is a line segment from a vertex to the midpoint of the opposite side.)

47. Plot the points $P(-1,-4)$, $Q(1,1)$, and $R(4,2)$ on a coordinate plane. Where should the point S be located so that the figure $PQRS$ is a parallelogram?

48. If $M(6,8)$ is the midpoint of the line segment AB and if A has coordinates $(2,3)$, find the coordinates of B.

49. (a) Sketch the parallelogram with vertices $A(-2,-1)$, $B(4,2)$, $C(7,7)$, and $D(1,4)$.
  (b) Find the midpoints of the diagonals of this parallelogram.
  (c) From part (b) show that the diagonals bisect each other.

50. The point M in the figure is the midpoint of the line segment AB. Show that M is equidistant from the vertices of triangle ABC.

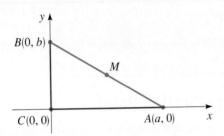

SKILLS Plus

51. Shifting the Coordinate Plane Suppose that each point in the coordinate plane is shifted 3 units to the right and 2 units upward.
  (a) The point $(5,3)$ is shifted to what new point?
  (b) The point (a,b) is shifted to what new point?
  (c) What point is shifted to $(3,4)$?
  (d) Triangle ABC in the figure has been shifted to triangle $A'B'C'$. Find the coordinates of the points A', B', and C'.

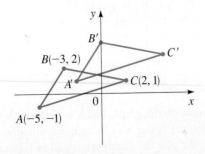

52. Reflecting in the Coordinate Plane Suppose that the y-axis acts as a mirror that reflects each point to the right of it into a point to the left of it.
  (a) The point $(3,7)$ is reflected to what point?
  (b) The point (a,b) is reflected to what point?
  (c) What point is reflected to $(-4,-1)$?
  (d) Triangle ABC in the figure is reflected to triangle $A'B'C'$. Find the coordinates of the points A', B', and C'.

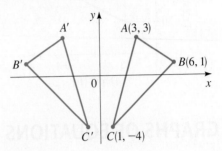

APPLICATIONS

53. Distances in a City A city has streets that run north and south and avenues that run east and west, all equally spaced. Streets and avenues are numbered sequentially, as shown in the figure. The *walking* distance between points A and B is 7 blocks— that is, 3 blocks east and 4 blocks north. To find the *straight-line* distance d, we must use the Distance Formula.
  (a) Find the straight-line distance (in blocks) between A and B.
  (b) Find the walking distance and the straight-line distance between the corner of 4th St. and 2nd Ave. and the corner of 11th St. and 26th Ave.
  (c) What must be true about the points P and Q if the walking distance between P and Q equals the straight-line distance between P and Q?

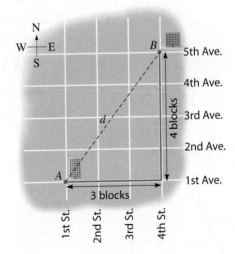

54. Halfway Point Two friends live in the city described in Exercise 53, one at the corner of 3rd St. and 7th Ave. and the other at the corner of 27th St. and 17th Ave. They frequently meet at a coffee shop halfway between their homes.
  (a) At what intersection is the coffee shop located?
  (b) How far must each of them walk to get to the coffee shop?

55. Pressure and Depth The graph shows the pressure experienced by an ocean diver at two different depths. Find and interpret the midpoint of the line segment shown in the graph.

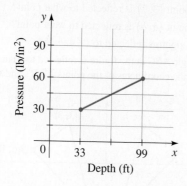

Depth (ft)

56. WRITE: Completing a Line Segment Plot the points $M(6, 8)$ and $A(2, 3)$ on a coordinate plane. If M is the midpoint of the line segment AB, find the coordinates of B. Write a brief description of the steps you took to find B and your reasons for taking them.

57. WRITE: Completing a Parallelogram Plot the points $P(0, 3)$, $Q(2, 2)$, and $R(5, 3)$ on a coordinate plane. Where should the point S be located so that the figure $PQRS$ is a parallelogram? Write a brief description of the steps you took and your reasons for taking them.

1.2 GRAPHS OF EQUATIONS IN TWO VARIABLES; CIRCLES

■ **Graphing Equations by Plotting Points** ■ **Intercepts** ■ **Circles** ■ **Symmetry**

Fundamental Principle of Analytic Geometry
A point (x, y) lies on the graph of an equation if and only if its coordinates satisfy the equation.

An **equation in two variables**, such as $y = x^2 + 1$, expresses a relationship between two quantities. A point (x, y) **satisfies** the equation if it makes the equation true when the values for x and y are substituted into the equation. For example, the point $(3, 10)$ satisfies the equation $y = x^2 + 1$ because $10 = 3^2 + 1$, but the point $(1, 3)$ does not, because $3 \neq 1^2 + 1$.

> **THE GRAPH OF AN EQUATION**
>
> The **graph** of an equation in x and y is the set of all points (x, y) in the coordinate plane that satisfy the equation.

■ Graphing Equations by Plotting Points

The graph of an equation is a curve, so to graph an equation, we plot as many points as we can, then connect them by a smooth curve.

EXAMPLE 1 ■ Sketching a Graph by Plotting Points

Sketch the graph of the equation $2x - y = 3$.

SOLUTION We first solve the given equation for y to get

$$y = 2x - 3$$

This helps us calculate the y-coordinates in the following table.

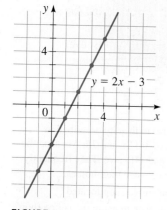

$y = 2x - 3$

FIGURE 1

x	$y = 2x - 3$	(x, y)
-1	-5	$(-1, -5)$
0	-3	$(0, -3)$
1	-1	$(1, -1)$
2	1	$(2, 1)$
3	3	$(3, 3)$
4	5	$(4, 5)$

Of course, there are infinitely many points on the graph, and it is impossible to plot all of them. But the more points we plot, the better we can imagine what the graph represented by the equation looks like. We plot the points we found in Figure 1; they appear to lie on a line. So we complete the graph by joining the points by a line. (In Section 1.3 we verify that the graph of an equation of this type is indeed a line.)

✎ Now Try Exercise 19

EXAMPLE 2 ■ Sketching a Graph by Plotting Points

Sketch the graph of the equation $y = x^2 - 2$.

SOLUTION We find some of the points that satisfy the equation in the following table. In Figure 2 we plot these points and then connect them by a smooth curve. A curve with this shape is called a *parabola*.

A detailed discussion of parabolas and their geometric properties is presented in Chapter 12.

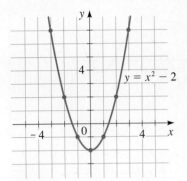

FIGURE 2

x	$y = x^2 - 2$	(x, y)
-3	7	$(-3, 7)$
-2	2	$(-2, 2)$
-1	-1	$(-1, -1)$
0	-2	$(0, -2)$
1	-1	$(1, -1)$
2	2	$(2, 2)$
3	7	$(3, 7)$

✎ Now Try Exercise 23

EXAMPLE 3 ■ Graphing an Absolute Value Equation

Sketch the graph of the equation $y = |x|$.

SOLUTION We make a table of values.

x	$y = |x|$	(x, y)
-3	3	$(-3, 3)$
-2	2	$(-2, 2)$
-1	1	$(-1, 1)$
0	0	$(0, 0)$
1	1	$(1, 1)$
2	2	$(2, 2)$
3	3	$(3, 3)$

FIGURE 3

In Figure 3 we plot these points and use them to sketch the graph of the equation.

✎ Now Try Exercise 33

See Appendix C, *Graphing with a Graphing Calculator*, for general guidelines on using a graphing calculator. See Appendix D, *Using the TI-83/84 Graphing Calculator*, for specific graphing instructions.

We can use a graphing calculator to graph equations. A graphing calculator draws the graph of an equation by plotting points, just as we would do by hand.

EXAMPLE 4 ■ Graphing an Equation with a Graphing Calculator

Use a graphing calculator to graph the following equation in the viewing rectangle $[-5, 5]$ by $[-1, 2]$.

$$y = \frac{1}{1 + x^2}$$

SOLUTION The graph is shown in Figure 4.

✎ Now Try Exercise 45

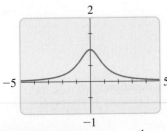

FIGURE 4 Graph of $y = \dfrac{1}{1 + x^2}$

■ Intercepts

The x-coordinates of the points where a graph intersects the x-axis are called the **x-intercepts** of the graph and are obtained by setting $y = 0$ in the equation of the graph. The y-coordinates of the points where a graph intersects the y-axis are called the **y-intercepts** of the graph and are obtained by setting $x = 0$ in the equation of the graph.

DEFINITION OF INTERCEPTS

Intercepts	How to find them	Where they are on the graph
x-intercepts:		
The x-coordinates of points where the graph of an equation intersects the x-axis	Set $y = 0$ and solve for x	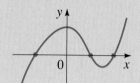
y-intercepts:		
The y-coordinates of points where the graph of an equation intersects the y-axis	Set $x = 0$ and solve for y	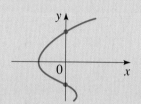

EXAMPLE 5 ■ Finding Intercepts

Find the x- and y-intercepts of the graph of the equation $y = x^2 - 2$.

SOLUTION To find the x-intercepts, we set $y = 0$ and solve for x. Thus

$$0 = x^2 - 2 \qquad \text{Set } y = 0$$
$$x^2 = 2 \qquad \text{Add 2 to each side}$$
$$x = \pm\sqrt{2} \qquad \text{Take the square root}$$

The x-intercepts are $\sqrt{2}$ and $-\sqrt{2}$.

To find the y-intercepts, we set $x = 0$ and solve for y. Thus

$$y = 0^2 - 2 \qquad \text{Set } x = 0$$
$$y = -2$$

The y-intercept is -2.

The graph of this equation was sketched in Example 2. It is repeated in Figure 5 with the x- and y-intercepts labeled.

✎ **Now Try Exercise 49** ■

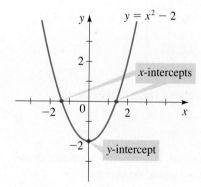

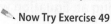

FIGURE 5

EXAMPLE 6 ■ Finding Intercepts

Find the x- and y-intercepts of the graph of the following equation:

$$\frac{x^2}{9} + \frac{y^2}{4} = 1$$

SOLUTION   To find the *x*-intercepts, we set $y = 0$ and solve for *x*.

$$\frac{x^2}{9} = 1 \qquad \text{Set } y = 0$$

$$x^2 = 9 \qquad \text{Multiply by 9}$$

$$x = \pm 3 \qquad \text{Solve for } x$$

So the *x*-intercepts are 3 and -3. To find the *y*-intercepts, we set $x = 0$ and solve for *y*.

$$\frac{y^2}{4} = 1 \qquad \text{Set } x = 0$$

$$y^2 = 4 \qquad \text{Multiply by 4}$$

$$y = \pm 2 \qquad \text{Solve for } y$$

So the *y*-intercepts are 2 and -2. A graph of the equation is shown in Figure 6. The shape of the graph is an ellipse. Ellipses are studied in more detail in Section 12.2.

✎. **Now Try Exercise 55**   ■

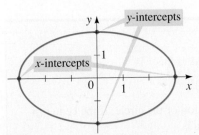

FIGURE 6 Graph of $\dfrac{x^2}{9} + \dfrac{y^2}{4} = 1$

EXAMPLE 7 ■ Finding Intercepts Graphically

Consider the equation $y = x^3 + 3x^2 - x - 3$.

(a) Graph the equation in the viewing rectangle $[-5, 3]$ by $[-5, 5]$.

(b) Find the *x*- and *y*-intercepts from the graph.

(c) Verify your answers to part (b) algebraically.

SOLUTION

(a) The graph is shown in Figure 7.

(b) From the graph we see that there are three *x*-intercepts: -3, -1, and 1. There is one *y*-intercept: -3.

(c) Setting $x = 0$ in the equation we get $y = -3$, so -3 is a *y*-intercept. Setting $x = -3$ in the equation, we get $y = 0$, so -3 is an *x*-intercept. We can similarly verify that -1, and 1 are *x*-intercepts.

$$y = (-3)^3 + 3(-3)^2 - (-3) - 3 = 0 \qquad \text{Set } x = -3$$

$$y = (-1)^3 + 3(-1)^2 - (-1) - 3 = 0 \qquad \text{Set } x = -1$$

$$y = (1)^3 + 3(1)^2 - (1) - 3 = 0 \qquad \text{Set } x = 1$$

✎. **Now Try Exercise 61**   ■

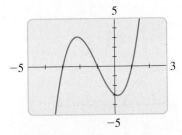

FIGURE 7 Graph of
$y = x^3 + 3x^2 - x - 3$

■ Circles

So far, we have discussed how to find the graph of an equation in *x* and *y*. The converse problem is to find an equation of a graph, that is, an equation that represents a given curve in the *xy*-plane. Such an equation is satisfied by the coordinates of the points on the curve and by no other point. This is the other half of the fundamental principle of analytic geometry as formulated by Descartes and Fermat. The idea is that if a geometric curve can be represented by an algebraic equation, then the rules of algebra can be used to analyze the curve.

As an example of this type of problem, let's find the equation of a circle with radius *r* and center (h, k). By definition the circle is the set of all points $P(x, y)$ whose

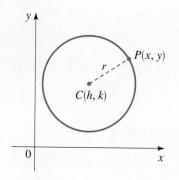

FIGURE 8

distance from the center $C(h, k)$ is r (see Figure 8). Thus P is on the circle if and only if $d(P, C) = r$. From the distance formula we have

$$\sqrt{(x - h)^2 + (y - k)^2} = r$$

$$(x - h)^2 + (y - k)^2 = r^2 \qquad \text{Square each side}$$

This is the desired equation.

EQUATION OF A CIRCLE

An equation of the circle with center (h, k) and radius r is

$$(x - h)^2 + (y - k)^2 = r^2$$

This is called the **standard form** for the equation of the circle. If the center of the circle is the origin $(0, 0)$, then the equation is

$$x^2 + y^2 = r^2$$

EXAMPLE 8 ■ Graphing a Circle

Graph each equation.

(a) $x^2 + y^2 = 25$ (b) $(x - 2)^2 + (y + 1)^2 = 25$

SOLUTION

(a) Rewriting the equation as $x^2 + y^2 = 5^2$, we see that this is an equation of the circle of radius 5 centered at the origin. Its graph is shown in Figure 9.

(b) Rewriting the equation as $(x - 2)^2 + (y + 1)^2 = 5^2$, we see that this is an equation of the circle of radius 5 centered at $(2, -1)$. Its graph is shown in Figure 10.

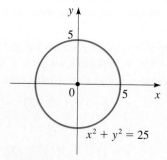

FIGURE 9

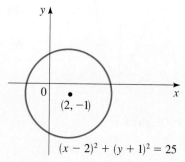

FIGURE 10

✎ Now Try Exercises 67 and 69

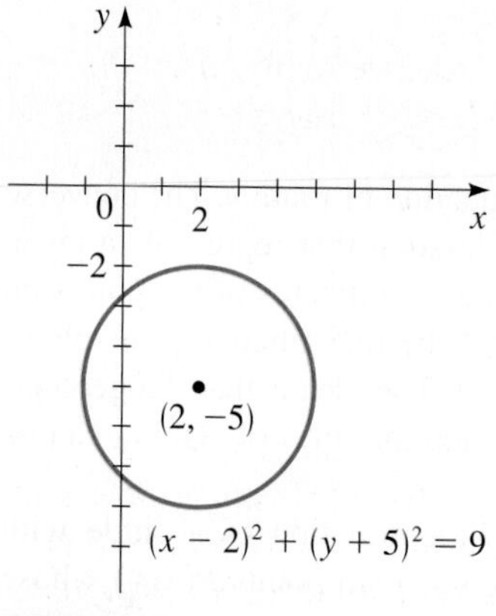

EXAMPLE 9 ■ Finding an Equation of a Circle

(a) Find an equation of the circle with radius 3 and center $(2, -5)$.

(b) Find an equation of the circle that has the points $P(1, 8)$ and $Q(5, -6)$ as the endpoints of a diameter.

SOLUTION

(a) Using the equation of a circle with $r = 3$, $h = 2$, and $k = -5$, we obtain

$$(x - 2)^2 + (y + 5)^2 = 9$$

The graph is shown in Figure 11.

FIGURE 11

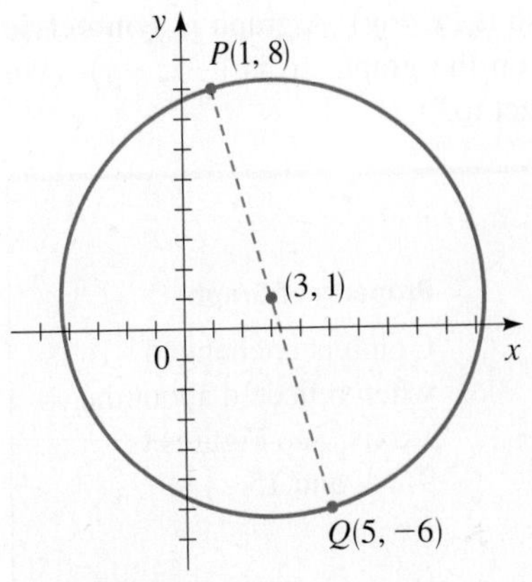

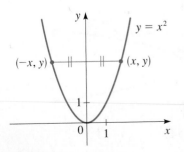

$P(1, 8)$

$(3, 1)$

$Q(5, -6)$

$(x - 3)^2 + (y - 1)^2 = 53$

FIGURE 12

(b) We first observe that the center is the midpoint of the diameter PQ, so by the Midpoint Formula the center is

$$\left(\frac{1 + 5}{2}, \frac{8 - 6}{2}\right) = (3, 1)$$

The radius r is the distance from P to the center, so by the Distance Formula

$$r^2 = (3 - 1)^2 + (1 - 8)^2 = 2^2 + (-7)^2 = 53$$

Therefore the equation of the circle is

$$(x - 3)^2 + (y - 1)^2 = 53$$

The graph is shown in Figure 12.

Now Try Exercises 73 and 77

Let's expand the equation of the circle in the preceding example.

$$(x - 3)^2 + (y - 1)^2 = 53 \qquad \text{Standard form}$$
$$x^2 - 6x + 9 + y^2 - 2y + 1 = 53 \qquad \text{Expand the squares}$$
$$x^2 - 6x + y^2 - 2y = 43 \qquad \text{Subtract 10 to get expanded form}$$

Completing the square is used in many contexts in algebra. In Section 1.4 we use completing the square to solve quadratic equations.

Suppose we are given the equation of a circle in expanded form. Then to find its center and radius, we must put the equation back in standard form. That means that we must reverse the steps in the preceding calculation, and to do that we need to know what to add to an expression like $x^2 - 6x$ to make it a perfect square—that is, we need to "complete the square." To **complete the square**, we must add the square of half the coefficient of x. For example, to complete the square for $x^2 - 6x$, we add the square of half of -6:

$$x^2 - 6x + \left(\tfrac{1}{2}(-6)\right)^2 = x^2 - 6x + 9 = (x - 3)^2$$

In general, to make $X^2 + bX$ a perfect square, add $(b/2)^2$.

EXAMPLE 10 ■ Identifying an Equation of a Circle

Show that the equation $x^2 + y^2 + 2x - 6y + 7 = 0$ represents a circle, and find the center and radius of the circle.

SOLUTION We first group the x-terms and y-terms. Then we complete the square within each grouping. That is, we complete the square for $x^2 + 2x$ by adding $\left(\tfrac{1}{2} \cdot 2\right)^2 = 1$, and we complete the square for $y^2 - 6y$ by adding $\left[\tfrac{1}{2} \cdot (-6)\right]^2 = 9$.

⊘ We must add the same numbers to *each side* to maintain equality.

$$(x^2 + 2x \qquad) + (y^2 - 6y \qquad) = -7 \qquad \text{Group terms}$$
$$(x^2 + 2x + 1) + (y^2 - 6y + 9) = -7 + 1 + 9 \qquad \text{Complete the square by adding 1 and 9 to each side}$$
$$(x + 1)^2 + (y - 3)^2 = 3 \qquad \text{Factor and simplify}$$

Comparing this equation with the standard equation of a circle, we see that $h = -1$, $k = 3$, and $r = \sqrt{3}$, so the given equation represents a circle with center $(-1, 3)$ and radius $\sqrt{3}$.

Now Try Exercise 83

■ Symmetry

$y = x^2$

$(-x, y)$ (x, y)

FIGURE 13

Figure 13 shows the graph of $y = x^2$. Notice that the part of the graph to the left of the y-axis is the mirror image of the part to the right of the y-axis. The reason is that if the point (x, y) is on the graph, then so is $(-x, y)$, and these points are reflections of each other about the y-axis. In this situation we say that the graph is **symmetric with respect to the y-axis**. Similarly, we say that a graph is **symmetric with respect to the x-axis** if whenever the point (x, y) is on the graph, then so is $(x, -y)$. A graph is **symmetric with respect to the origin** if whenever (x, y) is on the graph, so is $(-x, -y)$. (We often say symmetric "about" instead of "with respect to.")

TYPES OF SYMMETRY

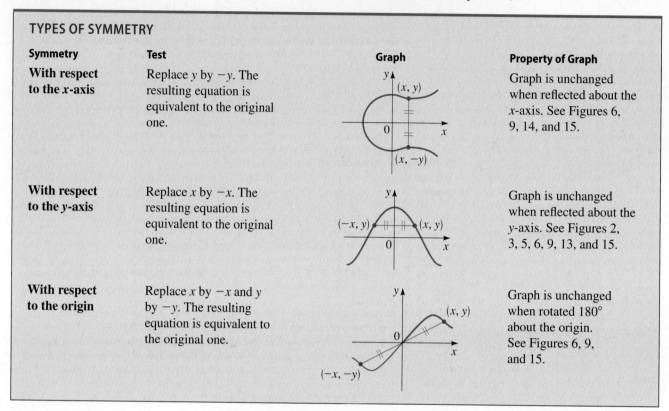

Symmetry	Test	Graph	Property of Graph
With respect to the x-axis	Replace y by $-y$. The resulting equation is equivalent to the original one.		Graph is unchanged when reflected about the x-axis. See Figures 6, 9, 14, and 15.
With respect to the y-axis	Replace x by $-x$. The resulting equation is equivalent to the original one.		Graph is unchanged when reflected about the y-axis. See Figures 2, 3, 5, 6, 9, 13, and 15.
With respect to the origin	Replace x by $-x$ and y by $-y$. The resulting equation is equivalent to the original one.		Graph is unchanged when rotated $180°$ about the origin. See Figures 6, 9, and 15.

The remaining examples in this section show how symmetry helps us to sketch the graphs of equations.

EXAMPLE 11 ■ Using Symmetry to Sketch a Graph

Test the equation $x = y^2$ for symmetry and sketch the graph.

SOLUTION If y is replaced by $-y$ in the equation $x = y^2$, we get

$$x = (-y)^2 \qquad \text{Replace } y \text{ by } -y$$

$$x = y^2 \qquad \text{Simplify}$$

and so the equation is equivalent to the original one. Therefore the graph is symmetric about the x-axis. But changing x to $-x$ gives the equation $-x = y^2$, which is not equivalent to the original equation, so the graph is not symmetric about the y-axis.

We use the symmetry about the x-axis to sketch the graph by first plotting points just for $y > 0$ and then reflecting the graph about the x-axis, as shown in Figure 14.

y	$x = y^2$	(x, y)
0	0	$(0, 0)$
1	1	$(1, 1)$
2	4	$(4, 2)$
3	9	$(9, 3)$

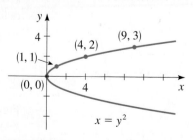

FIGURE 14

✏ Now Try Exercises 95 and 101

EXAMPLE 12 ■ Testing an Equation for Symmetry

Test the equation $y = x^3 - 9x$ for symmetry.

SOLUTION If we replace x by $-x$ and y by $-y$ in the equation, we get

$$-y = (-x)^3 - 9(-x) \qquad \text{Replace } x \text{ by } -x \text{ and } y \text{ by } -y$$
$$-y = -x^3 + 9x \qquad \text{Simplify}$$
$$y = x^3 - 9x \qquad \text{Multiply by } -1$$

and so the equation is equivalent to the original one. This means that the graph is symmetric with respect to the origin.

✎ Now Try Exercise 97

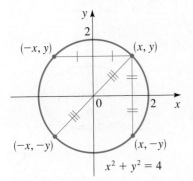

FIGURE 15

EXAMPLE 13 ■ A Circle That Has All Three Types of Symmetry

Test the equation of the circle $x^2 + y^2 = 4$ for symmetry.

SOLUTION The equation $x^2 + y^2 = 4$ is equivalent to the original one when x is replaced by $-x$ and y is replaced by $-y$, since $(-x)^2 = x^2$ and $(-y)^2 = y^2$, so the circle exhibits all three types of symmetry. It is symmetric with respect to the x-axis, the y-axis, and the origin, as shown in Figure 15.

✎ Now Try Exercise 99

1.2 EXERCISES

CONCEPTS

1. If the point $(2, 3)$ is on the graph of an equation in x and y, then the equation is satisfied when we replace x by

_____ and y by _____. Is the point $(2, 3)$ on the graph of the equation $2y = x + 1$? Complete the table, and sketch a graph.

x	y	(x, y)
-2		
-1		
0		
1		
2		

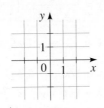

2. To find the x-intercept(s) of the graph of an equation, we

set _____ equal to 0 and solve for _____. So the

x-intercept of $2y = x + 1$ is _____.

3. To find the y-intercept(s) of the graph of an equation, we

set _____ equal to 0 and solve for _____. So the

y-intercept of $2y = x + 1$ is _____.

4. The graph of the equation $(x - 1)^2 + (y - 2)^2 = 9$ is a circle

with center (____, ____) and radius _____.

5. (a) If a graph is symmetric with respect to the x-axis and (a, b) is on the graph, then (____, ____) is also on the graph.

(b) If a graph is symmetric with respect to the y-axis and (a, b) is on the graph, then (____, ____) is also on the graph.

(c) If a graph is symmetric about the origin and (a, b) is on the graph, then (____, ____) is also on the graph.

6. The graph of an equation is shown below.

(a) The x-intercept(s) are _____, and the y-intercept(s)

are _____.

(b) The graph is symmetric about the _____ (x-axis/ y-axis/origin).

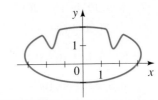

7–8 ■ *Yes or No? If No, give a reason.*

7. If the graph of an equation is symmetric with respect to both the *x*- and *y*-axes, is it necessarily symmetric with respect to the origin?

8. If the graph of an equation is symmetric with respect to the origin, is it necessarily symmetric with respect to the *x*- or *y*-axes?

SKILLS

9–14 ■ **Points on a Graph?** Determine whether the given points are on the graph of the equation.

9. $y = 3 - 4x$; $(0, 3), (4, 0), (1, -1)$

10. $y = \sqrt{1 - x}$; $(2, 1), (-3, 2), (0, 1)$

11. $x - 2y - 1 = 0$; $(0, 0), (1, 0), (-1, -1)$

12. $y(x^2 + 1) = 1$; $(1, 1), \left(1, \frac{1}{2}\right), \left(-1, \frac{1}{2}\right)$

13. $x^2 + 2xy + y^2 = 1$; $(0, 1), (2, -1), (-2, 3)$

14. $x^2 + y^2 = 1$; $(0, 1), \left(\frac{1}{\sqrt{2}}, \frac{1}{\sqrt{2}}\right), \left(\frac{\sqrt{3}}{2}, \frac{1}{2}\right)$

15–40 ■ **Graphing Equations** Make a table of values, and sketch a graph of the equation.

15. $y = 3x$

16. $y = -2x$

17. $y = 2 - x$

18. $y = 2x + 3$

19. $2x - y = 6$

20. $x - 4y = 8$

21. $y = 1 - x^2$

22. $y = x^2 + 2$

23. $y = x^2 - 2$

24. $y = -x^2 + 4$

25. $9y = x^2$

26. $4y = -x^2$

27. $x + y^2 = 4$

28. $xy = 2$

29. $y = \sqrt{x}$

30. $y = 2 + \sqrt{x}$

31. $y = -\sqrt{9 - x^2}$

32. $y = \sqrt{9 - x^2}$

33. $y = -|x|$

34. $x = |y|$

35. $y = 4 - |x|$

36. $y = |4 - x|$

37. $x = y^3$

38. $y = x^3 - 1$

39. $y = x^4$

40. $y = 16 - x^4$

41–46 ■ **Graphing Equations** Use a graphing calculator to graph the equation in the given viewing rectangle.

41. $y = 0.01x^3 - x^2 + 5$; $[-100, 150]$ by $[-2000, 2000]$

42. $y = 0.03x^2 + 1.7x - 3$; $[-100, 50]$ by $[-50, 100]$

43. $y = \sqrt{12x - 17}$; $[-1, 10]$ by $[-1, 20]$

44. $y = \sqrt[4]{256 - x^2}$; $[-20, 20]$ by $[-2, 6]$

45. $y = \dfrac{x}{x^2 + 25}$; $[-50, 50]$ by $[-0.2, 0.2]$

46. $y = x^4 - 4x^3$; $[-4, 6]$ by $[-50, 100]$

47–56 ■ **Intercepts** Find the *x*- and *y*-intercepts of the graph of the equation.

47. $y = x + 6$

48. $2x - 5y = 40$

49. $y = x^2 - 5$

50. $y^2 = 9 - x^2$

51. $y - 2xy + 2x = 1$

52. $x^2 - xy + y = 1$

53. $y = \sqrt{x + 1}$

54. $xy = 5$

55. $4x^2 + 25y^2 = 100$

56. $25x^2 - y^2 = 100$

57–60 ■ **Intercepts** An equation and its graph are given. Find the *x*- and *y*-intercepts.

57. $y = 4x - x^2$

58. $\dfrac{x^2}{9} + \dfrac{y^2}{4} = 1$

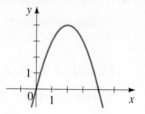

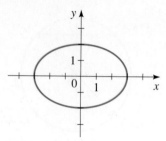

59. $x^4 + y^2 - xy = 16$

60. $x^2 + y^3 - x^2y^2 = 64$

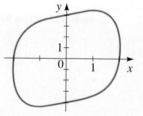

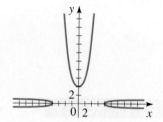

61–66 ■ **Graphing Equations** An equation is given. **(a)** Use a graphing calculator to graph the equation in the given viewing rectangle. **(b)** Find the *x*- and *y*-intercepts from the graph. **(c)** Verify your answers to part (b) algebraically (from the equation).

61. $y = x^3 - x^2$; $[-2, 2]$ by $[-1, 1]$

62. $y = x^4 - 2x^3$; $[-2, 3]$ by $[-3, 3]$

63. $y = -\dfrac{2}{x^2 + 1}$; $[-5, 5]$ by $[-3, 1]$

64. $y = \dfrac{x}{x^2 + 1}$; $[-5, 5]$ by $[-2, 2]$

65. $y = \sqrt[3]{x}$; $[-5, 5]$ by $[-2, 2]$

66. $y = \sqrt[3]{1 - x^2}$; $[-5, 5]$ by $[-5, 3]$

67–72 ■ **Graphing Circles** Find the center and radius of the circle, and sketch its graph.

67. $x^2 + y^2 = 9$

68. $x^2 + y^2 = 5$

69. $(x - 3)^2 + y^2 = 16$

70. $x^2 + (y - 2)^2 = 4$

71. $(x + 3)^2 + (y - 4)^2 = 25$

72. $(x + 1)^2 + (y + 2)^2 = 36$

73–80 ■ **Equations of Circles** Find an equation of the circle that satisfies the given conditions.

73. Center $(-3, 2)$, radius 5

74. Center $(-1, -3)$, radius 3

75. Center at the origin; passes through $(4, 7)$

76. Center $(-1, 5)$; passes through $(-4, -6)$

77. Endpoints of a diameter are $P(-1, 1)$ and $Q(5, 9)$

78. Endpoints of a diameter are $P(-1, 3)$ and $Q(7, -5)$

79. Center $(7, -3)$; tangent to the x-axis

80. Circle lies in the first quadrant, tangent to both x- and y-axes; radius 5

81–82 ■ Equations of Circles Find the equation of the circle shown in the figure.

81.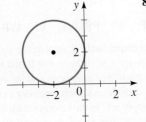

82.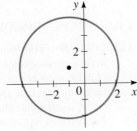

83–90 ■ Equations of Circles Show that the equation represents a circle, and find the center and radius of the circle.

83. $x^2 + y^2 - 2x + 4y + 1 = 0$

84. $x^2 + y^2 - 2x - 2y = 2$

85. $x^2 + y^2 - 4x + 10y + 13 = 0$

86. $x^2 + y^2 + 6y + 2 = 0$

87. $x^2 + y^2 + x = 0$ **88.** $x^2 + y^2 + 2x + y + 1 = 0$

89. $x^2 + y^2 - \frac{1}{2}x + \frac{1}{2}y = \frac{1}{8}$ **90.** $x^2 + y^2 + \frac{1}{2}x + 2y + \frac{1}{16} = 0$

91–94 ■ Graphing Circles Sketch the graph of the equation.

91. $x^2 + y^2 + 4x - 10y = 21$ **92.** $4x^2 + 4y^2 + 2x = 0$

93. $x^2 + y^2 + 6x - 12y + 45 = 0$

94. $x^2 + y^2 - 16x + 12y + 200 = 0$

95–100 ■ Symmetry Test the equation for symmetry.

95. $y = x^4 + x^2$ **96.** $x = y^4 - y^2$

97. $y = x^3 + 10x$ **98.** $y = x^2 + |x|$

99. $x^4 y^4 + x^2 y^2 = 1$ **100.** $x^2 y^2 + xy = 1$

101–104 ■ Symmetry Complete the graph using the given symmetry property.

101. Symmetric with respect to the y-axis

102. Symmetric with respect to the x-axis

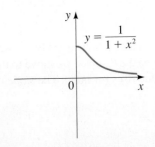

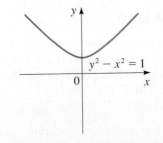

103. Symmetric with respect to the origin

104. Symmetric with respect to the origin

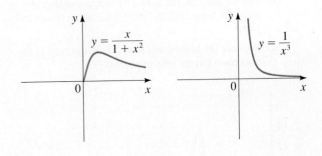

SKILLS Plus

105–106 ■ Graphing Regions Sketch the region given by the set.

105. $\{(x, y) \mid x^2 + y^2 \le 1\}$

106. $\{(x, y) \mid x^2 + y^2 > 4\}$

107. Area of a Region Find the area of the region that lies outside the circle $x^2 + y^2 = 4$ but inside the circle

$$x^2 + y^2 - 4y - 12 = 0$$

108. Area of a Region Sketch the region in the coordinate plane that satisfies both the inequalities $x^2 + y^2 \le 9$ and $y \ge |x|$. What is the area of this region?

109. Shifting the Coordinate Plane Suppose that each point in the coordinate plane is shifted 3 units to the right and 2 units upward.

  (a) The point $(5, 3)$ is shifted to what new point?

  (b) The point (a, b) is shifted to what new point?

110. Making a Graph Symmetric The graph shown in the figure is not symmetric about the x-axis, the y-axis, or the origin. Add more line segments to the graph so that it exhibits the indicated symmetry. In each case, add as little as possible.

  (a) Symmetry about the x-axis

  (b) Symmetry about the y-axis

  (c) Symmetry about the origin

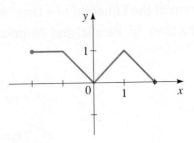

APPLICATIONS

111. U.S. Inflation Rates The following graph shows the annual inflation rate in the United States from 1975 to 2003.

  (a) Estimate the inflation rates in 1980, 1991, and 1999 to the nearest percent.

(b) For which years in this period did the inflation rate exceed 6%?

(c) Did the inflation rate generally increase or decrease in the years from 1980 to 1985? What about from 1987 to 1992?

(d) Estimate the highest and lowest inflation rates in this time period to the nearest percent.

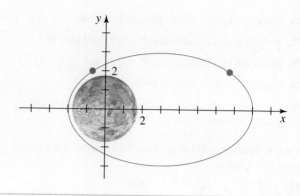

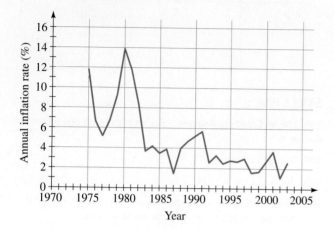

Year

112. Orbit of a Satellite A satellite is in orbit around the moon. A coordinate plane containing the orbit is set up with the center of the moon at the origin, as shown in the following graph, with distances measured in megameters (Mm). The equation of the satellite's orbit is

$$\frac{(x-3)^2}{25} + \frac{y^2}{16} = 1$$

(a) From the graph, determine the closest to and the farthest from the center of the moon that the satellite gets.

(b) There are two points in the orbit with y-coordinates 2. Find the x-coordinates of these points, and determine their distances to the center of the moon.

DISCUSS ■ **DISCOVER** ■ **PROVE** ■ **WRITE**

113. DISCOVER: Circle, Point, or Empty Set? Complete the squares in the general equation $x^2 + ax + y^2 + by + c = 0$, and simplify the result as much as possible. Under what conditions on the coefficients a, b, and c does this equation represent a circle? A single point? The empty set? In the case in which the equation does represent a circle, find its center and radius.

114. DISCOVER ■ **WRITE: Do the Circles Intersect?**

(a) Find the radius of each circle in the pair and the distance between their centers; then use this information to determine whether the circles intersect.

(i) $(x-2)^2 + (y-1)^2 = 9$;
$(x-6)^2 + (y-4)^2 = 16$

(ii) $x^2 + (y-2)^2 = 4$;
$(x-5)^2 + (y-14)^2 = 9$

(iii) $(x-3)^2 + (y+1)^2 = 1$;
$(x-2)^2 + (y-2)^2 = 25$

(b) How can you tell, just by knowing the radii of two circles and the distance between their centers, whether the circles intersect? Write a short paragraph describing how you would decide this, and draw graphs to illustrate your answer.

1.3 LINES

■ **The Slope of a Line** ■ **Point-Slope Form of the Equation of a Line** ■ **Slope-Intercept Form of the Equation of a Line** ■ **Vertical and Horizontal Lines** ■ **General Equation of a Line** ■ **Parallel and Perpendicular Lines**

In this section we find equations for straight lines lying in a coordinate plane. The equations will depend on how the line is inclined, so we begin by discussing the concept of slope.

■ The Slope of a Line

We first need a way to measure the "steepness" of a line, or how quickly it rises (or falls) as we move from left to right. We define *run* to be the distance we move to the right and *rise* to be the corresponding distance that the line rises (or falls). The *slope* of a line is the ratio of rise to run:

$$\text{slope} = \frac{\text{rise}}{\text{run}}$$

Figure 1 shows situations in which slope is important. Carpenters use the term *pitch* for the slope of a roof or a staircase; the term *grade* is used for the slope of a road.

Slope of a ramp
Slope $= \frac{1}{12}$

Pitch of a roof
Slope $= \frac{1}{3}$

Grade of a road
Slope $= \frac{8}{100}$

FIGURE 1

If a line lies in a coordinate plane, then the **run** is the change in the *x*-coordinate and the **rise** is the corresponding change in the *y*-coordinate between any two points on the line (see Figure 2). This gives us the following definition of slope.

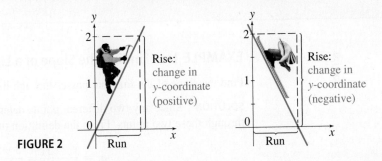

Rise:
change in
y-coordinate
(positive)

Rise:
change in
y-coordinate
(negative)

FIGURE 2 Run

Run

SLOPE OF A LINE

The **slope** m of a nonvertical line that passes through the points $A(x_1, y_1)$ and $B(x_2, y_2)$ is

$$m = \frac{\text{rise}}{\text{run}} = \frac{y_2 - y_1}{x_2 - x_1}$$

The slope of a vertical line is not defined.

The slope is independent of which two points are chosen on the line. We can see that this is true from the similar triangles in Figure 3.

$$\frac{y_2 - y_1}{x_2 - x_1} = \frac{y_2' - y_1'}{x_2' - x_1'}$$

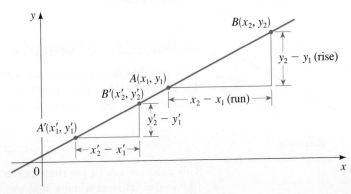

$B(x_2, y_2)$

$y_2 - y_1$ (rise)

$A(x_1, y_1)$

$B'(x_2', y_2')$

$x_2 - x_1$ (run)

$y_2' - y_1'$

$A'(x_1', y_1')$

$x_2' - x_1'$

FIGURE 3

The figures in the box below show several lines labeled with their slopes. Notice that lines with positive slope slant upward to the right, whereas lines with negative slope slant downward to the right. The steepest lines are those for which the absolute value of the slope is the largest; a horizontal line has slope 0. The slope of a vertical line is undefined (it has a 0 denominator), so we say that a vertical line has no slope.

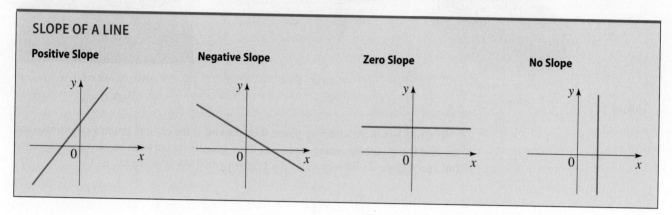

SLOPE OF A LINE

Positive Slope **Negative Slope** **Zero Slope** **No Slope**

EXAMPLE 1 ■ Finding the Slope of a Line Through Two Points

Find the slope of the line that passes through the points $P(2, 1)$ and $Q(8, 5)$.

SOLUTION Since any two different points determine a line, only one line passes through these two points. From the definition the slope is

$$m = \frac{y_2 - y_1}{x_2 - x_1} = \frac{5 - 1}{8 - 2} = \frac{4}{6} = \frac{2}{3}$$

This says that for every 3 units we move to the right, the line rises 2 units. The line is drawn in Figure 4.

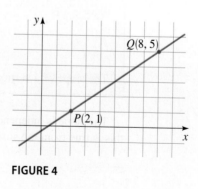

FIGURE 4

✎ Now Try Exercise 9

Point-Slope Form of the Equation of a Line

Now let's find the equation of the line that passes through a given point $P(x_1, y_1)$ and has slope m. A point $P(x, y)$ with $x \neq x_1$ lies on this line if and only if the slope of the line through P_1 and P is equal to m (see Figure 5), that is,

$$\frac{y - y_1}{x - x_1} = m$$

This equation can be rewritten in the form $y - y_1 = m(x - x_1)$; note that the equation is also satisfied when $x = x_1$ and $y = y_1$. Therefore it is an equation of the given line.

FIGURE 5

> ### POINT-SLOPE FORM OF THE EQUATION OF A LINE
>
> An equation of the line that passes through the point (x_1, y_1) and has slope m is
>
> $$y - y_1 = m(x - x_1)$$

EXAMPLE 2 ■ Finding an Equation of a Line with Given Point and Slope

(a) Find an equation of the line through $(1, -3)$ with slope $-\frac{1}{2}$.

(b) Sketch the line.

SOLUTION

(a) Using the point-slope form with $m = -\frac{1}{2}$, $x_1 = 1$, and $y_1 = -3$, we obtain an equation of the line as

$$y + 3 = -\tfrac{1}{2}(x - 1) \qquad \text{Slope } m = -\tfrac{1}{2}, \text{ point } (1, -3)$$

$$2y + 6 = -x + 1 \qquad \text{Multiply by 2}$$

$$x + 2y + 5 = 0 \qquad \text{Rearrange}$$

(b) The fact that the slope is $-\frac{1}{2}$ tells us that when we move to the right 2 units, the line drops 1 unit. This enables us to sketch the line in Figure 6.

✎ **Now Try Exercise 25** ■

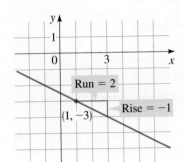

FIGURE 6

EXAMPLE 3 ■ Finding an Equation of a Line Through Two Given Points

Find an equation of the line through the points $(-1, 2)$ and $(3, -4)$.

SOLUTION The slope of the line is

$$m = \frac{-4 - 2}{3 - (-1)} = -\frac{6}{4} = -\frac{3}{2}$$

We can use *either* point, $(-1, 2)$ *or* $(3, -4)$, in the point-slope equation. We will end up with the same final answer.

Using the point-slope form with $x_1 = -1$ and $y_1 = 2$, we obtain

$$y - 2 = -\tfrac{3}{2}(x + 1) \qquad \text{Slope } m = -\tfrac{3}{2}, \text{ point } (-1, 2)$$

$$2y - 4 = -3x - 3 \qquad \text{Multiply by 2}$$

$$3x + 2y - 1 = 0 \qquad \text{Rearrange}$$

✎ **Now Try Exercise 29** ■

■ Slope-Intercept Form of the Equation of a Line

Suppose a nonvertical line has slope m and y-intercept b (see Figure 7). This means that the line intersects the y-axis at the point $(0, b)$, so the point-slope form of the equation of the line, with $x = 0$ and $y = b$, becomes

$$y - b = m(x - 0)$$

This simplifies to $y = mx + b$, which is called the **slope-intercept form** of the equation of a line.

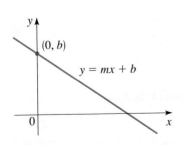

FIGURE 7

> ### SLOPE-INTERCEPT FORM OF THE EQUATION OF A LINE
>
> An equation of the line that has slope m and y-intercept b is
>
> $$y = mx + b$$

EXAMPLE 4 ■ Lines in Slope-Intercept Form

(a) Find an equation of the line with slope 3 and y-intercept -2.

(b) Find the slope and y-intercept of the line $3y - 2x = 1$.

SOLUTION

(a) Since $m = 3$ and $b = -2$, from the slope-intercept form of the equation of a line we get

$$y = 3x - 2$$

(b) We first write the equation in the form $y = mx + b$.

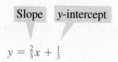

$$3y - 2x = 1 \qquad \text{Given equation}$$
$$3y = 2x + 1 \qquad \text{Add } 2x$$
$$y = \tfrac{2}{3}x + \tfrac{1}{3} \qquad \text{Divide by 3}$$

Slope y-intercept

$$y = \tfrac{2}{3}x + \tfrac{1}{3}$$

From the slope-intercept form of the equation of a line, we see that the slope is $m = \tfrac{2}{3}$ and the y-intercept is $b = \tfrac{1}{3}$.

Now Try Exercises 23 and 61 ∎

■ Vertical and Horizontal Lines

If a line is horizontal, its slope is $m = 0$, so its equation is $y = b$, where b is the y-intercept (see Figure 8). A vertical line does not have a slope, but we can write its equation as $x = a$, where a is the x-intercept, because the x-coordinate of every point on the line is a.

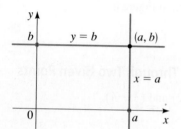

FIGURE 8

> **VERTICAL AND HORIZONTAL LINES**
>
> ■ An equation of the vertical line through (a, b) is $x = a$.
> ■ An equation of the horizontal line through (a, b) is $y = b$.

EXAMPLE 5 ■ Vertical and Horizontal Lines

(a) An equation for the vertical line through $(3, 5)$ is $x = 3$.

(b) The graph of the equation $x = 3$ is a vertical line with x-intercept 3.

(c) An equation for the horizontal line through $(8, -2)$ is $y = -2$.

(d) The graph of the equation $y = -2$ is a horizontal line with y-intercept -2.

The lines are graphed in Figure 9.

Now Try Exercises 35, 37, 63, and 65 ∎

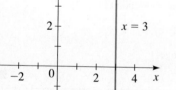
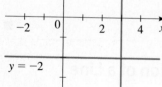

FIGURE 9

■ General Equation of a Line

A **linear equation** in the variables x and y is an equation of the form

$$Ax + By + C = 0$$

where A, B, and C are constants and A and B are not both 0. An equation of a line is a linear equation:

■ A nonvertical line has the equation $y = mx + b$ or $-mx + y - b = 0$, which is a linear equation with $A = -m$, $B = 1$, and $C = -b$.

■ A vertical line has the equation $x = a$ or $x - a = 0$, which is a linear equation with $A = 1$, $B = 0$, and $C = -a$.

Conversely, the graph of a linear equation is a line.

▪ If $B \neq 0$, the equation becomes

$$y = -\frac{A}{B}x - \frac{C}{B} \qquad \text{Divide by } B$$

and this is the slope-intercept form of the equation of a line (with $m = -A/B$ and $b = -C/B$).

▪ If $B = 0$, the equation becomes

$$Ax + C = 0 \qquad \text{Set } B = 0$$

or $x = -C/A$, which represents a vertical line.

We have proved the following.

GENERAL EQUATION OF A LINE

The graph of every **linear equation**

$$Ax + By + C = 0 \qquad (A, B \text{ not both zero})$$

is a line. Conversely, every line is the graph of a linear equation.

EXAMPLE 6 ■ Graphing a Linear Equation

Sketch the graph of the equation $2x - 3y - 12 = 0$.

SOLUTION 1 Since the equation is linear, its graph is a line. To draw the graph, it is enough to find any two points on the line. The intercepts are the easiest points to find.

x-intercept: Substitute $y = 0$, to get $2x - 12 = 0$, so $x = 6$

y-intercept: Substitute $x = 0$, to get $-3y - 12 = 0$, so $y = -4$

With these points we can sketch the graph in Figure 10.

SOLUTION 2 We write the equation in slope-intercept form.

$$2x - 3y - 12 = 0 \qquad \text{Given equation}$$

$$2x - 3y = 12 \qquad \text{Add 12}$$

$$-3y = -2x + 12 \qquad \text{Subtract } 2x$$

$$y = \tfrac{2}{3}x - 4 \qquad \text{Divide by } -3$$

This equation is in the form $y = mx + b$, so the slope is $m = \frac{2}{3}$ and the y-intercept is $b = -4$. To sketch the graph, we plot the y-intercept and then move 3 units to the right and 2 units up as shown in Figure 11.

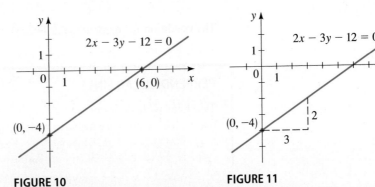

FIGURE 10   FIGURE 11

Now Try Exercise 67

■ Parallel and Perpendicular Lines

Since slope measures the steepness of a line, it seems reasonable that parallel lines should have the same slope. In fact, we can prove this.

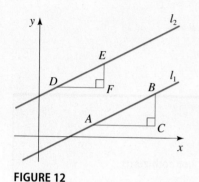

FIGURE 12

> ### PARALLEL LINES
>
> Two nonvertical lines are parallel if and only if they have the same slope.

Proof Let the lines l_1 and l_2 in Figure 12 have slopes m_1 and m_2. If the lines are parallel, then the right triangles ABC and DEF are similar, so

$$m_1 = \frac{d(B, C)}{d(A, C)} = \frac{d(E, F)}{d(D, F)} = m_2$$

Conversely, if the slopes are equal, then the triangles will be similar, so $\angle BAC = \angle EDF$ and the lines are parallel. ■

EXAMPLE 7 ■ Finding an Equation of a Line Parallel to a Given Line

Find an equation of the line through the point $(5, 2)$ that is parallel to the line $4x + 6y + 5 = 0$.

SOLUTION First we write the equation of the given line in slope-intercept form.

$$4x + 6y + 5 = 0 \qquad \text{Given equation}$$
$$6y = -4x - 5 \qquad \text{Subtract } 4x + 5$$
$$y = -\tfrac{2}{3}x - \tfrac{5}{6} \qquad \text{Divide by 6}$$

So the line has slope $m = -\tfrac{2}{3}$. Since the required line is parallel to the given line, it also has slope $m = -\tfrac{2}{3}$. From the point-slope form of the equation of a line we get

$$y - 2 = -\tfrac{2}{3}(x - 5) \qquad \text{Slope } m = -\tfrac{2}{3}, \text{ point } (5, 2)$$
$$3y - 6 = -2x + 10 \qquad \text{Multiply by 3}$$
$$2x + 3y - 16 = 0 \qquad \text{Rearrange}$$

Thus an equation of the required line is $2x + 3y - 16 = 0$.

✎ **Now Try Exercise 43** ■

The condition for perpendicular lines is not as obvious as that for parallel lines.

> ### PERPENDICULAR LINES
>
> Two lines with slopes m_1 and m_2 are perpendicular if and only if $m_1 m_2 = -1$, that is, their slopes are negative reciprocals:
>
> $$m_2 = -\frac{1}{m_1}$$
>
> Also, a horizontal line (slope 0) is perpendicular to a vertical line (no slope).

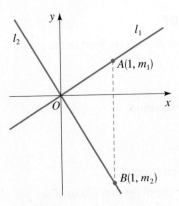

FIGURE 13

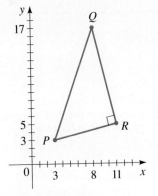

FIGURE 14

Proof   In Figure 13 we show two lines intersecting at the origin. (If the lines intersect at some other point, we consider lines parallel to these that intersect at the origin. These lines have the same slopes as the original lines.)

If the lines l_1 and l_2 have slopes m_1 and m_2, then their equations are $y = m_1 x$ and $y = m_2 x$. Notice that $A(1, m_1)$ lies on l_1 and $B(1, m_2)$ lies on l_2. By the Pythagorean Theorem and its converse (see page 277) $OA \perp OB$ if and only if

$$[d(O, A)]^2 + [d(O, B)]^2 = [d(A, B)]^2$$

By the Distance Formula this becomes

$$(1^2 + m_1^2) + (1^2 + m_2^2) = (1 - 1)^2 + (m_2 - m_1)^2$$
$$2 + m_1^2 + m_2^2 = m_2^2 - 2m_1 m_2 + m_1^2$$
$$2 = -2m_1 m_2$$
$$m_1 m_2 = -1$$
■

EXAMPLE 8 ▪ Perpendicular Lines

Show that the points $P(3, 3)$, $Q(8, 17)$, and $R(11, 5)$ are the vertices of a right triangle.

SOLUTION   The slopes of the lines containing PR and QR are, respectively,

$$m_1 = \frac{5 - 3}{11 - 3} = \frac{1}{4} \qquad \text{and} \qquad m_2 = \frac{5 - 17}{11 - 8} = -4$$

Since $m_1 m_2 = -1$, these lines are perpendicular, so PQR is a right triangle. It is sketched in Figure 14.

✎ **Now Try Exercise 81**
■

EXAMPLE 9 ▪ Finding an Equation of a Line Perpendicular to a Given Line

Find an equation of the line that is perpendicular to the line $4x + 6y + 5 = 0$ and passes through the origin.

SOLUTION   In Example 7 we found that the slope of the line $4x + 6y + 5 = 0$ is $-\frac{2}{3}$. Thus the slope of a perpendicular line is the negative reciprocal, that is, $\frac{3}{2}$. Since the required line passes through $(0, 0)$, the point-slope form gives

$$y - 0 = \tfrac{3}{2}(x - 0) \qquad \text{Slope } m = \tfrac{3}{2}, \text{ point } (0, 0)$$
$$y = \tfrac{3}{2}x \qquad \text{Simplify}$$

✎ **Now Try Exercise 47**
■

EXAMPLE 10 ▪ Graphing a Family of Lines

Use a graphing calculator to graph the family of lines

$$y = 0.5x + b$$

for $b = -2, -1, 0, 1, 2$. What property do the lines share?

SOLUTION   We use a graphing calculator to graph the lines in the viewing rectangle $[-6, 6]$ by $[-6, 6]$. The graphs are shown in Figure 15. The lines all have the same slope, so they are parallel.

✎ **Now Try Exercise 53**
■

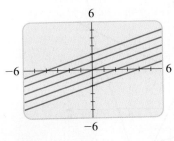

FIGURE 15 $y = 0.5x + b$

EXAMPLE 11 ■ Application: Interpreting Slope

A swimming pool is being filled with a hose. The water depth y (in feet) in the pool t hours after the hose is turned on is given by

$$y = 1.5t + 2$$

(a) Find the slope and y-intercept of the graph of this equation.

(b) What do the slope and y-intercept represent?

SOLUTION

(a) This is the equation of a line with slope 1.5 and y-intercept 2.

(b) The slope represents an increase of 1.5 ft. in water depth for every hour. The y-intercept indicates that the water depth was 2 ft. at the time the hose was turned on.

✎ **Now Try Exercise 87**

1.3 EXERCISES

CONCEPTS

1. We find the "steepness," or slope, of a line passing through two points by dividing the difference in the _____-coordinates of these points by the difference in the _____-coordinates. So the line passing through the points $(0, 1)$ and $(2, 5)$ has slope

_____.

2. A line has the equation $y = 3x + 2$.

  (a) This line has slope _____.

  (b) Any line parallel to this line has slope _____.

  (c) Any line perpendicular to this line has slope

    _____.

3. The point-slope form of the equation of the line with slope 3 passing through the point $(1, 2)$ is _____.

4. For the linear equation $2x + 3y - 12 = 0$, the x-intercept is _____ and the y-intercept is _____. The equation in slope-intercept form is $y = $ _____. The slope of the graph of this equation is _____.

5. The slope of a horizontal line is _____. The equation of the horizontal line passing through $(2, 3)$ is _____.

6. The slope of a vertical line is _____. The equation of the vertical line passing through $(2, 3)$ is _____.

7. *Yes or No*? If *No*, give a reason.

  (a) Is the graph of $y = -3$ a horizontal line?

  (b) Is the graph of $x = -3$ a vertical line?

  (c) Does a line perpendicular to a horizontal line have slope 0?

  (d) Does a line perpendicular to a vertical line have slope 0?

8. Sketch a graph of the lines $y = -3$ and $x = -3$. Are the lines perpendicular?

SKILLS

9–16 ■ Slope Find the slope of the line through P and Q.

9. $P(-1, 2)$, $Q(0, 0)$

10. $P(0, 0)$, $Q(3, -1)$

11. $P(2, -2)$, $Q(7, -1)$

12. $P(-5, 1)$, $Q(3, -2)$

13. $P(5, 4)$, $Q(0, 4)$

14. $P(4, 3)$, $Q(1, -1)$

15. $P(10, -2)$, $Q(6, -5)$

16. $P(3, -2)$, $Q(6, -2)$

17. Slope Find the slopes of the lines l_1, l_2, l_3, and l_4 in the figure below.

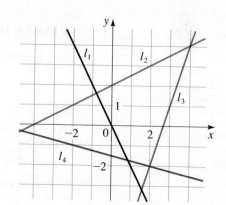

18. Slope

(a) Sketch lines through $(0,0)$ with slopes $1, 0, \frac{1}{2}, 2$, and -1.

(b) Sketch lines through $(0,0)$ with slopes $\frac{1}{3}, \frac{1}{2}, -\frac{1}{3}$, and 3.

19–22 ■ **Equations of Lines** Find an equation for the line whose graph is sketched.

19.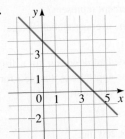

20.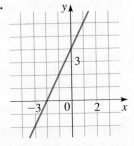

21.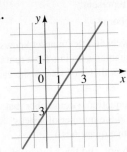

22.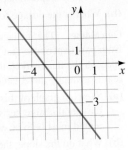

23–50 ■ **Finding Equations of Lines** Find an equation of the line that satisfies the given conditions.

23. Slope 3; y-intercept -2

24. Slope $\frac{2}{5}$; y-intercept 4

25. Through $(2,3)$; slope 5

26. Through $(-2,4)$; slope -1

27. Through $(1,7)$; slope $\frac{2}{3}$

28. Through $(-3,-5)$; slope $-\frac{7}{2}$

29. Through $(2,1)$ and $(1,6)$

30. Through $(-1,-2)$ and $(4,3)$

31. Through $(-2,5)$ and $(-1,-3)$

32. Through $(1,7)$ and $(4,7)$

33. x-intercept 1; y-intercept -3

34. x-intercept -8; y-intercept 6

35. Through $(1,3)$; slope 0

36. Through $(-1,4)$; slope undefined

37. Through $(2,-1)$; slope undefined

38. Through $(5,1)$; slope 0

39. Through $(1,2)$; parallel to the line $y = 3x - 5$

40. Through $(-3,2)$; perpendicular to the line $y = -\frac{1}{2}x + 7$

41. Through $(4,5)$; parallel to the x-axis

42. Through $(4,5)$; parallel to the y-axis

43. Through $(1,-6)$; parallel to the line $x + 2y = 6$

44. y-intercept 6; parallel to the line $2x + 3y + 4 = 0$

45. Through $(-1,2)$; parallel to the line $x = 5$

46. Through $(2,6)$; perpendicular to the line $y = 1$

47. Through $(-1,-2)$; perpendicular to the line $2x + 5y + 8 = 0$

48. Through $\left(\frac{1}{2}, -\frac{2}{3}\right)$; perpendicular to the line $4x - 8y = 1$

49. Through $(1,7)$; parallel to the line passing through $(2,5)$ and $(-2,1)$

50. Through $(-2,-11)$; perpendicular to the line passing through $(1,1)$ and $(5,-1)$

51. Finding Equations of Lines and Graphing

(a) Sketch the line with slope $\frac{3}{2}$ that passes through the point $(-2,1)$.

(b) Find an equation for this line.

52. Finding Equations of Lines and Graphing

(a) Sketch the line with slope -2 that passes through the point $(4,-1)$.

(b) Find an equation for this line.

53–56 ■ **Families of Lines** Use a graphing device to graph the given family of lines in the same viewing rectangle. What do the lines have in common?

53. $y = -2x + b$ for $b = 0, \pm 1, \pm 3, \pm 6$

54. $y = mx - 3$ for $m = 0, \pm 0.25, \pm 0.75, \pm 1.5$

55. $y = m(x - 3)$ for $m = 0, \pm 0.25, \pm 0.75, \pm 1.5$

56. $y = 2 + m(x + 3)$ for $m = 0, \pm 0.5, \pm 1, \pm 2, \pm 6$

57–66 ■ **Using Slopes and y-Intercepts to Graph Lines** Find the slope and y-intercept of the line, and draw its graph.

57. $y = 3 - x$

58. $y = \frac{2}{3}x - 2$

59. $-2x + y = 7$

60. $2x - 5y = 0$

61. $4x + 5y = 10$

62. $3x - 4y = 12$

63. $y = 4$

64. $x = -5$

65. $x = 3$

66. $y = -2$

67–72 ■ **Using x- and y-Intercepts to Graph Lines** Find the x- and y-intercepts of the line, and draw its graph.

67. $5x + 2y - 10 = 0$

68. $6x - 7y - 42 = 0$

69. $\frac{1}{2}x - \frac{1}{3}y + 1 = 0$

70. $\frac{1}{3}x - \frac{1}{5}y - 2 = 0$

71. $y = 6x + 4$

72. $y = -4x - 10$

73–78 ■ **Parallel and Perpendicular Lines** The equations of two lines are given. Determine whether the lines are parallel, perpendicular, or neither.

73. $y = 2x + 3$; $2y - 4x - 5 = 0$

74. $y = \frac{1}{2}x + 4$; $2x + 4y = 1$

75. $-3x + 4y = 4$; $4x + 3y = 5$

76. $2x - 3y = 10$; $3y - 2x - 7 = 0$

77. $7x - 3y = 2$; $9y + 21x = 1$

78. $6y - 2x = 5$; $2y + 6x = 1$

SKILLS Plus

79–82 ▪ **Using Slopes**   Verify the given geometric property.

79. Use slopes to show that $A(1, 1)$, $B(7, 4)$, $C(5, 10)$, and $D(-1, 7)$ are vertices of a parallelogram.

80. Use slopes to show that $A(-3, -1)$, $B(3, 3)$, and $C(-9, 8)$ are vertices of a right triangle.

81. Use slopes to show that $A(1, 1)$, $B(11, 3)$, $C(10, 8)$, and $D(0, 6)$ are vertices of a rectangle.

82. Use slopes to determine whether the given points are collinear (lie on a line).
  (a) $(1, 1), (3, 9), (6, 21)$ **(b)** $(-1, 3), (1, 7), (4, 15)$

83. Perpendicular Bisector   Find an equation of the perpendicular bisector of the line segment joining the points $A(1, 4)$ and $B(7, -2)$.

84. Area of a Triangle   Find the area of the triangle formed by the coordinate axes and the line

$$2y + 3x - 6 = 0$$

85. Two-Intercept Form

  (a) Show that if the x- and y-intercepts of a line are nonzero numbers a and b, then the equation of the line can be written in the form

$$\frac{x}{a} + \frac{y}{b} = 1$$

  This is called the **two-intercept form** of the equation of a line.

  (b) Use part (a) to find an equation of the line whose x-intercept is 6 and whose y-intercept is -8.

86. Tangent Line to a Circle

  (a) Find an equation for the line tangent to the circle $x^2 + y^2 = 25$ at the point $(3, -4)$. (See the figure.)

  (b) At what other point on the circle will a tangent line be parallel to the tangent line in part (a)?

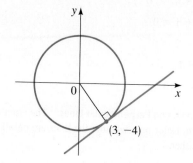

APPLICATIONS

87. Global Warming   Some scientists believe that the average surface temperature of the world has been rising steadily. The average surface temperature can be modeled by

$$T = 0.02t + 15.0$$

where T is temperature in °C and t is years since 1950.

  (a) What do the slope and T-intercept represent?

  (b) Use the equation to predict the average global surface temperature in 2050.

88. Drug Dosages   If the recommended adult dosage for a drug is D (in mg), then to determine the appropriate dosage c for a child of age a, pharmacists use the equation

$$c = 0.0417D(a + 1)$$

Suppose the dosage for an adult is 200 mg.

  (a) Find the slope. What does it represent?

  (b) What is the dosage for a newborn?

89. Flea Market   The manager of a weekend flea market knows from past experience that if she charges x dollars for a rental space at the flea market, then the number y of spaces she can rent is given by the equation $y = 200 - 4x$.

  (a) Sketch a graph of this linear equation. (Remember that the rental charge per space and the number of spaces rented must both be nonnegative quantities.)

  (b) What do the slope, the y-intercept, and the x-intercept of the graph represent?

90. Production Cost   A small-appliance manufacturer finds that if he produces x toaster ovens in a month, his production cost is given by the equation

$$y = 6x + 3000$$

(where y is measured in dollars).

  (a) Sketch a graph of this linear equation.

  (b) What do the slope and y-intercept of the graph represent?

91. Temperature Scales   The relationship between the Fahrenheit (F) and Celsius (C) temperature scales is given by the equation $F = \frac{9}{5}C + 32$.

  (a) Complete the table to compare the two scales at the given values.

  (b) Find the temperature at which the scales agree. [*Hint:* Suppose that a is the temperature at which the scales agree. Set $F = a$ and $C = a$. Then solve for a.]

C	F
$-30°$	
$-20°$	
$-10°$	
$0°$	
	$50°$
	$68°$
	$86°$

92. Crickets and Temperature Biologists have observed that the chirping rate of crickets of a certain species is related to temperature, and the relationship appears to be very nearly linear. A cricket produces 120 chirps per minute at 70°F and 168 chirps per minute at 80°F.

(a) Find the linear equation that relates the temperature t and the number of chirps per minute n.

(b) If the crickets are chirping at 150 chirps per minute, estimate the temperature.

93. Depreciation A small business buys a computer for $4000. After 4 years the value of the computer is expected to be $200. For accounting purposes the business uses *linear depreciation* to assess the value of the computer at a given time. This means that if V is the value of the computer at time t, then a linear equation is used to relate V and t.

(a) Find a linear equation that relates V and t.

(b) Sketch a graph of this linear equation.

(c) What do the slope and V-intercept of the graph represent?

(d) Find the depreciated value of the computer 3 years from the date of purchase.

94. Pressure and Depth At the surface of the ocean the water pressure is the same as the air pressure above the water, 15 lb/in². Below the surface the water pressure increases by 4.34 lb/in² for every 10 ft of descent.

(a) Find an equation for the relationship between pressure and depth below the ocean surface.

(b) Sketch a graph of this linear equation.

(c) What do the slope and y-intercept of the graph represent?

(d) At what depth is the pressure 100 lb/in²?

DISCUSS ■ **DISCOVER** ■ **PROVE** ■ **WRITE**

95. DISCUSS: What Does the Slope Mean? Suppose that the graph of the outdoor temperature over a certain period of time is a line. How is the weather changing if the slope of the line is positive? If it is negative? If it is zero?

96. DISCUSS: Collinear Points Suppose that you are given the coordinates of three points in the plane and you want to see whether they lie on the same line. How can you do this using slopes? Using the Distance Formula? Can you think of another method?

1.4 SOLVING QUADRATIC EQUATIONS

■ **Solving Quadratic Equations by Factoring** ■ **Solving Quadratic Equations by Completing the Square** ■ **The Quadratic Formula** ■ **The Discriminant** ■ **Modeling with Quadratic Equations**

Linear Equations

$$4x = -7$$
$$6x - 8 = 21$$
$$2 + 3x = \tfrac{1}{2} - \tfrac{3}{4}x$$

In Section P.8 we learned how to solve linear equations, which are first-degree equations such as $2x + 1 = 5$ or $4 - 3x = 2$. In this section we learn how to solve quadratic equations, which are second-degree equations such as $x^2 + 2x - 3 = 0$ or $2x^2 + 3 = 5x$. We will also see that many real-life problems can be modeled by using quadratic equations.

Quadratic Equations

$$x^2 - 2x - 8 = 0$$
$$3x + 10 = 4x^2$$
$$\tfrac{1}{2}x^2 + \tfrac{1}{3}x - \tfrac{1}{6} = 0$$

QUADRATIC EQUATIONS

A **quadratic equation** is an equation of the form

$$ax^2 + bx + c = 0$$

where a, b, and c are real numbers with $a \neq 0$.

■ Solving Quadratic Equations by Factoring

Some quadratic equations can be solved by factoring and using the following basic property of real numbers.

> ## ZERO-PRODUCT PROPERTY
>
> $$AB = 0 \qquad \text{if and only if} \qquad A = 0 \quad \text{or} \quad B = 0$$

 This means that if we can factor the left-hand side of a quadratic (or other) equation, then we can solve it by setting each factor equal to 0 in turn. This method works only when the right-hand side of the equation is 0.

EXAMPLE 1 ■ Solving a Quadratic Equation by Factoring

Find all real solutions of the equation $x^2 + 5x = 24$.

$x = 3$:

$(3)^2 + 5(3) = 9 + 15 = 24$ ✓

$x = -8$:

$(-8)^2 + 5(-8) = 64 - 40 = 24$ ✓

SOLUTION We must first rewrite the equation so that the right-hand side is 0.

$x^2 + 5x = 24$	Given equation
$x^2 + 5x - 24 = 0$	Subtract 24
$(x - 3)(x + 8) = 0$	Factor
$x - 3 = 0 \quad \text{or} \quad x + 8 = 0$	Zero-Product Property
$x = 3 \qquad\qquad x = -8$	Solve

The solutions are $x = 3$ and $x = -8$.

Now Try Exercise 7 ∎

Do you see why one side of the equation must be 0 in Example 1? Factoring the equation as $x(x + 5) = 24$ does not help us find the solutions, since 24 can be factored in infinitely many ways, such as $6 \cdot 4, \frac{1}{2} \cdot 48, \left(-\frac{2}{5}\right) \cdot (-60)$, and so on.

■ Solving Quadratic Equations by Completing the Square

Completing the Square

The area of the blue region is

$$x^2 + 2\left(\frac{b}{2}\right)x = x^2 + bx$$

Add a small square of area $(b/2)^2$ to "complete" the square.

As we saw in Section P.8, Example 5(b), if a quadratic equation is of the form $(x \pm a)^2 = c$, then we can solve it by taking the square root of each side. In an equation of this form, the left-hand side is a *perfect square*: the square of a linear expression in x. So if a quadratic equation does not factor readily, then we can solve it by **completing the square**.

> ## COMPLETING THE SQUARE
>
> To make $x^2 + bx$ a perfect square, add $\left(\dfrac{b}{2}\right)^2$, the square of half the coefficient of x. This gives the perfect square
>
> $$x^2 + bx + \left(\frac{b}{2}\right)^2 = \left(x + \frac{b}{2}\right)^2$$

To complete the square, we add a constant to a quadratic expression to make it a perfect square. For example, to make

$$x^2 + 6x$$

a perfect square, we must add $\left(\frac{6}{2}\right)^2 = 9$. Then

$$x^2 + 6x + 9 = (x + 3)^2$$

is a perfect square. The table gives some more examples of completing the square.

Expression	Add	Complete the square
$x^2 + 8x$	$\left(\dfrac{8}{2}\right)^2 = 16$	$x^2 + 8x + 16 = (x + 4)^2$
$x^2 - 12x$	$\left(-\dfrac{12}{2}\right)^2 = 36$	$x^2 - 12x + 36 = (x - 6)^2$
$x^2 + 3x$	$\left(\dfrac{3}{2}\right)^2 = \dfrac{9}{4}$	$x^2 + 3x + \dfrac{9}{4} = \left(x + \dfrac{3}{2}\right)^2$
$x^2 - \sqrt{3}x$	$\left(-\dfrac{\sqrt{3}}{2}\right)^2 = \dfrac{3}{4}$	$x^2 - \sqrt{3}x + \dfrac{3}{4} = \left(x - \dfrac{\sqrt{3}}{2}\right)^2$

See page 40 for how to recognize when a quadratic expression is a perfect square.

EXAMPLE 2 ■ Solving Quadratic Equations by Completing the Square

Find all real solutions of each equation.

(a) $x^2 - 8x + 13 = 0$

(b) $3x^2 - 12x + 6 = 0$

SOLUTION

(a)
$$x^2 - 8x + 13 = 0 \qquad \text{Given equation}$$
$$x^2 - 8x = -13 \qquad \text{Subtract 13}$$
$$x^2 - 8x + 16 = -13 + 16 \qquad \text{Complete the square: add } \left(\dfrac{-8}{2}\right)^2 = 16$$
$$(x - 4)^2 = 3 \qquad \text{Perfect square}$$
$$x - 4 = \pm\sqrt{3} \qquad \text{Take square root}$$
$$x = 4 \pm \sqrt{3} \qquad \text{Add 4}$$

⊘ When completing the square, make sure the coefficient of x^2 is 1. If it isn't, you must factor this coefficient from both terms that contain x:

$$ax^2 + bx = a\left(x^2 + \dfrac{b}{a}x\right)$$

Then complete the square inside the parentheses. Remember that the term added inside the parentheses is multiplied by a.

(b) After subtracting 6 from each side of the equation, we must factor the coefficient of x^2 (the 3) from the left side to put the equation in the correct form for completing the square.

$$3x^2 - 12x + 6 = 0 \qquad \text{Given equation}$$
$$3x^2 - 12x = -6 \qquad \text{Subtract 6}$$
$$3(x^2 - 4x) = -6 \qquad \text{Factor 3 from LHS}$$

Now we complete the square by adding $(-2)^2 = 4$ *inside* the parentheses. Since everything inside the parentheses is multiplied by 3, this means that we are actually adding $3 \cdot 4 = 12$ to the left side of the equation. Thus we must add 12 to the right side as well.

$$3(x^2 - 4x + 4) = -6 + 3\cdot 4 \qquad \text{Complete the square: add 4}$$
$$3(x - 2)^2 = 6 \qquad \text{Perfect square}$$
$$(x - 2)^2 = 2 \qquad \text{Divide by 3}$$
$$x - 2 = \pm\sqrt{2} \qquad \text{Take square root}$$
$$x = 2 \pm \sqrt{2} \qquad \text{Add 2}$$

✎ Now Try Exercises 17 and 25   ■

■ The Quadratic Formula

We can use the technique of completing the square to derive a formula for the roots of the general quadratic equation $ax^2 + bx + c = 0$.

THE QUADRATIC FORMULA

The roots of the quadratic equation $ax^2 + bx + c = 0$, where $a \neq 0$, are

$$x = \frac{-b \pm \sqrt{b^2 - 4ac}}{2a}$$

Proof   First, we divide each side of the equation by a and move the constant to the right side, giving

$$x^2 + \frac{b}{a}x = -\frac{c}{a} \qquad \text{Divide by } a$$

We now complete the square by adding $(b/2a)^2$ to each side of the equation.

$$x^2 + \frac{b}{a}x + \left(\frac{b}{2a}\right)^2 = -\frac{c}{a} + \left(\frac{b}{2a}\right)^2 \qquad \text{Complete the square: Add } \left(\frac{b}{2a}\right)^2$$

$$\left(x + \frac{b}{2a}\right)^2 = \frac{-4ac + b^2}{4a^2} \qquad \text{Perfect square}$$

$$x + \frac{b}{2a} = \pm\frac{\sqrt{b^2 - 4ac}}{2a} \qquad \text{Take square root}$$

$$x = \frac{-b \pm \sqrt{b^2 - 4ac}}{2a} \qquad \text{Subtract } \frac{b}{2a} \qquad ■$$

The Quadratic Formula could be used to solve the equations in Examples 1 and 2. You should carry out the details of these calculations.

EXAMPLE 3 ■ Using the Quadratic Formula

Find all real solutions of each equation.

(a) $3x^2 - 5x - 1 = 0$ **(b)** $4x^2 + 12x + 9 = 0$ **(c)** $x^2 + 2x + 2 = 0$

SOLUTION

(a) In this quadratic equation $a = 3$, $b = -5$, and $c = -1$:

$$b = -5$$
$$3x^2 - 5x - 1 = 0$$
$$a = 3 \qquad c = -1$$

By the Quadratic Formula,

$$x = \frac{-(-5) \pm \sqrt{(-5)^2 - 4(3)(-1)}}{2(3)} = \frac{5 \pm \sqrt{37}}{6}$$

If approximations are desired, we can use a calculator to obtain

$$x = \frac{5 + \sqrt{37}}{6} \approx 1.8471 \qquad \text{and} \qquad x = \frac{5 - \sqrt{37}}{6} \approx -0.1805$$

Another Method

$$4x^2 + 12x + 9 = 0$$
$$(2x + 3)^2 = 0$$
$$2x + 3 = 0$$
$$x = -\tfrac{3}{2}$$

(b) Using the Quadratic Formula with $a = 4$, $b = 12$, and $c = 9$ gives

$$x = \frac{-12 \pm \sqrt{(12)^2 - 4 \cdot 4 \cdot 9}}{2 \cdot 4} = \frac{-12 \pm 0}{8} = -\frac{3}{2}$$

This equation has only one solution, $x = -\tfrac{3}{2}$.

(c) Using the Quadratic Formula with $a = 1$, $b = 2$, and $c = 2$ gives

$$x = \frac{-2 \pm \sqrt{2^2 - 4 \cdot 2}}{2} = \frac{-2 \pm \sqrt{-4}}{2} = \frac{-2 \pm 2\sqrt{-1}}{2} = -1 \pm \sqrt{-1}$$

Since the square of any real number is nonnegative, $\sqrt{-1}$ is undefined in the real number system. The equation has no real solution.

✎ **Now Try Exercises 35, 37, and 41** ■

In the next section we study the complex number system, in which the square roots of negative numbers do exist. The equation in Example 3(c) does have solutions in the complex number system.

■ The Discriminant

The quantity $b^2 - 4ac$ that appears under the square root sign in the Quadratic Formula is called the *discriminant* of the equation $ax^2 + bx + c = 0$ and is given the symbol D. If $D < 0$, then $\sqrt{b^2 - 4ac}$ is undefined, and the quadratic equation has no real solution, as in Example 3(c). If $D = 0$, then the equation has only one real solution, as in Example 3(b). Finally, if $D > 0$, then the equation has two distinct real solutions, as in Example 3(a). The following box summarizes these observations.

THE DISCRIMINANT

The **discriminant** of the quadratic equation $ax^2 + bx + c = 0$ $(a \neq 0)$ is $D = b^2 - 4ac$.

1. If $D > 0$, then the equation has two distinct real solutions.
2. If $D = 0$, then the equation has exactly one real solution.
3. If $D < 0$, then the equation has no real solution.

EXAMPLE 4 ■ Using the Discriminant

Use the discriminant to determine how many real solutions each equation has.

(a) $x^2 + 4x - 1 = 0$ **(b)** $4x^2 - 12x + 9 = 0$ **(c)** $\frac{1}{3}x^2 - 2x + 4 = 0$

SOLUTION

(a) The discriminant is $D = 4^2 - 4(1)(-1) = 20 > 0$, so the equation has two distinct real solutions.

(b) The discriminant is $D = (-12)^2 - 4 \cdot 4 \cdot 9 = 0$, so the equation has exactly one real solution.

(c) The discriminant is $D = (-2)^2 - 4(\frac{1}{3})4 = -\frac{4}{3} < 0$, so the equation has no real solution.

✎ **Now Try Exercises 57, 59, and 61** ■

■ Modeling with Quadratic Equations

Let's look at some real-life problems that can be modeled by quadratic equations. The principles discussed in Section P.9 for setting up equations as models are useful here as well.

FRANÇOIS VIÈTE (1540–1603) had a successful political career before taking up mathematics late in life. He became one of the most famous French mathematicians of the 16th century. Viète introduced a new level of abstraction in algebra by using letters to stand for *known* quantities in an equation. Before Viète's time, each equation had to be solved on its own. For instance, the quadratic equations

$$3x^2 + 2x + 8 = 0$$
$$5x^2 - 6x + 4 = 0$$

had to be solved separately by completing the square. Viète's idea was to consider all quadratic equations at once by writing

$$ax^2 + bx + c = 0$$

where a, b, and c are known quantities. Thus he made it possible to write a *formula* (in this case the quadratic formula) involving a, b, and c that can be used to solve all such equations in one fell swoop.

Viète's mathematical genius proved quite valuable during a war between France and Spain. To communicate with their troops, the Spaniards used a complicated code that Viète managed to decipher. Unaware of Viète's accomplishment, the Spanish king, Philip II, protested to the Pope, claiming that the French were using witchcraft to read his messages.

EXAMPLE 5 ■ Dimensions of a Building Lot

A rectangular building lot is 8 ft longer than it is wide and has an area of 2900 ft^2. Find the dimensions of the lot.

SOLUTION **Identify the variable.**   We are asked to find the width and length of the lot. So let

$$w = \text{width of lot}$$

Translate from words to algebra.   Then we translate the information given in the problem into the language of algebra (see Figure 1):

In Words	In Algebra
Width of lot	w
Length of lot	$w + 8$

Set up the model.   Now we set up the model.

$$\boxed{\text{width of lot}} \times \boxed{\text{length of lot}} = \boxed{\text{area of lot}}$$

$$w(w + 8) = 2900$$

Solve.   Now we solve for w.

$$w^2 + 8w = 2900 \qquad \text{Expand}$$
$$w^2 + 8w - 2900 = 0 \qquad \text{Subtract 2900}$$
$$(w - 50)(w + 58) = 0 \qquad \text{Factor}$$
$$w = 50 \quad \text{or} \quad w = -58 \qquad \text{Zero-Product Property}$$

Since the width of the lot must be a positive number, we conclude that $w = 50$ ft. The length of the lot is $w + 8 = 50 + 8 = 58$ ft.

✎ Now Try Exercise 69

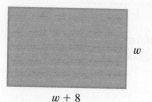

w

$w + 8$

FIGURE 1

EXAMPLE 6 ■ A Distance-Speed-Time Problem

A jet flew from New York to Los Angeles, a distance of 4200 km. The speed for the return trip was 100 km/h faster than the outbound speed. If the total trip took 13 hours, what was the jet's speed from New York to Los Angeles?

SOLUTION **Identify the variable.**   We are asked for the speed of the jet from New York to Los Angeles. So let

$$s = \text{speed from New York to Los Angeles}$$

Then

$$s + 100 = \text{speed from Los Angeles to New York}$$

Translate from words to algebra.   Now we organize the information in a table. We fill in the "Distance" column first, since we know that the cities are 4200 km apart. Then we fill in the "Speed" column, since we have expressed both speeds (rates) in terms of the variable s. Finally, we calculate the entries for the "Time" column, using

$$\text{time} = \frac{\text{distance}}{\text{rate}}$$

	Distance (km)	Speed (km/h)	Time (h)
N.Y. to L.A.	4200	s	$\dfrac{4200}{s}$
L.A. to N.Y.	4200	$s + 100$	$\dfrac{4200}{s + 100}$

Set up the model.   The total trip took 13 hours, so we have the model

$$\boxed{\text{time from N.Y. to L.A.}} + \boxed{\text{time from L.A. to N.Y.}} = \boxed{\text{total time}}$$

$$\frac{4200}{s} + \frac{4200}{s + 100} = 13$$

Solve.   Multiplying by the common denominator, $s(s + 100)$, we get

$$4200(s + 100) + 4200s = 13s(s + 100)$$

$$8400s + 420{,}000 = 13s^2 + 1300s$$

$$0 = 13s^2 - 7100s - 420{,}000$$

Although this equation does factor, with numbers this large it is probably quicker to use the Quadratic Formula and a calculator.

$$s = \frac{7100 \pm \sqrt{(-7100)^2 - 4(13)(-420{,}000)}}{2(13)}$$

$$= \frac{7100 \pm 8500}{26}$$

$$s = 600 \quad \text{or} \quad s = \frac{-1400}{26} \approx -53.8$$

Since s represents speed, we reject the negative answer and conclude that the jet's speed from New York to Los Angeles was 600 km/h.

◥. Now Try Exercise 79   ■

EXAMPLE 7 ■ The Path of a Projectile

This formula depends on the fact that acceleration due to gravity is constant near the earth's surface. Here we neglect the effect of air resistance.

An object thrown or fired straight upward at an initial speed of v_0 ft/s will reach a height of h feet after t seconds, where h and t are related by the formula

$$h = -16t^2 + v_0 t$$

Suppose that a bullet is shot straight upward with an initial speed of 800 ft/s. Its path is shown in Figure 2.

(a) When does the bullet fall back to ground level?

(b) When does it reach a height of 6400 ft?

(c) When does it reach a height of 2 mi?

(d) How high is the highest point the bullet reaches?

SOLUTION   Since the initial speed in this case is $v_0 = 800$ ft/s, the formula is

$$h = -16t^2 + 800t$$

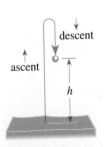

FIGURE 2

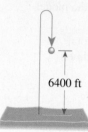

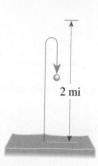

(a) Ground level corresponds to $h = 0$, so we must solve the equation

$$0 = -16t^2 + 800t \qquad \text{Set } h = 0$$

$$0 = -16t(t - 50) \qquad \text{Factor}$$

Thus $t = 0$ or $t = 50$. This means the bullet starts ($t = 0$) at ground level and returns to ground level after 50 s.

(b) Setting $h = 6400$ gives the equation

$$6400 = -16t^2 + 800t \qquad \text{Set } h = 6400$$

$$16t^2 - 800t + 6400 = 0 \qquad \text{All terms to LHS}$$

$$t^2 - 50t + 400 = 0 \qquad \text{Divide by 16}$$

$$(t - 10)(t - 40) = 0 \qquad \text{Factor}$$

$$t = 10 \quad \text{or} \quad t = 40 \qquad \text{Solve}$$

The bullet reaches 6400 ft after 10 s (on its ascent) and again after 40 s (on its descent to earth).

(c) Two miles is $2 \times 5280 = 10{,}560$ ft.

$$10{,}560 = -16t^2 + 800t \qquad \text{Set } h = 10{,}560$$

$$16t^2 - 800t + 10{,}560 = 0 \qquad \text{All terms to LHS}$$

$$t^2 - 50t + 660 = 0 \qquad \text{Divide by 16}$$

The discriminant of this equation is $D = (-50)^2 - 4(660) = -140$, which is negative. Thus the equation has no real solution. The bullet never reaches a height of 2 mi.

(d) Each height that the bullet reaches is attained twice: once on its ascent and once on its descent. The only exception is the highest point of its path, which is reached only once. This means that for the highest value of h, the following equation has only one solution for t.

$$h = -16t^2 + 800t$$

$$16t^2 - 800t + h = 0 \qquad \text{All terms to LHS}$$

This in turn means that the discriminant D of the equation is 0, so

$$D = (-800)^2 - 4(16)h = 0$$

$$640{,}000 - 64h = 0$$

$$h = 10{,}000$$

The maximum height reached is 10,000 ft.

Now Try Exercise 85

1.4 EXERCISES

CONCEPTS

1. The Quadratic Formula gives us the solutions of the equation $ax^2 + bx + c = 0$.

(a) State the Quadratic Formula: $x =$ _____.

(b) In the equation $\frac{1}{2}x^2 - x - 4 = 0$, $a =$ _____,

$b =$ _____, and $c =$ _____. So the solution of

the equation is $x =$ _____.

2. Explain how you would use each method to solve the equation $x^2 - 4x - 5 = 0$.

(a) By factoring: _____

(b) By completing the square: _____

(c) By using the Quadratic Formula: _____

3. For the quadratic equation $ax^2 + bx + c = 0$ the discriminant is $D = $ _____. The discriminant tells us how many real solutions a quadratic equation has.

If $D > 0$, the equation has _____ real solution(s).

If $D = 0$, the equation has _____ real solution(s).

If $D < 0$, the equation has _____ real solution(s).

4. Make up quadratic equations that have the following number of solutions:

Two solutions: _____

One solution: _____

No solution: _____

SKILLS

5–16 ■ Solving by Factoring Find all real solutions of the equation by factoring.

5. $x^2 - 8x + 15 = 0$ **6.** $x^2 + 5x + 6 = 0$

7. $x^2 - x = 6$ **8.** $x^2 - 4x = 21$

9. $5x^2 - 9x - 2 = 0$ **10.** $6x^2 - x - 12 = 0$

11. $2s^2 = 5s + 3$ **12.** $4y^2 - 9y = 28$

13. $12z^2 - 44z = 45$ **14.** $4w^2 = 4w + 3$

15. $x^2 = 5(x + 100)$ **16.** $6x(x - 1) = 21 - x$

17–28 ■ Completing the Square Find all real solutions of the equation by completing the square.

17. $x^2 - 8x + 1 = 0$ **18.** $x^2 + 6x - 2 = 0$

19. $x^2 - 6x - 11 = 0$ **20.** $x^2 + 3x - \frac{7}{4} = 0$

21. $x^2 + x - \frac{3}{4} = 0$ **22.** $x^2 - 5x + 1 = 0$

23. $x^2 + 22x + 21 = 0$ **24.** $x^2 - 18x = 19$

25. $5x^2 + 10x - 7 = 0$ **26.** $2x^2 + 16x + 5 = 0$

27. $2x^2 + 7x + 4 = 0$ **28.** $4x^2 + 5x - 8 = 0$

29–46 ■ Solving Quadratic Equations Find all real solutions of the equation.

29. $x^2 - 8x + 12 = 0$ **30.** $x^2 - 3x - 18 = 0$

31. $x^2 + 8x - 20 = 0$ **32.** $10x^2 + 9x - 7 = 0$

33. $2x^2 + x - 3 = 0$ **34.** $3x^2 + 7x + 4 = 0$

35. $3x^2 + 6x - 5 = 0$ **36.** $x^2 - 6x + 1 = 0$

37. $x^2 - \frac{4}{3}x + \frac{4}{9} = 0$ **38.** $2x^2 + 3x - \frac{1}{2} = 0$

39. $4x^2 + 16x - 9 = 0$ **40.** $0 = x^2 - 4x + 1$

41. $w^2 = 3(w - 1)$ **42.** $3 + 5z + z^2 = 0$

43. $10y^2 - 16y + 5 = 0$ **44.** $25x^2 + 70x + 49 = 0$

45. $3x^2 + 2x + 2 = 0$ **46.** $5x^2 - 7x + 5 = 0$

47–50 ■ Quadratic Formula Use the Quadratic Formula and a calculator to find all real solutions, rounded to three decimals.

47. $x^2 - 0.011x - 0.064 = 0$ **48.** $x^2 - 2.450x + 1.500 = 0$

49. $x^2 - 2.450x + 1.501 = 0$ **50.** $x^2 - 1.800x + 0.810 = 0$

51–56 ■ Solving for a Variable Solve the equation for the indicated variable.

51. $h = \frac{1}{2}gt^2 + v_0t$;   for t

52. $S = \dfrac{n(n + 1)}{2}$;   for n

53. $A = 2x^2 + 4xh$;   for x

54. $A = 2\pi r^2 + 2\pi rh$;   for r

55. $\dfrac{1}{s + a} + \dfrac{1}{s + b} = \dfrac{1}{c}$;   for s

56. $\dfrac{1}{r} + \dfrac{2}{1 - r} = \dfrac{4}{r^2}$;   for r

57–62 ■ Discriminant Use the discriminant to determine the number of real solutions of the equation. Do not solve the equation.

57. $x^2 - 6x + 1 = 0$ **58.** $x^2 = 6x - 9$

59. $x^2 + 2.20x + 1.21 = 0$ **60.** $x^2 + 2.21x + 1.21 = 0$

61. $4x^2 + 5x + \frac{13}{8} = 0$

62. $x^2 + rx - s = 0$ $(s > 0)$

SKILLS Plus

63–64 ■ Solving Quadratic Equations Solve the equation for x.

63. $a^2x^2 + 2ax + 1 = 0$ $(a \neq 0)$

64. $ax^2 - (2a + 1)x + (a + 1) = 0$ $(a \neq 0)$

65–66 ■ Quadratic Equations with One Solution Find all values of k that ensure that the given equation has exactly one solution.

65. $4x^2 + kx + 25 = 0$ **66.** $kx^2 + 36x + k = 0$

APPLICATIONS

67. Number Problem Find two numbers whose sum is 55 and whose product is 684.

68. Number Problem The sum of the squares of two consecutive even integers is 1252. Find the integers.

69. Dimensions of a Garden A rectangular garden is 10 ft longer than it is wide. Its area is 875 ft^2. What are its dimensions?

70. Dimensions of a Room A rectangular bedroom is 7 ft longer than it is wide. Its area is 228 ft^2. What is the width of the room?

71. Dimensions of a Garden A farmer has a rectangular garden plot surrounded by 200 ft of fence. Find the length and width of the garden if its area is 2400 ft^2.

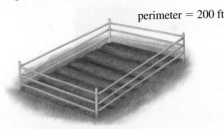

perimeter = 200 ft

72. Geometry Find the length x if the shaded area is 160 in².

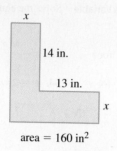

14 in.

13 in.

x

area = 160 in²

73. Geometry Find the length x if the shaded area is 1200 cm².

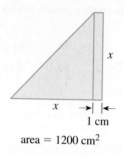

x

x 1 cm

area = 1200 cm²

74. Profit A small-appliance manufacturer finds that the profit P (in dollars) generated by producing x microwave ovens per week is given by the formula $P = \frac{1}{10}x(300 - x)$ provided that $0 \le x \le 200$. How many ovens must be manufactured in a given week to generate a profit of $1250?

75. Dimensions of a Box A box with a square base and no top is to be made from a square piece of cardboard by cutting 4-in. squares from each corner and folding up the sides, as shown in the figure. The box is to hold 100 in³. How big a piece of cardboard is needed?

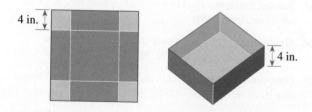

4 in.

4 in.

76. Dimensions of a Can A cylindrical can has a volume of 40π cm³ and is 10 cm tall. What is its diameter? [*Hint:* Use the volume formula listed on the inside front cover of this book.]

10 cm

77. Dimensions of a Lot A parcel of land is 6 ft longer than it is wide. Each diagonal from one corner to the opposite corner is 174 ft long. What are the dimensions of the parcel?

78. Height of a Flagpole A flagpole is secured on opposite sides by two guy wires, each of which is 5 ft longer than the pole. The distance between the points where the wires are fixed to the ground is equal to the length of one guy wire. How tall is the flagpole (to the nearest inch)?

79. Distance, Speed, and Time A salesman drives from Ajax to Barrington, a distance of 120 mi, at a steady speed. He then increases his speed by 10 mi/h to drive the 150 mi from Barrington to Collins. If the second leg of his trip took 6 min more time than the first leg, how fast was he driving between Ajax and Barrington?

80. Distance, Speed, and Time Kiran drove from Tortula to Cactus, a distance of 250 mi. She increased her speed by 10 mi/h for the 360-mi trip from Cactus to Dry Junction. If the total trip took 11 h, what was her speed from Tortula to Cactus?

81. Distance, Speed, and Time It took a crew 2 h 40 min to row 6 km upstream and back again. If the rate of flow of the stream was 3 km/h, what was the rowing speed of the crew in still water?

82. Speed of a Boat Two fishing boats depart a harbor at the same time, one traveling east, the other south. The eastbound boat travels at a speed 3 mi/h faster than the southbound boat. After two hours the boats are 30 mi apart. Find the speed of the southbound boat.

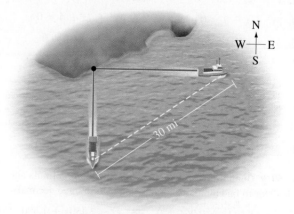

N

W—E

S

30 mi

83–84 ■ **Falling-Body Problems** Suppose an object is dropped from a height h_0 above the ground. Then its height after t seconds is given by $h = -16t^2 + h_0$, where h is measured in feet. Use this information to solve the problem.

83. If a ball is dropped from 288 ft above the ground, how long does it take to reach ground level?

84. A ball is dropped from the top of a building 96 ft tall.
  (a) How long will it take to fall half the distance to ground level?
  (b) How long will it take to fall to ground level?

85–86 ■ **Falling-Body Problems** Use the formula $h = -16t^2 + v_0 t$ discussed in Example 7.

85. A ball is thrown straight upward at an initial speed of $v_0 = 40$ ft/s.
  (a) When does the ball reach a height of 24 ft?
  (b) When does it reach a height of 48 ft?
  (c) What is the greatest height reached by the ball?
  (d) When does the ball reach the highest point of its path?
  (e) When does the ball hit the ground?

86. How fast would a ball have to be thrown upward to reach a maximum height of 100 ft? [*Hint:* Use the discriminant of the equation $16t^2 - v_0 t + h = 0$.]

87. Fish Population The fish population in a certain lake rises and falls according to the formula

$$F = 1000(30 + 17t - t^2)$$

Here F is the number of fish at time t, where t is measured in years since January 1, 2002, when the fish population was first estimated.
  (a) On what date will the fish population again be the same as it was on January 1, 2002?
  (b) By what date will all the fish in the lake have died?

88. Comparing Areas A wire 360 in. long is cut into two pieces. One piece is formed into a square, and the other is formed into a circle. If the two figures have the same area, what are the lengths of the two pieces of wire (to the nearest tenth of an inch)?

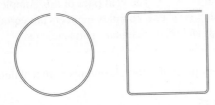

89. Width of a Lawn A factory is to be built on a lot measuring 180 ft by 240 ft. A local building code specifies that a lawn of uniform width and equal in area to the factory must surround the factory. What must the width of this lawn be, and what are the dimensions of the factory?

90. Reach of a Ladder A $19\frac{1}{2}$-ft ladder leans against a building. The base of the ladder is $7\frac{1}{2}$ ft from the building. How high up the building does the ladder reach?

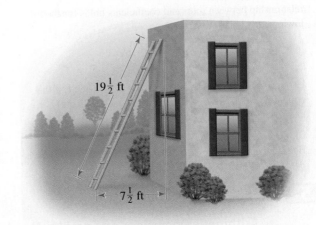

$19\frac{1}{2}$ ft

$7\frac{1}{2}$ ft

91. Sharing a Job Henry and Irene working together can wash all the windows of their house in 1 h 48 min. Working alone, it takes Henry $1\frac{1}{2}$ h more than Irene to do the job. How long does it take each person working alone to wash all the windows?

92. Sharing a Job Jack, Kay, and Lynn deliver advertising flyers in a small town. If each person works alone, it takes Jack 4 h to deliver all the flyers, and it takes Lynn 1 h longer than it takes Kay. Working together, they can deliver all the flyers in 40% of the time it takes Kay working alone. How long does it take Kay to deliver all the flyers alone?

93. Gravity If an imaginary line segment is drawn between the centers of the earth and the moon, then the net gravitational force F acting on an object situated on this line segment is

$$F = \frac{-K}{x^2} + \frac{0.012K}{(239 - x)^2}$$

where $K > 0$ is a constant and x is the distance of the object from the center of the earth, measured in thousands of miles. How far from the center of the earth is the "dead spot" where no net gravitational force acts upon the object? (Express your answer to the nearest thousand miles.)

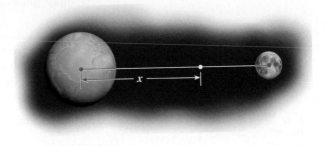

x

DISCUSS ■ **DISCOVER** ■ **PROVE** ■ **WRITE**

94. DISCOVER ■ **PROVE: Relationship Between Roots and Coefficients** The Quadratic Formula gives us the roots of a quadratic equation from its coefficients. We can also obtain the coefficients from the roots. For example, find the roots of the equation $x^2 - 9x + 20 = 0$ and show that the product of the roots is the constant term 20 and the sum of the roots is 9, the negative of the coefficient of x. Show that the same relationship between roots and coefficients holds for the following equations:

$$x^2 - 2x - 8 = 0$$
$$x^2 + 4x + 2 = 0$$

Use the Quadratic Formula to prove that in general, if the equation $x^2 + bx + c = 0$ has roots r_1 and r_2, then $c = r_1 r_2$ and $b = -(r_1 + r_2)$.

95. DISCUSS: A Babylonian Quadratic Equation   The ancient Babylonians knew how to solve quadratic equations. Here is a problem from a cuneiform tablet found in a Babylonian school dating back to about 2000 B.C.

> I have a reed, I know not its length. I broke from it one cubit, and it fit 60 times along the length of my field. I restored to the reed what I had broken off, and it fit 30 times along the width of my field. The area of my field is 375 square nindas. What was the original length of the reed?

Solve this problem. Use the fact that 1 ninda = 12 cubits.

1.5   COMPLEX NUMBERS

■ **Arithmetic Operations on Complex Numbers** ■ **Square Roots of Negative Numbers**
■ **Complex Solutions of Quadratic Equations**

In Section 1.4 we saw that if the discriminant of a quadratic equation is negative, the equation has no real solution. For example, the equation

$$x^2 + 4 = 0$$

has no real solution. If we try to solve this equation, we get $x^2 = -4$, so

$$x = \pm\sqrt{-4}$$

But this is impossible, since the square of any real number is positive. [For example, $(-2)^2 = 4$, a positive number.] Thus negative numbers don't have real square roots.

See the note on Cardano (page 328) for an example of how complex numbers are used to find real solutions of polynomial equations.

To make it possible to solve *all* quadratic equations, mathematicians invented an expanded number system, called the *complex number system*. First they defined the new number

$$i = \sqrt{-1}$$

This means that $i^2 = -1$. A complex number is then a number of the form $a + bi$, where a and b are real numbers.

DEFINITION OF COMPLEX NUMBERS

A **complex number** is an expression of the form

$$a + bi$$

where a and b are real numbers and $i^2 = -1$. The **real part** of this complex number is a, and the **imaginary part** is b. Two complex numbers are **equal** if and only if their real parts are equal and their imaginary parts are equal.

Note that both the real and imaginary parts of a complex number are real numbers.

EXAMPLE 1 ■ Complex Numbers

The following are examples of complex numbers.

$3 + 4i$	Real part 3, imaginary part 4
$\frac{1}{2} - \frac{2}{3}i$	Real part $\frac{1}{2}$, imaginary part $-\frac{2}{3}$
$6i$	Real part 0, imaginary part 6
-7	Real part -7, imaginary part 0

✎ **Now Try Exercises 7 and 11**

A number such as $6i$, which has real part 0, is called a **pure imaginary number**. A real number such as -7 can be thought of as a complex number with imaginary part 0.

In the complex number system every quadratic equation has solutions. The numbers $2i$ and $-2i$ are solutions of $x^2 = -4$ because

$$(2i)^2 = 2^2 i^2 = 4(-1) = -4 \qquad \text{and} \qquad (-2i)^2 = (-2)^2 i^2 = 4(-1) = -4$$

Although we use the term *imaginary* in this context, imaginary numbers should not be thought of as any less "real" (in the ordinary rather than the mathematical sense of that word) than negative numbers or irrational numbers. All numbers (except possibly the positive integers) are creations of the human mind—the numbers -1 and $\sqrt{2}$ as well as the number i. We study complex numbers because they complete, in a useful and elegant fashion, our study of the solutions of equations. In fact, imaginary numbers are useful not only in algebra and mathematics, but in the other sciences as well. To give just one example, in electrical theory the *reactance* of a circuit is a quantity whose measure is an imaginary number.

■ Arithmetic Operations on Complex Numbers

Complex numbers are added, subtracted, multiplied, and divided just as we would any number of the form $a + b\sqrt{c}$. The only difference that we need to keep in mind is that $i^2 = -1$. Thus the following calculations are valid.

$$
\begin{aligned}
(a + bi)(c + di) &= ac + (ad + bc)i + bdi^2 && \text{Multiply and collect like terms} \\
&= ac + (ad + bc)i + bd(-1) && i^2 = -1 \\
&= (ac - bd) + (ad + bc)i && \text{Combine real and imaginary parts}
\end{aligned}
$$

We therefore define the sum, difference, and product of complex numbers as follows.

ADDING, SUBTRACTING, AND MULTIPLYING COMPLEX NUMBERS

Definition	Description
Addition $(a + bi) + (c + di) = (a + c) + (b + d)i$	To add complex numbers, add the real parts and add the imaginary parts.
Subtraction $(a + bi) - (c + di) = (a - c) + (b - d)i$	To subtract complex numbers, subtract the real parts and subtract the imaginary parts.
Multiplication $(a + bi) \cdot (c + di) = (ac - bd) + (ad + bc)i$	Multiply complex numbers like binomials, using $i^2 = -1$.

EXAMPLE 2 ■ Adding, Subtracting, and Multiplying Complex Numbers

Graphing calculators can perform arithmetic operations on complex numbers. See Appendix D, *Using the TI-83/84 Graphing Calculator.*

```
(3+5i)+(4-2i)
            7+3i
(3+5i)*(4-2i)
           22+14i
```

Express the following in the form $a + bi$.

(a) $(3 + 5i) + (4 - 2i)$ **(b)** $(3 + 5i) - (4 - 2i)$

(c) $(3 + 5i)(4 - 2i)$ **(d)** i^{23}

SOLUTION

(a) According to the definition, we add the real parts and we add the imaginary parts:

$$(3 + 5i) + (4 - 2i) = (3 + 4) + (5 - 2)i = 7 + 3i$$

(b) $(3 + 5i) - (4 - 2i) = (3 - 4) + [5 - (-2)]i = -1 + 7i$

(c) $(3 + 5i)(4 - 2i) = [3 \cdot 4 - 5(-2)] + [3(-2) + 5 \cdot 4]i = 22 + 14i$

(d) $i^{23} = i^{22+1} = (i^2)^{11}i = (-1)^{11}i = (-1)i = -i$

✎ Now Try Exercises 19, 23, 29, and 47 ■

Complex Conjugates

Number	Conjugate
$3 + 2i$	$3 - 2i$
$1 - i$	$1 + i$
$4i$	$-4i$
5	5

Division of complex numbers is much like rationalizing the denominator of a radical expression, which we considered in Section P.7. For the complex number $z = a + bi$ we define its **complex conjugate** to be $\bar{z} = a - bi$. Note that

$$z \cdot \bar{z} = (a + bi)(a - bi) = a^2 + b^2$$

So the product of a complex number and its conjugate is always a nonnegative real number. We use this property to divide complex numbers.

DIVIDING COMPLEX NUMBERS

To simplify the quotient $\dfrac{a + bi}{c + di}$, multiply the numerator and the denominator by the complex conjugate of the denominator:

$$\frac{a + bi}{c + di} = \left(\frac{a + bi}{c + di}\right)\left(\frac{c - di}{c - di}\right) = \frac{(ac + bd) + (bc - ad)i}{c^2 + d^2}$$

Rather than memorizing this entire formula, it is easier to just remember the first step and then multiply out the numerator and the denominator as usual.

EXAMPLE 3 ■ Dividing Complex Numbers

Express the following in the form $a + bi$.

(a) $\dfrac{3 + 5i}{1 - 2i}$ **(b)** $\dfrac{7 + 3i}{4i}$

SOLUTION   We multiply both the numerator and denominator by the complex conjugate of the denominator to make the new denominator a real number.

(a) The complex conjugate of $1 - 2i$ is $\overline{1 - 2i} = 1 + 2i$. Therefore

$$\frac{3 + 5i}{1 - 2i} = \left(\frac{3 + 5i}{1 - 2i}\right)\left(\frac{1 + 2i}{1 + 2i}\right) = \frac{-7 + 11i}{5} = -\frac{7}{5} + \frac{11}{5}i$$

(b) The complex conjugate of $4i$ is $-4i$. Therefore

$$\frac{7 + 3i}{4i} = \left(\frac{7 + 3i}{4i}\right)\left(\frac{-4i}{-4i}\right) = \frac{12 - 28i}{16} = \frac{3}{4} - \frac{7}{4}i$$

✎ **Now Try Exercises 39 and 43**   ■

■ Square Roots of Negative Numbers

Just as every positive real number r has two square roots ($\sqrt{r}$ and $-\sqrt{r}$), every negative number has two square roots as well. If $-r$ is a negative number, then its square roots are $\pm i\sqrt{r}$, because $(i\sqrt{r})^2 = i^2 r = -r$ and $(-i\sqrt{r})^2 = (-1)^2 i^2 r = -r$.

SQUARE ROOTS OF NEGATIVE NUMBERS

If $-r$ is negative, then the **principal square root** of $-r$ is

$$\sqrt{-r} = i\sqrt{r}$$

The two square roots of $-r$ are $i\sqrt{r}$ and $-i\sqrt{r}$.

We usually write $i\sqrt{b}$ instead of $\sqrt{b}i$ to avoid confusion with $\sqrt{bi}$.

EXAMPLE 4 ■ Square Roots of Negative Numbers

(a) $\sqrt{-1} = i\sqrt{1} = i$ **(b)** $\sqrt{-16} = i\sqrt{16} = 4i$ **(c)** $\sqrt{-3} = i\sqrt{3}$

✎ Now Try Exercises 53 and 55 ■

Special care must be taken in performing calculations that involve square roots of negative numbers. Although $\sqrt{a} \cdot \sqrt{b} = \sqrt{ab}$ when a and b are positive, this is *not* true when both are negative. For example,

$$\sqrt{-2} \cdot \sqrt{-3} = i\sqrt{2} \cdot i\sqrt{3} = i^2\sqrt{6} = -\sqrt{6}$$

but

$$\sqrt{(-2)(-3)} = \sqrt{6}$$

so

$$\sqrt{-2} \cdot \sqrt{-3} \neq \sqrt{(-2)(-3)}$$

 When multiplying radicals of negative numbers, express them first in the form $i\sqrt{r}$ (where $r > 0$) to avoid possible errors of this type.

EXAMPLE 5 ■ Using Square Roots of Negative Numbers

Evaluate $(\sqrt{12} - \sqrt{-3})(3 + \sqrt{-4})$, and express the result in the form $a + bi$.

SOLUTION

$$\begin{aligned}(\sqrt{12} - \sqrt{-3})(3 + \sqrt{-4}) &= (\sqrt{12} - i\sqrt{3})(3 + i\sqrt{4}) \\ &= (2\sqrt{3} - i\sqrt{3})(3 + 2i) \\ &= (6\sqrt{3} + 2\sqrt{3}) + i(2 \cdot 2\sqrt{3} - 3\sqrt{3}) \\ &= 8\sqrt{3} + i\sqrt{3}\end{aligned}$$

✎ Now Try Exercise 57 ■

■ Complex Solutions of Quadratic Equations

We have already seen that if $a \neq 0$, then the solutions of the quadratic equation $ax^2 + bx + c = 0$ are

$$x = \frac{-b \pm \sqrt{b^2 - 4ac}}{2a}$$

If $b^2 - 4ac < 0$, then the equation has no real solution. But in the complex number system this equation will always have solutions, because negative numbers have square roots in this expanded setting.

EXAMPLE 6 ■ Quadratic Equations with Complex Solutions

Solve each equation.

(a) $x^2 + 9 = 0$ **(b)** $x^2 + 4x + 5 = 0$

SOLUTION

(a) The equation $x^2 + 9 = 0$ means $x^2 = -9$, so

$$x = \pm\sqrt{-9} = \pm i\sqrt{9} = \pm 3i$$

The solutions are therefore $3i$ and $-3i$.

LEONHARD EULER (1707–1783) was born in Basel, Switzerland, the son of a pastor. When Euler was 13, his father sent him to the University at Basel to study theology, but Euler soon decided to devote himself to the sciences. Besides theology he studied mathematics, medicine, astronomy, physics, and Asian languages. It is said that Euler could calculate as effortlessly as "men breathe or as eagles fly." One hundred years before Euler, Fermat (see page 154) had conjectured that $2^{2^n} + 1$ is a prime number for all n. The first five of these numbers are 5, 17, 257, 65537, and 4,294,967,297. It is easy to show that the first four are prime. The fifth was also thought to be prime until Euler, with his phenomenal calculating ability, showed that it is the product $641 \times 6{,}700{,}417$ and so is not prime. Euler published more than any other mathematician in history. His collected works comprise 75 large volumes. Although he was blind for the last 17 years of his life, he continued to work and publish. In his writings he popularized the use of the symbols π, e, and i, which you will find in this textbook. One of Euler's most lasting contributions is his development of complex numbers.

(b) By the Quadratic Formula we have

$$x = \frac{-4 \pm \sqrt{4^2 - 4 \cdot 5}}{2}$$

$$= \frac{-4 \pm \sqrt{-4}}{2}$$

$$= \frac{-4 \pm 2i}{2} = -2 \pm i$$

So the solutions are $-2 + i$ and $-2 - i$.

◥ **Now Try Exercises 61 and 63** ∎

We see from Example 6 that if a quadratic equation with real coefficients has complex solutions, then these solutions are complex conjugates of each other. So if $a + bi$ is a solution, then $a - bi$ is also a solution.

EXAMPLE 7 ■ Complex Conjugates as Solutions of a Quadratic

Show that the solutions of the equation

$$4x^2 - 24x + 37 = 0$$

are complex conjugates of each other.

SOLUTION   We use the Quadratic Formula to get

$$x = \frac{24 \pm \sqrt{(24)^2 - 4(4)(37)}}{2(4)}$$

$$= \frac{24 \pm \sqrt{-16}}{8}$$

$$= \frac{24 \pm 4i}{8} = 3 \pm \frac{1}{2}i$$

So the solutions are $3 + \frac{1}{2}i$ and $3 - \frac{1}{2}i$, and these are complex conjugates.

◥ **Now Try Exercise 69** ∎

1.5 EXERCISES

CONCEPTS

1. The imaginary number i has the property that $i^2 =$ _____.

2. For the complex number $3 + 4i$ the real part is _____, and the imaginary part is _____.

3. (a) The complex conjugate of $3 + 4i$ is $\overline{3 + 4i} =$ _____.

(b) $(3 + 4i)(\overline{3 + 4i}) =$ _____.

4. If $3 + 4i$ is a solution of a quadratic equation with real coefficients, then _____ is also a solution of the equation.

5–6 ■ *Yes or No?* If *No*, give a reason.

5. Is every real number also a complex number?

6. Is the sum of a complex number and its complex conjugate a real number?

SKILLS

7–16 ■ **Real and Imaginary Parts**   Find the real and imaginary parts of the complex number.

7. $5 - 7i$

8. $-6 + 4i$

9. $\dfrac{-2 - 5i}{3}$

10. $\dfrac{4 + 7i}{2}$

11. 3

12. $-\dfrac{1}{2}$

13. $-\dfrac{2}{3}i$

14. $i\sqrt{3}$

15. $\sqrt{3} + \sqrt{-4}$

16. $2 - \sqrt{-5}$

17–26 ■ Sums and Differences Evaluate the sum or difference, and write the result in the form $a + bi$.

17. $(3 + 2i) + 5i$

18. $3i - (2 - 3i)$

19. $(5 - 3i) + (-4 - 7i)$

20. $(-3 + 4i) - (2 - 5i)$

21. $(-6 + 6i) + (9 - i)$

22. $(3 - 2i) + \left(-5 - \frac{1}{3}i\right)$

23. $\left(7 - \frac{1}{2}i\right) - \left(5 + \frac{3}{2}i\right)$

24. $(-4 + i) - (2 - 5i)$

25. $(-12 + 8i) - (7 + 4i)$

26. $6i - (4 - i)$

27–36 ■ Products Evaluate the product, and write the result in the form $a + bi$.

27. $4(-1 + 2i)$

28. $-2(3 - 4i)$

29. $(7 - i)(4 + 2i)$

30. $(5 - 3i)(1 + i)$

31. $(6 + 5i)(2 - 3i)$

32. $(-2 + i)(3 - 7i)$

33. $(2 + 5i)(2 - 5i)$

34. $(3 - 7i)(3 + 7i)$

35. $(2 + 5i)^2$

36. $(3 - 7i)^2$

37–46 ■ Quotients Evaluate the quotient, and write the result in the form $a + bi$.

37. $\dfrac{1}{i}$

38. $\dfrac{1}{1 + i}$

39. $\dfrac{2 - 3i}{1 - 2i}$

40. $\dfrac{5 - i}{3 + 4i}$

41. $\dfrac{10i}{1 - 2i}$

42. $(2 - 3i)^{-1}$

43. $\dfrac{4 + 6i}{3i}$

44. $\dfrac{-3 + 5i}{15i}$

45. $\dfrac{1}{1 + i} - \dfrac{1}{1 - i}$

46. $\dfrac{(1 + 2i)(3 - i)}{2 + i}$

47–52 ■ Powers Evaluate the power, and write the result in the form $a + bi$.

47. i^3

48. i^{10}

49. $(3i)^5$

50. $(2i)^4$

51. i^{1000}

52. i^{1002}

53–60 ■ Radical Expressions Evaluate the radical expression, and express the result in the form $a + bi$.

53. $\sqrt{-49}$

54. $\sqrt{\dfrac{-81}{16}}$

55. $\sqrt{-3}\sqrt{-12}$

56. $\sqrt{\frac{1}{3}}\sqrt{-27}$

57. $(3 - \sqrt{-5})(1 + \sqrt{-1})$

58. $(\sqrt{3} - \sqrt{-4})(\sqrt{6} - \sqrt{-8})$

59. $\dfrac{2 + \sqrt{-8}}{1 + \sqrt{-2}}$

60. $\dfrac{\sqrt{-36}}{\sqrt{-2}\sqrt{-9}}$

61–72 ■ Quadratic Equations Find all solutions of the equation and express them in the form $a + bi$.

61. $x^2 + 49 = 0$

62. $3x^2 + 1 = 0$

63. $x^2 - x + 2 = 0$

64. $x^2 + 2x + 2 = 0$

65. $x^2 + 3x + 7 = 0$

66. $x^2 - 6x + 10 = 0$

67. $x^2 + x + 1 = 0$

68. $x^2 - 3x + 3 = 0$

69. $2x^2 - 2x + 1 = 0$

70. $t + 3 + \dfrac{3}{t} = 0$

71. $6x^2 + 12x + 7 = 0$

72. $x^2 + \frac{1}{2}x + 1 = 0$

SKILLS Plus

73–76 ■ Conjugates Evaluate the given expression for $z = 3 - 4i$ and $w = 5 + 2i$.

73. $\bar{z} + \bar{w}$

74. $\overline{z + w}$

75. $z \cdot \bar{z}$

76. $\bar{z} \cdot \bar{w}$

77–84 ■ Conjugates Recall that the symbol $\bar{z}$ represents the complex conjugate of z. If $z = a + bi$ and $w = c + di$, show that each statement is true.

77. $\bar{z} + \bar{w} = \overline{z + w}$

78. $\overline{zw} = \bar{z} \cdot \bar{w}$

79. $(\bar{z})^2 = \overline{z^2}$

80. $\bar{\bar{z}} = z$

81. $z + \bar{z}$ is a real number.

82. $z - \bar{z}$ is a pure imaginary number.

83. $z \cdot \bar{z}$ is a real number.

84. $z = \bar{z}$ if and only if z is real.

DISCUSS ■ DISCOVER ■ PROVE ■ WRITE

85. **PROVE: Complex Conjugate Roots** Suppose that the equation $ax^2 + bx + c = 0$ has real coefficients and complex roots. Why must the roots be complex conjugates of each other? [*Hint:* Think about how you would find the roots using the Quadratic Formula.]

86. **DISCUSS: Powers of i** Calculate the first 12 powers of i, that is, $i, i^2, i^3, \ldots, i^{12}$. Do you notice a pattern? Explain how you would calculate any whole number power of i, using the pattern that you have discovered. Use this procedure to calculate i^{4446}.

1.6   SOLVING OTHER TYPES OF EQUATIONS

■ **Polynomial Equations** ■ **Equations Involving Radicals** ■ **Equations of Quadratic Type**
■ **Applications**

So far, we have learned how to solve linear and quadratic equations. In this section we study other types of equations, including those that involve higher powers, fractional expressions, and radicals.

■ Polynomial Equations

Some equations can be solved by factoring and using the Zero-Product Property, which says that if a product equals 0, then at least one of the factors must equal 0.

EXAMPLE 1 ■ Solving an Equation by Factoring

Solve the equation $x^5 = 9x^3$.

SOLUTION   We bring all terms to one side and then factor:

$$x^5 - 9x^3 = 0 \qquad \text{Subtract } 9x^3$$
$$x^3(x^2 - 9) = 0 \qquad \text{Factor } x^3$$
$$x^3(x - 3)(x + 3) = 0 \qquad \text{Difference of squares}$$
$$x^3 = 0 \quad \text{or} \quad x - 3 = 0 \quad \text{or} \quad x + 3 = 0 \qquad \text{Zero-Product Property}$$
$$x = 0 \qquad\qquad x = 3 \qquad\qquad x = -3 \qquad \text{Solve}$$

The solutions are $x = 0$, $x = 3$, and $x = -3$. You should check that each of these satisfies the original equation.

✎ **Now Try Exercise 5**   ■

To divide each side of the equation in Example 1 by the common factor x^3 would be wrong, because in doing so, we would lose the solution $x = 0$. Never divide both sides of an equation by an expression that contains the variable unless you know that the expression cannot equal 0.

EXAMPLE 2 ■ Factoring by Grouping

Solve the equation $x^3 + 3x^2 - 4x - 12 = 0$.

SOLUTION   The left-hand side of the equation can be factored by grouping the terms in pairs:

$$(x^3 + 3x^2) - (4x + 12) = 0 \qquad \text{Group terms}$$
$$x^2(x + 3) - 4(x + 3) = 0 \qquad \text{Factor } x^2 \text{ and } 4$$
$$(x^2 - 4)(x + 3) = 0 \qquad \text{Factor } x + 3$$
$$(x - 2)(x + 2)(x + 3) = 0 \qquad \text{Difference of squares}$$
$$x - 2 = 0 \quad \text{or} \quad x + 2 = 0 \quad \text{or} \quad x + 3 = 0 \qquad \text{Zero-Product Property}$$
$$x = 2 \qquad\qquad x = -2 \qquad\qquad x = -3 \qquad \text{Solve}$$

The solutions are $x = 2$, -2, and -3.

✎ **Now Try Exercise 21**   ■

EXAMPLE 3 ■ An Equation Involving Fractional Expressions

Solve the equation $\dfrac{3}{x} - \dfrac{2}{x-3} = \dfrac{-12}{x^2-9}$.

SOLUTION   We eliminate the denominators by multiplying each side by the lowest common denominator.

$$\left(\dfrac{3}{x} - \dfrac{2}{x-3}\right)x(x^2-9) = \dfrac{-12}{x^2-9}x(x^2-9) \qquad \text{Multiply by LCD, } x(x^2-9)$$

$$3(x^2-9) - 2x(x+3) = -12x \qquad \text{Expand}$$

$$3x^2 - 27 - 2x^2 - 6x = -12x \qquad \text{Expand LHS}$$

$$x^2 - 6x - 27 = -12x \qquad \text{Add like terms on LHS}$$

$$x^2 + 6x - 27 = 0 \qquad \text{Add } 12x$$

$$(x-3)(x+9) = 0 \qquad \text{Factor}$$

$$x - 3 = 0 \quad \text{or} \quad x + 9 = 0 \qquad \text{Zero-Product Property}$$

$$x = 3 \qquad\qquad x = -9 \qquad \text{Solve}$$

We must check our answer because multiplying by an expression that contains the variable can introduce extraneous solutions. From *Check Your Answers* we see that the only solution is $x = -9$.

✎ **Now Try Exercise 27**   ∎

■ Equations Involving Radicals

When you solve an equation that involves radicals, you must be especially careful to check your final answers. The next example demonstrates why.

EXAMPLE 4 ■ An Equation Involving a Radical

Solve the equation $2x = 1 - \sqrt{2-x}$.

SOLUTION   To eliminate the square root, we first isolate it on one side of the equal sign, then square:

$$2x - 1 = -\sqrt{2-x} \qquad \text{Subtract 1}$$

$$(2x-1)^2 = 2 - x \qquad \text{Square each side}$$

$$4x^2 - 4x + 1 = 2 - x \qquad \text{Expand LHS}$$

$$4x^2 - 3x - 1 = 0 \qquad \text{Add } -2 + x$$

$$(4x+1)(x-1) = 0 \qquad \text{Factor}$$

$$4x + 1 = 0 \quad \text{or} \quad x - 1 = 0 \qquad \text{Zero-Product Property}$$

$$x = -\tfrac{1}{4} \qquad\qquad x = 1 \qquad \text{Solve}$$

The values $x = -\frac{1}{4}$ and $x = 1$ are only potential solutions. We must check them to see whether they satisfy the original equation. From *Check Your Answers* we see that $x = -\frac{1}{4}$ is a solution but $x = 1$ is not. The only solution is $x = -\frac{1}{4}$.

✎ **Now Try Exercise 43**   ∎

When we solve an equation, we may end up with one or more **extraneous solutions**, that is, potential solutions that do not satisfy the original equation. In Example 3 the value $x = 3$ is an extraneous solution, and in Example 4 the value $x = 1$ is an extraneous solution. In the case of equations involving fractional expressions, potential solutions may result in undefined expressions when substituted into the original equation and hence are extraneous solutions. In the case of equations involving radicals, extraneous solutions may be introduced when we square each side of an equation because the operation of squaring can turn a false equation into a true one. For example, $-1 \neq 1$, but $(-1)^2 = 1^2$. Thus the squared equation may be true for more values of the variable than the original equation. That is why you must always check your answers to make sure that each satisfies the original equation.

▪ Equations of Quadratic Type

An equation of the form $aW^2 + bW + c = 0$, where W is an algebraic expression, is an equation of **quadratic type**. We solve equations of quadratic type by substituting for the algebraic expression, as we see in the next two examples.

EXAMPLE 5 ▪ A Fourth-Degree Equation of Quadratic Type

Find all solutions of the equation $x^4 - 8x^2 + 8 = 0$.

SOLUTION   If we set $W = x^2$, then we get a quadratic equation in the new variable W.

$$(x^2)^2 - 8x^2 + 8 = 0 \qquad \text{Write } x^4 \text{ as } (x^2)^2$$

$$W^2 - 8W + 8 = 0 \qquad \text{Let } W = x^2$$

$$W = \frac{-(-8) \pm \sqrt{(-8)^2 - 4 \cdot 8}}{2} = 4 \pm 2\sqrt{2} \qquad \text{Quadratic Formula}$$

$$x^2 = 4 \pm 2\sqrt{2} \qquad W = x^2$$

$$x = \pm\sqrt{4 \pm 2\sqrt{2}} \qquad \text{Take square roots}$$

So there are four solutions:

$$\sqrt{4 + 2\sqrt{2}} \qquad \sqrt{4 - 2\sqrt{2}} \qquad -\sqrt{4 + 2\sqrt{2}} \qquad -\sqrt{4 - 2\sqrt{2}}$$

Using a calculator, we obtain the approximations $x \approx 2.61, 1.08, -2.61, -1.08$.

✎ **Now Try Exercise 49** ∎

EXAMPLE 6 ▪ An Equation of Quadratic Type

Solve the equation $\left(1 + \dfrac{1}{x}\right)^2 - 6\left(1 + \dfrac{1}{x}\right) + 8 = 0$.

SOLUTION   We could solve this equation by multiplying it out first. But it's easier to think of the expression $1 + \frac{1}{x}$ as the unknown in this equation and give it a new name, W. This turns the equation into a quadratic equation in the new variable W.

$$\left(1 + \frac{1}{x}\right)^2 - 6\left(1 + \frac{1}{x}\right) + 8 = 0 \qquad \text{Given equation}$$

$$W^2 - 6W + 8 = 0 \qquad \text{Let } W = 1 + \frac{1}{x}$$

$$(W - 4)(W - 2) = 0 \qquad \text{Factor}$$

$$W - 4 = 0 \quad \text{or} \quad W - 2 = 0 \qquad \text{Zero-Product Property}$$

$$W = 4 \qquad\qquad W = 2 \qquad \text{Solve}$$

Now we change these values of W back into the corresponding values of x.

$$1 + \frac{1}{x} = 4 \qquad 1 + \frac{1}{x} = 2 \qquad W = 1 + \frac{1}{x}$$

$$\frac{1}{x} = 3 \qquad \frac{1}{x} = 1 \qquad \text{Subtract 1}$$

$$x = \frac{1}{3} \qquad x = 1 \qquad \text{Take reciprocals}$$

The solutions are $x = \frac{1}{3}$ and $x = 1$.

✎ **Now Try Exercise 57**   ■

EXAMPLE 7 ■ An Equation Involving Fractional Powers

Find all solutions of the equation $x^{1/3} + x^{1/6} - 2 = 0$.

SOLUTION   This equation is of quadratic type because if we let $W = x^{1/6}$, then $W^2 = (x^{1/6})^2 = x^{1/3}$:

$$x^{1/3} + x^{1/6} - 2 = 0 \qquad \text{Given equation}$$

$$W^2 + W - 2 = 0 \qquad \text{Let } W = x^{1/6}$$

$$(W - 1)(W + 2) = 0 \qquad \text{Factor}$$

$$W - 1 = 0 \quad \text{or} \quad W + 2 = 0 \qquad \text{Zero-Product Property}$$

$$W = 1 \qquad\qquad W = -2 \qquad \text{Solve}$$

$$x^{1/6} = 1 \qquad\qquad x^{1/6} = -2 \qquad W = x^{1/6}$$

$$x = 1^6 = 1 \qquad\qquad x = (-2)^6 = 64 \quad \text{Take the 6th power}$$

From *Check Your Answers* we see that $x = 1$ is a solution but $x = 64$ is not. The only solution is $x = 1$.

> **CHECK YOUR ANSWERS**
>
> $x = 1$:
> $$\text{LHS} = 1^{1/3} + 1^{1/6} - 2 = 0$$
>
> $x = 64$:
> $$\text{LHS} = 64^{1/3} + 64^{1/6} - 2$$
> $$= 4 + 2 - 2 = 4$$
>
> $\text{RHS} = 0$
>
> $\text{RHS} = 0$
>
> $\text{LHS} = \text{RHS}$ ✓
>
> $\text{LHS} \neq \text{RHS}$ ✗

✎ **Now Try Exercise 59**   ■

■ Applications

Many real-life problems can be modeled with the types of equations that we have studied in this section.

EXAMPLE 8 ■ Dividing a Lottery Jackpot

For help in setting up equations that model real-life applications, see the Guidelines for Modeling with Equations, Section P.9, page 62.

A group of people come forward to claim a $1,000,000 lottery jackpot, which the winners are to share equally. Before the jackpot is divided, three more winning ticket holders show up. As a result, the share of each of the original winners is reduced by $75,000. How many winners were in the original group?

SOLUTION **Identify the variable.** We are asked for the number of people in the original group. So let

$$x = \text{number of winners in the original group}$$

Translate from words to algebra. We translate the information in the problem as follows:

In Words	In Algebra
Number of winners in original group	x
Number of winners in final group	$x + 3$
Winnings per person, originally	$\dfrac{1{,}000{,}000}{x}$
Winnings per person, finally	$\dfrac{1{,}000{,}000}{x + 3}$

Set up the model. Now we set up the model.

$$\boxed{\begin{array}{c}\text{winnings per}\\\text{person, originally}\end{array}} - \boxed{\$75{,}000} = \boxed{\begin{array}{c}\text{winnings per}\\\text{person, finally}\end{array}}$$

$$\frac{1{,}000{,}000}{x} - 75{,}000 = \frac{1{,}000{,}000}{x + 3}$$

Solve. We now solve for x.

$$1{,}000{,}000(x + 3) - 75{,}000x(x + 3) = 1{,}000{,}000x \qquad \text{Multiply by LCD } x(x + 3)$$

$$40(x + 3) - 3x(x + 3) = 40x \qquad \text{Divide by 25,000}$$

$$x^2 + 3x - 40 = 0 \qquad \text{Expand, simplify, and divide by 3}$$

$$(x + 8)(x - 5) = 0 \qquad \text{Factor}$$

$$x + 8 = 0 \quad \text{or} \quad x - 5 = 0 \qquad \text{Zero-Product Property}$$

$$x = -8 \qquad\qquad x = 5 \qquad \text{Solve}$$

Since we can't have a negative number of people, we conclude that there were five winners in the original group.

Mathematics in the Modern World

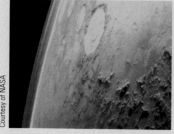

Courtesy of NASA

Error-Correcting Codes

The pictures sent back by the *Pathfinder* spacecraft from the surface of Mars on July 4, 1997, were astoundingly clear. But few viewing these pictures were aware of the complex mathematics used to accomplish that feat. The distance to Mars is enormous, and the background noise (or static) is many times stronger than the original signal emitted by the spacecraft. So when scientists receive the signal, it is full of errors. To get a clear picture, the errors must be found and corrected. This same problem of errors is routinely encountered in transmitting bank records when you use an ATM machine or voice when you are talking on the telephone.

To understand how errors are found and corrected, we must first understand that to transmit pictures, sound, or text, we transform them into bits (the digits 0 or 1; see page 40). To help the receiver recognize errors, the message is "coded" by inserting additional bits. For example, suppose you want to transmit the message "10100." A very simple-minded code is as follows: Send each digit a million times. The person receiving the message reads it in blocks of a million digits. If the first block is mostly 1's, he concludes that you are probably trying to transmit a 1, and so on. To say that this code is not efficient is a bit of an understatement; it requires sending a million times more data than the original message. Another method inserts "check digits." For example, for each block of eight digits insert a ninth digit; the inserted digit is 0 if there is an even number of 1's in the block and 1 if there is an odd number. So if a single digit is wrong (a 0 changed to a 1 or vice versa), the check digits allow us to recognize that an error has occurred. This method does not tell us where the error is, so we can't correct it. Modern error-correcting codes use interesting mathematical algorithms that require inserting relatively few digits but that allow the receiver to not only recognize, but also correct, errors. The first error-correcting code was developed in the 1940s by Richard Hamming at MIT. It is interesting to note that the English language has a built-in error correcting mechanism; to test it, try reading this error-laden sentence: Gve mo libty ox giv ne deth.

$$\text{winnings per person, originally} = \frac{\$1,000,000}{5} = \$200,000$$

$$\text{winnings per person, finally} = \frac{\$1,000,000}{8} = \$125,000$$

$$\$200,000 - \$75,000 = \$125,000 \;\checkmark$$

✎. Now Try Exercise 79 ■

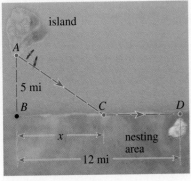

island

A

5 mi

B $\quad$ C $\qquad$ D

x $\qquad$ nesting area

12 mi

FIGURE 1

EXAMPLE 9 ■ Energy Expended in Bird Flight

Ornithologists have determined that some species of birds tend to avoid flights over large bodies of water during daylight hours, because air generally rises over land and falls over water in the daytime, so flying over water requires more energy. A bird is released from point A on an island, 5 mi from point B, the nearest point on a straight shoreline. The bird flies to a point C on the shoreline and then flies along the shoreline to its nesting area at point D, as shown in Figure 1. Suppose the bird has 170 kcal of energy reserves. It uses 10 kcal/mi flying over land and 14 kcal/mi flying over water.

(a) Where should the point C be located so that the bird uses exactly 170 kcal of energy during its flight?

(b) Does the bird have enough energy reserves to fly directly from A to D?

SOLUTION

(a) Identify the variable.   We are asked to find the location of C. So let

$$x = \text{distance from } B \text{ to } C$$

Translate from words to algebra.   From the figure and from the fact that

$$\text{energy used} = \text{energy per mile} \times \text{miles flown}$$

we determine the following:

In Words	In Algebra	
Distance from B to C	x	
Distance flown over water (from A to C)	$\sqrt{x^2 + 25}$	Pythagorean Theorem
Distance flown over land (from C to D)	$12 - x$	
Energy used over water	$14\sqrt{x^2 + 25}$	
Energy used over land	$10(12 - x)$	

Set up the model.   Now we set up the model.

$$\boxed{\text{total energy used}} = \boxed{\text{energy used over water}} + \boxed{\text{energy used over land}}$$

$$170 = 14\sqrt{x^2 + 25} + 10(12 - x)$$

Solve.   To solve this equation, we eliminate the square root by first bringing all other terms to the left of the equal sign and then squaring each side.

$$170 - 10(12 - x) = 14\sqrt{x^2 + 25} \qquad \text{Isolate square root term on RHS}$$

$$50 + 10x = 14\sqrt{x^2 + 25} \qquad \text{Simplify LHS}$$

$$(50 + 10x)^2 = (14)^2(x^2 + 25) \qquad \text{Square each side}$$

$$2500 + 1000x + 100x^2 = 196x^2 + 4900 \qquad \text{Expand}$$

$$0 = 96x^2 - 1000x + 2400 \qquad \text{All terms to RHS}$$

This equation could be factored, but because the numbers are so large, it is easier to use the Quadratic Formula and a calculator.

$$x = \frac{1000 \pm \sqrt{(-1000)^2 - 4(96)(2400)}}{2(96)} = \frac{1000 \pm 280}{192}$$

$$x = 6\tfrac{2}{3} \quad \text{or} \quad x = 3\tfrac{3}{4}$$

Point C should be either $6\tfrac{2}{3}$ mi or $3\tfrac{3}{4}$ mi from point B so that the bird uses exactly 170 kcal of energy during its flight.

(b) By the Pythagorean Theorem (see page 277) the length of the route directly from A to D is $\sqrt{5^2 + 12^2} = 13$ mi, so the energy the bird requires for that route is $14 \times 13 = 182$ kcal. This is more energy than the bird has available, so it can't use this route.

Now Try Exercise 87

We were able to solve all the equations in this section algebraically; however, not all equations can be solved this way. If our model leads to an equation that cannot be solved algebraically, we can solve it graphically as described in Section 1.9.

1.6 EXERCISES

CONCEPTS

1. (a) To solve the equation $x^3 - 4x^2 = 0$, we _____ the left-hand side.

(b) The solutions of the equation $x^2(x - 4) = 0$ are _____.

2. Solve the equation $\sqrt{2x} + x = 0$ by doing the following steps.

(a) Isolate the radical: _____.

(b) Square both sides: _____.

(c) The solutions of the resulting quadratic equation are

_____.

(d) The solution(s) that satisfy the original equation are

_____.

3. The equation $(x + 1)^2 - 5(x + 1) + 6 = 0$ is of _____ type. To solve the equation, we set $W = $ _____. The resulting quadratic equation is _____.

4. The equation $x^6 + 7x^3 - 8 = 0$ is of _____ type. To solve the equation, we set $W = $ _____. The resulting quadratic equation is _____.

SKILLS

5–24 ■ Polynomial Equations Find all real solutions of the equation.

5. $x^2 - x = 0$

6. $3x^3 - 6x^2 = 0$

7. $x^3 = 25x$

8. $x^5 = 5x^3$

9. $x^5 - 3x^2 = 0$

10. $6x^5 - 24x = 0$

11. $4z^5 - 10z^2 = 0$

12. $125t^{10} - 2t^7 = 0$

13. $x^5 + 8x^2 = 0$

14. $x^4 + 64x = 0$

15. $x^3 - 5x^2 + 6x = 0$

16. $x^4 - x^3 - 6x^2 = 0$

17. $x^4 + 4x^3 + 2x^2 = 0$

18. $y^5 - 8y^4 + 4y^3 = 0$

19. $(3x + 5)^4 - (3x + 5)^3 = 0$

20. $(x + 5)^4 - 16(x + 5)^2 = 0$

21. $x^3 - 5x^2 - 2x + 10 = 0$ **22.** $2x^3 + x^2 - 18x - 9 = 0$

23. $x^3 - x^2 + x - 1 = x^2 + 1$

24. $7x^3 - x + 1 = x^3 + 3x^2 + x$

25–36 ■ Equations Involving Rational Expressions Find all real solutions of the equation.

25. $z + \dfrac{4}{z + 1} = 3$

26. $\dfrac{10}{m + 5} + 15 = 3m$

27. $\dfrac{1}{x - 1} + \dfrac{1}{x + 2} = \dfrac{5}{4}$

28. $\dfrac{10}{x} - \dfrac{12}{x - 3} + 4 = 0$

29. $\dfrac{x^2}{x + 100} = 50$

30. $\dfrac{2x}{x^2 + 1} = 1$

31. $1 + \dfrac{1}{(x + 1)(x + 2)} = \dfrac{2}{x + 1} + \dfrac{1}{x + 2}$

32. $\dfrac{x}{x + 3} = \dfrac{2}{x - 3} - \dfrac{1}{x^2 - 9}$

33. $\dfrac{x}{2x + 7} - \dfrac{x + 1}{x + 3} = 1$

34. $\dfrac{1}{x - 1} - \dfrac{2}{x^2} = 0$

35. $\dfrac{x + \dfrac{2}{x}}{3 + \dfrac{4}{x}} = 5x$

36. $\dfrac{3 + \dfrac{1}{x}}{2 - \dfrac{4}{x}} = x$

37–48 ■ Equations Involving Radicals   Find all real solutions of the equation.

37. $5 = \sqrt{4x - 3}$

38. $\sqrt{8x - 1} = 3$

39. $\sqrt{2x - 1} = \sqrt{3x - 5}$

40. $\sqrt{3 + x} = \sqrt{x^2 + 1}$

41. $\sqrt{x + 2} = x$

42. $\sqrt{4 - 6x} = 2x$

43. $\sqrt{2x + 1} + 1 = x$

44. $x - \sqrt{9 - 3x} = 0$

45. $x - \sqrt{x - 1} = 3$

46. $\sqrt{3 - x} + 2 = 1 - x$

47. $\sqrt{3x + 1} = 2 + \sqrt{x + 1}$

48. $\sqrt{1 + x} + \sqrt{1 - x} = 2$

49–58 ■ Equations of Quadratic Type   Find all real solutions of the equation.

49. $x^4 - 4x^2 + 3 = 0$

50. $x^4 - 5x^2 + 6 = 0$

51. $2x^4 + 4x^2 + 1 = 0$

52. $x^6 - 2x^3 - 3 = 0$

53. $x^6 - 26x^3 - 27 = 0$

54. $x^8 + 15x^4 = 16$

55. $(x + 5)^2 - 3(x + 5) - 10 = 0$

56. $\left(\dfrac{x + 1}{x}\right)^2 + 4\left(\dfrac{x + 1}{x}\right) + 3 = 0$

57. $\left(\dfrac{1}{x + 1}\right)^2 - 2\left(\dfrac{1}{x + 1}\right) - 8 = 0$

58. $\left(\dfrac{x}{x + 2}\right)^2 = \dfrac{4x}{x + 2} - 4$

59–66 ■ Equations Involving Fractional Exponents   Find all real solutions of the equation.

59. $x^{4/3} - 5x^{2/3} + 6 = 0$

60. $\sqrt{x} - 3\sqrt[4]{x} - 4 = 0$

61. $4(x + 1)^{1/2} - 5(x + 1)^{3/2} + (x + 1)^{5/2} = 0$

62. $2(x - 4)^{7/3} - (x - 4)^{4/3} - (x - 4)^{1/3} = 0$

63. $x^{3/2} - 10x^{1/2} + 25x^{-1/2} = 0$

64. $x^{1/2} - x^{-1/2} - 6x^{-3/2} = 0$

65. $x^{1/2} - 3x^{1/3} = 3x^{1/6} - 9$

66. $x - 5\sqrt{x} + 6 = 0$

SKILLS Plus

67–74 ■ More on Solving Equations   Find all real solutions of the equation.

67. $\dfrac{1}{x^3} + \dfrac{4}{x^2} + \dfrac{4}{x} = 0$

68. $4x^{-4} - 16x^{-2} + 4 = 0$

69. $\sqrt{\sqrt{x + 5} + x} = 5$

70. $\sqrt[3]{4x^2 - 4x} = x$

71. $x^2\sqrt{x + 3} = (x + 3)^{3/2}$

72. $\sqrt{11 - x^2} - \dfrac{2}{\sqrt{11 - x^2}} = 1$

73. $\sqrt{x + \sqrt{x + 2}} = 2$

74. $\sqrt{1 + \sqrt{x + \sqrt{2x + 1}}} = \sqrt{5 + \sqrt{x}}$

75–78 ■ More on Solving Equations   Solve the equation for the variable x. The constants a and b represent positive real numbers.

75. $x^4 - 5ax^2 + 4a^2 = 0$

76. $a^3x^3 + b^3 = 0$

77. $\sqrt{x + a} + \sqrt{x - a} = \sqrt{2}\sqrt{x + 6}$

78. $\sqrt{x} - a\sqrt[3]{x} + b\sqrt[6]{x} - ab = 0$

APPLICATIONS

79. Chartering a Bus   A social club charters a bus at a cost of $900 to take a group of members on an excursion to Atlantic City. At the last minute, five people in the group decide not to go. This raises the transportation cost per person by $2. How many people originally intended to take the trip?

80. Buying a Cottage   A group of friends decides to buy a vacation home for $120,000, sharing the cost equally. If they can find one more person to join them, each person's contribution will drop by $6000. How many people are in the group?

81. Fish Population   A large pond is stocked with fish. The fish population P is modeled by the formula $P = 3t + 10\sqrt{t} + 140$, where t is the number of days since the fish were first introduced into the pond. How many days will it take for the fish population to reach 500?

82. The Lens Equation   If F is the focal length of a convex lens and an object is placed at a distance x from the lens, then its image will be at a distance y from the lens, where F, x, and y are related by the *lens equation*

$$\frac{1}{F} = \frac{1}{x} + \frac{1}{y}$$

Suppose that a lens has a focal length of 4.8 cm and that the image of an object is 4 cm closer to the lens than the object itself. How far from the lens is the object?

83. Volume of Grain   Grain is falling from a chute onto the ground, forming a conical pile whose diameter is always three times its height. How high is the pile (to the nearest hundredth of a foot) when it contains 1000 ft^3 of grain?

84. Radius of a Tank   A spherical tank has a capacity of 750 gallons. Using the fact that 1 gallon is about 0.1337 ft^3, find the radius of the tank (to the nearest hundredth of a foot).

85. Radius of a Sphere   A jeweler has three small solid spheres made of gold, of radius 2 mm, 3 mm, and 4 mm. He decides to melt these down and make just one sphere out of them. What will the radius of this larger sphere be?

86. Dimensions of a Box A large plywood box has a volume of 180 ft^3. Its length is 9 ft greater than its height, and its width is 4 ft less than its height. What are the dimensions of the box?

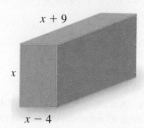

$x + 9$

x

$x - 4$

87. Construction Costs The town of Foxton lies 10 mi north of an abandoned east-west road that runs through Grimley, as shown in the figure. The point on the abandoned road closest to Foxton is 40 mi from Grimley. County officials are about to build a new road connecting the two towns. They have determined that restoring the old road would cost $100,000 per mile, while building a new road would cost $200,000 per mile. How much of the abandoned road should be used (as indicated in the figure) if the officials intend to spend exactly $6.8 million? Would it cost less than this amount to build a new road connecting the towns directly?

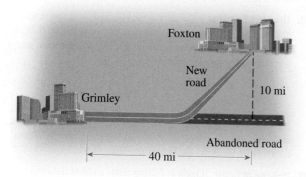

Foxton

New road

10 mi

Grimley

Abandoned road

40 mi

88. Distance, Speed, and Time A boardwalk is parallel to and 210 ft inland from a straight shoreline. A sandy beach lies between the boardwalk and the shoreline. A man is standing on the boardwalk, exactly 750 ft across the sand from his beach umbrella, which is right at the shoreline. The man walks 4 ft/s on the boardwalk and 2 ft/s on the sand. How far should he walk on the boardwalk before veering off onto the sand if he wishes to reach his umbrella in exactly 4 min 45 s?

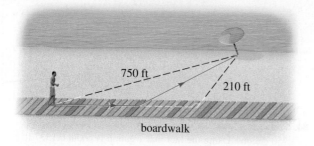

750 ft

210 ft

boardwalk

89. Dimensions of a Lot A city lot has the shape of a right triangle whose hypotenuse is 7 ft longer than one of the other sides. The perimeter of the lot is 392 ft. How long is each side of the lot?

90. Computer Monitors Two computer monitors sitting side by side on a shelf in an appliance store have the same screen height. One has a screen that is 7 in. wider than it is high. The other has a wider screen that is 1.8 times as wide as it is high. The diagonal measure of the wider screen is 3 in. more than the diagonal measure of the smaller screen. What is the height of the screens, correct to the nearest 0.1 in.?

91. Depth of a Well One method for determining the depth of a well is to drop a stone into it and then measure the time it takes until the splash is heard. If d is the depth of the well (in feet) and t_1 the time (in seconds) it takes for the stone to fall, then $d = 16t_1^2$, so $t_1 = \sqrt{d}/4$. Now if t_2 is the time it takes for the sound to travel back up, then $d = 1090t_2$ because the speed of sound is 1090 ft/s. So $t_2 = d/1090$. Thus the total time elapsed between dropping the stone and hearing the splash is

$$t_1 + t_2 = \frac{\sqrt{d}}{4} + \frac{d}{1090}$$

How deep is the well if this total time is 3 s? (See the following figure.)

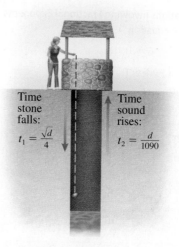

Time stone falls: $t_1 = \dfrac{\sqrt{d}}{4}$

Time sound rises: $t_2 = \dfrac{d}{1090}$

DISCUSS ■ **DISCOVER** ■ **PROVE** ■ **WRITE**

92. DISCUSS: Solving an Equation in Different Ways We have learned several different ways to solve an equation in this section. Some equations can be tackled by more than one method. For example, the equation $x - \sqrt{x} - 2 = 0$ is of quadratic type: We can solve it by letting $\sqrt{x} = u$ and $x = u^2$ and factoring. Or we could solve for $\sqrt{x}$, square each side, and then solve the resulting quadratic equation. Solve the following equations using both methods indicated, and show that you get the same final answers.

(a) $x - \sqrt{x} - 2 = 0$ Quadratic type; solve for the radical, and square

(b) $\dfrac{12}{(x-3)^2} + \dfrac{10}{x-3} + 1 = 0$ Quadratic type; multiply by LCD

1.7 SOLVING INEQUALITIES

■ Solving Linear Inequalities ■ Solving Nonlinear Inequalities
■ Modeling with Inequalities

Some problems in algebra lead to **inequalities** instead of equations. An inequality looks just like an equation, except that in the place of the equal sign is one of the symbols, $<$, $>$, $\leq$, or $\geq$. Here is an example of an inequality:

$$4x + 7 \leq 19$$

The table in the margin shows that some numbers satisfy the inequality and some numbers don't.

To **solve** an inequality that contains a variable means to find all values of the variable that make the inequality true. Unlike an equation, an inequality generally has infinitely many solutions, which form an interval or a union of intervals on the real line. The following illustration shows how an inequality differs from its corresponding equation:

x	$4x + 7 \leq 19$
1	$11 \leq 19$ ✓
2	$15 \leq 19$ ✓
3	$19 \leq 19$ ✓
4	$23 \leq 19$ ✗
5	$27 \leq 19$ ✗

		Solution	Graph
Equation:	$4x + 7 = 19$	$x = 3$	
Inequality:	$4x + 7 \leq 19$	$x \leq 3$	

To solve inequalities, we use the following rules to isolate the variable on one side of the inequality sign. These rules tell us when two inequalities are *equivalent* (the symbol $\Leftrightarrow$ means "is equivalent to"). In these rules the symbols A, B, and C stand for real numbers or algebraic expressions. Here we state the rules for inequalities involving the symbol $\leq$, but they apply to all four inequality symbols.

RULES FOR INEQUALITIES

Rule	**Description**
1. $A \leq B \quad \Leftrightarrow \quad A + C \leq B + C$	**Adding** the same quantity to each side of an inequality gives an equivalent inequality.
2. $A \leq B \quad \Leftrightarrow \quad A - C \leq B - C$	**Subtracting** the same quantity from each side of an inequality gives an equivalent inequality.
3. If $C > 0$, then $A \leq B \quad \Leftrightarrow \quad CA \leq CB$	**Multiplying** each side of an inequality by the same *positive* quantity gives an equivalent inequality.
4. If $C < 0$, then $A \leq B \quad \Leftrightarrow \quad CA \geq CB$	**Multiplying** each side of an inequality by the same *negative* quantity *reverses the direction* of the inequality.
5. If $A > 0$ and $B > 0$, then $A \leq B \quad \Leftrightarrow \quad \dfrac{1}{A} \geq \dfrac{1}{B}$	**Taking reciprocals** of each side of an inequality involving *positive* quantities *reverses the direction* of the inequality.
6. If $A \leq B$ and $C \leq D$, then $A + C \leq B + D$	Inequalities can be added.
7. If $A \leq B$ and $B \leq C$, then $A \leq C$	Inequality is transitive.

 Pay special attention to Rules 3 and 4. Rule 3 says that we can multiply (or divide) each side of an inequality by a *positive* number, but Rule 4 says that if we multiply each side of an inequality by a *negative* number, then we reverse the direction of the inequality. For example, if we start with the inequality

$$3 < 5$$

and multiply by 2, we get

$$6 < 10$$

but if we multiply by -2, we get

$$-6 > -10$$

■ Solving Linear Inequalities

An inequality is **linear** if each term is constant or a multiple of the variable. To solve a linear inequality, we isolate the variable on one side of the inequality sign.

EXAMPLE 1 ■ Solving a Linear Inequality

Solve the inequality $3x < 9x + 4$, and sketch the solution set.

SOLUTION

$$
\begin{aligned}
3x &< 9x + 4 && \text{Given inequality} \\
3x - 9x &< 9x + 4 - 9x && \text{Subtract } 9x \\
-6x &< 4 && \text{Simplify} \\
\left(-\tfrac{1}{6}\right)(-6x) &> \left(-\tfrac{1}{6}\right)(4) && \text{Multiply by } -\tfrac{1}{6} \text{ and reverse inequality} \\
x &> -\tfrac{2}{3} && \text{Simplify}
\end{aligned}
$$

The solution set consists of all numbers greater than $-\tfrac{2}{3}$. In other words the solution of the inequality is the interval $\left(-\tfrac{2}{3}, \infty\right)$. It is graphed in Figure 1.

✎· **Now Try Exercise 19**

Multiplying by the negative number $-\tfrac{1}{6}$ *reverses* the direction of the inequality.

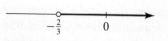

FIGURE 1

EXAMPLE 2 ■ Solving a Pair of Simultaneous Inequalities

Solve the inequalities $4 \le 3x - 2 < 13$.

SOLUTION The solution set consists of all values of x that satisfy both of the inequalities $4 \le 3x - 2$ and $3x - 2 < 13$. Using Rules 1 and 3, we see that the following inequalities are equivalent:

$$
\begin{aligned}
4 &\le 3x - 2 < 13 && \text{Given inequality} \\
6 &\le 3x < 15 && \text{Add 2} \\
2 &\le x < 5 && \text{Divide by 3}
\end{aligned}
$$

Therefore the solution set is $[2, 5)$, as shown in Figure 2.

✎· **Now Try Exercise 27**

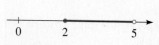

FIGURE 2

■ Solving Nonlinear Inequalities

To solve inequalities involving squares and other powers of the variable, we use factoring, together with the following principle.

THE SIGN OF A PRODUCT OR QUOTIENT

- If a product or a quotient has an *even* number of *negative* factors, then its value is *positive*.

- If a product or a quotient has an *odd* number of *negative* factors, then its value is *negative*.

For example, to solve the inequality $x^2 - 5x \leq -6$, we first move all terms to the left-hand side and factor to get

$$(x - 2)(x - 3) \leq 0$$

This form of the inequality says that the product $(x - 2)(x - 3)$ must be negative or zero, so to solve the inequality, we must determine where each factor is negative or positive (because the sign of a product depends on the sign of the factors). The details are explained in Example 3, in which we use the following guidelines.

GUIDELINES FOR SOLVING NONLINEAR INEQUALITIES

1. **Move All Terms to One Side.**   If necessary, rewrite the inequality so that all nonzero terms appear on one side of the inequality sign. If the nonzero side of the inequality involves quotients, bring them to a common denominator.

2. **Factor.**   Factor the nonzero side of the inequality.

3. **Find the Intervals.**   Determine the values for which each factor is zero. These numbers will divide the real line into intervals. List the intervals that are determined by these numbers.

4. **Make a Table or Diagram.**   Use **test values** to make a table or diagram of the signs of each factor on each interval. In the last row of the table determine the sign of the product (or quotient) of these factors.

5. **Solve.**   Use the sign table to find the intervals on which the inequality is satisfied. Check whether the **endpoints** of these intervals satisfy the inequality. (This may happen if the inequality involves $\leq$ or $\geq$.)

  The factoring technique that is described in these guidelines works only if all nonzero terms appear on one side of the inequality symbol. If the inequality is not written in this form, first rewrite it, as indicated in Step 1.

EXAMPLE 3 ■ Solving a Quadratic Inequality

Solve the inequality $x^2 \leq 5x - 6$.

SOLUTION   We will follow the guidelines given above.

Move all terms to one side.   We move all the terms to the left-hand side.

$$x^2 \leq 5x - 6 \qquad \text{Given inequality}$$

$$x^2 - 5x + 6 \leq 0 \qquad \text{Subtract } 5x, \text{ add } 6$$

Factor.   Factoring the left-hand side of the inequality, we get

$$(x - 2)(x - 3) \leq 0 \qquad \text{Factor}$$

Find the intervals.   The factors of the left-hand side are $x - 2$ and $x - 3$. These factors are zero when x is 2 and 3, respectively. As shown in Figure 3, the numbers 2 and 3 divide the real line into the three intervals

$$(-\infty, 2), (2, 3), (3, \infty)$$

The factors $x - 2$ and $x - 3$ change sign only at 2 and 3, respectively. So these factors maintain their sign on each of these three intervals.

Make a table or diagram.   To determine the sign of each factor on each of the intervals that we found, we use test values. We choose a number inside each interval and check the sign of the factors $x - 2$ and $x - 3$ at the number we chose. For the interval

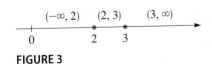

FIGURE 3

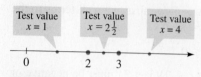

FIGURE 4

$(-\infty, 2)$, let's choose the test value 1 (see Figure 4). Substituting 1 for x in the factors $x - 2$ and $x - 3$, we get

$$x - 2 = 1 - 2 = -1 < 0$$

$$x - 3 = 1 - 3 = -2 < 0$$

So both factors are negative on this interval. Notice that we need to check only one test value for each interval because the factors $x - 2$ and $x - 3$ do not change sign on any of the three intervals we found.

Using the test values $x = 2\frac{1}{2}$ and $x = 4$ for the intervals $(2, 3)$ and $(3, \infty)$ (see Figure 4), respectively, we construct the following sign table. The final row of the table is obtained from the fact that the expression in the last row is the product of the two factors.

Interval	$(-\infty, 2)$	$(2, 3)$	$(3, \infty)$
Sign of $x - 2$ Sign of $x - 3$	$-$ $-$	$+$ $-$	$+$ $+$
Sign of $(x - 2)(x - 3)$	$+$	$-$	$+$

If you prefer, you can represent this information on a real line, as in the following sign diagram. The vertical lines indicate the points at which the real line is divided into intervals:

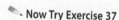

Sign of $x - 2$ $-$ $+$ $+$

Sign of $x - 3$ $-$ $-$ $+$

Sign of $(x - 2)(x - 3)$ $+$ $-$ $+$

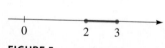

FIGURE 5

Solve. We read from the table or the diagram that $(x - 2)(x - 3)$ is negative on the interval $(2, 3)$. You can check that the endpoints 2 and 3 satisfy the inequality, so the solution is

$$\{x \mid 2 \le x \le 3\} = [2, 3]$$

The solution is illustrated in Figure 5.

✎ **Now Try Exercise 37**

EXAMPLE 4 ■ Solving an Inequality

Solve the inequality $2x^2 - x > 1$.

SOLUTION   We will follow the guidelines on page 143.

Move all terms to one side.   We move all the terms to the left-hand side.

$$2x^2 - x > 1 \qquad \text{Given inequality}$$

$$2x^2 - x - 1 > 0 \qquad \text{Subtract 1}$$

Factor.   Factoring the left-hand side of the inequality, we get

$$(2x + 1)(x - 1) > 0 \qquad \text{Factor}$$

Find the intervals.   The factors of the left-hand side are $2x + 1$ and $x - 1$. These factors are zero when x is $-\frac{1}{2}$ and 1. These numbers divide the real line into the intervals

$$\left(-\infty, -\tfrac{1}{2}\right), \left(-\tfrac{1}{2}, 1\right), (1, \infty)$$

Make a diagram. We make the following diagram, using test points to determine the sign of each factor in each interval:

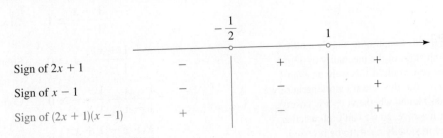

Sign of $2x + 1$

Sign of $x - 1$

Sign of $(2x + 1)(x - 1)$

Solve. From the diagram we see that $(2x + 1)(x - 1) > 0$ for x in the interval $\left(-\infty, -\frac{1}{2}\right)$ or for x in $(1, \infty)$. Since this inequality involves $<$, the endpoints of the intervals do not satisfy the inequality. So the solution set is the union of these two intervals:

$$\left(-\infty, -\tfrac{1}{2}\right) \cup (1, \infty)$$

The solution set is graphed in Figure 6.

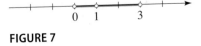

FIGURE 6

■. Now Try Exercise 39

EXAMPLE 5 ■ Solving an Inequality with Repeated Factors

Solve the inequality $x(x - 1)^2(x - 3) < 0$.

SOLUTION All nonzero terms are already on one side of the inequality, and the non-zero side of the inequality is already factored. So we begin by finding the intervals for this inequality.

Find the intervals. The factors of the left-hand side are x, $(x - 1)^2$, and $x - 3$. These are zero when $x = 0, 1$, and 3. These numbers divide the real line into the intervals

$$(-\infty, 0), (0, 1), (1, 3), (3, \infty)$$

Make a diagram. We make the following diagram, using test points to determine the sign of each factor in each interval.

Sign of x

Sign of $(x - 1)^2$

Sign of $(x - 3)$

Sign of $x(x - 1)^2(x - 3)$

Solve. From the diagram we see that the inequality is satisfied on the intervals $(0, 1)$ and $(1, 3)$. Since this inequality involves $<$, the endpoints of the intervals do not satisfy the inequality. So the solution set is the union of these two intervals:

$$(0, 1) \cup (1, 3)$$

The solution set is graphed in Figure 7.

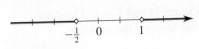

FIGURE 7

■. Now Try Exercise 51

EXAMPLE 6 ■ Solving an Inequality Involving a Quotient

Solve the inequality $\dfrac{1 + x}{1 - x} \geq 1$.

SOLUTION Move all terms to one side.   We move the terms to the left-hand side and simplify using a common denominator.

$$\frac{1+x}{1-x} \geq 1 \qquad \text{Given inequality}$$

$$\frac{1+x}{1-x} - 1 \geq 0 \qquad \text{Subtract 1}$$

$$\frac{1+x}{1-x} - \frac{1-x}{1-x} \geq 0 \qquad \text{Common denominator } 1-x$$

$$\frac{1+x-1+x}{1-x} \geq 0 \qquad \text{Combine the fractions}$$

$$\frac{2x}{1-x} \geq 0 \qquad \text{Simplify}$$

⊘ It is tempting to simply multiply both sides of the inequality by $1-x$ (as you would if this were an *equation*). But this doesn't work because we don't know whether $1-x$ is positive or negative, so we can't tell whether the inequality needs to be reversed. (See Exercise 95.)

Find the intervals.   The factors of the left-hand side are $2x$ and $1-x$. These are zero when x is 0 and 1. These numbers divide the real line into the intervals

$$(-\infty, 0), (0, 1), (1, \infty)$$

Make a diagram.   We make the following diagram using test points to determine the sign of each factor in each interval.

	0	1
Sign of $2x$	$-$ $+$	$+$
Sign of $1-x$	$+$ $+$	$-$
Sign of $\dfrac{2x}{1-x}$	$-$ $+$	$-$

Solve.   From the diagram we see that the inequality is satisfied on the interval $(0, 1)$. Checking the endpoints, we see that 0 satisfies the inequality but 1 does not (because the quotient in the inequality is not defined at 1). So the solution set is the interval

$$[0, 1)$$

The solution set is graphed in Figure 8.

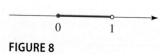

0   1

FIGURE 8

✎ Now Try Exercise 59

⊘   Example 6 shows that we should always check the endpoints of the solution set to see whether they satisfy the original inequality.

■ Modeling with Inequalities

Modeling real-life problems frequently leads to inequalities because we are often interested in determining when one quantity is more (or less) than another.

EXAMPLE 7 ■ Carnival Tickets

A carnival has two plans for tickets.

Plan A: $5 entrance fee and 25¢ each ride

Plan B: $2 entrance fee and 50¢ each ride

How many rides would you have to take for Plan A to be less expensive than Plan B?

SOLUTION Identify the variable. We are asked for the number of rides for which Plan A is less expensive than Plan B. So let

$$x = \text{number of rides}$$

Translate from words to algebra. The information in the problem may be organized as follows.

In Words	In Algebra
Number of rides	x
Cost with Plan A	$5 + 0.25x$
Cost with Plan B	$2 + 0.50x$

Set up the model. Now we set up the model.

$$\boxed{\text{cost with Plan A}} < \boxed{\text{cost with Plan B}}$$

$$5 + 0.25x < 2 + 0.50x$$

Solve. Now we solve for x.

$$3 + 0.25x < 0.50x \qquad \text{Subtract 2}$$

$$3 < 0.25x \qquad \text{Subtract } 0.25x$$

$$12 < x \qquad \text{Divide by } 0.25$$

So if you plan to take *more than* 12 rides, Plan A is less expensive.

✎. **Now Try Exercise 81**

EXAMPLE 8 ■ Relationship Between Fahrenheit and Celsius Scales

The instructions on a bottle of medicine indicate that the bottle should be stored at a temperature between 5 °C and 30 °C. What range of temperatures does this correspond to on the Fahrenheit scale?

SOLUTION The relationship between degrees Celsius (C) and degrees Fahrenheit (F) is given by the equation $C = \frac{5}{9}(F - 32)$. Expressing the statement on the bottle in terms of inequalities, we have

$$5 < C < 30$$

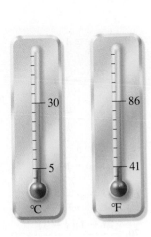

So the corresponding Fahrenheit temperatures satisfy the inequalities

$$5 < \tfrac{5}{9}(F - 32) < 30 \qquad \text{Substitute } C = \tfrac{5}{9}(F - 32)$$

$$\tfrac{9}{5} \cdot 5 < F - 32 < \tfrac{9}{5} \cdot 30 \qquad \text{Multiply by } \tfrac{9}{5}$$

$$9 < F - 32 < 54 \qquad \text{Simplify}$$

$$9 + 32 < F < 54 + 32 \qquad \text{Add 32}$$

$$41 < F < 86 \qquad \text{Simplify}$$

The medicine should be stored at a temperature between 41 °F and 86 °F.

✎. **Now Try Exercise 79**

1.7 EXERCISES

CONCEPTS

1. Fill in the blank with an appropriate inequality symbol.

  (a) If $x < 5$, then $x - 3$ _____ 2.

  (b) If $x \leq 5$, then $3x$ _____ 15.

  (c) If $x \geq 2$, then $-3x$ _____ -6.

  (d) If $x < -2$, then $-x$ _____ 2.

2. To solve the nonlinear inequality $\dfrac{x+1}{x-2} \leq 0$, we first observe that the numbers _____ and _____ are zeros of the numerator and denominator. These numbers divide the real line into three intervals. Complete the table.

Interval			
Sign of $x + 1$			
Sign of $x - 2$			
Sign of $(x+1)/(x-2)$			

Do any of the endpoints fail to satisfy the inequality? If so, which one(s)? _____. The solution of the inequality is

_____.

3. *Yes* or *No*? If *No*, give an example.

  (a) If $x(x + 1) > 0$, does it follow that x is positive?

  (b) If $x(x + 1) > 5$, does it follow that $x > 5$?

4. What is the logical first step in solving the inequality?

  (a) $3x \leq 7$ **(b)** $5x - 2 \geq 1$

SKILLS

5–10 ■ Solutions? Let $S = \{-5, -1, 0, \frac{2}{3}, \frac{5}{6}, 1, \sqrt{5}, 3, 5\}$. Determine which elements of S satisfy the inequality.

5. $-2 + 3x \geq \frac{1}{3}$

6. $1 - 2x \geq 5x$

7. $1 < 2x - 4 \leq 7$

8. $-2 \leq 3 - x < 2$

9. $\dfrac{1}{x} \leq \dfrac{1}{2}$

10. $x^2 + 2 < 4$

11–32 ■ Linear Inequalities Solve the linear inequality. Express the solution using interval notation and graph the solution set.

11. $5x \leq 6$

12. $2x \geq 8$

13. $2x - 5 > 3$

14. $3x + 11 < 5$

15. $2 - 3x > 8$

16. $1 < 5 - 2x$

17. $2x + 1 < 0$

18. $0 < 5 - 2x$

19. $1 + 4x \leq 5 - 2x$

20. $5 - 3x \leq 2 - 9x$

21. $\frac{1}{2}x - \frac{2}{3} > 2$

22. $\frac{2}{3} - \frac{1}{2}x \geq \frac{1}{6} + x$

23. $4 - 3x \leq -(1 + 8x)$

24. $2(7x - 3) \leq 12x + 16$

25. $2 \leq x + 5 < 4$

26. $5 \leq 3x - 4 \leq 14$

27. $-6 \leq 3x - 7 \leq 8$

28. $-8 \leq 5x - 4 \leq 5$

29. $-2 < 8 - 2x \leq -1$

30. $-3 \leq 3x + 7 \leq \frac{1}{2}$

31. $\dfrac{2}{3} \geq \dfrac{2x-3}{12} > \dfrac{1}{6}$

32. $-\dfrac{1}{2} \leq \dfrac{4-3x}{5} \leq \dfrac{1}{4}$

33–54 ■ Nonlinear Inequalities Solve the nonlinear inequality. Express the solution using interval notation, and graph the solution set.

33. $(x + 2)(x - 3) < 0$

34. $(x - 5)(x + 4) \geq 0$

35. $x(2x + 7) \geq 0$

36. $x(2 - 3x) \leq 0$

37. $x^2 - 3x - 18 \leq 0$

38. $x^2 + 5x + 6 > 0$

39. $2x^2 + x \geq 1$

40. $x^2 < x + 2$

41. $3x^2 - 3x < 2x^2 + 4$

42. $5x^2 + 3x \geq 3x^2 + 2$

43. $x^2 > 3(x + 6)$

44. $x^2 + 2x > 3$

45. $x^2 < 4$

46. $x^2 \geq 9$

47. $(x + 2)(x - 1)(x - 3) \leq 0$

48. $(x - 5)(x - 2)(x + 1) > 0$

49. $(x - 4)(x + 2)^2 < 0$

50. $(x + 3)^2(x + 1) > 0$

51. $(x - 2)^2(x - 3)(x + 1) \leq 0$

52. $x^2(x^2 - 1) \geq 0$

53. $x^3 - 4x > 0$

54. $16x \leq x^3$

55–72 ■ Inequalities Involving Quotients Solve the nonlinear inequality. Express the solution using interval notation, and graph the solution set.

55. $\dfrac{x+3}{2x-1} \geq 0$

56. $\dfrac{4-x}{x+4} < 0$

57. $\dfrac{4x}{2x+3} > 2$

58. $-2 < \dfrac{x+1}{x-3}$

59. $\dfrac{2x+1}{x-5} \leq 3$

60. $\dfrac{3+x}{3-x} \geq 1$

61. $\dfrac{4}{x} < x$

62. $\dfrac{x}{x+1} > 3x$

63. $1 + \dfrac{2}{x+1} \leq \dfrac{2}{x}$

64. $\dfrac{3}{x-1} - \dfrac{4}{x} \geq 1$

65. $\dfrac{6}{x-1} - \dfrac{6}{x} \geq 1$

66. $\dfrac{x}{2} \geq \dfrac{5}{x+1} + 4$

67. $\dfrac{x+2}{x+3} < \dfrac{x-1}{x-2}$

68. $\dfrac{1}{x+1} + \dfrac{1}{x+2} \leq 0$

69. $\dfrac{(x-1)(x+2)}{(x-2)^2} \geq 0$

70. $\dfrac{(2x-1)(x-3)^2}{x-4} < 0$

71. $x^4 > x^2$

72. $x^5 > x^2$

73–76 ■ Domain Determine the values of the variable for which the expression is defined as a real number.

73. $\sqrt{16 - 9x^2}$

74. $\sqrt{3x^2 - 5x + 2}$

75. $\left(\dfrac{1}{x^2 - 5x - 14}\right)^{1/2}$

76. $\sqrt[4]{\dfrac{1-x}{2+x}}$

SKILLS Plus

77–78 ■ Inequalities Solve the inequality for x, assuming that a, b, and c are positive constants.

77. $a(bx - c) \geq bc$

78. $a \leq bx + c < 2a$

APPLICATIONS

79. Temperature Scales Use the relationship between C and F given in Example 8 to find the interval on the Fahrenheit scale corresponding to the temperature range $20 \leq C \leq 30$.

80. Temperature Scales What interval on the Celsius scale corresponds to the temperature range $50 \leq F \leq 95$?

81. Car Rental Cost A car rental company offers two plans for renting a car.

Plan A: $30 per day and 10¢ per mile
Plan B: $50 per day with free unlimited mileage

For what range of miles will Plan B save you money?

82. Long-Distance Cost A telephone company offers two long-distance plans:

Plan A: $25 per month and 5¢ per minute
Plan B: $5 per month and 12¢ per minute

For how many minutes of long-distance calls would Plan B be financially advantageous?

83. Driving Cost It is estimated that the annual cost of driving a certain new car is given by the formula

$$C = 0.35m + 2200$$

where m represents the number of miles driven per year and C is the cost in dollars. Jane has purchased such a car and decides to budget between $6400 and $7100 for next year's driving costs. What is the corresponding range of miles that she can drive her new car?

84. Air Temperature As dry air moves upward, it expands and, in so doing, cools at a rate of about 1°C for each 100-meter rise, up to about 12 km.

(a) If the ground temperature is 20°C, write a formula for the temperature at height h.

(b) What range of temperatures can be expected if an airplane takes off and reaches a maximum height of 5 km?

85. Airline Ticket Price A charter airline finds that on its Saturday flights from Philadelphia to London all 120 seats will be sold if the ticket price is $200. However, for each $3 increase in ticket price, the number of seats sold decreases by one.

(a) Find a formula for the number of seats sold if the ticket price is P dollars.

(b) Over a certain period the number of seats sold for this flight ranged between 90 and 115. What was the corresponding range of ticket prices?

86. Accuracy of a Scale A coffee merchant sells a customer 3 lb of Hawaiian Kona at $6.50 per pound. The merchant's scale is accurate to within ±0.03 lb. By how much could the customer have been overcharged or undercharged because of possible inaccuracy in the scale?

87. Gravity The gravitational force F exerted by the earth on an object having a mass of 100 kg is given by the equation

$$F = \frac{4{,}000{,}000}{d^2}$$

where d is the distance (in km) of the object from the center of the earth, and the force F is measured in newtons (N). For what distances will the gravitational force exerted by the earth on this object be between 0.0004 N and 0.01 N?

88. Bonfire Temperature In the vicinity of a bonfire the temperature T in °C at a distance of x meters from the center of the fire was given by

$$T = \frac{600{,}000}{x^2 + 300}$$

At what range of distances from the fire's center was the temperature less than 500 °C?

89. Falling Ball Using calculus, it can be shown that if a ball is thrown upward with an initial velocity of 16 ft/s from the top of a building 128 ft high, then its height h above the ground t seconds later will be

$$h = 128 + 16t - 16t^2$$

During what time interval will the ball be at least 32 ft above the ground?

90. Gas Mileage The gas mileage g (measured in mi/gal) for a particular vehicle, driven at v mi/h, is given by the formula $g = 10 + 0.9v - 0.01v^2$, as long as v is between 10 mi/h and 75 mi/h. For what range of speeds is the vehicle's mileage 30 mi/gal or better?

91. Stopping Distance For a certain model of car the distance d required to stop the vehicle if it is traveling at v mi/h is given by the formula

$$d = v + \frac{v^2}{20}$$

where d is measured in feet. Kerry wants her stopping distance not to exceed 240 ft. At what range of speeds can she travel?

← 240 ft →

92. Manufacturer's Profit   If a manufacturer sells x units of a certain product, revenue R and cost C (in dollars) are given by

$$R = 20x$$
$$C = 2000 + 8x + 0.0025x^2$$

Use the fact that

$$\text{profit} = \text{revenue} - \text{cost}$$

to determine how many units the manufacturer should sell to enjoy a profit of at least $2400.

93. Fencing a Garden   A determined gardener has 120 ft of deer-resistant fence. She wants to enclose a rectangular vegetable garden in her backyard, and she wants the area that is enclosed to be at least 800 ft². What range of values is possible for the length of her garden?

DISCUSS ▪ **DISCOVER** ▪ **PROVE** ▪ **WRITE**

94. DISCUSS ▪ **DISCOVER: Do Powers Preserve Order?**   If $a < b$, is $a^2 < b^2$? (Check both positive and negative values for a and b.) If $a < b$, is $a^3 < b^3$? On the basis of your observations, state a general rule about the relationship between a^n and b^n when $a < b$ and n is a positive integer.

95. DISCUSS ▪ **DISCOVER: What's Wrong Here?**   It is tempting to try to solve an inequality as if it were an equation. For instance, we might try to solve $1 < 3/x$ by multiplying both sides by x, to get $x < 3$, so the solution would be $(-\infty, 3)$. But that's wrong; for example, $x = -1$ lies in this interval but does not satisfy the original inequality. Explain why this method doesn't work (think about the *sign* of x). Then solve the inequality correctly.

96–97 ▪ **PROVE: Inequalities**   Use the rules of inequalities to prove the following inequalities.

96. Rule 6 for Inequalities: If a, b, c, and d are any real numbers such that $a < b$ and $c < d$, then $a + c < b + d$. [*Hint:* Use Rule 1 to show that $a + c < b + c$ and $b + c < b + d$. Use Rule 7.]

97. If a, b, c, and d are positive numbers such that $\dfrac{a}{b} < \dfrac{c}{d}$, then

$$\frac{a}{b} < \frac{a + c}{b + d} < \frac{c}{d}. \quad [\textit{Hint:} \text{ Show that } \frac{ad}{b} + a < c + a \text{ and }$$
$$a + c < \frac{cb}{d} + c.]$$

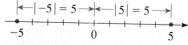

FIGURE 1

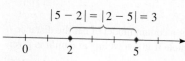

FIGURE 2

1.8   SOLVING ABSOLUTE VALUE EQUATIONS AND INEQUALITIES

▪ **Absolute Value Equations** ▪ **Absolute Value Inequalities**

Recall from Section P.2 that the absolute value of a number a is given by

$$|a| = \begin{cases} a & \text{if } a \geq 0 \\ -a & \text{if } a < 0 \end{cases}$$

and that it represents the distance from a to the origin on the real number line (see Figure 1). More generally, $|x - a|$ is the distance between x and a on the real number line. Figure 2 illustrates the fact that the distance between 2 and 5 is 3.

▪ Absolute Value Equations

We use the following property to solve equations that involve absolute value.

> $|x| = C$ is equivalent to $x = \pm C$

This property says that to solve an absolute value equation, we must solve *two* separate equations. For example, the equation $|x| = 5$ is equivalent to the two equations $x = 5$ and $x = -5$.

EXAMPLE 1 ▪ Solving an Absolute Value Equation

Solve the equation $|2x - 5| = 3$.

$x = 1$:

$$\text{LHS} = |2 \cdot 1 - 5|$$
$$= |-3| = 3 = \text{RHS} \;\checkmark$$

$x = 4$:

$$\text{LHS} = |2 \cdot 4 - 5|$$
$$= |3| = 3 = \text{RHS} \;\checkmark$$

SOLUTION   The equation $|2x - 5| = 3$ is equivalent to two equations:

$2x - 5 = 3$	or	$2x - 5 = -3$	
$2x = 8$		$2x = 2$	Add 5
$x = 4$		$x = 1$	Divide by 2

The solutions are 1 and 4.

✎ **Now Try Exercise 13**   ■

EXAMPLE 2 ■ Solving an Absolute Value Equation

Solve the equation $3|x - 7| + 5 = 14$.

SOLUTION   We first isolate the absolute value on one side of the equal sign.

$3|x - 7| + 5 = 14$	Given equation
$3|x - 7| = 9$	Subtract 5
$|x - 7| = 3$	Divide by 3
$x - 7 = 3$ or $x - 7 = -3$	Take cases
$x = 10$ $x = 4$	Add 7

The solutions are 4 and 10.

✎ **Now Try Exercise 17**   ■

■ Absolute Value Inequalities

We use the following properties to solve inequalities that involve absolute value.

These properties hold when x is replaced by any algebraic expression. (In the graphs we assume that $c > 0$.)

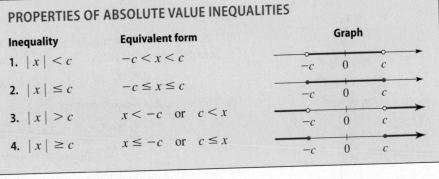

PROPERTIES OF ABSOLUTE VALUE INEQUALITIES

Inequality	Equivalent form	Graph
1. $|x| < c$	$-c < x < c$	
2. $|x| \le c$	$-c \le x \le c$	
3. $|x| > c$	$x < -c$ or $c < x$	
4. $|x| \ge c$	$x \le -c$ or $c \le x$	

These properties can be proved by using the definition of absolute value. To prove Property 1, for example, note that the inequality $|x| < c$ says that the distance from x to 0 is less than c, and from Figure 3 you can see that this is true if and only if x is between c and $-c$.

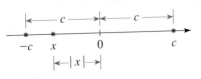

FIGURE 3

EXAMPLE 3 ■ Solving an Absolute Value Inequality

Solve the inequality $|x - 5| < 2$.

SOLUTION 1   The inequality $|x - 5| < 2$ is equivalent to

$-2 < x - 5 < 2$	Property 1
$3 < x < 7$	Add 5

The solution set is the open interval $(3, 7)$.

FIGURE 4

SOLUTION 2   Geometrically, the solution set consists of all numbers x whose distance from 5 is less than 2. From Figure 4 we see that this is the interval $(3, 7)$.

◥ **Now Try Exercise 27**

EXAMPLE 4 ■ Solving an Absolute Value Inequality

Solve the inequality $|3x + 2| \geq 4$.

SOLUTION   By Property 4 the inequality $|3x + 2| \geq 4$ is equivalent to

$$3x + 2 \geq 4 \qquad \text{or} \qquad 3x + 2 \leq -4$$
$$3x \geq 2 \qquad\qquad\qquad 3x \leq -6 \qquad \text{Subtract 2}$$
$$x \geq \tfrac{2}{3} \qquad\qquad\qquad x \leq -2 \qquad \text{Divide by 3}$$

So the solution set is

$$\left\{ x \mid x \leq -2 \quad \text{or} \quad x \geq \tfrac{2}{3} \right\} = (-\infty, -2] \cup \left[\tfrac{2}{3}, \infty \right)$$

The solution set is graphed in Figure 5.

◥ **Now Try Exercise 31**

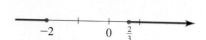

FIGURE 5

EXAMPLE 5 ■ Piston Tolerances

The specifications for a car engine indicate that the pistons have diameter 3.8745 in. with a tolerance of 0.0015 in. This means that the diameters can vary from the indicated specification by as much as 0.0015 in. and still be acceptable.

(a) Find an inequality involving absolute values that describes the range of possible diameters for the pistons.

(b) Solve the inequality.

SOLUTION

(a) Let d represent the actual diameter of a piston. Since the difference between the actual diameter (d) and the specified diameter (3.8745) is less than 0.0015, we have

$$|d - 3.8745| \leq 0.0015$$

(b) The inequality is equivalent to

$$-0.0015 \leq d - 3.8745 \leq 0.0015 \qquad \text{Property 1}$$
$$3.8730 \leq d \leq 3.8760 \qquad \text{Add 3.8745}$$

Acceptable piston diameters may vary between 3.8730 in. and 3.8760 in.

◥ **Now Try Exercise 57**

1.8 EXERCISES

CONCEPTS

1. The equation $|x| = 3$ has the two solutions _____ and _____.

2. (a) The solution of the inequality $|x| \leq 3$ is the interval _____.

(b) The solution of the inequality $|x| \geq 3$ is a union of two intervals _____ ∪ _____.

3. (a) The set of all points on the real line whose distance from zero is less than 3 can be described by the absolute value inequality $|x|$ _____.

(b) The set of all points on the real line whose distance from zero is greater than 3 can be described by the absolute value inequality $|x|$ _____ .

4. (a) What is the logical first step in solving the equation $|2x - 1| = 5$?

(b) What is the logical first step in solving the inequality $|3x + 2| \le 8$?

SKILLS

5–22 ■ Absolute Value Equations   Solve the equation.

5. $|5x| = 20$

6. $|-3x| = 10$

7. $5|x| + 3 = 28$

8. $\frac{1}{2}|x| - 7 = 2$

9. $|x - 3| = 2$

10. $|2x - 3| = 7$

11. $|x + 4| = 0.5$

12. $|x - 4| = -3$

13. $|2x - 3| = 11$

14. $|2 - x| = 11$

15. $4 - |3x + 6| = 1$

16. $|5 - 2x| + 6 = 14$

17. $3|x + 5| + 6 = 15$

18. $20 + |2x - 4| = 15$

19. $8 + 5|\frac{1}{3}x - \frac{5}{6}| = 33$

20. $|\frac{3}{5}x + 2| - \frac{1}{2} = 4$

21. $|x - 1| = |3x + 2|$

22. $|x + 3| = |2x + 1|$

23–48 ■ Absolute Value Inequalities   Solve the inequality. Express the answer using interval notation.

23. $|x| \le 5$

24. $|2x| \le 20$

25. $|2x| > 7$

26. $\frac{1}{2}|x| \ge 1$

27. $|x - 4| \le 10$

28. $|x - 3| > 9$

29. $|x + 1| \ge 1$

30. $|x + 4| \le 0$

31. $|2x + 1| \ge 3$

32. $|3x - 2| > 7$

33. $|2x - 3| \le 0.4$

34. $|5x - 2| < 6$

35. $\left|\dfrac{x - 2}{3}\right| < 2$

36. $\left|\dfrac{x + 1}{2}\right| \ge 4$

37. $|x + 6| < 0.001$

38. $|x - a| < d$

39. $4|x + 2| - 3 < 13$

40. $3 - |2x + 4| \le 1$

41. $8 - |2x - 1| \ge 6$

42. $7|x + 2| + 5 > 4$

43. $\frac{1}{2}|4x + \frac{1}{3}| > \frac{5}{6}$

44. $2|\frac{1}{2}x + 3| + 3 \le 51$

45. $1 \le |x| \le 4$

46. $0 < |x - 5| \le \frac{1}{2}$

47. $\dfrac{1}{|x + 7|} > 2$

48. $\dfrac{1}{|2x - 3|} \le 5$

49–52 ■ Words to Algebra   A phrase that describes a set of real numbers is given. Express the phrase as an inequality involving an absolute value.

49. All real numbers x less than 3 units from 0

50. All real numbers x more than 2 units from 0

51. All real numbers x at least 5 units from 7

52. All real numbers x at most 4 units from 2

53–56 ■ Algebraic Description of a Set   A set of real numbers is graphed. Find an inequality involving an absolute value that describes the set.

53.
```
-5 -4 -3 -2 -1  0  1  2  3  4  5
```

54.
```
-5 -4 -3 -2 -1  0  1  2  3  4  5
```

55.
```
-5 -4 -3 -2 -1  0  1  2  3  4  5
```

56.
```
-5 -4 -3 -2 -1  0  1  2  3  4  5
```

APPLICATIONS

57. Thickness of a Laminate   A company manufactures industrial laminates (thin nylon-based sheets) of thickness 0.020 in., with a tolerance of 0.003 in.

(a) Find an inequality involving absolute values that describes the range of possible thickness for the laminate.

(b) Solve the inequality that you found in part (a).

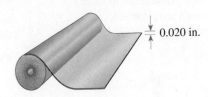

0.020 in.

58. Range of Height   The average height of adult males is 68.2 in., and 95% of adult males have height h that satisfies the inequality

$$\left|\frac{h - 68.2}{2.9}\right| \le 2$$

Solve the inequality to find the range of heights.

DISCUSS ■ DISCOVER ■ PROVE ■ WRITE

59. DISCUSS ■ DISCOVER: Using Distances to Solve Absolute Value Inequalities   Recall that $|a - b|$ is the distance between a and b on the number line. For any number x, what do $|x - 1|$ and $|x - 3|$ represent? Use this interpretation to solve the inequality $|x - 1| < |x - 3|$ geometrically. In general, if $a < b$, what is the solution of the inequality $|x - a| < |x - b|$?

1.9 SOLVING EQUATIONS AND INEQUALITIES GRAPHICALLY

■ Solving Equations Graphically ■ Solving Inequalities Graphically

"Algebra is a merry science," Uncle Jakob would say. "We go hunting for a little animal whose name we don't know, so we call it *x*. When we bag our game we pounce on it and give it its right name."

ALBERT EINSTEIN

In Sections P.8, 1.4, and 1.6 we learned how to solve equations by the **algebraic method**. In this method we view *x* as an *unknown* and then use the rules of algebra to "hunt it down," by isolating it on one side of the equation. In Section 1.7 we solved inequalities by this same method.

Sometimes an equation or inequality may be difficult or impossible to solve algebraically. In this case we use the **graphical method**. In this method we view *x* as a *variable* and sketch an appropriate graph. We can then obtain an approximate solution from the graph.

■ Solving Equations Graphically

To solve a one-variable equation such as $3x - 5 = 0$ graphically, we first draw a graph of the two-variable equation $y = 3x - 5$ obtained by setting the nonzero side of the equation equal to a variable *y*. The solutions of the given equation are the values of *x* for which *y* is equal to zero. That is, the solutions are the *x*-intercepts of the graph. The following describes the method.

SOLVING AN EQUATION

Algebraic Method

Use the rules of algebra to isolate the unknown *x* on one side of the equation.

Example: $3x - 4 = 1$

$3x = 5$ Add 4

$x = \frac{5}{3}$ Divide by 3

The solution is $x = \frac{5}{3}$.

Graphical Method

Move all terms to one side, and set equal to *y*. Graph the resulting equation, and find the *x*-intercepts.

Example: $3x - 4 = 1$

$3x - 5 = 0$ Subtract 1

Set $y = 3x - 5$ and graph. From the graph we see that the solution is $x \approx 1.7$

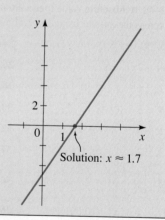

Solution: $x \approx 1.7$

The advantage of the algebraic method is that it gives exact answers. Also, the process of unraveling the equation to arrive at the answer helps us to understand the algebraic structure of the equation. On the other hand, for many equations it is difficult or impossible to isolate *x*.

Bettmann/Corbis

PIERRE DE FERMAT (1601–1665) was a French lawyer who became interested in mathematics at the age of 30. Because of his job as a magistrate, Fermat had little time to write complete proofs of his discoveries and often wrote them in the margin of whatever book he was reading at the time. After his death his copy of Diophantus' *Arithmetica* (see page 47) was found to contain a particularly tantalizing comment. Where Diophantus discusses the solutions of $x^2 + y^2 = z^2$ (for example, $x = 3$, $y = 4$, and $z = 5$), Fermat states in the margin that for $n \geq 3$ there are no natural number solutions to the equation $x^n + y^n = z^n$. In other words, it's impossible for a cube to equal the sum of two cubes, a fourth power to equal the sum of two fourth powers, and so on. Fermat writes, "I have discovered a truly wonderful proof for this but the margin is too small to contain it." All the other margin comments in Fermat's copy of *Arithmetica* have been proved. This one, however, remained unproved, and it came to be known as "Fermat's Last Theorem."

In 1994, Andrew Wiles of Princeton University announced a proof of Fermat's Last Theorem, an astounding 350 years after it was conjectured. His proof is one of the most widely reported mathematical results in the popular press.

The *Discovery Project* referenced on page 312 describes a numerical method for solving equations.

The graphical method gives a numerical approximation to the answer. This is an advantage when a numerical answer is desired. (For example, an engineer might find an answer expressed as $x \approx 2.6$ more immediately useful than $x = \sqrt{7}$.) Also, graphing an equation helps us to visualize how the solution is related to other values of the variable.

EXAMPLE 1 ■ Solving a Quadratic Equation Algebraically and Graphically

Find all real solutions of the quadratic equation. Use the algebraic method and the graphical method.

(a) $x^2 - 4x + 2 = 0$ **(b)** $x^2 - 4x + 4 = 0$ **(c)** $x^2 - 4x + 6 = 0$

SOLUTION 1: Algebraic

The Quadratic Formula is discussed on page 118.

You can check that the Quadratic Formula gives the following solutions.

(a) There are two real solutions, $x = 2 + \sqrt{2}$ and $x = 2 - \sqrt{2}$.

(b) There is one real solution, $x = 2$.

(c) There is no real solution. (The two complex solutions are $x = 2 + \sqrt{2}i$ and $x = 2 - \sqrt{2}i$.)

SOLUTION 2: Graphical

We use a graphing calculator to graph the equations $y = x^2 - 4x + 2$, $y = x^2 - 4x + 4$, and $y = x^2 - 4x + 6$ in Figure 1. By determining the x-intercepts of the graphs, we find the following solutions.

See Appendix D, *Using the TI-83/84 Graphing Calculator*, for specific instructions.

(a) The two x-intercepts give the two solutions $x \approx 0.6$ and $x \approx 3.4$.

(b) The one x-intercept gives the one solution $x = 2$.

(c) There is no x-intercept, so the equation has no real solutions.

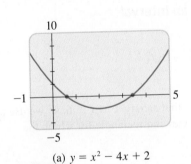

(a) $y = x^2 - 4x + 2$

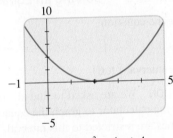

(b) $y = x^2 - 4x + 4$

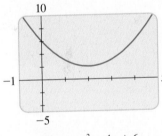

(c) $y = x^2 - 4x + 6$

FIGURE 1

✎ Now Try Exercises 9, 11, and 15

The graphs in Figure 1 show visually why a quadratic equation may have two solutions, one solution, or no real solution. We proved this fact algebraically in Section 1.4 when we studied the discriminant.

ALAN TURING (1912–1954) was at the center of two pivotal events of the 20th century: World War II and the invention of computers. At the age of 23 Turing made his mark on mathematics by solving an important problem in the foundations of mathematics that had been posed by David Hilbert at the 1928 International Congress of Mathematicians (see page 804). In this research he invented a theoretical machine, now called a Turing machine, which was the inspiration for modern digital computers. During World War II Turing was in charge of the British effort to decipher secret German codes. His complete success in this endeavor played a decisive role in the Allies' victory. To carry out the numerous logical steps that are required to break a coded message, Turing developed decision procedures similar to modern computer programs. After the war he helped to develop the first electronic computers in Britain. He also did pioneering work on artificial intelligence and computer models of biological processes. At the age of 42 Turing died of poisoning after eating an apple that had mysteriously been laced with cyanide.

Science Source

EXAMPLE 2 ■ Another Graphical Method

Solve the equation algebraically and graphically: $5 - 3x = 8x - 20$

SOLUTION 1: Algebraic

$$
\begin{aligned}
5 - 3x &= 8x - 20 && \text{Given equation} \\
-3x &= 8x - 25 && \text{Subtract 5} \\
-11x &= -25 && \text{Subtract } 8x \\
x &= \frac{-25}{-11} = 2\tfrac{3}{11} && \text{Divide by } -11 \text{ and simplify}
\end{aligned}
$$

SOLUTION 2: Graphical

We could move all terms to one side of the equal sign, set the result equal to y, and graph the resulting equation. But to avoid all this algebra, we use a graphing calculator to graph the two equations instead:

$$
y_1 = 5 - 3x \qquad \text{and} \qquad y_2 = 8x - 20
$$

The solution of the original equation will be the value of x that makes y_1 equal to y_2; that is, the solution is the x-coordinate of the intersection point of the two graphs. Using the $\boxed{\text{TRACE}}$ feature or the `intersect` command on a graphing calculator, we see from Figure 2 that the solution is $x \approx 2.27$.

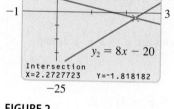

FIGURE 2

✎ **Now Try Exercise 5**

In the next example we use the graphical method to solve an equation that is extremely difficult to solve algebraically.

EXAMPLE 3 ■ Solving an Equation in an Interval

Solve the equation

$$
x^3 - 6x^2 + 9x = \sqrt{x}
$$

in the interval $[1, 6]$.

SOLUTION   We are asked to find all solutions x that satisfy $1 \le x \le 6$, so we use a graphing calculator to graph the equation in a viewing rectangle for which the x-values are restricted to this interval.

$$
\begin{aligned}
x^3 - 6x^2 + 9x &= \sqrt{x} && \text{Given equation} \\
x^3 - 6x^2 + 9x - \sqrt{x} &= 0 && \text{Subtract } \sqrt{x}
\end{aligned}
$$

We can also use the `zero` command to find the solutions, as shown in Figures 3(a) and 3(b).

Figure 3 shows the graph of the equation $y = x^3 - 6x^2 + 9x - \sqrt{x}$ in the viewing rectangle $[1, 6]$ by $[-5, 5]$. There are two x-intercepts in this viewing rectangle; zooming in, we see that the solutions are $x \approx 2.18$ and $x \approx 3.72$.

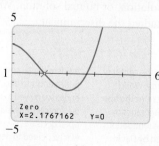

(a)

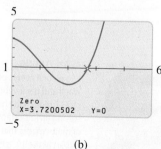

(b)

FIGURE 3

✎ **Now Try Exercise 17**

The equation in Example 3 actually has four solutions. You are asked to find the other two in Exercise 46.

■ Solving Inequalities Graphically

To solve a one-variable inequality such as $3x - 5 \geq 0$ graphically, we first draw a graph of the two-variable equation $y = 3x - 5$ obtained by setting the nonzero side of the inequality equal to a variable y. The solutions of the given inequality are the values of x for which y is greater than or equal to 0. That is, the solutions are the values of x for which the graph is above the x-axis.

SOLVING AN INEQUALITY

Algebraic Method

Use the rules of algebra to isolate the unknown x on one side of the inequality.

Example: $3x - 4 \geq 1$

$\qquad 3x \geq 5 \qquad$ Add 4

$\qquad x \geq \frac{5}{3} \qquad$ Divide by 3

The solution is $\left[\frac{5}{3}, \infty\right)$.

Graphical Method

Move all terms to one side, and set equal to y. Graph the resulting equation, and find the values of x where the graph is above or on the x-axis.

Example: $3x - 4 \geq 1$

$\qquad 3x - 5 \geq 0 \qquad$ Subtract 1

Set $y = 3x - 5$ and graph. From the graph we see that the solution is $[1.7, \infty)$.

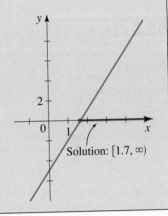

Solution: $[1.7, \infty)$

EXAMPLE 4 ■ Solving an Inequality Graphically

Solve the inequality $x^2 - 5x + 6 \leq 0$ graphically.

SOLUTION This inequality was solved algebraically in Example 3 of Section 1.7. To solve the inequality graphically, we use a graphing calculator to draw the graph of

$$y = x^2 - 5x + 6$$

Our goal is to find those values of x for which $y \leq 0$. These are simply the x-values for which the graph lies below the x-axis. From the graph in Figure 4 we see that the solution of the inequality is the interval $[2, 3]$.

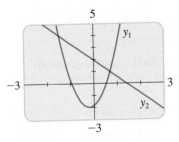

FIGURE 4

■. Now Try Exercise 33

EXAMPLE 5 ■ Solving an Inequality Graphically

Solve the inequality $3.7x^2 + 1.3x - 1.9 \leq 2.0 - 1.4x$.

SOLUTION We use a graphing calculator to graph the equations

$$y_1 = 3.7x^2 + 1.3x - 1.9 \qquad \text{and} \qquad y_2 = 2.0 - 1.4x$$

The graphs are shown in Figure 5. We are interested in those values of x for which $y_1 \leq y_2$; these are points for which the graph of y_2 lies on or above the graph of y_1. To determine the appropriate interval, we look for the x-coordinates of points where the graphs intersect. We conclude that the solution is (approximately) the interval $[-1.45, 0.72]$.

FIGURE 5
$y_1 = 3.7x^2 + 1.3x - 1.9$
$y_2 = 2.0 - 1.4x$

■. Now Try Exercise 35

EXAMPLE 6 ■ Solving an Inequality Graphically

Solve the inequality $x^3 - 5x^2 \geq -8$.

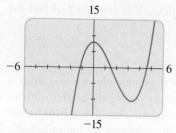

FIGURE 6 $x^3 - 5x^2 + 8 \geq 0$

SOLUTION We write the inequality as

$$x^3 - 5x^2 + 8 \geq 0$$

and then graph the equation

$$y = x^3 - 5x^2 + 8$$

in the viewing rectangle $[-6, 6]$ by $[-15, 15]$, as shown in Figure 6. The solution of the inequality consists of those intervals on which the graph lies on or above the x-axis. By moving the cursor to the x-intercepts, we find that, rounded to one decimal place, the solution is $[-1.1, 1.5] \cup [4.6, \infty)$.

✎ **Now Try Exercise 37**

1.9 EXERCISES

CONCEPTS

1. The solutions of the equation $x^2 - 2x - 3 = 0$ are the
_____-intercepts of the graph of $y = x^2 - 2x - 3$.

2. The solutions of the inequality $x^2 - 2x - 3 > 0$ are the
x-coordinates of the points on the graph of $y = x^2 - 2x - 3$
that lie _____ the x-axis.

3. The figure shows a graph of $y = x^4 - 3x^3 - x^2 + 3x$.
Use the graph to do the following.
   (a) Find the solutions of the equation $x^4 - 3x^3 - x^2 + 3x = 0$.
   (b) Find the solutions of the inequality $x^4 - 3x^3 - x^2 + 3x \leq 0$.

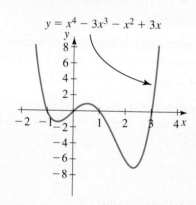

$$y = x^4 - 3x^3 - x^2 + 3x$$

4. The figure shows the graphs of $y = 5x - x^2$ and $y = 4$. Use the graphs to do the following.
   (a) Find the solutions of the equation $5x - x^2 = 4$.
   (b) Find the solutions of the inequality $5x - x^2 > 4$.

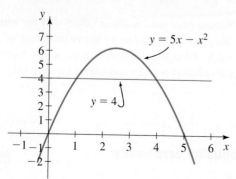

SKILLS

5–16 ■ **Solving Equations Algebraically and Graphically** Solve the equation both algebraically and graphically.

5. $x - 4 = 5x + 12$

6. $\frac{1}{2}x - 3 = 6 + 2x$

7. $\frac{2}{x} + \frac{1}{2x} = 7$

8. $\frac{4}{x+2} - \frac{6}{2x} = \frac{5}{2x+4}$

9. $x^2 - 32 = 0$

10. $x^3 + 16 = 0$

11. $x^2 + 9 = 0$

12. $x^2 + 3 = 2x$

13. $16x^4 = 625$

14. $2x^5 - 243 = 0$

15. $(x - 5)^4 - 80 = 0$

16. $6(x + 2)^5 = 64$

17–24 ■ **Solving Equations Graphically** Solve the equation graphically in the given interval. State each answer rounded to two decimals.

17. $x^2 - 7x + 12 = 0$; $[0, 6]$

18. $x^2 - 0.75x + 0.125 = 0$; $[-2, 2]$

19. $x^3 - 6x^2 + 11x - 6 = 0$; $[-1, 4]$

20. $16x^3 + 16x^2 = x + 1$; $[-2, 2]$

21. $x - \sqrt{x + 1} = 0$; $[-1, 5]$

22. $1 + \sqrt{x} = \sqrt{1 + x^2}$; $[-1, 5]$

23. $x^{1/3} - x = 0$; $[-3, 3]$

24. $x^{1/2} + x^{1/3} - x = 0$; $[-1, 5]$

25–28 ■ **Solving Equations Graphically** Use the graphical method to solve the equation in the indicated exercise from Section 1.6.

25. Exercise 43.

26. Exercise 46.

27. Exercise 51.

28. Exercise 52.

29–32 ■ **Solving Equations Graphically** Find all real solutions of the equation, rounded to two decimals.

29. $x^3 - 2x^2 - x - 1 = 0$

30. $x^4 - 8x^2 + 2 = 0$

31. $x(x - 1)(x + 2) = \frac{1}{6}x$

32. $x^4 = 16 - x^3$

33–40 ■ Solving Inequalities Graphically Find the solutions of the inequality by drawing appropriate graphs. State each answer rounded to two decimals.

33. $x^2 \leq 3x + 10$

34. $0.5x^2 + 0.875x \leq 0.25$

35. $x^3 + 11x \leq 6x^2 + 6$

36. $16x^3 + 24x^2 > -9x - 1$

37. $x^{1/3} < x$

38. $\sqrt{0.5x^2 + 1} \leq 2|x|$

39. $(x + 1)^2 < (x - 1)^2$

40. $(x + 1)^2 \leq x^3$

 41–44 ■ Solving Inequalities Graphically Use the graphical method to solve the inequality in the indicated exercise from Section 1.7.

41. Exercise 41.

42. Exercise 42.

43. Exercise 51.

44. Exercise 52.

SKILLS Plus

45. Another Graphical Method In Example 2 we solved the equation $5 - 3x = 8x - 20$ by drawing graphs of two equations. Solve the equation by drawing a graph of only one equation. Compare your answer to the one obtained in Example 2.

 46. Finding More Solutions In Example 3 we found two solutions of the equation $x^3 - 6x^2 + 9x = \sqrt{x}$ in the interval $[1, 6]$. Find two more solutions, rounded to two decimals.

APPLICATIONS

 47. Estimating Profit An appliance manufacturer estimates that the profit y (in dollars) generated by producing x cooktops per month is given by the equation

$$y = 10x + 0.5x^2 - 0.001x^3 - 5000$$

where $0 \leq x \leq 450$.

(a) Graph the equation.

(b) How many cooktops must be produced to begin generating a profit?

(c) For what range of values of x is the company's profit greater than $15,000?

 48. How Far Can You See? If you stand on a ship in a calm sea, then your height x (in ft) above sea level is related to the farthest distance y (in mi) that you can see by the equation

$$y = \sqrt{1.5x + \left(\frac{x}{5280}\right)^2}$$

(a) Graph the equation for $0 \leq x \leq 100$.

(b) How high up do you have to be to be able to see 10 mi?

DISCUSS ■ **DISCOVER** ■ **PROVE** ■ **WRITE**

49. WRITE: Algebraic and Graphical Solution Methods Write a short essay comparing the algebraic and graphical methods for solving equations. Make up your own examples to illustrate the advantages and disadvantages of each method.

50. DISCUSS: Enter Equations Carefully A student wishes to graph the equations

$$y = x^{1/3} \qquad \text{and} \qquad y = \frac{x}{x + 4}$$

on the same screen, so he enters the following information into his calculator:

$$Y_1 = X \wedge 1/3 \qquad Y_2 = X/X + 4$$

The calculator graphs two lines instead of the equations he wanted. What went wrong?

1.10 MODELING VARIATION

■ Direct Variation ■ Inverse Variation ■ Combining Different Types of Variation

When scientists talk about a *mathematical model* for a real-world phenomenon, they often mean a function that describes the dependence of one physical quantity on another. For instance, the model may describe the population of an animal species as a function of time or the pressure of a gas as a function of its volume. In this section we study a kind of modeling that occurs frequently in the sciences, called *variation*.

■ Direct Variation

One type of variation is called *direct variation*; it occurs when one quantity is a constant multiple of the other. We use a function of the form $f(x) = kx$ to model this dependence.

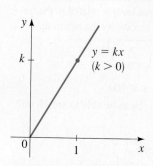

$y = kx$
$(k > 0)$

FIGURE 1

Recall that the graph of an equation of the form $y = mx + b$ is a line with slope m and y-intercept b. So the graph of an equation $y = kx$ that describes direct variation is a line with slope k and y-intercept 0 (see Figure 1).

EXAMPLE 1 ■ Direct Variation

During a thunderstorm you see the lightning before you hear the thunder because light travels much faster than sound. The distance between you and the storm varies directly as the time interval between the lightning and the thunder.

(a) Suppose that the thunder from a storm 5400 ft away takes 5 s to reach you. Determine the constant of proportionality, and write the equation for the variation.

(b) Sketch the graph of this equation. What does the constant of proportionality represent?

(c) If the time interval between the lightning and thunder is now 8 s, how far away is the storm?

SOLUTION

(a) Let d be the distance from you to the storm, and let t be the length of the time interval. We are given that d varies directly as t, so

$$d = kt$$

where k is a constant. To find k, we use the fact that $t = 5$ when $d = 5400$. Substituting these values in the equation, we get

$$5400 = k(5) \qquad \text{Substitute}$$

$$k = \frac{5400}{5} = 1080 \qquad \text{Solve for } k$$

Substituting this value of k in the equation for d, we obtain

$$d = 1080t$$

as the equation for d as a function of t.

(b) The graph of the equation $d = 1080t$ is a line through the origin with slope 1080 and is shown in Figure 2. The constant $k = 1080$ is the approximate speed of sound (in ft/s).

(c) When $t = 8$, we have

$$d = 1080 \cdot 8 = 8640$$

So the storm is 8640 ft $\approx$ 1.6 mi away.

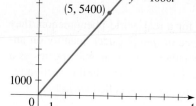

(8, 8640)

$y = 1080t$

(5, 5400)

1000

FIGURE 2

■. Now Try Exercises 19 and 35

Inverse Variation

Another function that is frequently used in mathematical modeling is $f(x) = k/x$, where k is a constant.

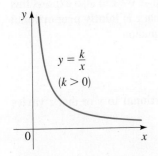

$y = \dfrac{k}{x}$
$(k > 0)$

FIGURE 3 Inverse variation

INVERSE VARIATION

If the quantities x and y are related by the equation

$$y = \frac{k}{x}$$

for some constant $k \neq 0$, we say that y **is inversely proportional to** x or y **varies inversely as** x. The constant k is called the **constant of proportionality**.

The graph of $y = k/x$ for $x > 0$ is shown in Figure 3 for the case $k > 0$. It gives a picture of what happens when y is inversely proportional to x.

EXAMPLE 2 ■ Inverse Variation

Boyle's Law states that when a sample of gas is compressed at a constant temperature, the pressure of the gas is inversely proportional to the volume of the gas.

(a) Suppose the pressure of a sample of air that occupies 0.106 m³ at 25°C is 50 kPa. Find the constant of proportionality, and write the equation that expresses the inverse proportionality. Sketch a graph of this equation.

(b) If the sample expands to a volume of 0.3 m³, find the new pressure.

SOLUTION

(a) Let P be the pressure of the sample of gas, and let V be its volume. Then, by the definition of inverse proportionality, we have

$$P = \frac{k}{V}$$

where k is a constant. To find k, we use the fact that $P = 50$ when $V = 0.106$. Substituting these values in the equation, we get

$$50 = \frac{k}{0.106} \qquad \text{Substitute}$$

$$k = (50)(0.106) = 5.3 \qquad \text{Solve for } k$$

Putting this value of k in the equation for P, we have

$$P = \frac{5.3}{V}$$

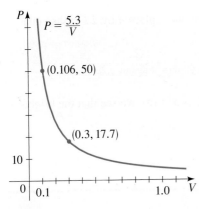

$P = \dfrac{5.3}{V}$

(0.106, 50)

(0.3, 17.7)

10

0   0.1   1.0   V

FIGURE 4

Since V represents volume (which is never negative), we sketch the part of the graph for which $V > 0$ only. The graph is shown in Figure 4.

(b) When $V = 0.3$, we have

$$P = \frac{5.3}{0.3} \approx 17.7$$

So the new pressure is about 17.7 kPa.

✎ Now Try Exercises 21 and 43

■ Combining Different Types of Variation

In the sciences, relationships between three or more variables are common, and any combination of the different types of proportionality that we have discussed is possible. For example, if the quantities x, y, and z are related by the equation

$$z = kxy$$

then we say that z is **proportional to the product** of x and y. We can also express this relationship by saying that z **varies jointly** as x and y or that z **is jointly proportional to** x and y. If the quantities x, y, and z are related by the equation

$$z = k\frac{x}{y}$$

we say that z **is proportional to** x **and inversely proportional to** y or that z **varies directly as** x **and inversely as** y.

EXAMPLE 3　■　Combining Variations

The apparent brightness B of a light source (measured in W/m^2) is directly proportional to the luminosity L (measured in W) of the light source and inversely proportional to the square of the distance d from the light source (measured in meters).

(a) Write an equation that expresses this variation.

(b) If the distance is doubled, by what factor will the brightness change?

(c) If the distance is cut in half and the luminosity is tripled, by what factor will the brightness change?

SOLUTION

(a) Since B is directly proportional to L and inversely proportional to d^2, we have

$$B = k\frac{L}{d^2} \qquad \text{Brightness at distance } d \text{ and luminosity } L$$

where k is a constant.

(b) To obtain the brightness at double the distance, we replace d by $2d$ in the equation we obtained in part (a).

$$B = k\frac{L}{(2d)^2} = \frac{1}{4}\left(k\frac{L}{d^2}\right) \qquad \text{Brightness at distance } 2d$$

Comparing this expression with that obtained in part (a), we see that the brightness is $\frac{1}{4}$ of the original brightness.

DISCOVERY PROJECT

Proportionality: Shape and Size

Many real-world quantities are related by proportionalities. We use the proportionality symbol $\propto$ to express proportionalities in the natural world. For example, for animals of the same shape, the skin area and volume are proportional, in different ways, to the length of the animal. In one situation we use proportionality to determine how a frog's size relates to its sensitivity to pollutants in the environment. You can find the project at **www.stewartmath.com**.

(c) To obtain the brightness at half the distance d and triple the luminosity L, we replace d by $d/2$ and L by $3L$ in the equation we obtained in part (a).

$$B = k\frac{3L}{\left(\frac{1}{2}d\right)^2} = \frac{3}{\frac{1}{4}}\left(k\frac{L}{d^2}\right) = 12\left(k\frac{L}{d^2}\right) \qquad \text{Brightness at distance } \tfrac{1}{2}d \text{ and luminosity } 3L$$

Comparing this expression with that obtained in part (a), we see that the brightness is 12 times the original brightness.

Now Try Exercises 23 and 45

The relationship between apparent brightness, actual brightness (or luminosity), and distance is used in estimating distances to stars (see Exercise 56).

EXAMPLE 4 ■ Newton's Law of Gravity

Newton's Law of Gravity says that two objects with masses m_1 and m_2 attract each other with a force F that is jointly proportional to their masses and inversely proportional to the square of the distance r between the objects. Express Newton's Law of Gravity as an equation.

SOLUTION Using the definitions of joint and inverse variation and the traditional notation G for the gravitational constant of proportionality, we have

$$F = G\frac{m_1m_2}{r^2}$$

Now Try Exercises 31 and 37

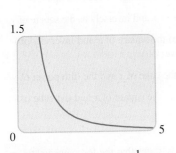

FIGURE 5 Graph of $F = \dfrac{1}{r^2}$

If m_1 and m_2 are fixed masses, then the gravitational force between them is $F = C/r^2$ (where $C = Gm_1m_2$ is a constant). Figure 5 shows the graph of this equation for $r > 0$ with $C = 1$. Observe how the gravitational attraction decreases with increasing distance.

Like the Law of Gravity, many laws of nature are *inverse square laws*. There is a geometric reason for this. Imagine a force or energy originating from a point source and spreading its influence equally in all directions, just like the light source in Example 3 or the gravitational force exerted by a planet in Example 4. The influence of the force or energy at a distance r from the source is spread out over the surface of a sphere of radius r, which has area $A = 4\pi r^2$ (see Figure 6). So the intensity I at a distance r from the source is the source strength S divided by the area A of the sphere:

$$I = \frac{S}{4\pi r^2} = \frac{k}{r^2}$$

where k is the constant $S/(4\pi)$. Thus point sources of light, sound, gravity, electromagnetic fields, and radiation must all obey inverse square laws, simply because of the geometry of space.

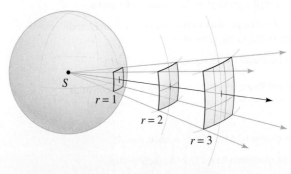

FIGURE 6 Energy from a point source S

1.10 EXERCISES

CONCEPTS

1. If the quantities x and y are related by the equation $y = 3x$, then we say that y is _____ _____ to x and the constant of _____ is 3.

2. If the quantities x and y are related by the equation $y = \dfrac{3}{x}$, then we say that y is _____ _____ to x and the constant of _____ is 3.

3. If the quantities x, y, and z are related by the equation $z = 3\dfrac{x}{y}$, then we say that z is _____ _____ to x and _____ _____ to y.

4. If z is directly proportional to the product of x and y and if z is 10 when x is 4 and y is 5, then x, y, and z are related by the equation $z =$ _____.

5–6 ■ In each equation, is y directly proportional, inversely proportional, or not proportional to x?

5. (a) $y = 3x$ (b) $y = 3x + 1$

6. (a) $y = \dfrac{3}{x + 1}$ (b) $y = \dfrac{3}{x}$

SKILLS

7–18 ■ **Equations of Proportionality** Write an equation that expresses the statement.

7. T varies directly as x.

8. P is directly proportional to w.

9. v is inversely proportional to z.

10. w is proportional to the product of m and n.

11. y is proportional to s and inversely proportional to t.

12. P varies inversely as T.

13. z is proportional to the square root of y.

14. A is proportional to the square of x and inversely proportional to the cube of t.

15. V is proportional to the product of l, w, and h.

16. S is proportional to the product of the squares of r and θ.

17. R is proportional to the product of the squares of P and t and inversely proportional to the cube of b.

18. A is jointly proportional to the square roots of x and y.

19–30 ■ **Constants of Proportionality** Express the statement as an equation. Use the given information to find the constant of proportionality.

19. y is directly proportional to x. If $x = 6$, then $y = 42$.

20. w is inversely proportional to t. If $t = 8$, then $w = 3$.

21. A varies inversely as r. If $r = 3$, then $A = 7$.

22. P is directly proportional to T. If $T = 300$, then $P = 20$.

23. A is directly proportional to x and inversely proportional to t. If $x = 7$ and $t = 3$, then $A = 42$.

24. S is proportional to the product of p and q. If $p = 4$ and $q = 5$, then $S = 180$.

25. W is inversely proportional to the square of r. If $r = 6$, then $W = 10$.

26. t is proportional to the product of x and y and inversely proportional to r. If $x = 2$, $y = 3$, and $r = 12$, then $t = 25$.

27. C is jointly proportional to l, w, and h. If $l = w = h = 2$, then $C = 128$.

28. H is jointly proportional to the squares of l and w. If $l = 2$ and $w = \frac{1}{3}$, then $H = 36$.

29. R is inversely proportional to the square root of x. If $x = 121$, then $R = 2.5$.

30. M is jointly proportional to a, b, and c and inversely proportional to d. If a and d have the same value and if b and c are both 2, then $M = 128$.

31–34 ■ **Proportionality** A statement describing the relationship between the variables x, y, and z is given. (a) Express the statement as an equation of proportionality. (b) If x is tripled and y is doubled, by what factor does z change? (See Example 3.)

31. z varies directly as the cube of x and inversely as the square of y.

32. z is directly proportional to the square of x and inversely proportional to the fourth power of y.

33. z is jointly proportional to the cube of x and the fifth power of y.

34. z is inversely proportional to the square of x and the cube of y.

APPLICATIONS

35. Hooke's Law Hooke's Law states that the force needed to keep a spring stretched x units beyond its natural length is directly proportional to x. Here the constant of proportionality is called the **spring constant**.

(a) Write Hooke's Law as an equation.

(b) If a spring has a natural length of 5 cm and a force of 30 N is required to maintain the spring stretched to a length of 9 cm, find the spring constant.

(c) What force is needed to keep the spring stretched to a length of 11 cm?

5 cm

36. Printing Costs The cost C of printing a magazine is jointly proportional to the number of pages p in the magazine and the number of magazines printed m.

(a) Write an equation that expresses this joint variation.

(b) Find the constant of proportionality if the printing cost is $60,000 for 4000 copies of a 120-page magazine.

(c) How much would the printing cost be for 5000 copies of a 92-page magazine?

37. Power from a Windmill The power P that can be obtained from a windmill is directly proportional to the cube of the wind speed s.

(a) Write an equation that expresses this variation.

(b) Find the constant of proportionality for a windmill that produces 96 watts of power when the wind is blowing at 20 mi/h.

(c) How much power will this windmill produce if the wind speed increases to 30 mi/h?

38. Power Needed to Propel a Boat The power P (measured in horsepower, hp) needed to propel a boat is directly proportional to the cube of the speed s.

(a) Write an equation that expresses this variation.

(b) Find the constant of proportionality for a boat that needs an 80-hp engine to propel the boat at 10 knots.

(c) How much power is needed to drive this boat at 15 knots?

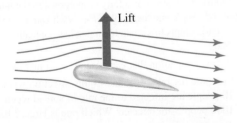

39. Stopping Distance The stopping distance D of a car after the brakes have been applied varies directly as the square of the speed s. A certain car traveling at 40 mi/h can stop in 150 ft. What is the maximum speed it can be traveling if it needs to stop in 200 ft?

40. Aerodynamic Lift The lift L on an airplane wing at takeoff varies jointly as the square of the speed s of the plane and the area A of its wings. A plane with a wing area of 500 ft² traveling at 50 mi/h experiences a lift of 1700 lb. How much lift would a plane with a wing area of 600 ft² traveling at 40 mi/h experience?

Lift

41. Drag Force on a Boat The drag force F on a boat is jointly proportional to the wetted surface area A on the hull and the square of the speed s of the boat. A boat experiences a drag force of 220 lb when traveling at 5 mi/h with a wetted surface area of 40 ft². How fast must a boat be traveling if it has 28 ft² of wetted surface area and is experiencing a drag force of 175 lb?

42. Kepler's Third Law Kepler's Third Law of planetary motion states that the square of the period T of a planet (the time it takes for the planet to make a complete revolution about the sun) is directly proportional to the cube of its average distance d from the sun.

(a) Express Kepler's Third Law as an equation.

(b) Find the constant of proportionality by using the fact that for our planet the period is about 365 days and the average distance is about 93 million miles.

(c) The planet Neptune is about 2.79×10^9 mi from the sun. Find the period of Neptune.

43. Ideal Gas Law The pressure P of a sample of gas is directly proportional to the temperature T and inversely proportional to the volume V.

(a) Write an equation that expresses this variation.

(b) Find the constant of proportionality if 100 L of gas exerts a pressure of 33.2 kPa at a temperature of 400 K (absolute temperature measured on the Kelvin scale).

(c) If the temperature is increased to 500 K and the volume is decreased to 80 L, what is the pressure of the gas?

44. Skidding in a Curve A car is traveling on a curve that forms a circular arc. The force F needed to keep the car from skidding is jointly proportional to the weight w of the car and the square of its speed s and is inversely proportional to the radius r of the curve.

(a) Write an equation that expresses this variation.

(b) A car weighing 1600 lb travels around a curve at 60 mi/h. The next car to round this curve weighs 2500 lb and requires the same force as the first car to keep from skidding. How fast is the second car traveling?

45. Loudness of Sound The loudness L of a sound (measured in decibels, dB) is inversely proportional to the square of the distance d from the source of the sound.

(a) Write an equation that expresses this variation.

(b) Find the constant of proportionality if a person 10 ft from a lawn mower experiences a sound level of 70 dB.

(c) If the distance in part (b) is doubled, by what factor is the loudness changed?

(d) If the distance in part (b) is cut in half, by what factor is the loudness changed?

46. A Jet of Water The power P of a jet of water is jointly proportional to the cross-sectional area A of the jet and to the cube of the velocity v.

(a) Write an equation that expresses this variation.

(b) If the velocity is doubled and the cross-sectional area is halved, by what factor is the power changed?

(c) If the velocity is halved and the cross-sectional area is tripled, by what factor is the power changed?

47. Electrical Resistance The resistance R of a wire varies directly as its length L and inversely as the square of its diameter d.

(a) Write an equation that expresses this joint variation.

(b) Find the constant of proportionality if a wire 1.2 m long and 0.005 m in diameter has a resistance of 140 ohms.

(c) Find the resistance of a wire made of the same material that is 3 m long and has a diameter of 0.008 m.

(d) If the diameter is doubled and the length is tripled, by what factor is the resistance changed?

48. Growing Cabbages In the short growing season of the Canadian arctic territory of Nunavut, some gardeners find it possible to grow gigantic cabbages in the midnight sun. Assume that the final size of a cabbage is proportional to the amount of nutrients it receives and inversely proportional to the number of other cabbages surrounding it. A cabbage that received 20 oz of nutrients and had 12 other cabbages around it grew to 30 lb. What size would it grow to if it received 10 oz of nutrients and had only 5 cabbage "neighbors"?

49. Radiation Energy The total radiation energy E emitted by a heated surface per unit area varies as the fourth power of its absolute temperature T. The temperature is 6000 K at the surface of the sun and 300 K at the surface of the earth.

(a) How many times more radiation energy per unit area is produced by the sun than by the earth?

(b) The radius of the earth is 3960 mi, and the radius of the sun is 435,000 mi. How many times more total radiation does the sun emit than the earth?

50. Value of a Lot The value of a building lot on Galiano Island is jointly proportional to its area and the quantity of water produced by a well on the property. A 200 ft by 300 ft lot has a well producing 10 gal of water per minute and is valued at $48,000. What is the value of a 400 ft by 400 ft lot if the well on the lot produces 4 gal of water per minute?

51. Law of the Pendulum The period of a pendulum (the time elapsed during one complete swing of the pendulum) varies directly with the square root of the length of the pendulum.

(a) Express this relationship by writing an equation.

(b) To double the period, how would we have to change the length l?

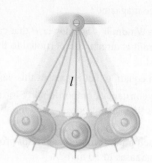

52. Heat of a Campfire The heat experienced by a hiker at a campfire is proportional to the amount of wood on the fire and inversely proportional to the cube of his distance from the fire. If the hiker is 20 ft from the fire and someone doubles the amount of wood burning, how far from the fire would he have to be so that he feels the same heat as before?

53. Frequency of Vibration The frequency f of vibration of a violin string is inversely proportional to its length L. The constant of proportionality k is positive and depends on the tension and density of the string.

(a) Write an equation that represents this variation.

(b) What effect does doubling the length of the string have on the frequency of its vibration?

54. Spread of a Disease The rate r at which a disease spreads in a population of size P is jointly proportional to the number x of infected people and the number $P - x$ who are not infected. An infection erupts in a small town that has population $P = 5000$.

(a) Write an equation that expresses r as a function of x.

(b) Compare the rate of spread of this infection when 10 people are infected to the rate of spread when 1000 people are infected. Which rate is larger? By what factor?

(c) Calculate the rate of spread when the entire population is infected. Why does this answer make intuitive sense?

55–56 ■ Combining Variations Solve the problem using the relationship between brightness B, luminosity L, and distance d derived in Example 3. The proportionality constant is $k = 0.080$.

55. Brightness of a Star The luminosity of a star is $L = 2.5 \times 10^{26}$ W, and its distance from the earth is $d = 2.4 \times 10^{19}$ m. How bright does the star appear on the earth?

56. Distance to a Star The luminosity of a star is $L = 5.8 \times 10^{30}$ W, and its brightness as viewed from the earth is $B = 8.2 \times 10^{-16}$ W/m². Find the distance of the star from the earth.

DISCUSS ■ DISCOVER ■ PROVE ■ WRITE

57. DISCUSS: Is Proportionality Everything? A great many laws of physics and chemistry are expressible as proportionalities. Give at least one example of a function that occurs in the sciences that is *not* a proportionality.

CHAPTER 1 ■ REVIEW

■ PROPERTIES AND FORMULAS

The Distance Formula (p. 90)

The distance between the points $A(x_1, y_1)$ and $B(x_2, y_2)$ is

$$d(A, B) = \sqrt{(x_2 - x_1)^2 + (y_2 - y_1)^2}$$

The Midpoint Formula (p. 91)

The midpoint of the line segment from $A(x_1, y_1)$ to $B(x_2, y_2)$ is

$$\left(\frac{x_1 + x_2}{2}, \frac{y_1 + y_2}{2} \right)$$

Intercepts (p. 96)

To find the **x-intercepts** of the graph of an equation, set $y = 0$ and solve for x.

To find the **y-intercepts** of the graph of an equation, set $x = 0$ and solve for y.

Circles (p. 98)

The circle with center $(0, 0)$ and radius r has equation

$$x^2 + y^2 = r^2$$

The circle with center (h, k) and radius r has equation

$$(x - h)^2 + (y - k)^2 = r^2$$

Symmetry (p. 100)

The graph of an equation is **symmetric with respect to the x-axis** if the equation remains unchanged when y is replaced by $-y$.

The graph of an equation is **symmetric with respect to the y-axis** if the equation remains unchanged when x is replaced by $-x$.

The graph of an equation is **symmetric with respect to the origin** if the equation remains unchanged when x is replaced by $-x$ and y by $-y$.

Slope of a Line (p. 105)

The slope of the nonvertical line that contains the points $A(x_1, y_1)$ and $B(x_2, y_2)$ is

$$m = \frac{\text{rise}}{\text{run}} = \frac{y_2 - y_1}{x_2 - x_1}$$

Equations of Lines (pp. 106–109)

If a line has slope m, has y-intercept b, and contains the point (x_1, y_1), then:

the **point-slope form** of its equation is

$$y - y_1 = m(x - x_1)$$

the **slope-intercept form** of its equation is

$$y = mx + b$$

The equation of any line can be expressed in the **general form**

$$Ax + By + C = 0$$

(where A and B both are not 0).

Vertical and Horizontal Lines (p. 108)

The **vertical** line containing the point (a, b) has the equation $x = a$.

The **horizontal** line containing the point (a, b) has the equation $y = b$.

Parallel and Perpendicular Lines (p. 110)

Two lines with slopes m_1 and m_2 are

parallel if and only if $m_1 = m_2$

perpendicular if and only if $m_1 m_2 = -1$

Zero-Product Property (p. 116)

$AB = 0$ if and only if $A = 0$ or $B = 0$.

Completing the Square (p. 116)

To make $x^2 + bx$ a perfect square, add $\left(\frac{b}{2} \right)^2$. This gives the perfect square

$$x^2 + bx + \left(\frac{b}{2} \right)^2 = \left(x + \frac{b}{2} \right)^2$$

Quadratic Formula (pp. 117–119)

A **quadratic equation** is an equation of the form

$$ax^2 + bx + c = 0$$

Its solutions are given by the **Quadratic Formula**:

$$x = \frac{-b \pm \sqrt{b^2 - 4ac}}{2a}$$

The **discriminant** is $D = b^2 - 4ac$.

If $D > 0$, the equation has two real solutions.

If $D = 0$, the equation has one solution.

If $D < 0$, the equation has two complex solutions.

Complex Numbers (pp. 126–129)

A **complex number** is a number of the form $a + bi$, where $i = \sqrt{-1}$.

The **complex conjugate** of $a + bi$ is

$$\overline{a + bi} = a - bi$$

To **multiply** complex numbers, treat them as binomials and use $i^2 = -1$ to simplify the result.

To **divide** complex numbers, multiply numerator and denominator by the complex conjugate of the denominator:

$$\frac{a + bi}{c + di} = \left(\frac{a + bi}{c + di}\right) \cdot \left(\frac{c - di}{c - di}\right) = \frac{(a + bi)(c - di)}{c^2 + d^2}$$

Inequalities (p. 141)

Adding the same quantity to each side of an inequality gives an equivalent inequality:

$$A < B \quad \Leftrightarrow \quad A + C < B + C$$

Multiplying each side of an inequality by the same *positive* quantity gives an equivalent inequality. Multiplying each side by the same *negative* quantity reverses the direction of the inequality:

$$\text{If } C > 0, \text{ then } A < B \quad \Leftrightarrow \quad CA < CB$$
$$\text{If } C < 0, \text{ then } A < B \quad \Leftrightarrow \quad CA > CB$$

Absolute Value Equations (p. 150)

To solve an absolute value equation, we use

$$|x| = C \quad \Leftrightarrow \quad x = C \ \text{ or } \ x = -C$$

Absolute Value Inequalities (p. 151)

To solve absolute value inequalities, we use

$$|x| < C \quad \Leftrightarrow \quad -C < x < C$$
$$|x| > C \quad \Leftrightarrow \quad x < -C \ \text{ or } \ x > C$$

Variation (pp. 160–162)

If y is **directly proportional** to x, then

$$y = kx$$

If y is **inversely proportional** to x, then

$$y = \frac{k}{x}$$

■ CONCEPT CHECK

1. (a) In the coordinate plane, what is the horizontal axis called and what is the vertical axis called?

   (b) To graph an ordered pair of numbers (x, y), you need the coordinate plane. For the point $(2, 3)$, which is the x-coordinate and which is the y-coordinate?

   (c) For an equation in the variables x and y, how do you determine whether a given point is on the graph? Is the point $(5, 3)$ on the graph of the equation $y = 2x - 1$?

2. (a) What is the formula for finding the distance between the points (x_1, y_1) and (x_2, y_2)?

   (b) What is the formula for finding the midpoint between (x_1, y_1) and (x_2, y_2)?

3. How do you find x-intercepts and y-intercepts of a graph of an equation?

4. (a) Write an equation of the circle with center (h, k) and radius r.

   (b) Find the equation of the circle with center $(2, -1)$ and radius 3.

5. (a) How do you test whether the graph of an equation is symmetric with respect to the (i) x-axis, (ii) y-axis, and (iii) origin?

   (b) What type of symmetry does the graph of the equation $xy^2 + y^2x^2 = 3x$ have?

6. (a) What is the slope of a line? How do you compute the slope of the line through the points $(-1, 4)$ and $(1, -2)$?

   (b) How do you find the slope and y-intercept of the line $6x + 3y = 12$?

   (c) How do you write the equation for a line that has slope 3 and passes through the point $(1, 2)$?

7. Give an equation of a vertical line and of a horizontal line that passes through the point $(2, 3)$.

8. State the general equation of a line.

9. Given lines with slopes m_1 and m_2, explain how you can tell whether the lines are (i) parallel, (ii) perpendicular.

10. Write the general form of each type of equation.

    (i) Linear equation   (ii) Quadratic equation

11. What are the three ways to solve a quadratic equation?

12. State the Zero-Product Property. Use the property to solve the equation $x(x - 1) = 0$.

13. What do you need to add to $ax^2 + bx$ to complete the square? Complete the square for the expression $x^2 + 6x$.

14. State the Quadratic Formula for the quadratic equation $ax^2 + bx + c = 0$, and use it to solve the equation $x^2 + 6x - 1 = 0$.

15. What is the discriminant of the quadratic equation $ax^2 + bx + c = 0$? Find the discriminant of $2x^2 - 3x + 5 = 0$. How many real solutions does this equation have?

16. What is a complex number? Give an example of a complex number, and identify the real and imaginary parts.

17. What is the complex conjugate of a complex number $a + bi$?

18. (a) How do you add complex numbers?
(b) How do you multiply $(3 + 5i)(2 - i)$?
(c) Is $(3 - i)(3 + i)$ a real number?
(d) How do you simplify the quotient $(3 + 5i)/(3 - i)$?

19. What is the logical first step in solving the equation $\sqrt{x - 1} = x - 3$? Why is it important to check your answers when solving equations of this type?

20. Explain how to solve the given type of problem.
(a) Linear inequality: $2x \geq 1$
(b) Nonlinear inequality: $(x - 1)(x - 4) < 0$
(c) Absolute value equation: $|2x - 5| = 7$
(d) Absolute value inequality: $|2x - 5| \leq 7$

21. How do you solve an equation (i) algebraically? (ii) graphically?

22. How do you solve an inequality (i) algebraically? (ii) graphically?

23. Write an equation that expresses each relationship.
(a) y is directly proportional to x.
(b) y is inversely proportional to x.
(c) z is jointly proportional to x and y.

ANSWERS TO THE CONCEPT CHECK CAN BE FOUND AT THE BACK OF THE BOOK.

■ EXERCISES

1–4 ■ Coordinate Plane Two points P and Q are given.
(a) Plot P and Q on a coordinate plane. (b) Find the distance from P to Q. (c) Find the midpoint of the segment PQ. (d) Sketch the line determined by P and Q, and find its equation in slope-intercept form. (e) Sketch the circle that passes through Q and has center P, and find the equation of this circle.

1. $P(2, 0)$, $Q(-5, 12)$ **2.** $P(7, -1)$, $Q(2, -11)$

3. $P(-6, 2)$, $Q(4, -14)$ **4.** $P(5, -2)$, $Q(-3, -6)$

5–6 ■ Graphing Regions Sketch the region given by the set.

5. $\{(x, y) \mid -4 < x < 4$ and $-2 < y < 2\}$

6. $\{(x, y) \mid x \geq 4$ or $y \geq 2\}$

7. Distance Formula Which of the points $A(4, 4)$ or $B(5, 3)$ is closer to the point $C(-1, -3)$?

8–10 ■ Circles In these exercises we find equations of circles.

8. Find an equation of the circle that has center $(2, -5)$ and radius $\sqrt{2}$.

9. Find an equation of the circle that has center $(-5, -1)$ and passes through the origin.

10. Find an equation of the circle that contains the points $P(2, 3)$ and $Q(-1, 8)$ and has the midpoint of the segment PQ as its center.

11–14 ■ Circles (a) Complete the square to determine whether the equation represents a circle or a point or has no graph. (b) If the equation is that of a circle, find its center and radius, and sketch its graph.

11. $x^2 + y^2 + 2x - 6y + 9 = 0$

12. $2x^2 + 2y^2 - 2x + 8y = \frac{1}{2}$

13. $x^2 + y^2 + 72 = 12x$

14. $x^2 + y^2 - 6x - 10y + 34 = 0$

15–22 ■ Graphing Equations Sketch the graph of the equation by making a table and plotting points.

15. $y = 2 - 3x$ **16.** $2x - y + 1 = 0$

17. $\dfrac{x}{2} - \dfrac{y}{7} = 1$ **18.** $\dfrac{x}{4} + \dfrac{y}{5} = 0$

19. $y = 16 - x^2$ **20.** $8x + y^2 = 0$

21. $x = \sqrt{y}$ **22.** $y = -\sqrt{1 - x^2}$

23–30 ■ Symmetry and Intercepts (a) Test the equation for symmetry with respect to the x-axis, the y-axis, and the origin. (b) Find the x- and y-intercepts of the graph of the equation.

23. $y = 9 - x^2$ **24.** $6x + y^2 = 36$

25. $x^2 + (y - 1)^2 = 1$ **26.** $x^4 = 16 + y$

27. $9x^2 - 16y^2 = 144$ **28.** $y = \dfrac{4}{x}$

29. $x^2 + 4xy + y^2 = 1$ **30.** $x^3 + xy^2 = 5$

31–34 ■ Graphing Equations (a) Use a graphing device to graph the equation in an appropriate viewing rectangle. (b) Use the graph to find the x- and y-intercepts.

31. $y = x^2 - 6x$ **32.** $y = \sqrt{5 - x}$

33. $y = x^3 - 4x^2 - 5x$ **34.** $\dfrac{x^2}{4} + y^2 = 1$

35–44 ■ Lines A description of a line is given. (a) Find an equation for the line in slope-intercept form. (b) Find an equation for the line in general form. (c) Graph the line.

35. The line that has slope 2 and y-intercept 6

36. The line that has slope $-\frac{1}{2}$ and passes through the point $(6, -3)$

37. The line that passes through the points $(-1, -6)$ and $(2, -4)$

38. The line that has x-intercept 4 and y-intercept 12

39. The vertical line that passes through the point $(3, -2)$

40. The horizontal line with y-intercept 5

41. The line that passes through the point $(1, 1)$ and is parallel to the line $2x - 5y = 10$

42. The line that passes through the origin and is parallel to the line containing $(2, 4)$ and $(4, -4)$

43. The line that passes through the origin and is perpendicular to the line $y = \frac{1}{2}x - 10$

44. The line that passes through the point $(1, 7)$ and is perpendicular to the line $x - 3y + 16 = 0$

45-46 ■ Parallel and Perpendicular Lines The equations of two lines are given. Determine whether the lines are parallel, perpendicular, or neither.

45. $y = -\frac{1}{3}x - 1$; $\quad 9y + 3x + 3 = 0$

46. $5x - 8y = 3$; $\quad 10y + 16x = 1$

47. Stretching a Spring Hooke's Law states that if a weight w is attached to a hanging spring, then the stretched length s of the spring is linearly related to w. For a particular spring we have

$$s = 0.3w + 2.5$$

where s is measured in inches and w in pounds.

(a) What do the slope and s-intercept in this equation represent?

(b) How long is the spring when a 5-lb weight is attached?

48. Annual Salary Margarita is hired by an accounting firm at a salary of $60,000 per year. Three years later her annual salary has increased to $70,500. Assume that her salary increases linearly.

(a) Find an equation that relates her annual salary S and the number of years t that she has worked for the firm.

(b) What do the slope and S-intercept of her salary equation represent?

(c) What will her salary be after 12 years with the firm?

49–64 ■ Solving Equations Find all real solutions of the equation.

49. $x^2 - 9x + 14 = 0$

50. $x^2 + 24x + 144 = 0$

51. $2x^2 + x = 1$

52. $3x^2 + 5x - 2 = 0$

53. $4x^3 - 25x = 0$

54. $x^3 - 2x^2 - 5x + 10 = 0$

55. $3x^2 + 4x - 1 = 0$

56. $x^2 - 3x + 9 = 0$

57. $\dfrac{1}{x} + \dfrac{2}{x - 1} = 3$

58. $\dfrac{x}{x - 2} + \dfrac{1}{x + 2} = \dfrac{8}{x^2 - 4}$

59. $x^4 - 8x^2 - 9 = 0$

60. $x - 4\sqrt{x} = 32$

61. $x^{-1/2} - 2x^{1/2} + x^{3/2} = 0$

62. $(1 + \sqrt{x})^2 - 2(1 + \sqrt{x}) - 15 = 0$

63. $|x - 7| = 4$

64. $|2x - 5| = 9$

65–68 ■ Complex Numbers Evaluate the expression and write in the form $a + bi$.

65. (a) $(2 - 3i) + (1 + 4i)$ **(b)** $(2 + i)(3 - 2i)$

66. (a) $(3 - 6i) - (6 - 4i)$ **(b)** $4i(2 - \frac{1}{2}i)$

67. (a) $\dfrac{4 + 2i}{2 - i}$ **(b)** $(1 - \sqrt{-1})(1 + \sqrt{-1})$

68. (a) $\dfrac{8 + 3i}{4 + 3i}$ **(b)** $\sqrt{-10} \cdot \sqrt{-40}$

69–74 ■ Real and Complex Solutions Find all real and complex solutions of the equation.

69. $x^2 + 16 = 0$

70. $x^2 = -12$

71. $x^2 + 6x + 10 = 0$

72. $2x^2 - 3x + 2 = 0$

73. $x^4 - 256 = 0$

74. $x^3 - 2x^2 + 4x - 8 = 0$

75. Distance and Time A woman cycles 8 mi/h faster than she runs. Every morning she cycles 4 mi and runs $2\frac{1}{2}$ mi, for a total of 1 h of exercise. How fast does she run?

76. The approximate distance d (in feet) that drivers travel after noticing that they must come to a sudden stop is given by the following formula, where x is the speed of the car (in mi/h):

$$d = x + \frac{x^2}{20}$$

If a car travels 75 ft before stopping, what was its speed before the brakes were applied?

77. Geometry The hypotenuse of a right triangle has length 20 cm. The sum of the lengths of the other two sides is 28 cm. Find the lengths of the other two sides of the triangle.

78. Dimensions of a Garden A homeowner wishes to fence in three adjoining garden plots, one for each of her children, as shown in the figure. If each plot is to be 80 ft² in area and she has 88 ft of fencing material at hand, what dimensions should each plot have?

79–92 ■ Inequalities Solve the inequality. Express the solution using interval notation and graph the solution set on the real number line.

79. $3x - 2 > -11$

80. $12 - x \geq 7x$

81. $3 - x \leq 2x - 7$

82. $-1 < 2x + 5 \leq 3$

83. $x^2 + 4x - 12 > 0$

84. $x^2 \leq 1$

85. $\dfrac{2x + 5}{x + 1} \leq 1$

86. $2x^2 \geq x + 3$

87. $\dfrac{x-4}{x^2-4} \le 0$

88. $\dfrac{5}{x^3 - x^2 - 4x + 4} < 0$

89. $|x-5| \le 3$

90. $|x-4| < 0.02$

91. $|2x+1| \ge 1$

92. $|x-1| < |x-3|$
[*Hint:* Interpret the quantities as distances.]

93. Values of a Radical Expression For what values of x is the algebraic expression defined as a real number?

(a) $\sqrt{24 - x - 3x^2}$

(b) $\dfrac{1}{\sqrt[4]{x - x^4}}$

94. Volume of a Sphere The volume of a sphere is given by $V = \frac{4}{3}\pi r^3$, where r is the radius. Find the interval of values of the radius so that the volume is between 8 ft³ and 12 ft³, inclusive.

95–100 ■ Solving Equations and Inequalities Graphically
Graphs of the equations $y = x^2 - 4x$ and $y = x + 6$ are given. Use the graphs to solve the equation or inequality.

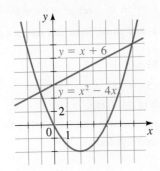

95. $x^2 - 4x = x + 6$

96. $x^2 - 4x = 0$

97. $x^2 - 4x \le x + 6$

98. $x^2 - 4x \ge x + 6$

99. $x^2 - 4x \ge 0$

100. $x^2 - 4x \le 0$

 101–104 ■ Solving Equations Graphically Solve the equation graphically.

101. $x^2 - 4x = 2x + 7$

102. $\sqrt{x+4} = x^2 - 5$

103. $x^4 - 9x^2 = x - 9$

104. $||x+3| - 5| = 2$

 105–108 ■ Solving Inequalities Graphically Solve the inequality graphically.

105. $4x - 3 \ge x^2$

106. $x^3 - 4x^2 - 5x > 2$

107. $x^4 - 4x^2 < \frac{1}{2}x - 1$

108. $|x^2 - 16| - 10 \ge 0$

109–110 ■ Circles and Lines Find equations for the circle and the line in the figure.

109.

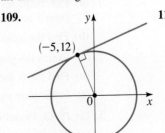

110.

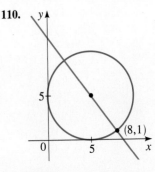

111. Variation Suppose that M varies directly as z and that $M = 120$ when $z = 15$. Write an equation that expresses this variation.

112. Variation Suppose that z is inversely proportional to y and that $z = 12$ when $y = 16$. Write an equation that expresses z in terms of y.

113. Light Intensity The intensity of illumination I from a light varies inversely as the square of the distance d from the light.

(a) Write this statement as an equation.

(b) Determine the constant of proportionality if it is known that a lamp has an intensity of 1000 candles at a distance of 8 m.

(c) What is the intensity of this lamp at a distance of 20 m?

114. Vibrating String The frequency of a vibrating string under constant tension is inversely proportional to its length. If a violin string 12 inches long vibrates 440 times per second, to what length must it be shortened to vibrate 660 times per second?

115. Terminal Velocity The terminal velocity of a parachutist is directly proportional to the square root of his weight. A 160-lb parachutist attains a terminal velocity of 9 mi/h. What is the terminal velocity for a parachutist weighing 240 lb?

116. Range of a Projectile The maximum range of a projectile is directly proportional to the square of its velocity. A baseball pitcher throws a ball at 60 mi/h, with a maximum range of 242 ft. What is his maximum range if he throws the ball at 70 mi/h?

1. **(a)** Plot the points $P(0, 3)$, $Q(3, 0)$, and $R(6, 3)$ in the coordinate plane. Where must the point S be located so that $PQRS$ is a square?

   (b) Find the area of $PQRS$.

2. **(a)** Sketch the graph of $y = x^2 - 4$.

   (b) Find the x- and y-intercepts of the graph.

   (c) Is the graph symmetric about the x-axis, the y-axis, or the origin?

3. Let $P(-3, 1)$ and $Q(5, 6)$ be two points in the coordinate plane.

   (a) Plot P and Q in the coordinate plane.

   (b) Find the distance between P and Q.

   (c) Find the midpoint of the segment PQ.

   (d) Find the slope of the line that contains P and Q.

   (e) Find the perpendicular bisector of the line that contains P and Q.

   (f) Find an equation for the circle for which the segment PQ is a diameter.

4. Find the center and radius of each circle, and sketch its graph.

   (a) $x^2 + y^2 = 25$ **(b)** $(x - 2)^2 + (y + 1)^2 = 9$ **(c)** $x^2 + 6x + y^2 - 2y + 6 = 0$

5. Test each equation for symmetry. Find the x- and y-intercepts, and sketch a graph of the equation.

   (a) $x = 4 - y^2$ **(b)** $y = |x - 2|$

6. A line has the general linear equation $3x - 5y = 15$.

   (a) Find the x- and y-intercepts of the graph of this line.

   (b) Graph the line. Use the intercepts that you found in part (a) to help you.

   (c) Write the equation of the line in slope-intercept form.

   (d) What is the slope of the line?

   (e) What is the slope of any line perpendicular to the given line?

7. Find an equation for the line with the given property.

   (a) It passes through the point $(3, -6)$ and is parallel to the line $3x + y - 10 = 0$.

   (b) It has x-intercept 6 and y-intercept 4.

8. A geologist measures the temperature T (in °C) of the soil at various depths below the surface and finds that at a depth of x cm, the temperature is given by $T = 0.08x - 4$.

   (a) What is the temperature at a depth of 1 m (100 cm)?

   (b) Sketch a graph of the linear equation.

   (c) What do the slope, the x-intercept, and T-intercept of the graph represent?

9. Find all real solutions.

   (a) $x^2 - x - 12 = 0$ **(b)** $2x^2 + 4x + 1 = 0$ **(c)** $3 - \sqrt{x - 3} = x$

   (d) $x^{1/2} - 3x^{1/4} + 2 = 0$ **(e)** $x^4 - 3x^2 + 2 = 0$ **(f)** $3|x - 4| = 10$

10. Perform the indicated operations, and write the result in the form $a + bi$.

    (a) $(3 - 2i) + (4 + 3i)$ **(b)** $(3 - 2i) - (4 + 3i)$

    (c) $(3 - 2i)(4 + 3i)$ **(d)** $\dfrac{3 - 2i}{4 + 3i}$

    (e) i^{48} **(f)** $(\sqrt{2} - \sqrt{-2})(\sqrt{8} + \sqrt{-2})$

11. Find all real and complex solutions of the equation $2x^2 + 4x + 3 = 0$.

12. A rectangular parcel of land is 70 ft longer than it is wide. Each diagonal between opposite corners is 130 ft. What are the dimensions of the parcel?

13. Solve each inequality. Write the answer using interval notation, and sketch the solution on the real number line.

(a) $-4 < 5 - 3x \le 17$

(b) $x(x - 1)(x + 2) > 0$

(c) $|x - 4| < 3$

(d) $\dfrac{2x - 3}{x + 1} \le 1$

14. A bottle of medicine is to be stored at a temperature between 5°C and 10°C. What range does this correspond to on the Fahrenheit scale? [*Note:* Fahrenheit (F) and Celsius (C) temperatures satisfy the relation $C = \frac{5}{9}(F - 32)$.]

15. For what values of x is the expression $\sqrt{6x - x^2}$ defined as a real number?

 16. Solve the equation and the inequality graphically.

(a) $x^3 - 9x - 1 = 0$

(b) $x^2 - 1 \le |x + 1|$

17. The maximum weight M that can be supported by a beam is jointly proportional to its width w and the square of its height h and inversely proportional to its length L.

(a) Write an equation that expresses this proportionality.

(b) Determine the constant of proportionality if a beam 4 in. wide, 6 in. high, and 12 ft long can support a weight of 4800 lb.

(c) If a 10-ft beam made of the same material is 3 in. wide and 10 in. high, what is the maximum weight it can support?

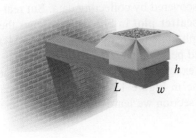

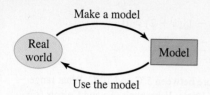

Make a model

Real world → Model

Use the model

A model is a representation of an object or process. For example, a toy Ferrari is a model of the actual car; a road map is a model of the streets in a city. A **mathematical model** is a mathematical representation (usually an equation) of an object or process. Once a mathematical model has been made, it can be used to obtain useful information or make predictions about the thing being modeled. The process is described in the diagram in the margin. In these *Focus on Modeling* sections we explore different ways in which mathematics is used to model real-world phenomena.

■ The Line That Best Fits the Data

In Section 1.10 we used linear equations to model relationships between varying quantities. In practice, such relationships are discovered by collecting data. But real-world data seldom fall into a precise line. The **scatter plot** in Figure 1(a) shows the result of a study on childhood obesity. The graph plots the body mass index (BMI) versus the number of hours of television watched per day for 25 adolescent subjects. Of course, we would not expect the data to be exactly linear as in Figure 1(b). But there is a linear *trend* indicated by the blue line in Figure 1(a): The more hours a subject watches TV, the higher the BMI. In this section we learn how to find the line that best fits the data.

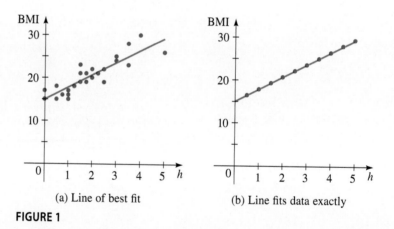

(a) Line of best fit   (b) Line fits data exactly

FIGURE 1

Table 1 gives the nationwide infant mortality rate for the period from 1950 to 2000. The *rate* is the number of infants who die before reaching their first birthday, out of every 1000 live births.

TABLE 1
U.S. Infant Mortality

Year	Rate
1950	29.2
1960	26.0
1970	20.0
1980	12.6
1990	9.2
2000	6.9

FIGURE 2 U.S. infant mortality rate

The scatter plot in Figure 2 shows that the data lie roughly on a straight line. We can try to fit a line visually to approximate the data points, but since the data aren't *exactly* linear, there are many lines that might seem to work. Figure 3 shows two attempts at "eyeballing" a line to fit the data.

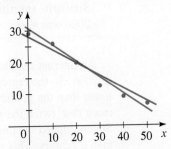

FIGURE 3 Visual attempts to fit line to data

Of all the lines that run through these data points, there is one that "best" fits the data, in the sense that it provides the most accurate linear model for the data. We now describe how to find this line.

It seems reasonable that the line of best fit is the line that is as close as possible to all the data points. This is the line for which the sum of the vertical distances from the data points to the line is as small as possible (see Figure 4). For technical reasons it is better to use the line where the sum of the squares of these distances is smallest. This is called the **regression line**. The formula for the regression line is found by using calculus, but fortunately, the formula is programmed into most graphing calculators. In Example 1 we see how to use a TI-83 calculator to find the regression line for the infant mortality data described above. (The process for other calculators is similar.)

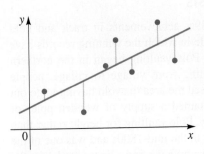

FIGURE 4 Distance from the data points to the line

EXAMPLE 1 ■ Regression Line for U.S. Infant Mortality Rates

(a) Find the regression line for the infant mortality data in Table 1.

(b) Graph the regression line on a scatter plot of the data.

(c) Use the regression line to estimate the infant mortality rates in 1995 and 2006.

SOLUTION

(a) To find the regression line using a TI-83 calculator, we must first enter the data into the lists L₁ and L₂, which are accessed by pressing the $\boxed{\text{STAT}}$ key and selecting Edit. Figure 5 shows the calculator screen after the data have been entered. (Note that we are letting $x = 0$ correspond to the year 1950 so that $x = 50$ corresponds to 2000. This makes the equations easier to work with.) We then press the $\boxed{\text{STAT}}$ key again and select Calc, then 4:LinReg(ax+b), which provides the output shown in Figure 6(a). This tells us that the regression line is

$$y = -0.48x + 29.4$$

Here x represents the number of years since 1950, and y represents the corresponding infant mortality rate.

(b) The scatter plot and the regression line have been plotted on a graphing calculator screen in Figure 6(b).

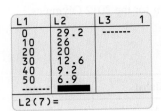

FIGURE 5 Entering the data

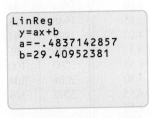

(a) Output of the LinReg command

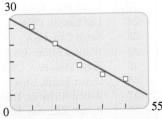

(b) Scatter plot and regression line

FIGURE 6

(c) The year 1995 is 45 years after 1950, so substituting 45 for x, we find that $y = -0.48(45) + 29.4 = 7.8$. So the infant mortality rate in 1995 was about 7.8. Similarly, substituting 56 for x, we find that the infant mortality rate predicted for 2006 was about $-0.48(56) + 29.4 \approx 2.5$. ∎

An Internet search shows that the actual infant mortality rate was 7.6 in 1995 and 6.4 in 2006. So the regression line is fairly accurate for 1995 (the actual rate was slightly lower than the predicted rate), but it is considerably off for 2006 (the actual rate was more than twice the predicted rate). The reason is that infant mortality in the United States stopped declining and actually started rising in 2002, for the first time in more than a century. This shows that we have to be very careful about extrapolating linear models outside the domain over which the data are spread.

■ Examples of Regression Analysis

Since the modern Olympic Games began in 1896, achievements in track and field events have been improving steadily. One example in which the winning records have shown an upward linear trend is the pole vault. Pole vaulting began in the northern Netherlands as a practical activity: When traveling from village to village, people would vault across the many canals that crisscrossed the area to avoid having to go out of their way to find a bridge. Households maintained a supply of wooden poles of lengths appropriate for each member of the family. Pole vaulting for height rather than distance became a collegiate track and field event in the mid-1800s and was one of the events in the first modern Olympics. In the next example we find a linear model for the gold-medal-winning records in the men's Olympic pole vault.

Renaud Lavillenie, 2012
Olympic gold medal winner,
men's pole vault

EXAMPLE 2 ■ Regression Line for Olympic Pole Vault Records

Table 2 gives the men's Olympic pole vault records up to 2008.

(a) Find the regression line for the data.

(b) Make a scatter plot of the data, and graph the regression line. Does the regression line appear to be a suitable model for the data?

(c) What does the slope of the regression line represent?

(d) Use the model to predict the winning pole vault height for the 2012 Olympics.

TABLE 2
Men's Olympic Pole Vault Records

Year	x	Gold medalist	Height (m)	Year	x	Gold medalist	Height (m)
1896	−4	William Hoyt, USA	3.30	1960	60	Don Bragg, USA	4.70
1900	0	Irving Baxter, USA	3.30	1964	64	Fred Hansen, USA	5.10
1904	4	Charles Dvorak, USA	3.50	1968	68	Bob Seagren, USA	5.40
1906	6	Fernand Gonder, France	3.50	1972	72	W. Nordwig, E. Germany	5.64
1908	8	A. Gilbert, E. Cook, USA	3.71	1976	76	Tadeusz Slusarski, Poland	5.64
1912	12	Harry Babcock, USA	3.95	1980	80	W. Kozakiewicz, Poland	5.78
1920	20	Frank Foss, USA	4.09	1984	84	Pierre Quinon, France	5.75
1924	24	Lee Barnes, USA	3.95	1988	88	Sergei Bubka, USSR	5.90
1928	28	Sabin Can, USA	4.20	1992	92	M. Tarassob, Unified Team	5.87
1932	32	William Miller, USA	4.31	1996	96	Jean Jaffione, France	5.92
1936	36	Earle Meadows, USA	4.35	2000	100	Nick Hysong, USA	5.90
1948	48	Guinn Smith, USA	4.30	2004	104	Timothy Mack, USA	5.95
1952	52	Robert Richards, USA	4.55	2008	108	Steven Hooker, Australia	5.96
1956	56	Robert Richards, USA	4.56				

Output of the LinReg
function on the TI-83

SOLUTION

(a) Let x = year − 1900, so 1896 corresponds to $x = -4$, 1900 to $x = 0$, and so on. Using a calculator, we find the following regression line:

$$y = 0.0260x + 3.42$$

(b) The scatter plot and the regression line are shown in Figure 7. The regression line appears to be a good model for the data.

(c) The slope is the average rate of increase in the pole vault record per year. So on average, the pole vault record increased by 0.0266 m/year.

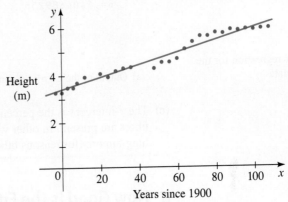

FIGURE 7 Scatter plot and regression line for pole vault data

(d) The year 2012 corresponds to $x = 112$ in our model. The model gives

$$y = 0.0260(112) + 3.42$$

$$\approx 6.33$$

So the model predicts that in 2012 the winning pole vault would be 6.33 m. ■

At the 2012 Olympics in London, England, the men's Olympic gold medal in the pole vault was won by Renaud Lavillenie of France, with a vault of 5.97 m. Although this height set an Olympic record, it was considerably lower than the 6.33 m predicted by the model of Example 2. In Problem 10 we find a regression line for the pole vault data from 1972 to 2008. Do the problem to see whether this restricted set of more recent data provides a better predictor for the 2012 record.

Is a linear model really appropriate for the data of Example 2? In subsequent *Focus on Modeling* sections we study regression models that use other types of functions, and we learn how to choose the best model for a given set of data.

In the next example we see how linear regression is used in medical research to investigate potential causes of diseases such as cancer.

EXAMPLE 3 ■ Regression Line for Links Between Asbestos and Cancer

When laboratory rats are exposed to asbestos fibers, some of the rats develop lung tumors. Table 3 lists the results of several experiments by different scientists.

(a) Find the regression line for the data.

(b) Make a scatter plot and graph the regression line. Does the regression line appear to be a suitable model for the data?

(c) What does the y-intercept of the regression line represent?

TABLE 3
Asbestos–Tumor Data

Asbestos exposure (fibers/mL)	Percent that develop lung tumors
50	2
400	6
500	5
900	10
1100	26
1600	42
1800	37
2000	28
3000	50

Eric and David Hosking/Terra/Corbis

FIGURE 8 Linear regression for the asbestos–tumor data

SOLUTION

(a) Using a calculator, we find the following regression line (see Figure 8(a)):

$$y = 0.0177x + 0.5405$$

(b) The scatter plot and regression line are graphed in Figure 8(b). The regression line appears to be a reasonable model for the data.

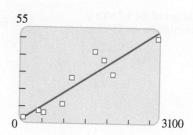

(a) Output of the `LinReg` command

(b) Scatter plot and regression line

(c) The y-intercept is the percentage of rats that develop tumors when no asbestos fibers are present. In other words, this is the percentage that normally develop lung tumors (for reasons other than asbestos).

■

■ How Good Is the Fit? The Correlation Coefficient

For any given set of two-variable data it is always possible to find a regression line, even if the data points do not tend to lie on a line and even if the variables don't seem to be related at all. Look at the three scatter plots in Figure 9. In the first scatter plot, the data points lie close to a line. In the second plot, there is still a linear trend but the points are more scattered. In the third plot there doesn't seem to be any trend at all, linear or otherwise.

A graphing calculator can give us a regression line for each of these scatter plots. But how well do these lines represent or "fit" the data? To answer this question, statisticians have invented the **correlation coefficient**, usually denoted r. The correlation coefficient is a number between -1 and 1 that measures how closely the data follow the regression line—or, in other words, how strongly the variables are **correlated**. Many graphing calculators give the value of r when they compute a regression line. If r is close to -1 or 1, then the variables are strongly correlated—that is, the scatter plot follows the regression line closely. If r is close to 0, then the variables are weakly correlated or not correlated at all. (The sign of r depends on the slope of the regression line.) The correlation coefficients of the scatter plots in Figure 9 are indicated on the graphs. For the first plot, r is close to 1 because the data are very close to linear. The second plot also has a relatively large r, but it is not as large as the first, because the data, while fairly linear, are more diffuse. The third plot has an r close to 0, since there is virtually no linear trend in the data.

There are no hard and fast rules for deciding what values of r are sufficient for deciding that a linear correlation is "significant." The correlation coefficient is only a rough guide in helping us decide how much faith to put into a given regression line. In Example 1 the correlation coefficient is -0.99, indicating a very high level of correlation, so we can safely say that the drop in infant mortality rates from 1950 to 2000 was strongly linear. (The value of r is negative, since infant mortality trended *down* over this period.) In Example 3 the correlation coefficient is 0.92, which also indicates a strong correlation between the variables. So exposure to asbestos is clearly associated with the growth of lung tumors in rats. Does this mean that asbestos *causes* lung cancer?

If two variables are correlated, it does not necessarily mean that a change in one variable *causes* a change in the other. For example, the mathematician John Allen Paulos points out that shoe size is strongly correlated to mathematics scores among schoolchildren. Does this mean that big feet cause high math scores? Certainly not—

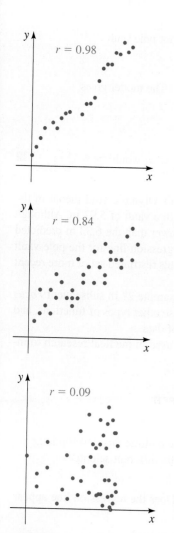

FIGURE 9

both shoe size and math skills increase independently as children get older. So it is important not to jump to conclusions: Correlation and causation are not the same thing. You can explore this topic further in *Discovery Project: Correlation and Causation* at **www.stewartmath.com**. Correlation is a useful tool in bringing important cause-and-effect relationships to light; but to prove causation, we must explain the mechanism by which one variable affects the other. For example, the link between smoking and lung cancer was observed as a correlation long before science found the mechanism through which smoking causes lung cancer.

PROBLEMS

1. **Femur Length and Height** Anthropologists use a linear model that relates femur length to height. The model allows an anthropologist to determine the height of an individual when only a partial skeleton (including the femur) is found. In this problem we find the model by analyzing the data on femur length and height for the eight males given in the table.

   (a) Make a scatter plot of the data.

   (b) Find and graph a linear function that models the data.

   (c) An anthropologist finds a femur of length 58 cm. How tall was the person?

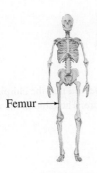

Femur ⟶

Femur length (cm)	Height (cm)
50.1	178.5
48.3	173.6
45.2	164.8
44.7	163.7
44.5	168.3
42.7	165.0
39.5	155.4
38.0	155.8

2. **Demand for Soft Drinks** A convenience store manager notices that sales of soft drinks are higher on hotter days, so he assembles the data in the table.

   (a) Make a scatter plot of the data.

   (b) Find and graph a linear function that models the data.

   (c) Use the model to predict soft drink sales if the temperature is 95°F.

High temperature (°F)	Number of cans sold
55	340
58	335
64	410
68	460
70	450
75	610
80	735
84	780

Diameter (in.)	Age (years)
2.5	15
4.0	24
6.0	32
8.0	56
9.0	49
9.5	76
12.5	90
15.5	89

3. **Tree Diameter and Age** To estimate ages of trees, forest rangers use a linear model that relates tree diameter to age. The model is useful because tree diameter is much easier to measure than tree age (which requires special tools for extracting a representative cross section of the tree and counting the rings). To find the model, use the data in the table, which were collected for a certain variety of oaks.

   (a) Make a scatter plot of the data.

   (b) Find and graph a linear function that models the data.

   (c) Use the model to estimate the age of an oak whose diameter is 18 in.

4. Carbon Dioxide Levels   The Mauna Loa Observatory, located on the island of Hawaii, has been monitoring carbon dioxide (CO_2) levels in the atmosphere since 1958. The table lists the average annual CO_2 levels measured in parts per million (ppm) from 1990 to 2012.

(a) Make a scatter plot of the data.

(b) Find and graph the regression line.

(c) Use the linear model in part (b) to estimate the CO_2 level in the atmosphere in 2011. Compare your answer with the actual CO_2 level of 391.6 that was measured in 2011.

Year	CO_2 level (ppm)
1990	354.4
1992	356.4
1994	358.8
1996	362.6
1998	366.7
2000	369.5
2002	373.2
2004	377.5
2006	381.9
2008	385.6
2010	389.9
2012	393.8

Source: Mauna Loa Observatory

Temperature (°F)	Chirping rate (chirps/min)
50	20
55	46
60	79
65	91
70	113
75	140
80	173
85	198
90	211

5. Temperature and Chirping Crickets   Biologists have observed that the chirping rate of crickets of a certain species appears to be related to temperature. The table in the margin shows the chirping rates for various temperatures.

(a) Make a scatter plot of the data.

(b) Find and graph the regression line.

(c) Use the linear model in part (b) to estimate the chirping rate at 100°F.

6. Extent of Arctic Sea Ice   The National Snow and Ice Data Center monitors the amount of ice in the Arctic year round. The table below gives approximate values for the sea ice extent in millions of square kilometers from 1986 to 2012, in two-year intervals.

(a) Make a scatter plot of the data.

(b) Find and graph the regression line.

(c) Use the linear model in part (b) to estimate the ice extent in the year 2016.

Year	Ice extent (million km²)	Year	Ice extent (million km²)
1986	7.5	2000	6.3
1988	7.5	2002	6.0
1990	6.2	2004	6.0
1992	7.5	2006	5.9
1994	7.2	2008	4.7
1996	7.9	2010	4.9
1998	6.6	2012	3.6

Source: National Snow and Ice Data Center

Flow rate (%)	Mosquito positive rate (%)
0	22
10	16
40	12
60	11
90	6
100	2

7. Mosquito Prevalence   The table in the margin lists the relative abundance of mosquitoes (as measured by the mosquito positive rate) versus the flow rate (measured as a percentage of maximum flow) of canal networks in Saga City, Japan.

(a) Make a scatter plot of the data.

(b) Find and graph the regression line.

(c) Use the linear model in part (b) to estimate the mosquito positive rate if the canal flow is 70% of maximum.

Noise level (dB)	MRT score (%)
80	99
84	91
88	84
92	70
96	47
100	23
104	11

Year	Life expectancy
1920	54.1
1930	59.7
1940	62.9
1950	68.2
1960	69.7
1970	70.8
1980	73.7
1990	75.4
2000	76.9

8. **Noise and Intelligibility** Audiologists study the intelligibility of spoken sentences under different noise levels. Intelligibility, the MRT score, is measured as the percent of a spoken sentence that the listener can decipher at a certain noise level in decibels (dB). The table shows the results of one such test.

(a) Make a scatter plot of the data.

(b) Find and graph the regression line.

(c) Find the correlation coefficient. Is a linear model appropriate?

(d) Use the linear model in part (b) to estimate the intelligibility of a sentence at a 94-dB noise level.

9. **Life Expectancy** The average life expectancy in the United States has been rising steadily over the past few decades, as shown in the table.

(a) Make a scatter plot of the data.

(b) Find and graph the regression line.

(c) Use the linear model you found in part (b) to predict the life expectancy in the year 2006.

(d) Search the Internet or your campus library to find the actual 2006 average life expectancy. Compare to your answer in part (c).

10. **Olympic Pole Vault** The graph in Figure 7 indicates that in recent years the winning Olympic men's pole vault height has fallen below the value predicted by the regression line in Example 2. This might have occurred because when the pole vault was a new event, there was much room for improvement in vaulters' performances, whereas now even the best training can produce only incremental advances. Let's see whether concentrating on more recent results gives a better predictor of future records.

(a) Use the data in Table 2 (page 176) to complete the table of winning pole vault heights shown in the margin. (Note that we are using $x = 0$ to correspond to the year 1972, where this restricted data set begins.)

(b) Find the regression line for the data in part (a).

(c) Plot the data and the regression line on the same axes. Does the regression line seem to provide a good model for the data?

(d) What does the regression line predict as the winning pole vault height for the 2012 Olympics? Compare this predicted value to the actual 2012 winning height of 5.97 m, as described on page 177. Has this new regression line provided a better prediction than the line in Example 2?

Year	x	Height (m)
1972	0	5.64
1976	4	
1980	8	
1984		
1988		
1992		
1996		
2000		
2004		
2008		

11. Shoe Size and Height Do you think that shoe size and height are correlated? Find out by surveying the shoe sizes and heights of people in your class. (Of course, the data for men and women should be separate.) Find the correlation coefficient.

12. Demand for Candy Bars In this problem you will determine a linear demand equation that describes the demand for candy bars in your class. Survey your classmates to determine what price they would be willing to pay for a candy bar. Your survey form might look like the sample to the left.

Would you buy a candy bar from the vending machine in the hallway if the price is as indicated?

Price	Yes or No
50¢	
75¢	
$1.00	
$1.25	
$1.50	
$1.75	
$2.00	

(a) Make a table of the number of respondents who answered "yes" at each price level.

(b) Make a scatter plot of your data.

(c) Find and graph the regression line $y = mp + b$, which gives the number of responents y who would buy a candy bar if the price were p cents. This is the *demand equation*. Why is the slope m negative?

(d) What is the p-intercept of the demand equation? What does this intercept tell you about pricing candy bars?

© iStockphoto.com/Jeff McDonald

2 Functions

A *function* **is a rule** that describes how one quantity depends on another. Many real-world situations follow precise rules, so they can be modeled by functions. For example, there is a rule that relates the distance a skydiver falls to the time he or she has been falling. So the distance traveled by the skydiver is a *function* of time. Knowing this function model allows skydivers to determine when to open their parachute. In this chapter we study functions and their graphs, as well as many real-world applications of functions. In the *Focus on Modeling* at the end of the chapter we explore different real-world situations that can be modeled by functions.

2.1   FUNCTIONS

■ Functions All Around Us ■ Definition of Function ■ Evaluating a Function
■ The Domain of a Function ■ Four Ways to Represent a Function

In this section we explore the idea of a function and then give the mathematical definition of function.

■ Functions All Around Us

In nearly every physical phenomenon we observe that one quantity depends on another. For example, your height depends on your age, the temperature depends on the date, the cost of mailing a package depends on its weight (see Figure 1). We use the term *function* to describe this dependence of one quantity on another. That is, we say the following:

- Height is a function of age.
- Temperature is a function of date.
- Cost of mailing a package is a function of weight.

The U.S. Post Office uses a simple rule to determine the cost of mailing a first-class parcel on the basis of its weight. But it's not so easy to describe the rule that relates height to age or the rule that relates temperature to date.

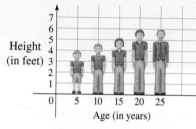

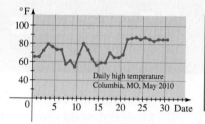

w (ounces)	2014 Postage (dollars)
$0 < w \leq 1$	0.98
$1 < w \leq 2$	1.19
$2 < w \leq 3$	1.40
$3 < w \leq 4$	1.61
$4 < w \leq 5$	1.82
$5 < w \leq 6$	2.03

FIGURE 1   Height is a function of age.   Temperature is a function of date.   Postage is a function of weight.

Can you think of other functions? Here are some more examples:

- The area of a circle is a function of its radius.
- The number of bacteria in a culture is a function of time.
- The weight of an astronaut is a function of her elevation.
- The price of a commodity is a function of the demand for that commodity.

The rule that describes how the area A of a circle depends on its radius r is given by the formula $A = \pi r^2$. Even when a precise rule or formula describing a function is not available, we can still describe the function by a graph. For example, when you turn on a hot water faucet, the temperature of the water depends on how long the water has been running. So we can say:

- The temperature of water from the faucet is a function of time.

Figure 2 shows a rough graph of the temperature T of the water as a function of the time t that has elapsed since the faucet was turned on. The graph shows that the initial temperature of the water is close to room temperature. When the water from the hot water tank reaches the faucet, the water's temperature T increases quickly. In the next phase,

T is constant at the temperature of the water in the tank. When the tank is drained, *T* decreases to the temperature of the cold water supply.

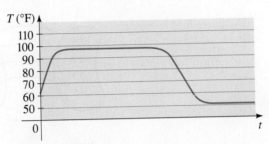

FIGURE 2 Graph of water temperature *T* as a function of time *t*

Definition of Function

We have previously used letters to stand for numbers. Here we do something quite different: We use letters to represent *rules*.

A function is a rule. To talk about a function, we need to give it a name. We will use letters such as *f*, *g*, *h*, . . . to represent functions. For example, we can use the letter *f* to represent a rule as follows:

"*f*" is the rule "square the number"

When we write *f*(2), we mean "apply the rule *f* to the number 2." Applying the rule gives $f(2) = 2^2 = 4$. Similarly, $f(3) = 3^2 = 9$, $f(4) = 4^2 = 16$, and in general $f(x) = x^2$.

DEFINITION OF A FUNCTION

A **function** *f* is a rule that assigns to each element *x* in a set *A* exactly one element, called *f*(*x*), in a set *B*.

We usually consider functions for which the sets *A* and *B* are sets of real numbers. The symbol *f*(*x*) is read "*f* of *x*" or "*f* at *x*" and is called the **value of *f* at *x***, or the **image of *x* under *f***. The set *A* is called the **domain** of the function. The **range** of *f* is the set of all possible values of *f*(*x*) as *x* varies throughout the domain, that is,

$$\text{range of } f = \{f(x) \mid x \in A\}$$

The symbol that represents an arbitrary number in the domain of a function *f* is called an **independent variable**. The symbol that represents a number in the range of *f* is called a **dependent variable**. So if we write $y = f(x)$, then *x* is the independent variable and *y* is the dependent variable.

It is helpful to think of a function as a **machine** (see Figure 3). If *x* is in the domain of the function *f*, then when *x* enters the machine, it is accepted as an **input** and the machine produces an **output** *f*(*x*) according to the rule of the function. Thus we can think of the domain as the set of all possible inputs and the range as the set of all possible outputs.

The ☑ key on your calculator is a good example of a function as a machine. First you input *x* into the display. Then you press the key labeled ☑. (On most *graphing* calculators the order of these operations is reversed.) If $x < 0$, then *x* is not in the domain of this function; that is, *x* is not an acceptable input, and the calculator will indicate an error. If $x \geq 0$, then an approximation to $\sqrt{x}$ appears in the display, correct to a certain number of decimal places. (Thus the ☑ key on your calculator is not quite the same as the exact mathematical function *f* defined by $f(x) = \sqrt{x}$.)

FIGURE 3 Machine diagram of *f*

Another way to picture a function *f* is by an **arrow diagram** as in Figure 4(a). Each arrow associates an input from *A* to the corresponding output in *B*. Since a function associates *exactly* one output to each input, the diagram in Figure 4(a) represents a function but the diagram in Figure 4(b) does *not* represent a function.

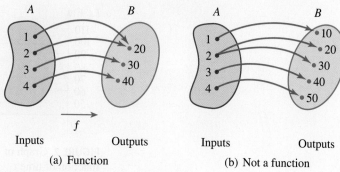

(a) Function   (b) Not a function

FIGURE 4 Arrow diagrams

EXAMPLE 1 ■ Analyzing a Function

A function f is defined by the formula

$$f(x) = x^2 + 4$$

(a) Express in words how f acts on the input x to produce the output $f(x)$.

(b) Evaluate $f(3)$, $f(-2)$, and $f(\sqrt{5})$.

(c) Find the domain and range of f.

(d) Draw a machine diagram for f.

SOLUTION

(a) The formula tells us that f first squares the input x and then adds 4 to the result. So f is the function

"square, then add 4"

(b) The values of f are found by substituting for x in the formula $f(x) = x^2 + 4$.

$$f(3) = 3^2 + 4 = 13 \qquad \text{Replace } x \text{ by } 3$$

$$f(-2) = (-2)^2 + 4 = 8 \qquad \text{Replace } x \text{ by } -2$$

$$f(\sqrt{5}) = (\sqrt{5})^2 + 4 = 9 \qquad \text{Replace } x \text{ by } \sqrt{5}$$

(c) The domain of f consists of all possible inputs for f. Since we can evaluate the formula $f(x) = x^2 + 4$ for every real number x, the domain of f is the set $\mathbb{R}$ of all real numbers.

The range of f consists of all possible outputs of f. Because $x^2 \geq 0$ for all real numbers x, we have $x^2 + 4 \geq 4$, so for every output of f we have $f(x) \geq 4$. Thus the range of f is $\{y \mid y \geq 4\} = [4, \infty)$.

(d) A machine diagram for f is shown in Figure 5.

✎ **Now Try Exercises 11, 15, 19, and 51**

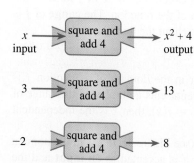

FIGURE 5 Machine diagram

■ Evaluating a Function

In the definition of a function the independent variable x plays the role of a placeholder. For example, the function $f(x) = 3x^2 + x - 5$ can be thought of as

$$f(\blacksquare) = 3 \cdot \blacksquare^2 + \blacksquare - 5$$

To evaluate f at a number, we substitute the number for the placeholder.

EXAMPLE 2 ■ Evaluating a Function

Let $f(x) = 3x^2 + x - 5$. Evaluate each function value.

(a) $f(-2)$ (b) $f(0)$ (c) $f(4)$ (d) $f\left(\frac{1}{2}\right)$

SOLUTION To evaluate f at a number, we substitute the number for x in the definition of f.

(a) $f(-2) = 3 \cdot (-2)^2 + (-2) - 5 = 5$

(b) $f(0) = 3 \cdot 0^2 + 0 - 5 = -5$

(c) $f(4) = 3 \cdot (4)^2 + 4 - 5 = 47$

(d) $f\left(\frac{1}{2}\right) = 3 \cdot \left(\frac{1}{2}\right)^2 + \frac{1}{2} - 5 = -\frac{15}{4}$

✎ **Now Try Exercise 21**

EXAMPLE 3 ■ A Piecewise Defined Function

A cell phone plan costs \$39 a month. The plan includes 2 gigabytes (GB) of free data and charges \$15 per gigabyte for any additional data used. The monthly charges are a function of the number of gigabytes of data used, given by

$$C(x) = \begin{cases} 39 & \text{if } 0 \le x \le 2 \\ 39 + 15(x - 2) & \text{if } x > 2 \end{cases}$$

Find $C(0.5)$, $C(2)$, and $C(4)$.

SOLUTION Remember that a function is a rule. Here is how we apply the rule for this function. First we look at the value of the input, x. If $0 \le x \le 2$, then the value of $C(x)$ is 39. On the other hand, if $x > 2$, then the value of $C(x)$ is $39 + 15(x - 2)$.

Since $0.5 \le 2$, we have $C(0.5) = 39$.

Since $2 \le 2$, we have $C(2) = 39$.

Since $4 > 2$, we have $C(4) = 39 + 15(4 - 2) = 69$.

Thus the plan charges \$39 for 0.5 GB, \$39 for 2 GB, and \$69 for 4 GB.

✎ **Now Try Exercises 31 and 85**

A **piecewise defined function** is defined by different formulas on different parts of its domain. The function C of Example 3 is piecewise defined.

From Examples 2 and 3 we see that the values of a function can change from one input to another. The **net change** in the value of a function f as the input changes from a to b (where $a \le b$) is given by

$$\boxed{f(b) - f(a)}$$

The next example illustrates this concept.

EXAMPLE 4 ■ Finding Net Change

Let $f(x) = x^2$. Find the net change in the value of f between the given inputs.

(a) From 1 to 3   (b) From -2 to 2

SOLUTION

(a) The net change is $f(3) - f(1) = 9 - 1 = 8$.

(b) The net change is $f(2) - f(-2) = 4 - 4 = 0$.

✎ **Now Try Exercise 39**

The values of the function in Example 4 decrease and then increase between -2 and 2, but the net change from -2 to 2 is 0 because $f(-2)$ and $f(2)$ have the same value.

EXAMPLE 5 ■ Evaluating a Function

If $f(x) = 2x^2 + 3x - 1$, evaluate the following.

Expressions like the one in part (d) of Example 5 occur frequently in calculus; they are called *difference quotients*, and they represent the average change in the value of f between $x = a$ and $x = a + h$.

(a) $f(a)$ **(b)** $f(-a)$ **(c)** $f(a + h)$ **(d)** $\dfrac{f(a + h) - f(a)}{h}$, $h \neq 0$

SOLUTION

(a) $f(a) = 2a^2 + 3a - 1$

(b) $f(-a) = 2(-a)^2 + 3(-a) - 1 = 2a^2 - 3a - 1$

(c) $f(a + h) = 2(a + h)^2 + 3(a + h) - 1$

$$= 2(a^2 + 2ah + h^2) + 3(a + h) - 1$$

$$= 2a^2 + 4ah + 2h^2 + 3a + 3h - 1$$

(d) Using the results from parts (c) and (a), we have

$$\frac{f(a + h) - f(a)}{h} = \frac{(2a^2 + 4ah + 2h^2 + 3a + 3h - 1) - (2a^2 + 3a - 1)}{h}$$

$$= \frac{4ah + 2h^2 + 3h}{h} = 4a + 2h + 3$$

 **Now Try Exercise 43**

A **table of values** for a function is a table with two headings, one for inputs and one for the corresponding outputs. A table of values helps us to analyze a function numerically, as in the next example.

EXAMPLE 6 ■ The Weight of an Astronaut

If an astronaut weighs 130 lb on the surface of the earth, then her weight when she is h miles above the earth is given by the function

$$w(h) = 130\left(\frac{3960}{3960 + h}\right)^2$$

(a) What is her weight when she is 100 mi above the earth?

(b) Construct a table of values for the function w that gives her weight at heights from 0 to 500 mi. What do you conclude from the table?

(c) Find the net change in the astronaut's weight from ground level to a height of 500 mi.

The weight of an object on or near the earth is the gravitational force that the earth exerts on it. When in orbit around the earth, an astronaut experiences the sensation of "weightlessness" because the centripetal force that keeps her in orbit is exactly the same as the gravitational pull of the earth.

SOLUTION

(a) We want the value of the function w when $h = 100$; that is, we must calculate $w(100)$:

$$w(100) = 130\left(\frac{3960}{3960 + 100}\right)^2 \approx 123.67$$

So at a height of 100 mi she weighs about 124 lb.

(b) The table gives the astronaut's weight, rounded to the nearest pound, at 100-mi increments. The values in the table are calculated as in part (a).

h	$w(h)$
0	130
100	124
200	118
300	112
400	107
500	102

The table indicates that the higher the astronaut travels, the less she weighs.

(c) The net change in the astronaut's weight from $h = 0$ to $h = 500$ is

$$w(500) - w(0) = 102 - 130 = -28$$

The negative sign indicates that the astronaut's weight *decreased* by about 28 lb.

▪ Now Try Exercise 79   ■

The Domain of a Function

Recall that the *domain* of a function is the set of all inputs for the function. The domain of a function may be stated explicitly. For example, if we write

$$f(x) = x^2 \qquad 0 \le x \le 5$$

then the domain is the set of all real numbers x for which $0 \le x \le 5$. If the function is given by an algebraic expression and the domain is not stated explicitly, then by convention *the domain of the function is the domain of the algebraic expression—that is, the set of all real numbers for which the expression is defined as a real number.* For example, consider the functions

Domains of algebraic expressions are discussed on page 44.

$$f(x) = \frac{1}{x - 4} \qquad g(x) = \sqrt{x}$$

The function f is not defined at $x = 4$, so its domain is $\{x \mid x \ne 4\}$. The function g is not defined for negative x, so its domain is $\{x \mid x \ge 0\}$.

EXAMPLE 7 ▪ Finding Domains of Functions

Find the domain of each function.

(a) $f(x) = \dfrac{1}{x^2 - x}$ (b) $g(x) = \sqrt{9 - x^2}$ (c) $h(t) = \dfrac{t}{\sqrt{t + 1}}$

SOLUTION

(a) A rational expression is not defined when the denominator is 0. Since

$$f(x) = \frac{1}{x^2 - x} = \frac{1}{x(x - 1)}$$

we see that $f(x)$ is not defined when $x = 0$ or $x = 1$. Thus the domain of f is

$$\{x \mid x \ne 0, x \ne 1\}$$

The domain may also be written in interval notation as

$$(\infty, 0) \cup (0, 1) \cup (1, \infty)$$

(b) We can't take the square root of a negative number, so we must have $9 - x^2 \ge 0$. Using the methods of Section 1.7, we can solve this inequality to find that $-3 \le x \le 3$. Thus the domain of g is

$$\{x \mid -3 \le x \le 3\} = [-3, 3]$$

(c) We can't take the square root of a negative number, and we can't divide by 0, so we must have $t + 1 > 0$, that is, $t > -1$. So the domain of h is

$$\{t \mid t > -1\} = (-1, \infty)$$

▪ Now Try Exercises 55, 59, and 69   ■

Four Ways to Represent a Function

To help us understand what a function is, we have used machine and arrow diagrams. We can describe a specific function in the following four ways:

- verbally (by a description in words)
- algebraically (by an explicit formula)
- visually (by a graph)
- numerically (by a table of values)

A single function may be represented in all four ways, and it is often useful to go from one representation to another to gain insight into the function. However, certain functions are described more naturally by one method than by the others. An example of a verbal description is the following rule for converting between temperature scales:

> "To find the Fahrenheit equivalent of a Celsius temperature, multiply the Celsius temperature by $\frac{9}{5}$, then add 32."

In Example 8 we see how to describe this verbal rule or function algebraically, graphically, and numerically. A useful representation of the area of a circle as a function of its radius is the algebraic formula

$$A(r) = \pi r^2$$

The graph produced by a seismograph (see the box below) is a visual representation of the vertical acceleration function $a(t)$ of the ground during an earthquake. As a final example, consider the function $C(w)$, which is described verbally as "the cost of mailing a large first-class letter with weight w." The most convenient way of describing this function is numerically—that is, using a table of values.

We will be using all four representations of functions throughout this book. We summarize them in the following box.

FOUR WAYS TO REPRESENT A FUNCTION

Verbal Using words:

"To convert from Celsius to Fahrenheit, multiply the Celsius temperature by $\frac{9}{5}$, then add 32."

Relation between Celsius and Fahrenheit temperature scales

Algebraic Using a formula:

$$A(r) = \pi r^2$$

Area of a circle

Visual Using a graph:

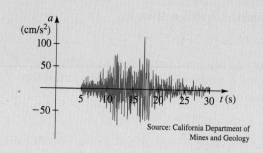

Source: California Department of Mines and Geology

Vertical acceleration during an earthquake

Numerical Using a table of values:

w (ounces)	$C(w)$ (dollars)
$0 < w \le 1$	\$0.98
$1 < w \le 2$	\$1.19
$2 < w \le 3$	\$1.40
$3 < w \le 4$	\$1.61
$4 < w \le 5$	\$1.82
⋮	⋮

Cost of mailing a large first-class envelope

EXAMPLE 8 ■ Representing a Function Verbally, Algebraically, Numerically, and Graphically

Let $F(C)$ be the Fahrenheit temperature corresponding to the Celsius temperature C. (Thus F is the function that converts Celsius inputs to Fahrenheit outputs.) The box on page 190 gives a verbal description of this function. Find ways to represent this function

(a) Algebraically (using a formula)

(b) Numerically (using a table of values)

(c) Visually (using a graph)

SOLUTION

(a) The verbal description tells us that we should first multiply the input C by $\frac{9}{5}$ and then add 32 to the result. So we get

$$F(C) = \tfrac{9}{5}C + 32$$

(b) We use the algebraic formula for F that we found in part (a) to construct a table of values:

C (Celsius)	F (Fahrenheit)
-10	14
0	32
10	50
20	68
30	86
40	104

(c) We use the points tabulated in part (b) to help us draw the graph of this function in Figure 6.

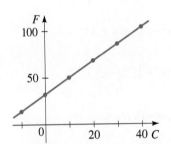

FIGURE 6 Celsius and Fahrenheit

✎ **Now Try Exercise 73**

2.1 EXERCISES

CONCEPTS

1. If $f(x) = x^3 + 1$, then

(a) the value of f at $x = -1$ is $f(\underline{\quad}) = \underline{\qquad}$.

(b) the value of f at $x = 2$ is $f(\underline{\quad}) = \underline{\qquad}$.

(c) the net change in the value of f between $x = -1$ and

$x = 2$ is $f(\underline{\quad}) - f(\underline{\quad}) = \underline{\qquad}$.

2. For a function f, the set of all possible inputs is called the

_____ of f, and the set of all possible outputs is called

the _____ of f.

3. (a) Which of the following functions have 5 in their domain?

$$f(x) = x^2 - 3x \qquad g(x) = \frac{x-5}{x} \qquad h(x) = \sqrt{x-10}$$

(b) For the functions from part (a) that *do* have 5 in their domain, find the value of the function at 5.

4. A function is given algebraically by the formula $f(x) = (x - 4)^2 + 3$. Complete these other ways to represent f:

(a) *Verbal:* "Subtract 4, then _____ and _____.

(b) *Numerical:*

x	$f(x)$
0	19
2	
4	
6	

5. A function f is a rule that assigns to each element x in a set A exactly _____ element(s) called $f(x)$ in a set B. Which of the following tables defines y as a function of x?

(i)

x	y
1	5
2	7
3	6
4	8

(ii)

x	y
1	5
1	7
2	6
3	8

6. *Yes or No?* If *No*, give a reason. Let f be a function.
  (a) Is it possible that $f(1) = 5$ and $f(2) = 5$?
  (b) Is it possible that $f(1) = 5$ and $f(1) = 6$?

SKILLS

7–10 ■ **Function Notation** Express the rule in function notation. (For example, the rule "square, then subtract 5" is expressed as the function $f(x) = x^2 - 5$.)

7. Multiply by 3, then subtract 5

8. Square, then add 2

9. Subtract 1, then square

10. Add 1, take the square root, then divide by 6

11–14 ■ **Functions in Words** Express the function (or rule) in words.

11. $f(x) = 2x + 3$

12. $g(x) = \dfrac{x + 2}{3}$

13. $h(x) = 5(x + 1)$

14. $k(x) = \dfrac{x^2 - 4}{3}$

15–16 ■ **Machine Diagram** Draw a machine diagram for the function.

15. $f(x) = \sqrt{x - 1}$

16. $f(x) = \dfrac{3}{x - 2}$

17–18 ■ **Table of Values** Complete the table.

17. $f(x) = 2(x - 1)^2$

x	$f(x)$
-1	
0	
1	
2	
3	

18. $g(x) = |2x + 3|$

x	$g(x)$
-3	
-2	
0	
1	
3	

19–30 ■ **Evaluating Functions** Evaluate the function at the indicated values.

19. $f(x) = x^2 - 6$; $f(-3), f(3), f(0), f(\tfrac{1}{2})$

20. $f(x) = x^3 + 2x$; $f(-2), f(-1), f(0), f(\tfrac{1}{2})$

21. $f(x) = \dfrac{1 - 2x}{3}$;
  $f(2), f(-2), f(\tfrac{1}{2}), f(a), f(-a), f(a - 1)$

22. $h(x) = \dfrac{x^2 + 4}{5}$;
  $h(2), h(-2), h(a), h(-x), h(a - 2), h(\sqrt{x})$

23. $f(x) = x^2 + 2x$;
  $f(0), f(3), f(-3), f(a), f(-x), f\left(\dfrac{1}{a}\right)$

24. $h(t) = t + \dfrac{1}{t}$;
  $h(-1), h(2), h(\tfrac{1}{2}), h(x - 1), h\left(\dfrac{1}{x}\right)$

25. $g(x) = \dfrac{1 - x}{1 + x}$;
  $g(2), g(-1), g(\tfrac{1}{2}), g(a), g(a - 1), g(x^2 - 1)$

26. $g(t) = \dfrac{t + 2}{t - 2}$;
  $g(-2), g(2), g(0), g(a), g(a^2 - 2), g(a + 1)$

27. $k(x) = -x^2 - 2x + 3$;
  $k(0), k(2), k(-2), k(\sqrt{2}), k(a + 2), k(-x), k(x^2)$

28. $k(x) = 2x^3 - 3x^2$;
  $k(0), k(3), k(-3), k(\tfrac{1}{2}), k(\tfrac{a}{2}), k(-x), k(x^3)$

29. $f(x) = 2|x - 1|$;
  $f(-2), f(0), f(\tfrac{1}{2}), f(2), f(x + 1), f(x^2 + 2)$

30. $f(x) = \dfrac{|x|}{x}$;
  $f(-2), f(-1), f(0), f(5), f(x^2), f\left(\dfrac{1}{x}\right)$

31–34 ■ **Piecewise Defined Functions** Evaluate the piecewise defined function at the indicated values.

31. $f(x) = \begin{cases} x^2 & \text{if } x < 0 \\ x + 1 & \text{if } x \geq 0 \end{cases}$
  $f(-2), f(-1), f(0), f(1), f(2)$

32. $f(x) = \begin{cases} 5 & \text{if } x \leq 2 \\ 2x - 3 & \text{if } x > 2 \end{cases}$
  $f(-3), f(0), f(2), f(3), f(5)$

33. $f(x) = \begin{cases} x^2 + 2x & \text{if } x \leq -1 \\ x & \text{if } -1 < x \leq 1 \\ -1 & \text{if } x > 1 \end{cases}$
  $f(-4), f(-\tfrac{3}{2}), f(-1), f(0), f(25)$

34. $f(x) = \begin{cases} 3x & \text{if } x < 0 \\ x + 1 & \text{if } 0 \leq x \leq 2 \\ (x - 2)^2 & \text{if } x > 2 \end{cases}$
  $f(-5), f(0), f(1), f(2), f(5)$

35–38 ■ Evaluating Functions Use the function to evaluate the indicated expressions and simplify.

35. $f(x) = x^2 + 1$; $f(x + 2), f(x) + f(2)$

36. $f(x) = 3x - 1$; $f(2x), 2f(x)$

37. $f(x) = x + 4$; $f(x^2), (f(x))^2$

38. $f(x) = 6x - 18$; $f\left(\dfrac{x}{3}\right), \dfrac{f(x)}{3}$

39–42 ■ Net Change Find the net change in the value of the function between the given inputs.

39. $f(x) = 3x - 2$; from 1 to 5

40. $f(x) = 4 - 5x$; from 3 to 5

41. $g(t) = 1 - t^2$; from -2 to 5

42. $h(t) = t^2 + 5$; from -3 to 6

43–50 ■ Difference Quotient Find $f(a)$, $f(a + h)$, and the difference quotient $\dfrac{f(a + h) - f(a)}{h}$, where $h \neq 0$.

43. $f(x) = 5 - 2x$ **44.** $f(x) = 3x^2 + 2$

45. $f(x) = 5$ **46.** $f(x) = \dfrac{1}{x + 1}$

47. $f(x) = \dfrac{x}{x + 1}$ **48.** $f(x) = \dfrac{2x}{x - 1}$

49. $f(x) = 3 - 5x + 4x^2$ **50.** $f(x) = x^3$

51–54 ■ Domain and Range Find the domain and range of the function.

51. $f(x) = 3x$ **52.** $f(x) = 5x^2 + 4$

53. $f(x) = 3x$, $-2 \leq x \leq 6$

54. $f(x) = 5x^2 + 4$, $0 \leq x \leq 2$

55–72 ■ Domain Find the domain of the function.

55. $f(x) = \dfrac{1}{x - 3}$ **56.** $f(x) = \dfrac{1}{3x - 6}$

57. $f(x) = \dfrac{x + 2}{x^2 - 1}$ **58.** $f(x) = \dfrac{x^4}{x^2 + x - 6}$

59. $f(t) = \sqrt{t + 1}$ **60.** $g(t) = \sqrt{t^2 + 9}$

61. $f(t) = \sqrt[3]{t - 1}$ **62.** $g(x) = \sqrt{7 - 3x}$

63. $f(x) = \sqrt{1 - 2x}$ **64.** $g(x) = \sqrt{x^2 - 4}$

65. $g(x) = \dfrac{\sqrt{2 + x}}{3 - x}$ **66.** $g(x) = \dfrac{\sqrt{x}}{2x^2 + x - 1}$

67. $g(x) = \sqrt[4]{x^2 - 6x}$ **68.** $g(x) = \sqrt{x^2 - 2x - 8}$

69. $f(x) = \dfrac{3}{\sqrt{x - 4}}$ **70.** $f(x) = \dfrac{x^2}{\sqrt{6 - x}}$

71. $f(x) = \dfrac{(x + 1)^2}{\sqrt{2x - 1}}$ **72.** $f(x) = \dfrac{x}{\sqrt[4]{9 - x^2}}$

73–76 ■ Four Ways to Represent a Function A verbal description of a function is given. Find **(a)** algebraic, **(b)** numerical, and **(c)** graphical representations for the function.

73. To evaluate $f(x)$, divide the input by 3 and add $\frac{2}{3}$ to the result.

74. To evaluate $g(x)$, subtract 4 from the input and multiply the result by $\frac{3}{4}$.

75. Let $T(x)$ be the amount of sales tax charged in Lemon County on a purchase of x dollars. To find the tax, take 8% of the purchase price.

76. Let $V(d)$ be the volume of a sphere of diameter d. To find the volume, take the cube of the diameter, then multiply by π and divide by 6.

SKILLS Plus

77–78 ■ Domain and Range Find the domain and range of f.

77. $f(x) = \begin{cases} 1 & \text{if } x \text{ is rational} \\ 5 & \text{if } x \text{ is irrational} \end{cases}$

78. $f(x) = \begin{cases} 1 & \text{if } x \text{ is rational} \\ 5x & \text{if } x \text{ is irrational} \end{cases}$

APPLICATIONS

79. Torricelli's Law A tank holds 50 gal of water, which drains from a leak at the bottom, causing the tank to empty in 20 min. The tank drains faster when it is nearly full because the pressure on the leak is greater. **Torricelli's Law** gives the volume of water remaining in the tank after t minutes as

$$V(t) = 50\left(1 - \dfrac{t}{20}\right)^2 \qquad 0 \leq t \leq 20$$

(a) Find $V(0)$ and $V(20)$.

(b) What do your answers to part (a) represent?

(c) Make a table of values of $V(t)$ for $t = 0, 5, 10, 15, 20$.

(d) Find the net change in the volume V as t changes from 0 min to 20 min.

80. Area of a Sphere The surface area S of a sphere is a function of its radius r given by

$$S(r) = 4\pi r^2$$

(a) Find $S(2)$ and $S(3)$.

(b) What do your answers in part (a) represent?

81. Relativity According to the Theory of Relativity, the length L of an object is a function of its velocity v with respect to an observer. For an object whose length at rest is 10 m, the function is given by

$$L(v) = 10\sqrt{1 - \frac{v^2}{c^2}}$$

where c is the speed of light (300,000 km/s).

(a) Find $L(0.5c)$, $L(0.75c)$, and $L(0.9c)$.

(b) How does the length of an object change as its velocity increases?

82. Pupil Size When the brightness x of a light source is increased, the eye reacts by decreasing the radius R of the pupil. The dependence of R on x is given by the function

$$R(x) = \sqrt{\frac{13 + 7x^{0.4}}{1 + 4x^{0.4}}}$$

where R is measured in millimeters and x is measured in appropriate units of brightness.

(a) Find $R(1)$, $R(10)$, and $R(100)$.

(b) Make a table of values of $R(x)$.

(c) Find the net change in the radius R as x changes from 10 to 100.

83. Blood Flow As blood moves through a vein or an artery, its velocity v is greatest along the central axis and decreases as the distance r from the central axis increases (see the figure). The formula that gives v as a function of r is called the **law of laminar flow**. For an artery with radius 0.5 cm, the relationship between v (in cm/s) and r (in cm) is given by the function

$$v(r) = 18,500(0.25 - r^2) \qquad 0 \le r \le 0.5$$

(a) Find $v(0.1)$ and $v(0.4)$.

(b) What do your answers to part (a) tell you about the flow of blood in this artery?

(c) Make a table of values of $v(r)$ for $r = 0, 0.1, 0.2, 0.3, 0.4, 0.5$.

(d) Find the net change in the velocity v as r changes from 0.1 cm to 0.5 cm.

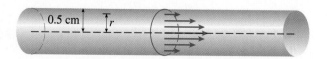

84. How Far Can You See? Because of the curvature of the earth, the maximum distance D that you can see from the top of a tall building or from an airplane at height h is given by the function

$$D(h) = \sqrt{2rh + h^2}$$

where $r = 3960$ mi is the radius of the earth and D and h are measured in miles.

(a) Find $D(0.1)$ and $D(0.2)$.

(b) How far can you see from the observation deck of Toronto's CN Tower, 1135 ft above the ground?

(c) Commercial aircraft fly at an altitude of about 7 mi. How far can the pilot see?

(d) Find the net change in the value of distance D as h changes from 1135 ft to 7 mi.

85. Income Tax In a certain country, income tax T is assessed according to the following function of income x:

$$T(x) = \begin{cases} 0 & \text{if } 0 \le x \le 10{,}000 \\ 0.08x & \text{if } 10{,}000 < x \le 20{,}000 \\ 1600 + 0.15x & \text{if } 20{,}000 < x \end{cases}$$

(a) Find $T(5{,}000)$, $T(12{,}000)$, and $T(25{,}000)$.

(b) What do your answers in part (a) represent?

86. Internet Purchases An Internet bookstore charges $15 shipping for orders under $100 but provides free shipping for orders of $100 or more. The cost C of an order is a function of the total price x of the books purchased, given by

$$C(x) = \begin{cases} x + 15 & \text{if } x < 100 \\ x & \text{if } x \ge 100 \end{cases}$$

(a) Find $C(75)$, $C(90)$, $C(100)$, and $C(105)$.

(b) What do your answers in part (a) represent?

87. Cost of a Hotel Stay A hotel chain charges $75 each night for the first two nights and $50 for each additional night's stay. The total cost T is a function of the number of nights x that a guest stays.

(a) Complete the expressions in the following piecewise defined function.

$$T(x) = \begin{cases} \rule{1.5em}{0.6em} & \text{if } 0 \le x \le 2 \\ \rule{1.5em}{0.6em} & \text{if } x > 2 \end{cases}$$

(b) Find $T(2)$, $T(3)$, and $T(5)$.

(c) What do your answers in part (b) represent?

88. Speeding Tickets In a certain state the maximum speed permitted on freeways is 65 mi/h, and the minimum is 40 mi/h. The fine F for violating these limits is $15 for every mile above the maximum or below the minimum.

(a) Complete the expressions in the following piecewise defined function, where x is the speed at which you are driving.

$$F(x) = \begin{cases} \rule{1.5em}{0.6em} & \text{if } 0 < x < 40 \\ \rule{1.5em}{0.6em} & \text{if } 40 \le x \le 65 \\ \rule{1.5em}{0.6em} & \text{if } x > 65 \end{cases}$$

(b) Find $F(30)$, $F(50)$, and $F(75)$.

(c) What do your answers in part (b) represent?

89. Height of Grass A home owner mows the lawn every Wednesday afternoon. Sketch a rough graph of the height of the grass as a function of time over the course of a four-week period beginning on a Sunday.

90. Temperature Change You place a frozen pie in an oven and bake it for an hour. Then you take the pie out and let it cool before eating it. Sketch a rough graph of the temperature of the pie as a function of time.

91. Daily Temperature Change Temperature readings T (in °F) were recorded every 2 hours from midnight to noon in Atlanta, Georgia, on March 18, 2014. The time t was measured in hours from midnight. Sketch a rough graph of T as a function of t.

t	0	2	4	6	8	10	12
T	58	57	53	50	51	57	61

92. Population Growth The population P (in thousands) of San Jose, California, from 1980 to 2010 is shown in the table. (Midyear estimates are given.) Draw a rough graph of P as a function of time t.

t	1980	1985	1990	1995	2000	2005	2010
P	629	714	782	825	895	901	946

Source: U.S. Census Bureau

DISCUSS ■ DISCOVER ■ PROVE ■ WRITE

93. DISCUSS: Examples of Functions At the beginning of this section we discussed three examples of everyday, ordinary functions: Height is a function of age, temperature is a function of date, and postage cost is a function of weight. Give three other examples of functions from everyday life.

94. DISCUSS: Four Ways to Represent a Function In the box on page 190 we represented four different functions verbally, algebraically, visually, and numerically. Think of a function that can be represented in all four ways, and give the four representations.

95. DISCUSS: Piecewise Defined Functions In Exercises 85–88 we worked with real-world situations modeled by piecewise defined functions. Find other examples of real-world situations that can be modeled by piecewise defined functions, and express the models in function notation.

2.2 GRAPHS OF FUNCTIONS

■ **Graphing Functions by Plotting Points** ■ **Graphing Functions with a Graphing Calculator** ■ **Graphing Piecewise Defined Functions** ■ **The Vertical Line Test: Which Graphs Represent Functions?** ■ **Which Equations Represent Functions?**

The most important way to visualize a function is through its graph. In this section we investigate in more detail the concept of graphing functions.

■ Graphing Functions by Plotting Points

To graph a function f, we plot the points $(x, f(x))$ in a coordinate plane. In other words, we plot the points (x, y) whose x-coordinate is an input and whose y-coordinate is the corresponding output of the function.

> **THE GRAPH OF A FUNCTION**
>
> If f is a function with domain A, then the **graph** of f is the set of ordered pairs
>
> $$\{(x, f(x)) \mid x \in A\}$$
>
> plotted in a coordinate plane. In other words, the graph of f is the set of all points (x, y) such that $y = f(x)$; that is, the graph of f is the graph of the equation $y = f(x)$.

The graph of a function f gives a picture of the behavior or "life history" of the function. We can read the value of $f(x)$ from the graph as being the height of the graph above the point x (see Figure 1).

FIGURE 1 The height of the graph above the point x is the value of $f(x)$.

A function f of the form $f(x) = mx + b$ is called a **linear function** because its graph is the graph of the equation $y = mx + b$, which represents a line with slope m and y-intercept b. A special case of a linear function occurs when the slope is $m = 0$. The function $f(x) = b$, where b is a given number, is called a **constant function** because all its values are the same number, namely, b. Its graph is the horizontal line $y = b$. Figure 2 shows the graphs of the constant function $f(x) = 3$ and the linear function $f(x) = 2x + 1$.

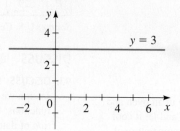

FIGURE 2   The constant function $f(x) = 3$ The linear function $f(x) = 2x + 1$

Functions of the form $f(x) = x^n$ are called **power functions**, and functions of the form $f(x) = x^{1/n}$ are called **root functions**. In the next example we graph two power functions and a root function.

EXAMPLE 1 ■ Graphing Functions by Plotting Points

Sketch graphs of the following functions.

(a) $f(x) = x^2$ **(b)** $g(x) = x^3$ **(c)** $h(x) = \sqrt{x}$

SOLUTION   We first make a table of values. Then we plot the points given by the table and join them by a smooth curve to obtain the graph. The graphs are sketched in Figure 3.

x	$f(x) = x^2$
0	0
$\pm\frac{1}{2}$	$\frac{1}{4}$
± 1	1
± 2	4
± 3	9

x	$g(x) = x^3$
0	0
$\frac{1}{2}$	$\frac{1}{8}$
1	1
2	8
$-\frac{1}{2}$	$-\frac{1}{8}$
-1	-1
-2	-8

x	$h(x) = \sqrt{x}$
0	0
1	1
2	$\sqrt{2}$
3	$\sqrt{3}$
4	2
5	$\sqrt{5}$

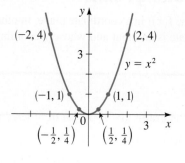

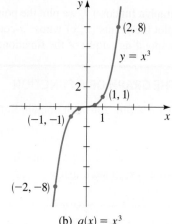

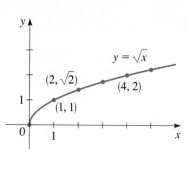

(a) $f(x) = x^2$ (b) $g(x) = x^3$ (c) $h(x) = \sqrt{x}$

FIGURE 3

✎ Now Try Exercises 9, 15, and 19

■ Graphing Functions with a Graphing Calculator

See Appendix C, *Graphing with a Graphing Calculator,* for general guidelines on using a graphing calculator. See Appendix D, *Using the TI-83/84 Graphing Calculator,* for specific instructions.

A convenient way to graph a function is to use a graphing calculator. To graph the function f, we use a calculator to graph the equation $y = f(x)$.

EXAMPLE 2 ■ Graphing a Function with a Graphing Calculator

Use a graphing calculator to graph the function $f(x) = x^3 - 8x^2$ in an appropriate viewing rectangle.

SOLUTION   To graph the function $f(x) = x^3 - 8x^2$, we must graph the equation $y = x^3 - 8x^2$. On the TI-83 graphing calculator the default viewing rectangle gives the graph in Figure 4(a). But this graph appears to spill over the top and bottom of the screen. We need to expand the vertical axis to get a better representation of the graph. The viewing rectangle $[-4, 10]$ by $[-100, 100]$ gives a more complete picture of the graph, as shown in Figure 4(b).

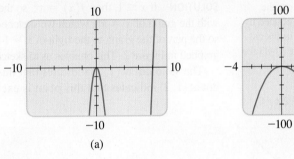

FIGURE 4 Graphing the function $f(x) = x^3 - 8x^2$

(a)   (b)

✎ Now Try Exercise 29

EXAMPLE 3 ■ A Family of Power Functions

(a) Graph the functions $f(x) = x^n$ for $n = 2, 4,$ and 6 in the viewing rectangle $[-2, 2]$ by $[-1, 3]$.

(b) Graph the functions $f(x) = x^n$ for $n = 1, 3,$ and 5 in the viewing rectangle $[-2, 2]$ by $[-2, 2]$.

(c) What conclusions can you draw from these graphs?

SOLUTION   To graph the function $f(x) = x^n$, we graph the equation $y = x^n$. The graphs for parts (a) and (b) are shown in Figure 5.

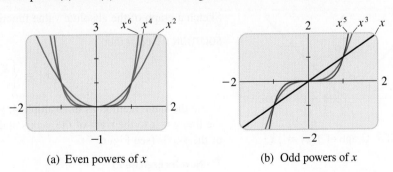

FIGURE 5 A family of power functions: $f(x) = x^n$

(a) Even powers of x (b) Odd powers of x

(c) We see that the general shape of the graph of $f(x) = x^n$ depends on whether n is even or odd.

If n is even, the graph of $f(x) = x^n$ is similar to the parabola $y = x^2$.

If n is odd, the graph of $f(x) = x^n$ is similar to that of $y = x^3$.

✎ Now Try Exercise 69

Notice from Figure 5 that as n increases, the graph of $y = x^n$ becomes flatter near 0 and steeper when $x > 1$. When $0 < x < 1$, the lower powers of x are the "bigger" functions. But when $x > 1$, the higher powers of x are the dominant functions.

■ Graphing Piecewise Defined Functions

A piecewise defined function is defined by different formulas on different parts of its domain. As you might expect, the graph of such a function consists of separate pieces.

EXAMPLE 4 ■ Graph of a Piecewise Defined Function

Sketch the graph of the function

$$f(x) = \begin{cases} x^2 & \text{if } x \le 1 \\ 2x + 1 & \text{if } x > 1 \end{cases}$$

On many graphing calculators the graph in Figure 6 can be produced by using the logical functions in the calculator. For example, on the TI-83 the following equation gives the required graph:

$$Y_1 = (X \le 1)X^2 + (X > 1)(2X + 1)$$

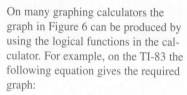

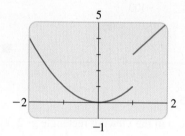

(To avoid the extraneous vertical line between the two parts of the graph, put the calculator in Dot mode.)

SOLUTION   If $x \le 1$, then $f(x) = x^2$, so the part of the graph to the left of $x = 1$ coincides with the graph of $y = x^2$, which we sketched in Figure 3. If $x > 1$, then $f(x) = 2x + 1$, so the part of the graph to the right of $x = 1$ coincides with the line $y = 2x + 1$, which we graphed in Figure 2. This enables us to sketch the graph in Figure 6.

The solid dot at $(1, 1)$ indicates that this point is included in the graph; the open dot at $(1, 3)$ indicates that this point is excluded from the graph.

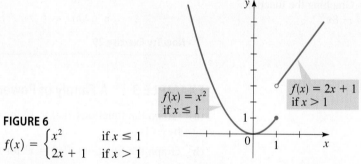

FIGURE 6
$$f(x) = \begin{cases} x^2 & \text{if } x \le 1 \\ 2x + 1 & \text{if } x > 1 \end{cases}$$

✎ Now Try Exercise 35

EXAMPLE 5 ■ Graph of the Absolute Value Function

Sketch a graph of the absolute value function $f(x) = |x|$.

SOLUTION   Recall that

$$|x| = \begin{cases} x & \text{if } x \ge 0 \\ -x & \text{if } x < 0 \end{cases}$$

Using the same method as in Example 4, we note that the graph of f coincides with the line $y = x$ to the right of the y-axis and coincides with the line $y = -x$ to the left of the y-axis (see Figure 7).

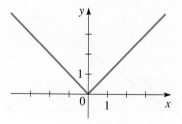

FIGURE 7 Graph of $f(x) = |x|$

✎ Now Try Exercise 23

The **greatest integer function** is defined by

$$[\![x]\!] = \text{greatest integer less than or equal to } x$$

For example, $[\![2]\!] = 2$, $[\![2.3]\!] = 2$, $[\![1.999]\!] = 1$, $[\![0.002]\!] = 0$, $[\![-3.5]\!] = -4$, and $[\![-0.5]\!] = -1$.

EXAMPLE 6 ■ Graph of the Greatest Integer Function

Sketch a graph of $f(x) = [\![x]\!]$.

SOLUTION   The table shows the values of f for some values of x. Note that $f(x)$ is constant between consecutive integers, so the graph between integers is a horizontal line segment, as shown in Figure 8.

x	$[\![x]\!]$
$\vdots$	$\vdots$
$-2 \le x < -1$	-2
$-1 \le x < 0$	-1
$0 \le x < 1$	0
$1 \le x < 2$	1
$2 \le x < 3$	2
$\vdots$	$\vdots$

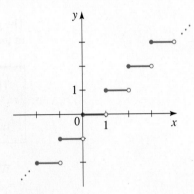

FIGURE 8 The greatest integer function, $y = [\![x]\!]$

The greatest integer function is an example of a **step function**. The next example gives a real-world example of a step function.

EXAMPLE 7 ■ The Cost Function for a Global Data Plan

A global data plan costs \$25 a month for the first 100 megabytes and \$20 for each additional 100 megabytes (or portion thereof). Draw a graph of the cost C (in dollars) as a function of the number of megabytes x used per month.

SOLUTION   Let $C(x)$ be the cost of using x megabytes of data in a month. Since $x \ge 0$, the domain of the function is $[0, \infty)$. From the given information we have

$$C(x) = 25 \qquad\qquad\quad \text{if } 0 < x \le 100$$
$$C(x) = 25 + 20 = 45 \qquad \text{if } 100 < x \le 200$$
$$C(x) = 25 + 2(20) = 65 \quad \text{if } 200 < x \le 300$$
$$C(x) = 25 + 3(20) = 85 \quad \text{if } 300 < x \le 400$$
$$\vdots \qquad\qquad\qquad\qquad \vdots$$

The graph is shown in Figure 9.

✎ **Now Try Exercise 83**

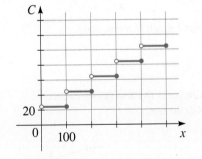

FIGURE 9 Cost of data usage

DISCOVERY PROJECT

Relations and Functions

Many real-world relationships are functions, but many are not. For example, the rule that assigns to each student his or her school ID number is a function. But what about the rule that assigns to each date those persons born in Chicago on that date? Do you see why this "relation" is not a function? A set of ordered pairs is called a *relation*. In this project we explore the question of which relations are functions. You can find the project at **www.stewartmath.com**.

A function is called **continuous** if its graph has no "breaks" or "holes." The functions in Examples 1, 2, 3, and 5 are continuous; the functions in Examples 4, 6, and 7 are not continuous.

■ The Vertical Line Test: Which Graphs Represent Functions?

The graph of a function is a curve in the xy-plane. But the question arises: Which curves in the xy-plane are graphs of functions? This is answered by the following test.

THE VERTICAL LINE TEST

A curve in the coordinate plane is the graph of a function if and only if no vertical line intersects the curve more than once.

We can see from Figure 10 why the Vertical Line Test is true. If each vertical line $x = a$ intersects a curve only once at (a, b), then exactly one functional value is defined by $f(a) = b$. But if a line $x = a$ intersects the curve twice, at (a, b) and at (a, c), then the curve cannot represent a function because a function cannot assign two different values to a.

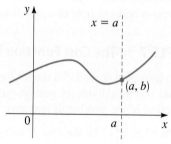
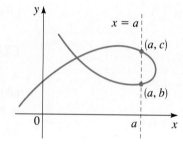

FIGURE 10 Vertical Line Test

Graph of a function

Not a graph of a function

EXAMPLE 8 ■ Using the Vertical Line Test

Using the Vertical Line Test, we see that the curves in parts (b) and (c) of Figure 11 represent functions, whereas those in parts (a) and (d) do not.

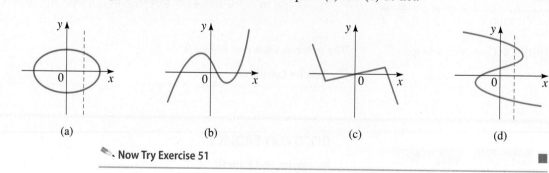

FIGURE 11

(a)   (b)   (c)   (d)

◤ Now Try Exercise 51   ■

■ Which Equations Represent Functions?

Any equation in the variables x and y defines a relationship between these variables. For example, the equation

$$y - x^2 = 0$$

defines a relationship between y and x. Does this equation define y as a *function* of x? To find out, we solve for y and get

$$y = x^2 \qquad \text{Equation form}$$

We see that the equation defines a rule, or function, that gives one value of y for each value of x. We can express this rule in function notation as

$$f(x) = x^2 \qquad \text{Function form}$$

But not every equation defines y as a function of x, as the following example shows.

EXAMPLE 9 ■ Equations That Define Functions

Does the equation define y as a function of x?

(a) $y - x^2 = 2$ **(b)** $x^2 + y^2 = 4$

SOLUTION

(a) Solving for y in terms of x gives

$$y - x^2 = 2$$
$$y = x^2 + 2 \qquad \text{Add } x^2$$

The last equation is a rule that gives one value of y for each value of x, so it defines y as a function of x. We can write the function as $f(x) = x^2 + 2$.

(b) We try to solve for y in terms of x.

$$x^2 + y^2 = 4$$
$$y^2 = 4 - x^2 \qquad \text{Subtract } x^2$$
$$y = \pm\sqrt{4 - x^2} \qquad \text{Take square roots}$$

The last equation gives two values of y for a given value of x. Thus the equation does not define y as a function of x.

✎ Now Try Exercises 57 and 61   ■

The graphs of the equations in Example 9 are shown in Figure 12. The Vertical Line Test shows graphically that the equation in Example 9(a) defines a function but the equation in Example 9(b) does not.

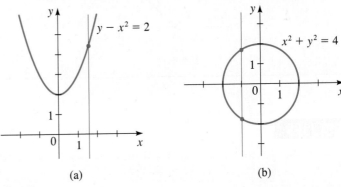

(a)   (b)

FIGURE 12

The following box shows the graphs of some functions that you will see frequently in this book.

SOME FUNCTIONS AND THEIR GRAPHS

Linear functions

$f(x) = mx + b$

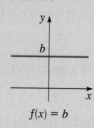

$f(x) = b$

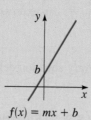

$f(x) = mx + b$

Power functions

$f(x) = x^n$

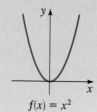

$f(x) = x^2$

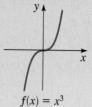

$f(x) = x^3$

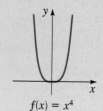

$f(x) = x^4$

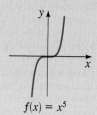

$f(x) = x^5$

Root functions

$f(x) = \sqrt[n]{x}$

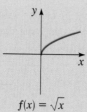

$f(x) = \sqrt{x}$

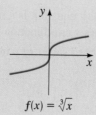

$f(x) = \sqrt[3]{x}$

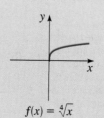

$f(x) = \sqrt[4]{x}$

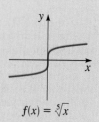

$f(x) = \sqrt[5]{x}$

Reciprocal functions

$f(x) = \dfrac{1}{x^n}$

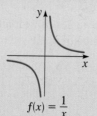

$f(x) = \dfrac{1}{x}$

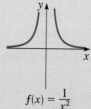

$f(x) = \dfrac{1}{x^2}$

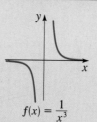

$f(x) = \dfrac{1}{x^3}$

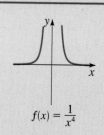

$f(x) = \dfrac{1}{x^4}$

Absolute value function

$f(x) = |x|$

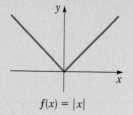

$f(x) = |x|$

Greatest integer function

$f(x) = [\![x]\!]$

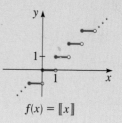

$f(x) = [\![x]\!]$

2.2 EXERCISES

CONCEPTS

1. To graph the function f, we plot the points $(x, \underline{\hspace{1cm}})$ in a coordinate plane. To graph $f(x) = x^2 - 2$, we plot the points $(x, \underline{\hspace{1cm}})$. So the point $(3, \underline{\hspace{1cm}})$ is on the graph of f. The height of the graph of f above the x-axis when $x = 3$ is _____ . Complete the table, and sketch a graph of f.

x	$f(x)$	(x, y)
-2		
-1		
0		
1		
2		

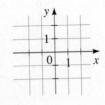

2. If $f(4) = 10$ then the point $(4,$ ___ $)$ is on the graph of f.

3. If the point $(3, 7)$ is on the graph of f, then $f(3) =$ _____ .

4. Match the function with its graph.

(a) $f(x) = x^2$ **(b)** $f(x) = x^3$

(c) $f(x) = \sqrt{x}$ **(d)** $f(x) = |x|$

I
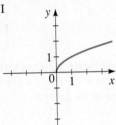

II
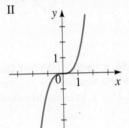

III
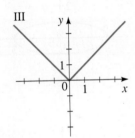

IV
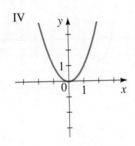

SKILLS

5–28 ■ Graphing Functions   Sketch a graph of the function by first making a table of values.

5. $f(x) = x + 2$ **6.** $f(x) = 4 - 2x$

7. $f(x) = -x + 3, \quad -3 \le x \le 3$

8. $f(x) = \dfrac{x - 3}{2}, \quad 0 \le x \le 5$

9. $f(x) = -x^2$ **10.** $f(x) = x^2 - 4$

11. $g(x) = -(x + 1)^2$ **12.** $g(x) = x^2 + 2x + 1$

13. $r(x) = 3x^4$ **14.** $r(x) = 1 - x^4$

15. $g(x) = x^3 - 8$ **16.** $g(x) = (x - 1)^3$

17. $k(x) = \sqrt[3]{-x}$ **18.** $k(x) = -\sqrt[3]{x}$

19. $f(x) = 1 + \sqrt{x}$ **20.** $f(x) = \sqrt{x - 2}$

21. $C(t) = \dfrac{1}{t^2}$ **22.** $C(t) = -\dfrac{1}{t + 1}$

23. $H(x) = |2x|$ **24.** $H(x) = |x + 1|$

25. $G(x) = |x| + x$ **26.** $G(x) = |x| - x$

27. $f(x) = |2x - 2|$ **28.** $f(x) = \dfrac{x}{|x|}$

 29–32 ■ Graphing Functions   Graph the function in each of the given viewing rectangles, and select the one that produces the most appropriate graph of the function.

29. $f(x) = 8x - x^2$
   (a) $[-5, 5]$ by $[-5, 5]$
   (b) $[-10, 10]$ by $[-10, 10]$
   (c) $[-2, 10]$ by $[-5, 20]$
   (d) $[-10, 10]$ by $[-100, 100]$

30. $g(x) = x^2 - x - 20$
   (a) $[-2, 2]$ by $[-5, 5]$
   (b) $[-10, 10]$ by $[-10, 10]$
   (c) $[-7, 7]$ by $[-25, 20]$
   (d) $[-10, 10]$ by $[-100, 100]$

31. $h(x) = x^3 - 5x - 4$
   (a) $[-2, 2]$ by $[-2, 2]$
   (b) $[-3, 3]$ by $[-10, 10]$
   (c) $[-3, 3]$ by $[-10, 5]$
   (d) $[-10, 10]$ by $[-10, 10]$

32. $k(x) = \frac{1}{32}x^4 - x^2 + 2$
   (a) $[-1, 1]$ by $[-1, 1]$
   (b) $[-2, 2]$ by $[-2, 2]$
   (c) $[-5, 5]$ by $[-5, 5]$
   (d) $[-10, 10]$ by $[-10, 10]$

33–46 ■ Graphing Piecewise Defined Functions   Sketch a graph of the piecewise defined function.

33. $f(x) = \begin{cases} 0 & \text{if } x < 2 \\ 1 & \text{if } x \ge 2 \end{cases}$

34. $f(x) = \begin{cases} 1 & \text{if } x \le 1 \\ x + 1 & \text{if } x > 1 \end{cases}$

35. $f(x) = \begin{cases} 3 & \text{if } x < 2 \\ x - 1 & \text{if } x \ge 2 \end{cases}$

36. $f(x) = \begin{cases} 1 - x & \text{if } x < -2 \\ 5 & \text{if } x \ge -2 \end{cases}$

37. $f(x) = \begin{cases} x & \text{if } x \le 0 \\ x + 1 & \text{if } x > 0 \end{cases}$

38. $f(x) = \begin{cases} 2x + 3 & \text{if } x < -1 \\ 3 - x & \text{if } x \ge -1 \end{cases}$

39. $f(x) = \begin{cases} -1 & \text{if } x < -1 \\ 1 & \text{if } -1 \le x \le 1 \\ -1 & \text{if } x > 1 \end{cases}$

40. $f(x) = \begin{cases} -1 & \text{if } x < -1 \\ x & \text{if } -1 \le x \le 1 \\ 1 & \text{if } x > 1 \end{cases}$

41. $f(x) = \begin{cases} 2 & \text{if } x \le -1 \\ x^2 & \text{if } x > -1 \end{cases}$

42. $f(x) = \begin{cases} 1 - x^2 & \text{if } x \le 2 \\ x & \text{if } x > 2 \end{cases}$

43. $f(x) = \begin{cases} 0 & \text{if } |x| \le 2 \\ 3 & \text{if } |x| > 2 \end{cases}$

44. $f(x) = \begin{cases} x^2 & \text{if } |x| \le 1 \\ 1 & \text{if } |x| > 1 \end{cases}$

45. $f(x) = \begin{cases} 4 & \text{if } x < -2 \\ x^2 & \text{if } -2 \le x \le 2 \\ -x + 6 & \text{if } x > 2 \end{cases}$

46. $f(x) = \begin{cases} -x & \text{if } x \le 0 \\ 9 - x^2 & \text{if } 0 < x \le 3 \\ x - 3 & \text{if } x > 3 \end{cases}$

 47–48 ■ **Graphing Piecewise Defined Functions** Use a graphing device to draw a graph of the piecewise defined function. (See the margin note on page 162.)

47. $f(x) = \begin{cases} x + 2 & \text{if } x \le -1 \\ x^2 & \text{if } x > -1 \end{cases}$

48. $f(x) = \begin{cases} 2x - x^2 & \text{if } x > 1 \\ (x - 1)^3 & \text{if } x \le 1 \end{cases}$

49–50 ■ **Finding Piecewise Defined Functions** A graph of a piecewise defined function is given. Find a formula for the function in the indicated form.

49.

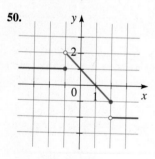

$f(x) = \begin{cases} \rule{1.5cm}{0.3cm} & \text{if } x < -2 \\ \rule{1.5cm}{0.3cm} & \text{if } -2 \le x \le 2 \\ \rule{1.5cm}{0.3cm} & \text{if } x > 2 \end{cases}$

50.

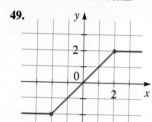

$f(x) = \begin{cases} \rule{1.5cm}{0.3cm} & \text{if } x \le -1 \\ \rule{1.5cm}{0.3cm} & \text{if } -1 < x \le 2 \\ \rule{1.5cm}{0.3cm} & \text{if } x > 2 \end{cases}$

51–52 ■ **Vertical Line Test** Use the Vertical Line Test to determine whether the curve is a graph of a function of x.

 51. (a)

(b)

(c)

(d)

52. (a)

(b)

(c)

(d)

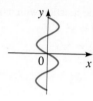

53–56 ■ **Vertical Line Test: Domain and Range** Use the Vertical Line Test to determine whether the curve is a graph of a function of x. If it is, state the domain and range of the function.

53.

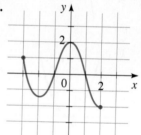

54.

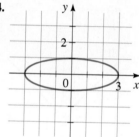

55.

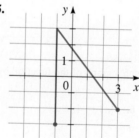

56.

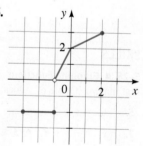

57–68 ■ **Equations That Define Functions** Determine whether the equation defines y as a function of x. (See Example 9.)

57. $3x - 5y = 7$

58. $3x^2 - y = 5$

59. $x = y^2$

60. $x^2 + (y - 1)^2 = 4$

61. $2x - 4y^2 = 3$

62. $2x^2 - 4y^2 = 3$

63. $2xy - 5y^2 = 4$

64. $\sqrt{y} - x = 5$

65. $2|x| + y = 0$

66. $2x + |y| = 0$

67. $x = y^3$

68. $x = y^4$

69–74 ▪ Families of Functions A family of functions is given. In parts (a) and (b) graph all the given members of the family in the viewing rectangle indicated. In part (c) state the conclusions that you can make from your graphs.

69. $f(x) = x^2 + c$

  (a) $c = 0, 2, 4, 6$; $[-5, 5]$ by $[-10, 10]$

  (b) $c = 0, -2, -4, -6$; $[-5, 5]$ by $[-10, 10]$

  (c) How does the value of c affect the graph?

70. $f(x) = (x - c)^2$

  (a) $c = 0, 1, 2, 3$; $[-5, 5]$ by $[-10, 10]$

  (b) $c = 0, -1, -2, -3$; $[-5, 5]$ by $[-10, 10]$

  (c) How does the value of c affect the graph?

71. $f(x) = (x - c)^3$

  (a) $c = 0, 2, 4, 6$; $[-10, 10]$ by $[-10, 10]$

  (b) $c = 0, -2, -4, -6$; $[-10, 10]$ by $[-10, 10]$

  (c) How does the value of c affect the graph?

72. $f(x) = cx^2$

  (a) $c = 1, \frac{1}{2}, 2, 4$; $[-5, 5]$ by $[-10, 10]$

  (b) $c = 1, -1, -\frac{1}{2}, -2$; $[-5, 5]$ by $[-10, 10]$

  (c) How does the value of c affect the graph?

73. $f(x) = x^c$

  (a) $c = \frac{1}{2}, \frac{1}{4}, \frac{1}{6}$; $[-1, 4]$ by $[-1, 3]$

  (b) $c = 1, \frac{1}{3}, \frac{1}{5}$; $[-3, 3]$ by $[-2, 2]$

  (c) How does the value of c affect the graph?

74. $f(x) = \dfrac{1}{x^n}$

  (a) $n = 1, 3$; $[-3, 3]$ by $[-3, 3]$

  (b) $n = 2, 4$; $[-3, 3]$ by $[-3, 3]$

  (c) How does the value of n affect the graph?

SKILLS Plus

75–78 ▪ Finding Functions for Certain Curves Find a function whose graph is the given curve.

75. The line segment joining the points $(-2, 1)$ and $(4, -6)$

76. The line segment joining the points $(-3, -2)$ and $(6, 3)$

77. The top half of the circle $x^2 + y^2 = 9$

78. The bottom half of the circle $x^2 + y^2 = 9$

APPLICATIONS

79. Weather Balloon As a weather balloon is inflated, the thickness T of its rubber skin is related to the radius of the balloon by

$$T(r) = \frac{0.5}{r^2}$$

where T and r are measured in centimeters. Graph the function T for values of r between 10 and 100.

80. Power from a Wind Turbine The power produced by a wind turbine depends on the speed of the wind. If a windmill has blades 3 meters long, then the power P produced by the turbine is modeled by

$$P(v) = 14.1v^3$$

where P is measured in watts (W) and v is measured in meters per second (m/s). Graph the function P for wind speeds between 1 m/s and 10 m/s.

81. Utility Rates Westside Energy charges its electric customers a base rate of $6.00 per month, plus 10¢ per kilowatt-hour (kWh) for the first 300 kWh used and 6¢ per kWh for all usage over 300 kWh. Suppose a customer uses x kWh of electricity in one month.

  (a) Express the monthly cost E as a piecewise defined function of x.

  (b) Graph the function E for $0 \le x \le 600$.

82. Taxicab Function A taxi company charges $2.00 for the first mile (or part of a mile) and 20 cents for each succeeding tenth of a mile (or part). Express the cost C (in dollars) of a ride as a piecewise defined function of the distance x traveled (in miles) for $0 < x < 2$, and sketch a graph of this function.

83. Postage Rates The 2014 domestic postage rate for first-class letters weighing 3.5 oz or less is 49 cents for the first ounce (or less), plus 21 cents for each additional ounce (or part of an ounce). Express the postage P as a piecewise defined function of the weight x of a letter, with $0 < x \le 3.5$, and sketch a graph of this function.

DISCUSS ▪ DISCOVER ▪ PROVE ▪ WRITE

84. DISCOVER: When Does a Graph Represent a Function? For every integer n, the graph of the equation $y = x^n$ is the graph of a function, namely $f(x) = x^n$. Explain why the graph of $x = y^2$ is *not* the graph of a function of x. Is the graph of $x = y^3$ the graph of a function of x? If so, of what function of x is it the graph? Determine for what integers n the graph of $x = y^n$ is a graph of a function of x.

85. DISCUSS: Step Functions In Example 7 and Exercises 82 and 83 we are given functions whose graphs consist of horizontal line segments. Such functions are often called *step functions*, because their graphs look like stairs. Give some other examples of step functions that arise in everyday life.

86. DISCOVER: Stretched Step Functions Sketch graphs of the functions $f(x) = [\![x]\!]$, $g(x) = [\![2x]\!]$, and $h(x) = [\![3x]\!]$ on separate graphs. How are the graphs related? If n is a positive integer, what does a graph of $k(x) = [\![nx]\!]$ look like?

87. DISCOVER: Graph of the Absolute Value of a Function

(a) Draw graphs of the functions

$$f(x) = x^2 + x - 6$$

and

$$g(x) = |x^2 + x - 6|$$

How are the graphs of f and g related?

(b) Draw graphs of the functions $f(x) = x^4 - 6x^2$ and $g(x) = |x^4 - 6x^2|$. How are the graphs of f and g related?

(c) In general, if $g(x) = |f(x)|$, how are the graphs of f and g related? Draw graphs to illustrate your answer.

2.3 GETTING INFORMATION FROM THE GRAPH OF A FUNCTION

■ Values of a Function; Domain and Range ■ Comparing Function Values: Solving Equations and Inequalities Graphically ■ Increasing and Decreasing Functions ■ Local Maximum and Minimum Values of a Function

Many properties of a function are more easily obtained from a graph than from the rule that describes the function. We will see in this section how a graph tells us whether the values of a function are increasing or decreasing and also where the maximum and minimum values of a function are.

■ Values of a Function; Domain and Range

A complete graph of a function contains all the information about a function, because the graph tells us which input values correspond to which output values. To analyze the graph of a function, we must keep in mind that *the height of the graph is the value of the function*. So we can read off the values of a function from its graph.

EXAMPLE 1 ■ Finding the Values of a Function from a Graph

The function T graphed in Figure 1 gives the temperature between noon and 6:00 P.M. at a certain weather station.

(a) Find $T(1)$, $T(3)$, and $T(5)$.

(b) Which is larger, $T(2)$ or $T(4)$?

(c) Find the value(s) of x for which $T(x) = 25$.

(d) Find the value(s) of x for which $T(x) \geq 25$.

(e) Find the net change in temperature from 1 P.M. to 3 P.M.

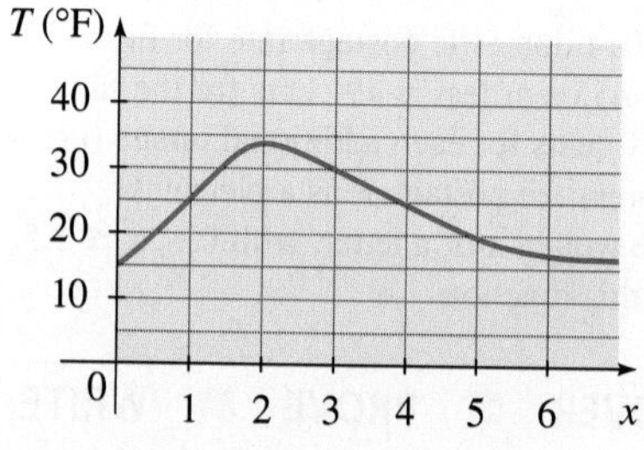

FIGURE 1 Temperature function

SOLUTION

(a) $T(1)$ is the temperature at 1:00 P.M. It is represented by the height of the graph above the x-axis at $x = 1$. Thus $T(1) = 25$. Similarly, $T(3) = 30$ and $T(5) = 20$.

(b) Since the graph is higher at $x = 2$ than at $x = 4$, it follows that $T(2)$ is larger than $T(4)$.

(c) The height of the graph is 25 when x is 1 and when x is 4. In other words, the temperature is 25 at 1:00 P.M. and 4:00 P.M.

(d) The graph is higher than 25 for x between 1 and 4. In other words, the temperature was 25 or greater between 1:00 P.M. and 4:00 P.M.

Net change is defined on page 187.

(e) The net change in temperature is

$$T(3) - T(1) = 30 - 25 = 5$$

So there was a net increase of 5°F from 1 P.M. to 3 P.M.

✎ **Now Try Exercises 7 and 55**

The graph of a function helps us to picture the domain and range of the function on the x-axis and y-axis, as shown in the box below.

DOMAIN AND RANGE FROM A GRAPH

The **domain** and **range** of a function $y = f(x)$ can be obtained from a graph of f as shown in the figure. The domain is the set of all x-values for which f is defined, and the range is all the corresponding y-values.

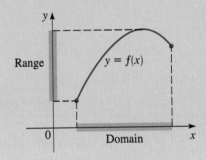

EXAMPLE 2 ▪ Finding the Domain and Range from a Graph

See Appendix C, *Graphing with a Graphing Calculator,* for guidelines on using a graphing calculator. See Appendix D, *Using the TI-83/84 Graphing Calculator,* for specific graphing instructions.

(a) Use a graphing calculator to draw the graph of $f(x) = \sqrt{4 - x^2}$.

(b) Find the domain and range of f.

SOLUTION

(a) The graph is shown in Figure 2.

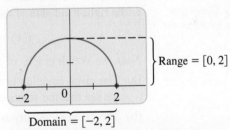

FIGURE 2 Graph of $f(x) = \sqrt{4 - x^2}$

(b) From the graph in Figure 2 we see that the domain is $[-2, 2]$ and the range is $[0, 2]$.

✎ Now Try Exercise 21   ▪

▪ Comparing Function Values: Solving Equations and Inequalities Graphically

We can compare the values of two functions f and g visually by drawing their graphs. The points at which the graphs intersect are the points where the values of the two functions are equal. So the solutions of the equation $f(x) = g(x)$ are the values of x at which the two graphs intersect. The points at which the graph of g is higher than the graph of f are the points where the values of g are greater than the values of f. So the solutions of the inequality $f(x) < g(x)$ are the values of x at which the graph of g is *higher than* the graph of f.

SOLVING EQUATIONS AND INEQUALITIES GRAPHICALLY

The **solution(s) of the equation** $f(x) = g(x)$ are the values of x where the graphs of f and g intersect.

The **solution(s) of the inequality** $f(x) < g(x)$ are the values of x where the graph of g is higher than the graph of f.

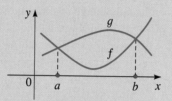

The solutions of $f(x) = g(x)$
are the values a and b.

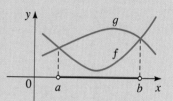

The solution of $f(x) < g(x)$
is the interval (a, b).

We can use these observations to solve equations and inequalities graphically, as the next example illustrates.

EXAMPLE 3 ■ Solving Graphically

Solve the given equation or inequality graphically.

(a) $2x^2 + 3 = 5x + 6$

(b) $2x^2 + 3 \leq 5x + 6$

(c) $2x^2 + 3 > 5x + 6$

You can also solve the equations and inequalities algebraically. Check that your solutions match the solutions we obtained graphically.

SOLUTION We first define functions f and g that correspond to the left-hand side and to the right-hand side of the equation or inequality. So we define

$$f(x) = 2x^2 + 3 \qquad \text{and} \qquad g(x) = 5x + 6$$

Next, we sketch graphs of f and g on the same set of axes.

(a) The given equation is equivalent to $f(x) = g(x)$. From the graph in Figure 3(a) we see that the solutions of the equation are $x = -0.5$ and $x = 3$.

(b) The given inequality is equivalent to $f(x) \leq g(x)$. From the graph in Figure 3(b) we see that the solution is the interval $[-0.5, 3]$.

(c) The given inequality is equivalent to $f(x) > g(x)$. From the graph in Figure 3(c) we see that the solution is $(-\infty, -0.5) \cup (3, \infty)$.

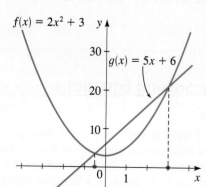

(a) Solution: $x = -0.5, 3$

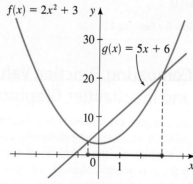

(b) Solution: $[-0.5, 3]$

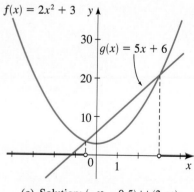

(c) Solution: $(-\infty, -0.5) \cup (3, \infty)$

FIGURE 3 Graphs of $f(x) = 2x^2 + 3$ and $g(x) = 5x + 6$

▶ Now Try Exercises 9 and 23

To solve an equation graphically, we can first move all terms to one side of the equation and then graph the function that corresponds to the nonzero side of the equation. In this case the solutions of the equation are the x-intercepts of the graph. We can use this same method to solve inequalities graphically, as the following example shows.

EXAMPLE 4 ■ Solving Graphically

Solve the given equation or inequality graphically.

(a) $x^3 + 6 = 2x^2 + 5x$

(b) $x^3 + 6 \geq 2x^2 + 5x$

SOLUTION   We first move all terms to one side to obtain an equivalent equation (or inequality). For the equation in part (a) we obtain

$$x^3 - 2x^2 - 5x + 6 = 0 \qquad \text{Move terms to LHS}$$

Then we define a function f by

$$f(x) = x^3 - 2x^2 - 5x + 6 \qquad \text{Define } f$$

Next, we use a graphing calculator to graph f, as shown in Figure 4.

(a) The given equation is the same as $f(x) = 0$, so the solutions are the x-intercepts of the graph. From Figure 4(a) we see that the solutions are $x = -2$, $x = 1$, and $x = 3$.

(b) The given inequality is the same as $f(x) \geq 0$, so the solutions are the x-values at which the graph of f is on or above the x-axis. From Figure 4(b) we see the solution is $[-2, 1] \cup [3, \infty]$.

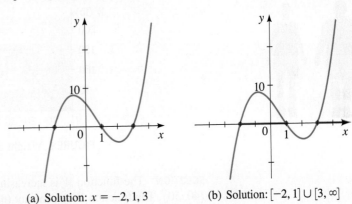

FIGURE 4 Graphs of
$f(x) = x^3 - 2x^2 - 5x + 6$

(a) Solution: $x = -2, 1, 3$ (b) Solution: $[-2, 1] \cup [3, \infty]$

✎ **Now Try Exercise 27**

■ Increasing and Decreasing Functions

It is very useful to know where the graph of a function rises and where it falls. The graph shown in Figure 5 rises, falls, then rises again as we move from left to right: It rises from A to B, falls from B to C, and rises again from C to D. The function f is said to be *increasing* when its graph rises and *decreasing* when its graph falls.

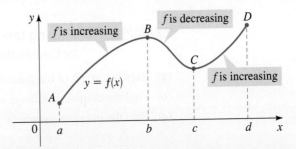

FIGURE 5 f is increasing on (a, b)
and (c, d); f is decreasing on (b, c)

We have the following definition.

From the definition we see that a function increases or decreases *on an interval*. It does not make sense to apply these definitions at a single point.

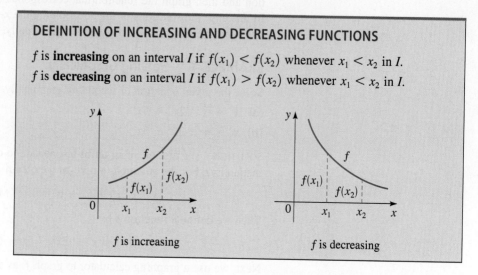

DEFINITION OF INCREASING AND DECREASING FUNCTIONS

f is **increasing** on an interval I if $f(x_1) < f(x_2)$ whenever $x_1 < x_2$ in I.
f is **decreasing** on an interval I if $f(x_1) > f(x_2)$ whenever $x_1 < x_2$ in I.

f is increasing f is decreasing

EXAMPLE 5 ■ Intervals on Which a Function Increases or Decreases

The graph in Figure 6 gives the weight W of a person at age x. Determine the intervals on which the function W is increasing and on which it is decreasing.

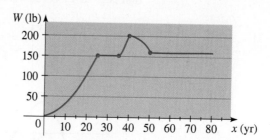

FIGURE 6 Weight as a function of age

SOLUTION The function W is increasing on $(0, 25)$ and $(35, 40)$. It is decreasing on $(40, 50)$. The function W is constant (neither increasing nor decreasing) on $(25, 35)$ and $(50, 80)$. This means that the person gained weight until age 25, then gained weight again between ages 35 and 40. He lost weight between ages 40 and 50.

✎ **Now Try Exercise 57**

By convention we write the intervals on which a function is increasing or decreasing as open intervals. (It would also be true to say that the function is increasing or decreasing on the corresponding closed interval. So for instance, it is also correct to say that the function W in Example 5 is decreasing on $[40, 50]$.)

EXAMPLE 6 ■ Finding Intervals on Which a Function Increases or Decreases

(a) Sketch a graph of the function $f(x) = 12x^2 + 4x^3 - 3x^4$.
(b) Find the domain and range of f.
(c) Find the intervals on which f is increasing and on which f is decreasing.

SOLUTION

(a) We use a graphing calculator to sketch the graph in Figure 7.

(b) The domain of f is $\mathbb{R}$ because f is defined for all real numbers. Using the $\boxed{\text{TRACE}}$ feature on the calculator, we find that the highest value is $f(2) = 32$. So the range of f is $(-\infty, 32]$.

(c) From the graph we see that f is increasing on the intervals $(-\infty, -1)$ and $(0, 2)$ and is decreasing on $(-1, 0)$ and $(2, \infty)$.

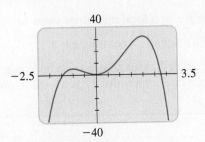

FIGURE 7 Graph of
$f(x) = 12x^2 + 4x^3 - 3x^4$

✎. **Now Try Exercise 35**   ■

EXAMPLE 7 ■ Finding Intervals Where a Function Increases and Decreases

(a) Sketch the graph of the function $f(x) = x^{2/3}$.

(b) Find the domain and range of the function.

(c) Find the intervals on which f is increasing and on which f is decreasing.

SOLUTION

(a) We use a graphing calculator to sketch the graph in Figure 8.

(b) From the graph we observe that the domain of f is $\mathbb{R}$ and the range is $[0, \infty)$.

(c) From the graph we see that f is decreasing on $(-\infty, 0)$ and increasing on $(0, \infty)$.

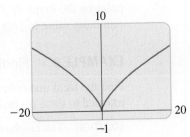

FIGURE 8 Graph of $f(x) = x^{2/3}$

✎. **Now Try Exercise 41**   ■

■ Local Maximum and Minimum Values of a Function

Finding the largest or smallest values of a function is important in many applications. For example, if a function represents revenue or profit, then we are interested in its maximum value. For a function that represents cost, we would want to find its minimum value. (See *Focus on Modeling: Modeling with Functions* on pages 273–280 for many such examples.) We can easily find these values from the graph of a function. We first define what we mean by a local maximum or minimum.

LOCAL MAXIMA AND MINIMA OF A FUNCTION

1. The function value $f(a)$ is a **local maximum value** of f if

$$f(a) \geq f(x) \quad \text{when } x \text{ is near } a$$

(This means that $f(a) \geq f(x)$ for all x in some open interval containing a.) In this case we say that f has a **local maximum** at $x = a$.

2. The function value $f(a)$ is a **local minimum value** of f if

$$f(a) \leq f(x) \quad \text{when } x \text{ is near } a$$

(This means that $f(a) \leq f(x)$ for all x in some open interval containing a.) In this case we say that f has a **local minimum** at $x = a$.

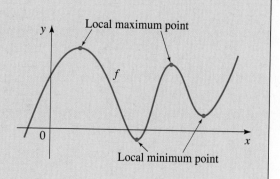

We can find the local maximum and minimum values of a function using a graphing calculator. If there is a viewing rectangle such that the point $(a, f(a))$ is the highest point on the graph of f *within* the viewing rectangle (not on the edge), then the number $f(a)$ is a local maximum value of f (see Figure 9). Notice that $f(a) \geq f(x)$ for all numbers x that are close to a.

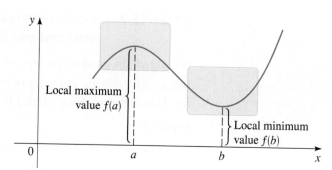

FIGURE 9

Similarly, if there is a viewing rectangle such that the point $(b, f(b))$ is the lowest point on the graph of f within the viewing rectangle, then the number $f(b)$ is a local minimum value of f. In this case $f(b) \leq f(x)$ for all numbers x that are close to b.

EXAMPLE 8 ■ Finding Local Maxima and Minima from a Graph

Find the local maximum and minimum values of the function $f(x) = x^3 - 8x + 1$, rounded to three decimal places.

SOLUTION   The graph of f is shown in Figure 10. There appears to be one local maximum between $x = -2$ and $x = -1$, and one local minimum between $x = 1$ and $x = 2$.

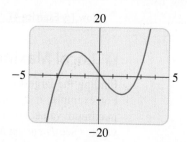

FIGURE 10 Graph of
$f(x) = x^3 - 8x + 1$

Let's find the coordinates of the local maximum point first. We zoom in to enlarge the area near this point, as shown in Figure 11. Using the $\boxed{\text{TRACE}}$ feature on the graphing device, we move the cursor along the curve and observe how the y-coordinates change. The local maximum value of y is 9.709, and this value occurs when x is -1.633, correct to three decimal places.

We locate the minimum value in a similar fashion. By zooming in to the viewing rectangle shown in Figure 12, we find that the local minimum value is about -7.709, and this value occurs when $x \approx 1.633$.

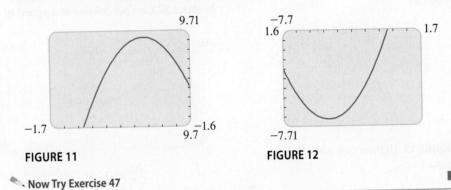

FIGURE 11

FIGURE 12

> ■ Now Try Exercise 47

The `maximum` and `minimum` commands on a TI-83 or TI-84 calculator provide another method for finding extreme values of functions. We use this method in the next example.

EXAMPLE 9 ■ A Model for Managing Traffic

See the *Discovery Project* referenced in Chapter 3, on page 331, for how this model is obtained.

A highway engineer develops a formula to estimate the number of cars that can safely travel a particular highway at a given speed. She assumes that each car is 17 ft long, travels at a speed of x mi/h, and follows the car in front of it at the safe following distance for that speed. She finds that the number N of cars that can pass a given point per minute is modeled by the function

$$N(x) = \frac{88x}{17 + 17\left(\dfrac{x}{20}\right)^2}$$

Graph the function in the viewing rectangle $[0, 100]$ by $[0, 60]$.

(a) Find the intervals on which the function N is increasing and on which it is decreasing.

(b) Find the maximum value of N. What is the maximum carrying capacity of the road, and at what speed is it achieved?

Dave Carpenter/www.CartoonStock.com

DISCOVERY PROJECT

Every Graph Tells a Story

A graph can often describe a real-world "story" much more quickly and effectively than many words. For example, the stock market crash of 1929 is effectively described by a graph of the Dow Jones Industrial Average. No words are needed to convey the message in the cartoon shown here. In this project we describe, or tell the story that corresponds to, a given graph as well as make graphs that correspond to a real-world "story." You can find the project at **www.stewartmath.com**.

SOLUTION   The graph is shown in Figure 13(a).

(a) From the graph we see that the function N is increasing on $(0, 20)$ and decreasing on $(20, \infty)$.

See Appendix D, *Using the TI-83/84 Graphing Calculator,* for specific instructions on using the maximum command.

(b) There appears to be a maximum between $x = 19$ and $x = 21$. Using the maximum command, as shown in Figure 13(b), we see that the maximum value of N is about 51.78, and it occurs when x is 20. So the maximum carrying capacity is about 52 cars per minute at a speed of 20 mi/h.

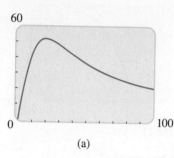

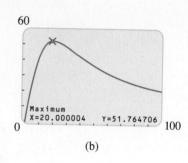

FIGURE 13 Highway capacity at speed x

(a)

(b)

▪ **Now Try Exercise 65**

2.3 EXERCISES

CONCEPTS

1–5 ■ The function f graphed below is defined by a polynomial expression of degree 4. Use the graph to solve the exercises.

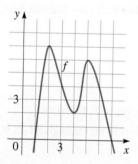

1. To find a function value $f(a)$ from the graph of f, we find the height of the graph above the x-axis at $x =$ _____.

From the graph of f we see that $f(3) =$ _____ and $f(1) =$ _____. The net change in f between $x = 1$ and $x = 3$ is $f(\_\_\_) - f(\_\_\_) =$ _____.

2. The domain of the function f is all the ___-values of the points on the graph, and the range is all the corresponding ___-values. From the graph of f we see that the domain of f is the interval _____ and the range of f is the interval _____.

3. (a) If f is increasing on an interval, then the y-values of the points on the graph _____ as the x-values increase. From the graph of f we see that f is increasing on the intervals _____ and _____.

(b) If f is decreasing on an interval, then the y-values of the points on the graph _____ as the x-values increase. From the graph of f we see that f is decreasing on the intervals _____ and _____.

4. (a) A function value $f(a)$ is a local maximum value of f if $f(a)$ is the _____ value of f on some open interval containing a. From the graph of f we see that there are two local maximum values of f: One local maximum is _____, and it occurs when $x = 2$; the other local maximum is _____, and it occurs when $x =$ _____.

(b) The function value $f(a)$ is a local minimum value of f if $f(a)$ is the _____ value of f on some open interval containing a. From the graph of f we see that there is one local minimum value of f. The local minimum value is _____, and it occurs when $x =$ _____.

5. The solutions of the equation $f(x) = 0$ are the _____-intercepts of the graph of f. The solution of the inequality $f(x) \geq 0$ is the set of x-values at which the graph of f is on or above the _____-axis. From the graph of f we find that the solutions of the equation $f(x) = 0$ are $x =$ _____ and $x =$ _____, and the solution of the inequality $f(x) \geq 0$ is _____.

6. (a) To solve the equation $2x + 1 = -x + 4$ graphically, we graph the functions $f(x) =$ _____ and $g(x) =$ _____ on the same set of axes and determine the values of x at which the graphs of f and g intersect. Graph f and g below, and use the graphs to solve the equation. The solution is $x =$ _____.

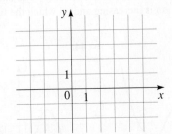

(b) To solve the inequality $2x + 1 < -x + 4$ graphically, we graph the functions $f(x) =$ _____ and $g(x) =$ _____ on the same set of axes and find the values of x at which the graph of g is

_____ (higher/lower) than the graph of f. From the graphs in part (a) we see that the solution of the inequality is the interval (____ , ____).

SKILLS

7. Values of a Function   The graph of a function h is given.
 (a) Find $h(-2)$, $h(0)$, $h(2)$, and $h(3)$.
 (b) Find the domain and range of h.
 (c) Find the values of x for which $h(x) = 3$.
 (d) Find the values of x for which $h(x) \le 3$.
 (e) Find the net change in h between $x = -3$ and $x = 3$.

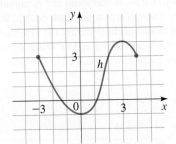

8. Values of a Function   The graph of a function g is given.
 (a) Find $g(-4)$, $g(-2)$, $g(0)$, $g(2)$, and $g(4)$.
 (b) Find the domain and range of g.
 (c) Find the values of x for which $g(x) = 3$.
 (d) Estimate the values of x for which $g(x) \le 0$.
 (e) Find the net change in g between $x = -1$ and $x = 2$.

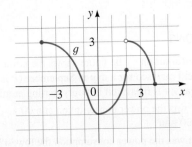

9. Solving Equations and Inequalities Graphically   Graphs of the functions f and g are given.
 (a) Which is larger, $f(0)$ or $g(0)$?
 (b) Which is larger, $f(-3)$ or $g(-3)$?
 (c) For which values of x is $f(x) = g(x)$?
 (d) Find the values of x for which $f(x) \le g(x)$.
 (e) Find the values of x for which $f(x) > g(x)$.

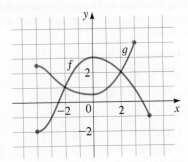

10. Solving Equations and Inequalities Graphically   Graphs of the functions f and g are given.
 (a) Which is larger, $f(6)$ or $g(6)$?
 (b) Which is larger, $f(3)$ or $g(3)$?
 (c) Find the values of x for which $f(x) = g(x)$.
 (d) Find the values of x for which $f(x) \le g(x)$.
 (e) Find the values of x for which $f(x) > g(x)$.

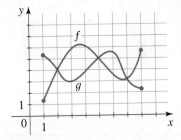

11–16 ■ Domain and Range from a Graph   A function f is given. **(a)** Sketch a graph of f. **(b)** Use the graph to find the domain and range of f.

11. $f(x) = 2x + 3$ **12.** $f(x) = 3x - 2$

13. $f(x) = x - 2$, $-2 \le x \le 5$

14. $f(x) = 4 - 2x$, $1 < x < 4$

15. $f(x) = x^2 - 1$, $-3 \le x \le 3$

16. $f(x) = 3 - x^2$, $-3 \le x \le 3$

17–22 ■ Finding Domain and Range Graphically   A function f is given. **(a)** Use a graphing calculator to draw the graph of f. **(b)** Find the domain and range of f from the graph.

17. $f(x) = x^2 + 4x + 3$ **18.** $f(x) = -x^2 + 2x + 1$

19. $f(x) = \sqrt{x - 1}$ **20.** $f(x) = \sqrt{x + 2}$

21. $f(x) = \sqrt{16 - x^2}$ **22.** $f(x) = -\sqrt{25 - x^2}$

23–26 ■ Solving Equations and Inequalities Graphically
Solve the given equation or inequality graphically.

 23. (a) $x - 2 = 4 - x$ (b) $x - 2 > 4 - x$

24. (a) $-2x + 3 = 3x - 7$ (b) $-2x + 3 \le 3x - 7$

25. (a) $x^2 = 2 - x$ (b) $x^2 \le 2 - x$

26. (a) $-x^2 = 3 - 4x$ (b) $-x^2 \ge 3 - 4x$

27–30 ■ Solving Equations and Inequalities Graphically Solve the given equation or inequality graphically. State your answers rounded to two decimals.

27. (a) $x^3 + 3x^2 = -x^2 + 3x + 7$
(b) $x^3 + 3x^2 \ge -x^2 + 3x + 7$

28. (a) $5x^2 - x^3 = -x^2 + 3x + 4$
(b) $5x^2 - x^3 \le -x^2 + 3x + 4$

29. (a) $16x^3 + 16x^2 = x + 1$
(b) $16x^3 + 16x^2 \ge x + 1$

30. (a) $1 + \sqrt{x} = \sqrt{x^2 + 1}$
(b) $1 + \sqrt{x} > \sqrt{x^2 + 1}$

31–34 ■ Increasing and Decreasing The graph of a function f is given. Use the graph to estimate the following. **(a)** The domain and range of f. **(b)** The intervals on which f is increasing and on which f is decreasing.

31.

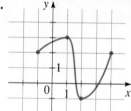

32.

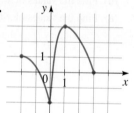

33.

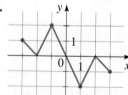

34.

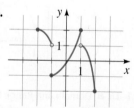

35–42 ■ Increasing and Decreasing A function f is given. **(a)** Use a graphing calculator to draw the graph of f. **(b)** Find the domain and range of f. **(c)** State approximately the intervals on which f is increasing and on which f is decreasing.

35. $f(x) = x^2 - 5x$

36. $f(x) = x^3 - 4x$

37. $f(x) = 2x^3 - 3x^2 - 12x$

38. $f(x) = x^4 - 16x^2$

39. $f(x) = x^3 + 2x^2 - x - 2$

40. $f(x) = x^4 - 4x^3 + 2x^2 + 4x - 3$

41. $f(x) = x^{2/5}$

42. $f(x) = 4 - x^{2/3}$

43–46 ■ Local Maximum and Minimum Values The graph of a function f is given. Use the graph to estimate the following. **(a)** All the local maximum and minimum values of the function and the value of x at which each occurs. **(b)** The intervals on which the function is increasing and on which the function is decreasing.

43.

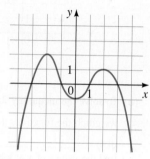

44.

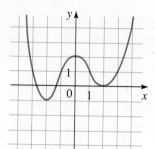

45.

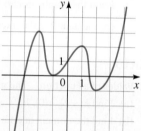

46.

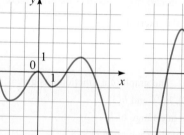

47–54 ■ Local Maximum and Minimum Values A function is given. **(a)** Find all the local maximum and minimum values of the function and the value of x at which each occurs. State each answer rounded to two decimal places. **(b)** Find the intervals on which the function is increasing and on which the function is decreasing. State each answer rounded to two decimal places.

47. $f(x) = x^3 - x$

48. $f(x) = 3 + x + x^2 - x^3$

49. $g(x) = x^4 - 2x^3 - 11x^2$

50. $g(x) = x^5 - 8x^3 + 20x$

51. $U(x) = x\sqrt{6 - x}$

52. $U(x) = x\sqrt{x - x^2}$

53. $V(x) = \dfrac{1 - x^2}{x^3}$

54. $V(x) = \dfrac{1}{x^2 + x + 1}$

APPLICATIONS

55. Power Consumption The figure shows the power consumption in San Francisco for a day in September (P is measured in megawatts; t is measured in hours starting at midnight).

(a) What was the power consumption at 6:00 A.M.? At 6:00 P.M.?

(b) When was the power consumption the lowest?

(c) When was the power consumption the highest?

(d) Find the net change in the power consumption from 9:00 A.M. to 7:00 P.M.

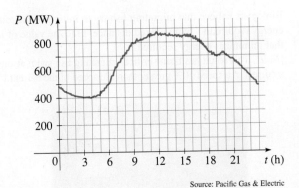

Source: Pacific Gas & Electric

56. Earthquake   The graph shows the vertical acceleration of the ground from the 1994 Northridge earthquake in Los Angeles, as measured by a seismograph. (Here *t* represents the time in seconds.)

(a) At what time *t* did the earthquake first make noticeable movements of the earth?

(b) At what time *t* did the earthquake seem to end?

(c) At what time *t* was the maximum intensity of the earthquake reached?

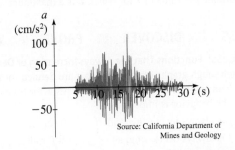

Source: California Department of Mines and Geology

57. Weight Function   The graph gives the weight *W* of a person at age *x*.

(a) Determine the intervals on which the function *W* is increasing and those on which it is decreasing.

(b) What do you think happened when this person was 30 years old?

(c) Find the net change in the person's weight *W* from age 10 to age 20.

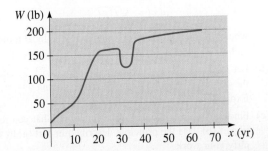

58. Distance Function   The graph gives a sales representative's distance from his home as a function of time on a certain day.

(a) Determine the time intervals on which his distance from home was increasing and those on which it was decreasing.

(b) Describe in words what the graph indicates about his travels on this day.

(c) Find the net change in his distance from home between noon and 1:00 P.M.

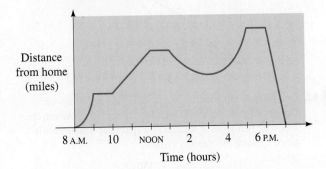

59. Changing Water Levels   The graph shows the depth of water *W* in a reservoir over a one-year period as a function of the number of days *x* since the beginning of the year.

(a) Determine the intervals on which the function *W* is increasing and on which it is decreasing.

(b) At what value of *x* does *W* achieve a local maximum? A local minimum?

(c) Find the net change in the depth *W* from 100 days to 300 days.

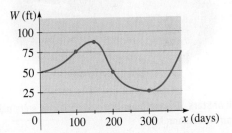

60. Population Growth and Decline   The graph shows the population *P* in a small industrial city from 1950 to 2000. The variable *x* represents the number of years since 1950.

(a) Determine the intervals on which the function *P* is increasing and on which it is decreasing.

(b) What was the maximum population, and in what year was it attained?

(c) Find the net change in the population *P* from 1970 to 1990.

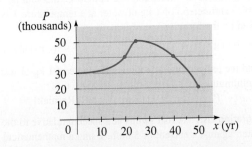

61. Hurdle Race   Three runners compete in a 100-meter hurdle race. The graph depicts the distance run as a function of time for each runner. Describe in words what the graph tells you about this race. Who won the race? Did each runner finish the race? What do you think happened to Runner B?

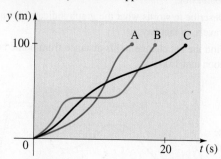

62. Gravity Near the Moon   We can use Newton's Law of Gravity to measure the gravitational attraction between the moon and an algebra student in a spaceship located a distance x above the moon's surface:

$$F(x) = \frac{350}{x^2}$$

Here F is measured in newtons (N), and x is measured in millions of meters.

(a) Graph the function F for values of x between 0 and 10.

(b) Use the graph to describe the behavior of the gravitational attraction F as the distance x increases.

63. Radii of Stars   Astronomers infer the radii of stars using the Stefan Boltzmann Law:

$$E(T) = (5.67 \times 10^{-8})T^4$$

where E is the energy radiated per unit of surface area measured in watts (W) and T is the absolute temperature measured in kelvins (K).

(a) Graph the function E for temperatures T between 100 K and 300 K.

(b) Use the graph to describe the change in energy E as the temperature T increases.

64. Volume of Water   Between 0°C and 30°C, the volume V (in cubic centimeters) of 1 kg of water at a temperature T is given by the formula

$$V = 999.87 - 0.06426T + 0.0085043T^2 - 0.0000679T^3$$

Find the temperature at which the volume of 1 kg of water is a minimum.
[*Source: Physics*, by D. Halliday and R. Resnick]

65. Migrating Fish   A fish swims at a speed v relative to the water, against a current of 5 mi/h. Using a mathematical model of energy expenditure, it can be shown that the total energy E required to swim a distance of 10 mi is given by

$$E(v) = 2.73v^3\frac{10}{v - 5}$$

Biologists believe that migrating fish try to minimize the total energy required to swim a fixed distance. Find the value of v that minimizes energy required.
[*Note:* This result has been verified; migrating fish swim against a current at a speed 50% greater than the speed of the current.]

66. Coughing   When a foreign object that is lodged in the trachea (windpipe) forces a person to cough, the diaphragm thrusts upward, causing an increase in pressure in the lungs. At the same time, the trachea contracts, causing the expelled air to move faster and increasing the pressure on the foreign object. According to a mathematical model of coughing, the velocity v (in cm/s) of the airstream through an average-sized person's trachea is related to the radius r of the trachea (in cm) by the function

$$v(r) = 3.2(1 - r)r^2 \qquad \tfrac{1}{2} \le r \le 1$$

Determine the value of r for which v is a maximum.

DISCUSS ■ **DISCOVER** ■ **PROVE** ■ **WRITE**

67. DISCUSS: Functions That Are Always Increasing or Decreasing   Sketch rough graphs of functions that are defined for all real numbers and that exhibit the indicated behavior (or explain why the behavior is impossible).

(a) f is always increasing, and $f(x) > 0$ for all x

(b) f is always decreasing, and $f(x) > 0$ for all x

(c) f is always increasing, and $f(x) < 0$ for all x

(d) f is always decreasing, and $f(x) < 0$ for all x

68. DISCUSS: Maximum and Minimum Values   In Example 9 we saw a real-world situation in which the maximum value of a function is important. Name several other everyday situations in which a maximum or minimum value is important.

69. DISCUSS ■ DISCOVER: Minimizing a Distance   When we seek a minimum or maximum value of a function, it is sometimes easier to work with a simpler function instead.

(a) Suppose

$$g(x) = \sqrt{f(x)}$$

where $f(x) \ge 0$ for all x. Explain why the local minima and maxima of f and g occur at the same values of x.

(b) Let $g(x)$ be the distance between the point $(3, 0)$ and the point (x, x^2) on the graph of the parabola $y = x^2$. Express g as a function of x.

(c) Find the minimum value of the function g that you found in part (b). Use the principle described in part (a) to simplify your work.

2.4 AVERAGE RATE OF CHANGE OF A FUNCTION

■ **Average Rate of Change** ■ **Linear Functions Have Constant Rate of Change**

Functions are often used to model changing quantities. In this section we learn how to find the rate at which the values of a function change as the input variable changes.

■ Average Rate of Change

We are all familiar with the concept of speed: If you drive a distance of 120 miles in 2 hours, then your average speed, or rate of travel, is $\frac{120 \text{ mi}}{2 \text{ h}} = 60$ mi/h. Now suppose you take a car trip and record the distance that you travel every few minutes. The distance s you have traveled is a function of the time t:

$$s(t) = \text{total distance traveled at time } t$$

We graph the function s as shown in Figure 1. The graph shows that you have traveled a total of 50 miles after 1 hour, 75 miles after 2 hours, 140 miles after 3 hours, and so on. To find your *average* speed between any two points on the trip, we divide the distance traveled by the time elapsed.

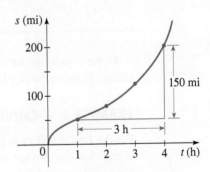

FIGURE 1 Average speed

Let's calculate your average speed between 1:00 P.M. and 4:00 P.M. The time elapsed is $4 - 1 = 3$ hours. To find the distance you traveled, we subtract the distance at 1:00 P.M. from the distance at 4:00 P.M., that is, $200 - 50 = 150$ mi. Thus your average speed is

$$\text{average speed} = \frac{\text{distance traveled}}{\text{time elapsed}} = \frac{150 \text{ mi}}{3 \text{ h}} = 50 \text{ mi/h}$$

The average speed that we have just calculated can be expressed by using function notation:

$$\text{average speed} = \frac{s(4) - s(1)}{4 - 1} = \frac{200 - 50}{3} = 50 \text{ mi/h}$$

Note that the average speed is different over different time intervals. For example, between 2:00 P.M. and 3:00 P.M. we find that

$$\text{average speed} = \frac{s(3) - s(2)}{3 - 2} = \frac{140 - 75}{1} = 65 \text{ mi/h}$$

Finding average rates of change is important in many contexts. For instance, we might be interested in knowing how quickly the air temperature is dropping as a storm approaches or how fast revenues are increasing from the sale of a new product. So we need to know how to determine the average rate of change of the functions that model these quantities. In fact, the concept of average rate of change can be defined for any function.

AVERAGE RATE OF CHANGE

The **average rate of change** of the function $y = f(x)$ between $x = a$ and $x = b$ is

$$\text{average rate of change} = \frac{\text{change in } y}{\text{change in } x} = \frac{f(b) - f(a)}{b - a}$$

The average rate of change is the slope of the **secant line** between $x = a$ and $x = b$ on the graph of f, that is, the line that passes through $(a, f(a))$ and $(b, f(b))$.

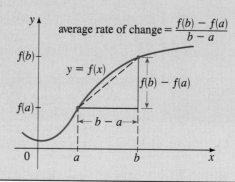

In the expression for average rate of change, the numerator $f(b) - f(a)$ is the net change in the value of f between $x = a$ and $x = b$ (see page 187).

EXAMPLE 1 ■ Calculating the Average Rate of Change

For the function $f(x) = (x - 3)^2$, whose graph is shown in Figure 2, find the net change and the average rate of change between the following points:

(a) $x = 1$ and $x = 3$ **(b)** $x = 4$ and $x = 7$

SOLUTION

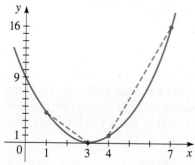

FIGURE 2 $f(x) = (x - 3)^2$

(a) Net change $= f(3) - f(1)$ Definition

$\qquad\qquad\qquad = (3 - 3)^2 - (1 - 3)^2$ Use $f(x) = (x - 3)^2$

$\qquad\qquad\qquad = -4$ Calculate

$\qquad$ Average rate of change $= \dfrac{f(3) - f(1)}{3 - 1}$ Definition

$\qquad\qquad\qquad\qquad\qquad = \dfrac{-4}{2} = -2$ Calculate

(b) Net change $= f(7) - f(4)$ Definition

$\qquad\qquad\qquad = (7 - 3)^2 - (4 - 3)^2$ Use $f(x) = (x - 3)^2$

$\qquad\qquad\qquad = 15$ Calculate

$\qquad$ Average rate of change $= \dfrac{f(7) - f(4)}{7 - 4}$ Definition

$\qquad\qquad\qquad\qquad\qquad = \dfrac{15}{3} = 5$ Calculate

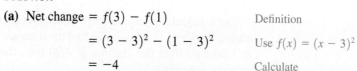 **Now Try Exercise 15**

EXAMPLE 2 ■ Average Speed of a Falling Object

If an object is dropped from a high cliff or a tall building, then the distance it has fallen after t seconds is given by the function $d(t) = 16t^2$. Find its average speed (average rate of change) over the following intervals:

(a) Between 1 s and 5 s   **(b)** Between $t = a$ and $t = a + h$

SOLUTION

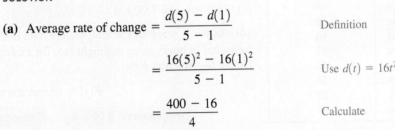

(a) Average rate of change $= \dfrac{d(5) - d(1)}{5 - 1}$ Definition

$$= \dfrac{16(5)^2 - 16(1)^2}{5 - 1}$$ Use $d(t) = 16t^2$

$$= \dfrac{400 - 16}{4}$$ Calculate

$$= 96 \text{ ft/s}$$ Calculate

(b) Average rate of change $= \dfrac{d(a + h) - d(a)}{(a + h) - a}$ Definition

$$= \dfrac{16(a + h)^2 - 16(a)^2}{(a + h) - a}$$ Use $d(t) = 16t^2$

$$= \dfrac{16(a^2 + 2ah + h^2 - a^2)}{h}$$ Expand and factor 16

$$= \dfrac{16(2ah + h^2)}{h}$$ Simplify numerator

$$= \dfrac{16h(2a + h)}{h}$$ Factor h

$$= 16(2a + h)$$ Simplify

Function: In t seconds the stone falls $16t^2$ ft.

$d(t) = 16t^2$

Now Try Exercise 19 ■

The average rate of change calculated in Example 2(b) is known as a *difference quotient*. In calculus we use difference quotients to calculate *instantaneous* rates of change. An example of an instantaneous rate of change is the speed shown on the speedometer of your car. This changes from one instant to the next as your car's speed changes.

The graphs in Figure 3 show that if a function is increasing on an interval, then the average rate of change between any two points is positive, whereas if a function is decreasing on an interval, then the average rate of change between any two points is negative.

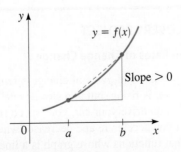

f increasing
Average rate of change positive

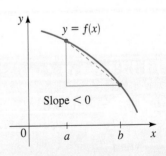

f decreasing
Average rate of change negative

FIGURE 3

Time	Temperature (°F)
8:00 A.M.	38
9:00 A.M.	40
10:00 A.M.	44
11:00 A.M.	50
12:00 NOON	56
1:00 P.M.	62
2:00 P.M.	66
3:00 P.M.	67
4:00 P.M.	64
5:00 P.M.	58
6:00 P.M.	55
7:00 P.M.	51

EXAMPLE 3 ■ Average Rate of Temperature Change

The table in the margin gives the outdoor temperatures observed by a science student on a spring day. Draw a graph of the data, and find the average rate of change of temperature between the following times:

(a) 8:00 A.M. and 9:00 A.M.

(b) 1:00 P.M. and 3:00 P.M.

(c) 4:00 P.M. and 7:00 P.M.

SOLUTION A graph of the temperature data is shown in Figure 4. Let t represent time, measured in hours since midnight (so, for example, 2:00 P.M. corresponds to $t = 14$). Define the function F by

$$F(t) = \text{temperature at time } t$$

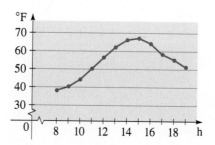
Temperature at 9:00 A.M.   Temperature at 8:00 A.M.

(a) Average rate of change $= \dfrac{F(9) - F(8)}{9 - 8} = \dfrac{40 - 38}{9 - 8} = 2$

The average rate of change was 2°F per hour.

FIGURE 4

(b) Average rate of change $= \dfrac{F(15) - F(13)}{15 - 13} = \dfrac{67 - 62}{2} = 2.5$

The average rate of change was 2.5°F per hour.

(c) Average rate of change $= \dfrac{F(19) - F(16)}{19 - 16} = \dfrac{51 - 64}{3} \approx -4.3$

The average rate of change was about −4.3°F per hour during this time interval. The negative sign indicates that the temperature was dropping.

✎ Now Try Exercise 31

DISCOVERY PROJECT

When Rates of Change Change

In the real world, rates of change often themselves change. A statement like "inflation is rising, but at a slower rate" involves a change of a rate of change. When you drive your car, your speed (rate of change of distance) increases when you accelerate and decreases when you decelerate. From Example 4 we see that functions whose graph is a line (linear functions) have constant rate of change. In this project we explore how the shape of a graph corresponds to a changing rate of change. You can find the project at **www.stewartmath.com**.

■ Linear Functions Have Constant Rate of Change

Recall that a function of the form $f(x) = mx + b$ is a linear function (see page 196). Its graph is a line with slope m. On the other hand, if a function f has constant rate of change, then it must be a linear function. (You are asked to prove these facts in Exercises 51 and 52 in Section 2.5.) In general, the average rate of change of a linear function between any two points is the constant m. In the next example we find the average rate of change for a particular linear function.

EXAMPLE 4 ■ Linear Functions Have Constant Rate of Change

Let $f(x) = 3x - 5$. Find the average rate of change of f between the following points.

(a) $x = 0$ and $x = 1$

(b) $x = 3$ and $x = 7$

(c) $x = a$ and $x = a + h$

What conclusion can you draw from your answers?

SOLUTION

(a) Average rate of change $= \dfrac{f(1) - f(0)}{1 - 0} = \dfrac{(3 \cdot 1 - 5) - (3 \cdot 0 - 5)}{1}$

$$= \dfrac{(-2) - (-5)}{1} = 3$$

(b) Average rate of change $= \dfrac{f(7) - f(3)}{7 - 3} = \dfrac{(3 \cdot 7 - 5) - (3 \cdot 3 - 5)}{4}$

$$= \dfrac{16 - 4}{4} = 3$$

(c) Average rate of change $= \dfrac{f(a + h) - f(a)}{(a + h) - a} = \dfrac{[3(a + h) - 5] - [3a - 5]}{h}$

$$= \dfrac{3a + 3h - 5 - 3a + 5}{h} = \dfrac{3h}{h} = 3$$

It appears that the average rate of change is always 3 for this function. In fact, part (c) proves that the rate of change between any two arbitrary points $x = a$ and $x = a + h$ is 3.

✎ Now Try Exercise 25   ■

2.4 EXERCISES

CONCEPTS

1. If you travel 100 miles in two hours, then your average speed for the trip is

average speed $= \dfrac{\rule{1.5cm}{0.4pt}}{\rule{1.5cm}{0.4pt}} = \rule{1.5cm}{0.4pt}$

2. The average rate of change of a function f between $x = a$ and $x = b$ is

average rate of change $= \dfrac{\rule{1.5cm}{0.4pt}}{\rule{1.5cm}{0.4pt}}$

3. The average rate of change of the function $f(x) = x^2$ between $x = 1$ and $x = 5$ is

average rate of change $= \dfrac{\rule{1.5cm}{0.4pt}}{\rule{1.5cm}{0.4pt}} = \rule{1.5cm}{0.4pt}$

4. (a) The average rate of change of a function f between $x = a$ and $x = b$ is the slope of the $\rule{1.5cm}{0.4pt}$ line between $(a, f(a))$ and $(b, f(b))$.

(b) The average rate of change of the linear function $f(x) = 3x + 5$ between any two points is $\rule{1.5cm}{0.4pt}$.

5–6 ■ *Yes or No? If No, give a reason.*

5. (a) Is the average rate of change of a function between $x = a$ and $x = b$ the slope of the secant line through $(a, f(a))$ and $(b, f(b))$?

(b) Is the average rate of change of a linear function the same for all intervals?

6. (a) Can the average rate of change of an increasing function ever be negative?

(b) If the average rate of change of a function between $x = a$ and $x = b$ is negative, then is the function necessarily decreasing on the interval (a, b)?

SKILLS

7–10 ■ **Net Change and Average Rate of Change** The graph of a function is given. Determine **(a)** the net change and **(b)** the average rate of change between the indicated points on the graph.

7.
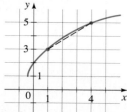

8.
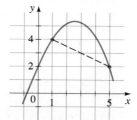

9.
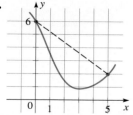

10.
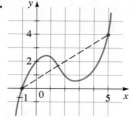

11–24 ■ **Net Change and Average Rate of Change** A function is given. Determine **(a)** the net change and **(b)** the average rate of change between the given values of the variable.

11. $f(x) = 3x - 2$; $\quad x = 2, x = 3$

12. $r(t) = 3 - \frac{1}{3}t$; $\quad t = 3, t = 6$

13. $h(t) = -t + \frac{3}{2}$; $\quad t = -4, t = 1$

14. $g(x) = 2 - \frac{2}{3}x$; $\quad x = -3, x = 2$

15. $h(t) = 2t^2 - t$; $\quad t = 3, t = 6$

16. $f(z) = 1 - 3z^2$; $\quad z = -2, z = 0$

17. $f(x) = x^3 - 4x^2$; $\quad x = 0, x = 10$

18. $g(t) = t^4 - t^3 + t^2$; $\quad t = -2, t = 2$

19. $f(t) = 5t^2$; $\quad t = 3, t = 3 + h$

20. $f(x) = 1 - 3x^2$; $\quad x = 2, x = 2 + h$

21. $g(x) = \frac{1}{x}$; $\quad x = 1, x = a$

22. $g(x) = \frac{2}{x + 1}$; $\quad x = 0, x = h$

23. $f(t) = \frac{2}{t}$; $\quad t = a, t = a + h$

24. $f(t) = \sqrt{t}$; $\quad t = a, t = a + h$

25–26 ■ **Average Rate of Change of a Linear Function** A linear function is given. **(a)** Find the average rate of change of the function between $x = a$ and $x = a + h$. **(b)** Show that the average rate of change is the same as the slope of the line.

25. $f(x) = \frac{1}{2}x + 3$ **26.** $g(x) = -4x + 2$

SKILLS Plus

27. Average Rate of Change The graphs of the functions f and g are shown. The function _____ (f or g) has a greater average rate of change between $x = 0$ and $x = 1$. The function _____ (f or g) has a greater average rate of change between $x = 1$ and $x = 2$. The functions f and g have the same average rate of change between $x =$ _____ and $x =$ _____.

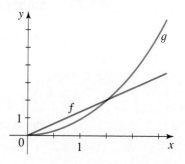

28. Average Rate of Change Graphs of the functions f, g, and h are shown below. What can you say about the average rate of change of each function on the successive intervals $[0, 1], [1, 2], [2, 3], \ldots$?

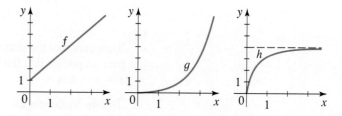

APPLICATIONS

29. Changing Water Levels The graph shows the depth of water W in a reservoir over a one-year period as a function of the number of days x since the beginning of the year. What was the average rate of change of W between $x = 100$ and $x = 200$?

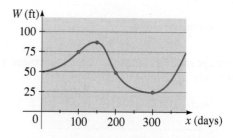

30. Population Growth and Decline The graph shows the population P in a small industrial city from 1950 to 2000. The variable x represents the number of years since 1950.

(a) What was the average rate of change of P between $x = 20$ and $x = 40$?

(b) Interpret the value of the average rate of change that you found in part (a).

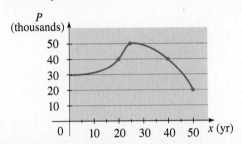

31. Population Growth and Decline The table gives the population in a small coastal community for the period 1997–2006. Figures shown are for January 1 in each year.

(a) What was the average rate of change of population between 1998 and 2001?

(b) What was the average rate of change of population between 2002 and 2004?

(c) For what period of time was the population increasing?

(d) For what period of time was the population decreasing?

Year	Population
1997	624
1998	856
1999	1,336
2000	1,578
2001	1,591
2002	1,483
2003	994
2004	826
2005	801
2006	745

32. Running Speed A man is running around a circular track that is 200 m in circumference. An observer uses a stopwatch to record the runner's time at the end of each lap, obtaining the data in the following table.

(a) What was the man's average speed (rate) between 68 s and 152 s?

(b) What was the man's average speed between 263 s and 412 s?

(c) Calculate the man's speed for each lap. Is he slowing down, speeding up, or neither?

Time (s)	Distance (m)
32	200
68	400
108	600
152	800
203	1000
263	1200
335	1400
412	1600

33. DVD Player Sales The table shows the number of DVD players sold in a small electronics store in the years 2003–2013.

Year	DVD players sold
2003	495
2004	513
2005	410
2006	402
2007	520
2008	580
2009	631
2010	719
2011	624
2012	582
2013	635

(a) What was the average rate of change of sales between 2003 and 2013?

(b) What was the average rate of change of sales between 2003 and 2004?

(c) What was the average rate of change of sales between 2004 and 2005?

(d) Between which two successive years did DVD player sales *increase* most quickly? *Decrease* most quickly?

34. Book Collection Between 1980 and 2000 a rare book collector purchased books for his collection at the rate of 40 books per year. Use this information to complete the following table. (Note that not every year is given in the table.)

Year	Number of books	Year	Number of books
1980	420	1995	
1981	460	1997	
1982		1998	
1985		1999	
1990		2000	1220
1992			

35. Cooling Soup When a bowl of hot soup is left in a room, the soup eventually cools down to room temperature. The temperature T of the soup is a function of time t. The table below gives the temperature (in °F) of a bowl of soup t minutes after it was set on the table. Find the average rate of change of the temperature of the soup over the first 20 minutes and over the next 20 minutes. During which interval did the soup cool off more quickly?

t (min)	T (°F)	t (min)	T (°F)
0	200	35	94
5	172	40	89
10	150	50	81
15	133	60	77
20	119	90	72
25	108	120	70
30	100	150	70

36. Farms in the United States The graph gives the number of farms in the United States from 1850 to 2000.

(a) Estimate the average rate of change in the number of farms between (i) 1860 and 1890 and (ii) 1950 and 1970.

(b) In which decade did the number of farms experience the greatest average rate of decline?

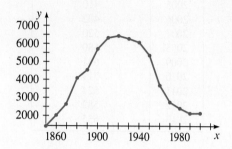

37. Three-Way Tie A downhill skiing race ends in a three-way tie for first place. The graph shows distance as a function of time for each of the three winners, A, B, and C.

(a) Find the average speed for each skier

(b) Describe the differences between the ways in which the three participants skied the race.

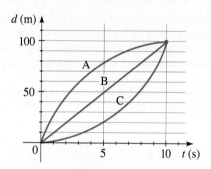

38. Speed Skating Two speed skaters, A and B, are racing in a 500-m event. The graph shows the distance they have traveled as a function of the time from the start of the race.

(a) Who won the race?

(b) Find the average speed during the first 10 s for each skater.

(c) Find the average speed during the last 15 s for each skater.

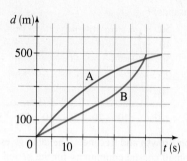

DISCUSS ■ **DISCOVER** ■ **PROVE** ■ **WRITE**

39. DISCOVER: Limiting Behavior of Average Speed An object is dropped from a high cliff, and the distance (in feet) it has fallen after t seconds is given by the function $d(t) = 16t^2$. Complete the table to find the average speed during the given time intervals. Use the table to determine what value the average speed approaches as the time intervals get smaller and smaller. Is it reasonable to say that this value is the speed of the object at the instant $t = 3$? Explain.

$t = a$	$t = b$	Average speed $= \dfrac{d(b) - d(a)}{b - a}$
3	3.5	
3	3.1	
3	3.01	
3	3.001	
3	3.0001	

2.5 ■ LINEAR FUNCTIONS AND MODELS

■ **Linear Functions** ■ **Slope and Rate of Change** ■ **Making and Using Linear Models**

In this section we study the simplest functions that can be expressed by an algebraic expression: linear functions.

■ Linear Functions

Recall that a *linear function* is a function of the form $f(x) = ax + b$. So in the expression defining a linear function the variable occurs to the first power only. We can also express a linear function in equation form as $y = ax + b$. From Section 1.3 we know that the graph of this equation is a line with slope a and y-intercept b.

> ## LINEAR FUNCTIONS
>
> A **linear function** is a function of the form $f(x) = ax + b$.
>
> The graph of a linear function is a line with slope a and y-intercept b.

EXAMPLE 1 ■ Identifying Linear Functions

Determine whether the given function is linear. If the function is linear, express the function in the form $f(x) = ax + b$.

(a) $f(x) = 2 + 3x$

(b) $g(x) = 3(1 - 2x)$

(c) $h(x) = x(4 + 3x)$

(d) $k(x) = \dfrac{1 - 5x}{4}$

SOLUTION

(a) We have $f(x) = 2 + 3x = 3x + 2$. So f is a linear function in which a is 3 and b is 2.

(b) We have $g(x) = 3(1 - 2x) = -6x + 3$. So g is a linear function in which a is -6 and b is 3.

(c) We have $h(x) = x(4 + 3x) = 4x + 3x^2$, which is not a linear function because the variable x is squared in the second term of the expression for h.

(d) We have $k(x) = \dfrac{1 - 5x}{4} = -\dfrac{5}{4}x + \dfrac{1}{4}$. So k is a linear function in which a is $-\frac{5}{4}$ and b is $\frac{1}{4}$.

■ Now Try Exercise 7

EXAMPLE 2 ■ Graphing a Linear Function

Let f be the linear function defined by $f(x) = 3x + 2$.

(a) Make a table of values, and sketch a graph.

(b) What is the slope of the graph of f?

SOLUTION

(a) A table of values is shown in the margin. Since f is a linear function, its graph is a line. So to obtain the graph of f, we plot any two points from the table and draw the straight line that contains the points. We use the points $(1, 5)$ and $(4, 14)$. The graph is the line shown in Figure 1. You can check that the other points in the table of values also lie on the line.

(b) Using the points given in Figure 1, we see that the slope is

$$\text{slope} = \frac{14 - 5}{4 - 1} = 3$$

So the slope is 3.

x	$f(x)$
-2	-4
-1	-1
0	2
1	5
2	8
3	11
4	14
5	17

From the box at the top of this page, you can see that the slope of the graph of $f(x) = 3x + 2$ is 3.

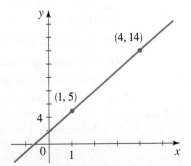

FIGURE 1 Graph of the linear function $f(x) = 3x + 2$

■ Now Try Exercise 15

■ Slope and Rate of Change

In Exercise 52 we prove that all functions with constant rate of change are linear.

Let $f(x) = ax + b$ be a linear function. If x_1 and x_2 are two different values for x and if $y_1 = f(x_1)$ and $y_2 = f(x_2)$, then the points (x_1, y_1) and (x_2, y_2) lie on the graph of f. From the definitions of slope and average rate of change we have

$$\text{slope} = \frac{y_2 - y_1}{x_2 - x_1} = \frac{f(x_2) - f(x_1)}{x_2 - x_1} = \text{average rate of change}$$

From Section 1.3 we know that the *slope* of a linear function is the same between any two points. From the above equation we conclude that the *average rate of change* of a linear function is the same between any two points. Moreover, the average rate of change is equal to the slope (see Exercise 51). Since the average rate of change of a linear function is the same between any two points, it is simply called the **rate of change**.

SLOPE AND RATE OF CHANGE

For the linear function $f(x) = ax + b$, the slope of the graph of f and the rate of change of f are both equal to a, the coefficient of x.

$$a = \text{slope of graph of } f = \text{rate of change of } f$$

The difference between "slope" and "rate of change" is simply a difference in point of view. For example, to describe how a reservoir fills up over time, it is natural to talk about the rate at which the water level is rising, but we can also think of the slope of the graph of the water level (see Example 3). To describe the steepness of a staircase, it is natural to talk about the slope of the trim board of the staircase, but we can also think of the rate at which the stairs rise (see Example 5).

EXAMPLE 3 ■ Slope and Rate of Change

A dam is built on a river to create a reservoir. The water level $f(t)$ in the reservoir at time t is given by

$$f(t) = 4.5t + 28$$

where t is the number of years since the dam was constructed and $f(t)$ is measured in feet.

(a) Sketch a graph of f.

(b) What is the slope of the graph?

(c) At what rate is the water level in the reservoir changing?

SOLUTION

(a) A graph of f is shown in Figure 2.

(b) The graph is a line with slope 4.5, the coefficient of t.

(c) The rate of change of f is 4.5, the coefficient of t. Since time t is measured in years and the water level $f(t)$ is measured in feet, the water level in the reservoir is changing at the rate of 4.5 ft per year. Since this rate of change is positive, the water level is rising.

■. Now Try Exercises 19 and 39

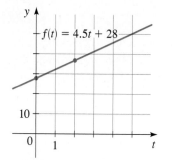

FIGURE 2 Water level as a function of time

■ Making and Using Linear Models

When a linear function is used to model the relationship between two quantities, the slope of the graph of the function is the rate of change of the one quantity with respect to the other. For example, the graph in Figure 3(a) gives the amount of gas in a tank that is being filled. The slope between the indicated points is

$$a = \frac{6 \text{ gal}}{3 \text{ min}} = 2 \text{ gal/min}$$

The slope is the rate at which the tank is being filled, 2 gal per minute. In Figure 3(b) the tank is being drained at the rate of 0.03 gal per minute, and the slope is -0.03.

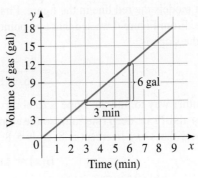
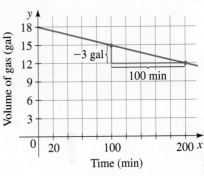

(a) Tank filled at 2 gal/min
    Slope of line is 2

(b) Tank drained at 0.03 gal/min
    Slope of line is -0.03

FIGURE 3 Amount of gas as a function of time

In the following examples we model real-world situations using linear functions. In each of these examples the model involves a constant rate of change (or a constant slope).

EXAMPLE 4 ■ Making a Linear Model from a Rate of Change

Water is being pumped into a swimming pool at the rate of 5 gal per min. Initially, the pool contains 200 gal of water.

(a) Find a linear function V that models the volume of water in the pool at any time t.

(b) If the pool has a capacity of 600 gal, how long does it take to completely fill the pool?

SOLUTION

(a) We need to find a linear function

$$V(t) = at + b$$

that models the volume $V(t)$ of water in the pool after t minutes. The rate of change of volume is 5 gal per min, so $a = 5$. Since the pool contains 200 gal to begin with, we have $V(0) = a \cdot 0 + b = 200$, so $b = 200$. Now that we know a and b, we get the model

$$V(t) = 5t + 200$$

(b) We want to find the time t at which $V(t) = 600$. So we need to solve the equation

$$600 = 5t + 200$$

Solving for t, we get $t = 80$. So it takes 80 min to fill the pool.

🔖 Now Try Exercise 41   ■

$t = 0$

There are 200 gallons of water in the pool at time $t = 0$.

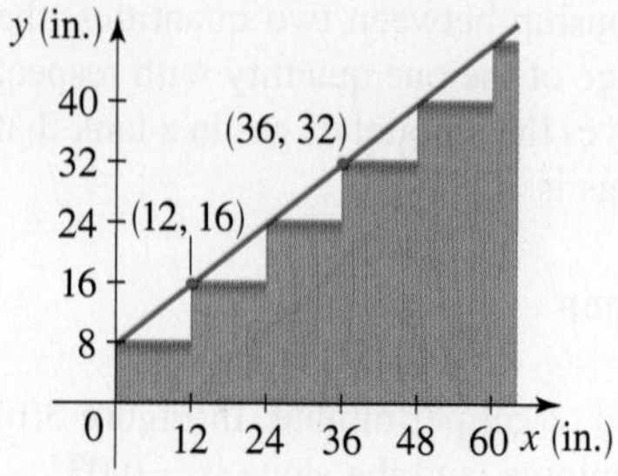

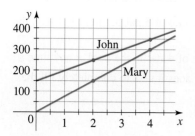

FIGURE 4 Slope of a staircase

EXAMPLE 5 ■ Making a Linear Model from a Slope

In Figure 4 we have placed a staircase in a coordinate plane, with the origin at the bottom left corner. The red line in the figure is the edge of the trim board of the staircase.

(a) Find a linear function H that models the height of the trim board above the floor.

(b) If the space available to build a staircase is 11 ft wide, how high does the staircase reach?

SOLUTION

(a) We need to find a function

$$H(x) = ax + b$$

that models the red line in the figure. First we find the value of a, the slope of the line. From Figure 4 we see that two points on the line are $(12, 16)$ and $(36, 32)$, so the slope is

$$a = \frac{32 - 16}{36 - 12} = \frac{2}{3}$$

Another way to find the slope is to observe that each of the steps is 8 in. high (the rise) and 12 in. deep (the run), so the slope of the line is $\frac{8}{12} = \frac{2}{3}$. From Figure 4 we see that the y-intercept is 8, so $b = 8$. So the model we want is

$$H(x) = \tfrac{2}{3}x + 8$$

(b) Since 11 ft is 132 in., we need to evaluate the function H when x is 132. We have

$$H(132) = \tfrac{2}{3}(132) + 8 = 96$$

So the staircase reaches a height of 96 in., or 8 ft.

. Now Try Exercise 43 ■

EXAMPLE 6 ■ Making Linear Models Involving Speed

John and Mary are driving westward along I-76 at constant speeds. The graphs in Figure 5 show the distance y (in miles) that they have traveled from Philadelphia at time x (in hours), where $x = 0$ corresponds to noon. (Note that at noon John has already traveled 150 mi.)

(a) At what speeds are John and Mary traveling? Who is traveling faster, and how does this show up in the graph?

(b) Find functions that model the distances that John and Mary have traveled as functions of x.

(c) How far will John and Mary have traveled at 5:00 P.M.?

(d) For what time period is Mary behind John? Will Mary overtake John? If so, at what time?

FIGURE 5 John and Mary's trips

SOLUTION

(a) From the graph we see that John has traveled 250 mi at 2:00 P.M. and 350 mi at 4:00 P.M. The speed is the rate of change of distance with respect to time. So the speed is the slope of the graph. Therefore John's speed is

$$\frac{350 \text{ mi} - 250 \text{ mi}}{4 \text{ h} - 2 \text{ h}} = 50 \text{ mi/h} \qquad \text{John's speed}$$

Mary has traveled 150 mi at 2:00 P.M. and 300 mi at 4:00 P.M., so we calculate Mary's speed to be

$$\frac{300 \text{ mi} - 150 \text{ mi}}{4 \text{ h} - 2 \text{ h}} = 75 \text{ mi/h} \qquad \text{Mary's speed}$$

Mary is traveling faster than John. We can see this from the graph because Mary's line is steeper (has a greater slope) than John's line.

(b) Let $f(x)$ be the distance John has traveled at time x. Since the speed (average rate of change) is constant, it follows that f is a linear function. Thus we can write f in the form $f(x) = ax + b$. From part (a) we know that the slope a is 50, and from the graph we see that the y-intercept b is 150. Thus the distance that John has traveled at time x is modeled by the linear function

$$f(x) = 50x + 150 \qquad \text{Model for John's distance}$$

Similarly, Mary is traveling at 75 mi/h, and the y-intercept of her graph is 0. Thus the distance she has traveled at time x is modeled by the linear function

$$g(x) = 75x \qquad \text{Model for Mary's distance}$$

(c) Replacing x by 5 in the models that we obtained in part (b), we find that at 5:00 P.M. John has traveled $f(5) = 50(5) + 150 = 400$ mi and Mary has traveled $g(5) = 75(5) = 375$ mi.

(d) Mary overtakes John at the time when each has traveled the same distance, that is, at the time x when $f(x) = g(x)$. So we must solve the equation

$$50x + 150 = 75x \qquad \text{John's distance} = \text{Mary's distance}$$

Solving this equation, we get $x = 6$. So Mary overtakes John after 6 h, that is, at 6:00 P.M. We can confirm our solution graphically by drawing the graphs of f and g on a larger domain as shown in Figure 6. The graphs intersect when $x = 6$. From the graph we see that the graph of Mary's trip is below the graph of John's trip from $x = 0$ to $x = 6$, so Mary is behind John from noon until 6:00 P.M.

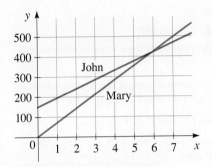

FIGURE 6 John and Mary's trips

✎. **Now Try Exercise 45**

2.5 EXERCISES

CONCEPTS

1. Let f be a function with constant rate of change. Then
   (a) f is a _____ function and f is of the form
   $f(x) = $ ____ $x + $ ____.
   (b) The graph of f is a _____.

2. Let f be the linear function $f(x) = -5x + 7$.
   (a) The rate of change of f is _____.
   (b) The graph of f is a _____ with slope _____ and y-intercept _____.

3–4 ■ A swimming pool is being filled. The graph shows the number of gallons y in the pool after x minutes.

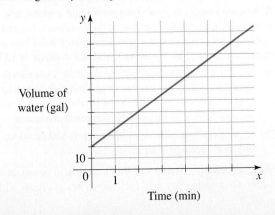

3. What is the slope of the graph?

4. At what rate is the pool being filled?

5. If a linear function has positive rate of change, does its graph slope upward or downward?

6. Is $f(x) = 3$ a linear function? If so, what are the slope and the rate of change?

SKILLS

7–14 ■ **Identifying Linear Functions** Determine whether the given function is linear. If the function is linear, express the function in the form $f(x) = ax + b$.

✎. **7.** $f(x) = 3 + \frac{1}{3}x$ **8.** $f(x) = 2 - 4x$

    9. $f(x) = x(4 - x)$ **10.** $f(x) = \sqrt{x} + 1$

   11. $f(x) = \dfrac{x + 1}{5}$ **12.** $f(x) = \dfrac{2x - 3}{x}$

   13. $f(x) = (x + 1)^2$ **14.** $f(x) = \frac{1}{2}(3x - 1)$

15–18 ■ **Graphing Linear Functions** For the given linear function, make a table of values and sketch its graph. What is the slope of the graph?

✎. **15.** $f(x) = 2x - 5$ **16.** $g(x) = 4 - 2x$

   17. $r(t) = -\frac{2}{3}t + 2$ **18.** $h(t) = \frac{1}{2} - \frac{3}{4}t$

19–26 ■ Slope and Rate of Change A linear function is given. **(a)** Sketch the graph. **(b)** Find the slope of the graph. **(c)** Find the rate of change of the function.

 19. $f(x) = 2x - 6$

20. $g(z) = -3z - 9$

21. $h(t) = -0.5t - 2$

22. $s(w) = -0.2w - 6$

23. $v(t) = -\frac{10}{3}t - 20$

24. $A(r) = -\frac{2}{3}r - 1$

25. $f(t) = -\frac{3}{2}t + 2$

26. $g(x) = \frac{5}{4}x - 10$

27–30 ■ Linear Functions Given Verbally A verbal description of a linear function f is given. Express the function f in the form $f(x) = ax + b$.

27. The linear function f has rate of change 3 and initial value -1.

28. The linear function g has rate of change -12 and initial value 100.

29. The graph of the linear function h has slope $\frac{1}{2}$ and y-intercept 3.

30. The graph of the linear function k has slope $-\frac{4}{5}$ and y-intercept -2.

31–32 ■ Linear Functions Given Numerically A table of values for a linear function f is given. **(a)** Find the rate of change of f. **(b)** Express f in the form $f(x) = ax + b$

31.

x	$f(x)$
0	7
2	10
4	13
6	16
8	19

32.

x	$f(x)$
-3	11
0	2
2	-4
5	-13
7	-19

33–36 ■ Linear Functions Given Graphically The graph of a linear function f is given. **(a)** Find the rate of change of f. **(b)** Express f in the form $f(x) = ax + b$.

33.

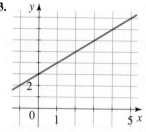

34.

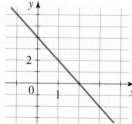

35.

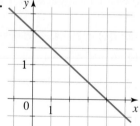

36.

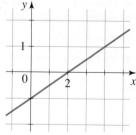

SKILLS Plus

37. Families of Linear Functions Graph $f(x) = ax$ for $a = \frac{1}{2}$, $a = 1$, and $a = 2$, all on the same set of axes. How does

increasing the value of a affect the graph of f? What about the rate of change of f?

38. Families of Linear Functions Graph $f(x) = x + b$ for $b = \frac{1}{2}$, $b = 1$, and $b = 2$, all on the same set of axes. How does increasing the value of b affect the graph of f? What about the rate of change of f?

APPLICATIONS

39. Landfill The amount of trash in a county landfill is modeled by the function

$$T(x) = 150x + 32,000$$

where x is the number of years since 1996 and $T(x)$ is measured in thousands of tons.

(a) Sketch a graph of T.

(b) What is the slope of the graph?

(c) At what rate is the amount of trash in the landfill increasing per year?

40. Copper Mining The amount of copper ore produced from a copper mine in Arizona is modeled by the function

$$f(x) = 200 + 32x$$

where x is the number of years since 2005 and $f(x)$ is measured in thousands of tons.

(a) Sketch a graph of f.

(b) What is the slope of the graph?

(c) At what rate is the amount of ore produced changing?

41. Weather Balloon Weather balloons are filled with hydrogen and released at various sites to measure and transmit data about conditions such as air pressure and temperature. A weather balloon is filled with hydrogen at the rate of 0.5 ft³/s. Initially, the balloon contains 2 ft³ of hydrogen.

(a) Find a linear function V that models the volume of hydrogen in the balloon at any time t.

(b) If the balloon has a capacity of 15 ft³, how long does it take to completely fill the balloon?

42. Filling a Pond A large koi pond is filled from a garden hose at the rate of 10 gal/min. Initially, the pond contains 300 gal of water.

(a) Find a linear function V that models the volume of water in the pond at any time t.

(b) If the pond has a capacity of 1300 gal, how long does it take to completely fill the pond?

43. Wheelchair Ramp A local diner must build a wheelchair ramp to provide handicap access to the restaurant. Federal building codes require that a wheelchair ramp must have a maximum rise of 1 in. for every horizontal distance of 12 in.

(a) What is the maximum allowable slope for a wheelchair ramp? Assuming that the ramp has maximum rise, find a linear function H that models the height of the ramp above the ground as a function of the horizontal distance x.

(b) If the space available to build a ramp is 150 in. wide, how high does the ramp reach?

44. Mountain Biking Meilin and Brianna are avid mountain bikers. On a spring day they cycle down straight roads with steep grades. The graphs give a representation of the elevation of the road on which each of them cycles. Find the grade of each road.

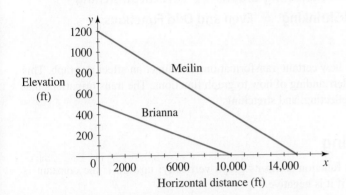

45. **Commute to Work** Jade and her roommate Jari commute to work each morning, traveling west on I-10. One morning Jade left for work at 6:50 A.M., but Jari left 10 minutes later. Both drove at a constant speed. The following graphs show the distance (in miles) each of them has traveled on I-10 at time t (in minutes), where $t = 0$ is 7:00 A.M.

(a) Use the graph to decide which of them is traveling faster.

(b) Find the speed (in mi/h) at which each of them is driving.

(c) Find linear functions f and g that model the distances that Jade and Jari travel as functions of t (in minutes).

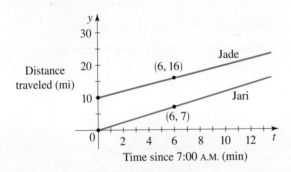

46. **Distance, Speed, and Time** Jacqueline leaves Detroit at 2:00 P.M. and drives at a constant speed, traveling west on I-90. She passes Ann Arbor, 40 mi from Detroit, at 2:50 P.M.

(a) Find a linear function d that models the distance (in mi) she has traveled after t min.

(b) Draw a graph of d. What is the slope of this line?

(c) At what speed (in mi/h) is Jacqueline traveling?

47. **Grade of Road** West of Albuquerque, New Mexico, Route 40 eastbound is straight and makes a steep descent toward the city. The highway has a 6% grade, which means that its slope is $-\frac{6}{100}$. Driving on this road, you notice from elevation signs that you have descended a distance of 1000 ft. What is the change in your horizontal distance in miles?

48. **Sedimentation** Devils Lake, North Dakota, has a layer of sedimentation at the bottom of the lake that increases every

year. The depth of the sediment layer is modeled by the function

$$D(x) = 20 + 0.24x$$

where x is the number of years since 1980 and $D(x)$ is measured in centimeters.

(a) Sketch a graph of D.

(b) What is the slope of the graph?

(c) At what rate (in cm) is the sediment layer increasing per year?

49. **Cost of Driving** The monthly cost of driving a car depends on the number of miles driven. Lynn found that in May her driving cost was $380 for 480 mi and in June her cost was $460 for 800 mi. Assume that there is a linear relationship between the monthly cost C of driving a car and the distance x driven.

(a) Find a linear function C that models the cost of driving x miles per month.

(b) Draw a graph of C. What is the slope of this line?

(c) At what rate does Lynn's cost increase for every additional mile she drives?

50. **Manufacturing Cost** The manager of a furniture factory finds that it costs $2200 to produce 100 chairs in one day and $4800 to produce 300 chairs in one day.

(a) Assuming that the relationship between cost and the number of chairs produced is linear, find a linear function C that models the cost of producing x chairs in one day.

(b) Draw a graph of C. What is the slope of this line?

(c) At what rate does the factory's cost increase for every additional chair produced?

DISCUSS ■ **DISCOVER** ■ **PROVE** ■ **WRITE**

51. **PROVE: Linear Functions Have Constant Rate of Change**
Suppose that $f(x) = ax + b$ is a linear function.

(a) Use the definition of the average rate of change of a function to calculate the average rate of change of f between any two real numbers x_1 and x_2.

(b) Use your calculation in part (a) to show that the average rate of change of f is the same as the slope a.

52. **PROVE: Functions with Constant Rate of Change Are Linear**
Suppose that the function f has the same average rate of change c between any two points.

(a) Find the average rate of change of f between the points a and x to show that

$$c = \frac{f(x) - f(a)}{x - a}$$

(b) Rearrange the equation in part (a) to show that

$$f(x) = cx + (f(a) - ca)$$

How does this show that f is a linear function? What is the slope, and what is the y-intercept?

2.6　TRANSFORMATIONS OF FUNCTIONS

■ Vertical Shifting ■ Horizontal Shifting ■ Reflecting Graphs ■ Vertical Stretching and Shrinking ■ Horizontal Stretching and Shrinking ■ Even and Odd Functions

In this section we study how certain transformations of a function affect its graph. This will give us a better understanding of how to graph functions. The transformations that we study are shifting, reflecting, and stretching.

■ Vertical Shifting

Adding a constant to a function shifts its graph vertically: upward if the constant is positive and downward if it is negative.

In general, suppose we know the graph of $y = f(x)$. How do we obtain from it the graphs of

Recall that the graph of the function f is the same as the graph of the equation $y = f(x)$.

$$y = f(x) + c \quad \text{and} \quad y = f(x) - c \quad (c > 0)$$

The y-coordinate of each point on the graph of $y = f(x) + c$ is c units above the y-coordinate of the corresponding point on the graph of $y = f(x)$. So we obtain the graph of $y = f(x) + c$ simply by shifting the graph of $y = f(x)$ upward c units. Similarly, we obtain the graph of $y = f(x) - c$ by shifting the graph of $y = f(x)$ downward c units.

VERTICAL SHIFTS OF GRAPHS

Suppose $c > 0$.

To graph $y = f(x) + c$, shift the graph of $y = f(x)$ upward c units.

To graph $y = f(x) - c$, shift the graph of $y = f(x)$ downward c units.

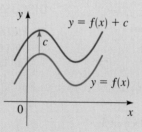　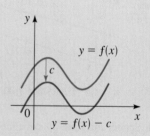

EXAMPLE 1 ■ Vertical Shifts of Graphs

Use the graph of $f(x) = x^2$ to sketch the graph of each function.

(a) $g(x) = x^2 + 3$ **(b)** $h(x) = x^2 - 2$

SOLUTION The function $f(x) = x^2$ was graphed in Example 1(a), Section 2.2. It is sketched again in Figure 1.

(a) Observe that

$$g(x) = x^2 + 3 = f(x) + 3$$

So the y-coordinate of each point on the graph of g is 3 units above the corresponding point on the graph of f. This means that to graph g, we shift the graph of f upward 3 units, as in Figure 1.

(b) Similarly, to graph h we shift the graph of f downward 2 units, as shown in Figure 1.

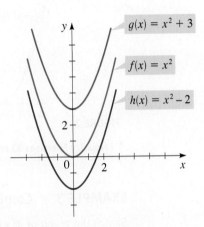

FIGURE 1

. Now Try Exercises 29 and 31   ■

■ Horizontal Shifting

Suppose that we know the graph of $y = f(x)$. How do we use it to obtain the graphs of

$$y = f(x + c) \quad \text{and} \quad y = f(x - c) \quad (c > 0)$$

The value of $f(x - c)$ at x is the same as the value of $f(x)$ at $x - c$. Since $x - c$ is c units to the left of x, it follows that the graph of $y = f(x - c)$ is just the graph of $y = f(x)$ shifted to the right c units. Similar reasoning shows that the graph of $y = f(x + c)$ is the graph of $y = f(x)$ shifted to the left c units. The following box summarizes these facts.

HORIZONTAL SHIFTS OF GRAPHS

Suppose $c > 0$.

To graph $y = f(x - c)$, shift the graph of $y = f(x)$ to the right c units.
To graph $y = f(x + c)$, shift the graph of $y = f(x)$ to the left c units.

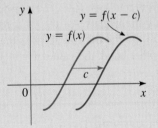   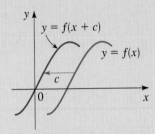

EXAMPLE 2 ■ Horizontal Shifts of Graphs

Use the graph of $f(x) = x^2$ to sketch the graph of each function.

(a) $g(x) = (x + 4)^2$ (b) $h(x) = (x - 2)^2$

SOLUTION

(a) To graph g, we shift the graph of f to the left 4 units.

(b) To graph h, we shift the graph of f to the right 2 units.

The graphs of g and h are sketched in Figure 2.

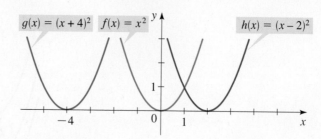

$g(x) = (x + 4)^2$ $f(x) = x^2$ $h(x) = (x - 2)^2$

FIGURE 2

✎ Now Try Exercises 33 and 35

EXAMPLE 3 ■ Combining Horizontal and Vertical Shifts

Sketch the graph of $f(x) = \sqrt{x - 3} + 4$.

SOLUTION   We start with the graph of $y = \sqrt{x}$ (Example 1(c), Section 2.2) and shift it to the right 3 units to obtain the graph of $y = \sqrt{x - 3}$. Then we shift the resulting graph upward 4 units to obtain the graph of $f(x) = \sqrt{x - 3} + 4$ shown in Figure 3.

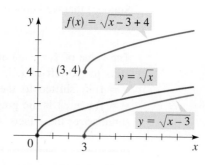

$f(x) = \sqrt{x - 3} + 4$

$(3, 4)$

$y = \sqrt{x}$

$y = \sqrt{x - 3}$

FIGURE 3

✎ Now Try Exercise 45

■ Reflecting Graphs

Suppose we know the graph of $y = f(x)$. How do we use it to obtain the graphs of $y = -f(x)$ and $y = f(-x)$? The y-coordinate of each point on the graph of $y = -f(x)$ is simply the negative of the y-coordinate of the corresponding point on the graph of $y = f(x)$. So the desired graph is the reflection of the graph of $y = f(x)$ in the x-axis. On the other hand, the value of $y = f(-x)$ at x is the same as the value of $y = f(x)$ at

---

DISCOVERY PROJECT

Transformation Stories

If a real-world situation, or "story," is modeled by a function, how does transforming the function change the story? For example, if the distance traveled on a road trip is modeled by a function, then how does shifting or stretching the function change the story of the trip? How does changing the story of the trip transform the function that models the trip? In this project we explore some real-world stories and transformations of these stories. You can find the project at **www.stewartmath.com**.

$-x$, so the desired graph here is the reflection of the graph of $y = f(x)$ in the y-axis. The following box summarizes these observations.

REFLECTING GRAPHS

To graph $y = -f(x)$, reflect the graph of $y = f(x)$ in the x-axis.

To graph $y = f(-x)$, reflect the graph of $y = f(x)$ in the y-axis.

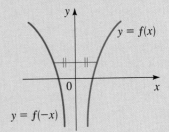

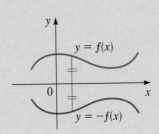

EXAMPLE 4 ■ Reflecting Graphs

Sketch the graph of each function.

(a) $f(x) = -x^2$ **(b)** $g(x) = \sqrt{-x}$

SOLUTION

(a) We start with the graph of $y = x^2$. The graph of $f(x) = -x^2$ is the graph of $y = x^2$ reflected in the x-axis (see Figure 4).

(b) We start with the graph of $y = \sqrt{x}$ (Example 1(c) in Section 2.2). The graph of $g(x) = \sqrt{-x}$ is the graph of $y = \sqrt{x}$ reflected in the y-axis (see Figure 5). Note that the domain of the function $g(x) = \sqrt{-x}$ is $\{x \mid x \le 0\}$.

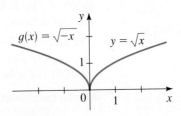

FIGURE 5

FIGURE 4

✎ Now Try Exercises 37 and 39 ■

RENÉ DESCARTES (1596–1650) was born in the town of La Haye in southern France. From an early age Descartes liked mathematics because of "the certainty of its results and the clarity of its reasoning." He believed that to arrive at truth, one must begin by doubting everything, including one's own existence; this led him to formulate perhaps the best-known sentence in all of philosophy: "I think, therefore I am." In his book *Discourse on Method* he described what is now called the Cartesian plane. This idea of combining algebra and geometry enabled mathematicians for the first time to graph functions and thus "see" the equations they were studying. The philosopher John Stuart Mill called this invention "the greatest single step ever made in the progress of the exact sciences." Descartes liked to get up late and spend the morning in bed thinking and writing. He invented the coordinate plane while lying in bed watching a fly crawl on the ceiling, reasoning that he could describe the exact location of the fly by knowing its distance from two perpendicular walls. In 1649 Descartes became the tutor of Queen Christina of Sweden. She liked her lessons at 5 o'clock in the morning, when, she said, her mind was sharpest. However, the change from his usual habits and the ice-cold library where they studied proved too much for Descartes. In February 1650, after just two months of this, he caught pneumonia and died.

■ Vertical Stretching and Shrinking

Suppose we know the graph of $y = f(x)$. How do we use it to obtain the graph of $y = cf(x)$? The y-coordinate of $y = cf(x)$ at x is the same as the corresponding y-coordinate of $y = f(x)$ multiplied by c. Multiplying the y-coordinates by c has the effect of vertically stretching or shrinking the graph by a factor of c (if $c > 0$).

VERTICAL STRETCHING AND SHRINKING OF GRAPHS

To graph $y = cf(x)$:

If $c > 1$, stretch the graph of $y = f(x)$ vertically by a factor of c.

If $0 < c < 1$, shrink the graph of $y = f(x)$ vertically by a factor of c.

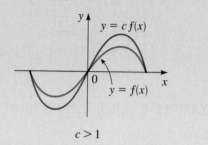
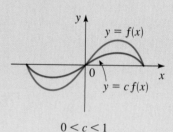

$$c > 1 \qquad\qquad 0 < c < 1$$

EXAMPLE 5 ■ Vertical Stretching and Shrinking of Graphs

Use the graph of $f(x) = x^2$ to sketch the graph of each function.

(a) $g(x) = 3x^2$ **(b)** $h(x) = \frac{1}{3}x^2$

SOLUTION

(a) The graph of g is obtained by multiplying the y-coordinate of each point on the graph of f by 3. That is, to obtain the graph of g, we stretch the graph of f vertically by a factor of 3. The result is the narrowest parabola in Figure 6.

(b) The graph of h is obtained by multiplying the y-coordinate of each point on the graph of f by $\frac{1}{3}$. That is, to obtain the graph of h, we shrink the graph of f vertically by a factor of $\frac{1}{3}$. The result is the widest parabola in Figure 6.

✎ **Now Try Exercises 41 and 43**

■

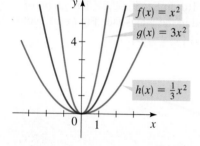

FIGURE 6

We illustrate the effect of combining shifts, reflections, and stretching in the following example.

EXAMPLE 6 ■ Combining Shifting, Stretching, and Reflecting

Sketch the graph of the function $f(x) = 1 - 2(x - 3)^2$.

SOLUTION   Starting with the graph of $y = x^2$, we first shift to the right 3 units to get the graph of $y = (x - 3)^2$. Then we reflect in the x-axis and stretch by a factor of 2 to get the graph of $y = -2(x - 3)^2$. Finally, we shift upward 1 unit to get the graph of $f(x) = 1 - 2(x - 3)^2$ shown in Figure 7.

Note that the shifts and stretches follow the normal order of operations when evaluating the function. In particular, the upward shift must be performed *last*.

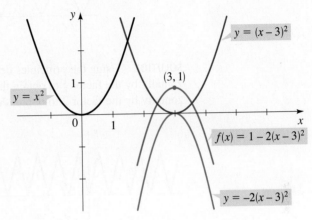

FIGURE 7

➤ **Now Try Exercise 47**

■ Horizontal Stretching and Shrinking

Now we consider horizontal shrinking and stretching of graphs. If we know the graph of $y = f(x)$, then how is the graph of $y = f(cx)$ related to it? The y-coordinate of $y = f(cx)$ at x is the same as the y-coordinate of $y = f(x)$ at cx. Thus the x-coordinates in the graph of $y = f(x)$ correspond to the x-coordinates in the graph of $y = f(cx)$ multiplied by c. Looking at this the other way around, we see that the x-coordinates in the graph of $y = f(cx)$ are the x-coordinates in the graph of $y = f(x)$ multiplied by $1/c$. In other words, to change the graph of $y = f(x)$ to the graph of $y = f(cx)$, we must shrink (or stretch) the graph horizontally by a factor of $1/c$ (if $c > 0$), as summarized in the following box.

HORIZONTAL SHRINKING AND STRETCHING OF GRAPHS

To graph $y = f(cx)$:

If $c > 1$, shrink the graph of $y = f(x)$ horizontally by a factor of $1/c$.

If $0 < c < 1$, stretch the graph of $y = f(x)$ horizontally by a factor of $1/c$.

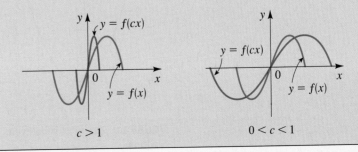

EXAMPLE 7 ■ Horizontal Stretching and Shrinking of Graphs

The graph of $y = f(x)$ is shown in Figure 8. Sketch the graph of each function.

(a) $y = f(2x)$ **(b)** $y = f(\frac{1}{2}x)$

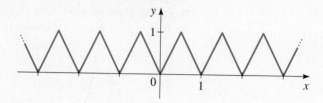

FIGURE 8 $y = f(x)$

SOLUTION Using the principles described on page 239, we **(a)** *shrink* the graph horizontally by the factor $\frac{1}{2}$ to obtain the graph in Figure 9, and **(b)** *stretch* the graph horizontally by the factor 2 to obtain the graph in Figure 10.

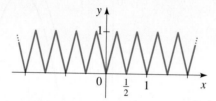

FIGURE 9 $y = f(2x)$

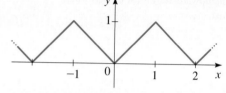

FIGURE 10 $y = f(\frac{1}{2}x)$

✎ **Now Try Exercise 71**

■ Even and Odd Functions

If a function f satisfies $f(-x) = f(x)$ for every number x in its domain, then f is called an **even function**. For instance, the function $f(x) = x^2$ is even because

$$f(-x) = (-x)^2 = (-1)^2 x^2 = x^2 = f(x)$$

The graph of an even function is symmetric with respect to the y-axis (see Figure 11). This means that if we have plotted the graph of f for $x \geq 0$, then we can obtain the entire graph simply by reflecting this portion in the y-axis.

If f satisfies $f(-x) = -f(x)$ for every number x in its domain, then f is called an **odd function**. For example, the function $f(x) = x^3$ is odd because

$$f(-x) = (-x)^3 = (-1)^3 x^3 = -x^3 = -f(x)$$

The graph of an odd function is symmetric about the origin (see Figure 12). If we have plotted the graph of f for $x \geq 0$, then we can obtain the entire graph by rotating this portion through 180° about the origin. (This is equivalent to reflecting first in the x-axis and then in the y-axis.)

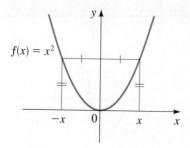

FIGURE 11 $f(x) = x^2$ is an even function.

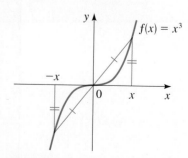

FIGURE 12 $f(x) = x^3$ is an odd function.

SONYA KOVALEVSKY (1850–1891) is considered the most important woman mathematician of the 19th century. She was born in Moscow to an aristocratic family. While a child, she was exposed to the principles of calculus in a very unusual fashion: Her bedroom was temporarily wallpapered with the pages of a calculus book. She later wrote that she "spent many hours in front of that wall, trying to understand it." Since Russian law forbade women from studying in universities, she entered a marriage of convenience, which allowed her to travel to Germany and obtain a doctorate in mathematics from the University of Göttingen. She eventually was awarded a full professorship at the University of Stockholm, where she taught for eight years before dying in an influenza epidemic at the age of 41. Her research was instrumental in helping to put the ideas and applications of functions and calculus on a sound and logical foundation. She received many accolades and prizes for her research work.

EVEN AND ODD FUNCTIONS

Let f be a function.

f is **even** if $f(-x) = f(x)$ for all x in the domain of f.

f is **odd** if $f(-x) = -f(x)$ for all x in the domain of f.

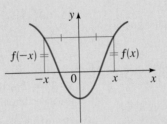

The graph of an even function is symmetric with respect to the y-axis.

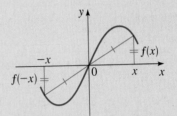

The graph of an odd function is symmetric with respect to the origin.

EXAMPLE 8 ■ Even and Odd Functions

Determine whether the functions are even, odd, or neither even nor odd.

(a) $f(x) = x^5 + x$

(b) $g(x) = 1 - x^4$

(c) $h(x) = 2x - x^2$

SOLUTION

(a) $f(-x) = (-x)^5 + (-x)$
$$= -x^5 - x = -(x^5 + x)$$
$$= -f(x)$$

Therefore f is an odd function.

(b) $g(-x) = 1 - (-x)^4 = 1 - x^4 = g(x)$

So g is even.

(c) $h(-x) = 2(-x) - (-x)^2 = -2x - x^2$

Since $h(-x) \neq h(x)$ and $h(-x) \neq -h(x)$, we conclude that h is neither even nor odd.

Now Try Exercises 83, 85, and 87

The graphs of the functions in Example 8 are shown in Figure 13. The graph of f is symmetric about the origin, and the graph of g is symmetric about the y-axis. The graph of h is not symmetric about either the y-axis or the origin.

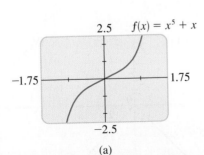

(a)

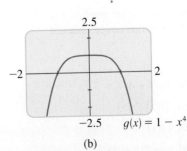

(b)

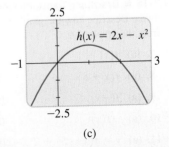

(c)

FIGURE 13

2.6 EXERCISES

CONCEPTS

1–2 ■ Fill in the blank with the appropriate direction (left, right, up, or down).

1. (a) The graph of $y = f(x) + 3$ is obtained from the graph of $y = f(x)$ by shifting _____ 3 units.

    (b) The graph of $y = f(x + 3)$ is obtained from the graph of $y = f(x)$ by shifting _____ 3 units.

2. (a) The graph of $y = f(x) - 3$ is obtained from the graph of $y = f(x)$ by shifting _____ 3 units.

    (b) The graph of $y = f(x - 3)$ is obtained from the graph of $y = f(x)$ by shifting _____ 3 units.

3. Fill in the blank with the appropriate axis (x-axis or y-axis).

    (a) The graph of $y = -f(x)$ is obtained from the graph of $y = f(x)$ by reflecting in the _____.

    (b) The graph of $y = f(-x)$ is obtained from the graph of $y = f(x)$ by reflecting in the _____.

4. A graph of a function f is given. Match each equation with one of the graphs labeled I–IV.

    (a) $f(x) + 2$ **(b)** $f(x + 3)$

    (c) $f(x - 2)$ **(d)** $f(x) - 4$

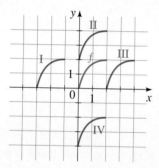

5. If a function f is an even function, then what type of symmetry does the graph of f have?

6. If a function f is an odd function, then what type of symmetry does the graph of f have?

SKILLS

7–18 ■ **Describing Transformations** Suppose the graph of f is given. Describe how the graph of each function can be obtained from the graph of f.

7. (a) $f(x) - 1$ **(b)** $f(x - 2)$

8. (a) $f(x + 5)$ **(b)** $f(x) + 4$

9. (a) $f(-x)$ **(b)** $3f(x)$

10. (a) $-f(x)$ **(b)** $\frac{1}{3}f(x)$

11. (a) $y = f(x - 5) + 2$ **(b)** $y = f(x + 1) - 1$

12. (a) $y = f(x + 3) + 2$ **(b)** $y = f(x - 7) - 3$

13. (a) $y = -f(x) + 5$ **(b)** $y = 3f(x) - 5$

14. (a) $1 - f(-x)$ **(b)** $2 - \frac{1}{5}f(x)$

15. (a) $2f(x + 5) - 1$ **(b)** $\frac{1}{4}f(x - 3) + 5$

16. (a) $\frac{1}{3}f(x - 2) + 5$ **(b)** $4f(x + 1) + 3$

17. (a) $y = f(4x)$ **(b)** $y = f(\frac{1}{4}x)$

18. (a) $y = f(2x) - 1$ **(b)** $y = 2f(\frac{1}{2}x)$

19–22 ■ **Describing Transformations** Explain how the graph of g is obtained from the graph of f.

19. (a) $f(x) = x^2$, $g(x) = (x + 2)^2$

    (b) $f(x) = x^2$, $g(x) = x^2 + 2$

20. (a) $f(x) = x^3$, $g(x) = (x - 4)^3$

    (b) $f(x) = x^3$, $g(x) = x^3 - 4$

21. (a) $f(x) = |x|$, $g(x) = |x + 2| - 2$

    (b) $f(x) = |x|$, $g(x) = |x - 2| + 2$

22. (a) $f(x) = \sqrt{x}$, $g(x) = -\sqrt{x} + 1$

    (b) $f(x) = \sqrt{x}$, $g(x) = \sqrt{-x} + 1$

23. Graphing Transformations Use the graph of $y = x^2$ in Figure 4 to graph the following.

    (a) $g(x) = x^2 + 1$ **(b)** $g(x) = (x - 1)^2$

    (c) $g(x) = -x^2$ **(d)** $g(x) = (x - 1)^2 + 3$

24. Graphing Transformations Use the graph of $y = \sqrt{x}$ in Figure 5 to graph the following.

    (a) $g(x) = \sqrt{x - 2}$ **(b)** $g(x) = \sqrt{x} + 1$

    (c) $g(x) = \sqrt{x + 2} + 2$ **(d)** $g(x) = -\sqrt{x} + 1$

25–28 ■ **Identifying Transformations** Match the graph with the function. (See the graph of $y = |x|$ on page 202.)

25. $y = |x + 1|$ **26.** $y = |x - 1|$

27. $y = |x| - 1$ **28.** $y = -|x|$

I

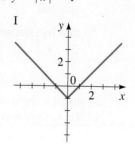

II

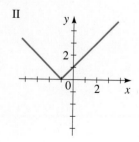

III

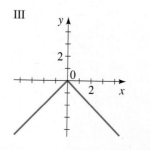

IV

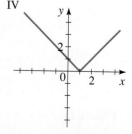

29–52 ■ Graphing Transformations Sketch the graph of the function, not by plotting points, but by starting with the graph of a standard function and applying transformations.

29. $f(x) = x^2 + 3$

30. $f(x) = x^2 - 4$

31. $f(x) = |x| - 1$

32. $f(x) = \sqrt{x} + 1$

33. $f(x) = (x - 5)^2$

34. $f(x) = (x + 1)^2$

35. $f(x) = |x + 2|$

36. $f(x) = \sqrt{x - 4}$

37. $f(x) = -x^3$

38. $f(x) = -|x|$

39. $y = \sqrt[4]{-x}$

40. $y = \sqrt[3]{-x}$

41. $y = \frac{1}{4}x^2$

42. $y = -5\sqrt{x}$

43. $y = 3|x|$

44. $y = \frac{1}{2}|x|$

45. $y = (x - 3)^2 + 5$

46. $y = \sqrt{x + 4} - 3$

47. $y = 3 - \frac{1}{2}(x - 1)^2$

48. $y = 2 - \sqrt{x + 1}$

49. $y = |x + 2| + 2$

50. $y = 2 - |x|$

51. $y = \frac{1}{2}\sqrt{x + 4} - 3$

52. $y = 3 - 2(x - 1)^2$

53–62 ■ Finding Equations for Transformations A function f is given, and the indicated transformations are applied to its graph (in the given order). Write an equation for the final transformed graph.

53. $f(x) = x^2$; shift downward 3 units

54. $f(x) = x^3$; shift upward 5 units

55. $f(x) = \sqrt{x}$; shift 2 units to the left

56. $f(x) = \sqrt[3]{x}$; shift 1 unit to the right

57. $f(x) = |x|$; shift 2 units to the left and shift downward 5 units

58. $f(x) = |x|$; reflect in the x-axis, shift 4 units to the right, and shift upward 3 units.

59. $f(x) = \sqrt[4]{x}$; reflect in the y-axis and shift upward 1 unit

60. $f(x) = x^2$; shift 2 units to the left and reflect in the x-axis

61. $f(x) = x^2$; stretch vertically by a factor of 2, shift downward 2 units, and shift 3 units to the right

62. $f(x) = |x|$; shrink vertically by a factor of $\frac{1}{2}$, shift to the left 1 unit, and shift upward 3 units

63–68 ■ Finding Formulas for Transformations The graphs of f and g are given. Find a formula for the function g.

63.
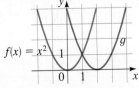
$f(x) = x^2$

64.
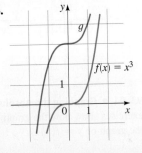
g
$f(x) = x^3$

65.
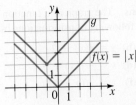
g
$f(x) = |x|$

66.
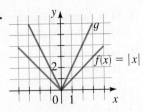
g
$f(x) = |x|$

67.
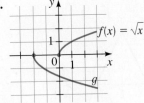
$f(x) = \sqrt{x}$
g

68.
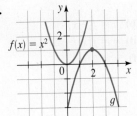
$f(x) = x^2$
g

69–70 ■ Identifying Transformations The graph of $y = f(x)$ is given. Match each equation with its graph.

69. (a) $y = f(x - 4)$ **(b)** $y = f(x) + 3$

(c) $y = 2f(x + 6)$ **(d)** $y = -f(2x)$

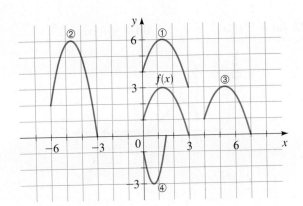

70. (a) $y = \frac{1}{3}f(x)$ **(b)** $y = -f(x + 4)$

(c) $y = f(x - 4) + 3$ **(d)** $y = f(-x)$

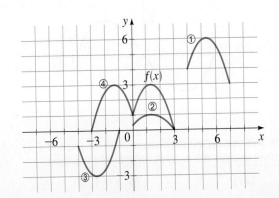

71–74 ■ Graphing Transformations The graph of a function f is given. Sketch the graphs of the following transformations of f.

71. (a) $y = f(x - 2)$ (b) $y = f(x) - 2$
(c) $y = 2f(x)$ (d) $y = -f(x) + 3$
(e) $y = f(-x)$ (f) $y = \frac{1}{2}f(x - 1)$

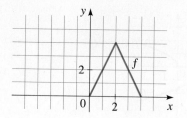

72. (a) $y = f(x + 1)$ (b) $y = f(-x)$
(c) $y = f(x - 2)$ (d) $y = f(x) - 2$
(e) $y = -f(x)$ (f) $y = 2f(x)$

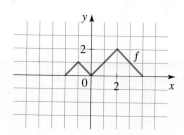

73. (a) $y = f(2x)$ (b) $y = f(\frac{1}{2}x)$

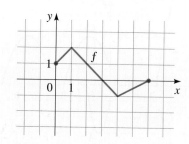

74. (a) $y = f(3x)$ (b) $y = f(\frac{1}{3}x)$

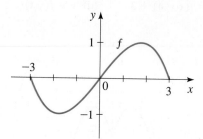

75–76 ■ Graphing Transformations Use the graph of $f(x) = [\![x]\!]$ described on page 199 to graph the indicated function.

75. $y = [\![2x]\!]$ **76.** $y = [\![\frac{1}{4}x]\!]$

 77–80 ■ Graphing Transformations Graph the functions on the same screen using the given viewing rectangle. How is each graph related to the graph in part (a)?

77. Viewing rectangle $[-8, 8]$ by $[-2, 8]$
(a) $y = \sqrt[4]{x}$ (b) $y = \sqrt[4]{x + 5}$
(c) $y = 2\sqrt[4]{x + 5}$ (d) $y = 4 + 2\sqrt[4]{x + 5}$

78. Viewing rectangle $[-8, 8]$ by $[-6, 6]$
(a) $y = |x|$ (b) $y = -|x|$
(c) $y = -3|x|$ (d) $y = -3|x - 5|$

79. Viewing rectangle $[-4, 6]$ by $[-4, 4]$
(a) $y = x^6$ (b) $y = \frac{1}{3}x^6$
(c) $y = -\frac{1}{3}x^6$ (d) $y = -\frac{1}{3}(x - 4)^6$

80. Viewing rectangle $[-6, 6]$ by $[-4, 4]$
(a) $y = \dfrac{1}{\sqrt{x}}$ (b) $y = \dfrac{1}{\sqrt{x + 3}}$
(c) $y = \dfrac{1}{2\sqrt{x + 3}}$ (d) $y = \dfrac{1}{2\sqrt{x + 3}} - 3$

81–82 ■ Graphing Transformations If $f(x) = \sqrt{2x - x^2}$, graph the following functions in the viewing rectangle $[-5, 5]$ by $[-4, 4]$. How is each graph related to the graph in part (a)?

81. (a) $y = f(x)$ (b) $y = f(2x)$ (c) $y = f(\frac{1}{2}x)$

82. (a) $y = f(x)$ (b) $y = f(-x)$
(c) $y = -f(-x)$ (d) $y = f(-2x)$
(e) $y = f(-\frac{1}{2}x)$

83–90 ■ Even and Odd Functions Determine whether the function f is even, odd, or neither. If f is even or odd, use symmetry to sketch its graph.

83. $f(x) = x^4$ **84.** $f(x) = x^3$

85. $f(x) = x^2 + x$ **86.** $f(x) = x^4 - 4x^2$

87. $f(x) = x^3 - x$ **88.** $f(x) = 3x^3 + 2x^2 + 1$

89. $f(x) = 1 - \sqrt[3]{x}$ **90.** $f(x) = x + \dfrac{1}{x}$

SKILLS Plus

91–92 ■ Graphing Even and Odd Functions The graph of a function defined for $x \geq 0$ is given. Complete the graph for $x < 0$ to make (a) an even function and (b) an odd function.

91.

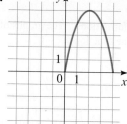

92.

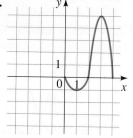

93–94 ■ Graphing the Absolute Value of a Function These exercises show how the graph of $y = |f(x)|$ is obtained from the graph of $y = f(x)$.

93. The graphs of $f(x) = x^2 - 4$ and $g(x) = |x^2 - 4|$ are shown. Explain how the graph of g is obtained from the graph of f.

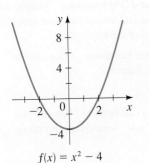

$f(x) = x^2 - 4$

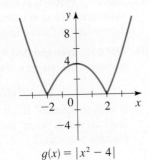

$g(x) = |x^2 - 4|$

94. The graph of $f(x) = x^4 - 4x^2$ is shown. Use this graph to sketch the graph of $g(x) = |x^4 - 4x^2|$.

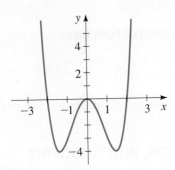

95–96 ■ **Graphing the Absolute Value of a Function** Sketch the graph of each function.

95. (a) $f(x) = 4x - x^2$ (b) $g(x) = |4x - x^2|$

96. (a) $f(x) = x^3$ (b) $g(x) = |x^3|$

APPLICATIONS

97. Bungee Jumping Luisa goes bungee jumping from a 500-ft-high bridge. The graph shows Luisa's height $h(t)$ (in ft) after t seconds.

(a) Describe in words what the graph indicates about Luisa's bungee jump.

(b) Suppose Luisa goes bungee jumping from a 400-ft-high bridge. Sketch a new graph that shows Luisa's height $H(t)$ after t seconds.

(c) What transformation must be performed on the function h to obtain the function H? Express the function H in terms of h.

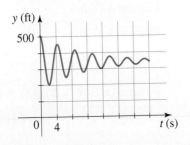

98. Swimming Laps Miyuki practices swimming laps with her team. The function $y = f(t)$ graphed below gives her distance (in meters) from the starting edge of the pool t seconds after she starts her laps.

(a) Describe in words Miyuki's swim practice. What is her average speed for the first 30 s?

(b) Graph the function $y = 1.2f(t)$. How is the graph of the new function related to the graph of the original function?

(c) What is Miyuki's new average speed for the first 30 s?

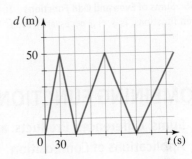

99. Field Trip A class of fourth graders walks to a park on a field trip. The function $y = f(t)$ graphed below gives their distance from school (in ft) t minutes after they left school.

(a) What is the average speed going to the park? How long was the class at the park? How far away is the park?

(b) Graph the function $y = 0.5f(t)$. How is the graph of the new function related to the graph of the original function? What is the average speed going to the new park? How far away is the new park?

(c) Graph the function $y = f(t - 10)$. How is the graph of the new function related to the graph of the original function? How does the field trip descibed by this function differ from the original trip?

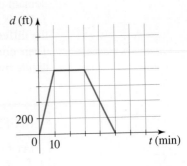

DISCUSS ■ **DISCOVER** ■ **PROVE** ■ **WRITE**

100–101 ■ **DISCUSS: Obtaining Transformations** Can the function g be obtained from f by transformations? If so, describe the transformations needed.

100. The functions f and g are described algebraically as follows:

$$f(x) = (x + 2)^2 \qquad g(x) = (x - 2)^2 + 5$$

101. The functions f and g are described graphically in the figure.

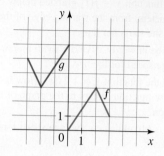

102. DISCUSS: Sums of Even and Odd Functions If f and g are both even functions, is $f + g$ necessarily even? If both are odd, is their sum necessarily odd? What can you say about the sum if one is odd and one is even? In each case, prove your answer.

103. DISCUSS: Products of Even and Odd Functions Answer the same questions as in Exercise 102, except this time consider the product of f and g instead of the sum.

104. DISCUSS: Even and Odd Power Functions What must be true about the integer n if the function

$$f(x) = x^n$$

is an even function? If it is an odd function? Why do you think the names "even" and "odd" were chosen for these function properties?

2.7 COMBINING FUNCTIONS

■ **Sums, Differences, Products, and Quotients**   ■ **Composition of Functions**
■ **Applications of Composition**

In this section we study different ways to combine functions to make new functions.

■ Sums, Differences, Products, and Quotients

The sum of f and g is defined by

$$(f + g)(x) = f(x) + g(x)$$

The name of the new function is "$f + g$." So this $+$ sign stands for the operation of addition of *functions*. The $+$ sign on the right side, however, stands for addition of the *numbers* $f(x)$ and $g(x)$.

Two functions f and g can be combined to form new functions $f + g$, $f - g$, fg, and f/g in a manner similar to the way we add, subtract, multiply, and divide real numbers. For example, we define the function $f + g$ by

$$(f + g)(x) = f(x) + g(x)$$

The new function $f + g$ is called the **sum** of the functions f and g; its value at x is $f(x) + g(x)$. Of course, the sum on the right-hand side makes sense only if both $f(x)$ and $g(x)$ are defined, that is, if x belongs to the domain of f and also to the domain of g. So if the domain of f is A and the domain of g is B, then the domain of $f + g$ is the intersection of these domains, that is, $A \cap B$. Similarly, we can define the **difference** $f - g$, the **product** fg, and the **quotient** f/g of the functions f and g. Their domains are $A \cap B$, but in the case of the quotient we must remember not to divide by 0.

ALGEBRA OF FUNCTIONS

Let f and g be functions with domains A and B. Then the functions $f + g$, $f - g$, fg, and f/g are defined as follows.

$$(f + g)(x) = f(x) + g(x) \qquad \text{Domain } A \cap B$$

$$(f - g)(x) = f(x) - g(x) \qquad \text{Domain } A \cap B$$

$$(fg)(x) = f(x)g(x) \qquad \text{Domain } A \cap B$$

$$\left(\frac{f}{g}\right)(x) = \frac{f(x)}{g(x)} \qquad \text{Domain } \{x \in A \cap B \mid g(x) \neq 0\}$$

EXAMPLE 1 ■ Combinations of Functions and Their Domains

Let $f(x) = \dfrac{1}{x-2}$ and $g(x) = \sqrt{x}$.

(a) Find the functions $f + g$, $f - g$, fg, and f/g and their domains.

(b) Find $(f + g)(4)$, $(f - g)(4)$, $(fg)(4)$, and $(f/g)(4)$.

SOLUTION

(a) The domain of f is $\{x \mid x \neq 2\}$, and the domain of g is $\{x \mid x \geq 0\}$. The intersection of the domains of f and g is

$$\{x \mid x \geq 0 \text{ and } x \neq 2\} = [0, 2) \cup (2, \infty)$$

Thus we have

$$(f + g)(x) = f(x) + g(x) = \frac{1}{x-2} + \sqrt{x} \qquad \text{Domain } \{x \mid x \geq 0 \text{ and } x \neq 2\}$$

$$(f - g)(x) = f(x) - g(x) = \frac{1}{x-2} - \sqrt{x} \qquad \text{Domain } \{x \mid x \geq 0 \text{ and } x \neq 2\}$$

$$(fg)(x) = f(x)g(x) = \frac{\sqrt{x}}{x-2} \qquad \text{Domain } \{x \mid x \geq 0 \text{ and } x \neq 2\}$$

$$\left(\frac{f}{g}\right)(x) = \frac{f(x)}{g(x)} = \frac{1}{(x-2)\sqrt{x}} \qquad \text{Domain } \{x \mid x > 0 \text{ and } x \neq 2\}$$

To divide fractions, invert the denominator and multiply:

$$\frac{1/(x-2)}{\sqrt{x}} = \frac{1/(x-2)}{\sqrt{x}/1}$$

$$= \frac{1}{x-2} \cdot \frac{1}{\sqrt{x}}$$

$$= \frac{1}{(x-2)\sqrt{x}}$$

Note that in the domain of f/g we exclude 0 because $g(0) = 0$.

(b) Each of these values exist because $x = 4$ is in the domain of each function:

$$(f + g)(4) = f(4) + g(4) = \frac{1}{4-2} + \sqrt{4} = \frac{5}{2}$$

$$(f - g)(4) = f(4) - g(4) = \frac{1}{4-2} - \sqrt{4} = -\frac{3}{2}$$

$$(fg)(4) = f(4)g(4) = \left(\frac{1}{4-2}\right)\sqrt{4} = 1$$

$$\left(\frac{f}{g}\right)(4) = \frac{f(4)}{g(4)} = \frac{1}{(4-2)\sqrt{4}} = \frac{1}{4}$$

✎ Now Try Exercise 9

■

© Mr. Green/Shutterstock.com

DISCOVERY PROJECT

Iteration and Chaos

The *iterates* of a function f at a point x are the numbers $f(x)$, $f(f(x))$, $f(f(f(x)))$, and so on. We examine iterates of the *logistic function*, which models the population of a species with limited potential for growth (such as lizards on an island or fish in a pond). Iterates of the model can help us to predict whether the population will eventually stabilize or whether it will fluctuate chaotically. You can find the project at **www.stewartmath.com**.

The graph of the function $f + g$ can be obtained from the graphs of f and g by **graphical addition**. This means that we add corresponding y-coordinates, as illustrated in the next example.

EXAMPLE 2 ■ Using Graphical Addition

The graphs of f and g are shown in Figure 1. Use graphical addition to graph the function $f + g$.

SOLUTION   We obtain the graph of $f + g$ by "graphically adding" the value of $f(x)$ to $g(x)$ as shown in Figure 2. This is implemented by copying the line segment PQ on top of PR to obtain the point S on the graph of $f + g$.

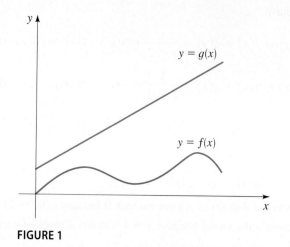

FIGURE 1

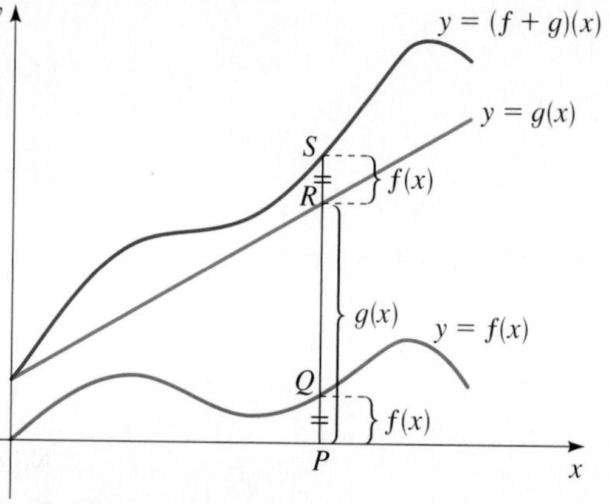

FIGURE 2 Graphical addition

✎ Now Try Exercise 21   ■

■ Composition of Functions

Now let's consider a very important way of combining two functions to get a new function. Suppose $f(x) = \sqrt{x}$ and $g(x) = x^2 + 1$. We may define a new function h as

$$h(x) = f(g(x)) = f(x^2 + 1) = \sqrt{x^2 + 1}$$

The function h is made up of the functions f and g in an interesting way: Given a number x, we first apply the function g to it, then apply f to the result. In this case, f is the rule "take the square root," g is the rule "square, then add 1," and h is the rule "square, then add 1, then take the square root." In other words, we get the rule h by applying the rule g and then the rule f. Figure 3 shows a machine diagram for h.

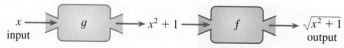

FIGURE 3 The h machine is composed of the g machine (first) and then the f machine.

In general, given any two functions f and g, we start with a number x in the domain of g and find its image $g(x)$. If this number $g(x)$ is in the domain of f, we can then calculate the value of $f(g(x))$. The result is a new function $h(x) = f(g(x))$ that is obtained by substituting g into f. It is called the *composition* (or *composite*) of f and g and is denoted by $f \circ g$ ("f composed with g").

COMPOSITION OF FUNCTIONS

Given two functions f and g, the **composite function** $f \circ g$ (also called the **composition** of f and g) is defined by

$$(f \circ g)(x) = f(g(x))$$

The domain of $f \circ g$ is the set of all x in the domain of g such that $g(x)$ is in the domain of f. In other words, $(f \circ g)(x)$ is defined whenever both $g(x)$ and $f(g(x))$ are defined. We can picture $f \circ g$ using an arrow diagram (Figure 4).

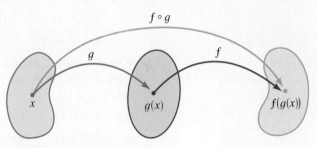

FIGURE 4 Arrow diagram for $f \circ g$

EXAMPLE 3 ■ Finding the Composition of Functions

Let $f(x) = x^2$ and $g(x) = x - 3$.

(a) Find the functions $f \circ g$ and $g \circ f$ and their domains.

(b) Find $(f \circ g)(5)$ and $(g \circ f)(7)$.

SOLUTION

In Example 3, f is the rule "square," and g is the rule "subtract 3." The function $f \circ g$ *first* subtracts 3 and *then* squares; the function $g \circ f$ *first* squares and *then* subtracts 3.

(a) We have

$$
\begin{aligned}
(f \circ g)(x) &= f(g(x)) && \text{Definition of } f \circ g \\
&= f(x - 3) && \text{Definition of } g \\
&= (x - 3)^2 && \text{Definition of } f
\end{aligned}
$$

and

$$
\begin{aligned}
(g \circ f)(x) &= g(f(x)) && \text{Definition of } g \circ f \\
&= g(x^2) && \text{Definition of } f \\
&= x^2 - 3 && \text{Definition of } g
\end{aligned}
$$

The domains of both $f \circ g$ and $g \circ f$ are $\mathbb{R}$.

(b) We have

$$(f \circ g)(5) = f(g(5)) = f(2) = 2^2 = 4$$

$$(g \circ f)(7) = g(f(7)) = g(49) = 49 - 3 = 46$$

Now Try Exercises 27 and 49

You can see from Example 3 that, in general, $f \circ g \neq g \circ f$. Remember that the notation $f \circ g$ means that the function g is applied first and then f is applied second.

The graphs of f and g of Example 4, as well as those of $f \circ g$, $g \circ f$, $f \circ f$, and $g \circ g$, are shown below. These graphs indicate that the operation of composition can produce functions that are quite different from the original functions.

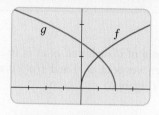

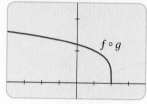

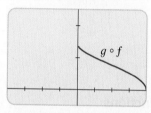

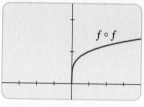

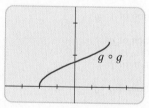

EXAMPLE 4 ■ Finding the Composition of Functions

If $f(x) = \sqrt{x}$ and $g(x) = \sqrt{2 - x}$, find the following functions and their domains.

(a) $f \circ g$ **(b)** $g \circ f$ **(c)** $f \circ f$ **(d)** $g \circ g$

SOLUTION

(a)
$$
\begin{aligned}
(f \circ g)(x) &= f(g(x)) &&\text{Definition of } f \circ g \\
&= f(\sqrt{2 - x}) &&\text{Definition of } g \\
&= \sqrt{\sqrt{2 - x}} &&\text{Definition of } f \\
&= \sqrt[4]{2 - x}
\end{aligned}
$$

The domain of $f \circ g$ is $\{x \mid 2 - x \geq 0\} = \{x \mid x \leq 2\} = (-\infty, 2]$.

(b)
$$
\begin{aligned}
(g \circ f)(x) &= g(f(x)) &&\text{Definition of } g \circ f \\
&= g(\sqrt{x}) &&\text{Definition of } f \\
&= \sqrt{2 - \sqrt{x}} &&\text{Definition of } g
\end{aligned}
$$

For $\sqrt{x}$ to be defined, we must have $x \geq 0$. For $\sqrt{2 - \sqrt{x}}$ to be defined, we must have $2 - \sqrt{x} \geq 0$, that is, $\sqrt{x} \leq 2$, or $x \leq 4$. Thus we have $0 \leq x \leq 4$, so the domain of $g \circ f$ is the closed interval $[0, 4]$.

(c)
$$
\begin{aligned}
(f \circ f)(x) &= f(f(x)) &&\text{Definition of } f \circ f \\
&= f(\sqrt{x}) &&\text{Definition of } f \\
&= \sqrt{\sqrt{x}} &&\text{Definition of } f \\
&= \sqrt[4]{x}
\end{aligned}
$$

The domain of $f \circ f$ is $[0, \infty)$.

(d)
$$
\begin{aligned}
(g \circ g)(x) &= g(g(x)) &&\text{Definition of } g \circ g \\
&= g(\sqrt{2 - x}) &&\text{Definition of } g \\
&= \sqrt{2 - \sqrt{2 - x}} &&\text{Definition of } g
\end{aligned}
$$

This expression is defined when both $2 - x \geq 0$ and $2 - \sqrt{2 - x} \geq 0$. The first inequality means $x \leq 2$, and the second is equivalent to $\sqrt{2 - x} \leq 2$, or $2 - x \leq 4$, or $x \geq -2$. Thus $-2 \leq x \leq 2$, so the domain of $g \circ g$ is $[-2, 2]$.

✎ **Now Try Exercise 55** ■

It is possible to take the composition of three or more functions. For instance, the composite function $f \circ g \circ h$ is found by first applying h, then g, and then f as follows:

$$(f \circ g \circ h)(x) = f(g(h(x)))$$

EXAMPLE 5 ■ A Composition of Three Functions

Find $f \circ g \circ h$ if $f(x) = x/(x + 1)$, $g(x) = x^{10}$, and $h(x) = x + 3$.

SOLUTION

$$
\begin{aligned}
(f \circ g \circ h)(x) &= f(g(h(x))) &&\text{Definition of } f \circ g \circ h \\
&= f(g(x + 3)) &&\text{Definition of } h \\
&= f((x + 3)^{10}) &&\text{Definition of } g \\
&= \frac{(x + 3)^{10}}{(x + 3)^{10} + 1} &&\text{Definition of } f
\end{aligned}
$$

✎ **Now Try Exercise 59** ■

So far, we have used composition to build complicated functions from simpler ones. But in calculus it is useful to be able to "decompose" a complicated function into simpler ones, as shown in the following example.

EXAMPLE 6 ■ Recognizing a Composition of Functions

Given $F(x) = \sqrt[4]{x + 9}$, find functions f and g such that $F = f \circ g$.

SOLUTION   Since the formula for F says to first add 9 and then take the fourth root, we let

$$g(x) = x + 9 \qquad \text{and} \qquad f(x) = \sqrt[4]{x}$$

Then

$$
\begin{aligned}
(f \circ g)(x) &= f(g(x)) & &\text{Definition of } f \circ g \\
&= f(x + 9) & &\text{Definition of } g \\
&= \sqrt[4]{x + 9} & &\text{Definition of } f \\
&= F(x)
\end{aligned}
$$

✎ **Now Try Exercise 63** ■

■ Applications of Composition

When working with functions that model real-world situations, we name the variables using letters that suggest the quantity being modeled. We may use t for time, d for distance, V for volume, and so on. For example, if air is being pumped into a balloon, then the radius R of the balloon is a function of the volume V of air pumped into the balloon, say, $R = f(V)$. Also the volume V is a function of the time t that the pump has been working, say, $V = g(t)$. It follows that the radius R is a function of the time t given by $R = f(g(t))$.

EXAMPLE 7 ■ An Application of Composition of Functions

A ship is traveling at 20 mi/h parallel to a straight shoreline. The ship is 5 mi from shore. It passes a lighthouse at noon.

(a) Express the distance s between the lighthouse and the ship as a function of d, the distance the ship has traveled since noon; that is, find f so that $s = f(d)$.

(b) Express d as a function of t, the time elapsed since noon; that is, find g so that $d = g(t)$.

(c) Find $f \circ g$. What does this function represent?

SOLUTION   We first draw a diagram as in Figure 5.

(a) We can relate the distances s and d by the Pythagorean Theorem. Thus s can be expressed as a function of d by

$$s = f(d) = \sqrt{25 + d^2}$$

(b) Since the ship is traveling at 20 mi/h, the distance d it has traveled is a function of t as follows:

$$d = g(t) = 20t$$

(c) We have

$$
\begin{aligned}
(f \circ g)(t) &= f(g(t)) & &\text{Definition of } f \circ g \\
&= f(20t) & &\text{Definition of } g \\
&= \sqrt{25 + (20t)^2} & &\text{Definition of } f
\end{aligned}
$$

The function $f \circ g$ gives the distance of the ship from the lighthouse as a function of time.

✎ **Now Try Exercise 77** ■

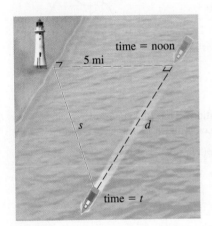

FIGURE 5

distance = rate × time

2.7 EXERCISES

CONCEPTS

1. From the graphs of f and g in the figure, we find

$(f + g)(2) =$ _____ $(f - g)(2) =$ _____

$(fg)(2) =$ _____ $\left(\dfrac{f}{g}\right)(2) =$ _____

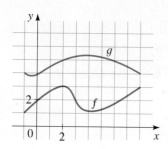

2. By definition, $(f \circ g)(x) =$ _____. So if $g(2) = 5$ and $f(5) = 12$, then $(f \circ g)(2) =$ _____.

3. If the rule of the function f is "add one" and the rule of the function g is "multiply by 2," then the rule of $f \circ g$ is

"_____,"

and the rule of $g \circ f$ is

"_____."

4. We can express the functions in Exercise 3 algebraically as

$f(x) =$ _____ $g(x) =$ _____

$(f \circ g)(x) =$ _____ $(g \circ f)(x) =$ _____

5–6 ■ Let f and g be functions.

5. (a) The function $(f + g)(x)$ is defined for all values of x that are in the domains of both _____ and _____.

(b) The function $(fg)(x)$ is defined for all values of x that are in the domains of both _____ and _____.

(c) The function $(f/g)(x)$ is defined for all values of x that are in the domains of both _____ and _____, and $g(x)$ is not equal to _____.

6. The composition $(f \circ g)(x)$ is defined for all values of x for which x is in the domain of _____ and $g(x)$ is in the domain of _____.

SKILLS

7–16 ■ **Combining Functions**   Find $f + g$, $f - g$, fg, and f/g and their domains.

7. $f(x) = x, \quad g(x) = 2x$

8. $f(x) = x, \quad g(x) = \sqrt{x}$

9. $f(x) = x^2 + x, \quad g(x) = x^2$

10. $f(x) = 3 - x^2, \quad g(x) = x^2 - 4$

11. $f(x) = 5 - x, \quad g(x) = x^2 - 3x$

12. $f(x) = x^2 + 2x, \quad g(x) = 3x^2 - 1$

13. $f(x) = \sqrt{25 - x^2}, \quad g(x) = \sqrt{x + 3}$

14. $f(x) = \sqrt{16 - x^2}, \quad g(x) = \sqrt{x^2 - 1}$

15. $f(x) = \dfrac{2}{x}, \quad g(x) = \dfrac{4}{x + 4}$

16. $f(x) = \dfrac{2}{x + 1}, \quad g(x) = \dfrac{x}{x + 1}$

17–20 ■ **Domain**   Find the domain of the function.

17. $f(x) = \sqrt{x} + \sqrt{3 - x}$

18. $f(x) = \sqrt{x + 4} - \dfrac{\sqrt{1 - x}}{x}$

19. $h(x) = (x - 3)^{-1/4}$

20. $k(x) = \dfrac{\sqrt{x + 3}}{x - 1}$

21–22 ■ **Graphical Addition**   Use graphical addition to sketch the graph of $f + g$.

21.

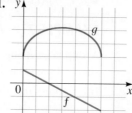

22.

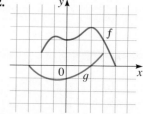

 23–26 ■ **Graphical Addition**   Draw the graphs of f, g, and $f + g$ on a common screen to illustrate graphical addition.

23. $f(x) = \sqrt{1 + x}, \quad g(x) = \sqrt{1 - x}$

24. $f(x) = x^2, \quad g(x) = \sqrt{x}$

25. $f(x) = x^2, \quad g(x) = \frac{1}{3}x^3$

26. $f(x) = \sqrt[4]{1 - x}, \quad g(x) = \sqrt{1 - \dfrac{x^2}{9}}$

27–32 ■ **Evaluating Composition of Functions**   Use $f(x) = 2x - 3$ and $g(x) = 4 - x^2$ to evaluate the expression.

27. (a) $f(g(0))$ (b) $g(f(0))$

28. (a) $f(f(2))$ (b) $g(g(3))$

29. (a) $(f \circ g)(-2)$ (b) $(g \circ f)(-2)$

30. (a) $(f \circ f)(-1)$ (b) $(g \circ g)(-1)$

31. (a) $(f \circ g)(x)$ (b) $(g \circ f)(x)$

32. (a) $(f \circ f)(x)$ (b) $(g \circ g)(x)$

33–38 ■ Composition Using a Graph   Use the given graphs of f and g to evaluate the expression.

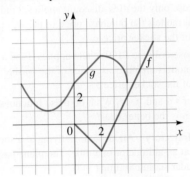

33. $f(g(2))$

34. $g(f(0))$

35. $(g \circ f)(4)$

36. $(f \circ g)(0)$

37. $(g \circ g)(-2)$

38. $(f \circ f)(4)$

39–46 ■ Composition Using a Table   Use the table to evaluate the expression.

x	1	2	3	4	5	6
$f(x)$	2	3	5	1	6	3
$g(x)$	3	5	6	2	1	4

39. $f(g(2))$

40. $g(f(2))$

41. $f(f(1))$

42. $g(g(2))$

43. $(f \circ g)(6)$

44. $(g \circ f)(2)$

45. $(f \circ f)(5)$

46. $(g \circ g)(2)$

47–58 ■ Composition of Functions   Find the functions $f \circ g$, $g \circ f$, $f \circ f$, and $g \circ g$ and their domains.

47. $f(x) = 2x + 3$, $g(x) = 4x - 1$

48. $f(x) = 6x - 5$, $g(x) = \dfrac{x}{2}$

49. $f(x) = x^2$, $g(x) = x + 1$

50. $f(x) = x^3 + 2$, $g(x) = \sqrt[3]{x}$

51. $f(x) = \dfrac{1}{x}$, $g(x) = 2x + 4$

52. $f(x) = x^2$, $g(x) = \sqrt{x - 3}$

53. $f(x) = |x|$, $g(x) = 2x + 3$

54. $f(x) = x - 4$, $g(x) = |x + 4|$

55. $f(x) = \dfrac{x}{x + 1}$, $g(x) = 2x - 1$

56. $f(x) = \dfrac{1}{\sqrt{x}}$, $g(x) = x^2 - 4x$

57. $f(x) = \dfrac{x}{x + 1}$, $g(x) = \dfrac{1}{x}$

58. $f(x) = \dfrac{2}{x}$, $g(x) = \dfrac{x}{x + 2}$

59–62 ■ Composition of Three Functions   Find $f \circ g \circ h$.

59. $f(x) = x - 1$, $g(x) = \sqrt{x}$, $h(x) = x - 1$

60. $f(x) = \dfrac{1}{x}$, $g(x) = x^3$, $h(x) = x^2 + 2$

61. $f(x) = x^4 + 1$, $g(x) = x - 5$, $h(x) = \sqrt{x}$

62. $f(x) = \sqrt{x}$, $g(x) = \dfrac{x}{x - 1}$, $h(x) = \sqrt[3]{x}$

63–68 ■ Expressing a Function as a Composition   Express the function in the form $f \circ g$.

63. $F(x) = (x - 9)^5$

64. $F(x) = \sqrt{x} + 1$

65. $G(x) = \dfrac{x^2}{x^2 + 4}$

66. $G(x) = \dfrac{1}{x + 3}$

67. $H(x) = |1 - x^3|$

68. $H(x) = \sqrt{1 + \sqrt{x}}$

69–72 ■ Expressing a Function as a Composition   Express the function in the form $f \circ g \circ h$.

69. $F(x) = \dfrac{1}{x^2 + 1}$

70. $F(x) = \sqrt[3]{\sqrt{x} - 1}$

71. $G(x) = (4 + \sqrt[3]{x})^9$

72. $G(x) = \dfrac{2}{(3 + \sqrt{x})^2}$

SKILLS Plus

73. Composing Linear Functions   The graphs of the functions

$$f(x) = m_1 x + b_1$$
$$g(x) = m_2 x + b_2$$

are lines with slopes m_1 and m_2, respectively. Is the graph of $f \circ g$ a line? If so, what is its slope?

74. Solving an Equation for an Unknown Function   Suppose that

$$g(x) = 2x + 1$$
$$h(x) = 4x^2 + 4x + 7$$

Find a function f such that $f \circ g = h$. (Think about what operations you would have to perform on the formula for g to end up with the formula for h.) Now suppose that

$$f(x) = 3x + 5$$
$$h(x) = 3x^2 + 3x + 2$$

Use the same sort of reasoning to find a function g such that $f \circ g = h$.

APPLICATIONS

75–76 ■ Revenue, Cost, and Profit   A print shop makes bumper stickers for election campaigns. If x stickers are ordered (where $x < 10{,}000$), then the price per bumper sticker is $0.15 - 0.000002x$ dollars, and the total cost of producing the order is $0.095x - 0.0000005x^2$ dollars.

75. Use the fact that

$$\boxed{\text{revenue}} = \boxed{\text{price per item}} \times \boxed{\text{number of items sold}}$$

to express $R(x)$, the revenue from an order of x stickers, as a product of two functions of x.

76. Use the fact that

$$\boxed{\text{profit}} = \boxed{\text{revenue}} - \boxed{\text{cost}}$$

to express $P(x)$, the profit on an order of x stickers, as a difference of two functions of x.

77. Area of a Ripple A stone is dropped in a lake, creating a circular ripple that travels outward at a speed of 60 cm/s.

   (a) Find a function g that models the radius as a function of time.

   (b) Find a function f that models the area of the circle as a function of the radius.

   (c) Find $f \circ g$. What does this function represent?

78. Inflating a Balloon A spherical balloon is being inflated. The radius of the balloon is increasing at the rate of 1 cm/s.

   (a) Find a function f that models the radius as a function of time.

   (b) Find a function g that models the volume as a function of the radius.

   (c) Find $g \circ f$. What does this function represent?

79. Area of a Balloon A spherical weather balloon is being inflated. The radius of the balloon is increasing at the rate of 2 cm/s. Express the surface area of the balloon as a function of time t (in seconds).

80. Multiple Discounts You have a $50 coupon from the manufacturer that is good for the purchase of a cell phone. The store where you are purchasing your cell phone is offering a 20% discount on all cell phones. Let x represent the regular price of the cell phone.

   (a) Suppose only the 20% discount applies. Find a function f that models the purchase price of the cell phone as a function of the regular price x.

   (b) Suppose only the $50 coupon applies. Find a function g that models the purchase price of the cell phone as a function of the sticker price x.

   (c) If you can use the coupon and the discount, then the purchase price is either $(f \circ g)(x)$ or $(g \circ f)(x)$, depending on the order in which they are applied to the price. Find both $(f \circ g)(x)$ and $(g \circ f)(x)$. Which composition gives the lower price?

81. Multiple Discounts An appliance dealer advertises a 10% discount on all his washing machines. In addition, the manufacturer offers a $100 rebate on the purchase of a washing machine. Let x represent the sticker price of the washing machine.

   (a) Suppose only the 10% discount applies. Find a function f that models the purchase price of the washer as a function of the sticker price x.

   (b) Suppose only the $100 rebate applies. Find a function g that models the purchase price of the washer as a function of the sticker price x.

   (c) Find $f \circ g$ and $g \circ f$. What do these functions represent? Which is the better deal?

82. Airplane Trajectory An airplane is flying at a speed of 350 mi/h at an altitude of one mile. The plane passes directly above a radar station at time $t = 0$.

   (a) Express the distance s (in miles) between the plane and the radar station as a function of the horizontal distance d (in miles) that the plane has flown.

   (b) Express d as a function of the time t (in hours) that the plane has flown.

   (c) Use composition to express s as a function of t.

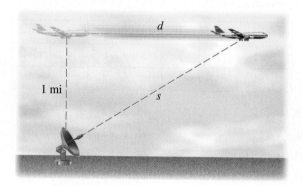

DISCUSS ■ DISCOVER ■ PROVE ■ WRITE

83. DISCOVER: Compound Interest A savings account earns 5% interest compounded annually. If you invest x dollars in such an account, then the amount $A(x)$ of the investment after one year is the initial investment plus 5%; that is,

$$A(x) = x + 0.05x = 1.05x$$

Find

$$A \circ A$$
$$A \circ A \circ A$$
$$A \circ A \circ A \circ A$$

What do these compositions represent? Find a formula for what you get when you compose n copies of A.

84. DISCUSS: Compositions of Odd and Even Functions Suppose that

$$h = f \circ g$$

If g is an even function, is h necessarily even? If g is odd, is h odd? What if g is odd and f is odd? What if g is odd and f is even?

2.8 ONE-TO-ONE FUNCTIONS AND THEIR INVERSES

■ One-to-One Functions ■ The Inverse of a Function ■ Finding the Inverse of a Function
■ Graphing the Inverse of a Function ■ Applications of Inverse Functions

The *inverse* of a function is a rule that acts on the output of the function and produces the corresponding input. So the inverse "undoes" or reverses what the function has done. Not all functions have inverses; those that do are called *one-to-one*.

■ One-to-One Functions

Let's compare the functions f and g whose arrow diagrams are shown in Figure 1. Note that f never takes on the same value twice (any two numbers in A have different images), whereas g does take on the same value twice (both 2 and 3 have the same image, 4). In symbols, $g(2) = g(3)$ but $f(x_1) \neq f(x_2)$ whenever $x_1 \neq x_2$. Functions that have this latter property are called *one-to-one*.

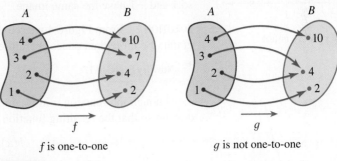

f is one-to-one g is not one-to-one

FIGURE 1

DEFINITION OF A ONE-TO-ONE FUNCTION

A function with domain A is called a **one-to-one function** if no two elements of A have the same image, that is,

$$f(x_1) \neq f(x_2) \quad \text{whenever } x_1 \neq x_2$$

An equivalent way of writing the condition for a one-to-one function is this:

$$\text{If } f(x_1) = f(x_2), \text{ then } x_1 = x_2.$$

If a horizontal line intersects the graph of f at more than one point, then we see from Figure 2 that there are numbers $x_1 \neq x_2$ such that $f(x_1) = f(x_2)$. This means that f is not one-to-one. Therefore we have the following geometric method for determining whether a function is one-to-one.

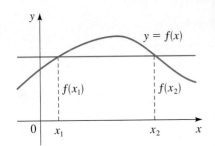

FIGURE 2 This function is not one-to-one because $f(x_1) = f(x_2)$.

HORIZONTAL LINE TEST

A function is one-to-one if and only if no horizontal line intersects its graph more than once.

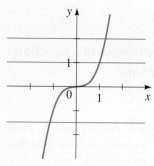

FIGURE 3 $f(x) = x^3$ is one-to-one.

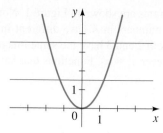

FIGURE 4 $g(x) = x^2$ is not one-to-one.

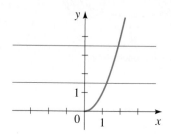

FIGURE 5 $h(x) = x^2\ (x \geq 0)$ is one-to-one.

EXAMPLE 1 ■ Deciding Whether a Function Is One-to-One

Is the function $f(x) = x^3$ one-to-one?

SOLUTION 1 If $x_1 \neq x_2$, then $x_1^3 \neq x_2^3$ (two different numbers cannot have the same cube). Therefore $f(x) = x^3$ is one-to-one.

SOLUTION 2 From Figure 3 we see that no horizontal line intersects the graph of $f(x) = x^3$ more than once. Therefore by the Horizontal Line Test, f is one-to-one.

■ Now Try Exercise 15

Notice that the function f of Example 1 is increasing and is also one-to-one. In fact, it can be proved that *every increasing function and every decreasing function is one-to-one.*

EXAMPLE 2 ■ Deciding Whether a Function Is One-to-One

Is the function $g(x) = x^2$ one-to-one?

SOLUTION 1 This function is not one-to-one because, for instance,

$$g(1) = 1 \quad \text{and} \quad g(-1) = 1$$

so 1 and -1 have the same image.

SOLUTION 2 From Figure 4 we see that there are horizontal lines that intersect the graph of g more than once. Therefore by the Horizontal Line Test, g is not one-to-one.

■ Now Try Exercise 17

Although the function g in Example 2 is not one-to-one, it is possible to restrict its domain so that the resulting function is one-to-one. In fact, if we define

$$h(x) = x^2 \qquad x \geq 0$$

then h is one-to-one, as you can see from Figure 5 and the Horizontal Line Test.

EXAMPLE 3 ■ Showing That a Function Is One-to-One

Show that the function $f(x) = 3x + 4$ is one-to-one.

SOLUTION Suppose there are numbers x_1 and x_2 such that $f(x_1) = f(x_2)$. Then

$$3x_1 + 4 = 3x_2 + 4 \qquad \text{Suppose } f(x_1) = f(x_2)$$
$$3x_1 = 3x_2 \qquad \text{Subtract 4}$$
$$x_1 = x_2 \qquad \text{Divide by 3}$$

Therefore f is one-to-one.

■ Now Try Exercise 13

■ The Inverse of a Function

One-to-one functions are important because they are precisely the functions that possess inverse functions according to the following definition.

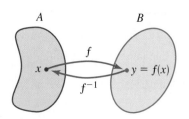

FIGURE 6

DEFINITION OF THE INVERSE OF A FUNCTION

Let f be a one-to-one function with domain A and range B. Then its **inverse function** f^{-1} has domain B and range A and is defined by

$$f^{-1}(y) = x \quad \Leftrightarrow \quad f(x) = y$$

for any y in B.

This definition says that if f takes x to y, then f^{-1} takes y back to x. (If f were not one-to-one, then f^{-1} would not be defined uniquely.) The arrow diagram in Figure 6 indicates that f^{-1} reverses the effect of f. From the definition we have

$$\text{domain of } f^{-1} = \text{range of } f$$

$$\text{range of } f^{-1} = \text{domain of } f$$

EXAMPLE 4 ■ Finding f^{-1} for Specific Values

🚫 Don't mistake the -1 in f^{-1} for an exponent.

$$f^{-1}(x) \quad \textit{does not mean} \quad \frac{1}{f(x)}$$

The reciprocal $1/f(x)$ is written as $(f(x))^{-1}$.

If $f(1) = 5$, $f(3) = 7$, and $f(8) = -10$, find $f^{-1}(5)$, $f^{-1}(7)$, and $f^{-1}(-10)$.

SOLUTION From the definition of f^{-1} we have

$$f^{-1}(5) = 1 \quad \text{because} \quad f(1) = 5$$

$$f^{-1}(7) = 3 \quad \text{because} \quad f(3) = 7$$

$$f^{-1}(-10) = 8 \quad \text{because} \quad f(8) = -10$$

Figure 7 shows how f^{-1} reverses the effect of f in this case.

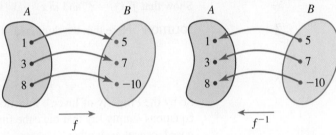

FIGURE 7

🖊 **Now Try Exercise 25** ■

EXAMPLE 5 ■ Finding Values of an Inverse Function

We can find specific values of an inverse function from a table or graph of the function itself.

(a) The table below gives values of a function h. From the table we see that $h^{-1}(8) = 3$, $h^{-1}(12) = 4$, and $h^{-1}(3) = 6$.

(b) A graph of a function f is shown in Figure 8. From the graph we see that $f^{-1}(5) = 7$ and $f^{-1}(3) = 4$.

x	$h(x)$
2	5
3 ←	8
4 ←—	12
5	1
6 ←	3
7	15

Finding values of h^{-1} from a table of h

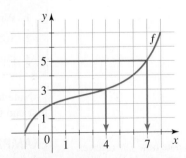

FIGURE 8 Finding values of f^{-1} from a graph of f

🖊 **Now Try Exercises 29 and 31**

By definition the inverse function f^{-1} undoes what f does: If we start with x, apply f, and then apply f^{-1}, we arrive back at x, where we started. Similarly, f undoes what f^{-1} does. In general, any function that reverses the effect of f in this way must be the inverse of f. These observations are expressed precisely as follows.

INVERSE FUNCTION PROPERTY

Let f be a one-to-one function with domain A and range B. The inverse function f^{-1} satisfies the following cancellation properties:

$$f^{-1}(f(x)) = x \quad \text{for every } x \text{ in } A$$
$$f(f^{-1}(x)) = x \quad \text{for every } x \text{ in } B$$

Conversely, any function f^{-1} satisfying these equations is the inverse of f.

These properties indicate that f is the inverse function of f^{-1}, so we say that f and f^{-1} are *inverses of each other*.

EXAMPLE 6 ■ Verifying That Two Functions Are Inverses

Show that $f(x) = x^3$ and $g(x) = x^{1/3}$ are inverses of each other.

SOLUTION Note that the domain and range of both f and g are $\mathbb{R}$. We have

$$g(f(x)) = g(x^3) = (x^3)^{1/3} = x$$
$$f(g(x)) = f(x^{1/3}) = (x^{1/3})^3 = x$$

So by the Property of Inverse Functions, f and g are inverses of each other. These equations simply say that the cube function and the cube root function, when composed, cancel each other.

✎ Now Try Exercise 39 ■

■ Finding the Inverse of a Function

Now let's examine how we compute inverse functions. We first observe from the definition of f^{-1} that

$$y = f(x) \quad \Leftrightarrow \quad f^{-1}(y) = x$$

So if $y = f(x)$ and if we are able to solve this equation for x in terms of y, then we must have $x = f^{-1}(y)$. If we then interchange x and y, we have $y = f^{-1}(x)$, which is the desired equation.

HOW TO FIND THE INVERSE OF A ONE-TO-ONE FUNCTION

1. Write $y = f(x)$.
2. Solve this equation for x in terms of y (if possible).
3. Interchange x and y. The resulting equation is $y = f^{-1}(x)$.

Note that Steps 2 and 3 can be reversed. In other words, we can interchange x and y first and then solve for y in terms of x.

In Example 7 note how f^{-1} reverses the effect of f. The function f is the rule "Multiply by 3, then subtract 2," whereas f^{-1} is the rule "Add 2, then divide by 3."

EXAMPLE 7 ■ Finding the Inverse of a Function

Find the inverse of the function $f(x) = 3x - 2$.

SOLUTION First we write $y = f(x)$.

$$y = 3x - 2$$

We use the Inverse Function Property:

$$f^{-1}(f(x)) = f^{-1}(3x - 2)$$

$$= \frac{(3x - 2) + 2}{3}$$

$$= \frac{3x}{3} = x$$

$$f(f^{-1}(x)) = f\left(\frac{x + 2}{3}\right)$$

$$= 3\left(\frac{x + 2}{3}\right) - 2$$

$$= x + 2 - 2 = x \;\checkmark$$

In Example 8 note how f^{-1} reverses the effect of f. The function f is the rule "Take the fifth power, subtract 3, then divide by 2," whereas f^{-1} is the rule "Multiply by 2, add 3, then take the fifth root."

We use the Inverse Function Property:

$$f^{-1}(f(x)) = f^{-1}\left(\frac{x^5 - 3}{2}\right)$$

$$= \left[2\left(\frac{x^5 - 3}{2}\right) + 3\right]^{1/5}$$

$$= (x^5 - 3 + 3)^{1/5}$$

$$= (x^5)^{1/5} = x$$

$$f(f^{-1}(x)) = f((2x + 3)^{1/5})$$

$$= \frac{[(2x + 3)^{1/5}]^5 - 3}{2}$$

$$= \frac{2x + 3 - 3}{2}$$

$$= \frac{2x}{2} = x \;\checkmark$$

Rational functions are studied in Section 3.6.

Then we solve this equation for x:

$$3x = y + 2 \qquad \text{Add 2}$$

$$x = \frac{y + 2}{3} \qquad \text{Divide by 3}$$

Finally, we interchange x and y:

$$y = \frac{x + 2}{3}$$

Therefore, the inverse function is $f^{-1}(x) = \dfrac{x + 2}{3}$.

✎ **Now Try Exercise 49**

EXAMPLE 8 ■ Finding the Inverse of a Function

Find the inverse of the function $f(x) = \dfrac{x^5 - 3}{2}$.

SOLUTION   We first write $y = (x^5 - 3)/2$ and solve for x.

$$y = \frac{x^5 - 3}{2} \qquad \text{Equation defining function}$$

$$2y = x^5 - 3 \qquad \text{Multiply by 2}$$

$$x^5 = 2y + 3 \qquad \text{Add 3 (and switch sides)}$$

$$x = (2y + 3)^{1/5} \qquad \text{Take fifth root of each side}$$

Then we interchange x and y to get $y = (2x + 3)^{1/5}$. Therefore the inverse function is $f^{-1}(x) = (2x + 3)^{1/5}$.

✎ **Now Try Exercise 61**

A **rational function** is a function defined by a rational expression. In the next example we find the inverse of a rational function.

EXAMPLE 9 ■ Finding the Inverse of a Rational Function

Find the inverse of the function $f(x) = \dfrac{2x + 3}{x - 1}$.

SOLUTION   We first write $y = (2x + 3)/(x - 1)$ and solve for x.

$$y = \frac{2x + 3}{x - 1} \qquad \text{Equation defining function}$$

$$y(x - 1) = 2x + 3 \qquad \text{Multiply by } x - 1$$

$$yx - y = 2x + 3 \qquad \text{Expand}$$

$$yx - 2x = y + 3 \qquad \text{Bring } x\text{-terms to LHS}$$

$$x(y - 2) = y + 3 \qquad \text{Factor } x$$

$$x = \frac{y + 3}{y - 2} \qquad \text{Divide by } y - 2$$

Therefore the inverse function is $f^{-1}(x) = \dfrac{x + 3}{x - 2}$.

✎ **Now Try Exercise 55**

Graphing the Inverse of a Function

The principle of interchanging x and y to find the inverse function also gives us a method for obtaining the graph of f^{-1} from the graph of f. If $f(a) = b$, then $f^{-1}(b) = a$. Thus the point (a, b) is on the graph of f if and only if the point (b, a) is on the graph of f^{-1}. But we get the point (b, a) from the point (a, b) by reflecting in the line $y = x$ (see Figure 9). Therefore, as Figure 10 illustrates, the following is true.

> The graph of f^{-1} is obtained by reflecting the graph of f in the line $y = x$.

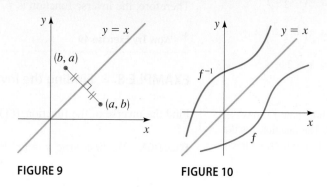

FIGURE 9   **FIGURE 10**

EXAMPLE 10 ■ Graphing the Inverse of a Function

(a) Sketch the graph of $f(x) = \sqrt{x - 2}$.

(b) Use the graph of f to sketch the graph of f^{-1}.

(c) Find an equation for f^{-1}.

SOLUTION

(a) Using the transformations from Section 2.6, we sketch the graph of $y = \sqrt{x - 2}$ by plotting the graph of the function $y = \sqrt{x}$ (Example 1(c) in Section 2.2) and shifting it to the right 2 units.

(b) The graph of f^{-1} is obtained from the graph of f in part (a) by reflecting it in the line $y = x$, as shown in Figure 11.

(c) Solve $y = \sqrt{x - 2}$ for x, noting that $y \geq 0$.

$$\sqrt{x - 2} = y$$
$$x - 2 = y^2 \qquad \text{Square each side}$$
$$x = y^2 + 2 \qquad y \geq 0 \qquad \text{Add 2}$$

Interchange x and y, as follows:

$$y = x^2 + 2 \qquad x \geq 0$$

Thus $\qquad\qquad\qquad f^{-1}(x) = x^2 + 2 \qquad x \geq 0$

This expression shows that the graph of f^{-1} is the right half of the parabola $y = x^2 + 2$, and from the graph shown in Figure 11 this seems reasonable.

◗ Now Try Exercise 73 ■

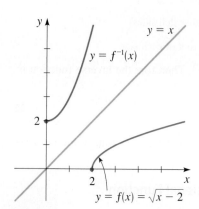

FIGURE 11

In Example 10 note how f^{-1} reverses the effect of f. The function f is the rule "Subtract 2, then take the square root," whereas f^{-1} is the rule "Square, then add 2."

Applications of Inverse Functions

When working with functions that model real-world situations, we name the variables using letters that suggest the quantity being modeled. For instance we may use t for time, d for distance, V for volume, and so on. When using inverse functions, we follow this convention. For example, suppose that the variable R is a function of the variable N, say, $R = f(N)$. Then $f^{-1}(R) = N$. So the function f^{-1} defines N as a function of R.

EXAMPLE 11 ■ An Inverse Function

At a local pizza parlor the daily special is $12 for a plain cheese pizza plus $2 for each additional topping.

(a) Find a function f that models the price of a pizza with n toppings.

(b) Find the inverse of the function f. What does f^{-1} represent?

(c) If a pizza costs $22, how many toppings does it have?

SOLUTION   Note that the price p of a pizza is a function of the number n of toppings.

(a) The price of a pizza with n toppings is given by the function

$$f(n) = 12 + 2n$$

(b) To find the inverse function, we first write $p = f(n)$, where we use the letter p instead of our usual y because $f(n)$ is the price of the pizza. We have

$$p = 12 + 2n$$

Next we solve for n:

$$p = 12 + 2n$$

$$p - 12 = 2n$$

$$n = \frac{p - 12}{2}$$

So $n = f^{-1}(p) = \dfrac{p - 12}{2}$. The function f^{-1} gives the number n of toppings for a pizza with price p.

(c) We have $n = f^{-1}(22) = (22 - 12)/2 = 5$. So the pizza has five toppings.

Now Try Exercise 93   ■

2.8 EXERCISES

CONCEPTS

1. A function f is one-to-one if different inputs produce

_____ outputs. You can tell from the graph that a function

is one-to-one by using the _____ Test.

2. (a) For a function to have an inverse, it must be _____.
So which one of the following functions has an inverse?

$$f(x) = x^2 \qquad g(x) = x^3$$

(b) What is the inverse of the function that you chose in part (a)?

3. A function f has the following verbal description: "Multiply by 3, add 5, and then take the third power of the result."

(a) Write a verbal description for f^{-1}.

(b) Find algebraic formulas that express f and f^{-1} in terms of the input x.

4. A graph of a function f is given. Does f have an inverse? If

so, find $f^{-1}(1) =$ _____ and $f^{-1}(3) =$ _____.

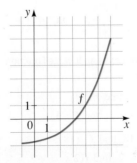

5. If the point $(3, 4)$ is on the graph of the function f, then the

point (____, ____) is on the graph of f^{-1}.

6. *True or false?*

(a) If f has an inverse, then $f^{-1}(x)$ is always the same as $\dfrac{1}{f(x)}$.

(b) If f has an inverse, then $f^{-1}(f(x)) = x$.

SKILLS

7–12 ■ One-to-One Function? A graph of a function f is given. Determine whether f is one-to-one.

7.

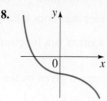

8.

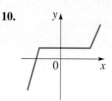

9.

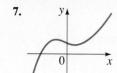

10.

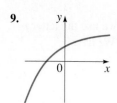

11.

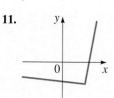

12.

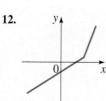

13–24 ■ One-to-One Function? Determine whether the function is one-to-one.

13. $f(x) = -2x + 4$

14. $f(x) = 3x - 2$

15. $g(x) = \sqrt{x}$

16. $g(x) = |x|$

17. $h(x) = x^2 - 2x$

18. $h(x) = x^3 + 8$

19. $f(x) = x^4 + 5$

20. $f(x) = x^4 + 5, \quad 0 \le x \le 2$

21. $r(t) = t^6 - 3, \quad 0 \le t \le 5$

22. $r(t) = t^4 - 1$

23. $f(x) = \dfrac{1}{x^2}$

24. $f(x) = \dfrac{1}{x}$

25–28 ■ Finding Values of an Inverse Function Assume that f is a one-to-one function.

25. (a) If $f(2) = 7$, find $f^{-1}(7)$.

(b) If $f^{-1}(3) = -1$, find $f(-1)$.

26. (a) If $f(5) = 18$, find $f^{-1}(18)$.

(b) If $f^{-1}(4) = 2$, find $f(2)$.

27. If $f(x) = 5 - 2x$, find $f^{-1}(3)$.

28. If $g(x) = x^2 + 4x$ with $x \ge -2$, find $g^{-1}(5)$.

29–30 ■ Finding Values of an Inverse from a Graph A graph of a function is given. Use the graph to find the indicated values.

29. (a) $f^{-1}(2)$ (b) $f^{-1}(5)$ (c) $f^{-1}(6)$

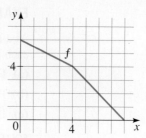

30. (a) $g^{-1}(2)$ (b) $g^{-1}(5)$ (c) $g^{-1}(6)$

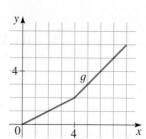

31–36 ■ Finding Values of an Inverse Using a Table A table of values for a one-to-one function is given. Find the indicated values.

31. $f^{-1}(5)$

32. $f^{-1}(0)$

33. $f^{-1}(f(1))$

34. $f(f^{-1}(6))$

35. $f^{-1}(f^{-1}(1))$

36. $f^{-1}(f^{-1}(0))$

x	1	2	3	4	5	6
$f(x)$	4	6	2	5	0	1

37–48 ■ Inverse Function Property Use the Inverse Function Property to show that f and g are inverses of each other.

37. $f(x) = x - 6; \quad g(x) = x + 6$

38. $f(x) = 3x; \quad g(x) = \dfrac{x}{3}$

39. $f(x) = 3x + 4; \quad g(x) = \dfrac{x - 4}{3}$

40. $f(x) = 2 - 5x; \quad g(x) = \dfrac{2 - x}{5}$

41. $f(x) = \dfrac{1}{x}; \quad g(x) = \dfrac{1}{x}$ **42.** $f(x) = x^5; \quad g(x) = \sqrt[5]{x}$

43. $f(x) = x^2 - 9, \quad x \ge 0; \quad g(x) = \sqrt{x + 9}, \quad x \ge -9$

44. $f(x) = x^3 + 1; \quad g(x) = (x - 1)^{1/3}$

45. $f(x) = \dfrac{1}{x - 1}; \quad g(x) = \dfrac{1}{x} + 1$

46. $f(x) = \sqrt{4 - x^2}, \quad 0 \le x \le 2;$

$\quad g(x) = \sqrt{4 - x^2}, \quad 0 \le x \le 2$

47. $f(x) = \dfrac{x + 2}{x - 2}; \quad g(x) = \dfrac{2x + 2}{x - 1}$

48. $f(x) = \dfrac{x - 5}{3x + 4}; \quad g(x) = \dfrac{5 + 4x}{1 - 3x}$

49–70 ■ Finding Inverse Functions Find the inverse function of f.

49. $f(x) = 3x + 5$

50. $f(x) = 7 - 5x$

51. $f(x) = 5 - 4x^3$

52. $f(x) = 3x^3 + 8$

53. $f(x) = \dfrac{1}{x + 2}$

54. $f(x) = \dfrac{x - 2}{x + 2}$

55. $f(x) = \dfrac{x}{x + 4}$

56. $f(x) = \dfrac{3x}{x - 2}$

57. $f(x) = \dfrac{2x + 5}{x - 7}$

58. $f(x) = \dfrac{4x - 2}{3x + 1}$

59. $f(x) = \dfrac{2x + 3}{1 - 5x}$

60. $f(x) = \dfrac{3 - 4x}{8x - 1}$

61. $f(x) = 4 - x^2, \quad x \ge 0$

62. $f(x) = x^2 + x, \quad x \ge -\frac{1}{2}$

63. $f(x) = x^6, \quad x \ge 0$

64. $f(x) = \dfrac{1}{x^2}, \quad x > 0$

65. $f(x) = \dfrac{2 - x^3}{5}$

66. $f(x) = (x^5 - 6)^7$

67. $f(x) = \sqrt{5 + 8x}$

68. $f(x) = 2 + \sqrt{3 + x}$

69. $f(x) = 2 + \sqrt[3]{x}$

70. $f(x) = \sqrt{4 - x^2}, \quad 0 \le x \le 2$

71–74 ■ Graph of an Inverse Function A function f is given. **(a)** Sketch the graph of f. **(b)** Use the graph of f to sketch the graph of f^{-1}. **(c)** Find f^{-1}.

71. $f(x) = 3x - 6$

72. $f(x) = 16 - x^2, \quad x \ge 0$

73. $f(x) = \sqrt{x + 1}$

74. $f(x) = x^3 - 1$

75–80 ■ One-to-One Functions from a Graph Draw the graph of f, and use it to determine whether the function is one-to-one.

75. $f(x) = x^3 - x$

76. $f(x) = x^3 + x$

77. $f(x) = \dfrac{x + 12}{x - 6}$

78. $f(x) = \sqrt{x^3 - 4x + 1}$

79. $f(x) = |x| - |x - 6|$

80. $f(x) = x \cdot |x|$

81–84 ■ Finding Inverse Functions A one-to-one function is given. **(a)** Find the inverse of the function. **(b)** Graph both the function and its inverse on the same screen to verify that the graphs are reflections of each other in the line $y = x$.

81. $f(x) = 2 + x$

82. $f(x) = 2 - \frac{1}{2}x$

83. $g(x) = \sqrt{x + 3}$

84. $g(x) = x^2 + 1, \quad x \ge 0$

85–88 ■ Restricting the Domain The given function is not one-to-one. Restrict its domain so that the resulting function *is*

one-to-one. Find the inverse of the function with the restricted domain. (There is more than one correct answer.)

85. $f(x) = 4 - x^2$

86. $g(x) = (x - 1)^2$

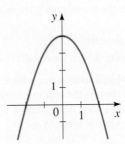

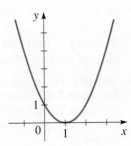

87. $h(x) = (x + 2)^2$

88. $k(x) = |x - 3|$

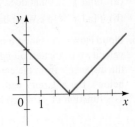

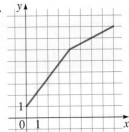

89–90 ■ Graph of an Inverse Function Use the graph of f to sketch the graph of f^{-1}.

89.

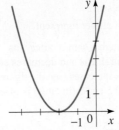

90.

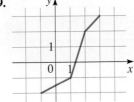

SKILLS Plus

91–92 ■ Functions That Are Their Own Inverse If a function f is its own inverse, then the graph of f is symmetric about the line $y = x$. **(a)** Graph the given function. **(b)** Does the graph indicate that f and f^{-1} are the same function? **(c)** Find the function f^{-1}. Use your result to verify your answer to part (b).

91. $f(x) = \dfrac{1}{x}$

92. $f(x) = \dfrac{x + 3}{x - 1}$

APPLICATIONS

93. Pizza Cost Marcello's Pizza charges a base price of $16 for a large pizza plus $1.50 for each additional topping.

  (a) Find a function f that models the price of a pizza with n toppings.

  (b) Find the inverse of the function f. What does f^{-1} represent?

  (c) If a pizza costs $25, how many toppings does it have?

94. Fee for Service For his services, a private investigator requires a $500 retainer fee plus $80 per hour. Let x represent the number of hours the investigator spends working on a case.

(a) Find a function f that models the investigator's fee as a function of x.

(b) Find f^{-1}. What does f^{-1} represent?

(c) Find $f^{-1}(1220)$. What does your answer represent?

95. Torricelli's Law A tank holds 100 gallons of water, which drains from a leak at the bottom, causing the tank to empty in 40 minutes. According to Torricelli's Law, the volume V of water remaining in the tank after t min is given by the function

$$V = f(t) = 100\left(1 - \frac{t}{40}\right)^2$$

(a) Find f^{-1}. What does f^{-1} represent?

(b) Find $f^{-1}(15)$. What does your answer represent?

96. Blood Flow As blood moves through a vein or artery, its velocity v is greatest along the central axis and decreases as the distance r from the central axis increases (see the figure below). For an artery with radius 0.5 cm, v (in cm/s) is given as a function of r (in cm) by

$$v = g(r) = 18{,}500(0.25 - r^2)$$

(a) Find g^{-1}. What does g^{-1} represent?

(b) Find $g^{-1}(30)$. What does your answer represent?

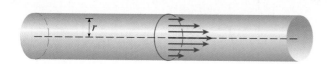

97. Demand Function The amount of a commodity that is sold is called the *demand* for the commodity. The demand D for a certain commodity is a function of the price given by

$$D = f(p) = -3p + 150$$

(a) Find f^{-1}. What does f^{-1} represent?

(b) Find $f^{-1}(30)$. What does your answer represent?

98. Temperature Scales The relationship between the Fahrenheit (F) and Celsius (C) scales is given by

$$F = g(C) = \tfrac{9}{5}C + 32$$

(a) Find g^{-1}. What does g^{-1} represent?

(b) Find $g^{-1}(86)$. What does your answer represent?

99. Exchange Rates The relative value of currencies fluctuates every day. When this problem was written, one Canadian dollar was worth 0.9766 U.S. dollars.

(a) Find a function f that gives the U.S. dollar value $f(x)$ of x Canadian dollars.

(b) Find f^{-1}. What does f^{-1} represent?

(c) How much Canadian money would $12,250 in U.S. currency be worth?

100. Income Tax In a certain country the tax on incomes less than or equal to €20,000 is 10%. For incomes that are more than €20,000 the tax is €2000 plus 20% of the amount over €20,000.

(a) Find a function f that gives the income tax on an income x. Express f as a piecewise defined function.

(b) Find f^{-1}. What does f^{-1} represent?

(c) How much income would require paying a tax of €10,000?

101. Multiple Discounts A car dealership advertises a 15% discount on all its new cars. In addition, the manufacturer offers a $1000 rebate on the purchase of a new car. Let x represent the sticker price of the car.

(a) Suppose that only the 15% discount applies. Find a function f that models the purchase price of the car as a function of the sticker price x.

(b) Suppose that only the $1000 rebate applies. Find a function g that models the purchase price of the car as a function of the sticker price x.

(c) Find a formula for $H = f \circ g$.

(d) Find H^{-1}. What does H^{-1} represent?

(e) Find $H^{-1}(13{,}000)$. What does your answer represent?

DISCUSS ■ **DISCOVER** ■ **PROVE** ■ **WRITE**

102. DISCUSS: Determining When a Linear Function Has an Inverse For the linear function $f(x) = mx + b$ to be one-to-one, what must be true about its slope? If it is one-to-one, find its inverse. Is the inverse linear? If so, what is its slope?

103. DISCUSS: Finding an Inverse "in Your Head" In the margin notes in this section we pointed out that the inverse of a function can be found by simply reversing the operations that make up the function. For instance, in Example 7 we saw that the inverse of

$$f(x) = 3x - 2 \quad \text{is} \quad f^{-1}(x) = \frac{x + 2}{3}$$

because the "reverse" of "Multiply by 3 and subtract 2" is "Add 2 and divide by 3." Use the same procedure to find the inverse of the following functions.

(a) $f(x) = \dfrac{2x + 1}{5}$ (b) $f(x) = 3 - \dfrac{1}{x}$

(c) $f(x) = \sqrt{x^3 + 2}$ (d) $f(x) = (2x - 5)^3$

Now consider another function:

$$f(x) = x^3 + 2x + 6$$

Is it possible to use the same sort of simple reversal of operations to find the inverse of this function? If so, do it. If not, explain what is different about this function that makes this task difficult.

104. PROVE: The Identity Function The function $I(x) = x$ is called the **identity function**. Show that for any function f we have $f \circ I = f$, $I \circ f = f$, and $f \circ f^{-1} = f^{-1} \circ f = I$. (This means that the identity function I behaves for functions and composition just the way the number 1 behaves for real numbers and multiplication.)

105. DISCUSS: Solving an Equation for an Unknown Function
In Exercises 69–72 of Section 2.7 you were asked to solve equations in which the unknowns are functions. Now that we know about inverses and the identity function (see Exercise 104), we can use algebra to solve such equations. For instance, to solve $f \circ g = h$ for the unknown function f, we perform the following steps:

$$f \circ g = h \qquad \text{Problem: Solve for } f$$
$$f \circ g \circ g^{-1} = h \circ g^{-1} \qquad \text{Compose with } g^{-1} \text{ on the right}$$
$$f \circ I = h \circ g^{-1} \qquad \text{Because } g \circ g^{-1} = I$$
$$f = h \circ g^{-1} \qquad \text{Because } f \circ I = f$$

So the solution is $f = h \circ g^{-1}$. Use this technique to solve the equation $f \circ g = h$ for the indicated unknown function.

(a) Solve for f, where $g(x) = 2x + 1$ and $h(x) = 4x^2 + 4x + 7$.

(b) Solve for g, where $f(x) = 3x + 5$ and $h(x) = 3x^2 + 3x + 2$.

CHAPTER 2 ■ REVIEW

■ PROPERTIES AND FORMULAS

Function Notation (p. 185)

If a function is given by the formula $y = f(x)$, then x is the independent variable and denotes the **input**; y is the dependent variable and denotes the **output**; the **domain** is the set of all possible inputs x; the **range** is the set of all possible outputs y.

Net Change (p. 187)

The **net change** in the value of the function f between $x = a$ and $x = b$ is

$$\text{net change} = f(b) - f(a)$$

The Graph of a Function (p. 195)

The graph of a function f is the graph of the equation $y = f(x)$ that defines f.

The Vertical Line Test (p. 200)

A curve in the coordinate plane is the graph of a function if and only if no vertical line intersects the graph more than once.

Increasing and Decreasing Functions (p. 210)

A function f is **increasing** on an interval if $f(x_1) < f(x_2)$ whenever $x_1 < x_2$ in the interval.

A function f is **decreasing** on an interval if $f(x_1) > f(x_2)$ whenever $x_1 < x_2$ in the interval.

Local Maximum and Minimum Values (p. 212)

The function value $f(a)$ is a **local maximum value** of the function f if $f(a) \geq f(x)$ for all x near a. In this case we also say that f has a **local maximum** at $x = a$.

The function value $f(b)$ is a **local minimum value** of the function f if $f(b) \leq f(x)$ for all x near b. In this case we also say that f has a **local minimum** at $x = b$.

Average Rate of Change (p. 220)

The **average rate of change** of the function f between $x = a$ and $x = b$ is the slope of the **secant** line between $(a, f(a))$ and $(b, f(b))$:

$$\text{average rate of change} = \frac{f(b) - f(a)}{b - a}$$

Linear Functions (pp. 227–228)

A **linear function** is a function of the form $f(x) = ax + b$. The graph of f is a line with slope a and y-intercept b. The average rate of change of f has the constant value a between any two points.

$$a = \text{slope of graph of } f = \text{rate of change of } f$$

Vertical and Horizontal Shifts of Graphs (pp. 234–235)

Let c be a positive constant.

To graph $y = f(x) + c$, shift the graph of $y = f(x)$ **upward** by c units.

To graph $y = f(x) - c$, shift the graph of $y = f(x)$ **downward** by c units.

To graph $y = f(x - c)$, shift the graph of $y = f(x)$ **to the right** by c units.

To graph $y = f(x + c)$, shift the graph of $y = f(x)$ **to the left** by c units.

Reflecting Graphs (p. 237)

To graph $y = -f(x)$, **reflect** the graph of $y = f(x)$ in the **x-axis**.

To graph $y = f(-x)$, **reflect** the graph of $y = f(x)$ in the **y-axis**.

Vertical and Horizontal Stretching and Shrinking of Graphs (pp. 238, 239)

If $c > 1$, then to graph $y = cf(x)$, **stretch** the graph of $y = f(x)$ **vertically** by a factor of c.

If $0 < c < 1$, then to graph $y = cf(x)$, **shrink** the graph of $y = f(x)$ **vertically** by a factor of c.

If $c > 1$, then to graph $y = f(cx)$, **shrink** the graph of $y = f(x)$ **horizontally** by a factor of $1/c$.

If $0 < c < 1$, then to graph $y = f(cx)$, **stretch** the graph of $y = f(x)$ **horizontally** by a factor of $1/c$.

Even and Odd Functions (p. 240)

A function f is

even if $f(-x) = f(x)$

odd if $f(-x) = -f(x)$

for every x in the domain of f.

Composition of Functions (p. 249)

Given two functions f and g, the **composition** of f and g is the function $f \circ g$ defined by

$$(f \circ g)(x) = f(g(x))$$

The **domain** of $f \circ g$ is the set of all x for which both $g(x)$ and $f(g(x))$ are defined.

One-to-One Functions (p. 255)

A function f is **one-to-one** if $f(x_1) \neq f(x_2)$ whenever x_1 and x_2 are *different* elements of the domain of f.

Horizontal Line Test (p. 255)

A function is one-to-one if and only if no horizontal line intersects its graph more than once.

Inverse of a Function (p. 256)

Let f be a one-to-one function with domain A and range B.

The **inverse** of f is the function f^{-1} defined by

$$f^{-1}(y) = x \quad \Leftrightarrow \quad f(x) = y$$

The inverse function f^{-1} has domain B and range A.

The functions f and f^{-1} satisfy the following **cancellation properties**:

$$f^{-1}(f(x)) = x \quad \text{for every } x \text{ in } A$$
$$f(f^{-1}(x)) = x \quad \text{for every } x \text{ in } B$$

■ CONCEPT CHECK

1. Define each concept.
   (a) Function
   (b) Domain and range of a function
   (c) Graph of a function
   (d) Independent and dependent variables

2. Describe the four ways of representing a function.

3. Sketch graphs of the following functions by hand.
   (a) $f(x) = x^2$ (b) $g(x) = x^3$
   (c) $h(x) = |x|$ (d) $k(x) = \sqrt{x}$

4. What is a piecewise defined function? Give an example.

5. (a) What is the Vertical Line Test, and what is it used for?
   (b) What is the Horizontal Line Test, and what is it used for?

6. Define each concept, and give an example of each.
   (a) Increasing function
   (b) Decreasing function
   (c) Constant function

7. Suppose we know that the point $(3, 5)$ is a point on the graph of a function f. Explain how to find $f(3)$ and $f^{-1}(5)$.

8. What does it mean to say that $f(4)$ is a local maximum value of f?

9. Explain how to find the average rate of change of a function f between $x = a$ and $x = b$.

10. (a) What is the slope of a linear function? How do you find it? What is the rate of change of a linear function?
    (b) Is the rate of change of a linear function constant? Explain.
    (c) Give an example of a linear function, and sketch its graph.

11. Suppose the graph of a function f is given. Write an equation for each of the graphs that are obtained from the graph of f as follows.
    (a) Shift upward 3 units
    (b) Shift downward 3 units
    (c) Shift 3 units to the right
    (d) Shift 3 units to the left
    (e) Reflect in the x-axis
    (f) Reflect in the y-axis
    (g) Stretch vertically by a factor of 3
    (h) Shrink vertically by a factor of $\frac{1}{3}$
    (i) Shrink horizontally by a factor of $\frac{1}{3}$
    (j) Stretch horizontally by a factor of 3

12. (a) What is an even function? How can you tell that a function is even by looking at its graph? Give an example of an even function.
    (b) What is an odd function? How can you tell that a function is odd by looking at its graph? Give an example of an odd function.

13. Suppose that f has domain A and g has domain B. What are the domains of the following functions?
    (a) Domain of $f + g$
    (b) Domain of fg
    (c) Domain of f/g

14. (a) How is the composition function $f \circ g$ defined? What is its domain?
    (b) If $g(a) = b$ and $f(b) = c$, then explain how to find $(f \circ g)(a)$.

15. (a) What is a one-to-one function?

(b) How can you tell from the graph of a function whether it is one-to-one?

(c) Suppose that f is a one-to-one function with domain A and range B. How is the inverse function f^{-1} defined? What are the domain and range of f^{-1}?

(d) If you are given a formula for f, how do you find a formula for f^{-1}? Find the inverse of the function $f(x) = 2x$.

(e) If you are given a graph of f, how do you find a graph of the inverse function f^{-1}?

ANSWERS TO THE CONCEPT CHECK CAN BE FOUND AT THE BACK OF THE BOOK.

■ EXERCISES

1–2 ■ Function Notation A verbal description of a function f is given. Find a formula that expresses f in function notation.

1. "Square, then subtract 5."

2. "Divide by 2, then add 9."

3–4 ■ Function in Words A formula for a function f is given. Give a verbal description of the function.

3. $f(x) = 3(x + 10)$

4. $f(x) = \sqrt{6x - 10}$

5–6 ■ Table of Values Complete the table of values for the given function.

5. $g(x) = x^2 - 4x$

6. $h(x) = 3x^2 + 2x - 5$

x	$g(x)$
-1	
0	
1	
2	
3	

x	$h(x)$
-2	
-1	
0	
1	
2	

7. Printing Cost A publisher estimates that the cost $C(x)$ of printing a run of x copies of a certain mathematics textbook is given by the function $C(x) = 5000 + 30x - 0.001x^2$.

(a) Find $C(1000)$ and $C(10,000)$.

(b) What do your answers in part (a) represent?

(c) Find $C(0)$. What does this number represent?

(d) Find the net change and the average rate of change of the cost C between $x = 1000$ and $x = 10,000$.

8. Earnings Reynalda works as a salesperson in the electronics division of a department store. She earns a base weekly salary plus a commission based on the retail price of the goods she has sold. If she sells x dollars worth of goods in a week, her earnings for that week are given by the function $E(x) = 400 + 0.03x$.

(a) Find $E(2000)$ and $E(15,000)$.

(b) What do your answers in part (a) represent?

(c) Find $E(0)$. What does this number represent?

(d) Find the net change and the average rate of change of her earnings E between $x = 2000$ and $x = 15,000$.

(e) From the formula for E, determine what percentage Reynalda earns on the goods that she sells.

9–10 ■ Evaluating Functions Evaluate the function at the indicated values.

9. $f(x) = x^2 - 4x + 6$; $\quad f(0), f(2), f(-2), f(a), f(-a),$ $f(x + 1), f(2x)$

10. $f(x) = 4 - \sqrt{3x - 6}$; $\quad f(5), f(9), f(a + 2), f(-x), f(x^2)$

11. Functions Given by a Graph Which of the following figures are graphs of functions? Which of the functions are one-to-one?

(a)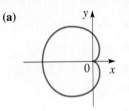

(b)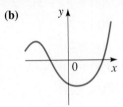

(c)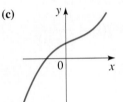

(d)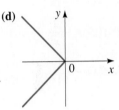

12. Getting Information from a Graph A graph of a function f is given.

(a) Find $f(-2)$ and $f(2)$.

(b) Find the net change and the average rate of change of f between $x = -2$ and $x = 2$.

(c) Find the domain and range of f.

(d) On what intervals is f increasing? On what intervals is f decreasing?

(e) What are the local maximum values of f?

(f) Is f one-to-one?

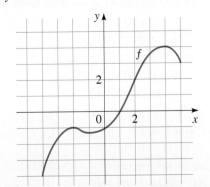

13–14 ■ Domain and Range   Find the domain and range of the function.

13. $f(x) = \sqrt{x + 3}$

14. $F(t) = t^2 + 2t + 5$

15–22 ■ Domain   Find the domain of the function.

15. $f(x) = 7x + 15$

16. $f(x) = \dfrac{2x + 1}{2x - 1}$

17. $f(x) = \sqrt{x + 4}$

18. $f(x) = 3x - \dfrac{2}{\sqrt{x + 1}}$

19. $f(x) = \dfrac{1}{x} + \dfrac{1}{x + 1} + \dfrac{1}{x + 2}$

20. $g(x) = \dfrac{2x^2 + 5x + 3}{2x^2 - 5x - 3}$

21. $h(x) = \sqrt{4 - x} + \sqrt{x^2 - 1}$

22. $f(x) = \dfrac{\sqrt[3]{2x + 1}}{\sqrt[3]{2x + 2}}$

23–38 ■ Graphing Functions   Sketch a graph of the function. Use transformations of functions whenever possible.

23. $f(x) = 1 - 2x$

24. $f(x) = \frac{1}{3}(x - 5), \quad 2 \le x \le 8$

25. $f(x) = 3x^2$

26. $f(x) = -\frac{1}{4}x^2$

27. $f(x) = 2x^2 - 1$

28. $f(x) = -(x - 1)^4$

29. $f(x) = 1 + \sqrt{x}$

30. $f(x) = 1 - \sqrt{x + 2}$

31. $f(x) = \frac{1}{2}x^3$

32. $f(x) = \sqrt[3]{-x}$

33. $f(x) = -|x|$

34. $f(x) = |x + 1|$

35. $f(x) = -\dfrac{1}{x^2}$

36. $f(x) = \dfrac{1}{(x - 1)^3}$

37. $f(x) = \begin{cases} 1 - x & \text{if } x < 0 \\ 1 & \text{if } x \ge 0 \end{cases}$

38. $f(x) = \begin{cases} -x & \text{if } x < 0 \\ x^2 & \text{if } 0 \le x < 2 \\ 1 & \text{if } x \ge 2 \end{cases}$

39–42 ■ Equations That Represent Functions   Determine whether the equation defines y as a function of x.

39. $x + y^2 = 14$

40. $3x - \sqrt{y} = 8$

41. $x^3 - y^3 = 27$

42. $2x = y^4 - 16$

 43–44 ■ Graphing Functions   Determine which viewing rectangle produces the most appropriate graph of the function.

43. $f(x) = 6x^3 - 15x^2 + 4x - 1$
   (i) $[-2, 2]$ by $[-2, 2]$
   (ii) $[-8, 8]$ by $[-8, 8]$
   (iii) $[-4, 4]$ by $[-12, 12]$
   (iv) $[-100, 100]$ by $[-100, 100]$

44. $f(x) = \sqrt{100 - x^3}$.
   (i) $[-4, 4]$ by $[-4, 4]$
   (ii) $[-10, 10]$ by $[-10, 10]$
   (iii) $[-10, 10]$ by $[-10, 40]$
   (iv) $[-100, 100]$ by $[-100, 100]$

 45–48 ■ Domain and Range from a Graph   A function f is given. **(a)** Use a graphing calculator to draw the graph of f. **(b)** Find the domain and range of f from the graph.

45. $f(x) = \sqrt{9 - x^2}$

46. $f(x) = -\sqrt{x^2 - 3}$

47. $f(x) = \sqrt{x^3 - 4x + 1}$

48. $f(x) = x^4 - x^3 + x^2 + 3x - 6$

 49–50 ■ Getting Information from a Graph   Draw a graph of the function f, and determine the intervals on which f is increasing and on which f is decreasing.

49. $f(x) = x^3 - 4x^2$

50. $f(x) = |x^4 - 16|$

51–56 ■ Net Change and Average Rate of Change   A function is given (either numerically, graphically, or algebraically). Find the net change and the average rate of change of the function between the indicated values.

51. Between $x = 4$ and $x = 8$

52. Between $x = 10$ and $x = 30$

x	$f(x)$
2	14
4	12
6	12
8	8
10	6

x	$g(x)$
0	25
10	-5
20	-2
30	30
40	0

53. Between $x = -1$ and $x = 2$

54. Between $x = 1$ and $x = 3$

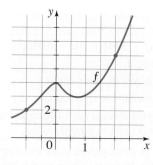

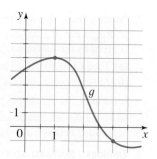

55. $f(x) = x^2 - 2x$;   between $x = 1$ and $x = 4$

56. $g(x) = (x + 1)^2$;   between $x = a$ and $x = a + h$

57–58 ■ Linear?   Determine whether the given function is linear.

57. $f(x) = (2 + 3x)^2$

58. $g(x) = \dfrac{x + 3}{5}$

59–60 ■ Linear Functions   A linear function is given. **(a)** Sketch a graph of the function. **(b)** What is the slope of the graph? **(c)** What is the rate of change of the function?

59. $f(x) = 3x + 2$

60. $g(x) = 3 - \frac{1}{2}x$

61–66 ■ **Linear Functions** A linear function is described either verbally, numerically, or graphically. Express f in the form $f(x) = ax + b$.

61. The function has rate of change -2 and initial value 3.

62. The graph of the function has slope $\frac{1}{2}$ and y-intercept -1.

63.

x	$f(x)$
0	3
1	5
2	7
3	9
4	11

64.

x	$f(x)$
0	6
2	5.5
4	5
6	4.5
8	4

65.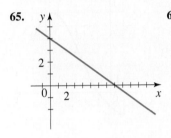

66.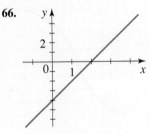

67. Population The population of a planned seaside community in Florida is given by the function $P(t) = 3000 + 200t + 0.1t^2$, where t represents the number of years since the community was incorporated in 1985.

  (a) Find $P(10)$ and $P(20)$. What do these values represent?

  (b) Find the average rate of change of P between $t = 10$ and $t = 20$. What does this number represent?

68. Retirement Savings Ella is saving for her retirement by making regular deposits into a 401(k) plan. As her salary rises, she finds that she can deposit increasing amounts each year. Between 1995 and 2008 the annual amount (in dollars) that she deposited was given by the function $D(t) = 3500 + 15t^2$, where t represents the year of the deposit measured from the start of the plan (so 1995 corresponds to $t = 0$, 1996 corresponds to $t = 1$, and so on).

  (a) Find $D(0)$ and $D(15)$. What do these values represent?

  (b) Assuming that her deposits continue to be modeled by the function D, in what year will she deposit $17,000?

  (c) Find the average rate of change of D between $t = 0$ and $t = 15$. What does this number represent?

69–70 ■ **Average Rate of Change** A function f is given. **(a)** Find the average rate of change of f between $x = 0$ and $x = 2$, and the average rate of change of f between $x = 15$ and $x = 50$. **(b)** Were the two average rates of change that you found in part (a) the same? **(c)** Is the function linear? If so, what is its rate of change?

69. $f(x) = \frac{1}{2}x - 6$ **70.** $f(x) = 8 - 3x$

71. Transformations Suppose the graph of f is given. Describe how the graphs of the following functions can be obtained from the graph of f.

  (a) $y = f(x) + 8$ (b) $y = f(x + 8)$

  (c) $y = 1 + 2f(x)$ (d) $y = f(x - 2) - 2$

  (e) $y = f(-x)$ (f) $y = -f(-x)$

  (g) $y = -f(x)$ (h) $y = f^{-1}(x)$

72. Transformations The graph of f is given. Draw the graphs of the following functions.

  (a) $y = f(x - 2)$ (b) $y = -f(x)$

  (c) $y = 3 - f(x)$ (d) $y = \frac{1}{2}f(x) - 1$

  (e) $y = f^{-1}(x)$ (f) $y = f(-x)$

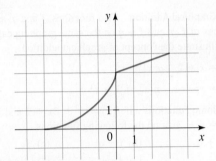

73. Even and Odd Functions Determine whether f is even, odd, or neither.

  (a) $f(x) = 2x^5 - 3x^2 + 2$ (b) $f(x) = x^3 - x^7$

  (c) $f(x) = \dfrac{1 - x^2}{1 + x^2}$ (d) $f(x) = \dfrac{1}{x + 2}$

74. Even and Odd Functions Determine whether the function in the figure is even, odd, or neither.

  (a) 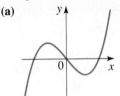   (b)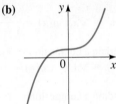

  (c) 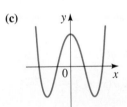   (d)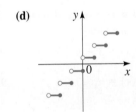

75–78 ■ **Local Maxima and Minima** Find the local maximum and minimum values of the function and the values of x at which they occur. State each answer rounded to two decimal places.

75. $g(x) = 2x^2 + 4x - 5$

76. $f(x) = 1 - x - x^2$

77. $f(x) = 3.3 + 1.6x - 2.5x^3$

78. $f(x) = x^{2/3}(6 - x)^{1/3}$

79. Maximum Height of Projectile A stone is thrown upward from the top of a building. Its height (in feet) above the ground after t seconds is given by

$$h(t) = -16t^2 + 48t + 32$$

What maximum height does it reach?

80. Maximum Profit The profit P (in dollars) generated by selling x units of a certain commodity is given by

$$P(x) = -1500 + 12x - 0.0004x^2$$

What is the maximum profit, and how many units must be sold to generate it?

 81–82 ■ Graphical Addition Two functions, f and g, are given. Draw graphs of f, g, and $f + g$ on the same graphing calculator screen to illustrate the concept of graphical addition.

81. $f(x) = x + 2$, $g(x) = x^2$

82. $f(x) = x^2 + 1$, $g(x) = 3 - x^2$

83. Combining Functions If $f(x) = x^2 - 3x + 2$ and $g(x) = 4 - 3x$, find the following functions.

(a) $f + g$ (b) $f - g$ (c) fg

(d) f/g (e) $f \circ g$ (f) $g \circ f$

84. If $f(x) = 1 + x^2$ and $g(x) = \sqrt{x - 1}$, find the following.

(a) $f \circ g$ (b) $g \circ f$ (c) $(f \circ g)(2)$

(d) $(f \circ f)(2)$ (e) $f \circ g \circ f$ (f) $g \circ f \circ g$

85–86 ■ Composition of Functions Find the functions $f \circ g$, $g \circ f$, $f \circ f$, and $g \circ g$ and their domains.

85. $f(x) = 3x - 1$, $g(x) = 2x - x^2$

86. $f(x) = \sqrt{x}$, $g(x) = \dfrac{2}{x - 4}$

87. Finding a Composition Find $f \circ g \circ h$, where $f(x) = \sqrt{1 - x}, g(x) = 1 - x^2$, and $h(x) = 1 + \sqrt{x}$.

88. Finding a Composition If $T(x) = \dfrac{1}{\sqrt{1 + \sqrt{x}}}$, find functions f, g, and h such that $f \circ g \circ h = T$.

89–94 ■ One-to-One Functions Determine whether the function is one-to-one.

89. $f(x) = 3 + x^3$

90. $g(x) = 2 - 2x + x^2$

91. $h(x) = \dfrac{1}{x^4}$

92. $r(x) = 2 + \sqrt{x + 3}$

 93. $p(x) = 3.3 + 1.6x - 2.5x^3$

 94. $q(x) = 3.3 + 1.6x + 2.5x^3$

95–98 ■ Finding Inverse Functions Find the inverse of the function.

95. $f(x) = 3x - 2$

96. $f(x) = \dfrac{2x + 1}{3}$

97. $f(x) = (x + 1)^3$

98. $f(x) = 1 + \sqrt[5]{x - 2}$

99–100 ■ Inverse Functions from a Graph A graph of a function f is given. Does f have an inverse? If so, find $f^{-1}(0)$ and $f^{-1}(4)$.

99.

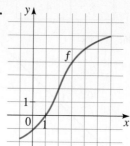

100.

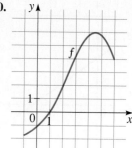

101. Graphing Inverse Functions

(a) Sketch a graph of the function

$$f(x) = x^2 - 4 \qquad x \geq 0$$

(b) Use part (a) to sketch the graph of f^{-1}.

(c) Find an equation for f^{-1}.

102. Graphing Inverse Functions

(a) Show that the function $f(x) = 1 + \sqrt[4]{x}$ is one-to-one.

(b) Sketch the graph of f.

(c) Use part (b) to sketch the graph of f^{-1}.

(d) Find an equation for f^{-1}.

1. Which of the following are graphs of functions? If the graph is that of a function, is it one-to-one?

(a)

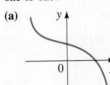

(b)

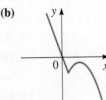

(c)

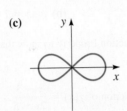

(d)

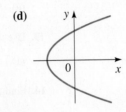

2. Let $f(x) = \dfrac{\sqrt{x}}{x + 1}$.

(a) Evaluate $f(0)$, $f(2)$, and $f(a + 2)$.

(b) Find the domain of f.

(c) What is the average rate of change of f between $x = 2$ and $x = 10$?

3. A function f has the following verbal description: "Subtract 2, then cube the result."

(a) Find a formula that expresses f algebraically.

(b) Make a table of values of f, for the inputs -1, 0, 1, 2, 3, and 4.

(c) Sketch a graph of f, using the table of values from part (b) to help you.

(d) How do we know that f has an inverse? Give a verbal description for f^{-1}.

(e) Find a formula that expresses f^{-1} algebraically.

4. A graph of a function f is given in the margin.

(a) Find the local minimum and maximum values of f and the values of x at which they occur.

(b) Find the intervals on which f is increasing and on which f is decreasing.

5. A school fund-raising group sells chocolate bars to help finance a swimming pool for their physical education program. The group finds that when they set their price at x dollars per bar (where $0 < x \le 5$), their total sales revenue (in dollars) is given by the function $R(x) = -500x^2 + 3000x$.

(a) Evaluate $R(2)$ and $R(4)$. What do these values represent?

(b) Use a graphing calculator to draw a graph of R. What does the graph tell us about what happens to revenue as the price increases from 0 to 5 dollars?

(c) What is the maximum revenue, and at what price is it achieved?

6. Determine the net change and the average rate of change for the function $f(t) = t^2 - 2t$ between $t = 2$ and $t = 2 + h$.

7. Let $f(x) = (x + 5)^2$ and $g(x) = 1 - 5x$.

(a) Only one of the two functions f and g is linear. Which one is linear, and why is the other one not linear?

(b) Sketch a graph of each function.

(c) What is the rate of change of the linear function?

8. (a) Sketch the graph of the function $f(x) = x^3$.

(b) Use part (a) to graph the function $g(x) = (x - 1)^3 - 2$.

9. (a) How is the graph of $y = f(x - 3) + 2$ obtained from the graph of f?

(b) How is the graph of $y = f(-x)$ obtained from the graph of f?

271

10. Let $f(x) = \begin{cases} 1 - x & \text{if } x \leq 1 \\ 2x + 1 & \text{if } x > 1 \end{cases}$

  (a) Evaluate $f(-2)$ and $f(1)$.

  (b) Sketch the graph of f.

11. If $f(x) = x^2 + x + 1$ and $g(x) = x - 3$, find the following.

  (a) $f + g$ **(b)** $f - g$ **(c)** $f \circ g$ **(d)** $g \circ f$

  (e) $f(g(2))$ **(f)** $g(f(2))$ **(g)** $g \circ g \circ g$

12. Determine whether the function is one-to-one.

  (a) $f(x) = x^3 + 1$ **(b)** $g(x) = |x + 1|$

13. Use the Inverse Function Property to show that $f(x) = \dfrac{1}{x - 2}$ is the inverse of $g(x) = \dfrac{1}{x} + 2$.

14. Find the inverse function of $f(x) = \dfrac{x - 3}{2x + 5}$.

15. (a) If $f(x) = \sqrt{3 - x}$, find the inverse function f^{-1}.

  (b) Sketch the graphs of f and f^{-1} on the same coordinate axes.

16–21 ■ A graph of a function f is given below.

16. Find the domain and range of f.

17. Find $f(0)$ and $f(4)$.

18. Graph $f(x - 2)$ and $f(x) + 2$.

19. Find the net change and the average rate of change of f between $x = 2$ and $x = 6$.

20. Find $f^{-1}(1)$ and $f^{-1}(3)$.

21. Sketch the graph of f^{-1}.

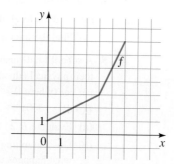

22. Let $f(x) = 3x^4 - 14x^2 + 5x - 3$.

  (a) Draw the graph of f in an appropriate viewing rectangle.

  (b) Is f one-to-one?

  (c) Find the local maximum and minimum values of f and the values of x at which they occur. State each answer correct to two decimal places.

  (d) Use the graph to determine the range of f.

  (e) Find the intervals on which f is increasing and on which f is decreasing.

A CUMULATIVE REVIEW TEST FOR CHAPTERS 1 AND 2 CAN BE FOUND AT THE BOOK COMPANION WEBSITE: **www.stewartmath.com**.

Modeling with Functions

Many of the processes that are studied in the physical and social sciences involve understanding how one quantity varies with respect to another. Finding a function that describes the dependence of one quantity on another is called *modeling*. For example, a biologist observes that the number of bacteria in a certain culture increases with time. He tries to model this phenomenon by finding the precise function (or rule) that relates the bacteria population to the elapsed time.

In this *Focus on Modeling* we will learn how to find models that can be constructed using geometric or algebraic properties of the object under study. Once the model is found, we use it to analyze and predict properties of the object or process being studied.

■ Modeling with Functions

We begin by giving some general guidelines for making a function model.

GUIDELINES FOR MODELING WITH FUNCTIONS

1. **Express the Model in Words.** Identify the quantity you want to model, and express it, in words, as a function of the other quantities in the problem.

2. **Choose the Variable.** Identify all the variables that are used to express the function in Step 1. Assign a symbol, such as x, to one variable, and express the other variables in terms of this symbol.

3. **Set up the Model.** Express the function in the language of algebra by writing it as a function of the single variable chosen in Step 2.

4. **Use the Model.** Use the function to answer the questions posed in the problem. (To find a maximum or a minimum, use the methods described in Section 2.3.)

EXAMPLE 1 ■ Fencing a Garden

A gardener has 140 feet of fencing to fence in a rectangular vegetable garden.

(a) Find a function that models the area of the garden she can fence.

(b) For what range of widths is the area greater than 825 ft²?

(c) Can she fence a garden with area 1250 ft²?

(d) Find the dimensions of the largest area she can fence.

> **THINKING ABOUT THE PROBLEM**
>
> If the gardener fences a plot with width 10 ft, then the length must be 60 ft, because $10 + 10 + 60 + 60 = 140$. So the area is
>
> $$A = \text{width} \times \text{length} = 10 \cdot 60 = 600 \text{ ft}^2$$
>
> The table shows various choices for fencing the garden. We see that as the width increases, the fenced area increases, then decreases.

Width	Length	Area
10	60	600
20	50	1000
30	40	1200
40	30	1200
50	20	1000
60	10	600

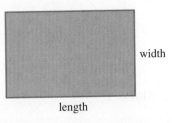

length

width

273

SOLUTION

(a) The model that we want is a function that gives the area she can fence.

Express the model in words.   We know that the area of a rectangular garden is

$$\text{area} = \text{width} \times \text{length}$$

Choose the variable.   There are two varying quantities: width and length. Because the function we want depends on only one variable, we let

$$x = \text{width of the garden}$$

Then we must express the length in terms of x. The perimeter is fixed at 140 ft, so the length is determined once we choose the width. If we let the length be l, as in Figure 1, then $2x + 2l = 140$, so $l = 70 - x$. We summarize these facts:

In Words	In Algebra
Width	x
Length	$70 - x$

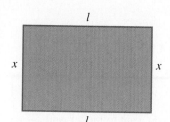

FIGURE 1

Set up the model.   The model is the function A that gives the area of the garden for any width x.

$$\text{area} = \text{width} \times \text{length}$$

$$A(x) = x(70 - x)$$

$$A(x) = 70x - x^2$$

The area that she can fence is modeled by the function $A(x) = 70x - x^2$.

Use the model.   We use the model to answer the questions in parts (b)–(d).

(b) We need to solve the inequality $A(x) \geq 825$. To solve graphically, we graph $y = 70x - x^2$ and $y = 825$ in the same viewing rectangle (see Figure 2). We see that $15 \leq x \leq 55$.

(c) From Figure 3 we see that the graph of $A(x)$ always lies below the line $y = 1250$, so an area of 1250 ft^2 is never attained.

Maximum values of functions are discussed on page 212.

(d) We need to find where the maximum value of the function $A(x) = 70x - x^2$ occurs. The function is graphed in Figure 4. Using the $\boxed{\text{TRACE}}$ feature on a graphing calculator, we find that the function achieves its maximum value at $x = 35$. So the maximum area that she can fence is that when the garden's width is 35 ft and its length is $70 - 35 = 35$ ft. The maximum area then is $35 \times 35 = 1225$ ft^2.

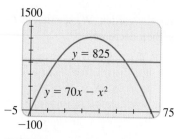

FIGURE 2

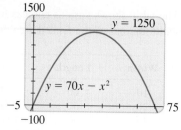

FIGURE 3

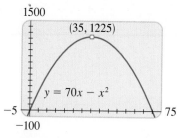

FIGURE 4

EXAMPLE 2 ■ Minimizing the Metal in a Can

A manufacturer makes a metal can that holds 1 L (liter) of oil. What radius minimizes the amount of metal in the can?

THINKING ABOUT THE PROBLEM

To use the least amount of metal, we must minimize the surface area of the can, that is, the area of the top, bottom, and the sides. The area of the top and bottom is $2\pi r^2$ and the area of the sides is $2\pi rh$ (see Figure 5), so the surface area of the can is

$$S = 2\pi r^2 + 2\pi rh$$

The radius and height of the can must be chosen so that the volume is exactly 1 L, or 1000 cm³. If we want a small radius, say, $r = 3$, then the height must be just tall enough to make the total volume 1000 cm³. In other words, we must have

$$\pi(3)^2 h = 1000 \qquad \text{Volume of the can is } \pi r^2 h$$

$$h = \frac{1000}{9\pi} \approx 35.37 \text{ cm} \qquad \text{Solve for } h$$

Now that we know the radius and height, we can find the surface area of the can:

$$\text{surface area} = 2\pi(3)^2 + 2\pi(3)(35.4) \approx 723.2 \text{ cm}^3$$

If we want a different radius, we can find the corresponding height and surface area in a similar fashion.

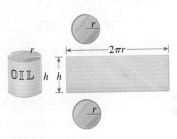

FIGURE 5

SOLUTION   The model that we want is a function that gives the surface area of the can.

Express the model in words.   We know that for a cylindrical can

$$\boxed{\text{surface area}} \;=\; \boxed{\text{area of top and bottom}} \;+\; \boxed{\text{area of sides}}$$

Choose the variable.   There are two varying quantities: radius and height. Because the function we want depends on the radius, we let

$$r = \text{radius of can}$$

Next, we must express the height in terms of the radius r. Because the volume of a cylindrical can is $V = \pi r^2 h$ and the volume must be 1000 cm³, we have

$$\pi r^2 h = 1000 \qquad \text{Volume of can is 1000 cm}^3$$

$$h = \frac{1000}{\pi r^2} \qquad \text{Solve for } h$$

We can now express the areas of the top, bottom, and sides in terms of r only:

In Words	In Algebra
Radius of can	r
Height of can	$\dfrac{1000}{\pi r^2}$
Area of top and bottom	$2\pi r^2$
Area of sides $(2\pi rh)$	$2\pi r\left(\dfrac{1000}{\pi r^2}\right)$

Set up the model. The model is the function S that gives the surface area of the can as a function of the radius r.

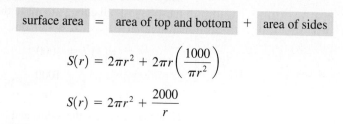

$$\text{surface area} = \text{area of top and bottom} + \text{area of sides}$$

$$S(r) = 2\pi r^2 + 2\pi r\left(\frac{1000}{\pi r^2}\right)$$

$$S(r) = 2\pi r^2 + \frac{2000}{r}$$

Use the model. We use the model to find the minimum surface area of the can. We graph S in Figure 6 and zoom in on the minimum point to find that the minimum value of S is about 554 cm² and occurs when the radius is about 5.4 cm. ∎

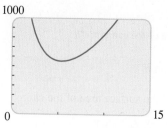

FIGURE 6 $S(r) = 2\pi r^2 + \dfrac{2000}{r}$

PROBLEMS

1–18 ■ In these problems you are asked to find a function that models a real-life situation. Use the principles of modeling described in this Focus to help you.

1. Area A rectangular building lot is three times as long as it is wide. Find a function that models its area A in terms of its width w.

2. Area A poster is 10 in. longer than it is wide. Find a function that models its area A in terms of its width w.

3. Volume A rectangular box has a square base. Its height is half the width of the base. Find a function that models its volume V in terms of its width w.

4. Volume The height of a cylinder is four times its radius. Find a function that models the volume V of the cylinder in terms of its radius r.

5. Area A rectangle has a perimeter of 20 ft. Find a function that models its area A in terms of the length x of one of its sides.

6. Perimeter A rectangle has an area of 16 m². Find a function that models its perimeter P in terms of the length x of one of its sides.

7. Area Find a function that models the area A of an equilateral triangle in terms of the length x of one of its sides.

8. Area Find a function that models the surface area S of a cube in terms of its volume V.

9. Radius Find a function that models the radius r of a circle in terms of its area A.

10. Area Find a function that models the area A of a circle in terms of its circumference C.

11. Area A rectangular box with a volume of 60 ft³ has a square base. Find a function that models its surface area S in terms of the length x of one side of its base.

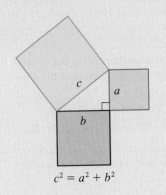
12. Length   A woman 5 ft tall is standing near a street lamp that is 12 ft tall, as shown in the figure. Find a function that models the length L of her shadow in terms of her distance d from the base of the lamp.

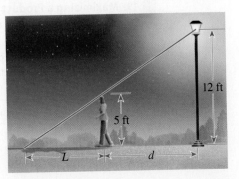

13. Distance   Two ships leave port at the same time. One sails south at 15 mi/h, and the other sails east at 20 mi/h. Find a function that models the distance D between the ships in terms of the time t (in hours) elapsed since their departure.

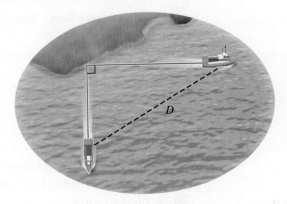

14. Product   The sum of two positive numbers is 60. Find a function that models their product P in terms of x, one of the numbers.

15. Area   An isosceles triangle has a perimeter of 8 cm. Find a function that models its area A in terms of the length of its base b.

16. Perimeter   A right triangle has one leg twice as long as the other. Find a function that models its perimeter P in terms of the length x of the shorter leg.

17. Area   A rectangle is inscribed in a semicircle of radius 10, as shown in the figure. Find a function that models the area A of the rectangle in terms of its height h.

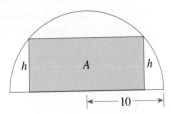

18. Height   The volume of a cone is 100 in^3. Find a function that models the height h of the cone in terms of its radius r.

19–32 ■ In these problems you are asked to find a function that models a real-life situation and then use the model to answer questions about the situation. Use the guidelines on page 273 to help you.

19. Maximizing a Product   Consider the following problem: Find two numbers whose sum is 19 and whose product is as large as possible.

(a) Experiment with the problem by making a table like the one following, showing the product of different pairs of numbers that add up to 19. On the basis of the evidence in your table, estimate the answer to the problem.

First number	Second number	Product
1	18	18
2	17	34
3	16	48
⋮	⋮	⋮

(b) Find a function that models the product in terms of one of the two numbers.

(c) Use your model to solve the problem, and compare with your answer to part (a).

20. Minimizing a Sum   Find two positive numbers whose sum is 100 and the sum of whose squares is a minimum.

21. Fencing a Field   Consider the following problem: A farmer has 2400 ft of fencing and wants to fence off a rectangular field that borders a straight river. He does not need a fence along the river (see the figure). What are the dimensions of the field of largest area that he can fence?

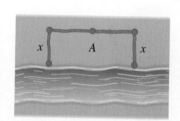

(a) Experiment with the problem by drawing several diagrams illustrating the situation. Calculate the area of each configuration, and use your results to estimate the dimensions of the largest possible field.

(b) Find a function that models the area of the field in terms of one of its sides.

(c) Use your model to solve the problem, and compare with your answer to part (a).

22. Dividing a Pen   A rancher with 750 ft of fencing wants to enclose a rectangular area and then divide it into four pens with fencing parallel to one side of the rectangle (see the figure).

(a) Find a function that models the total area of the four pens.

(b) Find the largest possible total area of the four pens.

23. Fencing a Garden Plot   A property owner wants to fence a garden plot adjacent to a road, as shown in the figure. The fencing next to the road must be sturdier and costs $5 per foot, but the other fencing costs just $3 per foot. The garden is to have an area of 1200 ft².

(a) Find a function that models the cost of fencing the garden.

(b) Find the garden dimensions that minimize the cost of fencing.

(c) If the owner has at most $600 to spend on fencing, find the range of lengths he can fence along the road.

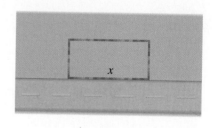

24. Maximizing Area A wire 10 cm long is cut into two pieces, one of length x and the other of length $10 - x$, as shown in the figure. Each piece is bent into the shape of a square.

(a) Find a function that models the total area enclosed by the two squares.

(b) Find the value of x that minimizes the total area of the two squares.

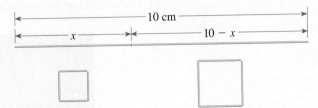

25. Light from a Window A Norman window has the shape of a rectangle surmounted by a semicircle, as shown in the figure to the left. A Norman window with perimeter 30 ft is to be constructed.

(a) Find a function that models the area of the window.

(b) Find the dimensions of the window that admits the greatest amount of light.

26. Volume of a Box A box with an open top is to be constructed from a rectangular piece of cardboard with dimensions 12 in. by 20 in. by cutting out equal squares of side x at each corner and then folding up the sides (see the figure).

(a) Find a function that models the volume of the box.

(b) Find the values of x for which the volume is greater than 200 in^3.

(c) Find the largest volume that such a box can have.

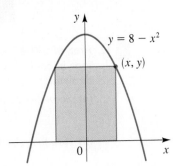

27. Area of a Box An open box with a square base is to have a volume of 12 ft^3.

(a) Find a function that models the surface area of the box.

(b) Find the box dimensions that minimize the amount of material used.

28. Inscribed Rectangle Find the dimensions that give the largest area for the rectangle shown in the figure. Its base is on the x-axis, and its other two vertices are above the x-axis, lying on the parabola $y = 8 - x^2$.

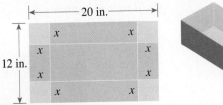

29. Minimizing Costs A rancher wants to build a rectangular pen with an area of 100 m^2.

(a) Find a function that models the length of fencing required.

(b) Find the pen dimensions that require the minimum amount of fencing.

30. Minimizing Time A man stands at a point A on the bank of a straight river, 2 mi wide. To reach point B, 7 mi downstream on the opposite bank, he first rows his boat to point P on the opposite bank and then walks the remaining distance x to B, as shown in the figure. He can row at a speed of 2 mi/h and walk at a speed of 5 mi/h.

(a) Find a function that models the time needed for the trip.

(b) Where should he land so that he reaches B as soon as possible?

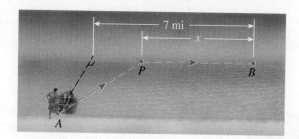

31. Bird Flight A bird is released from point A on an island, 5 mi from the nearest point B on a straight shoreline. The bird flies to a point C on the shoreline and then flies along the shoreline to its nesting area D (see the figure). Suppose the bird requires 10 kcal/mi of energy to fly over land and 14 kcal/mi to fly over water.

(a) Use the fact that

$$\text{energy used} = \text{energy per mile} \times \text{miles flown}$$

to show that the total energy used by the bird is modeled by the function

$$E(x) = 14\sqrt{x^2 + 25} + 10(12 - x)$$

(b) If the bird instinctively chooses a path that minimizes its energy expenditure, to what point does it fly?

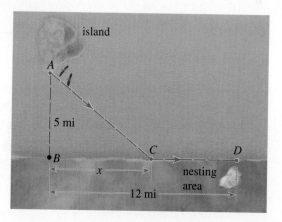

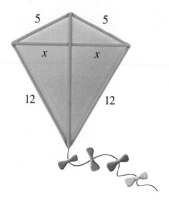

32. Area of a Kite A kite frame is to be made from six pieces of wood. The four pieces that form its border have been cut to the lengths indicated in the figure. Let x be as shown in the figure.

(a) Show that the area of the kite is given by the function

$$A(x) = x\left(\sqrt{25 - x^2} + \sqrt{144 - x^2}\right)$$

(b) How long should each of the two crosspieces be to maximize the area of the kite?

© Porojnicu Stelian/Shutterstock.com

3 Polynomial and Rational Functions

Functions defined by polynomial expressions are called *polynomial functions*. The graphs of polynomial functions can have many peaks and valleys. This property makes them suitable models for many real-world situations. For example, a factory owner notices that if she increases the number of workers, productivity increases, but if there are too many workers, productivity begins to decrease. This situation is modeled by a polynomial function of degree 2 (a quadratic function). The growth of many animal species follows a predictable pattern, beginning with a period of rapid growth, followed by a period of slow growth and then a final growth spurt. This variability in growth is modeled by a polynomial of degree 3.

In the *Focus on Modeling* at the end of this chapter we explore different ways of using polynomial functions to model real-world situations.

3.1 # QUADRATIC FUNCTIONS AND MODELS

■ Graphing Quadratic Functions Using the Standard Form ■ Maximum and Minimum Values of Quadratic Functions ■ Modeling with Quadratic Functions

Polynomial expressions are defined in Section P.5.

A polynomial function is a function that is defined by a polynomial expression. So a **polynomial function of degree n** is a function of the form

$$P(x) = a_n x^n + a_{n-1} x^{n-1} + \cdots + a_1 x + a_0 \qquad a_n \neq 0$$

We have already studied polynomial functions of degree 0 and 1. These are functions of the form $P(x) = a_0$ and $P(x) = a_1 x + a_0$, respectively, whose graphs are lines. In this section we study polynomial functions of degree 2. These are called quadratic functions.

QUADRATIC FUNCTIONS

A **quadratic function** is a polynomial function of degree 2. So a quadratic function is a function of the form

$$f(x) = ax^2 + bx + c \qquad a \neq 0$$

We see in this section how quadratic functions model many real-world phenomena. We begin by analyzing the graphs of quadratic functions.

■ Graphing Quadratic Functions Using the Standard Form

For a geometric definition of parabolas, see Section 12.1.

If we take $a = 1$ and $b = c = 0$ in the quadratic function $f(x) = ax^2 + bx + c$, we get the quadratic function $f(x) = x^2$, whose graph is the parabola graphed in Example 1 of Section 2.2. In fact, the graph of any quadratic function is a **parabola**; it can be obtained from the graph of $f(x) = x^2$ by the transformations given in Section 2.6.

STANDARD FORM OF A QUADRATIC FUNCTION

A quadratic function $f(x) = ax^2 + bx + c$ can be expressed in the **standard form**

$$f(x) = a(x - h)^2 + k$$

by completing the square. The graph of f is a parabola with **vertex** (h, k); the parabola opens upward if $a > 0$ or downward if $a < 0$.

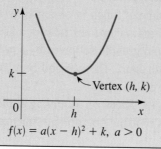

$f(x) = a(x - h)^2 + k,\ a > 0$

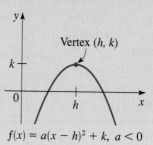

$f(x) = a(x - h)^2 + k,\ a < 0$

EXAMPLE 1 ■ Standard Form of a Quadratic Function

Let $f(x) = 2x^2 - 12x + 13$.

(a) Express f in standard form.

(b) Find the vertex and x- and y-intercepts of f.

(c) Sketch a graph of f.

(d) Find the domain and range of f.

SOLUTION

(a) Since the coefficient of x^2 is not 1, we must factor this coefficient from the terms involving x before we complete the square.

$$f(x) = 2x^2 - 12x + 13$$

$$= 2(x^2 - 6x) + 13 \qquad \text{Factor 2 from the } x\text{-terms}$$

$$= 2(x^2 - 6x + 9) + 13 - 2 \cdot 9 \qquad \begin{array}{l}\text{Complete the square: Add 9 inside} \\ \text{parentheses, subtract } 2 \cdot 9 \text{ outside}\end{array}$$

$$= 2(x - 3)^2 - 5 \qquad \text{Factor and simplify}$$

Completing the square is discussed in Section 1.4.

The standard form is $f(x) = 2(x - 3)^2 - 5$.

(b) From the standard form of f we can see that the vertex of f is $(3, -5)$. The y-intercept is $f(0) = 13$. To find the x-intercepts, we set $f(x) = 0$ and solve the resulting equation. We can solve a quadratic equation by any of the methods we studied in Section 1.4. In this case we solve the equation by using the Quadratic Formula.

$$0 = 2x^2 - 12x + 13 \qquad \text{Set } f(x) = 0$$

$$x = \frac{12 \pm \sqrt{144 - 4 \cdot 2 \cdot 13}}{4} \qquad \text{Solve for } x \text{ using the Quadratic Formula}$$

$$x = \frac{6 \pm \sqrt{10}}{2} \qquad \text{Simplify}$$

Thus the x-intercepts are $x = (6 \pm \sqrt{10})/2$. So the intercepts are approximately 1.42 and 4.58.

(c) The standard form tells us that we get the graph of f by taking the parabola $y = x^2$, shifting it to the right 3 units, stretching it vertically by a factor of 2, and moving it downward 5 units. We sketch a graph of f in Figure 1, including the x- and y-intercepts found in part (b).

(d) The domain of f is the set of all real numbers $(-\infty, \infty)$. From the graph we see that the range of f is $[-5, \infty)$.

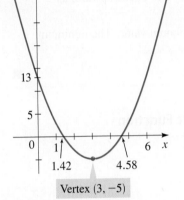

FIGURE 1 $f(x) = 2x^2 - 12x + 13$

✎ **Now Try Exercise 15** ∎

■ Maximum and Minimum Values of Quadratic Functions

If a quadratic function has vertex (h, k), then the function has a minimum value at the vertex if its graph opens upward and a maximum value at the vertex if its graph opens downward. For example, the function graphed in Figure 1 has minimum value 5 when $x = 3$, since the vertex $(3, 5)$ is the lowest point on the graph.

MAXIMUM OR MINIMUM VALUE OF A QUADRATIC FUNCTION

Let f be a quadratic function with standard form $f(x) = a(x - h)^2 + k$. The maximum or minimum value of f occurs at $x = h$.

If $a > 0$, then the **minimum value** of f is $f(h) = k$.

If $a < 0$, then the **maximum value** of f is $f(h) = k$.

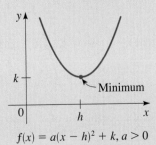

$f(x) = a(x - h)^2 + k, a > 0$

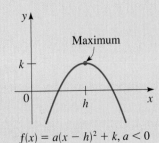

$f(x) = a(x - h)^2 + k, a < 0$

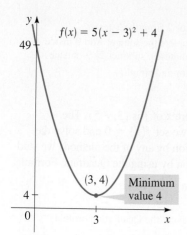

FIGURE 2

EXAMPLE 2 ■ Minimum Value of a Quadratic Function

Consider the quadratic function $f(x) = 5x^2 - 30x + 49$.

(a) Express f in standard form.

(b) Sketch a graph of f.

(c) Find the minimum value of f.

SOLUTION

(a) To express this quadratic function in standard form, we complete the square.

$$f(x) = 5x^2 - 30x + 49$$

$$= 5(x^2 - 6x) + 49 \qquad \text{Factor 5 from the } x\text{-terms}$$

$$= 5(x^2 - 6x + 9) + 49 - 5 \cdot 9 \qquad \begin{array}{l}\text{Complete the square: Add 9 inside}\\ \text{parentheses, subtract } 5 \cdot 9 \text{ outside}\end{array}$$

$$= 5(x - 3)^2 + 4 \qquad \text{Factor and simplify}$$

(b) The graph is a parabola that has its vertex at $(3, 4)$ and opens upward, as sketched in Figure 2.

(c) Since the coefficient of x^2 is positive, f has a minimum value. The minimum value is $f(3) = 4$.

✎ **Now Try Exercise 27**

EXAMPLE 3 ■ Maximum Value of a Quadratic Function

Consider the quadratic function $f(x) = -x^2 + x + 2$.

(a) Express f in standard form.

(b) Sketch a graph of f.

(c) Find the maximum value of f.

SOLUTION

(a) To express this quadratic function in standard form, we complete the square.

$$f(x) = -x^2 + x + 2$$

$$= -(x^2 - x) + 2 \qquad \text{Factor } -1 \text{ from the } x\text{-terms}$$

$$= -\left(x^2 - x + \tfrac{1}{4}\right) + 2 - (-1)\tfrac{1}{4} \qquad \begin{array}{l}\text{Complete the square: Add } \frac{1}{4} \text{ inside}\\ \text{parentheses, subtract } (-1)\frac{1}{4} \text{ outside}\end{array}$$

$$= -\left(x - \tfrac{1}{2}\right)^2 + \tfrac{9}{4} \qquad \text{Factor and simplify}$$

In Example 3 you can check that the x-intercepts of the parabola are -1 and 2. These are obtained by solving the equation $f(x) = 0$.

(b) From the standard form we see that the graph is a parabola that opens downward and has vertex $\left(\frac{1}{2}, \frac{9}{4}\right)$. The graph of f is sketched in Figure 3.

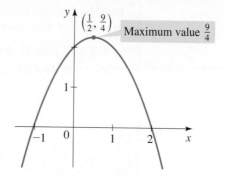

FIGURE 3 Graph of $f(x) = -x^2 + x + 2$

(c) Since the coefficient of x^2 is negative, f has a maximum value, which is $f\left(\frac{1}{2}\right) = \frac{9}{4}$.

✎ **Now Try Exercise 29**

Expressing a quadratic function in standard form helps us to sketch its graph as well as to find its maximum or minimum value. If we are interested only in finding the maximum or minimum value, then a formula is available for doing so. This formula is obtained by completing the square for the general quadratic function as follows.

$$f(x) = ax^2 + bx + c$$

$$= a\left(x^2 + \frac{b}{a}x\right) + c \qquad \text{Factor } a \text{ from the } x\text{-terms}$$

$$= a\left(x^2 + \frac{b}{a}x + \frac{b^2}{4a^2}\right) + c - a\left(\frac{b^2}{4a^2}\right) \qquad \begin{array}{l}\text{Complete the square: Add } \dfrac{b^2}{4a^2} \\ \text{inside parentheses, subtract} \\ a\left(\dfrac{b^2}{4a^2}\right) \text{ outside}\end{array}$$

$$= a\left(x + \frac{b}{2a}\right)^2 + c - \frac{b^2}{4a} \qquad \text{Factor}$$

This equation is in standard form with $h = -b/(2a)$ and $k = c - b^2/(4a)$. Since the maximum or minimum value occurs at $x = h$, we have the following result.

MAXIMUM OR MINIMUM VALUE OF A QUADRATIC FUNCTION

The maximum or minimum value of a quadratic function $f(x) = ax^2 + bx + c$ occurs at

$$x = -\frac{b}{2a}$$

If $a > 0$, then the **minimum value** is $f\left(-\dfrac{b}{2a}\right)$.

If $a < 0$, then the **maximum value** is $f\left(-\dfrac{b}{2a}\right)$.

EXAMPLE 4 ■ Finding Maximum and Minimum Values of Quadratic Functions

Find the maximum or minimum value of each quadratic function.

(a) $f(x) = x^2 + 4x$

(b) $g(x) = -2x^2 + 4x - 5$

SOLUTION

(a) This is a quadratic function with $a = 1$ and $b = 4$. Thus the maximum or minimum value occurs at

$$x = -\frac{b}{2a} = -\frac{4}{2 \cdot 1} = -2$$

Since $a > 0$, the function has the *minimum* value

$$f(-2) = (-2)^2 + 4(-2) = -4$$

(b) This is a quadratic function with $a = -2$ and $b = 4$. Thus the maximum or minimum value occurs at

$$x = -\frac{b}{2a} = -\frac{4}{2 \cdot (-2)} = 1$$

Since $a < 0$, the function has the *maximum* value

$$f(1) = -2(1)^2 + 4(1) - 5 = -3$$

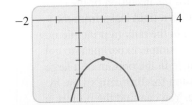

The minimum value occurs at $x = -2$.

The maximum value occurs at $x = 1$.

Now Try Exercises 35 and 37

■ Modeling with Quadratic Functions

We study some examples of real-world phenomena that are modeled by quadratic functions. These examples and the *Applications* exercises for this section show some of the variety of situations that are naturally modeled by quadratic functions.

EXAMPLE 5 ■ Maximum Gas Mileage for a Car

Most cars get their best gas mileage when traveling at a relatively modest speed. The gas mileage M for a certain new car is modeled by the function

$$M(s) = -\frac{1}{28}s^2 + 3s - 31 \qquad 15 \le s \le 70$$

where s is the speed in mi/h and M is measured in mi/gal. What is the car's best gas mileage, and at what speed is it attained?

SOLUTION   The function M is a quadratic function with $a = -\frac{1}{28}$ and $b = 3$. Thus its maximum value occurs when

$$s = -\frac{b}{2a} = -\frac{3}{2\left(-\frac{1}{28}\right)} = 42$$

The maximum value is $M(42) = -\frac{1}{28}(42)^2 + 3(42) - 31 = 32$. So the car's best gas mileage is 32 mi/gal when it is traveling at 42 mi/h.

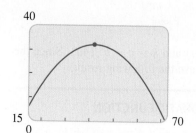

40

15
0   70

The maximum gas
mileage occurs at 42 mi/h.

✎ Now Try Exercise 55   ■

EXAMPLE 6 ■ Maximizing Revenue from Ticket Sales

A hockey team plays in an arena that has a seating capacity of 15,000 spectators. With the ticket price set at $14, average attendance at recent games has been 9500. A market survey indicates that for each dollar the ticket price is lowered, the average attendance increases by 1000.

(a) Find a function that models the revenue in terms of ticket price.

(b) Find the price that maximizes revenue from ticket sales.

(c) What ticket price is so high that no one attends and so no revenue is generated?

SOLUTION

(a) **Express the model in words.**   The model that we want is a function that gives the revenue for any ticket price:

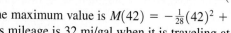

revenue = ticket price × attendance

DISCOVERY PROJECT

Torricelli's Law

Evangelista Torricelli (1608–1647) is best known for his invention of the barometer. He also discovered that the speed at which a fluid leaks from the bottom of a tank is related to the height of the fluid in the tank (a principle now called Torricelli's Law). In this project we conduct a simple experiment to collect data on the speed of water leaking through a hole in the bottom of a large soft-drink bottle. We then find an algebraic expression for Torricelli's Law by fitting a quadratic function to the data we obtained. You can find the project at **www.stewartmath.com**.

Choose the variable. There are two varying quantities: ticket price and attendance. Since the function we want depends on price, we let

$$x = \text{ticket price}$$

Next, we express attendance in terms of x.

In Words	In Algebra
Ticket price	x
Amount ticket price is lowered	$14 - x$
Increase in attendance	$1000(14 - x)$
Attendance	$9500 + 1000(14 - x)$

Set up the model. The model that we want is the function R that gives the revenue for a given ticket price x.

$$\boxed{\text{revenue} = \text{ticket price} \times \text{attendance}}$$

$$R(x) = x \times [9500 + 1000(14 - x)]$$

$$R(x) = x(23{,}500 - 1000x)$$

$$R(x) = 23{,}500x - 1000x^2$$

(b) Use the model. Since R is a quadratic function with $a = -1000$ and $b = 23{,}500$, the maximum occurs at

$$x = -\frac{b}{2a} = -\frac{23{,}500}{2(-1000)} = 11.75$$

So a ticket price of $11.75 gives the maximum revenue.

(c) Use the model. We want to find the ticket price for which $R(x) = 0$.

$$23{,}500x - 1000x^2 = 0 \qquad \text{Set } R(x) = 0$$

$$23.5x - x^2 = 0 \qquad \text{Divide by 1000}$$

$$x(23.5 - x) = 0 \qquad \text{Factor}$$

$$x = 0 \quad \text{or} \quad x = 23.5 \qquad \text{Solve for } x$$

So according to this model, a ticket price of $23.50 is just too high; at that price no one attends to watch this team play. (Of course, revenue is also zero if the ticket price is zero.)

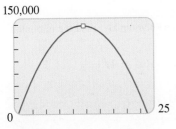

150,000

0   25

Maximum attendance occurs
when ticket price is $11.75.

✎ **Now Try Exercise 65**

3.1 EXERCISES

CONCEPTS

1. To put the quadratic function $f(x) = ax^2 + bx + c$ in

standard form, we complete the _____.

2. The quadratic function $f(x) = a(x - h)^2 + k$ is in standard form.

(a) The graph of f is a parabola with vertex

(____, ____).

(b) If $a > 0$, the graph of f opens _____. In this case

$f(h) = k$ is the _____ value of f.

(c) If $a < 0$, the graph of f opens _____. In this case

$f(h) = k$ is the _____ value of f.

3. The graph of $f(x) = 3(x - 2)^2 - 6$ is a parabola that opens

_____, with its vertex at (____, ____), and $f(2) =$

_____ is the (minimum/maximum) _____ value of f.

4. The graph of $f(x) = -3(x - 2)^2 - 6$ is a parabola that

opens _____, with its vertex at (____, ____), and

$f(2) =$ _____ is the (minimum/maximum) _____

value of f.

SKILLS

5–8 ■ **Graphs of Quadratic Functions** The graph of a quadratic function f is given. **(a)** Find the coordinates of the vertex and the x- and y-intercepts. **(b)** Find the maximum or minimum value of f. **(c)** Find the domain and range of f.

5. $f(x) = -x^2 + 6x - 5$ **6.** $f(x) = -\frac{1}{2}x^2 - 2x + 6$

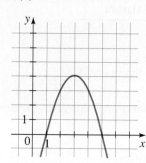
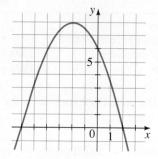

7. $f(x) = 2x^2 - 4x - 1$ **8.** $f(x) = 3x^2 + 6x - 1$

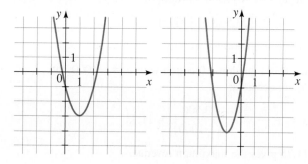

9–24 ■ **Graphing Quadratic Functions** A quadratic function f is given. **(a)** Express f in standard form. **(b)** Find the vertex and x- and y-intercepts of f. **(c)** Sketch a graph of f. **(d)** Find the domain and range of f.

9. $f(x) = x^2 - 2x + 3$ **10.** $f(x) = x^2 + 4x - 1$

11. $f(x) = x^2 - 6x$ **12.** $f(x) = x^2 + 8x$

13. $f(x) = 3x^2 + 6x$ **14.** $f(x) = -x^2 + 10x$

15. $f(x) = x^2 + 4x + 3$ **16.** $f(x) = x^2 - 2x + 2$

17. $f(x) = -x^2 + 6x + 4$ **18.** $f(x) = -x^2 - 4x + 4$

19. $f(x) = 2x^2 + 4x + 3$ **20.** $f(x) = -3x^2 + 6x - 2$

21. $f(x) = 2x^2 - 20x + 57$ **22.** $f(x) = 2x^2 + 12x + 10$

23. $f(x) = -4x^2 - 12x + 1$ **24.** $f(x) = 3x^2 + 2x - 2$

25–34 ■ **Maximum and Minimum Values** A quadratic function f is given. **(a)** Express f in standard form. **(b)** Sketch a graph of f. **(c)** Find the maximum or minimum value of f.

25. $f(x) = x^2 + 2x - 1$ **26.** $f(x) = x^2 - 8x + 8$

27. $f(x) = 3x^2 - 6x + 1$ **28.** $f(x) = 5x^2 + 30x + 4$

29. $f(x) = -x^2 - 3x + 3$ **30.** $f(x) = 1 - 6x - x^2$

31. $g(x) = 3x^2 - 12x + 13$ **32.** $g(x) = 2x^2 + 8x + 11$

33. $h(x) = 1 - x - x^2$ **34.** $h(x) = 3 - 4x - 4x^2$

35–44 ■ **Formula for Maximum and Minimum Values** Find the maximum or minimum value of the function.

35. $f(x) = 2x^2 + 4x - 1$ **36.** $f(x) = 3 - 4x - x^2$

37. $f(t) = -3 + 80t - 20t^2$ **38.** $f(x) = 6x^2 - 24x - 100$

39. $f(s) = s^2 - 1.2s + 16$ **40.** $g(x) = 100x^2 - 1500x$

41. $h(x) = \frac{1}{2}x^2 + 2x - 6$ **42.** $f(x) = -\frac{x^2}{3} + 2x + 7$

43. $f(x) = 3 - x - \frac{1}{2}x^2$ **44.** $g(x) = 2x(x - 4) + 7$

45–46 ■ **Maximum and Minimum Values** A quadratic function is given. **(a)** Use a graphing device to find the maximum or minimum value of the quadratic function f, rounded to two decimal places. **(b)** Find the exact maximum or minimum value of f, and compare it with your answer to part (a).

45. $f(x) = x^2 + 1.79x - 3.21$

46. $f(x) = 1 + x - \sqrt{2}x^2$

SKILLS Plus

47–48 ■ **Finding Quadratic Functions** Find a function f whose graph is a parabola with the given vertex and that passes through the given point.

47. Vertex $(2, -3)$;   point $(3, 1)$

48. Vertex $(-1, 5)$;   point $(-3, -7)$

49. **Maximum of a Fourth-Degree Polynomial** Find the maximum value of the function

$$f(x) = 3 + 4x^2 - x^4$$

[*Hint:* Let $t = x^2$.]

50. **Minimum of a Sixth-Degree Polynomial** Find the minimum value of the function

$$f(x) = 2 + 16x^3 + 4x^6$$

[*Hint:* Let $t = x^3$.]

APPLICATIONS

51. **Height of a Ball** If a ball is thrown directly upward with a velocity of 40 ft/s, its height (in feet) after t seconds is given by $y = 40t - 16t^2$. What is the maximum height attained by the ball?

52. **Path of a Ball** A ball is thrown across a playing field from a height of 5 ft above the ground at an angle of 45° to the horizontal at a speed of 20 ft/s. It can be deduced from physical principles that the path of the ball is modeled by the function

$$y = -\frac{32}{(20)^2}x^2 + x + 5$$

where x is the distance in feet that the ball has traveled horizontally.

(a) Find the maximum height attained by the ball.

(b) Find the horizontal distance the ball has traveled when it hits the ground.

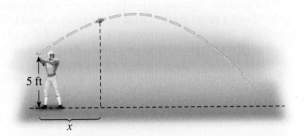

5 ft

x

53. **Revenue** A manufacturer finds that the revenue generated by selling x units of a certain commodity is given by the function $R(x) = 80x - 0.4x^2$, where the revenue $R(x)$ is measured in dollars. What is the maximum revenue, and how many units should be manufactured to obtain this maximum?

54. **Sales** A soft-drink vendor at a popular beach analyzes his sales records and finds that if he sells x cans of soda pop in one day, his profit (in dollars) is given by

$$P(x) = -0.001x^2 + 3x - 1800$$

What is his maximum profit per day, and how many cans must he sell for maximum profit?

55. **Advertising** The effectiveness of a television commercial depends on how many times a viewer watches it. After some experiments an advertising agency found that if the effectiveness E is measured on a scale of 0 to 10, then

$$E(n) = \tfrac{2}{3}n - \tfrac{1}{90}n^2$$

where n is the number of times a viewer watches a given commercial. For a commercial to have maximum effectiveness, how many times should a viewer watch it?

56. **Pharmaceuticals** When a certain drug is taken orally, the concentration of the drug in the patient's bloodstream after t minutes is given by $C(t) = 0.06t - 0.0002t^2$, where $0 \le t \le 240$ and the concentration is measured in mg/L. When is the maximum serum concentration reached, and what is that maximum concentration?

57. **Agriculture** The number of apples produced by each tree in an apple orchard depends on how densely the trees are planted. If n trees are planted on an acre of land, then each tree produces $900 - 9n$ apples. So the number of apples produced per acre is

$$A(n) = n(900 - 9n)$$

How many trees should be planted per acre to obtain the maximum yield of apples?

58. **Agriculture** At a certain vineyard it is found that each grape vine produces about 10 lb of grapes in a season when about 700 vines are planted per acre. For each additional vine that is planted, the production of each vine decreases by about 1 percent. So the number of pounds of grapes produced per acre is modeled by

$$A(n) = (700 + n)(10 - 0.01n)$$

where n is the number of additional vines planted. Find the number of vines that should be planted to maximize grape production.

59–62 ■ **Maxima and Minima** Use the formulas of this section to give an alternative solution to the indicated problem in *Focus on Modeling: Modeling with Functions* on pages 237–244.

59. Problem 21
60. Problem 22
61. Problem 25
62. Problem 24

63. **Fencing a Horse Corral** Carol has 2400 ft of fencing to fence in a rectangular horse corral.

(a) Find a function that models the area of the corral in terms of the width x of the corral.

(b) Find the dimensions of the rectangle that maximize the area of the corral.

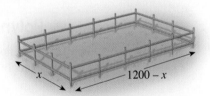

x $1200 - x$

64. **Making a Rain Gutter** A rain gutter is formed by bending up the sides of a 30-in.-wide rectangular metal sheet as shown in the figure.

(a) Find a function that models the cross-sectional area of the gutter in terms of x.

(b) Find the value of x that maximizes the cross-sectional area of the gutter.

(c) What is the maximum cross-sectional area for the gutter?

x 30 in.

65. **Stadium Revenue** A baseball team plays in a stadium that holds 55,000 spectators. With the ticket price at $10, the average attendance at recent games has been 27,000. A market survey indicates that for every dollar the ticket price is lowered, attendance increases by 3000.

(a) Find a function that models the revenue in terms of ticket price.

(b) Find the price that maximizes revenue from ticket sales.

(c) What ticket price is so high that no revenue is generated?

66. Maximizing Profit A community bird-watching society makes and sells simple bird feeders to raise money for its conservation activities. The materials for each feeder cost $6, and the society sells an average of 20 per week at a price of $10 each. The society has been considering raising the price, so it conducts a survey and finds that for every dollar increase, it will lose 2 sales per week.

(a) Find a function that models weekly profit in terms of price per feeder.

(b) What price should the society charge for each feeder to maximize profits? What is the maximum weekly profit?

DISCUSS ■ DISCOVER ■ PROVE ■ WRITE

67. DISCOVER: Vertex and x-Intercepts We know that the graph of the quadratic function $f(x) = (x - m)(x - n)$ is a parabola. Sketch a rough graph of what such a parabola would look like. What are the x-intercepts of the graph of f? Can you tell from your graph the x-coordinate of the vertex in terms of m and n? (Use the symmetry of the parabola.) Confirm your answer by expanding and using the formulas of this section.

3.2 POLYNOMIAL FUNCTIONS AND THEIR GRAPHS

■ Polynomial Functions ■ Graphing Basic Polynomial Functions ■ Graphs of Polynomial Functions: End Behavior ■ Using Zeros to Graph Polynomials ■ Shape of the Graph Near a Zero ■ Local Maxima and Minima of Polynomials

■ Polynomial Functions

In this section we study polynomial functions of any degree. But before we work with polynomial functions, we must agree on some terminology.

POLYNOMIAL FUNCTIONS

A **polynomial function of degree n** is a function of the form

$$P(x) = a_n x^n + a_{n-1} x^{n-1} + \cdots + a_1 x + a_0$$

where n is a nonnegative integer and $a_n \neq 0$.

The numbers $a_0, a_1, a_2, \ldots, a_n$ are called the **coefficients** of the polynomial.

The number a_0 is the **constant coefficient** or **constant term**.

The number a_n, the coefficient of the highest power, is the **leading coefficient**, and the term $a_n x^n$ is the **leading term**.

We often refer to polynomial functions simply as *polynomials*. The following polynomial has degree 5, leading coefficient 3, and constant term -6.

Leading coefficient 3 Degree 5 Constant term -6

$$3x^5 + 6x^4 - 2x^3 + x^2 + 7x - 6$$

Leading term $3x^5$

Coefficients 3, 6, -2, 1, 7, and -6

The table lists some more examples of polynomials.

Polynomial	Degree	Leading term	Constant term
$P(x) = 4x - 7$	1	$4x$	-7
$P(x) = x^2 + x$	2	x^2	0
$P(x) = 2x^3 - 6x^2 + 10$	3	$2x^3$	10
$P(x) = -5x^4 + x - 2$	4	$-5x^4$	-2

If a polynomial consists of just a single term, then it is called a **monomial**. For example, $P(x) = x^3$ and $Q(x) = -6x^5$ are monomials.

■ Graphing Basic Polynomial Functions

The simplest polynomial functions are the monomials $P(x) = x^n$, whose graphs are shown in Figure 1. As the figure suggests, the graph of $P(x) = x^n$ has the same general shape as the graph of $y = x^2$ when n is even and the same general shape as the graph of $y = x^3$ when n is odd. However, as the degree n becomes larger, the graphs become flatter around the origin and steeper elsewhere.

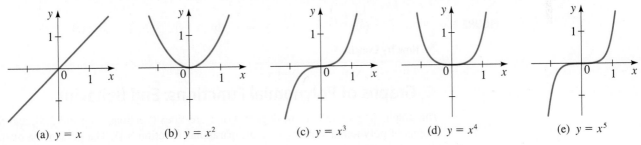

(a) $y = x$ (b) $y = x^2$ (c) $y = x^3$ (d) $y = x^4$ (e) $y = x^5$

FIGURE 1 Graphs of monomials

EXAMPLE 1 ■ Transformations of Monomials

Sketch graphs of the following functions.

(a) $P(x) = -x^3$ (b) $Q(x) = (x - 2)^4$

(c) $R(x) = -2x^5 + 4$

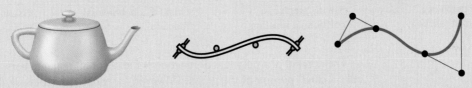

Mathematics in the Modern World

Splines

A spline is a long strip of wood that is curved while held fixed at certain points. In the old days shipbuilders used splines to create the curved shape of a boat's hull. Splines are also used to make the curves of a piano, a violin, or the spout of a teapot.

Mathematicians discovered that the shapes of splines can be obtained by piecing together parts of polynomials. For example, the graph of a cubic polynomial can be made to fit specified points by adjusting the coefficients of the polynomial (see Example 10, page 301).

Curves obtained in this way are called cubic splines. In modern computer design programs, such as Adobe Illustrator or Microsoft Paint, a curve can be drawn by fixing two points, then using the mouse to drag one or more anchor points. Moving the anchor points amounts to adjusting the coefficients of a cubic polynomial.

SOLUTION We use the graphs in Figure 1 and transform them using the techniques of Section 2.6.

(a) The graph of $P(x) = -x^3$ is the reflection of the graph of $y = x^3$ in the x-axis, as shown in Figure 2(a) below.

(b) The graph of $Q(x) = (x - 2)^4$ is the graph of $y = x^4$ shifted to the right 2 units, as shown in Figure 2(b).

(c) We begin with the graph of $y = x^5$. The graph of $y = -2x^5$ is obtained by stretching the graph vertically and reflecting it in the x-axis (see the dashed blue graph in Figure 2(c)). Finally, the graph of $R(x) = -2x^5 + 4$ is obtained by shifting upward 4 units (see the red graph in Figure 2(c)).

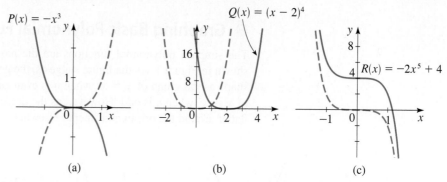

FIGURE 2

(a)　　　　　　(b)　　　　　　(c)

▨ **Now Try Exercise 5**

■

Graphs of Polynomial Functions: End Behavior

The graphs of polynomials of degree 0 or 1 are lines (Sections 1.10 and 2.5), and the graphs of polynomials of degree 2 are parabolas (Section 3.1). The greater the degree of a polynomial, the more complicated its graph can be. However, the graph of a polynomial function is **continuous**. This means that the graph has no breaks or holes (see Figure 3). Moreover, the graph of a polynomial function is a smooth curve; that is, it has no corners or sharp points (cusps) as shown in Figure 3.

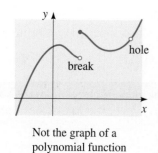

Not the graph of a polynomial function

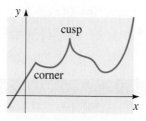

Not the graph of a polynomial function

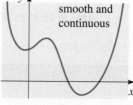

Graph of a polynomial function

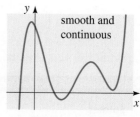

Graph of a polynomial function

FIGURE 3

The domain of a polynomial function is the set of all real numbers, so we can sketch only a small portion of the graph. However, for values of x outside the portion of the graph we have drawn, we can describe the behavior of the graph.

The **end behavior** of a polynomial is a description of what happens as x becomes large in the positive or negative direction. To describe end behavior, we use the following **arrow notation**.

Symbol	Meaning
$x \to \infty$	x goes to infinity; that is, x increases without bound
$x \to -\infty$	x goes to negative infinity; that is, x decreases without bound

For example, the monomial $y = x^2$ in Figure 1(b) has the following end behavior.

$$y \to \infty \quad \text{as} \quad x \to \infty \qquad \text{and} \qquad y \to \infty \quad \text{as} \quad x \to -\infty$$

The monomial $y = x^3$ in Figure 1(c) has the following end behavior.

$$y \to \infty \quad \text{as} \quad x \to \infty \qquad \text{and} \qquad y \to -\infty \quad \text{as} \quad x \to -\infty$$

For any polynomial *the end behavior is determined by the term that contains the high-est power of x*, because when x is large, the other terms are relatively insignificant in size. The following box shows the four possible types of end behavior, based on the highest power and the sign of its coefficient.

END BEHAVIOR OF POLYNOMIALS

The end behavior of the polynomial $P(x) = a_n x^n + a_{n-1} x^{n-1} + \cdots + a_1 x + a_0$ is determined by the degree n and the sign of the leading coefficient a_n, as indicated in the following graphs.

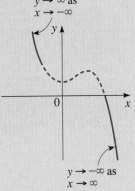

P has odd degree

$y \to \infty$ as $x \to \infty$

$y \to -\infty$ as $x \to -\infty$

Leading coefficient positive

$y \to \infty$ as $x \to -\infty$

$y \to -\infty$ as $x \to \infty$

Leading coefficient negative

P has even degree

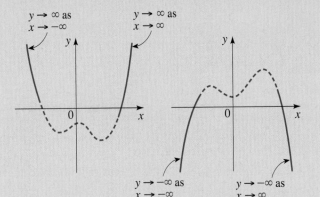

$y \to \infty$ as $x \to -\infty$

$y \to \infty$ as $x \to \infty$

$y \to -\infty$ as $x \to -\infty$

Leading coefficient positive

$y \to \infty$ as $x \to \infty$

$y \to -\infty$ as $x \to -\infty$

$y \to -\infty$ as $x \to \infty$

Leading coefficient negative

EXAMPLE 2 ■ End Behavior of a Polynomial

Determine the end behavior of the polynomial

$$P(x) = -2x^4 + 5x^3 + 4x - 7$$

SOLUTION The polynomial P has degree 4 and leading coefficient -2. Thus P has *even* degree and *negative* leading coefficient, so it has the following end behavior.

$$y \to -\infty \quad \text{as} \quad x \to \infty \qquad \text{and} \qquad y \to -\infty \quad \text{as} \quad x \to -\infty$$

The graph in Figure 4 illustrates the end behavior of P.

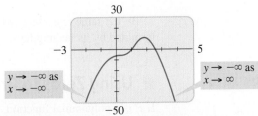

30

-3 5

$y \to -\infty$ as $x \to -\infty$

$y \to -\infty$ as $x \to \infty$

-50

FIGURE 4 $P(x) = -2x^4 + 5x^3 + 4x - 7$

✎ Now Try Exercise 11

EXAMPLE 3 ■ End Behavior of a Polynomial

(a) Determine the end behavior of the polynomial $P(x) = 3x^5 - 5x^3 + 2x$.

(b) Confirm that P and its leading term $Q(x) = 3x^5$ have the same end behavior by graphing them together.

SOLUTION

(a) Since P has odd degree and positive leading coefficient, it has the following end behavior.

$$y \to \infty \quad \text{as} \quad x \to \infty \qquad \text{and} \qquad y \to -\infty \quad \text{as} \quad x \to -\infty$$

(b) Figure 5 shows the graphs of P and Q in progressively larger viewing rectangles. The larger the viewing rectangle, the more the graphs look alike. This confirms that they have the same end behavior.

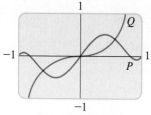 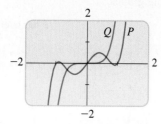 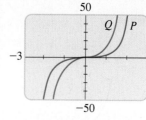 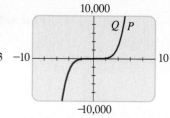

FIGURE 5
$P(x) = 3x^5 - 5x^3 + 2x$
$Q(x) = 3x^5$

✎. Now Try Exercise 45 ■

To see algebraically why P and Q in Example 3 have the same end behavior, factor P as follows and compare with Q.

$$P(x) = 3x^5\left(1 - \frac{5}{3x^2} + \frac{2}{3x^4}\right) \qquad Q(x) = 3x^5$$

When x is large, the terms $5/(3x^2)$ and $2/(3x^4)$ are close to 0 (see Exercise 90 on page 17). So for large x we have

$$P(x) \approx 3x^5(1 - 0 - 0) = 3x^5 = Q(x)$$

So when x is large, P and Q have approximately the same values. We can also see this numerically by making a table like the one shown below.

x	$P(x)$	$Q(x)$
15	2,261,280	2,278,125
30	72,765,060	72,900,000
50	936,875,100	937,500,000

By the same reasoning we can show that the end behavior of *any* polynomial is determined by its leading term.

■ Using Zeros to Graph Polynomials

If P is a polynomial function, then c is called a **zero** of P if $P(c) = 0$. In other words, the zeros of P are the solutions of the polynomial equation $P(x) = 0$. Note that if $P(c) = 0$, then the graph of P has an x-intercept at $x = c$, so the x-intercepts of the graph are the zeros of the function.

REAL ZEROS OF POLYNOMIALS

If P is a polynomial and c is a real number, then the following are equivalent:

1. c is a zero of P.
2. $x = c$ is a solution of the equation $P(x) = 0$.
3. $x - c$ is a factor of $P(x)$.
4. c is an x-intercept of the graph of P.

To find the zeros of a polynomial P, we factor and then use the Zero-Product Property (see page 116). For example, to find the zeros of $P(x) = x^2 + x - 6$, we factor P to get

$$P(x) = (x - 2)(x + 3)$$

From this factored form we easily see that

1. 2 is a zero of P.
2. $x = 2$ is a solution of the equation $x^2 + x - 6 = 0$.
3. $x - 2$ is a factor of $x^2 + x - 6$.
4. 2 is an x-intercept of the graph of P.

The same facts are true for the other zero, -3.

The following theorem has many important consequences. (See, for instance, the *Discovery Project* referenced on page 312.) Here we use it to help us graph polynomial functions.

INTERMEDIATE VALUE THEOREM FOR POLYNOMIALS

If P is a polynomial function and $P(a)$ and $P(b)$ have opposite signs, then there exists at least one value c between a and b for which $P(c) = 0$.

We will not prove this theorem, but Figure 6 shows why it is intuitively plausible.

One important consequence of this theorem is that between any two successive zeros the values of a polynomial are either all positive or all negative. That is, between two successive zeros the graph of a polynomial lies *entirely above* or *entirely below* the x-axis. To see why, suppose c_1 and c_2 are successive zeros of P. If P has both positive and negative values between c_1 and c_2, then by the Intermediate Value Theorem, P must have another zero between c_1 and c_2. But that's not possible because c_1 and c_2 are successive zeros. This observation allows us to use the following guidelines to graph polynomial functions.

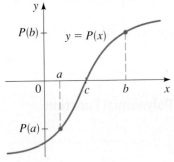

FIGURE 6

GUIDELINES FOR GRAPHING POLYNOMIAL FUNCTIONS

1. **Zeros.**   Factor the polynomial to find all its real zeros; these are the x-intercepts of the graph.
2. **Test Points.**   Make a table of values for the polynomial. Include test points to determine whether the graph of the polynomial lies above or below the x-axis on the intervals determined by the zeros. Include the y-intercept in the table.
3. **End Behavior.**   Determine the end behavior of the polynomial.
4. **Graph.**   Plot the intercepts and other points you found in the table. Sketch a smooth curve that passes through these points and exhibits the required end behavior.

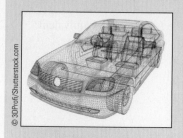
EXAMPLE 4 ■ Using Zeros to Graph a Polynomial Function

Sketch the graph of the polynomial function $P(x) = (x + 2)(x - 1)(x - 3)$.

SOLUTION The zeros are $x = -2, 1,$ and 3. These determine the intervals $(-\infty, -2)$, $(-2, 1)$, $(1, 3)$, and $(3, \infty)$. Using test points in these intervals, we get the information in the following sign diagram (see Section 1.7).

	Test point $x = -3$ $P(-3) < 0$	Test point $x = -1$ $P(-1) > 0$	Test point $x = 2$ $P(2) < 0$	Test point $x = 4$ $P(3) > 0$
		-2	1	3
Sign of $P(x) = (x + 2)(x - 1)(x - 3)$	$-$	$+$	$-$	$+$
Graph of P	below x-axis	above x-axis	below x-axis	above x-axis

Plotting a few additional points and connecting them with a smooth curve helps us to complete the graph in Figure 7.

	x	$P(x)$
Test point →	-3	-24
	-2	0
Test point →	-1	8
	0	6
	1	0
Test point →	2	-4
	3	0
Test point →	4	18

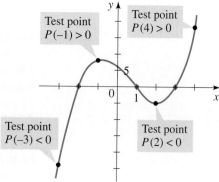

FIGURE 7 $P(x) = (x + 2)(x - 1)(x - 3)$

Test point $P(-1) > 0$

Test point $P(4) > 0$

Test point $P(-3) < 0$

Test point $P(2) < 0$

■ Now Try Exercise 17

EXAMPLE 5 ■ Finding Zeros and Graphing a Polynomial Function

Let $P(x) = x^3 - 2x^2 - 3x$.

(a) Find the zeros of P.   **(b)** Sketch a graph of P.

SOLUTION

(a) To find the zeros, we factor completely.

$$P(x) = x^3 - 2x^2 - 3x$$
$$= x(x^2 - 2x - 3) \qquad \text{Factor } x$$
$$= x(x - 3)(x + 1) \qquad \text{Factor quadratic}$$

Thus the zeros are $x = 0$, $x = 3$, and $x = -1$.

(b) The x-intercepts are $x = 0$, $x = 3$, and $x = -1$. The y-intercept is $P(0) = 0$. We make a table of values of $P(x)$, making sure that we choose test points between (and to the right and left of) successive zeros.

Since P is of odd degree and its leading coefficient is positive, it has the following end behavior:

$$y \to \infty \quad \text{as} \quad x \to \infty \qquad \text{and} \qquad y \to -\infty \quad \text{as} \quad x \to -\infty$$

We plot the points in the table and connect them by a smooth curve to complete the graph, as shown in Figure 8.

A table of values is most easily calculated by using a programmable calculator or a graphing calculator. See Appendix D, *Using the TI-83/84 Graphing Calculator,* for specific instructions.

	x	$P(x)$
Test point →	-2	-10
	-1	0
Test point →	$-\frac{1}{2}$	$\frac{7}{8}$
	0	0
Test point →	1	-4
	2	-6
	3	0
Test point →	4	20

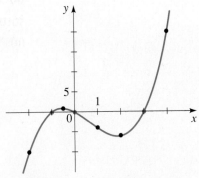

FIGURE 8 $P(x) = x^3 - 2x^2 - 3x$

Now Try Exercise 31

EXAMPLE 6 ■ Finding Zeros and Graphing a Polynomial Function

Let $P(x) = -2x^4 - x^3 + 3x^2$.

(a) Find the zeros of P.   **(b)** Sketch a graph of P.

SOLUTION

(a) To find the zeros, we factor completely.

$$P(x) = -2x^4 - x^3 + 3x^2$$
$$= -x^2(2x^2 + x - 3) \qquad \text{Factor } -x^2$$
$$= -x^2(2x + 3)(x - 1) \qquad \text{Factor quadratic}$$

Thus the zeros are $x = 0$, $x = -\frac{3}{2}$, and $x = 1$.

(b) The x-intercepts are $x = 0$, $x = -\frac{3}{2}$, and $x = 1$. The y-intercept is $P(0) = 0$. We make a table of values of $P(x)$, making sure that we choose test points between (and to the right and left of) successive zeros.

Since P is of even degree and its leading coefficient is negative, it has the following end behavior.

$$y \to -\infty \quad \text{as} \quad x \to \infty \qquad \text{and} \qquad y \to -\infty \quad \text{as} \quad x \to -\infty$$

We plot the points from the table and connect the points by a smooth curve to complete the graph in Figure 9.

x	$P(x)$
-2	-12
-1.5	0
-1	2
-0.5	0.75
0	0
0.5	0.5
1	0
1.5	-6.75

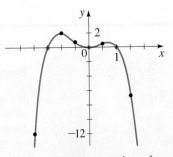

FIGURE 9 $P(x) = -2x^4 - x^3 + 3x^2$

Now Try Exercise 35

EXAMPLE 7 ■ **Finding Zeros and Graphing a Polynomial Function**

Let $P(x) = x^3 - 2x^2 - 4x + 8$.

(a) Find the zeros of P.   **(b)** Sketch a graph of P.

SOLUTION

(a) To find the zeros, we factor completely.

$$
\begin{aligned}
P(x) &= x^3 - 2x^2 - 4x + 8 \\
&= x^2(x - 2) - 4(x - 2) && \text{Group and factor} \\
&= (x^2 - 4)(x - 2) && \text{Factor } x - 2 \\
&= (x + 2)(x - 2)(x - 2) && \text{Difference of squares} \\
&= (x + 2)(x - 2)^2 && \text{Simplify}
\end{aligned}
$$

Thus the zeros are $x = -2$ and $x = 2$.

(b) The x-intercepts are $x = -2$ and $x = 2$. The y-intercept is $P(0) = 8$. The table gives additional values of $P(x)$.

Since P is of odd degree and its leading coefficient is positive, it has the following end behavior.

$$y \to \infty \quad \text{as} \quad x \to \infty \qquad \text{and} \qquad y \to -\infty \quad \text{as} \quad x \to -\infty$$

We connect the points by a smooth curve to complete the graph in Figure 10.

x	$P(x)$
-3	-25
-2	0
-1	9
0	8
1	3
2	0
3	5

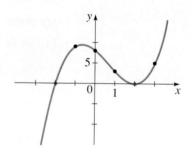

FIGURE 10
$P(x) = x^3 - 2x^2 - 4x + 8$

✎ **Now Try Exercise 37**   ■

■ Shape of the Graph Near a Zero

Although $x = 2$ is a zero of the polynomial in Example 7, the graph does not cross the x-axis at the x-intercept 2. This is because the factor $(x - 2)^2$ corresponding to that zero is raised to an even power, so it doesn't change sign as we test points on either side of 2. In the same way the graph does not cross the x-axis at $x = 0$ in Example 6.

DISCOVERY PROJECT

Bridge Science

If you want to build a bridge, how can you be sure that your bridge design is strong enough to support the cars that will drive over it? In this project we perform a simple experiment using paper "bridges" to collect data on the weight our bridges can support. We model the data with linear and power functions to determine which model best fits the data. The model we obtain allows us to predict the strength of a large bridge *before* it is built. You can find the project at **www.stewartmath.com**.

In general, if c is a zero of P and the corresponding factor $x - c$ occurs exactly m times in the factorization of P, then we say that c is a **zero of multiplicity m**. By considering test points on either side of the x-intercept c, we conclude that the graph crosses the x-axis at c if the multiplicity m is odd and does not cross the x-axis if m is even. Moreover, it can be shown by using calculus that near $x = c$ the graph has the same general shape as the graph of $y = A(x - c)^m$.

SHAPE OF THE GRAPH NEAR A ZERO OF MULTIPLICITY m

If c is a zero of P of multiplicity m, then the shape of the graph of P near c is as follows.

Multiplicity of c	Shape of the graph of P near the x-intercept c
m odd, $m > 1$	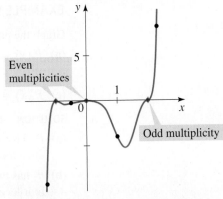
m even, $m > 1$	

EXAMPLE 8 ■ Graphing a Polynomial Function Using Its Zeros

Graph the polynomial $P(x) = x^4(x - 2)^3(x + 1)^2$.

SOLUTION   The zeros of P are -1, 0, and 2 with multiplicities 2, 4, and 3, respectively:

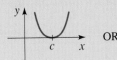 0 is a zero of multiplicity 4    2 is a zero of multiplicity 3   −1 is a zero of multiplicity 2

$$P(x) = x^4(x - 2)^3(x + 1)^2$$

The zero 2 has *odd* multiplicity, so the graph crosses the x-axis at the x-intercept 2. But the zeros 0 and -1 have *even* multiplicity, so the graph does not cross the x-axis at the x-intercepts 0 and -1.

Since P is a polynomial of degree 9 and has positive leading coefficient, it has the following end behavior:

$$y \to \infty \quad \text{as} \quad x \to \infty \quad \text{and} \quad y \to -\infty \quad \text{as} \quad x \to -\infty$$

With this information and a table of values we sketch the graph in Figure 11.

x	$P(x)$
-1.3	-9.2
-1	0
-0.5	-3.9
0	0
1	-4
2	0
2.3	8.2

FIGURE 11 $P(x) = x^4(x - 2)^3(x + 1)^2$

Even multiplicities

Odd multiplicity

Now Try Exercise 29

■ Local Maxima and Minima of Polynomials

Recall from Section 2.3 that if the point $(a, f(a))$ is the highest point on the graph of f within some viewing rectangle, then $f(a)$ is a local maximum value of f, and if $(b, f(b))$ is the lowest point on the graph of f within a viewing rectangle, then $f(b)$ is a local minimum value (see Figure 12). We say that such a point $(a, f(a))$ is a **local maximum point** on the graph and that $(b, f(b))$ is a **local minimum point**. The local maximum and minimum points on the graph of a function are called its **local extrema**.

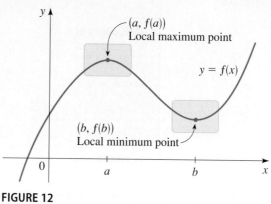

FIGURE 12

For a polynomial function the number of local extrema must be less than the degree, as the following principle indicates. (A proof of this principle requires calculus.)

LOCAL EXTREMA OF POLYNOMIALS

If $P(x) = a_n x^n + a_{n-1} x^{n-1} + \cdots + a_1 x + a_0$ is a polynomial of degree n, then the graph of P has at most $n - 1$ local extrema.

 A polynomial of degree n may in fact have fewer than $n - 1$ local extrema. For example, $P(x) = x^5$ (graphed in Figure 1) has *no* local extrema, even though it is of degree 5. The preceding principle tells us only that a polynomial of degree n can have no more than $n - 1$ local extrema.

EXAMPLE 9 ■ The Number of Local Extrema

Graph the polynomial and determine how many local extrema it has.

(a) $P_1(x) = x^4 + x^3 - 16x^2 - 4x + 48$

(b) $P_2(x) = x^5 + 3x^4 - 5x^3 - 15x^2 + 4x - 15$

(c) $P_3(x) = 7x^4 + 3x^2 - 10x$

SOLUTION The graphs are shown in Figure 13.

(a) P_1 has two local minimum points and one local maximum point, for a total of three local extrema.

(b) P_2 has two local minimum points and two local maximum points, for a total of four local extrema.

(c) P_3 has just one local extremum, a local minimum.

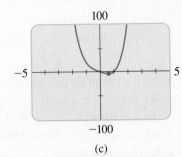

(a)

$$P_1(x) = x^4 + x^3 - 16x^2 - 4x + 48$$

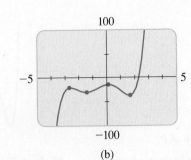

(b)

$$P_2(x) = x^5 + 3x^4 - 5x^3 - 15x^2 + 4x - 15$$

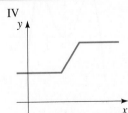

(c)

$$P_3(x) = 7x^4 + 3x^2 - 10x$$

FIGURE 13

✎ **Now Try Exercises 65 and 67**

With a graphing calculator we can quickly draw the graphs of many functions at once, on the same viewing screen. This allows us to see how changing a value in the definition of the functions affects the shape of its graph. In the next example we apply this principle to a family of third-degree polynomials.

EXAMPLE 10 ■ A Family of Polynomials

Sketch the family of polynomials $P(x) = x^3 - cx^2$ for $c = 0, 1, 2,$ and 3. How does changing the value of c affect the graph?

SOLUTION The polynomials

$$P_0(x) = x^3 \qquad\qquad P_1(x) = x^3 - x^2$$
$$P_2(x) = x^3 - 2x^2 \qquad\qquad P_3(x) = x^3 - 3x^2$$

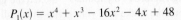
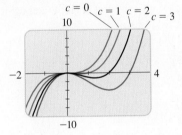

FIGURE 14 A family of polynomials
$P(x) = x^3 - cx^2$

are graphed in Figure 14. We see that increasing the value of c causes the graph to develop an increasingly deep "valley" to the right of the y-axis, creating a local maximum at the origin and a local minimum at a point in Quadrant IV. This local minimum moves lower and farther to the right as c increases. To see why this happens, factor $P(x) = x^2(x - c)$. The polynomial P has zeros at 0 and c, and the larger c gets, the farther to the right the minimum between 0 and c will be.

✎ **Now Try Exercise 75**

3.2 EXERCISES

CONCEPTS

1. Only one of the following graphs could be the graph of a polynomial function. Which one? Why are the others not graphs of polynomials?

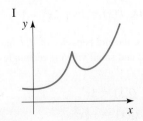

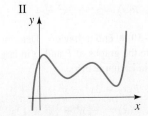

III

IV

2. Describe the end behavior of each polynomial.

(a) $y = x^3 - 8x^2 + 2x - 15$

End behavior: $y \to$ _____ as $x \to \infty$

$y \to$ _____ as $x \to -\infty$

(b) $y = -2x^4 + 12x + 100$

End behavior: $y \rightarrow$ _____ as $x \rightarrow \infty$

$y \rightarrow$ _____ as $x \rightarrow -\infty$

3. If c is a zero of the polynomial P, then
   (a) $P(c) =$ _____.
   (b) $x - c$ is a _____ of $P(x)$.
   (c) c is a(n) _____ -intercept of the graph of P.

4. Which of the following statements couldn't possibly be true about the polynomial function P?
   (a) P has degree 3, two local maxima, and two local minima.
   (b) P has degree 3 and no local maxima or minima.
   (c) P has degree 4, one local maximum, and no local minima.

SKILLS

5–8 ■ Transformations of Monomials Sketch the graph of each function by transforming the graph of an appropriate function of the form $y = x^n$ from Figure 1. Indicate all x- and y-intercepts on each graph.

5. (a) $P(x) = x^2 - 4$ **(b)** $Q(x) = (x - 4)^2$
   (c) $P(x) = 2x^2 + 3$ **(d)** $P(x) = -(x + 2)^2$

6. (a) $P(x) = x^4 - 16$ **(b)** $P(x) = -(x + 5)^4$
   (c) $P(x) = -5x^4 + 5$ **(d)** $P(x) = (x - 5)^4$

7. (a) $P(x) = x^3 - 8$ **(b)** $Q(x) = -x^3 + 27$
   (c) $R(x) = -(x + 2)^3$ **(d)** $S(x) = \frac{1}{2}(x - 1)^3 + 4$

8. (a) $P(x) = (x + 3)^5$ **(b)** $Q(x) = 2(x + 3)^5 - 64$
   (c) $R(x) = -\frac{1}{2}(x - 2)^5$ **(d)** $S(x) = -\frac{1}{2}(x - 2)^5 + 16$

9–14 ■ End Behavior A polynomial function is given.
(a) Describe the end behavior of the polynomial function.
(b) Match the polynomial function with one of the graphs I–VI.

9. $P(x) = x(x^2 - 4)$ **10.** $Q(x) = -x^2(x^2 - 4)$

11. $R(x) = -x^5 + 5x^3 - 4x$ **12.** $S(x) = \frac{1}{2}x^6 - 2x^4$

13. $T(x) = x^4 + 2x^3$ **14.** $U(x) = -x^3 + 2x^2$

I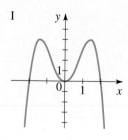

II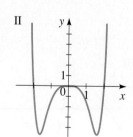

III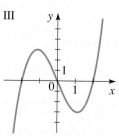

IV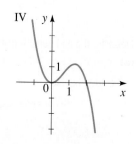

V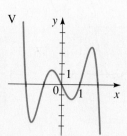

VI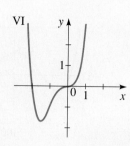

15–30 ■ Graphing Factored Polynomials Sketch the graph of the polynomial function. Make sure your graph shows all intercepts and exhibits the proper end behavior.

15. $P(x) = (x - 1)(x + 2)$

16. $P(x) = (2 - x)(x + 5)$

17. $P(x) = -x(x - 3)(x + 2)$

18. $P(x) = x(x - 3)(x + 2)$

19. $P(x) = -(2x - 1)(x + 1)(x + 3)$

20. $P(x) = (x - 3)(x + 2)(3x - 2)$

21. $P(x) = (x + 2)(x + 1)(x - 2)(x - 3)$

22. $P(x) = x(x + 1)(x - 1)(2 - x)$

23. $P(x) = -2x(x - 2)^2$

24. $P(x) = \frac{1}{5}x(x - 5)^2$

25. $P(x) = (x + 2)(x + 1)^2(2x - 3)$

26. $P(x) = -(x + 1)^2(x - 1)^3(x - 2)$

27. $P(x) = \frac{1}{12}(x + 2)^2(x - 3)^2$

28. $P(x) = (x - 1)^2(x + 2)^3$

29. $P(x) = x^3(x + 2)(x - 3)^2$

30. $P(x) = (x - 3)^2(x + 1)^2$

31–44 ■ Graphing Polynomials Factor the polynomial and use the factored form to find the zeros. Then sketch the graph.

31. $P(x) = x^3 - x^2 - 6x$ **32.** $P(x) = x^3 + 2x^2 - 8x$

33. $P(x) = -x^3 + x^2 + 12x$ **34.** $P(x) = -2x^3 - x^2 + x$

35. $P(x) = x^4 - 3x^3 + 2x^2$ **36.** $P(x) = x^5 - 9x^3$

37. $P(x) = x^3 + x^2 - x - 1$

38. $P(x) = x^3 + 3x^2 - 4x - 12$

39. $P(x) = 2x^3 - x^2 - 18x + 9$

40. $P(x) = \frac{1}{8}(2x^4 + 3x^3 - 16x - 24)^2$

41. $P(x) = x^4 - 2x^3 - 8x + 16$

42. $P(x) = x^4 - 2x^3 + 8x - 16$

43. $P(x) = x^4 - 3x^2 - 4$ **44.** $P(x) = x^6 - 2x^3 + 1$

45–50 ■ End Behavior Determine the end behavior of P. Compare the graphs of P and Q in large and small viewing rectangles, as in Example 3(b).

45. $P(x) = 3x^3 - x^2 + 5x + 1$; $Q(x) = 3x^3$

46. $P(x) = -\frac{1}{8}x^3 + \frac{1}{4}x^2 + 12x$; $Q(x) = -\frac{1}{8}x^3$

47. $P(x) = x^4 - 7x^2 + 5x + 5$; $Q(x) = x^4$

48. $P(x) = -x^5 + 2x^2 + x; \quad Q(x) = -x^5$

49. $P(x) = x^{11} - 9x^9; \quad Q(x) = x^{11}$

50. $P(x) = 2x^2 - x^{12}; \quad Q(x) = -x^{12}$

51–54 ■ **Local Extrema** The graph of a polynomial function is given. From the graph, find **(a)** the x- and y-intercepts, and **(b)** the coordinates of all local extrema.

51. $P(x) = -x^2 + 4x$

52. $P(x) = \frac{2}{9}x^3 - x^2$

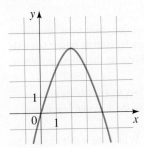

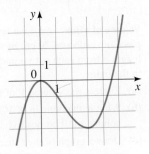

53. $P(x) = -\frac{1}{2}x^3 + \frac{3}{2}x - 1$

54. $P(x) = \frac{1}{9}x^4 - \frac{4}{9}x^3$

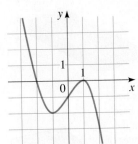

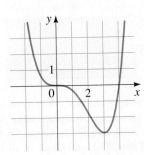

55–62 ■ **Local Extrema** Graph the polynomial in the given viewing rectangle. Find the coordinates of all local extrema. State each answer rounded to two decimal places. State the domain and range.

55. $y = -x^2 + 8x, \quad [-4, 12]$ by $[-50, 30]$

56. $y = x^3 - 3x^2, \quad [-2, 5]$ by $[-10, 10]$

57. $y = x^3 - 12x + 9, \quad [-5, 5]$ by $[-30, 30]$

58. $y = 2x^3 - 3x^2 - 12x - 32, \quad [-5, 5]$ by $[-60, 30]$

59. $y = x^4 + 4x^3, \quad [-5, 5]$ by $[-30, 30]$

60. $y = x^4 - 18x^2 + 32, \quad [-5, 5]$ by $[-100, 100]$

61. $y = 3x^5 - 5x^3 + 3, \quad [-3, 3]$ by $[-5, 10]$

62. $y = x^5 - 5x^2 + 6, \quad [-3, 3]$ by $[-5, 10]$

63–72 ■ **Number of Local Extrema** Graph the polynomial, and determine how many local maxima and minima it has.

63. $y = -2x^2 + 3x + 5$

64. $y = x^3 + 12x$

65. $y = x^3 - x^2 - x$

66. $y = 6x^3 + 3x + 1$

67. $y = x^4 - 5x^2 + 4$

68. $y = 1.2x^5 + 3.75x^4 - 7x^3 - 15x^2 + 18x$

69. $y = (x - 2)^5 + 32$

70. $y = (x^2 - 2)^3$

71. $y = x^8 - 3x^4 + x$

72. $y = \frac{1}{3}x^7 - 17x^2 + 7$

73–78 ■ **Families of Polynomials** Graph the family of polynomials in the same viewing rectangle, using the given values of c. Explain how changing the value of c affects the graph.

73. $P(x) = cx^3; \quad c = 1, 2, 5, \frac{1}{2}$

74. $P(x) = (x - c)^4; \quad c = -1, 0, 1, 2$

75. $P(x) = x^4 + c; \quad c = -1, 0, 1, 2$

76. $P(x) = x^3 + cx; \quad c = 2, 0, -2, -4$

77. $P(x) = x^4 - cx; \quad c = 0, 1, 8, 27$

78. $P(x) = x^c; \quad c = 1, 3, 5, 7$

SKILLS Plus

79. Intersection Points of Two Polynomials

(a) On the same coordinate axes, sketch graphs (as accurately as possible) of the functions

$$y = x^3 - 2x^2 - x + 2 \quad \text{and} \quad y = -x^2 + 5x + 2$$

(b) On the basis of your sketch in part (a), at how many points do the two graphs appear to intersect?

(c) Find the coordinates of all intersection points.

80. Power Functions Portions of the graphs of $y = x^2$, $y = x^3$, $y = x^4$, $y = x^5$, and $y = x^6$ are plotted in the figures. Determine which function belongs to each graph.

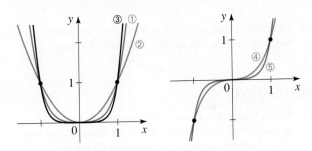

81. Odd and Even Functions Recall that a function f is *odd* if $f(-x) = -f(x)$ or *even* if $f(-x) = f(x)$ for all real x.

(a) Show that a polynomial $P(x)$ that contains only odd powers of x is an odd function.

(b) Show that a polynomial $P(x)$ that contains only even powers of x is an even function.

(c) Show that if a polynomial $P(x)$ contains both odd and even powers of x, then it is neither an odd nor an even function.

(d) Express the function

$$P(x) = x^5 + 6x^3 - x^2 - 2x + 5$$

as the sum of an odd function and an even function.

82. Number of Intercepts and Local Extrema

(a) How many x-intercepts and how many local extrema does the polynomial $P(x) = x^3 - 4x$ have?

(b) How many x-intercepts and how many local extrema does the polynomial $Q(x) = x^3 + 4x$ have?

(c) If $a > 0$, how many x-intercepts and how many local extrema does each of the polynomials $P(x) = x^3 - ax$ and $Q(x) = x^3 + ax$ have? Explain your answer.

83–86 ■ **Local Extrema** These exercises involve local maxima and minima of polynomial functions.

 83. (a) Graph the function $P(x) = (x - 1)(x - 3)(x - 4)$ and find all local extrema, correct to the nearest tenth.

(b) Graph the function

$$Q(x) = (x - 1)(x - 3)(x - 4) + 5$$

and use your answers to part (a) to find all local extrema, correct to the nearest tenth.

 84. (a) Graph the function $P(x) = (x - 2)(x - 4)(x - 5)$ and determine how many local extrema it has.

(b) If $a < b < c$, explain why the function

$$P(x) = (x - a)(x - b)(x - c)$$

must have two local extrema.

85. Maximum Number of Local Extrema What is the smallest possible degree that the polynomial whose graph is shown can have? Explain.

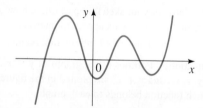

86. Impossible Situation? Is it possible for a polynomial to have two local maxima and no local minimum? Explain.

APPLICATIONS

 87. Market Research A market analyst working for a small-appliance manufacturer finds that if the firm produces and sells x blenders annually, the total profit (in dollars) is

$$P(x) = 8x + 0.3x^2 - 0.0013x^3 - 372$$

Graph the function P in an appropriate viewing rectangle and use the graph to answer the following questions.

(a) When just a few blenders are manufactured, the firm loses money (profit is negative). (For example, $P(10) = -263.3$, so the firm loses \$263.30 if it produces and sells only 10 blenders.) How many blenders must the firm produce to break even?

(b) Does profit increase indefinitely as more blenders are produced and sold? If not, what is the largest possible profit the firm could have?

 88. Population Change The rabbit population on a small island is observed to be given by the function

$$P(t) = 120t - 0.4t^4 + 1000$$

where t is the time (in months) since observations of the island began.

(a) When is the maximum population attained, and what is that maximum population?

(b) When does the rabbit population disappear from the island?

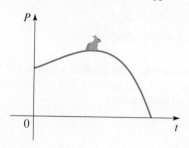

89. Volume of a Box An open box is to be constructed from a piece of cardboard 20 cm by 40 cm by cutting squares of side length x from each corner and folding up the sides, as shown in the figure.

(a) Express the volume V of the box as a function of x.

(b) What is the domain of V? (Use the fact that length and volume must be positive.)

 (c) Draw a graph of the function V, and use it to estimate the maximum volume for such a box.

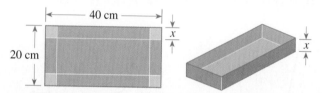

90. Volume of a Box A cardboard box has a square base, with each edge of the base having length x inches, as shown in the figure. The total length of all 12 edges of the box is 144 in.

(a) Show that the volume of the box is given by the function $V(x) = 2x^2(18 - x)$.

(b) What is the domain of V? (Use the fact that length and volume must be positive.)

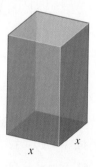

(c) Draw a graph of the function V and use it to estimate the maximum volume for such a box.

DISCUSS ■ **DISCOVER** ■ **PROVE** ■ **WRITE**

91. DISCOVER: Graphs of Large Powers Graph the functions $y = x^2$, $y = x^3$, $y = x^4$, and $y = x^5$, for $-1 \leq x \leq 1$, on the same coordinate axes. What do you think the graph of $y = x^{100}$ would look like on this same interval? What about $y = x^{101}$? Make a table of values to confirm your answers.

92. DISCUSS ■ **DISCOVER: Possible Number of Local Extrema** Is it possible for a third-degree polynomial to have exactly one local extremum? Can a fourth-degree polynomial have exactly two local extrema? How many local extrema can polynomials of third, fourth, fifth, and sixth degree have? (Think about the end behavior of such polynomials.) Now give an example of a polynomial that has six local extrema.

3.3 DIVIDING POLYNOMIALS

■ Long Division of Polynomials ■ Synthetic Division ■ The Remainder and Factor Theorems

So far in this chapter we have been studying polynomial functions *graphically*. In this section we begin to study polynomials *algebraically*. Most of our work will be concerned with factoring polynomials, and to factor, we need to know how to divide polynomials.

■ Long Division of Polynomials

Dividing polynomials is much like the familiar process of dividing numbers. When we divide 38 by 7, the quotient is 5 and the remainder is 3. We write

$$\frac{38}{7} = 5 + \frac{3}{7}$$

with labels: Dividend (38), Remainder (3), Divisor (7), Quotient (5).

To divide polynomials, we use long division, as follows.

DIVISION ALGORITHM

If $P(x)$ and $D(x)$ are polynomials, with $D(x) \neq 0$, then there exist unique polynomials $Q(x)$ and $R(x)$, where $R(x)$ is either 0 or of degree less than the degree of $D(x)$, such that

$$\frac{P(x)}{D(x)} = Q(x) + \frac{R(x)}{D(x)} \qquad \text{or} \qquad P(x) = D(x) \cdot Q(x) + R(x)$$

with labels: Dividend $P(x)$, Divisor $D(x)$, Quotient $Q(x)$, Remainder $R(x)$.

The polynomials $P(x)$ and $D(x)$ are called the **dividend** and **divisor**, respectively, $Q(x)$ is the **quotient**, and $R(x)$ is the **remainder**.

EXAMPLE 1 ■ Long Division of Polynomials

Divide $6x^2 - 26x + 12$ by $x - 4$. Express the result in each of the two forms shown in the above box.

SOLUTION The *dividend* is $6x^2 - 26x + 12$, and the *divisor* is $x - 4$. We begin by arranging them as follows.

$$x - 4 \overline{)6x^2 - 26x + 12}$$

Next we divide the leading term in the dividend by the leading term in the divisor to get the first term of the quotient: $6x^2/x = 6x$. Then we multiply the divisor by $6x$ and subtract the result from the dividend.

$$
\begin{array}{r}
6x \\
x - 4 \overline{)6x^2 - 26x + 12} \\
6x^2 - 24x \\
\hline
-2x + 12
\end{array}
$$

Divide leading terms: $\dfrac{6x^2}{x} = 6x$

Multiply: $6x(x - 4) = 6x^2 - 24x$

Subtract and "bring down" 12

We repeat the process using the last line $-2x + 12$ as the dividend.

$$
\begin{array}{r}
6x - 2 \\
x - 4 \overline{\smash{\big)}\, 6x^2 - 26x + 12} \\
\underline{6x^2 - 24x} \\
-2x + 12 \\
\underline{-2x + 8} \\
4
\end{array}
$$

Divide leading terms: $\dfrac{-2x}{x} = -2$

Multiply: $-2(x - 4) = -2x + 8$

Subtract

The division process ends when the last line is of lesser degree than the divisor. The last line then contains the *remainder*, and the top line contains the *quotient*. The result of the division can be interpreted in either of two ways:

$$
\underbrace{\frac{\overbrace{6x^2 - 26x + 12}^{\text{Dividend}}}{\underbrace{x - 4}_{\text{Divisor}}}} = \overbrace{6x - 2}^{\text{Quotient}} + \frac{\overbrace{4}^{\text{Remainder}}}{x - 4}
$$

or

$$
\underbrace{6x^2 - 26x + 12}_{\text{Dividend}} = \underbrace{(x - 4)}_{\text{Divisor}}\underbrace{(6x - 2)}_{\text{Quotient}} + \overbrace{4}^{\text{Remainder}}
$$

✎ **Now Try Exercises 3 and 9** ■

EXAMPLE 2 ■ Long Division of Polynomials

Let $P(x) = 8x^4 + 6x^2 - 3x + 1$ and $D(x) = 2x^2 - x + 2$. Find polynomials $Q(x)$ and $R(x)$ such that $P(x) = D(x) \cdot Q(x) + R(x)$.

SOLUTION We use long division after first inserting the term $0x^3$ into the dividend to ensure that the columns line up correctly.

$$
\begin{array}{r}
4x^2 + 2x \\
2x^2 - x + 2 \overline{\smash{\big)}\, 8x^4 + 0x^3 + 6x^2 - 3x + 1} \\
\underline{8x^4 - 4x^3 + 8x^2} \\
4x^3 - 2x^2 - 3x \\
\underline{4x^3 - 2x^2 + 4x} \\
-7x + 1
\end{array}
$$

Multiply divisor by $4x^2$

Subtract

Multiply divisor by $2x$

Subtract

The process is complete at this point because $-7x + 1$ is of lesser degree than the divisor $2x^2 - x + 2$. From the above long division we see that $Q(x) = 4x^2 + 2x$ and $R(x) = -7x + 1$, so

$$
8x^4 + 6x^2 - 3x + 1 = (2x^2 - x + 2)(4x^2 + 2x) + (-7x + 1)
$$

✎ **Now Try Exercise 19** ■

■ Synthetic Division

Synthetic division is a quick method of dividing polynomials; it can be used when the divisor is of the form $x - c$. In synthetic division we write only the essential parts of the long division. Compare the following long and synthetic divisions, in which we divide $2x^3 - 7x^2 + 5$ by $x - 3$. (We'll explain how to perform the synthetic division in Example 3.)

Long Division

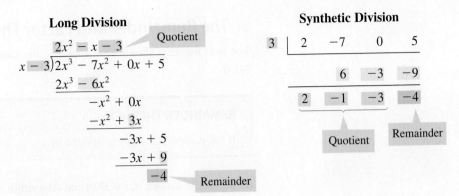

$$2x^2 - x - 3 \quad \text{Quotient}$$

$$x - 3 \overline{\smash{)}2x^3 - 7x^2 + 0x + 5}$$
$$\underline{2x^3 - 6x^2}$$
$$-x^2 + 0x$$
$$\underline{-x^2 + 3x}$$
$$-3x + 5$$
$$\underline{-3x + 9}$$
$$-4 \quad \text{Remainder}$$

Synthetic Division

Note that in synthetic division we abbreviate $2x^3 - 7x^2 + 5$ by writing only the coefficients: 2   −7   0   5, and instead of $x - 3$, we simply write 3. (Writing 3 instead of −3 allows us to add instead of subtract, but this changes the sign of all the numbers that appear in the gold boxes.)

The next example shows how synthetic division is performed.

EXAMPLE 3 ■ Synthetic Division

Use synthetic division to divide $2x^3 - 7x^2 + 5$ by $x - 3$.

SOLUTION   We begin by writing the appropriate coefficients to represent the divisor and the dividend:

Divisor $x - 3$ ⟶   3 │ 2   −7   0   5   ⟵ Dividend $2x^3 - 7x^2 + 0x + 5$

We bring down the 2, multiply $3 \cdot 2 = 6$, and write the result in the middle row. Then we add.

$$
\begin{array}{c|cccc}
3 & 2 & -7 & 0 & 5 \\
  &   & 6 &   &   \\
\hline
  & 2 & -1 &   &
\end{array}
$$

Multiply: $3 \cdot 2 = 6$

Add: $-7 + 6 = -1$

We repeat this process of multiplying and then adding until the table is complete.

$$
\begin{array}{c|cccc}
3 & 2 & -7 & 0 & 5 \\
  &   & 6 & -3 &   \\
\hline
  & 2 & -1 & -3 &
\end{array}
$$

Multiply: $3(-1) = -3$

Add: $0 + (-3) = -3$

$$
\begin{array}{c|cccc}
3 & 2 & -7 & 0 & 5 \\
  &   & 6 & -3 & -9 \\
\hline
  & 2 & -1 & -3 & -4
\end{array}
$$

Multiply: $3(-3) = -9$

Add: $5 + (-9) = -4$

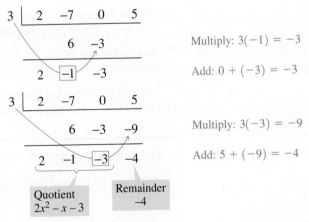

Quotient $2x^2 - x - 3$

Remainder −4

From the last line of the synthetic division we see that the quotient is $2x^2 - x - 3$ and the remainder is −4. Thus

$$2x^3 - 7x^2 + 5 = (x - 3)(2x^2 - x - 3) - 4$$

✎ **Now Try Exercise 31** ■

■ The Remainder and Factor Theorems

The next theorem shows how synthetic division can be used to evaluate polynomials easily.

REMAINDER THEOREM

If the polynomial $P(x)$ is divided by $x - c$, then the remainder is the value $P(c)$.

Proof If the divisor in the Division Algorithm is of the form $x - c$ for some real number c, then the remainder must be a constant (since the degree of the remainder is less than the degree of the divisor). If we call this constant r, then

$$P(x) = (x - c) \cdot Q(x) + r$$

Replacing x by c in this equation, we get $P(c) = (c - c) \cdot Q(c) + r = 0 + r = r$, that is, $P(c)$ is the remainder r. ■

EXAMPLE 4 ■ Using the Remainder Theorem to Find the Value of a Polynomial

Let $P(x) = 3x^5 + 5x^4 - 4x^3 + 7x + 3$.

(a) Find the quotient and remainder when $P(x)$ is divided by $x + 2$.

(b) Use the Remainder Theorem to find $P(-2)$.

SOLUTION

(a) Since $x + 2 = x - (-2)$, the synthetic division for this problem takes the following form:

$$
\begin{array}{r|rrrrrr}
-2 & 3 & 5 & -4 & 0 & 7 & 3 \\
   &   & -6 & 2 & 4 & -8 & 2 \\
\hline
   & 3 & -1 & -2 & 4 & -1 & 5
\end{array}
$$

Remainder is 5, so $P(-2) = 5$

The quotient is $3x^4 - x^3 - 2x^2 + 4x - 1$, and the remainder is 5.

(b) By the Remainder Theorem, $P(-2)$ is the remainder when $P(x)$ is divided by $x - (-2) = x + 2$. From part (a) the remainder is 5, so $P(-2) = 5$.

Now Try Exercise 39 ■

The next theorem says that *zeros* of polynomials correspond to *factors*. We used this fact in Section 3.2 to graph polynomials.

FACTOR THEOREM

c is a zero of P if and only if $x - c$ is a factor of $P(x)$.

Proof If $P(x)$ factors as $P(x) = (x - c)Q(x)$, then

$$P(c) = (c - c)Q(c) = 0 \cdot Q(c) = 0$$

Conversely, if $P(c) = 0$, then by the Remainder Theorem

$$P(x) = (x - c)Q(x) + 0 = (x - c)Q(x)$$

so $x - c$ is a factor of $P(x)$. ■

EXAMPLE 5 ■ Factoring a Polynomial Using the Factor Theorem

Let $P(x) = x^3 - 7x + 6$. Show that $P(1) = 0$, and use this fact to factor $P(x)$ completely.

SOLUTION Substituting, we see that $P(1) = 1^3 - 7 \cdot 1 + 6 = 0$. By the Factor Theorem this means that $x - 1$ is a factor of $P(x)$. Using synthetic or long division (shown in the margin), we see that

$$P(x) = x^3 - 7x + 6 \qquad \text{Given polynomial}$$
$$= (x - 1)(x^2 + x - 6) \qquad \text{See margin}$$
$$= (x - 1)(x - 2)(x + 3) \qquad \text{Factor quadratic } x^2 + x - 6$$

✏ **Now Try Exercises 53 and 57** ■

$$\begin{array}{r|rrrr} 1 & 1 & 0 & -7 & 6 \\ & & 1 & 1 & -6 \\ \hline & 1 & 1 & -6 & 0 \end{array}$$

$$\begin{array}{r} x^2 + x - 6 \\ x - 1 \overline{)x^3 + 0x^2 - 7x + 6} \\ \underline{x^3 - x^2} \\ x^2 - 7x \\ \underline{x^2 - x} \\ -6x + 6 \\ \underline{-6x + 6} \\ 0 \end{array}$$

EXAMPLE 6 ■ Finding a Polynomial with Specified Zeros

Find a polynomial of degree four that has zeros $-3, 0, 1$, and 5, and the coefficient of x^3 is -6.

SOLUTION By the Factor Theorem, $x - (-3)$, $x - 0$, $x - 1$, and $x - 5$ must all be factors of the desired polynomial. Let

$$P(x) = (x + 3)(x - 0)(x - 1)(x - 5)$$
$$= x^4 - 3x^3 - 13x^2 + 15x$$

The polynomial $P(x)$ is of degree 4 with the desired zeros, but the coefficient of x^3 is -3, not -6. Multiplication by a nonzero constant does not change the degree, so the desired polynomial is a constant multiple of $P(x)$. If we multiply $P(x)$ by the constant 2, we get

$$Q(x) = 2x^4 - 6x^3 - 26x^2 + 30x$$

which is a polynomial with all the desired properties. The polynomial Q is graphed in Figure 1. Note that the zeros of Q correspond to the x-intercepts of the graph.

✏ **Now Try Exercises 63 and 67** ■

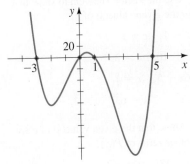

FIGURE 1
$Q(x) = 2x(x + 3)(x - 1)(x - 5)$
has zeros $-3, 0, 1$, and 5, and the coefficient of x^3 is -6.

3.3 EXERCISES

CONCEPTS

1. If we divide the polynomial P by the factor $x - c$ and we obtain the equation $P(x) = (x - c)Q(x) + R(x)$, then we say that $x - c$ is the divisor, $Q(x)$ is the _____, and $R(x)$ is the _____.

2. (a) If we divide the polynomial $P(x)$ by the factor $x - c$ and we obtain a remainder of 0, then we know that c is a _____ of P.

(b) If we divide the polynomial $P(x)$ by the factor $x - c$ and we obtain a remainder of k, then we know that $P(c) =$ _____.

SKILLS

3–8 ■ Division of Polynomials Two polynomials P and D are given. Use either synthetic or long division to divide $P(x)$ by $D(x)$, and express the quotient $P(x)/D(x)$ in the form

$$\frac{P(x)}{D(x)} = Q(x) + \frac{R(x)}{D(x)}$$

✏ **3.** $P(x) = 2x^2 - 5x - 7$, $\quad D(x) = x - 2$

4. $P(x) = 3x^3 + 9x^2 - 5x - 1$, $\quad D(x) = x + 4$

5. $P(x) = 4x^2 - 3x - 7$, $\quad D(x) = 2x - 1$

6. $P(x) = 6x^3 + x^2 - 12x + 5$, $\quad D(x) = 3x - 4$

7. $P(x) = 2x^4 - x^3 + 9x^2$, $\quad D(x) = x^2 + 4$

8. $P(x) = 2x^5 + x^3 - 2x^2 + 3x - 5$, $\quad D(x) = x^2 - 3x + 1$

9–14 ■ Division of Polynomials Two polynomials P and D are given. Use either synthetic or long division to divide $P(x)$ by $D(x)$, and express P in the form

$$P(x) = D(x) \cdot Q(x) + R(x)$$

9. $P(x) = -x^3 - 2x + 6, \quad D(x) = x + 1$

10. $P(x) = x^4 + 2x^3 - 10x, \quad D(x) = x - 3$

11. $P(x) = 2x^3 - 3x^2 - 2x, \quad D(x) = 2x - 3$

12. $P(x) = 4x^3 + 7x + 9, \quad D(x) = 2x + 1$

13. $P(x) = 8x^4 + 4x^3 + 6x^2, \quad D(x) = 2x^2 + 1$

14. $P(x) = 27x^5 - 9x^4 + 3x^2 - 3, \quad D(x) = 3x^2 - 3x + 1$

15–24 ■ Long Division of Polynomials Find the quotient and remainder using long division.

15. $\dfrac{x^2 - 3x + 7}{x - 2}$

16. $\dfrac{x^3 + 2x^2 - x + 1}{x + 3}$

17. $\dfrac{4x^3 + 2x^2 - 2x - 3}{2x + 1}$

18. $\dfrac{x^3 + 3x^2 + 4x + 3}{3x + 6}$

19. $\dfrac{x^3 + 2x + 1}{x^2 - x + 3}$

20. $\dfrac{x^4 - 3x^3 + x - 2}{x^2 - 5x + 1}$

21. $\dfrac{6x^3 + 2x^2 + 22x}{2x^2 + 5}$

22. $\dfrac{9x^2 - x + 5}{3x^2 - 7x}$

23. $\dfrac{x^6 + x^4 + x^2 + 1}{x^2 + 1}$

24. $\dfrac{2x^5 - 7x^4 - 13}{4x^2 - 6x + 8}$

25–38 ■ Synthetic Division of Polynomials Find the quotient and remainder using synthetic division.

25. $\dfrac{2x^2 - 5x + 3}{x - 3}$

26. $\dfrac{-x^2 + x - 4}{x + 1}$

27. $\dfrac{3x^2 + x}{x + 1}$

28. $\dfrac{4x^2 - 3}{x - 2}$

29. $\dfrac{x^3 + 2x^2 + 2x + 1}{x + 2}$

30. $\dfrac{3x^3 - 12x^2 - 9x + 1}{x - 5}$

31. $\dfrac{x^3 - 8x + 2}{x + 3}$

32. $\dfrac{x^4 - x^3 + x^2 - x + 2}{x - 2}$

33. $\dfrac{x^5 + 3x^3 - 6}{x - 1}$

34. $\dfrac{x^3 - 9x^2 + 27x - 27}{x - 3}$

35. $\dfrac{2x^3 + 3x^2 - 2x + 1}{x - \frac{1}{2}}$

36. $\dfrac{6x^4 + 10x^3 + 5x^2 + x + 1}{x + \frac{2}{3}}$

37. $\dfrac{x^3 - 27}{x - 3}$

38. $\dfrac{x^4 - 16}{x + 2}$

39–51 ■ Remainder Theorem Use synthetic division and the Remainder Theorem to evaluate $P(c)$.

39. $P(x) = 4x^2 + 12x + 5, \quad c = -1$

40. $P(x) = 2x^2 + 9x + 1, \quad c = \frac{1}{2}$

41. $P(x) = x^3 + 3x^2 - 7x + 6, \quad c = 2$

42. $P(x) = x^3 - x^2 + x + 5, \quad c = -1$

43. $P(x) = x^3 + 2x^2 - 7, \quad c = -2$

44. $P(x) = 2x^3 - 21x^2 + 9x - 200, \quad c = 11$

45. $P(x) = 5x^4 + 30x^3 - 40x^2 + 36x + 14, \quad c = -7$

46. $P(x) = 6x^5 + 10x^3 + x + 1, \quad c = -2$

47. $P(x) = x^7 - 3x^2 - 1, \quad c = 3$

48. $P(x) = -2x^6 + 7x^5 + 40x^4 - 7x^2 + 10x + 112, \quad c = -3$

49. $P(x) = 3x^3 + 4x^2 - 2x + 1, \quad c = \frac{2}{3}$

50. $P(x) = x^3 - x + 1, \quad c = \frac{1}{4}$

51. $P(x) = x^3 + 2x^2 - 3x - 8, \quad c = 0.1$

52. Remainder Theorem Let

$$P(x) = 6x^7 - 40x^6 + 16x^5 - 200x^4$$
$$- 60x^3 - 69x^2 + 13x - 139$$

Calculate $P(7)$ by **(a)** using synthetic division and **(b)** substituting $x = 7$ into the polynomial and evaluating directly.

53–56 ■ Factor Theorem Use the Factor Theorem to show that $x - c$ is a factor of $P(x)$ for the given value(s) of c.

53. $P(x) = x^3 - 3x^2 + 3x - 1, \quad c = 1$

54. $P(x) = x^3 + 2x^2 - 3x - 10, \quad c = 2$

55. $P(x) = 2x^3 + 7x^2 + 6x - 5, \quad c = \frac{1}{2}$

56. $P(x) = x^4 + 3x^3 - 16x^2 - 27x + 63, \quad c = 3, -3$

57–62 ■ Factor Theorem Show that the given value(s) of c are zeros of $P(x)$, and find all other zeros of $P(x)$.

57. $P(x) = x^3 + 2x^2 - 9x - 18, \quad c = -2$

58. $P(x) = x^3 - 5x^2 - 2x + 10, \quad c = 5$

59. $P(x) = x^3 - x^2 - 11x + 15, \quad c = 3$

60. $P(x) = 3x^4 - x^3 - 21x^2 - 11x + 6, \quad c = -2, \frac{1}{3}$

61. $P(x) = 3x^4 - 8x^3 - 14x^2 + 31x + 6, \quad c = -2, 3$

62. $P(x) = 2x^4 - 13x^3 + 7x^2 + 37x + 15, \quad c = -1, 3$

63–66 ■ Finding a Polynomial with Specified Zeros Find a polynomial of the specified degree that has the given zeros.

63. Degree 3; zeros $-1, 1, 3$

64. Degree 4; zeros $-2, 0, 2, 4$

65. Degree 4; zeros $-1, 1, 3, 5$

66. Degree 5; zeros $-2, -1, 0, 1, 2$

67–70 ■ Polynomials with Specified Zeros Find a polynomial of the specified degree that satisfies the given conditions.

67. Degree 4; zeros $-2, 0, 1, 3$; coefficient of x^3 is 4

68. Degree 4; zeros $-1, 0, 2, \frac{1}{2}$; coefficient of x^3 is 3

69. Degree 4; zeros $-1, 1, \sqrt{2}$; integer coefficients and constant term 6

70. Degree 5; zeros $-2, -1, 2, \sqrt{5}$; integer coefficients and constant term 40

SKILLS Plus

71–74 ■ **Finding a Polynomial from a Graph**   Find the polynomial of the specified degree whose graph is shown.

71. Degree 3

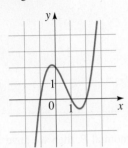

72. Degree 3

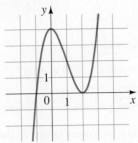

73. Degree 4

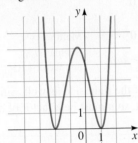

74. Degree 4

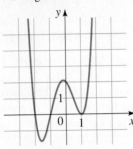

75. DISCUSS: Impossible Division?   Suppose you were asked to solve the following two problems on a test:
  A. Find the remainder when $6x^{1000} - 17x^{562} + 12x + 26$ is divided by $x + 1$.
  B. Is $x - 1$ a factor of $x^{567} - 3x^{400} + x^9 + 2$?

Obviously, it's impossible to solve these problems by dividing, because the polynomials are of such large degree. Use one or more of the theorems in this section to solve these problems *without* actually dividing.

76. DISCOVER: Nested Form of a Polynomial   Expand Q to prove that the polynomials P and Q are the same.

$$P(x) = 3x^4 - 5x^3 + x^2 - 3x + 5$$

$$Q(x) = (((3x - 5)x + 1)x - 3)x + 5$$

Try to evaluate $P(2)$ and $Q(2)$ in your head, using the forms given. Which is easier? Now write the polynomial $R(x) = x^5 - 2x^4 + 3x^3 - 2x^2 + 3x + 4$ in "nested" form, like the polynomial Q. Use the nested form to find $R(3)$ in your head.
  Do you see how calculating with the nested form follows the same arithmetic steps as calculating the value of a polynomial using synthetic division?

3.4 REAL ZEROS OF POLYNOMIALS

■ **Rational Zeros of Polynomials** ■ **Descartes' Rule of Signs** ■ **Upper and Lower Bounds Theorem** ■ **Using Algebra and Graphing Devices to Solve Polynomial Equations**

The Factor Theorem tells us that finding the zeros of a polynomial is really the same thing as factoring it into linear factors. In this section we study some algebraic methods that help us to find the real zeros of a polynomial and thereby factor the polynomial. We begin with the *rational* zeros of a polynomial.

■ Rational Zeros of Polynomials

To help us understand the next theorem, let's consider the polynomial

$$P(x) = (x - 2)(x - 3)(x + 4) \qquad \text{Factored form}$$
$$= x^3 - x^2 - 14x + 24 \qquad \text{Expanded form}$$

From the factored form we see that the zeros of P are 2, 3, and -4. When the polynomial is expanded, the constant 24 is obtained by multiplying $(-2) \times (-3) \times 4$. This means that the zeros of the polynomial are all factors of the constant term. The following generalizes this observation.

RATIONAL ZEROS THEOREM

If the polynomial $P(x) = a_n x^n + a_{n-1} x^{n-1} + \cdots + a_1 x + a_0$ has integer coefficients (where $a_n \neq 0$ and $a_0 \neq 0$), then every rational zero of P is of the form

$$\frac{p}{q}$$

where p and q are integers and

p is a factor of the constant coefficient a_0

q is a factor of the leading coefficient a_n

Proof If p/q is a rational zero, in lowest terms, of the polynomial P, then we have

$$a_n\left(\frac{p}{q}\right)^n + a_{n-1}\left(\frac{p}{q}\right)^{n-1} + \cdots + a_1\left(\frac{p}{q}\right) + a_0 = 0$$

$$a_n p^n + a_{n-1} p^{n-1} q + \cdots + a_1 p q^{n-1} + a_0 q^n = 0 \qquad \text{Multiply by } q^n$$

$$p(a_n p^{n-1} + a_{n-1} p^{n-2} q + \cdots + a_1 q^{n-1}) = -a_0 q^n \qquad \begin{array}{l}\text{Subtract } a_0 q^n \\ \text{and factor LHS}\end{array}$$

Now p is a factor of the left side, so it must be a factor of the right side as well. Since p/q is in lowest terms, p and q have no factor in common, so p must be a factor of a_0. A similar proof shows that q is a factor of a_n. ∎

We see from the Rational Zeros Theorem that if the leading coefficient is 1 or −1, then the rational zeros must be factors of the constant term.

EXAMPLE 1 ■ Using the Rational Zeros Theorem

Find the rational zeros of $P(x) = x^3 - 3x + 2$.

SOLUTION Since the leading coefficient is 1, any rational zero must be a divisor of the constant term 2. So the possible rational zeros are ± 1 and ± 2. We test each of these possibilities.

$$P(1) = (1)^3 - 3(1) + 2 = 0$$

$$P(-1) = (-1)^3 - 3(-1) + 2 = 4$$

$$P(2) = (2)^3 - 3(2) + 2 = 4$$

$$P(-2) = (-2)^3 - 3(-2) + 2 = 0$$

The rational zeros of P are 1 and −2.

✎ Now Try Exercise 15

■

DISCOVERY PROJECT

Zeroing in on a Zero

We have learned how to find the zeros of a polynomial function algebraically and graphically. In this project we investigate a *numerical* method for finding the zeros of a polynomial. With this method we can approximate the zeros of a polynomial to as many decimal places as we wish. The method involves finding smaller and smaller intervals that zoom in on a zero of a polynomial. You can find the project at **www.stewartmath.com**.

The following box explains how we use the Rational Zeros Theorem with synthetic division to factor a polynomial.

EVARISTE GALOIS (1811–1832) is one of the very few mathematicians to have an entire theory named in his honor. Not yet 21 when he died, he completely settled the central problem in the theory of equations by describing a criterion that reveals whether a polynomial equation can be solved by algebraic operations. Galois was one of the greatest mathematicians in the world at that time, although no one knew it but him. He repeatedly sent his work to the eminent mathematicians Cauchy and Poisson, who either lost his letters or did not understand his ideas. Galois wrote in a terse style and included few details, which probably played a role in his failure to pass the entrance exams at the Ecole Polytechnique in Paris. A political radical, Galois spent several months in prison for his revolutionary activities. His brief life came to a tragic end when he was killed in a duel over a love affair. The night before his duel, fearing that he would die, Galois wrote down the essence of his ideas and entrusted them to his friend Auguste Chevalier. He concluded by writing "there will, I hope, be people who will find it to their advantage to decipher all this mess." The mathematician Camille Jordan did just that, 14 years later.

> **FINDING THE RATIONAL ZEROS OF A POLYNOMIAL**
>
> 1. **List Possible Zeros.** List all possible rational zeros, using the Rational Zeros Theorem.
> 2. **Divide.** Use synthetic division to evaluate the polynomial at each of the candidates for the rational zeros that you found in Step 1. When the remainder is 0, note the quotient you have obtained.
> 3. **Repeat.** Repeat Steps 1 and 2 for the quotient. Stop when you reach a quotient that is quadratic or factors easily, and use the quadratic formula or factor to find the remaining zeros.

EXAMPLE 2 ■ Finding Rational Zeros

Write the polynomial $P(x) = 2x^3 + x^2 - 13x + 6$ in factored form, and find all its zeros.

SOLUTION   By the Rational Zeros Theorem the rational zeros of P are of the form

$$\text{possible rational zero of } P = \frac{\text{factor of constant term}}{\text{factor of leading coefficient}}$$

The constant term is 6 and the leading coefficient is 2, so

$$\text{possible rational zero of } P = \frac{\text{factor of 6}}{\text{factor of 2}}$$

The factors of 6 are $\pm 1, \pm 2, \pm 3, \pm 6$, and the factors of 2 are $\pm 1, \pm 2$. Thus the possible rational zeros of P are

$$\pm\frac{1}{1}, \quad \pm\frac{2}{1}, \quad \pm\frac{3}{1}, \quad \pm\frac{6}{1}, \quad \pm\frac{1}{2}, \quad \pm\frac{2}{2}, \quad \pm\frac{3}{2}, \quad \pm\frac{6}{2}$$

Simplifying the fractions and eliminating duplicates, we get the following list of possible rational zeros:

$$\pm 1, \quad \pm 2, \quad \pm 3, \quad \pm 6, \quad \pm\frac{1}{2}, \quad \pm\frac{3}{2}$$

To check which of these *possible* zeros actually *are* zeros, we need to evaluate P at each of these numbers. An efficient way to do this is to use synthetic division.

Test whether 1 is a zero

$$
\begin{array}{r|rrrr}
1 & 2 & 1 & -13 & 6 \\
  &   & 2 & 3 & -10 \\
\hline
  & 2 & 3 & -10 & -4
\end{array}
$$

Remainder is *not* 0, so 1 is *not* a zero

Test whether 2 is a zero

$$
\begin{array}{r|rrrr}
2 & 2 & 1 & -13 & 6 \\
  &   & 4 & 10 & -6 \\
\hline
  & 2 & 5 & -3 & 0
\end{array}
$$

Remainder *is* 0, so 2 *is* a zero

From the last synthetic division we see that 2 is a zero of P and that P factors as

$$P(x) = 2x^3 + x^2 - 13x + 6 \qquad \text{Given polynomial}$$
$$= (x - 2)(2x^2 + 5x - 3) \qquad \text{From synthetic division}$$
$$= (x - 2)(2x - 1)(x + 3) \qquad \text{Factor } 2x^2 + 5x - 3$$

From the factored form we see that the zeros of P are 2, $\frac{1}{2}$, and -3.

✎ **Now Try Exercise 29** ■

EXAMPLE 3 ■ Using the Rational Zeros Theorem and the Quadratic Formula

Let $P(x) = x^4 - 5x^3 - 5x^2 + 23x + 10$.

(a) Find the zeros of P. **(b)** Sketch a graph of P.

SOLUTION

(a) The leading coefficient of P is 1, so all the rational zeros are integers: They are divisors of the constant term 10. Thus the possible candidates are

$$\pm 1, \quad \pm 2, \quad \pm 5, \quad \pm 10$$

$$
\begin{array}{r|rrrr}
1 & 1 & -5 & -5 & 23 & 10 \\
  &   & 1 & -4 & -9 & 14 \\
\hline
  & 1 & -4 & -9 & 14 & \boxed{24} \\
\end{array}
$$

$$
\begin{array}{r|rrrr}
2 & 1 & -5 & -5 & 23 & 10 \\
  &   & 2 & -6 & -22 & 2 \\
\hline
  & 1 & -3 & -11 & 1 & \boxed{12} \\
\end{array}
$$

$$
\begin{array}{r|rrrr}
5 & 1 & -5 & -5 & 23 & 10 \\
  &   & 5 & 0 & -25 & -10 \\
\hline
  & 1 & 0 & -5 & -2 & \boxed{0} \\
\end{array}
$$

Using synthetic division (see the margin), we find that 1 and 2 are not zeros but that 5 is a zero and that P factors as

$$x^4 - 5x^3 - 5x^2 + 23x + 10 = (x - 5)(x^3 - 5x - 2)$$

We now try to factor the quotient $x^3 - 5x - 2$. Its possible zeros are the divisors of -2, namely,

$$\pm 1, \quad \pm 2$$

Since we already know that 1 and 2 are not zeros of the original polynomial P, we don't need to try them again. Checking the remaining candidates, -1 and -2, we see that -2 is a zero (see the margin), and P factors as

$$x^4 - 5x^3 - 5x^2 + 23x + 10 = (x - 5)(x^3 - 5x - 2)$$
$$= (x - 5)(x + 2)(x^2 - 2x - 1)$$

$$
\begin{array}{r|rrr}
-2 & 1 & 0 & -5 & -2 \\
   &   & -2 & 4 & 2 \\
\hline
   & 1 & -2 & -1 & \boxed{0} \\
\end{array}
$$

Now we use the Quadratic Formula to obtain the two remaining zeros of P:

$$x = \frac{2 \pm \sqrt{(-2)^2 - 4(1)(-1)}}{2} = 1 \pm \sqrt{2}$$

The zeros of P are 5, -2, $1 + \sqrt{2}$, and $1 - \sqrt{2}$.

(b) Now that we know the zeros of P, we can use the methods of Section 3.2 to sketch the graph. If we want to use a graphing calculator instead, knowing the zeros allows us to choose an appropriate viewing rectangle—one that is wide enough to contain all the x-intercepts of P. Numerical approximations to the zeros of P are

$$5, \quad -2, \quad 2.4, \quad -0.4$$

So in this case we choose the rectangle $[-3, 6]$ by $[-50, 50]$ and draw the graph shown in Figure 1.

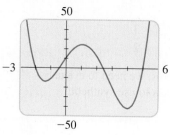

FIGURE 1
$P(x) = x^4 - 5x^3 - 5x^2 + 23x + 10$

✎ **Now Try Exercises 45 and 55** ■

■ Descartes' Rule of Signs

In some cases, the following rule—discovered by the French philosopher and mathematician René Descartes around 1637 (see page 237)—is helpful in eliminating candidates from lengthy lists of possible rational roots. To describe this rule, we need the concept

Polynomial	Variations in sign
$x^2 + 4x + 1$	0
$2x^3 + x - 6$	1
$x^4 - 3x^2 - x + 4$	2

of *variation in sign.* If $P(x)$ is a polynomial with real coefficients, written with descending powers of x (and omitting powers with coefficient 0), then a **variation in sign** occurs whenever adjacent coefficients have opposite signs. For example,

$$P(x) = 5x^7 - 3x^5 - x^4 + 2x^2 + x - 3$$

has three variations in sign.

DESCARTES' RULE OF SIGNS

Let P be a polynomial with real coefficients.

1. The number of positive real zeros of $P(x)$ either is equal to the number of variations in sign in $P(x)$ or is less than that by an even whole number.
2. The number of negative real zeros of $P(x)$ either is equal to the number of variations in sign in $P(-x)$ or is less than that by an even whole number.

Multiplicity is discussed on page 299.

In Descartes' Rule of Signs a zero with multiplicity m is counted m times. For example, the polynomial $P(x) = x^2 - 2x + 1$ has two sign changes and has the positive zero $x = 1$. But this zero is counted twice because it has multiplicity 2.

EXAMPLE 4 ▪ Using Descartes' Rule

Use Descartes' Rule of Signs to determine the possible number of positive and negative real zeros of the polynomial

$$P(x) = 3x^6 + 4x^5 + 3x^3 - x - 3$$

SOLUTION   The polynomial has one variation in sign, so it has one positive zero. Now

$$P(-x) = 3(-x)^6 + 4(-x)^5 + 3(-x)^3 - (-x) - 3$$

$$= 3x^6 - 4x^5 - 3x^3 + x - 3$$

So $P(-x)$ has three variations in sign. Thus $P(x)$ has either three or one negative zero(s), making a total of either two or four real zeros.

◤ Now Try Exercise 63   ▪

Upper and Lower Bounds Theorem

We say that a is a **lower bound** and b is an **upper bound** for the zeros of a polynomial if every real zero c of the polynomial satisfies $a \le c \le b$. The next theorem helps us to find such bounds for the zeros of a polynomial.

THE UPPER AND LOWER BOUNDS THEOREM

Let P be a polynomial with real coefficients.

1. If we divide $P(x)$ by $x - b$ (with $b > 0$) using synthetic division and if the row that contains the quotient and remainder has no negative entry, then b is an upper bound for the real zeros of P.
2. If we divide $P(x)$ by $x - a$ (with $a < 0$) using synthetic division and if the row that contains the quotient and remainder has entries that are alternately nonpositive and nonnegative, then a is a lower bound for the real zeros of P.

A proof of this theorem is suggested in Exercise 109. The phrase "alternately non-positive and nonnegative" simply means that the signs of the numbers alternate, with 0 considered to be positive or negative as required.

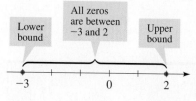

EXAMPLE 5 ■ Upper and Lower Bounds for the Zeros of a Polynomial

Show that all the real zeros of the polynomial $P(x) = x^4 - 3x^2 + 2x - 5$ lie between -3 and 2.

SOLUTION   We divide $P(x)$ by $x - 2$ and $x + 3$ using synthetic division:

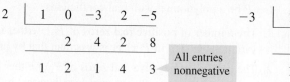

2	1	0	-3	2	-5
		2	4	2	8
	1	2	1	4	3

All entries nonnegative

-3	1	0	-3	2	-5
		-3	9	-18	48
	1	-3	6	-16	43

Entries alternate in sign

By the Upper and Lower Bounds Theorem -3 is a lower bound and 2 is an upper bound for the zeros. Since neither -3 nor 2 is a zero (the remainders are not 0 in the division table), all the real zeros lie between these numbers.

✎ Now Try Exercise 69   ■

EXAMPLE 6 ■ A Lower Bound for the Zeros of a Polynomial

Show that all the real zeros of the polynomial $P(x) = x^4 + 4x^3 + 3x^2 + 7x - 5$ are greater than or equal to -4.

SOLUTION   We divide $P(x)$ by $x + 4$ using synthetic division:

-4	1	4	3	7	-5
		-4	0	-12	20
	1	0	3	-5	15

Alternately nonnegative and nonpositive

Since 0 can be considered either nonnegative or nonpositive, the entries alternate in sign. So -4 is a lower bound for the real zeros of P.

✎ Now Try Exercise 73   ■

EXAMPLE 7 ■ Factoring a Fifth-Degree Polynomial

Factor completely the polynomial

$$P(x) = 2x^5 + 5x^4 - 8x^3 - 14x^2 + 6x + 9$$

SOLUTION   The possible rational zeros of P are $\pm\frac{1}{2}$, ± 1, $\pm\frac{3}{2}$, ± 3, $\pm\frac{9}{2}$, and ± 9. We check the positive candidates first, beginning with the smallest:

$\frac{1}{2}$	2	5	-8	-14	6	9
		1	3	$-\frac{5}{2}$	$-\frac{33}{4}$	$-\frac{9}{8}$
	2	6	-5	$-\frac{33}{2}$	$-\frac{9}{4}$	$\frac{63}{8}$

$\frac{1}{2}$ is not a zero

1	2	5	-8	-14	6	9
		2	7	-1	-15	-9
	2	7	-1	-15	-9	0

$P(1) = 0$

So 1 is a zero, and $P(x) = (x - 1)(2x^4 + 7x^3 - x^2 - 15x - 9)$. We continue by factoring the quotient. We still have the same list of possible zeros except that $\frac{1}{2}$ has been eliminated.

$$
\begin{array}{r|rrrrr}
1 & 2 & 7 & -1 & -15 & -9 \\
  &   & 2 & 9 & 8 & -7 \\
\hline
  & 2 & 9 & 8 & -7 & -16
\end{array}
$$

1 is not a zero

$$
\begin{array}{r|rrrrr}
\frac{3}{2} & 2 & 7 & -1 & -15 & -9 \\
  &   & 3 & 15 & 21 & 9 \\
\hline
  & 2 & 10 & 14 & 6 & 0
\end{array}
$$

$P(\frac{3}{2}) = 0$, all entries nonnegative

We see that $\frac{3}{2}$ is both a zero and an upper bound for the zeros of $P(x)$, so we do not need to check any further for positive zeros, because all the remaining candidates are greater than $\frac{3}{2}$.

$$P(x) = (x - 1)(x - \tfrac{3}{2})(2x^3 + 10x^2 + 14x + 6)$$

From synthetic division

$$= (x - 1)(2x - 3)(x^3 + 5x^2 + 7x + 3)$$

Factor 2 from last factor, multiply into second factor

By Descartes' Rule of Signs, $x^3 + 5x^2 + 7x + 3$ has no positive zero, so its only possible rational zeros are -1 and -3:

$$
\begin{array}{r|rrrr}
-1 & 1 & 5 & 7 & 3 \\
   &   & -1 & -4 & -3 \\
\hline
   & 1 & 4 & 3 & 0
\end{array}
$$

$P(-1) = 0$

Therefore,

$$P(x) = (x - 1)(2x - 3)(x + 1)(x^2 + 4x + 3)$$

From synthetic division

$$= (x - 1)(2x - 3)(x + 1)^2(x + 3)$$

Factor quadratic

This means that the zeros of P are 1, $\frac{3}{2}$, -1, and -3. The graph of the polynomial is shown in Figure 2.

🖙 **Now Try Exercise 81**   ■

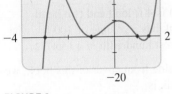

FIGURE 2
$P(x) = 2x^5 + 5x^4 - 8x^3 - 14x^2 + 6x + 9$
$= (x - 1)(2x - 3)(x + 1)^2(x + 3)$

■ Using Algebra and Graphing Devices to Solve Polynomial Equations

In Section 1.9 we used graphing devices to solve equations graphically. We can now use the algebraic techniques that we've learned to select an appropriate viewing rectangle when solving a polynomial equation graphically.

EXAMPLE 8 ■ Solving a Fourth-Degree Equation Graphically

Find all real solutions of the following equation, rounded to the nearest tenth:

$$3x^4 + 4x^3 - 7x^2 - 2x - 3 = 0$$

SOLUTION To solve the equation graphically, we graph

$$P(x) = 3x^4 + 4x^3 - 7x^2 - 2x - 3$$

We use the Upper and Lower Bounds Theorem to see where the solutions can be found.

First we use the Upper and Lower Bounds Theorem to find two numbers between which all the solutions must lie. This allows us to choose a viewing rectangle that is certain to contain all the x-intercepts of P. We use synthetic division and proceed by trial and error.

To find an upper bound, we try the whole numbers, 1, 2, 3, . . . , as potential candidates. We see that 2 is an upper bound for the solutions:

$$
\begin{array}{r|rrrrr}
2 & 3 & 4 & -7 & -2 & -3 \\
  &   & 6 & 20 & 26 & 48 \\
\hline
  & 3 & 10 & 13 & 24 & 45
\end{array}
$$

All positive

Now we look for a lower bound, trying the numbers -1, -2, and -3 as potential candidates. We see that -3 is a lower bound for the solutions:

$$
\begin{array}{r|rrrrr}
-3 & 3 & 4 & -7 & -2 & -3 \\
   &   & -9 & 15 & -24 & 78 \\
\hline
   & 3 & -5 & 8 & -26 & 75
\end{array}
$$

Entries alternate in sign

Thus all the solutions lie between -3 and 2. So the viewing rectangle $[-3, 2]$ by $[-20, 20]$ contains all the x-intercepts of P. The graph in Figure 3 has two x-intercepts, one between -3 and -2 and the other between 1 and 2. Zooming in, we find that the solutions of the equation, to the nearest tenth, are -2.3 and 1.3.

✎ **Now Try Exercise 95** ∎

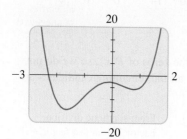

FIGURE 3
$y = 3x^4 + 4x^3 - 7x^2 - 2x - 3$

EXAMPLE 9 ▪ Determining the Size of a Fuel Tank

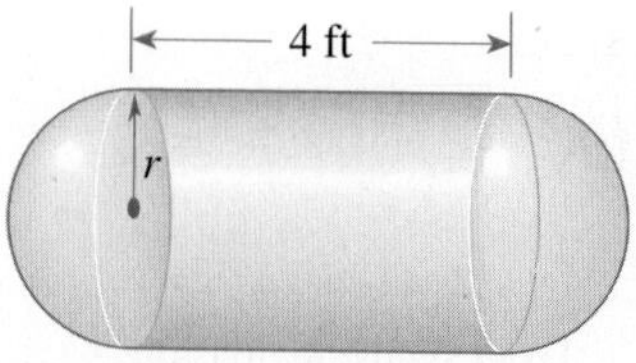

A fuel tank consists of a cylindrical center section that is 4 ft long and two hemispherical end sections, as shown in Figure 4. If the tank has a volume of 100 ft³, what is the radius r shown in the figure, rounded to the nearest hundredth of a foot?

SOLUTION Using the volume formula listed on the inside front cover of this book, we see that the volume of the cylindrical section of the tank is

$$\pi \cdot r^2 \cdot 4$$

The two hemispherical parts together form a complete sphere whose volume is

$$\tfrac{4}{3}\pi r^3$$

Because the total volume of the tank is 100 ft³, we get the following equation:

$$\tfrac{4}{3}\pi r^3 + 4\pi r^2 = 100$$

A negative solution for r would be meaningless in this physical situation, and by substitution we can verify that $r = 3$ leads to a tank that is over 226 ft³ in volume, much larger than the required 100 ft³. Thus we know the correct radius lies somewhere between 0 and 3 ft, so we use a viewing rectangle of $[0, 3]$ by $[50, 150]$ to graph the function $y = \tfrac{4}{3}\pi x^3 + 4\pi x^2$, as shown in Figure 5. Since we want the value of this function to be 100, we also graph the horizontal line $y = 100$ in the same viewing rectangle. The correct radius will be the x-coordinate of the point of intersection of the curve and the line. Using the cursor and zooming in, we see that at the point of intersection $x \approx 2.15$, rounded to two decimal places. Thus the tank has a radius of about 2.15 ft.

✎ **Now Try Exercise 99** ∎

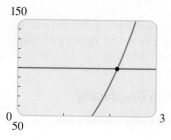

FIGURE 4

Volume of a cylinder: $V = \pi r^2 h$

Volume of a sphere: $V = \tfrac{4}{3}\pi r^3$

FIGURE 5
$y = \tfrac{4}{3}\pi x^3 + 4\pi x^2$ and $y = 100$

Note that we also could have solved the equation in Example 9 by first writing it as

$$\tfrac{4}{3}\pi r^3 + 4\pi r^2 - 100 = 0$$

and then finding the x-intercept of the function $y = \tfrac{4}{3}\pi x^3 + 4\pi x^2 - 100$.

3.4 EXERCISES

CONCEPTS

1. If the polynomial function

$$P(x) = a_n x^n + a_{n-1} x^{n-1} + \cdots + a_1 x + a_0$$

has integer coefficients, then the only numbers that could possibly be rational zeros of P are all of the form $\dfrac{p}{q}$, where p is a factor of _____ and q is a factor of _____. The possible rational zeros of $P(x) = 6x^3 + 5x^2 - 19x - 10$ are

_____.

2. Using Descartes' Rule of Signs, we can tell that the polynomial $P(x) = x^5 - 3x^4 + 2x^3 - x^2 + 8x - 8$ has

_____, _____, or _____ positive real zeros and

_____ negative real zeros.

3. *True or False?* If c is a real zero of the polynomial P, then all the other zeros of P are zeros of $P(x)/(x - c)$.

4. *True or False?* If a is an upper bound for the real zeros of the polynomial P, then $-a$ is necessarily a lower bound for the real zeros of P.

SKILLS

5–10 ■ Possible Rational Zeros List all possible rational zeros given by the Rational Zeros Theorem (but don't check to see which actually are zeros).

5. $P(x) = x^3 - 4x^2 + 3$

6. $Q(x) = x^4 - 3x^3 - 6x + 8$

7. $R(x) = 2x^5 + 3x^3 + 4x^2 - 8$

8. $S(x) = 6x^4 - x^2 + 2x + 12$

9. $T(x) = 4x^4 - 2x^2 - 7$

10. $U(x) = 12x^5 + 6x^3 - 2x - 8$

11–14 ■ Possible Rational Zeros A polynomial function P and its graph are given. **(a)** List all possible rational zeros of P given by the Rational Zeros Theorem. **(b)** From the graph, determine which of the possible rational zeros actually turn out to be zeros.

11. $P(x) = 5x^3 - x^2 - 5x + 1$

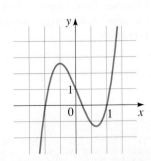

12. $P(x) = 3x^3 + 4x^2 - x - 2$

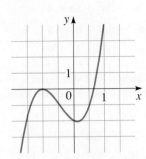

13. $P(x) = 2x^4 - 9x^3 + 9x^2 + x - 3$

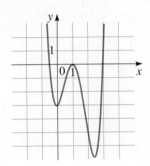

14. $P(x) = 4x^4 - x^3 - 4x + 1$

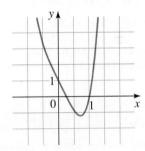

15–28 ■ Integer Zeros All the real zeros of the given polynomial are integers. Find the zeros, and write the polynomial in factored form.

15. $P(x) = x^3 + 2x^2 - 13x + 10$

16. $P(x) = x^3 - 4x^2 - 19x - 14$

17. $P(x) = x^3 + 3x^2 - 4$

18. $P(x) = x^3 - 3x - 2$

19. $P(x) = x^3 - 6x^2 + 12x - 8$

20. $P(x) = x^3 + 12x^2 + 48x + 64$

21. $P(x) = x^3 - 19x - 30$

22. $P(x) = x^3 + 11x^2 + 8x - 20$

23. $P(x) = x^3 + 3x^2 - x - 3$

24. $P(x) = x^3 - 4x^2 - 11x + 30$

25. $P(x) = x^4 - 5x^2 + 4$

26. $P(x) = x^4 - 2x^3 - 3x^2 + 8x - 4$

27. $P(x) = x^4 + 6x^3 + 7x^2 - 6x - 8$

28. $P(x) = x^4 - x^3 - 23x^2 - 3x + 90$

29–44 ■ **Rational Zeros** Find all rational zeros of the polynomial, and write the polynomial in factored form.

29. $P(x) = 4x^4 - 37x^2 + 9$

30. $P(x) = 6x^4 - 23x^3 - 13x^2 + 32x + 16$

31. $P(x) = 3x^4 - 10x^3 - 9x^2 + 40x - 12$

32. $P(x) = 2x^3 + 7x^2 + 4x - 4$

33. $P(x) = 4x^3 + 4x^2 - x - 1$

34. $P(x) = 2x^3 - 3x^2 - 2x + 3$

35. $P(x) = 4x^3 - 7x + 3$

36. $P(x) = 12x^3 - 25x^2 + x + 2$

37. $P(x) = 24x^3 + 10x^2 - 13x - 6$

38. $P(x) = 12x^3 - 20x^2 + x + 3$

39. $P(x) = 2x^4 - 7x^3 + 3x^2 + 8x - 4$

40. $P(x) = 6x^4 - 7x^3 - 12x^2 + 3x + 2$

41. $P(x) = x^5 + 3x^4 - 9x^3 - 31x^2 + 36$

42. $P(x) = x^5 - 4x^4 - 3x^3 + 22x^2 - 4x - 24$

43. $P(x) = 3x^5 - 14x^4 - 14x^3 + 36x^2 + 43x + 10$

44. $P(x) = 2x^6 - 3x^5 - 13x^4 + 29x^3 - 27x^2 + 32x - 12$

45–54 ■ **Real Zeros of a Polynomial** Find all the real zeros of the polynomial. Use the Quadratic Formula if necessary, as in Example 3(a).

45. $P(x) = 3x^3 + 5x^2 - 2x - 4$

46. $P(x) = 3x^4 - 5x^3 - 16x^2 + 7x + 15$

47. $P(x) = x^4 - 6x^3 + 4x^2 + 15x + 4$

48. $P(x) = x^4 + 2x^3 - 2x^2 - 3x + 2$

49. $P(x) = x^4 - 7x^3 + 14x^2 - 3x - 9$

50. $P(x) = x^5 - 4x^4 - x^3 + 10x^2 + 2x - 4$

51. $P(x) = 4x^3 - 6x^2 + 1$

52. $P(x) = 3x^3 - 5x^2 - 8x - 2$

53. $P(x) = 2x^4 + 15x^3 + 17x^2 + 3x - 1$

54. $P(x) = 4x^5 - 18x^4 - 6x^3 + 91x^2 - 60x + 9$

55–62 ■ **Real Zeros of a Polynomial** A polynomial P is given. **(a)** Find all the real zeros of P. **(b)** Sketch a graph of P.

55. $P(x) = x^3 - 3x^2 - 4x + 12$

56. $P(x) = -x^3 - 2x^2 + 5x + 6$

57. $P(x) = 2x^3 - 7x^2 + 4x + 4$

58. $P(x) = 3x^3 + 17x^2 + 21x - 9$

59. $P(x) = x^4 - 5x^3 + 6x^2 + 4x - 8$

60. $P(x) = -x^4 + 10x^2 + 8x - 8$

61. $P(x) = x^5 - x^4 - 5x^3 + x^2 + 8x + 4$

62. $P(x) = x^5 - x^4 - 6x^3 + 14x^2 - 11x + 3$

63–68 ■ **Descartes' Rule of Signs** Use Descartes' Rule of Signs to determine how many positive and how many negative real zeros the polynomial can have. Then determine the possible total number of real zeros.

63. $P(x) = x^3 - x^2 - x - 3$

64. $P(x) = 2x^3 - x^2 + 4x - 7$

65. $P(x) = 2x^6 + 5x^4 - x^3 - 5x - 1$

66. $P(x) = x^4 + x^3 + x^2 + x + 12$

67. $P(x) = x^5 + 4x^3 - x^2 + 6x$

68. $P(x) = x^8 - x^5 + x^4 - x^3 + x^2 - x + 1$

69–76 ■ **Upper and Lower Bounds** Show that the given values for a and b are lower and upper bounds for the real zeros of the polynomial.

69. $P(x) = 2x^3 + 5x^2 + x - 2$; $a = -3, b = 1$

70. $P(x) = x^4 - 2x^3 - 9x^2 + 2x + 8$; $a = -3, b = 5$

71. $P(x) = 8x^3 + 10x^2 - 39x + 9$; $a = -3, b = 2$

72. $P(x) = 3x^4 - 17x^3 + 24x^2 - 9x + 1$; $a = 0, b = 6$

73. $P(x) = x^4 + 2x^3 + 3x^2 + 5x - 1$; $a = -2, b = 1$

74. $P(x) = x^4 + 3x^3 - 4x^2 - 2x - 7$; $a = -4, b = 2$

75. $P(x) = 2x^4 - 6x^3 + x^2 - 2x + 3$; $a = -1, b = 3$

76. $P(x) = 3x^4 - 5x^3 - 2x^2 + x - 1$; $a = -1, b = 2$

77–80 ■ **Upper and Lower Bounds** Find integers that are upper and lower bounds for the real zeros of the polynomial.

77. $P(x) = x^3 - 3x^2 + 4$

78. $P(x) = 2x^3 - 3x^2 - 8x + 12$

79. $P(x) = x^4 - 2x^3 + x^2 - 9x + 2$

80. $P(x) = x^5 - x^4 + 1$

81–86 ■ **Zeros of a Polynomial** Find all rational zeros of the polynomial, and then find the irrational zeros, if any. Whenever appropriate, use the Rational Zeros Theorem, the Upper and Lower Bounds Theorem, Descartes' Rule of Signs, the Quadratic Formula, or other factoring techniques.

81. $P(x) = 2x^4 + 3x^3 - 4x^2 - 3x + 2$

82. $P(x) = 2x^4 + 15x^3 + 31x^2 + 20x + 4$

83. $P(x) = 4x^4 - 21x^2 + 5$

84. $P(x) = 6x^4 - 7x^3 - 8x^2 + 5x$

85. $P(x) = x^5 - 7x^4 + 9x^3 + 23x^2 - 50x + 24$

86. $P(x) = 8x^5 - 14x^4 - 22x^3 + 57x^2 - 35x + 6$

87–90 ■ **Polynomials With No Rational Zeros**   Show that the polynomial does not have any rational zeros.

87. $P(x) = x^3 - x - 2$

88. $P(x) = 2x^4 - x^3 + x + 2$

89. $P(x) = 3x^3 - x^2 - 6x + 12$

90. $P(x) = x^{50} - 5x^{25} + x^2 - 1$

91–94 ■ **Verifying Zeros Using a Graphing Device**   The real solutions of the given equation are rational. List all possible rational roots using the Rational Zeros Theorem, and then graph the polynomial in the given viewing rectangle to determine which values are actually solutions. (All solutions can be seen in the given viewing rectangle.)

91. $x^3 - 3x^2 - 4x + 12 = 0$; $[-4, 4]$ by $[-15, 15]$

92. $x^4 - 5x^2 + 4 = 0$; $[-4, 4]$ by $[-30, 30]$

93. $2x^4 - 5x^3 - 14x^2 + 5x + 12 = 0$; $[-2, 5]$ by $[-40, 40]$

94. $3x^3 + 8x^2 + 5x + 2 = 0$; $[-3, 3]$ by $[-10, 10]$

95–98 ■ **Finding Zeros Using a Graphing Device**   Use a graphing device to find all real solutions of the equation, rounded to two decimal places.

95. $x^4 - x - 4 = 0$

96. $2x^3 - 8x^2 + 9x - 9 = 0$

97. $4.00x^4 + 4.00x^3 - 10.96x^2 - 5.88x + 9.09 = 0$

98. $x^5 + 2.00x^4 + 0.96x^3 + 5.00x^2 + 10.00x + 4.80 = 0$

APPLICATIONS

99. Volume of a Silo   A grain silo consists of a cylindrical main section and a hemispherical roof. If the total volume of the silo (including the part inside the roof section) is 15,000 ft^3 and the cylindrical part is 30 ft tall, what is the radius of the silo, rounded to the nearest tenth of a foot?

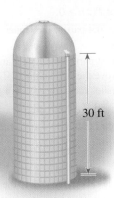

30 ft

100. Dimensions of a Lot   A rectangular parcel of land has an area of 5000 ft^2. A diagonal between opposite corners is measured to be 10 ft longer than one side of the parcel.

What are the dimensions of the land, rounded to the nearest foot?

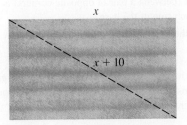

x

$x + 10$

101. Depth of Snowfall   Snow began falling at noon on Sunday. The amount of snow on the ground at a certain location at time t was given by the function

$$h(t) = 11.60t - 12.41t^2 + 6.20t^3$$
$$- 1.58t^4 + 0.20t^5 - 0.01t^6$$

where t is measured in days from the start of the snowfall and $h(t)$ is the depth of snow in inches. Draw a graph of this function, and use your graph to answer the following questions.

(a) What happened shortly after noon on Tuesday?

(b) Was there ever more than 5 in. of snow on the ground? If so, on what day(s)?

(c) On what day and at what time (to the nearest hour) did the snow disappear completely?

102. Volume of a Box   An open box with a volume of 1500 cm^3 is to be constructed by taking a piece of cardboard 20 cm by 40 cm, cutting squares of side length x cm from each corner, and folding up the sides. Show that this can be done in two different ways, and find the exact dimensions of the box in each case.

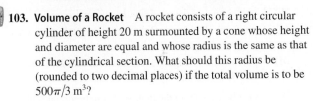

40 cm

20 cm

x

x

103. Volume of a Rocket   A rocket consists of a right circular cylinder of height 20 m surmounted by a cone whose height and diameter are equal and whose radius is the same as that of the cylindrical section. What should this radius be (rounded to two decimal places) if the total volume is to be $500\pi/3$ m^3?

20 m

104. Volume of a Box   A rectangular box with a volume of $2\sqrt{2}$ ft³ has a square base as shown below. The diagonal of the box (between a pair of opposite corners) is 1 ft longer than each side of the base.

(a) If the base has sides of length x feet, show that
$$x^6 - 2x^5 - x^4 + 8 = 0$$

(b) Show that two different boxes satisfy the given conditions. Find the dimensions in each case, rounded to the nearest hundredth of a foot.

105. Girth of a Box   A box with a square base has length plus girth of 108 in. (Girth is the distance "around" the box.) What is the length of the box if its volume is 2200 in³?

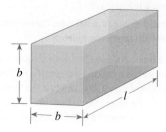

DISCUSS ■ **DISCOVER** ■ **PROVE** ■ **WRITE**

106. DISCUSS ■ DISCOVER: How Many Real Zeros Can a Polynomial Have?   Give examples of polynomials that have the following properties, or explain why it is impossible to find such a polynomial.

(a) A polynomial of degree 3 that has no real zeros

(b) A polynomial of degree 4 that has no real zeros

(c) A polynomial of degree 3 that has three real zeros, only one of which is rational

(d) A polynomial of degree 4 that has four real zeros, none of which is rational

What must be true about the degree of a polynomial with integer coefficients if it has no real zeros?

107. DISCUSS ■ PROVE: The Depressed Cubic   The most general cubic (third-degree) equation with rational coefficients can be written as
$$x^3 + ax^2 + bx + c = 0$$

(a) Prove that if we replace x by $X - a/3$ and simplify, we end up with an equation that doesn't have an X^2 term, that is, an equation of the form
$$X^3 + pX + q = 0$$
This is called a *depressed cubic*, because we have "depressed" the quadratic term.

(b) Use the procedure described in part (a) to depress the equation $x^3 + 6x^2 + 9x + 4 = 0$.

108. DISCUSS: The Cubic Formula   The Quadratic Formula can be used to solve any quadratic (or second-degree) equation. You might have wondered whether similar formulas exist for cubic (third-degree), quartic (fourth-degree), and higher-degree equations. For the depressed cubic $x^3 + px + q = 0$, Cardano (page 328) found the following formula for one solution:

$$x = \sqrt[3]{-\frac{q}{2} + \sqrt{\frac{q^2}{4} + \frac{p^3}{27}}} + \sqrt[3]{-\frac{q}{2} - \sqrt{\frac{q^2}{4} + \frac{p^3}{27}}}$$

A formula for quartic equations was discovered by the Italian mathematician Ferrari in 1540. In 1824 the Norwegian mathematician Niels Henrik Abel proved that it is impossible to write a quintic formula, that is, a formula for fifth-degree equations. Finally, Galois (page 313) gave a criterion for determining which equations can be solved by a formula involving radicals.

Use the formula given above to find a solution for the following equations. Then solve the equations using the methods you learned in this section. Which method is easier?

(a) $x^3 - 3x + 2 = 0$

(b) $x^3 - 27x - 54 = 0$

(c) $x^3 + 3x + 4 = 0$

109. PROVE: Upper and Lower Bounds Theorem   Let $P(x)$ be a polynomial with real coefficients, and let $b > 0$. Use the Division Algorithm to write
$$P(x) = (x - b) \cdot Q(x) + r$$

Suppose that $r \geq 0$ and that all the coefficients in $Q(x)$ are nonnegative. Let $z > b$.

(a) Show that $P(z) > 0$.

(b) Prove the first part of the Upper and Lower Bounds Theorem.

(c) Use the first part of the Upper and Lower Bounds Theorem to prove the second part. [*Hint:* Show that if $P(x)$ satisfies the second part of the theorem, then $P(-x)$ satisfies the first part.]

110. PROVE: Number of Rational and Irrational Roots   Show that the equation
$$x^5 - x^4 - x^3 - 5x^2 - 12x - 6 = 0$$
has exactly one rational root, and then prove that it must have either two or four irrational roots.

3.5 COMPLEX ZEROS AND THE FUNDAMENTAL THEOREM OF ALGEBRA

▪ The Fundamental Theorem of Algebra and Complete Factorization ▪ Zeros and Their Multiplicities ▪ Complex Zeros Come in Conjugate Pairs ▪ Linear and Quadratic Factors

We have already seen that an nth-degree polynomial can have at most n real zeros. In the complex number system an nth-degree polynomial has exactly n zeros (counting multiplicity) and so can be factored into exactly n linear factors. This fact is a consequence of the Fundamental Theorem of Algebra, which was proved by the German mathematician C. F. Gauss in 1799 (see page 326).

▪ The Fundamental Theorem of Algebra and Complete Factorization

The following theorem is the basis for much of our work in factoring polynomials and solving polynomial equations.

FUNDAMENTAL THEOREM OF ALGEBRA

Every polynomial

$$P(x) = a_n x^n + a_{n-1}x^{n-1} + \cdots + a_1 x + a_0 \qquad (n \geq 1, a_n \neq 0)$$

with complex coefficients has at least one complex zero.

Complex numbers are discussed in Section 1.5.

Because any real number is also a complex number, the theorem applies to polynomials with real coefficients as well.

The Fundamental Theorem of Algebra and the Factor Theorem together show that a polynomial can be factored completely into linear factors, as we now prove.

COMPLETE FACTORIZATION THEOREM

If $P(x)$ is a polynomial of degree $n \geq 1$, then there exist complex numbers $a, c_1, c_2, \ldots, c_n$ (with $a \neq 0$) such that

$$P(x) = a(x - c_1)(x - c_2) \cdots (x - c_n)$$

Proof By the Fundamental Theorem of Algebra, P has at least one zero. Let's call it c_1. By the Factor Theorem (see page 308), $P(x)$ can be factored as

$$P(x) = (x - c_1)Q_1(x)$$

where $Q_1(x)$ is of degree $n - 1$. Applying the Fundamental Theorem to the quotient $Q_1(x)$ gives us the factorization

$$P(x) = (x - c_1)(x - c_2)Q_2(x)$$

where $Q_2(x)$ is of degree $n - 2$ and c_2 is a zero of $Q_1(x)$. Continuing this process for n steps, we get a final quotient $Q_n(x)$ of degree 0, a nonzero constant that we will call a. This means that P has been factored as

$$P(x) = a(x - c_1)(x - c_2) \cdots (x - c_n)$$ ▪

To actually find the complex zeros of an nth-degree polynomial, we usually first factor as much as possible, then use the Quadratic Formula on parts that we can't factor further.

EXAMPLE 1 ■ Factoring a Polynomial Completely

Let $P(x) = x^3 - 3x^2 + x - 3$.

(a) Find all the zeros of P.

(b) Find the complete factorization of P.

SOLUTION

(a) We first factor P as follows.

$$
\begin{aligned}
P(x) &= x^3 - 3x^2 + x - 3 && \text{Given} \\
&= x^2(x - 3) + (x - 3) && \text{Group terms} \\
&= (x - 3)(x^2 + 1) && \text{Factor } x - 3
\end{aligned}
$$

We find the zeros of P by setting each factor equal to 0:

$$P(x) = (x - 3)(x^2 + 1)$$

This factor is 0 when $x = 3$ This factor is 0 when $x = i$ or $-i$

Setting $x - 3 = 0$, we see that $x = 3$ is a zero. Setting $x^2 + 1 = 0$, we get $x^2 = -1$, so $x = \pm i$. So the zeros of P are 3, i, and $-i$.

(b) Since the zeros are 3, i, and $-i$, the complete factorization of P is

$$
\begin{aligned}
P(x) &= (x - 3)(x - i)[x - (-i)] \\
&= (x - 3)(x - i)(x + i)
\end{aligned}
$$

✎. **Now Try Exercise 7**   ■

EXAMPLE 2 ■ Factoring a Polynomial Completely

Let $P(x) = x^3 - 2x + 4$.

(a) Find all the zeros of P.

(b) Find the complete factorization of P.

SOLUTION

$$
\begin{array}{r|rrrr}
-2 & 1 & 0 & -2 & 4 \\
& & -2 & 4 & -4 \\
\hline
& 1 & -2 & -2 & 0
\end{array}
$$

(a) The possible rational zeros are the factors of 4, which are ± 1, ± 2, ± 4. Using synthetic division (see the margin), we find that -2 is a zero, and the polynomial factors as

$$P(x) = (x + 2)(x^2 - 2x + 2)$$

This factor is 0 when $x = -2$ Use the Quadratic Formula to find when this factor is 0

To find the zeros, we set each factor equal to 0. Of course, $x + 2 = 0$ means that $x = -2$. We use the Quadratic Formula to find when the other factor is 0.

$$
\begin{aligned}
x^2 - 2x + 2 &= 0 && \text{Set factor equal to 0} \\
x &= \frac{2 \pm \sqrt{4 - 8}}{2} && \text{Quadratic Formula} \\
x &= \frac{2 \pm 2i}{2} && \text{Take square root} \\
x &= 1 \pm i && \text{Simplify}
\end{aligned}
$$

So the zeros of P are -2, $1 + i$, and $1 - i$.

(b) Since the zeros are -2, $1 + i$, and $1 - i$, the complete factorization of P is

$$P(x) = [x - (-2)][x - (1 + i)][x - (1 - i)]$$
$$= (x + 2)(x - 1 - i)(x - 1 + i)$$

■ Now Try Exercise 9

Zeros and Their Multiplicities

In the Complete Factorization Theorem the numbers $c_1, c_2, \ldots, c_n$ are the zeros of P. These zeros need not all be different. If the factor $x - c$ appears k times in the complete factorization of $P(x)$, then we say that c is a zero of **multiplicity k** (see page 299). For example, the polynomial

$$P(x) = (x - 1)^3(x + 2)^2(x + 3)^5$$

has the following zeros:

$$1 \text{ (multiplicity 3)} \qquad -2 \text{ (multiplicity 2)} \qquad -3 \text{ (multiplicity 5)}$$

The polynomial P has the same number of zeros as its degree: It has degree 10 and has 10 zeros, provided that we count multiplicities. This is true for all polynomials, as we prove in the following theorem.

ZEROS THEOREM

Every polynomial of degree $n \geq 1$ has exactly n zeros, provided that a zero of multiplicity k is counted k times.

Proof Let P be a polynomial of degree n. By the Complete Factorization Theorem

$$P(x) = a(x - c_1)(x - c_2) \cdots (x - c_n)$$

Now suppose that c is any given zero of P. Then

$$P(c) = a(c - c_1)(c - c_2) \cdots (c - c_n) = 0$$

Thus by the Zero-Product Property, one of the factors $c - c_i$ must be 0, so $c = c_i$ for some i. It follows that P has exactly the n zeros $c_1, c_2, \ldots, c_n$. ■

EXAMPLE 3 ■ Factoring a Polynomial with Complex Zeros

Find the complete factorization and all five zeros of the polynomial

$$P(x) = 3x^5 + 24x^3 + 48x$$

SOLUTION Since $3x$ is a common factor, we have

$$P(x) = 3x(x^4 + 8x^2 + 16)$$
$$= 3x(x^2 + 4)^2$$

This factor is 0 when $x = 0$

This factor is 0 when $x = 2i$ or $x = -2i$

CARL FRIEDRICH GAUSS (1777–1855) is considered the greatest mathematician of modern times. His contemporaries called him the "Prince of Mathematics." He was born into a poor family; his father made a living as a mason. As a very small child, Gauss found a calculation error in his father's accounts, the first of many incidents that gave evidence of his mathematical precocity. (See also page 898.) At 19, Gauss demonstrated that the regular 17-sided polygon can be constructed with straight-edge and compass alone. This was remarkable because, since the time of Euclid, it had been thought that the only regular polygons constructible in this way were the triangle and pentagon. Because of this discovery Gauss decided to pursue a career in mathematics instead of languages, his other passion. In his doctoral dissertation, written at the age of 22, Gauss proved the Fundamental Theorem of Algebra: A polynomial of degree n with complex coefficients has n roots. His other accomplishments range over every branch of mathematics, as well as physics and astronomy.

To factor $x^2 + 4$, note that $2i$ and $-2i$ are zeros of this polynomial. Thus $x^2 + 4 = (x - 2i)(x + 2i)$, so

$$P(x) = 3x[(x - 2i)(x + 2i)]^2$$
$$= 3x(x - 2i)^2(x + 2i)^2$$

| 0 is a zero of multiplicity 1 | $2i$ is a zero of multiplicity 2 | $-2i$ is a zero of multiplicity 2 |

The zeros of P are 0, $2i$, and $-2i$. Since the factors $x - 2i$ and $x + 2i$ each occur twice in the complete factorization of P, the zeros $2i$ and $-2i$ are of multiplicity 2 (or *double* zeros). Thus we have found all five zeros.

◆ **Now Try Exercise 31** ■

The following table gives further examples of polynomials with their complete factorizations and zeros.

Degree	Polynomial	Zero(s)	Number of zeros
1	$P(x) = x - 4$	4	1
2	$P(x) = x^2 - 10x + 25$ $= (x - 5)(x - 5)$	5 (multiplicity 2)	2
3	$P(x) = x^3 + x$ $= x(x - i)(x + i)$	$0, i, -i$	3
4	$P(x) = x^4 + 18x^2 + 81$ $= (x - 3i)^2(x + 3i)^2$	$3i$ (multiplicity 2), $-3i$ (multiplicity 2)	4
5	$P(x) = x^5 - 2x^4 + x^3$ $= x^3(x - 1)^2$	0 (multiplicity 3), 1 (multiplicity 2)	5

EXAMPLE 4 ▪ Finding Polynomials with Specified Zeros

(a) Find a polynomial $P(x)$ of degree 4, with zeros i, $-i$, 2, and -2, and with $P(3) = 25$.

(b) Find a polynomial $Q(x)$ of degree 4, with zeros -2 and 0, where -2 is a zero of multiplicity 3.

SOLUTION

(a) The required polynomial has the form

$$P(x) = a(x - i)(x - (-i))(x - 2)(x - (-2))$$
$$= a(x^2 + 1)(x^2 - 4) \qquad \text{Difference of squares}$$
$$= a(x^4 - 3x^2 - 4) \qquad \text{Multiply}$$

We know that $P(3) = a(3^4 - 3 \cdot 3^2 - 4) = 50a = 25$, so $a = \frac{1}{2}$. Thus

$$P(x) = \tfrac{1}{2}x^4 - \tfrac{3}{2}x^2 - 2$$

(b) We require

$$Q(x) = a[x - (-2)]^3(x - 0)$$
$$= a(x + 2)^3 x$$
$$= a(x^3 + 6x^2 + 12x + 8)x \qquad \text{Special Product Formula 4 (Section P.5)}$$
$$= a(x^4 + 6x^3 + 12x^2 + 8x)$$

Since we are given no information about Q other than its zeros and their multiplicity, we can choose any number for a. If we use $a = 1$, we get

$$Q(x) = x^4 + 6x^3 + 12x^2 + 8x$$

▸ Now Try Exercise 37

■

EXAMPLE 5 ■ Finding All the Zeros of a Polynomial

Find all four zeros of $P(x) = 3x^4 - 2x^3 - x^2 - 12x - 4$.

SOLUTION   Using the Rational Zeros Theorem from Section 3.4, we obtain the following list of possible rational zeros: $\pm 1, \pm 2, \pm 4, \pm\frac{1}{3}, \pm\frac{2}{3}, \pm\frac{4}{3}$. Checking these using synthetic division, we find that 2 and $-\frac{1}{3}$ are zeros, and we get the following factorization.

$$P(x) = 3x^4 - 2x^3 - x^2 - 12x - 4$$
$$= (x - 2)(3x^3 + 4x^2 + 7x + 2) \qquad \text{Factor } x - 2$$
$$= (x - 2)(x + \tfrac{1}{3})(3x^2 + 3x + 6) \qquad \text{Factor } x + \tfrac{1}{3}$$
$$= 3(x - 2)(x + \tfrac{1}{3})(x^2 + x + 2) \qquad \text{Factor } 3$$

The zeros of the quadratic factor are

$$x = \frac{-1 \pm \sqrt{1 - 8}}{2} = -\frac{1}{2} \pm i\frac{\sqrt{7}}{2} \qquad \text{Quadratic Formula}$$

so the zeros of $P(x)$ are

$$2, \quad -\frac{1}{3}, \quad -\frac{1}{2} + i\frac{\sqrt{7}}{2}, \quad \text{and} \quad -\frac{1}{2} - i\frac{\sqrt{7}}{2}$$

▸ Now Try Exercise 47

■

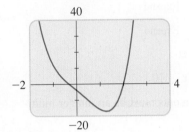

FIGURE 1
$P(x) = 3x^4 - 2x^3 - x^2 - 12x - 4$

Figure 1 shows the graph of the polynomial P in Example 5. The x-intercepts correspond to the real zeros of P. The imaginary zeros cannot be determined from the graph.

■ Complex Zeros Come in Conjugate Pairs

As you might have noticed from the examples so far, the complex zeros of polynomials with real coefficients come in pairs. Whenever $a + bi$ is a zero, its complex conjugate $a - bi$ is also a zero.

CONJUGATE ZEROS THEOREM

If the polynomial P has real coefficients and if the complex number z is a zero of P, then its complex conjugate $\bar{z}$ is also a zero of P.

Proof   Let

$$P(x) = a_n x^n + a_{n-1}x^{n-1} + \cdots + a_1 x + a_0$$

where each coefficient is real. Suppose that $P(z) = 0$. We must prove that $P(\bar{z}) = 0$. We use the facts that the complex conjugate of a sum of two complex numbers is the sum of the conjugates and that the conjugate of a product is the product of the conjugates.

$$P(\bar{z}) = a_n(\bar{z})^n + a_{n-1}(\bar{z})^{n-1} + \cdots + a_1\bar{z} + a_0$$
$$= \overline{a_n}\,\overline{z^n} + \overline{a_{n-1}}\,\overline{z^{n-1}} + \cdots + \overline{a_1}\,\overline{z} + \overline{a_0} \qquad \text{Because the coefficients are real}$$
$$= \overline{a_n z^n} + \overline{a_{n-1}z^{n-1}} + \cdots + \overline{a_1 z} + \overline{a_0}$$
$$= \overline{a_n z^n + a_{n-1}z^{n-1} + \cdots + a_1 z + a_0}$$
$$= \overline{P(z)} = \overline{0} = 0$$

This shows that $\bar{z}$ is also a zero of $P(x)$, which proves the theorem.

■

GEROLAMO CARDANO (1501–1576) is certainly one of the most colorful figures in the history of mathematics. He was the best-known physician in Europe in his day, yet throughout his life he was plagued by numerous maladies, including ruptures, hemorrhages, and an irrational fear of encountering rabid dogs. He was a doting father, but his beloved sons broke his heart—his favorite was eventually beheaded for murdering his own wife. Cardano was also a compulsive gambler; indeed, this vice might have driven him to write the *Book on Games of Chance,* the first study of probability from a mathematical point of view.

In Cardano's major mathematical work, the *Ars Magna,* he detailed the solution of the general third- and fourth-degree polynomial equations. At the time of its publication, mathematicians were uncomfortable even with negative numbers, but Cardano's formulas paved the way for the acceptance not just of negative numbers, but also of imaginary numbers, because they occurred naturally in solving polynomial equations. For example, for the cubic equation

$$x^3 - 15x - 4 = 0$$

one of his formulas gives the solution

$$x = \sqrt[3]{2 + \sqrt{-121}} + \sqrt[3]{2 - \sqrt{-121}}$$

(See page 322, Exercise 108.) This value for *x* actually turns out to be the *integer* 4, yet to find it, Cardano had to use the imaginary number $\sqrt{-121} = 11i$.

EXAMPLE 6 ■ A Polynomial with a Specified Complex Zero

Find a polynomial $P(x)$ of degree 3 that has integer coefficients and zeros $\frac{1}{2}$ and $3 - i$.

SOLUTION   Since $3 - i$ is a zero, then so is $3 + i$ by the Conjugate Zeros Theorem. This means that $P(x)$ must have the following form.

$$
\begin{aligned}
P(x) &= a\left(x - \tfrac{1}{2}\right)[x - (3 - i)][x - (3 + i)] \\
&= a\left(x - \tfrac{1}{2}\right)[(x - 3) + i][(x - 3) - i] && \text{Regroup} \\
&= a\left(x - \tfrac{1}{2}\right)[(x - 3)^2 - i^2] && \text{Difference of Squares Formula} \\
&= a\left(x - \tfrac{1}{2}\right)(x^2 - 6x + 10) && \text{Expand} \\
&= a\left(x^3 - \tfrac{13}{2}x^2 + 13x - 5\right) && \text{Expand}
\end{aligned}
$$

To make all coefficients integers, we set $a = 2$ and get

$$P(x) = 2x^3 - 13x^2 + 26x - 10$$

Any other polynomial that satisfies the given requirements must be an integer multiple of this one.

✎ **Now Try Exercise 41** ■

■ Linear and Quadratic Factors

We have seen that a polynomial factors completely into linear factors if we use complex numbers. If we don't use complex numbers, then a polynomial with real coefficients can always be factored into linear and quadratic factors. We use this property in Section 11.7 when we study partial fractions. A quadratic polynomial with no real zeros is called **irreducible** over the real numbers. Such a polynomial cannot be factored without using complex numbers.

LINEAR AND QUADRATIC FACTORS THEOREM

Every polynomial with real coefficients can be factored into a product of linear and irreducible quadratic factors with real coefficients.

Proof   We first observe that if $c = a + bi$ is a complex number, then

$$
\begin{aligned}
(x - c)(x - \bar{c}) &= [x - (a + bi)][x - (a - bi)] \\
&= [(x - a) - bi][(x - a) + bi] \\
&= (x - a)^2 - (bi)^2 \\
&= x^2 - 2ax + (a^2 + b^2)
\end{aligned}
$$

The last expression is a quadratic with *real* coefficients.

Now, if P is a polynomial with real coefficients, then by the Complete Factorization Theorem

$$P(x) = a(x - c_1)(x - c_2) \cdots (x - c_n)$$

Since the complex roots occur in conjugate pairs, we can multiply the factors corresponding to each such pair to get a quadratic factor with real coefficients. This results in P being factored into linear and irreducible quadratic factors.   ■

EXAMPLE 7 ■ Factoring a Polynomial into Linear and Quadratic Factors

Let $P(x) = x^4 + 2x^2 - 8$.

(a) Factor P into linear and irreducible quadratic factors with real coefficients.

(b) Factor P completely into linear factors with complex coefficients.

SOLUTION

(a)
$$P(x) = x^4 + 2x^2 - 8$$
$$= (x^2 - 2)(x^2 + 4)$$
$$= (x - \sqrt{2})(x + \sqrt{2})(x^2 + 4)$$

The factor $x^2 + 4$ is irreducible, since it has no real zeros.

(b) To get the complete factorization, we factor the remaining quadratic factor:
$$P(x) = (x - \sqrt{2})(x + \sqrt{2})(x^2 + 4)$$
$$= (x - \sqrt{2})(x + \sqrt{2})(x - 2i)(x + 2i)$$

➤ Now Try Exercise 67   ■

3.5 EXERCISES

CONCEPTS

1. The polynomial $P(x) = 5x^2(x - 4)^3(x + 7)$ has degree

_____. It has zeros 0, 4, and _____. The zero 0 has

multiplicity _____, and the zero 4 has multiplicity

_____.

2. **(a)** If a is a zero of the polynomial P, then _____ must
be a factor of $P(x)$.

   (b) If a is a zero of multiplicity m of the polynomial P, then

   _____ must be a factor of $P(x)$ when we factor P
   completely.

3. A polynomial of degree $n \geq 1$ has exactly _____ zeros if
a zero of multiplicity m is counted m times.

4. If the polynomial function P has real coefficients and if $a + bi$

is a zero of P, then _____ is also a zero of P. So if $3 + i$

is a zero of P, then _____ is also a zero of P.

5–6 ■ *True or False?* If *False*, give a reason.

5. Let $P(x) = x^4 + 1$.

   (a) The polynomial P has four complex zeros.

   (b) The polynomial P can be factored into linear factors with
   complex coefficients.

   (c) Some of the zeros of P are real.

6. Let $P(x) = x^3 + x$.

   (a) The polynomial P has three real zeros.

   (b) The polynomial P has at least one real zero.

   (c) The polynomial P can be factored into linear factors with
   real coefficients.

SKILLS

7–18 ■ **Complete Factorization**   A polynomial P is given.
(a) Find all zeros of P, real and complex. **(b)** Factor P
completely.

7. $P(x) = x^4 + 4x^2$

8. $P(x) = x^5 + 9x^3$

9. $P(x) = x^3 - 2x^2 + 2x$

10. $P(x) = x^3 + x^2 + x$

11. $P(x) = x^4 + 2x^2 + 1$

12. $P(x) = x^4 - x^2 - 2$

13. $P(x) = x^4 - 16$

14. $P(x) = x^4 + 6x^2 + 9$

15. $P(x) = x^3 + 8$

16. $P(x) = x^3 - 8$

17. $P(x) = x^6 - 1$

18. $P(x) = x^6 - 7x^3 - 8$

19–36 ■ **Complete Factorization**   Factor the polynomial
completely, and find all its zeros. State the multiplicity of
each zero.

19. $P(x) = x^2 + 25$

20. $P(x) = 4x^2 + 9$

21. $Q(x) = x^2 + 2x + 2$

22. $Q(x) = x^2 - 8x + 17$

23. $P(x) = x^3 + 4x$

24. $P(x) = x^3 - x^2 + x$

25. $Q(x) = x^4 - 1$

26. $Q(x) = x^4 - 625$

27. $P(x) = 16x^4 - 81$

28. $P(x) = x^3 - 64$

29. $P(x) = x^3 + x^2 + 9x + 9$

30. $P(x) = x^6 - 729$

31. $Q(x) = x^4 + 2x^2 + 1$

32. $Q(x) = x^4 + 10x^2 + 25$

33. $P(x) = x^4 + 3x^2 - 4$

34. $P(x) = x^5 + 7x^3$

35. $P(x) = x^5 + 6x^3 + 9x$

36. $P(x) = x^6 + 16x^3 + 64$

37–46 ■ Finding a Polynomial with Specified Zeros Find a polynomial with integer coefficients that satisfies the given conditions.

37. P has degree 2 and zeros $1 + i$ and $1 - i$.

38. P has degree 2 and zeros $1 + i\sqrt{2}$ and $1 - i\sqrt{2}$.

39. Q has degree 3 and zeros 3, $2i$, and $-2i$.

40. Q has degree 3 and zeros 0 and i.

41. P has degree 3 and zeros 2 and i.

42. Q has degree 3 and zeros -3 and $1 + i$.

43. R has degree 4 and zeros $1 - 2i$ and 1, with 1 a zero of multiplicity 2.

44. S has degree 4 and zeros $2i$ and $3i$.

45. T has degree 4, zeros i and $1 + i$, and constant term 12.

46. U has degree 5, zeros $\frac{1}{2}$, -1, and $-i$, and leading coefficient 4; the zero -1 has multiplicity 2.

47–64 ■ Finding Complex Zeros Find all zeros of the polynomial.

47. $P(x) = x^3 + 2x^2 + 4x + 8$

48. $P(x) = x^3 - 7x^2 + 17x - 15$

49. $P(x) = x^3 - 2x^2 + 2x - 1$

50. $P(x) = x^3 + 7x^2 + 18x + 18$

51. $P(x) = x^3 - 3x^2 + 3x - 2$

52. $P(x) = x^3 - x - 6$

53. $P(x) = 2x^3 + 7x^2 + 12x + 9$

54. $P(x) = 2x^3 - 8x^2 + 9x - 9$

55. $P(x) = x^4 + x^3 + 7x^2 + 9x - 18$

56. $P(x) = x^4 - 2x^3 - 2x^2 - 2x - 3$

57. $P(x) = x^5 - x^4 + 7x^3 - 7x^2 + 12x - 12$

58. $P(x) = x^5 + x^3 + 8x^2 + 8$ [*Hint:* Factor by grouping.]

59. $P(x) = x^4 - 6x^3 + 13x^2 - 24x + 36$

60. $P(x) = x^4 - x^2 + 2x + 2$

61. $P(x) = 4x^4 + 4x^3 + 5x^2 + 4x + 1$

62. $P(x) = 4x^4 + 2x^3 - 2x^2 - 3x - 1$

63. $P(x) = x^5 - 3x^4 + 12x^3 - 28x^2 + 27x - 9$

64. $P(x) = x^5 - 2x^4 + 2x^3 - 4x^2 + x - 2$

65–70 ■ Linear and Quadratic Factors A polynomial P is given. **(a)** Factor P into linear and irreducible quadratic factors with real coefficients. **(b)** Factor P completely into linear factors with complex coefficients.

65. $P(x) = x^3 - 5x^2 + 4x - 20$

66. $P(x) = x^3 - 2x - 4$

67. $P(x) = x^4 + 8x^2 - 9$

68. $P(x) = x^4 + 8x^2 + 16$

69. $P(x) = x^6 - 64$

70. $P(x) = x^5 - 16x$

SKILLS Plus

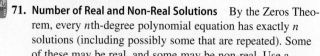

71. Number of Real and Non-Real Solutions By the Zeros Theorem, every nth-degree polynomial equation has exactly n solutions (including possibly some that are repeated). Some of these may be real, and some may be non-real. Use a graphing device to determine how many real and non-real solutions each equation has.

  (a) $x^4 - 2x^3 - 11x^2 + 12x = 0$

  (b) $x^4 - 2x^3 - 11x^2 + 12x - 5 = 0$

  (c) $x^4 - 2x^3 - 11x^2 + 12x + 40 = 0$

72–74 ■ Real and Non-Real Coefficients So far, we have worked only with polynomials that have real coefficients. These exercises involve polynomials with real and imaginary coefficients.

72. Find all solutions of the equation.

  (a) $2x + 4i = 1$ **(b)** $x^2 - ix = 0$

  (c) $x^2 + 2ix - 1 = 0$ **(d)** $ix^2 - 2x + i = 0$

73. (a) Show that $2i$ and $1 - i$ are both solutions of the equation

$$x^2 - (1 + i)x + (2 + 2i) = 0$$

  but that their complex conjugates $-2i$ and $1 + i$ are not.

  (b) Explain why the result of part (a) does not violate the Conjugate Zeros Theorem.

74. (a) Find the polynomial with *real* coefficients of the smallest possible degree for which i and $1 + i$ are zeros and in which the coefficient of the highest power is 1.

  (b) Find the polynomial with *complex* coefficients of the smallest possible degree for which i and $1 + i$ are zeros and in which the coefficient of the highest power is 1.

DISCUSS ■ DISCOVER ■ PROVE ■ WRITE

75. DISCUSS: Polynomials of Odd Degree The Conjugate Zeros Theorem says that the complex zeros of a polynomial with real coefficients occur in complex conjugate pairs. Explain how this fact proves that a polynomial with real coefficients and odd degree has at least one real zero.

76. DISCUSS ■ DISCOVER: Roots of Unity There are two square roots of 1, namely, 1 and -1. These are the solutions of $x^2 = 1$. The fourth roots of 1 are the solutions of the equation $x^4 = 1$ or $x^4 - 1 = 0$. How many fourth roots of 1 are there? Find them. The cube roots of 1 are the solutions of the equation $x^3 = 1$ or $x^3 - 1 = 0$. How many cube roots of 1 are there? Find them. How would you find the sixth roots of 1? How many are there? Make a conjecture about the number of nth roots of 1.

3.6 RATIONAL FUNCTIONS

■ Rational Functions and Asymptotes ■ Transformations of $y = 1/x$ ■ Asymptotes of Rational Functions ■ Graphing Rational Functions ■ Common Factors in Numerator and Denominator ■ Slant Asymptotes and End Behavior ■ Applications

A rational function is a function of the form

$$r(x) = \frac{P(x)}{Q(x)}$$

where P and Q are polynomials. We assume that $P(x)$ and $Q(x)$ have no factor in common. Even though rational functions are constructed from polynomials, their graphs look quite different from the graphs of polynomial functions.

■ Rational Functions and Asymptotes

Domains of rational expressions are discussed in Section P.7.

The *domain* of a rational function consists of all real numbers x except those for which the denominator is zero. When graphing a rational function, we must pay special attention to the behavior of the graph near those x-values. We begin by graphing a very simple rational function.

EXAMPLE 1 ■ A Simple Rational Function

Graph the rational function $f(x) = 1/x$, and state the domain and range.

SOLUTION The function f is not defined for $x = 0$. The following tables show that when x is close to zero, the value of $|f(x)|$ is large, and the closer x gets to zero, the larger $|f(x)|$ gets.

For positive real numbers,

$$\frac{1}{\text{BIG NUMBER}} = \text{small number}$$

$$\frac{1}{\text{small number}} = \text{BIG NUMBER}$$

x	$f(x)$
-0.1	-10
-0.01	-100
-0.00001	$-100,000$

Approaching 0^- Approaching $-\infty$

x	$f(x)$
0.1	10
0.01	100
0.00001	$100,000$

Approaching 0^+ Approaching ∞

We describe this behavior in words and in symbols as follows. The first table shows that as x approaches 0 from the left, the values of $y = f(x)$ decrease without bound. In symbols,

$$f(x) \to -\infty \quad \text{as} \quad x \to 0^-$$

"y approaches negative infinity as x approaches 0 from the left"

DISCOVERY PROJECT

Managing Traffic

A highway engineer wants to determine the optimal safe driving speed for a road. The higher the speed limit, the more cars the road can accommodate, but safety requires a greater following distance at higher speeds. In this project we find a rational function that models the carrying capacity of a road at a given traffic speed. The model can be used to determine the speed limit at which the road has its maximum carrying capacity. You can find the project at **www.stewartmath.com**.

The second table shows that as x approaches 0 from the right, the values of $f(x)$ increase without bound. In symbols,

$$f(x) \to \infty \quad \text{as} \quad x \to 0^+ \qquad \text{"y approaches infinity as } x \text{ approaches 0 from the right"}$$

The next two tables show how $f(x)$ changes as $|x|$ becomes large.

x	$f(x)$
-10	-0.1
-100	-0.01
$-100,000$	-0.00001

x	$f(x)$
10	0.1
100	0.01
$100,000$	0.00001

Approaching $-\infty$ Approaching 0   Approaching ∞ Approaching 0

These tables show that as $|x|$ becomes large, the value of $f(x)$ gets closer and closer to zero. We describe this situation in symbols by writing

$$f(x) \to 0 \quad \text{as} \quad x \to -\infty \qquad \text{and} \qquad f(x) \to 0 \quad \text{as} \quad x \to \infty$$

Using the information in these tables and plotting a few additional points, we obtain the graph shown in Figure 1.

x	$f(x) = 1/x$
-2	$-\frac{1}{2}$
-1	-1
$-\frac{1}{2}$	-2
$\frac{1}{2}$	2
1	1
2	$\frac{1}{2}$

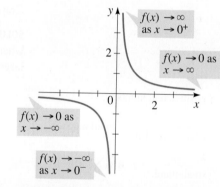

FIGURE 1
$f(x) = 1/x$

$f(x) \to \infty$ as $x \to 0^+$

$f(x) \to 0$ as $x \to \infty$

$f(x) \to 0$ as $x \to -\infty$

$f(x) \to -\infty$ as $x \to 0^-$

Obtaining the domain and range of a function from its graph is explained in Section 2.3, page 207.

The function f is defined for all values of x other than 0, so the domain is $\{x \mid x \neq 0\}$. From the graph we see that the range is $\{y \mid y \neq 0\}$.

◢ Now Try Exercise 9 ■

In Example 1 we used the following **arrow notation**.

Symbol	Meaning
$x \to a^-$	x approaches a from the left
$x \to a^+$	x approaches a from the right
$x \to -\infty$	x goes to negative infinity; that is, x decreases without bound
$x \to \infty$	x goes to infinity; that is, x increases without bound

The line $x = 0$ is called a *vertical asymptote* of the graph in Figure 1, and the line $y = 0$ is a *horizontal asymptote*. Informally speaking, an asymptote of a function is a line to which the graph of the function gets closer and closer as one travels along that line.

DEFINITION OF VERTICAL AND HORIZONTAL ASYMPTOTES

1. The line $x = a$ is a **vertical asymptote** of the function $y = f(x)$ if y approaches $\pm\infty$ as x approaches a from the right or left.

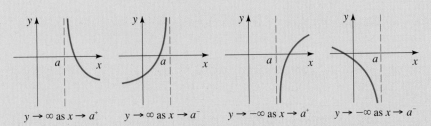

$$y \to \infty \text{ as } x \to a^+ \qquad y \to \infty \text{ as } x \to a^- \qquad y \to -\infty \text{ as } x \to a^+ \qquad y \to -\infty \text{ as } x \to a^-$$

2. The line $y = b$ is a **horizontal asymptote** of the function $y = f(x)$ if y approaches b as x approaches $\pm\infty$.

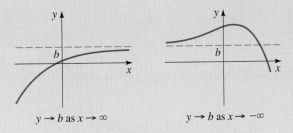

$$y \to b \text{ as } x \to \infty \qquad y \to b \text{ as } x \to -\infty$$

Recall that for a rational function $R(x) = P(x)/Q(x)$, we assume that $P(x)$ and $Q(x)$ have no factor in common.

A rational function has vertical asymptotes where the function is undefined, that is, where the denominator is zero.

■ Transformations of $y = 1/x$

A rational function of the form

$$r(x) = \frac{ax + b}{cx + d}$$

can be graphed by shifting, stretching, and/or reflecting the graph of $f(x) = 1/x$ shown in Figure 1, using the transformations studied in Section 2.6. (Such functions are called *linear fractional transformations*.)

EXAMPLE 2 ■ Using Transformations to Graph Rational Functions

Graph each rational function, and state the domain and range.

(a) $r(x) = \dfrac{2}{x - 3}$ **(b)** $s(x) = \dfrac{3x + 5}{x + 2}$

SOLUTION

(a) Let $f(x) = 1/x$. Then we can express r in terms of f as follows:

$$r(x) = \frac{2}{x - 3}$$

$$= 2\left(\frac{1}{x - 3}\right) \qquad \text{Factor 2}$$

$$= 2(f(x - 3)) \qquad \text{Since } f(x) = 1/x$$

From this form we see that the graph of r is obtained from the graph of f by shifting 3 units to the right and stretching vertically by a factor of 2. Thus r has vertical asymptote $x = 3$ and horizontal asymptote $y = 0$. The graph of r is shown in Figure 2.

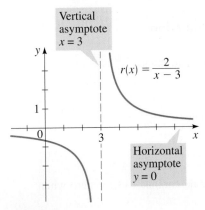

Vertical asymptote $x = 3$

$r(x) = \dfrac{2}{x - 3}$

Horizontal asymptote $y = 0$

FIGURE 2

The function r is defined for all x other than 3, so the domain is $\{x \mid x \neq 3\}$. From the graph we see that the range is $\{y \mid y \neq 0\}$.

(b) Using long division (see the margin), we get $s(x) = 3 - \dfrac{1}{x + 2}$. Thus we can express s in terms of f as follows.

$$s(x) = 3 - \frac{1}{x + 2}$$

$$= -\frac{1}{x + 2} + 3 \qquad \text{Rearrange terms}$$

$$= -f(x + 2) + 3 \qquad \text{Since } f(x) = 1/x$$

From this form we see that the graph of s is obtained from the graph of f by shifting 2 units to the left, reflecting in the x-axis, and shifting upward 3 units. Thus s has vertical asymptote $x = -2$ and horizontal asymptote $y = 3$. The graph of s is shown in Figure 3.

$$\begin{array}{r} 3 \\ x + 2 \overline{\smash)3x + 5} \\ \underline{3x + 6} \\ -1 \end{array}$$

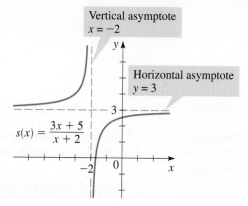

FIGURE 3

The function s is defined for all x other than -2, so the domain is $\{x \mid x \neq -2\}$. From the graph we see that the range is $\{y \mid y \neq 3\}$.

➤ **Now Try Exercises 15 and 17**

■ Asymptotes of Rational Functions

The methods of Example 2 work only for simple rational functions. To graph more complicated ones, we need to take a closer look at the behavior of a rational function near its vertical and horizontal asymptotes.

EXAMPLE 3 ■ Asymptotes of a Rational Function

Graph $r(x) = \dfrac{2x^2 - 4x + 5}{x^2 - 2x + 1}$, and state the domain and range.

SOLUTION

Vertical asymptote. We first factor the denominator

$$r(x) = \frac{2x^2 - 4x + 5}{(x - 1)^2}$$

The line $x = 1$ is a vertical asymptote because the denominator of r is zero when $x = 1$.

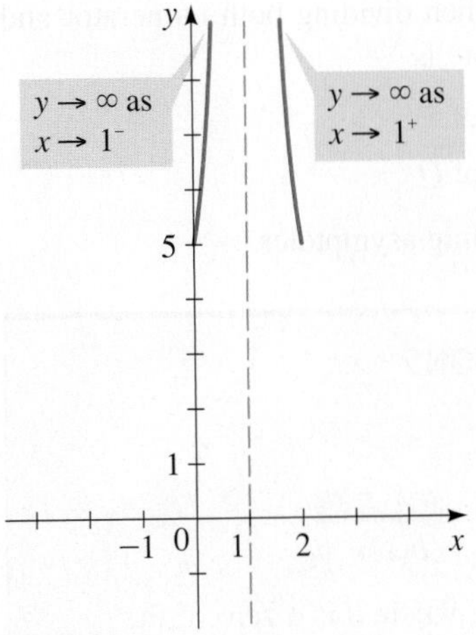

To see what the graph of r looks like near the vertical asymptote, we make tables of values for x-values to the left and to the right of 1. From the tables shown below we see that

$$y \to \infty \quad \text{as} \quad x \to 1^- \quad \text{and} \quad y \to \infty \quad \text{as} \quad x \to 1^+$$

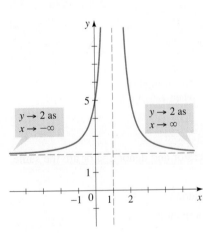

$y \to \infty$ as $x \to 1^-$

$y \to \infty$ as $x \to 1^+$

FIGURE 4

$x \to 1^-$

x	y
0	5
0.5	14
0.9	302
0.99	30,002

Approaching 1^- Approaching ∞

$x \to 1^+$

x	y
2	5
1.5	14
1.1	302
1.01	30,002

Approaching 1^+ Approaching ∞

Thus near the vertical asymptote $x = 1$, the graph of r has the shape shown in Figure 4.

Horizontal asymptote. The horizontal asymptote is the value that y approaches as $x \to \pm\infty$. To help us find this value, we divide both numerator and denominator by x^2, the highest power of x that appears in the expression:

$$y = \frac{2x^2 - 4x + 5}{x^2 - 2x + 1} \cdot \frac{\dfrac{1}{x^2}}{\dfrac{1}{x^2}} = \frac{2 - \dfrac{4}{x} + \dfrac{5}{x^2}}{1 - \dfrac{2}{x} + \dfrac{1}{x^2}}$$

The fractional expressions $\dfrac{4}{x}, \dfrac{5}{x^2}, \dfrac{2}{x}$, and $\dfrac{1}{x^2}$ all approach 0 as $x \to \pm\infty$ (see Exercise 90, Section P.2, page 17). So as $x \to \pm\infty$, we have

These terms approach 0

$$y = \frac{2 - \dfrac{4}{x} + \dfrac{5}{x^2}}{1 - \dfrac{2}{x} + \dfrac{1}{x^2}} \longrightarrow \frac{2 - 0 + 0}{1 - 0 + 0} = 2$$

These terms approach 0

$y \to 2$ as $x \to -\infty$

$y \to 2$ as $x \to \infty$

FIGURE 5

$$r(x) = \frac{2x^2 - 4x + 5}{x^2 - 2x + 1}$$

Thus the horizontal asymptote is the line $y = 2$.

Since the graph must approach the horizontal asymptote, we can complete it as in Figure 5.

Domain and range. The function r is defined for all values of x other than 1, so the domain is $\{x \mid x \neq 1\}$. From the graph we see that the range is $\{y \mid y > 2\}$.

✎ **Now Try Exercise 45** ∎

From Example 3 we see that the horizontal asymptote is determined by the leading coefficients of the numerator and denominator, since after dividing through by x^2 (the highest power of x), all other terms approach zero. In general, if $r(x) = P(x)/Q(x)$ and the degrees of P and Q are the same (both n, say), then dividing both numerator and denominator by x^n shows that the horizontal asymptote is

$$y = \frac{\text{leading coefficient of } P}{\text{leading coefficient of } Q}$$

The following box summarizes the procedure for finding asymptotes.

Recall that for a rational function $R(x) = P(x)/Q(x)$ we assume that $P(x)$ and $Q(x)$ have no factor in common. (See page 331.)

FINDING ASYMPTOTES OF RATIONAL FUNCTIONS

Let r be the rational function

$$r(x) = \frac{a_n x^n + a_{n-1} x^{n-1} + \cdots + a_1 x + a_0}{b_m x^m + b_{m-1} x^{m-1} + \cdots + b_1 x + b_0}$$

1. The vertical asymptotes of r are the lines $x = a$, where a is a zero of the denominator.

2. **(a)** If $n < m$, then r has horizontal asymptote $y = 0$.

   (b) If $n = m$, then r has horizontal asymptote $y = \dfrac{a_n}{b_m}$.

   (c) If $n > m$, then r has no horizontal asymptote.

EXAMPLE 4 ■ Asymptotes of a Rational Function

Find the vertical and horizontal asymptotes of $r(x) = \dfrac{3x^2 - 2x - 1}{2x^2 + 3x - 2}$.

SOLUTION

Vertical asymptotes.   We first factor

$$r(x) = \frac{3x^2 - 2x - 1}{(2x - 1)(x + 2)}$$

> This factor is 0 when $x = \frac{1}{2}$

> This factor is 0 when $x = -2$

The vertical asymptotes are the lines $x = \frac{1}{2}$ and $x = -2$.

Horizontal asymptote.   The degrees of the numerator and denominator are the same, and

$$\frac{\text{leading coefficient of numerator}}{\text{leading coefficient of denominator}} = \frac{3}{2}$$

Thus the horizontal asymptote is the line $y = \frac{3}{2}$.

To confirm our results, we graph r using a graphing calculator (see Figure 6).

FIGURE 6

$r(x) = \dfrac{3x^2 - 2x - 1}{2x^2 + 3x - 2}$

Graph is drawn using dot mode to avoid extraneous lines.

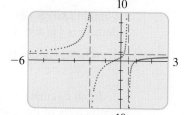

■ **Now Try Exercises 33 and 35**

Graphing Rational Functions

We have seen that asymptotes are important when graphing rational functions. In general, we use the following guidelines to graph rational functions.

SKETCHING GRAPHS OF RATIONAL FUNCTIONS

1. **Factor.** Factor the numerator and denominator.
2. **Intercepts.** Find the x-intercepts by determining the zeros of the numerator and the y-intercept from the value of the function at $x = 0$.
3. **Vertical Asymptotes.** Find the vertical asymptotes by determining the zeros of the denominator, and then see whether $y \to \infty$ or $y \to -\infty$ on each side of each vertical asymptote by using test values.
4. **Horizontal Asymptote.** Find the horizontal asymptote (if any), using the procedure described in the box on page 336.
5. **Sketch the Graph.** Graph the information provided by the first four steps. Then plot as many additional points as needed to fill in the rest of the graph of the function.

A fraction is 0 only if its numerator is 0.

EXAMPLE 5 ■ Graphing a Rational Function

Graph $r(x) = \dfrac{2x^2 + 7x - 4}{x^2 + x - 2}$, and state the domain and range.

SOLUTION We factor the numerator and denominator, find the intercepts and asymptotes, and sketch the graph.

Factor. $\quad y = \dfrac{(2x - 1)(x + 4)}{(x - 1)(x + 2)}$

x-Intercepts. The x-intercepts are the zeros of the numerator, $x = \frac{1}{2}$ and $x = -4$.

y-Intercept. To find the y-intercept, we substitute $x = 0$ into the original form of the function.

$$r(0) = \frac{2(0)^2 + 7(0) - 4}{(0)2 + (0) - 2} = \frac{-4}{-2} = 2$$

The y-intercept is 2.

Vertical asymptotes. The vertical asymptotes occur where the denominator is 0, that is, where the function is undefined. From the factored form we see that the vertical asymptotes are the lines $x = 1$ and $x = -2$.

When choosing test values, we must make sure that there is no x-intercept between the test point and the vertical asymptote.

Behavior near vertical asymptotes. We need to know whether $y \to \infty$ or $y \to -\infty$ on each side of each vertical asymptote. To determine the sign of y for x-values near the vertical asymptotes, we use test values. For instance, as $x \to 1^-$, we use a test value close to and to the left of 1 ($x = 0.9$, say) to check whether y is positive or negative to the left of $x = 1$.

$$y = \frac{(2(0.9) - 1)((0.9) + 4)}{((0.9) - 1)((0.9) + 2)} \quad \text{whose sign is} \quad \frac{(+)(+)}{(-)(+)} \quad \text{(negative)}$$

So $y \to -\infty$ as $x \to 1^-$. On the other hand, as $x \to 1^+$, we use a test value close to and to the right of 1 ($x = 1.1$, say), to get

$$y = \frac{(2(1.1) - 1)((1.1) + 4)}{((1.1) - 1)((1.1) + 2)} \quad \text{whose sign is} \quad \frac{(+)(+)}{(+)(+)} \quad \text{(positive)}$$

So $y \to \infty$ as $x \to 1^+$. The other entries in the following table are calculated similarly.

As $x \to$		-2^-	-2^+	1^-	1^+
the sign of $y = \dfrac{(2x-1)(x+4)}{(x-1)(x+2)}$ is		$\dfrac{(-)(+)}{(-)(-)}$	$\dfrac{(-)(+)}{(-)(+)}$	$\dfrac{(+)(+)}{(-)(+)}$	$\dfrac{(+)(+)}{(+)(+)}$
so $y \to$		$-\infty$	∞	$-\infty$	∞

Horizontal asymptote. The degrees of the numerator and denominator are the same, and

$$\frac{\text{leading coefficient of numerator}}{\text{leading coefficient of denominator}} = \frac{2}{1} = 2$$

Thus the horizontal asymptote is the line $y = 2$.

Graph. We use the information we have found, together with some additional values, to sketch the graph in Figure 7.

x	y
-6	0.93
-3	-1.75
-1	4.50
1.5	6.29
2	4.50
3	3.50

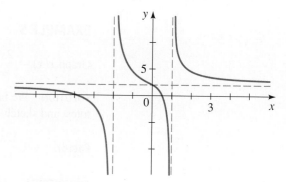

FIGURE 7

$$r(x) = \frac{2x^2 + 7x - 4}{x^2 + x - 2}$$

Domain and range. The domain is $\{x \mid x \neq 1, x \neq -2\}$. From the graph we see that the range is all real numbers.

✎. **Now Try Exercise 53**

■

EXAMPLE 6 ■ Graphing a Rational Function

Graph the rational function $r(x) = \dfrac{x^2 - 4}{2x^2 + 2x}$, and state the domain and range.

SOLUTION

Factor. $y = \dfrac{(x+2)(x-2)}{2x(x+1)}$

x-intercepts. -2 and 2, from $x + 2 = 0$ and $x - 2 = 0$

y-intercept. None, because $r(0)$ is undefined

Vertical asymptotes. $x = 0$ and $x = -1$, from the zeros of the denominator

Behavior near vertical asymptote.

As $x \to$		-1^-	-1^+	0^-	0^+
the sign of $y = \dfrac{(x+2)(x-2)}{2x(x+1)}$ is		$\dfrac{(+)(-)}{(-)(-)}$	$\dfrac{(+)(-)}{(-)(+)}$	$\dfrac{(+)(-)}{(-)(+)}$	$\dfrac{(+)(-)}{(+)(+)}$
so $y \to$		$-\infty$	∞	∞	$-\infty$

Horizontal asymptote. $y = \frac{1}{2}$, because the degree of the numerator and the degree of the denominator are the same and

$$\frac{\text{leading coefficient of numerator}}{\text{leading coefficient of denominator}} = \frac{1}{2}$$

Graph. We use the information we have found, together with some additional values, to sketch the graph in Figure 8.

x	y
-0.9	17.72
-0.5	7.50
-0.45	7.67
-0.4	8.00
-0.3	9.31
-0.1	22.17

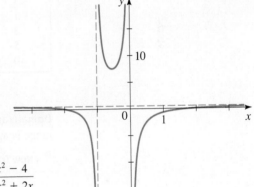

FIGURE 8

$$r(x) = \frac{x^2 - 4}{2x^2 + 2x}$$

Domain and range. The domain is $\{x \mid x \neq 0, x \neq -1\}$. From the graph we see that the range is $\{x \mid x < \frac{1}{2} \text{ or } x > 7.5\}$.

■ **Now Try Exercise 55** ■

EXAMPLE 7 ■ Graphing a Rational Function

Graph $r(x) = \dfrac{5x + 21}{x^2 + 10x + 25}$, and state the domain and range.

SOLUTION

Factor. $y = \dfrac{5x + 21}{(x + 5)^2}$

x-Intercept. $-\dfrac{21}{5}$, from $5x + 21 = 0$

y-Intercept. $\dfrac{21}{25}$, because $r(0) = \dfrac{5 \cdot 0 + 21}{0^2 + 10 \cdot 0 + 25}$

$$= \dfrac{21}{25}$$

Vertical asymptote. $x = -5$, from the zeros of the denominator

Behavior near vertical asymptote.

As $x \to$	-5^-	-5^+
the sign of $y = \dfrac{5x + 21}{(x + 5)^2}$ is	$\dfrac{(-)}{(-)(-)}$	$\dfrac{(-)}{(+)(+)}$
so $y \to$	$-\infty$	$-\infty$

Horizontal asymptote. $y = 0$, because the degree of the numerator is less than the degree of the denominator

Graph. We use the information we have found, together with some additional values, to sketch the graph in Figure 9.

x	y
-15	-0.5
-10	-1.2
-3	1.5
-1	1.0
3	0.6
5	0.5
10	0.3

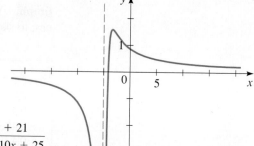

FIGURE 9

$$r(x) = \frac{5x + 21}{x^2 + 10x + 25}$$

Domain and range. The domain is $\{x \mid x \neq -5\}$. From the graph we see that the range is approximately the interval $(-\infty, 1.6]$.

✎. **Now Try Exercise 59**

■

 From the graph in Figure 9 we see that, contrary to common misconception, a graph may cross a horizontal asymptote. The graph in Figure 9 crosses the x-axis (the horizontal asymptote) from below, reaches a maximum value near $x = -3$, and then approaches the x-axis from above as $x \to \infty$.

■ Common Factors in Numerator and Denominator

We have adopted the convention that the numerator and denominator of a rational function have no factor in common. If $s(x) = p(x)/q(x)$ and if p and q do have a factor in common, then we may cancel that factor, but only for those values of x for which that factor is *not zero* (because division by zero is not defined). Since s is not defined at those values of x, its graph has a **"hole"** at those points, as the following example illustrates.

EXAMPLE 8 ■ Common Factor in Numerator and Denominator

Graph the following functions.

(a) $s(x) = \dfrac{x - 3}{x^2 - 3x}$ **(b)** $t(x) = \dfrac{x^3 - 2x^2}{x - 2}$

SOLUTION

(a) We factor the numerator and denominator:

$$s(x) = \frac{x - 3}{x^2 - 3x} = \frac{(x - 3)}{x(x - 3)} = \frac{1}{x} \quad \text{for } x \neq 3$$

So s has the same graph as the rational function $r(x) = 1/x$ but with a "hole" when x is 3, as shown in Figure 10(a).

(b) We factor the numerator and denominator:

$$t(x) = \frac{x^3 - 2x^2}{x - 2} = \frac{x^2(x - 2)}{x - 2} = x^2 \quad \text{for } x \neq 2$$

So the graph of t is the same as the graph of $r(x) = x^2$ but with a "hole" when x is 2, as shown in Figure 10(b).

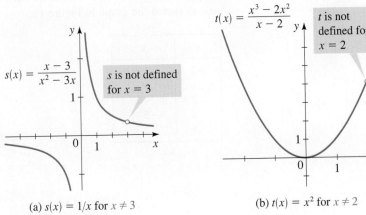

(a) $s(x) = 1/x$ for $x \neq 3$ (b) $t(x) = x^2$ for $x \neq 2$

FIGURE 10 Graphs with "holes"

Now Try Exercise 63

■ Slant Asymptotes and End Behavior

If $r(x) = P(x)/Q(x)$ is a rational function in which the degree of the numerator is one more than the degree of the denominator, we can use the Division Algorithm to express the function in the form

$$r(x) = ax + b + \frac{R(x)}{Q(x)}$$

where the degree of R is less than the degree of Q and $a \neq 0$. This means that as $x \to \pm\infty$, $R(x)/Q(x) \to 0$, so for large values of $|x|$ the graph of $y = r(x)$ approaches the graph of the line $y = ax + b$. In this situation we say that $y = ax + b$ is a **slant asymptote**, or an **oblique asymptote**.

EXAMPLE 9 ■ A Rational Function with a Slant Asymptote

Graph the rational function $r(x) = \dfrac{x^2 - 4x - 5}{x - 3}$.

SOLUTION

Factor. $y = \dfrac{(x + 1)(x - 5)}{x - 3}$

x-Intercepts. -1 and 5, from $x + 1 = 0$ and $x - 5 = 0$

y-Intercept. $\dfrac{5}{3}$, because $r(0) = \dfrac{0^2 - 4 \cdot 0 - 5}{0 - 3} = \dfrac{5}{3}$

Vertical asymptote. $x = 3$, from the zero of the denominator

Behavior near vertical asymptote. $y \to \infty$ as $x \to 3^-$ and $y \to -\infty$ as $x \to 3^+$

Horizontal asymptote. None, because the degree of the numerator is greater than the degree of the denominator

$$\begin{array}{r} x - 1 \\ x - 3 \overline{)\smash{\big)}\, x^2 - 4x - 5} \\ \underline{x^2 - 3x} \\ -x - 5 \\ \underline{-x + 3} \\ -8 \end{array}$$

Slant asymptote.   Since the degree of the numerator is one more than the degree of the denominator, the function has a slant asymptote. Dividing (see the margin), we obtain

$$r(x) = x - 1 - \frac{8}{x - 3}$$

Thus $y = x - 1$ is the slant asymptote.

Graph.   We use the information we have found, together with some additional values, to sketch the graph in Figure 11.

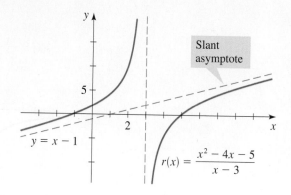

x	y
-2	-1.4
1	4
2	9
4	-5
6	2.33

FIGURE 11

✎ Now Try Exercise 69

So far, we have considered only horizontal and slant asymptotes as end behaviors for rational functions. In the next example we graph a function whose end behavior is like that of a parabola.

EXAMPLE 10 ■ **End Behavior of a Rational Function**

Graph the rational function

$$r(x) = \frac{x^3 - 2x^2 + 3}{x - 2}$$

and describe its end behavior.

SOLUTION

Factor. $y = \dfrac{(x + 1)(x^2 - 3x + 3)}{x - 2}$

x-Intercept. -1, from $x + 1 = 0$ (The other factor in the numerator has no real zeros.)

y-Intercept. $-\dfrac{3}{2}$, because $r(0) = \dfrac{0^3 - 2 \cdot 0^2 + 3}{0 - 2} = -\dfrac{3}{2}$

Vertical asymptote. $x = 2$, from the zero of the denominator

Behavior near vertical asymptote. $y \to -\infty$ as $x \to 2^-$ and $y \to \infty$ as $x \to 2^+$

Horizontal asymptote.   None, because the degree of the numerator is greater than the degree of the denominator

End behavior.   Dividing (see the margin), we get

$$r(x) = x^2 + \frac{3}{x - 2}$$

$$\begin{array}{r} x^2 \\ x - 2 \overline{)\smash{\big)}\, x^3 - 2x^2 + 0x + 3} \\ \underline{x^3 - 2x^2} \\ 3 \end{array}$$

This shows that the end behavior of r is like that of the parabola $y = x^2$ because $3/(x - 2)$ is small when $|x|$ is large. That is, $3/(x - 2) \to 0$ as $x \to \pm\infty$. This means that the graph of r will be close to the graph of $y = x^2$ for large $|x|$.

Graph. In Figure 12(a) we graph r in a small viewing rectangle; we can see the intercepts, the vertical asymptotes, and the local minimum. In Figure 12(b) we graph r in a larger viewing rectangle; here the graph looks almost like the graph of a parabola. In Figure 12(c) we graph both $y = r(x)$ and $y = x^2$; these graphs are very close to each other except near the vertical asymptote.

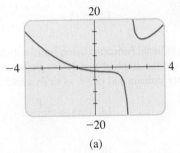

(a)

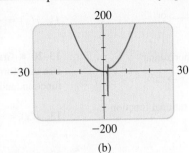

(b)

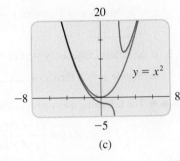

(c)

FIGURE 12

$r(x) = \dfrac{x^3 - 2x^2 + 3}{x - 2}$

 Now Try Exercise 77

■ Applications

Rational functions occur frequently in scientific applications of algebra. In the next example we analyze the graph of a function from the theory of electricity.

EXAMPLE 11 ■ Electrical Resistance

When two resistors with resistances R_1 and R_2 are connected in parallel, their combined resistance R is given by the formula

$$R = \frac{R_1 R_2}{R_1 + R_2}$$

Suppose that a fixed 8-ohm resistor is connected in parallel with a variable resistor, as shown in Figure 13. If the resistance of the variable resistor is denoted by x, then the combined resistance R is a function of x. Graph R, and give a physical interpretation of the graph.

SOLUTION Substituting $R_1 = 8$ and $R_2 = x$ into the formula gives the function

$$R(x) = \frac{8x}{8 + x}$$

Since resistance cannot be negative, this function has physical meaning only when $x > 0$. The function is graphed in Figure 14(a) using the viewing rectangle $[0, 20]$ by $[0, 10]$. The function has no vertical asymptote when x is restricted to positive values. The combined resistance R increases as the variable resistance x increases. If we widen the viewing rectangle to $[0, 100]$ by $[0, 10]$, we obtain the graph in Figure 14(b). For large x the combined resistance R levels off, getting closer and closer to the horizontal asymptote $R = 8$. No matter how large the variable resistance x, the combined resistance is never greater than 8 ohms.

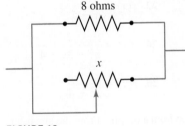

8 ohms

x

FIGURE 13

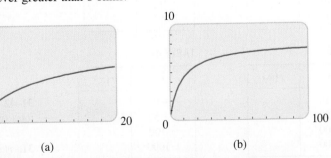

(a)

(b)

FIGURE 14

$R(x) = \dfrac{8x}{8 + x}$

 Now Try Exercise 87

3.6 EXERCISES

CONCEPTS

1. If the rational function $y = r(x)$ has the vertical asymptote $x = 2$, then as $x \to 2^+$, either $y \to$ _____ or $y \to$ _____.

2. If the rational function $y = r(x)$ has the horizontal asymptote $y = 2$, then $y \to$ _____ as $x \to \pm\infty$.

3–6 ■ The following questions are about the rational function

$$r(x) = \frac{(x + 1)(x - 2)}{(x + 2)(x - 3)}$$

3. The function r has x-intercepts _____ and _____.

4. The function r has y-intercept _____.

5. The function r has vertical asymptotes $x =$ _____ and $x =$ _____.

6. The function r has horizontal asymptote $y =$ _____.

7–8 ■ *True or False?*

7. Let $r(x) = \dfrac{x^2 + x}{(x + 1)(2x - 4)}$. The graph of r has

  (a) vertical asymptote $x = -1$.

  (b) vertical asymptote $x = 2$.

  (c) horizontal asymptote $y = 1$.

  (d) horizontal asymptote $y = \frac{1}{2}$.

8. The graph of a rational function may cross a horizontal asymptote.

SKILLS

9–12 ■ **Table of Values** A rational function is given. **(a)** Complete each table for the function. **(b)** Describe the behavior of the function near its vertical asymptote, based on Tables 1 and 2. **(c)** Determine the horizontal asymptote, based on Tables 3 and 4.

TABLE 1

x	$r(x)$
1.5	
1.9	
1.99	
1.999	

TABLE 2

x	$r(x)$
2.5	
2.1	
2.01	
2.001	

TABLE 3

x	$r(x)$
10	
50	
100	
1000	

TABLE 4

x	$r(x)$
-10	
-50	
-100	
-1000	

9. $r(x) = \dfrac{x}{x - 2}$

10. $r(x) = \dfrac{4x + 1}{x - 2}$

11. $r(x) = \dfrac{3x - 10}{(x - 2)^2}$

12. $r(x) = \dfrac{3x^2 + 1}{(x - 2)^2}$

13–20 ■ **Graphing Rational Functions Using Transformations** Use transformations of the graph of $y = 1/x$ to graph the rational function, and state the domain and range, as in Example 2.

13. $r(x) = \dfrac{1}{x - 1}$

14. $r(x) = \dfrac{1}{x + 4}$

15. $s(x) = \dfrac{3}{x + 1}$

16. $s(x) = \dfrac{-2}{x - 2}$

17. $t(x) = \dfrac{2x - 3}{x - 2}$

18. $t(x) = \dfrac{3x - 3}{x + 2}$

19. $r(x) = \dfrac{x + 2}{x + 3}$

20. $r(x) = \dfrac{2x - 9}{x - 4}$

21–26 ■ **Intercepts of Rational Functions** Find the x- and y-intercepts of the rational function.

21. $r(x) = \dfrac{x - 1}{x + 4}$

22. $s(x) = \dfrac{3x}{x - 5}$

23. $t(x) = \dfrac{x^2 - x - 2}{x - 6}$

24. $r(x) = \dfrac{2}{x^2 + 3x - 4}$

25. $r(x) = \dfrac{x^2 - 9}{x^2}$

26. $r(x) = \dfrac{x^3 + 8}{x^2 + 4}$

27–30 ■ **Getting Information from a Graph** From the graph, determine the x- and y-intercepts and the vertical and horizontal asymptotes.

27.

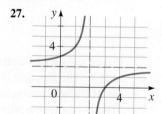

28.

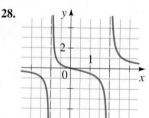

29.

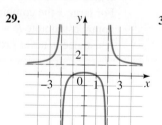

30.

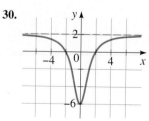

31–42 ■ **Asymptotes** Find all horizontal and vertical asymptotes (if any).

31. $r(x) = \dfrac{5}{x - 2}$

32. $r(x) = \dfrac{2x - 3}{x^2 - 1}$

33. $r(x) = \dfrac{3x + 1}{4x^2 + 1}$ **34.** $r(x) = \dfrac{3x^2 + 5x}{x^4 - 1}$

35. $s(x) = \dfrac{6x^2 + 1}{2x^2 + x - 1}$ **36.** $s(x) = \dfrac{8x^2 + 1}{4x^2 + 2x - 6}$

37. $r(x) = \dfrac{(x + 1)(2x - 3)}{(x - 2)(4x + 7)}$ **38.** $r(x) = \dfrac{(x - 3)(x + 2)}{(5x + 1)(2x - 3)}$

39. $r(x) = \dfrac{6x^3 - 2}{2x^3 + 5x^2 + 6x}$ **40.** $r(x) = \dfrac{5x^3}{x^3 + 2x^2 + 5x}$

41. $t(x) = \dfrac{x^2 + 2}{x - 1}$ **42.** $r(x) = \dfrac{x^3 + 3x^2}{x^2 - 4}$

43–62 ■ **Graphing Rational Functions** Find the intercepts and asymptotes, and then sketch a graph of the rational function and state the domain and range. Use a graphing device to confirm your answer.

43. $r(x) = \dfrac{4x - 4}{x + 2}$ **44.** $r(x) = \dfrac{2x + 6}{-6x + 3}$

45. $r(x) = \dfrac{3x^2 - 12x + 13}{x^2 - 4x + 4}$ **46.** $r(x) = \dfrac{-2x^2 - 8x - 9}{x^2 + 4x + 4}$

47. $r(x) = \dfrac{-x^2 + 8x - 18}{x^2 - 8x + 16}$ **48.** $r(x) = \dfrac{x^2 + 2x + 3}{2x^2 + 4x + 2}$

49. $s(x) = \dfrac{4x - 8}{(x - 4)(x + 1)}$ **50.** $s(x) = \dfrac{6}{x^2 - 5x - 6}$

51. $s(x) = \dfrac{2x - 4}{x^2 + x - 2}$ **52.** $s(x) = \dfrac{x + 2}{(x + 3)(x - 1)}$

53. $r(x) = \dfrac{(x - 1)(x + 2)}{(x + 1)(x - 3)}$ **54.** $r(x) = \dfrac{2x^2 + 10x - 12}{x^2 + x - 6}$

55. $r(x) = \dfrac{2x^2 + 2x - 4}{x^2 + x}$ **56.** $r(x) = \dfrac{3x^2 + 6}{x^2 - 2x - 3}$

57. $s(x) = \dfrac{x^2 - 2x + 1}{x^3 - 3x^2}$ **58.** $r(x) = \dfrac{x^2 - x - 6}{x^2 + 3x}$

59. $r(x) = \dfrac{x^2 - 2x + 1}{x^2 + 2x + 1}$ **60.** $r(x) = \dfrac{4x^2}{x^2 - 2x - 3}$

61. $r(x) = \dfrac{5x^2 + 5}{x^2 + 4x + 4}$ **62.** $t(x) = \dfrac{x^3 - x^2}{x^3 - 3x - 2}$

63–68 ■ **Rational Functions with Holes** Find the factors that are common in the numerator and the denominator. Then find the intercepts and asymptotes, and sketch a graph of the rational function. State the domain and range of the function.

63. $r(x) = \dfrac{x^2 + 4x - 5}{x^2 + x - 2}$

64. $r(x) = \dfrac{x^2 + 3x - 10}{(x + 1)(x - 3)(x + 5)}$

65. $r(x) = \dfrac{x^2 - 2x - 3}{x + 1}$

66. $r(x) = \dfrac{x^3 - 2x^2 - 3x}{x - 3}$

67. $r(x) = \dfrac{x^3 - 5x^2 + 3x + 9}{x + 1}$

[*Hint:* Check that $x + 1$ is a factor of the numerator.]

68. $r(x) = \dfrac{x^2 + 4x - 5}{x^3 + 7x^2 + 10x}$

69–76 ■ **Slant Asymptotes** Find the slant asymptote and the vertical asymptotes, and sketch a graph of the function.

69. $r(x) = \dfrac{x^2}{x - 2}$ **70.** $r(x) = \dfrac{x^2 + 2x}{x - 1}$

71. $r(x) = \dfrac{x^2 - 2x - 8}{x}$ **72.** $r(x) = \dfrac{3x - x^2}{2x - 2}$

73. $r(x) = \dfrac{x^2 + 5x + 4}{x - 3}$ **74.** $r(x) = \dfrac{x^3 + 4}{2x^2 + x - 1}$

75. $r(x) = \dfrac{x^3 + x^2}{x^2 - 4}$ **76.** $r(x) = \dfrac{2x^3 + 2x}{x^2 - 1}$

SKILLS Plus

77–80 ■ **End Behavior** Graph the rational function f, and determine all vertical asymptotes from your graph. Then graph f and g in a sufficiently large viewing rectangle to show that they have the same end behavior.

77. $f(x) = \dfrac{2x^2 + 6x + 6}{x + 3}$, $g(x) = 2x$

78. $f(x) = \dfrac{-x^3 + 6x^2 - 5}{x^2 - 2x}$, $g(x) = -x + 4$

79. $f(x) = \dfrac{x^3 - 2x^2 + 16}{x - 2}$, $g(x) = x^2$

80. $f(x) = \dfrac{-x^4 + 2x^3 - 2x}{(x - 1)^2}$, $g(x) = 1 - x^2$

81–86 ■ **End Behavior** Graph the rational function, and find all vertical asymptotes, x- and y-intercepts, and local extrema, correct to the nearest tenth. Then use long division to find a polynomial that has the same end behavior as the rational function, and graph both functions in a sufficiently large viewing rectangle to verify that the end behaviors of the polynomial and the rational function are the same.

81. $y = \dfrac{2x^2 - 5x}{2x + 3}$

82. $y = \dfrac{x^4 - 3x^3 + x^2 - 3x + 3}{x^2 - 3x}$

83. $y = \dfrac{x^5}{x^3 - 1}$ **84.** $y = \dfrac{x^4}{x^2 - 2}$

85. $r(x) = \dfrac{x^4 - 3x^3 + 6}{x - 3}$ **86.** $r(x) = \dfrac{4 + x^2 - x^4}{x^2 - 1}$

APPLICATIONS

87. Population Growth Suppose that the rabbit population on Mr. Jenkins' farm follows the formula

$$p(t) = \frac{3000t}{t + 1}$$

where $t \geq 0$ is the time (in months) since the beginning of the year.

(a) Draw a graph of the rabbit population.

(b) What eventually happens to the rabbit population?

88. Drug Concentration After a certain drug is injected into a patient, the concentration c of the drug in the bloodstream is monitored. At time $t \geq 0$ (in minutes since the injection) the concentration (in mg/L) is given by

$$c(t) = \frac{30t}{t^2 + 2}$$

(a) Draw a graph of the drug concentration.

(b) What eventually happens to the concentration of drug in the bloodstream?

89. Drug Concentration A drug is administered to a patient, and the concentration of the drug in the bloodstream is monitored. At time $t \geq 0$ (in hours since giving the drug) the concentration (in mg/L) is given by

$$c(t) = \frac{5t}{t^2 + 1}$$

Graph the function c with a graphing device.

(a) What is the highest concentration of drug that is reached in the patient's bloodstream?

(b) What happens to the drug concentration after a long period of time?

(c) How long does it take for the concentration to drop below 0.3 mg/L?

90. Flight of a Rocket Suppose a rocket is fired upward from the surface of the earth with an initial velocity v (measured in meters per second). Then the maximum height h (in meters) reached by the rocket is given by the function

$$h(v) = \frac{Rv^2}{2gR - v^2}$$

where $R = 6.4 \times 10^6$ m is the radius of the earth and $g = 9.8$ m/s^2 is the acceleration due to gravity. Use a graphing device to draw a graph of the function h. (Note that h and v must both be positive, so the viewing rectangle need not contain negative values.) What does the vertical asymptote represent physically?

91. The Doppler Effect As a train moves toward an observer (see the figure), the pitch of its whistle sounds higher to the observer than it would if the train were at rest, because the crests of the sound waves are compressed closer together. This phenomenon is called the *Doppler effect*. The observed pitch P is a function of the speed v of the train and is given by

$$P(v) = P_0 \left(\frac{s_0}{s_0 - v} \right)$$

where P_0 is the actual pitch of the whistle at the source and

$s_0 = 332$ m/s is the speed of sound in air. Suppose that a train has a whistle pitched at $P_0 = 440$ Hz. Graph the function $y = P(v)$ using a graphing device. How can the vertical asymptote of this function be interpreted physically?

92. Focusing Distance For a camera with a lens of fixed focal length F to focus on an object located a distance x from the lens, the film must be placed a distance y behind the lens, where F, x, and y are related by

$$\frac{1}{x} + \frac{1}{y} = \frac{1}{F}$$

(See the figure.) Suppose the camera has a 55-mm lens ($F = 55$).

(a) Express y as a function of x, and graph the function.

(b) What happens to the focusing distance y as the object moves far away from the lens?

(c) What happens to the focusing distance y as the object moves close to the lens?

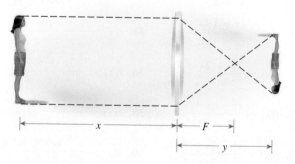

DISCUSS ■ DISCOVER ■ PROVE ■ WRITE

93. DISCUSS: Constructing a Rational Function from Its Asymptotes Give an example of a rational function that has vertical asymptote $x = 3$. Now give an example of one that has vertical asymptote $x = 3$ *and* horizontal asymptote $y = 2$. Now give an example of a rational function with vertical asymptotes $x = 1$ and $x = -1$, horizontal asymptote $y = 0$, and x-intercept 4.

94. DISCUSS: A Rational Function with No Asymptote Explain how you can tell (without graphing it) that the function

$$r(x) = \frac{x^6 + 10}{x^4 + 8x^2 + 15}$$

has no x-intercept and no horizontal, vertical, or slant asymptote. What is its end behavior?'

95. DISCOVER: Transformations of $y = 1/x^2$ In Example 2 we saw that some simple rational functions can be graphed by shifting, stretching, or reflecting the graph of $y = 1/x$. In this exercise we consider rational functions that can be graphed by transforming the graph of $y = 1/x^2$.

(a) Graph the function

$$r(x) = \frac{1}{(x - 2)^2}$$

by transforming the graph of $y = 1/x^2$.

(b) Use long division and factoring to show that the function

$$s(x) = \frac{2x^2 + 4x + 5}{x^2 + 2x + 1}$$

can be written as

$$s(x) = 2 + \frac{3}{(x + 1)^2}$$

Then graph s by transforming the graph of $y = 1/x^2$.

(c) One of the following functions can be graphed by transforming the graph of $y = 1/x^2$; the other cannot. Use transformations to graph the one that can be, and explain why this method doesn't work for the other one.

$$p(x) = \frac{2 - 3x^2}{x^2 - 4x + 4} \qquad q(x) = \frac{12x - 3x^2}{x^2 - 4x + 4}$$

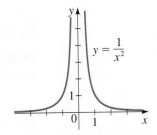

3.7 POLYNOMIAL AND RATIONAL INEQUALITIES

■ **Polynomial Inequalities** ■ **Rational Inequalities**

In Section 1.7 we solved basic inequalities. In this section we solve more advanced inequalities by using the methods we learned in Section 3.4 for factoring and graphing polynomials.

■ Polynomial Inequalities

An important consequence of the Intermediate Value Theorem (page 295) is that the values of a polynomial function P do not change sign between successive zeros. In other words, the values of P between successive zeros are either all positive or all negative. Graphically, this means that between successive x-intercepts, the graph of P is entirely above or entirely below the x-axis. Figure 1 illustrates this property of polynomials. This property of polynomials allows us to solve **polynomial inequalities** like $P(x) \geq 0$ by finding the zeros of the polynomial and using test points between successive zeros to determine the intervals that satisfy the inequality. We use the following guidelines.

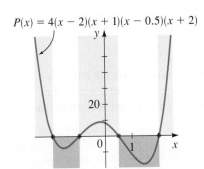

$P(x) = 4(x - 2)(x + 1)(x - 0.5)(x + 2)$

FIGURE 1 $P(x) > 0$ or $P(x) < 0$ for x between successive zeros of P

> **SOLVING POLYNOMIAL INEQUALITIES**
>
> 1. **Move All Terms to One Side.** Rewrite the inequality so that all nonzero terms appear on one side of the inequality symbol.
> 2. **Factor the Polynomial.** Factor the polynomial into irreducible factors, and find the **real zeros** of the polynomial.
> 3. **Find the Intervals.** List the intervals determined by the real zeros.
> 4. **Make a Table or Diagram.** Use test values to make a table or diagram of the signs of each factor in each interval. In the last row of the table determine the sign of the polynomial on that interval.
> 5. **Solve.** Determine the solutions of the inequality from the last row of the table. Check whether the **endpoints** of these intervals satisfy the inequality. (This may happen if the inequality involves $\leq$ or $\geq$.)

EXAMPLE 1 ■ Solving a Polynomial Inequality

Solve the inequality $2x^3 + x^2 + 6 \geq 13x$.

SOLUTION We follow the preceding guidelines.

Move all terms to one side. We move all terms to the left-hand side of the inequality to get

$$2x^3 + x^2 - 13x + 6 \geq 0$$

The left-hand side is a polynomial.

Factor the polynomial. This polynomial is factored in Example 2, Section 3.4, on page 313. We get

$$(x - 2)(2x - 1)(x + 3) \geq 0$$

The zeros of the polynomial are -3, $\frac{1}{2}$, and 2.

Find the intervals. The intervals determined by the zeros of the polynomial are

$$(-\infty, -3), \left(-3, \tfrac{1}{2}\right), \left(\tfrac{1}{2}, 2\right), (2, \infty)$$

Make a table or diagram. We make a diagram indicating the sign of each factor on each interval.

	-3	$\frac{1}{2}$	2	
Sign of $x - 2$	$-$	$-$	$-$	$+$
Sign of $2x - 1$	$-$	$-$	$+$	$+$
Sign of $x + 3$	$-$	$+$	$+$	$+$
Sign of $(x - 2)(2x - 1)(x + 3)$	$-$	$+$	$-$	$+$

Solve. From the diagram we see that the inequality is satisfied on the intervals $\left(-3, \tfrac{1}{2}\right)$ and $(2, \infty)$. Checking the endpoints, we see that -3, $\frac{1}{2}$, and 2 satisfy the inequality, so the solution is $\left[-3, \tfrac{1}{2}\right] \cup [2, \infty)$. The graph in Figure 2 confirms our solution.

✎ **Now Try Exercise 7**

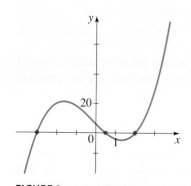

FIGURE 2

EXAMPLE 2 ■ Solving a Polynomial Inequality

Solve the inequality $3x^4 - x^2 - 4 < 2x^3 + 12x$.

SOLUTION We follow the above guidelines.

Move all terms to one side. We move all terms to the left-hand side of the inequality to get

$$3x^4 - 2x^3 - x^2 - 12x - 4 < 0$$

The left-hand side is a polynomial.

Factor the polynomial. This polynomial is factored into linear and irreducible quadratic factors in Example 5, Section 3.5, page 327. We get

$$(x - 2)(3x + 1)(x^2 + x + 2) < 0$$

From the first two factors we obtain the zeros 2 and $-\frac{1}{3}$. The third factor has no real zeros.

Find the intervals. The intervals determined by the zeros of the polynomial are

$$\left(-\infty, -\tfrac{1}{3}\right), \left(-\tfrac{1}{3}, 2\right), (2, \infty)$$

Make a table or diagram. We make a sign diagram.

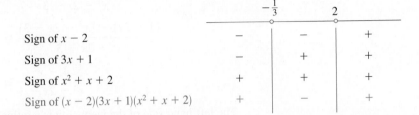

	$-\tfrac{1}{3}$		2	
Sign of $x - 2$	$-$		$-$	$+$
Sign of $3x + 1$	$-$		$+$	$+$
Sign of $x^2 + x + 2$	$+$		$+$	$+$
Sign of $(x - 2)(3x + 1)(x^2 + x + 2)$	$+$		$-$	$+$

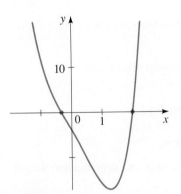

FIGURE 3

Solve. From the diagram we see that the inequality is satisfied on the interval $\left(-\tfrac{1}{3}, 2\right)$. You can check that the two endpoints do not satisfy the inequality, so the solution is $\left(-\tfrac{1}{3}, 2\right)$. The graph in Figure 3 confirms our solution.

✎ **Now Try Exercise 13** ▪

▪ Rational Inequalities

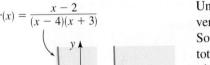

$$r(x) = \frac{x - 2}{(x - 4)(x + 3)}$$

FIGURE 4 $r(x) > 0$ or $r(x) < 0$ for x between successive cut points of r

Unlike polynomial functions, rational functions are not necessarily continuous. The vertical asymptotes of a rational function r break up the graph into separate "branches." So the intervals on which r does not change sign are determined by the vertical asymptotes as well as the zeros of r. This is the reason for the following definition: If $r(x) = P(x)/Q(x)$ is a rational function, the **cut points** of r are the values of x at which either $P(x) = 0$ or $Q(x) = 0$. In other words, the cut points of r are the zeros of the numerator and the zeros of the denominator (see Figure 4). So to solve a **rational inequality** like $r(x) \geq 0$, we use test points between successive cut points to determine the intervals that satisfy the inequality. We use the following guidelines.

SOLVING RATIONAL INEQUALITIES

1. **Move All Terms to One Side.** Rewrite the inequality so that all nonzero terms appear on one side of the inequality symbol. Bring all quotients to a common denominator.

2. **Factor Numerator and Denominator.** Factor the numerator and denominator into irreducible factors, and then find the **cut points**.

3. **Find the Intervals.** List the intervals determined by the cut points.

4. **Make a Table or Diagram.** Use test values to make a table or diagram of the signs of each factor in each interval. In the last row of the table determine the sign of the rational function on that interval.

5. **Solve.** Determine the solution of the inequality from the last row of the table. Check whether the **endpoints** of these intervals satisfy the inequality. (This may happen if the inequality involves $\leq$ or $\geq$.)

EXAMPLE 3 ▪ Solving a Rational Inequality

Solve the inequality

$$\frac{1 - 2x}{x^2 - 2x - 3} \geq 1$$

SOLUTION   We follow the above guidelines.

Move all terms to one side.   We move all terms to the left-hand side of the inequality.

$$\frac{1 - 2x}{x^2 - 2x - 3} - 1 \geq 0 \qquad \text{Move terms to LHS}$$

$$\frac{(1 - 2x) - (x^2 - 2x - 3)}{x^2 - 2x - 3} \geq 0 \qquad \text{Common denominator}$$

$$\frac{4 - x^2}{x^2 - 2x - 3} \geq 0 \qquad \text{Simplify}$$

The left-hand side of the inequality is a rational function.

Factor numerator and denominator.   Factoring the numerator and denominator, we get

$$\frac{(2 - x)(2 + x)}{(x - 3)(x + 1)} \geq 0$$

The zeros of the numerator are 2 and -2, and the zeros of the denominator are -1 and 3, so the cut points are -2, -1, 2, and 3.

Find the intervals.   The intervals determined by the cut points are

$$(-\infty, -2), \ (-2, -1), \ (-1, 2), \ (2, 3), (3, \infty)$$

Make a table or diagram.   We make a sign diagram.

	-2	-1	2	3
Sign of $2 - x$	$+$	$+$	$+$	$-$	$-$
Sign of $2 + x$	$-$	$+$	$+$	$+$	$+$
Sign of $x - 3$	$-$	$-$	$-$	$-$	$+$
Sign of $x + 1$	$-$	$-$	$+$	$+$	$+$
Sign of $\dfrac{(2 - x)(2 + x)}{(x - 3)(x + 1)}$	$-$	$+$	$-$	$+$	$-$

Solve.   From the diagram we see that the inequality is satisfied on the intervals $(-2, -1)$ and $(2, 3)$. Checking the endpoints, we see that -2 and 2 satisfy the inequality, so the solution is $[-2, -1) \cup [2, 3)$. The graph in Figure 5 confirms our solution.

✎ **Now Try Exercise 27** ■

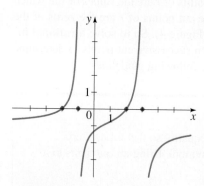

FIGURE 5

EXAMPLE 4 ■ Solving a Rational Inequality

Solve the inequality

$$\frac{x^2 - 4x + 3}{x^2 - 4x - 5} \geq 0$$

SOLUTION   Since all nonzero terms are already on one side of the inequality symbol, we begin by factoring.

Factor numerator and denominator.   Factoring the numerator and denominator, we get

$$\frac{(x - 3)(x - 1)}{(x - 5)(x + 1)} \geq 0$$

The cut points are -1, 1, 3, and 5.

Find the intervals. The intervals determined by the cut points are

$$(-\infty, -1), (-1, 1), (1, 3), (3, 5), (5, \infty)$$

Make a table or diagram. We make a sign diagram.

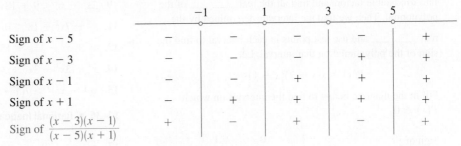

	-1	1	3	5
Sign of $x - 5$	$-$	$-$	$-$	$-$	$+$
Sign of $x - 3$	$-$	$-$	$-$	$+$	$+$
Sign of $x - 1$	$-$	$-$	$+$	$+$	$+$
Sign of $x + 1$	$-$	$+$	$+$	$+$	$+$
Sign of $\dfrac{(x-3)(x-1)}{(x-5)(x+1)}$	$+$	$-$	$+$	$-$	$+$

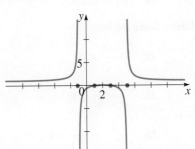

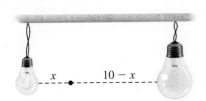

FIGURE 6

Solve. From the diagram we see that the inequality is satisfied on the intervals $(-\infty, -1), (1, 3),$ and $(5, \infty)$. Checking the endpoints, we see that 1 and 3 satisfy the inequality, so the solution is $(-\infty, -1) \cup [1, 3] \cup (5, \infty)$. The graph in Figure 6 confirms our solution.

◀ **Now Try Exercise 23**

We can also solve polynomial and rational inequalities graphically (see pages 120 and 172). In the next example we graph each side of the inequality and compare the values of left- and right-hand sides graphically.

EXAMPLE 5 ■ Solving a Rational Inequality Graphically

Two light sources are 10 m apart. One is three times as intense as the other. The light intensity L (in lux) at a point x meters from the weaker source is given by

$$L(x) = \frac{10}{x^2} + \frac{30}{(10 - x)^2}$$

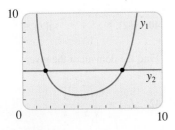

FIGURE 7

(See Figure 7.) Find the points at which the light intensity is 4 lux or less.

SOLUTION We need to solve the inequality

$$\frac{10}{x^2} + \frac{30}{(10 - x)^2} \le 4$$

See Appendix D, *Using the TI-83/84 Graphing Calculator,* for specific instructions.

We solve the inequality graphically by graphing the two functions

$$y_1 = \frac{10}{x^2} + \frac{30}{(10 - x)^2} \quad \text{and} \quad y_2 = 4$$

In this physical problem the possible values of x are between 0 and 10, so we graph the two functions in a viewing rectangle with x-values between 0 and 10, as shown in Figure 8. We want those values of x for which $y_1 \le y_2$. Zooming in (or using the `intersect` command), we find that the graphs intersect at $x \approx 1.67431$ and at $x \approx 7.19272$, and between these x-values the graph of y_1 lies below the graph of y_2. So the solution of the inequality is the interval $(1.67, 7.19)$, rounded to two decimal places. Thus the light intensity is less than or equal to 4 lux when the distance from the weaker source is between 1.67 m and 7.19 m.

FIGURE 8

◀ **Now Try Exercises 45 and 55**

3.7 EXERCISES

CONCEPTS

1. To solve a polynomial inequality, we factor the polynomial into irreducible factors and find all the real _____ of the polynomial. Then we find the intervals determined by the

real _____ and use test points in each interval to find the sign of the polynomial on that interval. Let

$$P(x) = x(x + 2)(x - 1)$$

Fill in the diagram below to find the intervals on which $P(x) \geq 0$.

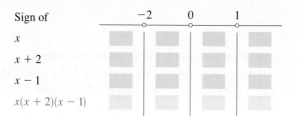

From the diagram above we see that $P(x) \geq 0$ on the

intervals _____ and _____.

2. To solve a rational inequality, we factor the numerator and the denominator into irreducible factors. The cut points are

the real _____ of the numerator and the real _____

denominator. Then we find the intervals determined by the

_____ _____, and we use test points to find the sign of the rational function on each interval. Let

$$r(x) = \frac{(x + 2)(x - 1)}{(x - 3)(x + 4)}$$

Fill in the diagram below to find the intervals on which $r(x) \geq 0$.

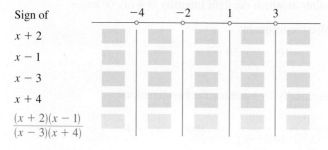

From the diagram we see that $r(x) \geq 0$ on the intervals

_____, _____, and _____.

SKILLS

3–16 ■ Polynomial Inequalities   Solve the inequality.

3. $(x - 3)(x + 5)(2x + 5) < 0$

4. $(x - 1)(x + 2)(x - 3)(x + 4) \geq 0$

5. $(x + 5)^2(x + 3)(x - 1) > 0$

6. $(2x - 7)^4(x - 1)^3(x + 1) \leq 0$

7. $x^3 + 4x^2 \geq 4x + 16$

8. $2x^3 - 18x < x^2 - 9$

9. $2x^3 - x^2 < 9 - 18x$

10. $x^4 + 3x^3 < x + 3$

11. $x^4 - 7x^2 - 18 < 0$

12. $4x^4 - 25x^2 + 36 \leq 0$

13. $x^3 + x^2 - 17x + 15 \geq 0$

14. $x^4 + 3x^3 - 3x^2 + 3x - 4 < 0$

15. $x(1 - x^2)^3 > 7(1 - x^2)^3$

16. $x^2(7 - 6x) \leq 1$

17–36 ■ Rational Inequalities   Solve the inequality.

17. $\dfrac{x - 1}{x - 10} < 0$

18. $\dfrac{3x - 7}{x + 2} \leq 0$

19. $\dfrac{2x + 5}{x^2 + 2x - 35} \geq 0$

20. $\dfrac{4x^2 - 25}{x^2 - 9} \leq 0$

21. $\dfrac{x}{x^2 + 2x - 2} \leq 0$

22. $\dfrac{x + 1}{2x^2 - 4x + 1} > 0$

23. $\dfrac{x^2 + 2x - 3}{3x^2 - 7x - 6} > 0$

24. $\dfrac{x - 1}{x^3 + 1} \geq 0$

25. $\dfrac{x^3 + 3x^2 - 9x - 27}{x + 4} \leq 0$

26. $\dfrac{x^2 - 16}{x^4 - 16} < 0$

27. $\dfrac{x - 3}{2x + 5} \geq 1$

28. $\dfrac{1}{x} + \dfrac{1}{x + 1} < \dfrac{2}{x + 2}$

29. $2 + \dfrac{1}{1 - x} \leq \dfrac{3}{x}$

30. $\dfrac{1}{x - 3} + \dfrac{1}{x + 2} \geq \dfrac{2x}{x^2 + x - 2}$

31. $\dfrac{(x - 1)^2}{(x + 1)(x + 2)} > 0$

32. $\dfrac{x^2 - 2x + 1}{x^3 + 3x^2 + 3x + 1} \leq 0$

33. $\dfrac{6}{x - 1} - \dfrac{6}{x} \geq 1$

34. $\dfrac{x}{2} \geq \dfrac{5}{x + 1} + 4$

35. $\dfrac{x + 2}{x + 3} < \dfrac{x - 1}{x - 2}$

36. $\dfrac{1}{x + 1} + \dfrac{1}{x + 2} \leq \dfrac{1}{x + 3}$

37–40 ■ Graphs of Two Functions   Find all values of x for which the graph of f lies above the graph of g.

37. $f(x) = x^2; \quad g(x) = 3x + 10$

38. $f(x) = \dfrac{1}{x}; \quad g(x) = \dfrac{1}{x - 1}$

39. $f(x) = 4x; \quad g(x) = \dfrac{1}{x}$

40. $f(x) = x^2 + x; \quad g(x) = \dfrac{2}{x}$

41–44 ■ Domain of a Function   Find the domain of the given function.

41. $f(x) = \sqrt{6 + x - x^2}$

42. $g(x) = \sqrt{\dfrac{5 + x}{5 - x}}$

43. $h(x) = \sqrt[4]{x^4 - 1}$

44. $f(x) = \dfrac{1}{\sqrt{x^4 - 5x^2 + 4}}$

45–50 ■ **Solving Inequalities Graphically** Use a graphing device to solve the inequality, as in Example 5. Express your answer using interval notation, with the endpoints of the intervals rounded to two decimals.

45. $x^3 - 2x^2 - 5x + 6 \geq 0$ **46.** $2x^3 + x^2 - 8x - 4 \leq 0$

47. $2x^3 - 3x + 1 < 0$ **48.** $x^4 - 4x^3 + 8x > 0$

49. $5x^4 < 8x^3$ **50.** $x^5 + x^3 \geq x^2 + 6x$

SKILLS Plus

51–52 ■ **Rational Inequalities** Solve the inequality. (These exercises involve expressions that arise in calculus.)

51. $\dfrac{(1-x)^2}{\sqrt{x}} \geq 4\sqrt{x}(x-1)$

52. $\frac{2}{3}x^{-1/3}(x+2)^{1/2} + \frac{1}{2}x^{2/3}(x+2)^{-1/2} < 0$

53. General Polynomial Inequality Solve the inequality

$$(x - a)(x - b)(x - c)(x - d) \geq 0$$

where $a < b < c < d$.

54. General Rational Inequality Solve the inequality

$$\frac{x^2 + (a - b)x - ab}{x + c} \leq 0$$

where $0 < a < b < c$.

APPLICATIONS

55. Bonfire Temperature In the vicinity of a bonfire the temperature T (in °C) at a distance of x meters from the center of the fire is given by

$$T(x) = \frac{500{,}000}{x^2 + 400}$$

At what range of distances from the fire's center is the temperature less than 300°C?

56. Stopping Distance For a certain model of car the distance d required to stop the vehicle if it is traveling at v mi/h is given by the function

$$d(t) = v + \frac{v^2}{25}$$

where d is measured in feet. Kerry wants her stopping distance not to exceed 175 ft. At what range of speeds can she travel?

 57. Managing Traffic A highway engineer develops a formula to estimate the number of cars that can safely travel a particular highway at a given speed. She finds that the number N of cars that can pass a given point per minute is modeled by the function

$$N(x) = \frac{88x}{17 + 17\left(\dfrac{x}{20}\right)^2}$$

Graph the function in the viewing rectangle $[0, 100]$ by $[0, 60]$. If the number of cars that pass by the given point is greater than 40, at what range of speeds can the cars travel?

 58. Estimating Solar Panel Profits A solar panel manufacturer estimates that the profit y (in dollars) generated by producing x solar panels per month is given by the equation

$$S(x) = 8x + 0.8x^2 - 0.002x^3 - 4000$$

Graph the function in the viewing rectangle $[0, 400]$ by $[-10{,}000, 20{,}000]$. For what range of values of x is the company's profit greater than \$12,000?

CHAPTER 3 ■ REVIEW

■ PROPERTIES AND FORMULAS

Quadratic Functions (pp. 282–287)

A **quadratic function** is a function of the form

$$f(x) = ax^2 + bx + c$$

It can be expressed in the **standard form**

$$f(x) = a(x - h)^2 + k$$

by completing the square.

The graph of a quadratic function in standard form is a **parabola** with **vertex** (h, k).

If $a > 0$, then the quadratic function f has the **minimum value** k at $x = h = -b/(2a)$.

If $a < 0$, then the quadratic function f has the **maximum value** k at $x = h = -b/(2a)$.

Polynomial Functions (p. 290)

A **polynomial function** of **degree** n is a function P of the form

$$P(x) = a_n x^n + a_{n-1} x^{n-1} + \cdots + a_1 x + a_0$$

(where $a_n \neq 0$). The numbers a_i are the **coefficients** of the polynomial; a_n is the **leading coefficient**, and a_0 is the **constant coefficient** (or **constant term**).

The graph of a polynomial function is a smooth, continuous curve.

Real Zeros of Polynomials (p. 295)

A **zero** of a polynomial P is a number c for which $P(c) = 0$. The following are equivalent ways of describing real zeros of polynomials:

1. c is a real zero of P.

2. $x = c$ is a solution of the equation $P(x) = 0$.

3. $x - c$ is a factor of $P(x)$.

4. c is an x-intercept of the graph of P.

Multiplicity of a Zero (p. 299)

A zero c of a polynomial P has multiplicity m if m is the highest power for which $(x - c)^m$ is a factor of $P(x)$.

Local Maxima and Minima (p. 300)

A polynomial function P of degree n has $n - 1$ or fewer **local extrema** (i.e., local maxima and minima).

Division of Polynomials (p. 305)

If P and D are any polynomials (with $D(x) \neq 0$), then we can divide P by D using either **long division** or (if D is linear) **synthetic division**. The result of the division can be expressed in one of the following equivalent forms:

$$P(x) = D(x) \cdot Q(x) + R(x)$$

$$\frac{P(x)}{D(x)} = Q(x) + \frac{R(x)}{D(x)}$$

In this division, P is the **dividend**, D is the **divisor**, Q is the **quotient**, and R is the **remainder**. When the division is continued to its completion, the degree of R will be less than the degree of D (or $R(x) = 0$).

Remainder Theorem (p. 308)

When $P(x)$ is divided by the linear divisor $D(x) = x - c$, the **remainder** is the constant $P(c)$. So one way to **evaluate** a polynomial function P at c is to use synthetic division to divide $P(x)$ by $x - c$ and observe the value of the remainder.

Rational Zeros of Polynomials (pp. 311–312)

If the polynomial P given by

$$P(x) = a_n x^n + a_{n-1} x^{n-1} + \cdots + a_1 x + a_0$$

has integer coefficients, then all the **rational zeros** of P have the form

$$x = \pm \frac{p}{q}$$

where p is a divisor of the constant term a_0 and q is a divisor of the leading coefficient a_n.

So to find all the rational zeros of a polynomial, we list all the *possible* rational zeros given by this principle and then check to see which *actually* are zeros by using synthetic division.

Descartes' Rule of Signs (pp. 314–315)

Let P be a polynomial with real coefficients. Then:

The number of positive real zeros of P either is the number of **changes of sign** in the coefficients of $P(x)$ or is less than that by an even number.

The number of negative real zeros of P either is the number of **changes of sign** in the coefficients of $P(-x)$ or is less than that by an even number.

Upper and Lower Bounds Theorem (p. 315)

Suppose we divide the polynomial P by the linear expression $x - c$ and arrive at the result

$$P(x) = (x - c) \cdot Q(x) + r$$

If $c > 0$ and the coefficients of Q, followed by r, are all nonnegative, then c is an **upper bound** for the zeros of P.

If $c < 0$ and the coefficients of Q, followed by r (including zero coefficients), are alternately nonnegative and nonpositive, then c is a **lower bound** for the zeros of P.

The Fundamental Theorem of Algebra, Complete Factorization, and the Zeros Theorem (p. 323)

Every polynomial P of degree n with complex coefficients has exactly n complex zeros, provided that each zero of multiplicity m is counted m times. P factors into n linear factors as follows:

$$P(x) = a(x - c_1)(x - c_2) \cdots (x - c_n)$$

where a is the leading coefficient of P and $c_1, c_1, \ldots, c_n$ are the zeros of P.

Conjugate Zeros Theorem (p. 327)

If the polynomial P has real coefficients and if $a + bi$ is a zero of P, then its complex conjugate $a - bi$ is also a zero of P.

Linear and Quadratic Factors Theorem (p. 328)

Every polynomial with real coefficients can be factored into linear and irreducible quadratic factors with real coefficients.

Rational Functions (p. 331)

A **rational function** r is a quotient of polynomial functions:

$$r(x) = \frac{P(x)}{Q(x)}$$

We generally assume that the polynomials P and Q have no factors in common.

Asymptotes (pp. 332–333)

The line $x = a$ is a **vertical asymptote** of the function $y = f(x)$ if

$$y \to \infty \quad \text{or} \quad y \to -\infty \quad \text{as} \quad x \to a^+ \quad \text{or} \quad x \to a^-$$

The line $y = b$ is a **horizontal asymptote** of the function $y = f(x)$ if

$$y \to b \quad \text{as} \quad x \to \infty \quad \text{or} \quad x \to -\infty$$

Asymptotes of Rational Functions (pp. 334–336)

Let $r(x) = \dfrac{P(x)}{Q(x)}$ be a rational function.

The vertical asymptotes of r are the lines $x = a$ where a is a zero of Q.

If the degree of P is less than the degree of Q, then the horizontal asymptote of r is the line $y = 0$.

If the degrees of P and Q are the same, then the horizontal asymptote of r is the line $y = b$, where

$$b = \frac{\text{leading coefficient of } P}{\text{leading coefficient of } Q}$$

If the degree of P is greater than the degree of Q, then r has no horizontal asymptote.

Polynomial and Rational Inequalities (pp. 347, 349)

A **polynomial inequality** is an inequality of the form $P(x) \geq 0$, where P is a polynomial. We solve $P(x) \geq 0$ by finding the zeros of P and using test points between successive zeros to determine the intervals that satisfy the inequality.

A **rational inequality** is an inequality of the form $r(x) \geq 0$, where

$$r(x) = \frac{P(x)}{Q(x)}$$

is a rational function. The cut points of r are the values of x at which either $P(x) = 0$ or $Q(x) = 0$. We solve $r(x) \geq 0$ by using test points between successive cut points to determine the intervals that satisfy the inequality.

■ CONCEPT CHECK

1. (a) What is the degree of a quadratic function f? What is the standard form of a quadratic function? How do you put a quadratic function into standard form?

   (b) The quadratic function $f(x) = a(x - h)^2 + k$ is in standard form. The graph of f is a parabola. What is the vertex of the graph of f? How do you determine whether $f(h) = k$ is a minimum or a maximum value?

   (c) Express $f(x) = x^2 + 4x + 1$ in standard form. Find the vertex of the graph and the maximum or minimum value of f.

2. (a) Give the general form of polynomial function P of degree n.

   (b) What does it mean to say that c is a zero of P? Give two equivalent conditions that tell us that c is a zero of P.

3. Sketch graphs showing the possible end behaviors of polynomials of odd degree and of even degree.

4. What steps do you follow to graph a polynomial function P?

5. (a) What is a local maximum point or local minimum point of a polynomial P?

   (b) How many local extrema can a polynomial P of degree n have?

6. When we divide a polynomial $P(x)$ by a divisor $D(x)$, the Division Algorithm tells us that we can always obtain a quotient $Q(x)$ and a remainder $R(x)$. State the two forms in which the result of this division can be written.

7. (a) State the Remainder Theorem.

   (b) State the Factor Theorem.

   (c) State the Rational Zeros Theorem.

8. What steps would you take to find the rational zeros of a polynomial P?

9. Let $P(x) = 2x^4 - 3x^3 + x - 15$.

   (a) Explain how Descartes' Rule of Signs is used to determine the possible number of positive and negative real roots of P.

   (b) What does it mean to say that a is a lower bound and b is an upper bound for the zeros of a polynomial?

   (c) Explain how the Upper and Lower Bounds Theorem is used to show that all the real zeros of P lie between -3 and 3.

10. (a) State the Fundamental Theorem of Algebra.

    (b) State the Complete Factorization Theorem.

    (c) State the Zeros Theorem.

    (d) State the Conjugate Zeros Theorem.

11. (a) What is a rational function?

    (b) What does it mean to say that $x = a$ is a vertical asymptote of $y = f(x)$?

    (c) What does it mean to say that $y = b$ is a horizontal asymptote of $y = f(x)$?

12. (a) How do you find vertical asymptotes of rational functions?

    (b) Let s be the rational function

    $$s(x) = \frac{a_n x^n + a_{n-1} x^{n-1} + \cdots + a_1 x + a_0}{b_m x^m + b_{m-1} x^{m-1} + \cdots + b_1 x + b_0}$$

    How do you find the horizontal asymptote of s?

    (c) Find the vertical and horizontal asymptotes of

    $$f(x) = \frac{5x^2 + 3}{x^2 - 4}$$

13. (a) Under what circumstances does a rational function have a slant asymptote?

    (b) How do you determine the end behavior of a rational function?

14. (a) Explain how to solve a polynomial inequality.

    (b) What are the cut points of a rational function? Explain how to solve a rational inequality.

    (c) Solve the inequality $x^2 - 9 \leq 8x$.

ANSWERS TO THE CONCEPT CHECK CAN BE FOUND AT THE BACK OF THE BOOK.

▪ EXERCISES

1–4 ▪ Graphs of Quadratic Functions   A quadratic function is given. **(a)** Express the function in standard form. **(b)** Graph the function.

1. $f(x) = x^2 + 6x + 2$ **2.** $f(x) = 2x^2 - 8x + 4$

3. $f(x) = 1 - 10x - x^2$ **4.** $g(x) = -2x^2 + 12x$

5–6 ▪ Maximum and Minimum Values   Find the maximum or minimum value of the quadratic function.

5. $f(x) = -x^2 + 3x - 1$ **6.** $f(x) = 3x^2 - 18x + 5$

7. Height of a Stone   A stone is thrown upward from the top of a building. Its height (in feet) above the ground after t seconds is given by the function $h(t) = -16t^2 + 48t + 32$. What maximum height does the stone reach?

8. Profit   The profit P (in dollars) generated by selling x units of a certain commodity is given by the function

$$P(x) = -1500 + 12x - 0.004x^2$$

What is the maximum profit, and how many units must be sold to generate it?

9–14 ▪ Transformations of Monomials   Graph the polynomial by transforming an appropriate graph of the form $y = x^n$. Show clearly all x- and y-intercepts.

9. $P(x) = -x^3 + 64$ **10.** $P(x) = 2x^3 - 16$

11. $P(x) = 2(x + 1)^4 - 32$ **12.** $P(x) = 81 - (x - 3)^4$

13. $P(x) = 32 + (x - 1)^5$ **14.** $P(x) = -3(x + 2)^5 + 96$

15–18 ▪ Graphing Polynomials in Factored Form   A polynomial function P is given. **(a)** Describe the end behavior. **(b)** Sketch a graph of P. Make sure your graph shows all intercepts.

15. $P(x) = (x - 3)(x + 1)(x - 5)$

16. $P(x) = -(x - 5)(x^2 - 9)(x + 2)$

17. $P(x) = -(x - 1)^2(x - 4)(x + 2)^2$

18. $P(x) = x^2(x^2 - 4)(x^2 - 9)$

19–20 ▪ Graphing Polynomials   A polynomial function P is given. **(a)** Determine the multiplicity of each zero of P. **(b)** Sketch a graph of P.

19. $P(x) = x^3(x - 2)^2$ **20.** $P(x) = x(x + 1)^3(x - 1)^2$

 21–24 ▪ Graphing Polynomials   Use a graphing device to graph the polynomial. Find the x- and y-intercepts and the coordinates of all local extrema, correct to the nearest decimal. Describe the end behavior of the polynomial.

21. $P(x) = x^3 - 4x + 1$ **22.** $P(x) = -2x^3 + 6x^2 - 2$

23. $P(x) = 3x^4 - 4x^3 - 10x - 1$

24. $P(x) = x^5 + x^4 - 7x^3 - x^2 + 6x + 3$

25. Strength of a Beam   The strength S of a wooden beam of width x and depth y is given by the formula $S = 13.8xy^2$.

A beam is to be cut from a log of diameter 10 in., as shown in the figure.

(a) Express the strength S of this beam as a function of x only.

(b) What is the domain of the function S?

 (c) Draw a graph of S.

(d) What width will make the beam the strongest?

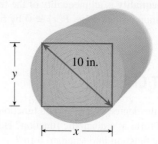

26. Volume   A small shelter for delicate plants is to be constructed of thin plastic material. It will have square ends and a rectangular top and back, with an open bottom and front, as shown in the figure. The total area of the four plastic sides is to be 1200 in^2.

(a) Express the volume V of the shelter as a function of the depth x.

 (b) Draw a graph of V.

(c) What dimensions will maximize the volume of the shelter?

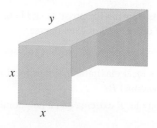

27–34 ▪ Division of Polynomials   Find the quotient and remainder.

27. $\dfrac{x^2 - 5x + 2}{x - 3}$ **28.** $\dfrac{3x^2 + x - 5}{x + 2}$

29. $\dfrac{2x^3 - x^2 + 3x - 4}{x + 5}$ **30.** $\dfrac{-x^3 + 2x + 4}{x - 7}$

31. $\dfrac{x^4 - 8x^2 + 2x + 7}{x + 5}$ **32.** $\dfrac{2x^4 + 3x^3 - 12}{x + 4}$

33. $\dfrac{2x^3 + x^2 - 8x + 15}{x^2 + 2x - 1}$ **34.** $\dfrac{x^4 - 2x^2 + 7x}{x^2 - x + 3}$

35–38 ▪ Remainder Theorem   These exercises involve the Remainder Theorem.

35. If $P(x) = 2x^3 - 9x^2 - 7x + 13$, find $P(5)$.

36. If $Q(x) = x^4 + 4x^3 + 7x^2 + 10x + 15$, find $Q(-3)$.

37. What is the remainder when the polynomial
$P(x) = x^{500} + 6x^{101} - x^2 - 2x + 4$ is divided by $x - 1$?

38. What is the remainder when the polynomial
$Q(x) = x^{101} - x^4 + 2$ is divided by $x + 1$?

39–40 ■ Factor Theorem   Use the Factor Theorem to show that the statement in the exercise is true.

39. Show that $\frac{1}{2}$ is a zero of the polynomial
$$P(x) = 2x^4 + x^3 - 5x^2 + 10x - 4$$

40. Show that $x + 4$ is a factor of the polynomial
$$P(x) = x^5 + 4x^4 - 7x^3 - 23x^2 + 23x + 12$$

41–44 ■ Number of Possible Zeros   A polynomial P is given. **(a)** List all possible rational zeros (without testing to see whether they actually are zeros). **(b)** Determine the possible number of positive and negative real zeros using Descartes' Rule of Signs.

41. $P(x) = x^5 - 6x^3 - x^2 + 2x + 18$

42. $P(x) = 6x^4 + 3x^3 + x^2 + 3x + 4$

43. $P(x) = 3x^7 - x^5 + 5x^4 + x^3 + 8$

44. $P(x) = 6x^{10} - 2x^8 - 5x^3 + 2x^2 + 12$

45–52 ■ Finding Real Zeros and Graphing Polynomials   A polynomial P is given. **(a)** Find all real zeros of P, and state their multiplicities. **(b)** Sketch the graph of P.

45. $P(x) = x^3 - 16x$ **46.** $P(x) = x^3 - 3x^2 - 4x$

47. $P(x) = x^4 + x^3 - 2x^2$ **48.** $P(x) = x^4 - 5x^2 + 4$

49. $P(x) = x^4 - 2x^3 - 7x^2 + 8x + 12$

50. $P(x) = x^4 - 2x^3 - 2x^2 + 8x - 8$

51. $P(x) = 2x^4 + x^3 + 2x^2 - 3x - 2$

52. $P(x) = 9x^5 - 21x^4 + 10x^3 + 6x^2 - 3x - 1$

53–56 ■ Polynomials with Specified Zeros   Find a polynomial with real coefficients of the specified degree that satisfies the given conditions.

53. Degree 3;   zeros $-\frac{1}{2}, 2, 3$;   constant coefficient 12

54. Degree 4;   zeros 4 (multiplicity 2) and $3i$;   integer coefficients;   coefficient of x^2 is -25

55. Complex Zeros of Polynomials   Does there exist a polynomial of degree 4 with integer coefficients that has zeros i, $2i$, $3i$, and $4i$? If so, find it. If not, explain why.

56. Polynomial with no Real Roots   Prove that the equation $3x^4 + 5x^2 + 2 = 0$ has no real root.

57–68 ■ Finding Real and Complex Zeros of Polynomials   Find all rational, irrational, and complex zeros (and state their multiplicities). Use Descartes' Rule of Signs, the Upper and Lower Bounds Theorem, the Quadratic Formula, or other factoring techniques to help you whenever possible.

57. $P(x) = x^3 - x^2 + x - 1$ **58.** $P(x) = x^3 - 8$

59. $P(x) = x^3 - 3x^2 - 13x + 15$

60. $P(x) = 2x^3 + 5x^2 - 6x - 9$

61. $P(x) = x^4 + 6x^3 + 17x^2 + 28x + 20$

62. $P(x) = x^4 + 7x^3 + 9x^2 - 17x - 20$

63. $P(x) = x^5 - 3x^4 - x^3 + 11x^2 - 12x + 4$

64. $P(x) = x^4 - 81$

65. $P(x) = x^6 - 64$

66. $P(x) = 18x^3 + 3x^2 - 4x - 1$

67. $P(x) = 6x^4 - 18x^3 + 6x^2 - 30x + 36$

68. $P(x) = x^4 + 15x^2 + 54$

69–72 ■ Solving Polynomials Graphically   Use a graphing device to find all real solutions of the equation.

69. $2x^2 = 5x + 3$

70. $x^3 + x^2 - 14x - 24 = 0$

71. $x^4 - 3x^3 - 3x^2 - 9x - 2 = 0$

72. $x^5 = x + 3$

73–74 ■ Complete Factorization   A polynomial function P is given. Find all the real zeros of P, and factor P completely into linear and irreducible quadratic factors with real coefficients.

73. $P(x) = x^3 - 2x - 4$ **74.** $P(x) = x^4 + 3x^2 - 4$

75–78 ■ Transformations of $y = 1/x$ A rational function is given. **(a)** Find all vertical and horizontal asymptotes, all x- and y-intercepts, and state the domain and range. **(b)** Use transformations of the graph of $y = 1/x$ to sketch a graph of the rational function, and state the domain and range of r.

75. $r(x) = \dfrac{3}{x + 4}$ **76.** $r(x) = \dfrac{-1}{x - 5}$

77. $r(x) = \dfrac{3x - 4}{x - 1}$ **78.** $r(x) = \dfrac{2x + 5}{x + 2}$

79–84 ■ Graphing Rational Functions   Graph the rational function. Show clearly all x- and y-intercepts and asymptotes, and state the domain and range of r.

79. $r(x) = \dfrac{3x - 12}{x + 1}$ **80.** $r(x) = \dfrac{1}{(x + 2)^2}$

81. $r(x) = \dfrac{x - 2}{x^2 - 2x - 8}$ **82.** $r(x) = \dfrac{x^3 + 27}{x + 4}$

83. $r(x) = \dfrac{x^2 - 9}{2x^2 + 1}$ **84.** $r(x) = \dfrac{2x^2 - 6x - 7}{x - 4}$

85–88 ■ Rational Functions with Holes   Find the common factors of the numerator and denominator of the rational function. Then find the intercepts and asymptotes, and sketch a graph. State the domain and range.

85. $r(x) = \dfrac{x^2 + 5x - 14}{x - 2}$

86. $r(x) = \dfrac{x^3 - 3x^2 - 10x}{x + 2}$

87. $r(x) = \dfrac{x^2 + 3x - 18}{x^2 - 8x + 15}$

 88. $r(x) = \dfrac{x^2 + 2x - 15}{x^3 + 4x^2 - 7x - 10}$

 89–92 ▪ **Graphing Rational Functions** Use a graphing device to analyze the graph of the rational function. Find all x- and y-intercepts and all vertical, horizontal, and slant asymptotes. If the function has no horizontal or slant asymptote, find a polynomial that has the same end behavior as the rational function.

89. $r(x) = \dfrac{x - 3}{2x + 6}$

90. $r(x) = \dfrac{2x - 7}{x^2 + 9}$

91. $r(x) = \dfrac{x^3 + 8}{x^2 - x - 2}$

92. $r(x) = \dfrac{2x^3 - x^2}{x + 1}$

93–96 ▪ **Polynomial Inequalities** Solve the inequality.

93. $2x^2 \ge x + 3$

94. $x^3 - 3x^2 - 4x + 12 \le 0$

95. $x^4 - 7x^2 - 18 < 0$

96. $x^8 - 17x^4 + 16 > 0$

97–100 ▪ **Rational Inequalities** Solve the inequality.

97. $\dfrac{5}{x^3 - x^2 - 4x + 4} < 0$

98. $\dfrac{3x + 1}{x + 2} \le \dfrac{2}{3}$

99. $\dfrac{1}{x - 2} + \dfrac{2}{x + 3} \ge \dfrac{3}{x}$

100. $\dfrac{1}{x + 2} + \dfrac{3}{x - 3} \le \dfrac{4}{x}$

101–102 ▪ **Domain of a Function** Find the domain of the given function.

101. $f(x) = \sqrt{24 - x - 3x^2}$

102. $g(x) = \dfrac{1}{\sqrt[4]{x - x^4}}$

 103–104 ▪ **Solving Inequalities Graphically** Use a graphing device to solve the inequality. Express your answer using interval notation, with the endpoints of the intervals rounded to two decimals.

103. $x^4 + x^3 \le 5x^2 + 4x - 5$

104. $x^5 - 4x^4 + 7x^3 - 12x + 2 > 0$

105. **Application of Descartes' Rule of Signs** We use Descartes' Rule of Signs to show that a polynomial $Q(x) = 2x^3 + 3x^2 - 3x + 4$ has no positive real zeros.

   (a) Show that -1 is a zero of the polynomial $P(x) = 2x^4 + 5x^3 + x + 4$.

   (b) Use the information from part (a) and Descartes' Rule of Signs to show that the polynomial $Q(x) = 2x^3 + 3x^2 - 3x + 4$ has no positive real zeros. [*Hint:* Compare the coefficients of the latter polynomial to your synthetic division table from part (a).]

106. **Points of Intersection** Find the coordinates of all points of intersection of the graphs of

$$y = x^4 + x^2 + 24x \quad \text{and} \quad y = 6x^3 + 20$$

1. Express the quadratic function $f(x) = x^2 - x - 6$ in standard form, and sketch its graph.

2. Find the maximum or minimum value of the quadratic function $g(x) = 2x^2 + 6x + 3$.

3. A cannonball fired out to sea from a shore battery follows a parabolic trajectory given by the graph of the equation

$$h(x) = 10x - 0.01x^2$$

where $h(x)$ is the height of the cannonball above the water when it has traveled a horizontal distance of x feet.

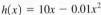

   (a) What is the maximum height that the cannonball reaches?

   (b) How far does the cannonball travel horizontally before splashing into the water?

4. Graph the polynomial $P(x) = -(x + 2)^3 + 27$, showing clearly all x- and y-intercepts.

5. (a) Use synthetic division to find the quotient and remainder when $x^4 - 4x^2 + 2x + 5$ is divided by $x - 2$.

   (b) Use long division to find the quotient and remainder when $2x^5 + 4x^4 - x^3 - x^2 + 7$ is divided by $2x^2 - 1$.

6. Let $P(x) = 2x^3 - 5x^2 - 4x + 3$.

   (a) List all possible rational zeros of P.

   (b) Find the complete factorization of P.

   (c) Find the zeros of P.

   (d) Sketch the graph of P.

7. Find all real and complex zeros of $P(x) = x^3 - x^2 - 4x - 6$.

8. Find the complete factorization of $P(x) = x^4 - 2x^3 + 5x^2 - 8x + 4$.

9. Find a fourth-degree polynomial with integer coefficients that has zeros $3i$ and -1, with -1 a zero of multiplicity 2.

10. Let $P(x) = 2x^4 - 7x^3 + x^2 - 18x + 3$.

   (a) Use Descartes' Rule of Signs to determine how many positive and how many negative real zeros P can have.

   (b) Show that 4 is an upper bound and -1 is a lower bound for the real zeros of P.

   (c) Draw a graph of P, and use it to estimate the real zeros of P, rounded to two decimal places.

   (d) Find the coordinates of all local extrema of P, rounded to two decimals.

11. Consider the following rational functions:

$$r(x) = \frac{2x - 1}{x^2 - x - 2} \qquad s(x) = \frac{x^3 + 27}{x^2 + 4} \qquad t(x) = \frac{x^3 - 9x}{x + 2} \qquad u(x) = \frac{x^2 + x - 6}{x^2 - 25} \qquad w(x) = \frac{x^3 + 6x^2 + 9x}{x + 3}$$

   (a) Which of these rational functions has a horizontal asymptote?

   (b) Which of these functions has a slant asymptote?

   (c) Which of these functions has no vertical asymptote?

   (d) Which of these functions has a "hole"?

   (e) What are the asymptotes of the function $r(x)$?

   (f) Graph $y = u(x)$, showing clearly any asymptotes and x- and y-intercepts the function may have.

   (g) Use long division to find a polynomial P that has the same end behavior as t. Graph both P and t on the same screen to verify that they have the same end behavior.

12. Solve the rational inequality $x \leq \dfrac{6-x}{2x-5}$.

13. Find the domain of the function $f(x) = \dfrac{1}{\sqrt{4-2x-x^2}}$.

14. (a) Choosing an appropriate viewing rectangle, graph the following function and find all its x-intercepts and local extrema, rounded to two decimals.

$$P(x) = x^4 - 4x^3 + 8x$$

(b) Use your graph from part (a) to solve the inequality

$$x^4 - 4x^3 + 8x \geq 0$$

Express your answer in interval form, with the endpoints rounded to two decimals.

Fitting Polynomial Curves to Data

We have learned how to fit a line to data (see *Focus on Modeling*, page 174). The line models the increasing or decreasing trend in the data. If the data exhibit more variability, such as an increase followed by a decrease, then to model the data, we need to use a curve rather than a line. Figure 1 shows a scatter plot with three possible models that appear to fit the data. Which model fits the data best?

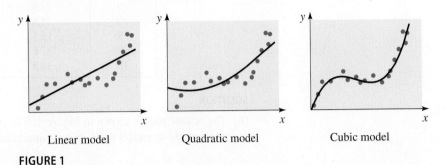

| Linear model | Quadratic model | Cubic model |

FIGURE 1

■ Polynomial Functions as Models

Polynomial functions are ideal for modeling data for which the scatter plot has peaks or valleys (that is, local maxima or minima). For example, if the data have a single peak as in Figure 2(a), then it may be appropriate to use a quadratic polynomial to model the data. The more peaks or valleys the data exhibit, the higher the degree of the polynomial needed to model the data (see Figure 2).

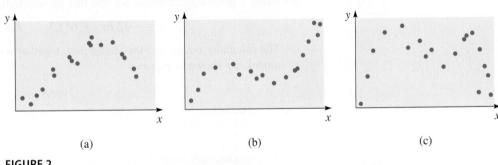

| (a) | (b) | (c) |

FIGURE 2

Graphing calculators are programmed to find the **polynomial of best fit** of a specified degree. As is the case for lines (see page 175), a polynomial of a given degree fits the data *best* if the sum of the squares of the distances between the graph of the polynomial and the data points is minimized.

EXAMPLE 1 ■ Rainfall and Crop Yield

Rain is essential for crops to grow, but too much rain can diminish crop yields. The data on the next page give rainfall and cotton yield per acre for several seasons in a certain county.

(a) Make a scatter plot of the data. What degree polynomial seems appropriate for modeling the data?

(b) Use a graphing calculator to find the polynomial of best fit. Graph the polynomial on the scatter plot.

(c) Use the model that you found to estimate the yield if there are 25 in. of rainfall.

Season	Rainfall (in.)	Yield (kg/acre)
1	23.3	5311
2	20.1	4382
3	18.1	3950
4	12.5	3137
5	30.9	5113
6	33.6	4814
7	35.8	3540
8	15.5	3850
9	27.6	5071
10	34.5	3881

SOLUTION

(a) The scatter plot is shown in Figure 3. The data appear to have a peak, so it is appropriate to model the data by a quadratic polynomial (degree 2).

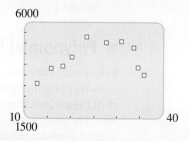

FIGURE 3 Scatter plot of yield versus rainfall data

(b) Using a graphing calculator, we find that the quadratic polynomial of best fit is

$$y = -12.6x^2 + 651.5x - 3283.2$$

The calculator output and the scatter plot, together with the graph of the quadratic model, are shown in Figure 4.

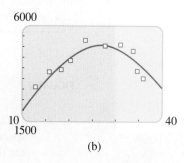

```
QuadReg
y=ax²+bx+c
a=-12.6271745
b=651.5470392
c=-3283.15741
```

FIGURE 4

(a)   (b)

(c) Using the model with $x = 25$, we get

$$y = -12.6(25)^2 + 651.5(25) - 3283.2 \approx 5129.3$$

We estimate the yield to be about 5130 kg/acre. ∎

EXAMPLE 2 ■ Length-at-Age Data for Fish

Otoliths ("earstones") are tiny structures that are found in the heads of fish. Microscopic growth rings on the otoliths, not unlike growth rings on a tree, record the age of a fish. The following table gives the lengths of rock bass caught at different ages, as determined by the otoliths. Scientists have proposed a cubic polynomial to model this data.

(a) Use a graphing calculator to find the cubic polynomial of best fit for the data.

(b) Make a scatter plot of the data, and graph the polynomial from part (a).

(c) A fisherman catches a rock bass 20 in. long. Use the model to estimate its age.

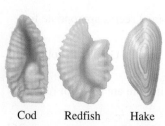

Cod   Redfish   Hake

Otoliths for several fish species

Age (yr)	Length (in.)	Age (yr)	Length (in.)
1	4.8	9	18.2
2	8.8	9	17.1
2	8.0	10	18.8
3	7.9	10	19.5
4	11.9	11	18.9
5	14.4	12	21.7
6	14.1	12	21.9
6	15.8	13	23.8
7	15.6	14	26.9
8	17.8	14	25.1

SOLUTION

(a) Using a graphing calculator (see Figure 5(a)), we find the cubic polynomial of best fit:

$$y = 0.0155x^3 - 0.372x^2 + 3.95x + 1.21$$

(b) The scatter plot of the data and the cubic polynomial are graphed in Figure 5(b).

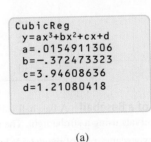

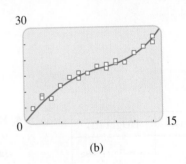

FIGURE 5

(a)   (b)

(c) Moving the cursor along the graph of the polynomial, we find that $y = 20$ when $x \approx 10.8$. Thus the fish is about 11 years old. ∎

PROBLEMS

1. Tire Inflation and Treadwear Car tires need to be inflated properly. Overinflation or underinflation can cause premature treadwear. The data in the margin show tire life for different inflation values for a certain type of tire.

(a) Find the quadratic polynomial that best fits the data.

(b) Draw a graph of the polynomial from part (a) together with a scatter plot of the data.

(c) Use your result from part (b) to estimate the pressure that gives the longest tire life.

Pressure (lb/in²)	Tire life (mi)
26	50,000
28	66,000
31	78,000
35	81,000
38	74,000
42	70,000
45	59,000

2. Too Many Corn Plants per Acre? The more corn a farmer plants per acre, the greater is the yield the farmer can expect, but only up to a point. Too many plants per acre can cause overcrowding and decrease yields. The data give crop yields per acre for various densities of corn plantings, as found by researchers at a university test farm.

(a) Find the quadratic polynomial that best fits the data.

(b) Draw a graph of the polynomial from part (a) together with a scatter plot of the data.

(c) Use your result from part (b) to estimate the yield for 37,000 plants per acre.

Density (plants/acre)	15,000	20,000	25,000	30,000	35,000	40,000	45,000	50,000
Crop yield (bushels/acre)	43	98	118	140	142	122	93	67

3. **How Fast Can You List Your Favorite Things?** If you are asked to make a list of objects in a certain category, how fast you can list them follows a predictable pattern. For example, if you try to name as many vegetables as you can, you'll probably think of several right away—for example, carrots, peas, beans, corn, and so on. Then after a pause you might think of ones you eat less frequently—perhaps zucchini, eggplant, and asparagus. Finally, a few more exotic vegetables might come to mind—artichokes, jicama, bok choy, and the like. A psychologist performs this experiment on a number of subjects. The table below gives the average number of vegetables that the subjects named by a given number of seconds.

   (a) Find the cubic polynomial that best fits the data.

   (b) Draw a graph of the polynomial from part (a) together with a scatter plot of the data.

   (c) Use your result from part (b) to estimate the number of vegetables that subjects would be able to name in 40 s.

   (d) According to the model, how long (to the nearest 0.1 s) would it take a person to name five vegetables?

Seconds	Number of vegetables
1	2
2	6
5	10
10	12
15	14
20	15
25	18
30	21

Time (s)	Height (ft)
0	4.2
0.5	26.1
1.0	40.1
1.5	46.0
2.0	43.9
2.5	33.7
3.0	15.8

4. **Height of a Baseball** A baseball is thrown upward, and its height is measured at 0.5-s intervals using a strobe light. The resulting data are given in the table.

   (a) Draw a scatter plot of the data. What degree polynomial is appropriate for modeling the data?

   (b) Find a polynomial model that best fits the data, and graph it on the scatter plot.

   (c) Find the times when the ball is 20 ft above the ground.

   (d) What is the maximum height attained by the ball?

5. **Torricelli's Law** Water in a tank will flow out of a small hole in the bottom faster when the tank is nearly full than when it is nearly empty. According to Torricelli's Law, the height $h(t)$ of water remaining at time t is a quadratic function of t.

   A certain tank is filled with water and allowed to drain. The height of the water is measured at different times as shown in the table.

   (a) Find the quadratic polynomial that best fits the data.

   (b) Draw a graph of the polynomial from part (a) together with a scatter plot of the data.

   (c) Use your graph from part (b) to estimate how long it takes for the tank to drain completely.

Time (min)	Height (ft)
0	5.0
4	3.1
8	1.9
12	0.8
16	0.2

© TonyV3112/Shutterstock.com

4 Exponential and Logarithmic Functions

In this chapter we study *exponential functions*. These are functions like $f(x) = 2^x$, where the independent variable is in the exponent. Exponential functions are used in modeling many real-world phenomena, such as the growth of a population, the growth of an investment that earns compound interest, or the decay of a radioactive substance. Once an exponential model has been obtained, we can use the model to predict the size of a population, calculate the amount of an investment, or find the amount of a radioactive substance that remains. The inverse functions of exponential functions are called *logarithmic functions*. With exponential models and logarithmic functions we can answer questions such as these: When will my city be as crowded as the city street pictured here? When will my bank account have a million dollars? When will radiation from a radioactive spill decay to a safe level?

In the *Focus on Modeling* at the end of the chapter we learn how to fit exponential and power curves to data.

365

4.1 EXPONENTIAL FUNCTIONS

▪ Exponential Functions ▪ Graphs of Exponential Functions ▪ Compound Interest

In this chapter we study a new class of functions called *exponential functions*. For example,

$$f(x) = 2^x$$

is an exponential function (with base 2). Notice how quickly the values of this function increase.

$$f(3) = 2^3 = 8$$

$$f(10) = 2^{10} = 1024$$

$$f(30) = 2^{30} = 1{,}073{,}741{,}824$$

Compare this with the function $g(x) = x^2$, where $g(30) = 30^2 = 900$. The point is that when the variable is in the exponent, even a small change in the variable can cause a dramatic change in the value of the function.

▪ Exponential Functions

To study exponential functions, we must first define what we mean by the exponential expression a^x when x is any real number. In Section P.4 we defined a^x for $a > 0$ and x a rational number, but we have not yet defined irrational powers. So what is meant by $5^{\sqrt{3}}$ or 2^{π}? To define a^x when x is irrational, we approximate x by rational numbers.

For example, since

$$\sqrt{3} \approx 1.73205 \ldots$$

is an irrational number, we successively approximate $a^{\sqrt{3}}$ by the following rational powers:

$$a^{1.7}, a^{1.73}, a^{1.732}, a^{1.7320}, a^{1.73205}, \ldots$$

Intuitively, we can see that these rational powers of a are getting closer and closer to $a^{\sqrt{3}}$. It can be shown by using advanced mathematics that there is exactly one number that these powers approach. We define $a^{\sqrt{3}}$ to be this number.

For example, using a calculator, we find

$$5^{\sqrt{3}} \approx 5^{1.732}$$

$$\approx 16.2411 \ldots$$

The more decimal places of $\sqrt{3}$ we use in our calculation, the better our approximation of $5^{\sqrt{3}}$.

It can be proved that the *Laws of Exponents are still true when the exponents are real numbers.*

The Laws of Exponents are listed on page 19.

EXPONENTIAL FUNCTIONS

The **exponential function with base a** is defined for all real numbers x by

$$f(x) = a^x$$

where $a > 0$ and $a \neq 1$.

We assume that $a \neq 1$ because the function $f(x) = 1^x = 1$ is just a constant function. Here are some examples of exponential functions:

$$f(x) = 2^x \qquad g(x) = 3^x \qquad h(x) = 10^x$$

Base 2   Base 3   Base 10

EXAMPLE 1 ■ Evaluating Exponential Functions

Let $f(x) = 3^x$, and evaluate the following:

(a) $f(5)$ **(b)** $f\left(-\frac{2}{3}\right)$

(c) $f(\pi)$ **(d)** $f(\sqrt{2})$

SOLUTION We use a calculator to obtain the values of f.

	Calculator keystrokes	Output
(a) $f(5) = 3^5 = 243$	3 ∧ 5 ENTER	243
(b) $f\left(-\frac{2}{3}\right) = 3^{-2/3} \approx 0.4807$	3 ∧ ((−) 2 ÷ 3) ENTER	0.4807498
(c) $f(\pi) = 3^\pi \approx 31.544$	3 ∧ π ENTER	31.5442807
(d) $f(\sqrt{2}) = 3^{\sqrt{2}} \approx 4.7288$	3 ∧ √ 2 ENTER	4.7288043

✎ **Now Try Exercise 7** ■

■ Graphs of Exponential Functions

We first graph exponential functions by plotting points. We will see that the graphs of such functions have an easily recognizable shape.

EXAMPLE 2 ■ Graphing Exponential Functions by Plotting Points

Draw the graph of each function.

(a) $f(x) = 3^x$ **(b)** $g(x) = \left(\frac{1}{3}\right)^x$

SOLUTION We calculate values of $f(x)$ and $g(x)$ and plot points to sketch the graphs in Figure 1.

x	$f(x) = 3^x$	$g(x) = \left(\frac{1}{3}\right)^x$
-3	$\frac{1}{27}$	27
-2	$\frac{1}{9}$	9
-1	$\frac{1}{3}$	3
0	1	1
1	3	$\frac{1}{3}$
2	9	$\frac{1}{9}$
3	27	$\frac{1}{27}$

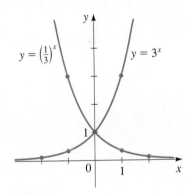

FIGURE 1

Notice that

$$g(x) = \left(\frac{1}{3}\right)^x = \frac{1}{3^x} = 3^{-x} = f(-x)$$

Reflecting graphs is explained in Section 2.6.

so we could have obtained the graph of g from the graph of f by reflecting in the y-axis.

✎ **Now Try Exercise 17** ■

Figure 2 shows the graphs of the family of exponential functions $f(x) = a^x$ for various values of the base a. All of these graphs pass through the point $(0, 1)$ because

To see just how quickly $f(x) = 2^x$ increases, let's perform the following thought experiment. Suppose we start with a piece of paper that is a thousandth of an inch thick, and we fold it in half 50 times. Each time we fold the paper, the thickness of the paper stack doubles, so the thickness of the resulting stack would be $2^{50}/1000$ inches. How thick do you think that is? It works out to be more than 17 million miles!

$a^0 = 1$ for $a \neq 0$. You can see from Figure 2 that there are two kinds of exponential functions: If $0 < a < 1$, the exponential function decreases rapidly. If $a > 1$, the function increases rapidly (see the margin note).

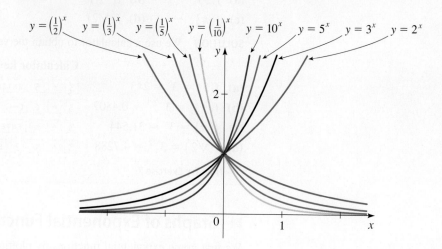

FIGURE 2 A family of exponential functions

See Section 3.6, page 331, where the arrow notation used here is explained.

The x-axis is a horizontal asymptote for the exponential function $f(x) = a^x$. This is because when $a > 1$, we have $a^x \to 0$ as $x \to -\infty$, and when $0 < a < 1$, we have $a^x \to 0$ as $x \to \infty$ (see Figure 2). Also, $a^x > 0$ for all $x \in \mathbb{R}$, so the function $f(x) = a^x$ has domain $\mathbb{R}$ and range $(0, \infty)$. These observations are summarized in the following box.

GRAPHS OF EXPONENTIAL FUNCTIONS

The exponential function

$$f(x) = a^x \qquad a > 0, a \neq 1$$

has domain $\mathbb{R}$ and range $(0, \infty)$. The line $y = 0$ (the x-axis) is a horizontal asymptote of f. The graph of f has one of the following shapes.

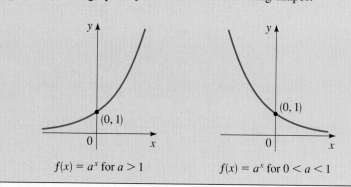

$f(x) = a^x$ for $a > 1$ $f(x) = a^x$ for $0 < a < 1$

EXAMPLE 3 ■ Identifying Graphs of Exponential Functions

Find the exponential function $f(x) = a^x$ whose graph is given.

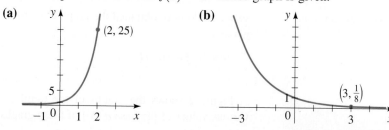

SOLUTION

(a) Since $f(2) = a^2 = 25$, we see that the base is $a = 5$. So $f(x) = 5^x$.

(b) Since $f(3) = a^3 = \frac{1}{8}$, we see that the base is $a = \frac{1}{2}$. So $f(x) = \left(\frac{1}{2}\right)^x$.

✎ **Now Try Exercise 21** ■

In the next example we see how to graph certain functions, not by plotting points, but by taking the basic graphs of the exponential functions in Figure 2 and applying the shifting and reflecting transformations of Section 2.6.

EXAMPLE 4 ■ Transformations of Exponential Functions

Use the graph of $f(x) = 2^x$ to sketch the graph of each function. State the domain, range, and asymptote.

(a) $g(x) = 1 + 2^x$ **(b)** $h(x) = -2^x$ **(c)** $k(x) = 2^{x-1}$

SOLUTION

Shifting and reflecting of graphs are explained in Section 2.6.

(a) To obtain the graph of $g(x) = 1 + 2^x$, we start with the graph of $f(x) = 2^x$ and shift it upward 1 unit to get the graph shown in Figure 3(a). From the graph we see that the domain of g is the set $\mathbb{R}$ of real numbers, the range is the interval $(1, \infty)$, and the line $y = 1$ is a horizontal asymptote.

(b) Again we start with the graph of $f(x) = 2^x$, but here we reflect in the x-axis to get the graph of $h(x) = -2^x$ shown in Figure 3(b). From the graph we see that the domain of h is the set $\mathbb{R}$ of all real numbers, the range is the interval $(-\infty, 0)$, and the line $y = 0$ is a horizontal asymptote.

(c) This time we start with the graph of $f(x) = 2^x$ and shift it to the right by 1 unit to get the graph of $k(x) = 2^{x-1}$ shown in Figure 3(c). From the graph we see that the domain of k is the set $\mathbb{R}$ of all real numbers, the range is the interval $(0, \infty)$, and the line $y = 0$ is a horizontal asymptote.

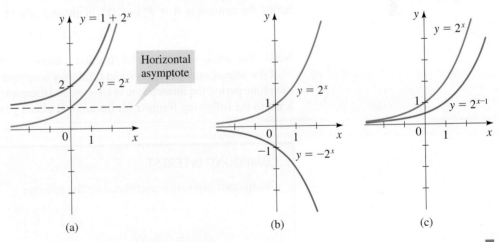

FIGURE 3   (a)   (b)   (c)

✎ **Now Try Exercises 27, 29, and 31** ■

EXAMPLE 5 ■ Comparing Exponential and Power Functions

Compare the rates of growth of the exponential function $f(x) = 2^x$ and the power function $g(x) = x^2$ by drawing the graphs of both functions in the following viewing rectangles.

(a) $[0, 3]$ by $[0, 8]$ **(b)** $[0, 6]$ by $[0, 25]$ **(c)** $[0, 20]$ by $[0, 1000]$

SOLUTION

(a) Figure 4(a) shows that the graph of $g(x) = x^2$ catches up with, and becomes higher than, the graph of $f(x) = 2^x$ at $x = 2$.

(b) The larger viewing rectangle in Figure 4(b) shows that the graph of $f(x) = 2^x$ overtakes that of $g(x) = x^2$ when $x = 4$.

(c) Figure 4(c) gives a more global view and shows that when x is large, $f(x) = 2^x$ is much larger than $g(x) = x^2$.

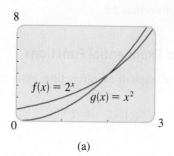

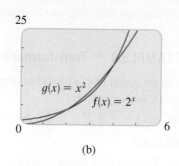

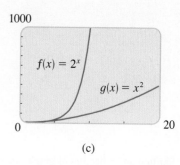

FIGURE 4   (a)   (b)   (c)

✎ **Now Try Exercise 45**   ■

■ Compound Interest

Exponential functions occur in calculating compound interest. If an amount of money P, called the **principal**, is invested at an interest rate i per time period, then after one time period the interest is Pi, and the amount A of money is

$$A = P + Pi = P(1 + i)$$

If the interest is reinvested, then the new principal is $P(1 + i)$, and the amount after another time period is $A = P(1 + i)(1 + i) = P(1 + i)^2$. Similarly, after a third time period the amount is $A = P(1 + i)^3$. In general, after k periods the amount is

$$A = P(1 + i)^k$$

Notice that this is an exponential function with base $1 + i$.

If the annual interest rate is r and if interest is compounded n times per year, then in each time period the interest rate is $i = r/n$, and there are nt time periods in t years. This leads to the following formula for the amount after t years.

COMPOUND INTEREST

Compound interest is calculated by the formula

$$A(t) = P\left(1 + \frac{r}{n}\right)^{nt}$$

where $A(t)$ = amount after t years

P = principal

r = interest rate per year

n = number of times interest is compounded per year

t = number of years

---

r is often referred to as the nominal annual interest rate.

EXAMPLE 6 ■ Calculating Compound Interest

A sum of $1000 is invested at an interest rate of 12% per year. Find the amounts in the account after 3 years if interest is compounded annually, semiannually, quarterly, monthly, and daily.

SOLUTION We use the compound interest formula with $P = \$1000$, $r = 0.12$, and $t = 3$.

Compounding	n	Amount after 3 years	
Annual	1	$1000\left(1 + \dfrac{0.12}{1}\right)^{1(3)}$	$= \$1404.93$
Semiannual	2	$1000\left(1 + \dfrac{0.12}{2}\right)^{2(3)}$	$= \$1418.52$
Quarterly	4	$1000\left(1 + \dfrac{0.12}{4}\right)^{4(3)}$	$= \$1425.76$
Monthly	12	$1000\left(1 + \dfrac{0.12}{12}\right)^{12(3)}$	$= \$1430.77$
Daily	365	$1000\left(1 + \dfrac{0.12}{365}\right)^{365(3)}$	$= \$1433.24$

✎ **Now Try Exercise 57**

■

If an investment earns compound interest, then the **annual percentage yield** (APY) is the *simple* interest rate that yields the same amount at the end of one year.

EXAMPLE 7 ■ Calculating the Annual Percentage Yield

Find the annual percentage yield for an investment that earns interest at a rate of 6% per year, compounded daily.

SOLUTION After one year, a principal P will grow to the amount

$$A = P\left(1 + \frac{0.06}{365}\right)^{365} = P(1.06183)$$

Simple interest is studied in Section P.9.   The formula for simple interest is

$$A = P(1 + r)$$

Comparing, we see that $1 + r = 1.06183$, so $r = 0.06183$. Thus the annual percentage yield is 6.183%.

✎ **Now Try Exercise 63**

■

DISCOVERY PROJECT

So You Want to Be a Millionaire?

In this project we explore how rapidly the values of an exponential function increase by examining some real-world situations. For example, if you save a penny today, two pennies tomorrow, four pennies the next day, and so on, how long do you have to continue saving in this way before you become a millionaire? You can find out the surprising answer to this and other questions by completing this discovery project. You can find the project at **www.stewartmath.com**.

4.1 EXERCISES

CONCEPTS

1. The function $f(x) = 5^x$ is an exponential function with base _____; $f(-2) = $ _____, $f(0) = $ _____, $f(2) = $ _____, and $f(6) = $ _____.

2. Match the exponential function with one of the graphs labeled I, II, III, or IV, shown below.

(a) $f(x) = 2^x$ (b) $f(x) = 2^{-x}$

(c) $f(x) = -2^x$ (d) $f(x) = -2^{-x}$

I
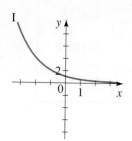

II
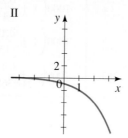

III
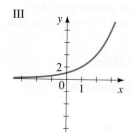

IV
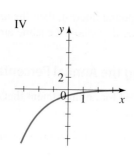

3. (a) To obtain the graph of $g(x) = 2^x - 1$, we start with the graph of $f(x) = 2^x$ and shift it _____ (upward/downward) 1 unit.

(b) To obtain the graph of $h(x) = 2^{x-1}$, we start with the graph of $f(x) = 2^x$ and shift it to the _____ (left/right) 1 unit.

4. In the formula $A(t) = P\left(1 + \frac{r}{n}\right)^{nt}$ for compound interest the letters P, r, n, and t stand for _____, _____, _____, and _____, respectively, and $A(t)$ stands for _____. So if \$100 is invested at an interest rate of 6% compounded quarterly, then the amount after 2 years is _____.

5. The exponential function $f(x) = \left(\frac{1}{2}\right)^x$ has the _____ asymptote $y = $ _____. This means that as $x \to \infty$, we have $\left(\frac{1}{2}\right)^x \to$ _____.

6. The exponential function $f(x) = \left(\frac{1}{2}\right)^x + 3$ has the _____ asymptote $y = $ _____. This means that as $x \to \infty$, we have $\left(\frac{1}{2}\right)^x + 3 \to$ _____.

SKILLS

7–10 ■ Evaluating Exponential Functions   Use a calculator to evaluate the function at the indicated values. Round your answers to three decimals.

7. $f(x) = 4^x$; $f\left(\frac{1}{2}\right), f(\sqrt{5}), f(-2), f(0.3)$

8. $f(x) = 3^{x-1}$; $f\left(\frac{1}{2}\right), f(2.5), f(-1), f\left(\frac{1}{4}\right)$

9. $g(x) = \left(\frac{1}{3}\right)^{x+1}$; $g\left(\frac{1}{2}\right), g(\sqrt{2}), g(-3.5), g(-1.4)$

10. $g(x) = \left(\frac{4}{3}\right)^{3x}$; $g\left(-\frac{1}{2}\right), g(\sqrt{6}), g(-3), g\left(\frac{4}{3}\right)$

11–16 ■ Graphing Exponential Functions   Sketch the graph of the function by making a table of values. Use a calculator if necessary.

11. $f(x) = 2^x$ **12.** $g(x) = 8^x$

13. $f(x) = \left(\frac{1}{3}\right)^x$ **14.** $h(x) = (1.1)^x$

15. $g(x) = 3(1.3)^x$ **16.** $h(x) = 2\left(\frac{1}{4}\right)^x$

17–20 ■ Graphing Exponential Functions   Graph both functions on one set of axes.

17. $f(x) = 2^x$ and $g(x) = 2^{-x}$

18. $f(x) = 3^{-x}$ and $g(x) = \left(\frac{1}{3}\right)^x$

19. $f(x) = 4^x$ and $g(x) = 7^x$

20. $f(x) = \left(\frac{2}{3}\right)^x$ and $g(x) = 1.5^x$

21–24 ■ Exponential Functions from a Graph   Find the exponential function $f(x) = a^x$ whose graph is given.

21.
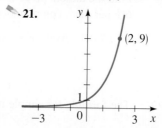

22.
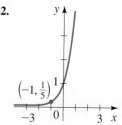

23.
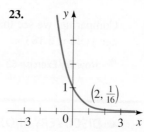

24.
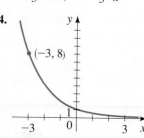

25–26 ■ Exponential Functions from a Graph   Match the exponential function with one of the graphs labeled I or II.

25. $f(x) = 5^{x+1}$ **26.** $f(x) = 5^x + 1$

I
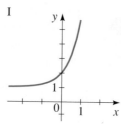

II
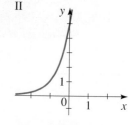

27–40 ■ Graphing Exponential Functions Graph the function, not by plotting points, but by starting from the graphs in Figure 2. State the domain, range, and asymptote.

27. $g(x) = 2^x - 3$

28. $h(x) = 4 + \left(\frac{1}{2}\right)^x$

29. $f(x) = -3^x$

30. $f(x) = 10^{-x}$

31. $f(x) = 10^{x+3}$

32. $g(x) = 2^{x-3}$

33. $y = 5^{-x} + 1$

34. $h(x) = 6 - 3^x$

35. $y = 2 - \left(\frac{1}{3}\right)^x$

36. $y = 5^{-x} - 3$

37. $h(x) = 2^{x-4} + 1$

38. $y = 3 - 10^{x-1}$

39. $g(x) = 1 - 3^{-x}$

40. $y = 3 - \left(\frac{1}{5}\right)^x$

41–42 ■ Comparing Exponential Functions In these exercises we compare the graphs of two exponential functions.

41. (a) Sketch the graphs of $f(x) = 2^x$ and $g(x) = 3(2^x)$.

  (b) How are the graphs related?

42. (a) Sketch the graphs of $f(x) = 9^{x/2}$ and $g(x) = 3^x$.

  (b) Use the Laws of Exponents to explain the relationship between these graphs.

43–44 ■ Comparing Exponential and Power Functions Compare the graphs of the power function f and exponential function g by evaluating both of them for $x = 0, 1, 2, 3, 4, 6, 8,$ and 10. Then draw the graphs of f and g on the same set of axes.

43. $f(x) = x^3$; $g(x) = 3^x$ **44.** $f(x) = x^4$; $g(x) = 4^x$

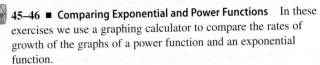

45–46 ■ Comparing Exponential and Power Functions In these exercises we use a graphing calculator to compare the rates of growth of the graphs of a power function and an exponential function.

45. (a) Compare the rates of growth of the functions $f(x) = 2^x$ and $g(x) = x^5$ by drawing the graphs of both functions in the following viewing rectangles.

   (i) $[0, 5]$ by $[0, 20]$

   (ii) $[0, 25]$ by $[0, 10^7]$

   (iii) $[0, 50]$ by $[0, 10^8]$

  (b) Find the solutions of the equation $2^x = x^5$, rounded to one decimal place.

46. (a) Compare the rates of growth of the functions $f(x) = 3^x$ and $g(x) = x^4$ by drawing the graphs of both functions in the following viewing rectangles:

   (i) $[-4, 4]$ by $[0, 20]$

   (ii) $[0, 10]$ by $[0, 5000]$

   (iii) $[0, 20]$ by $[0, 10^5]$

  (b) Find the solutions of the equation $3^x = x^4$, rounded to two decimal places.

SKILLS Plus

 47–48 ■ Families of Functions Draw graphs of the given family of functions for $c = 0.25, 0.5, 1, 2, 4$. How are the graphs related?

47. $f(x) = c2^x$

48. $f(x) = 2^{cx}$

49–50 ■ Getting Information from a Graph Find, rounded to two decimal places, **(a)** the intervals on which the function is increasing or decreasing and **(b)** the range of the function.

49. $y = 10^{x-x^2}$

50. $y = x2^x$

51–52 ■ Difference Quotients These exercises involve a difference quotient for an exponential function.

51. If $f(x) = 10^x$, show that

$$\frac{f(x+h) - f(x)}{h} = 10^x\left(\frac{10^h - 1}{h}\right)$$

52. If $f(x) = 3^{x-1}$, show that

$$\frac{f(x+h) - f(x)}{h} = 3^{x-1}\left(\frac{3^h - 1}{h}\right)$$

APPLICATIONS

53. Bacteria Growth A bacteria culture contains 1500 bacteria initially and doubles every hour.

  (a) Find a function N that models the number of bacteria after t hours.

  (b) Find the number of bacteria after 24 hours.

54. Mouse Population A certain breed of mouse was introduced onto a small island with an initial population of 320 mice, and scientists estimate that the mouse population is doubling every year.

  (a) Find a function N that models the number of mice after t years.

  (b) Estimate the mouse population after 8 years.

55–56 ■ Compound Interest An investment of $5000 is deposited into an account in which interest is compounded monthly. Complete the table by filling in the amounts to which the investment grows at the indicated times or interest rates.

55. $r = 4\%$ **56.** $t = 5$ years

Time (years)	Amount		Rate per year	Amount
1			1%	
2			2%	
3			3%	
4			4%	
5			5%	
6			6%	

57. Compound Interest If $10,000 is invested at an interest rate of 3% per year, compounded semiannually, find the value of the investment after the given number of years.

  (a) 5 years   **(b)** 10 years   **(c)** 15 years

58. Compound Interest If $2500 is invested at an interest rate of 2.5% per year, compounded daily, find the value of the investment after the given number of years.

  (a) 2 years   **(b)** 3 years   **(c)** 6 years

59. Compound Interest If $500 is invested at an interest rate of 3.75% per year, compounded quarterly, find the value of the investment after the given number of years.

  (a) 1 year   **(b)** 2 years   **(c)** 10 years

60. Compound Interest If $4000 is borrowed at a rate of 5.75% interest per year, compounded quarterly, find the amount due at the end of the given number of years.

  (a) 4 years   **(b)** 6 years   **(c)** 8 years

61–62 ■ Present Value   The **present value** of a sum of money is the amount that must be invested now, at a given rate of interest, to produce the desired sum at a later date.

61. Find the present value of $10,000 if interest is paid at a rate of 9% per year, compounded semiannually, for 3 years.

62. Find the present value of $100,000 if interest is paid at a rate of 8% per year, compounded monthly, for 5 years.

63. Annual Percentage Yield   Find the annual percentage yield for an investment that earns 8% per year, compounded monthly.

64. Annual Percentage Yield   Find the annual percentage yield for an investment that earns $5\frac{1}{2}$% per year, compounded quarterly.

DISCUSS ■ DISCOVER ■ PROVE ■ WRITE

65. DISCUSS ■ DISCOVER: Growth of an Exponential Function   Suppose you are offered a job that lasts one month, and you are to be very well paid. Which of the following methods of payment is more profitable for you?

(a) One million dollars at the end of the month

(b) Two cents on the first day of the month, 4 cents on the second day, 8 cents on the third day, and, in general, 2^n cents on the nth day

66. DISCUSS ■ DISCOVER: The Height of the Graph of an Exponential Function   Your mathematics instructor asks you to sketch a graph of the exponential function

$$f(x) = 2^x$$

for x between 0 and 40, using a scale of 10 units to one inch. What are the dimensions of the sheet of paper you will need to sketch this graph?

4.2   THE NATURAL EXPONENTIAL FUNCTION

■ The Number e   ■ The Natural Exponential Function   ■ Continuously Compounded Interest

Any positive number can be used as a base for an exponential function. In this section we study the special base e, which is convenient for applications involving calculus.

■ The Number e

The number e is defined as the value that $(1 + 1/n)^n$ approaches as n becomes large. (In calculus this idea is made more precise through the concept of a limit.) The table shows the values of the expression $(1 + 1/n)^n$ for increasingly large values of n.

The **Gateway Arch** in St. Louis, Missouri, is shaped in the form of the graph of a combination of exponential functions (*not* a parabola, as it might first appear). Specifically, it is a **catenary**, which is the graph of an equation of the form

$$y = a(e^{bx} + e^{-bx})$$

(see Exercises 17 and 19). This shape was chosen because it is optimal for distributing the internal structural forces of the arch. Chains and cables suspended between two points (for example, the stretches of cable between pairs of telephone poles) hang in the shape of a catenary.

n	$\left(1 + \dfrac{1}{n}\right)^n$
1	2.00000
5	2.48832
10	2.59374
100	2.70481
1000	2.71692
10,000	2.71815
100,000	2.71827
1,000,000	2.71828

It appears that, rounded to five decimal places, $e \approx 2.71828$; in fact, the approximate value to 20 decimal places is

$$e \approx 2.71828182845904523536$$

It can be shown that e is an irrational number, so we cannot write its exact value in decimal form.

■ The Natural Exponential Function

The notation e was chosen by Leonhard Euler (see page 130), probably because it is the first letter of the word *exponential*.

The number e is the base for the natural exponential function. Why use such a strange base for an exponential function? It might seem at first that a base such as 10 is easier to work with. We will see, however, that in certain applications the number e is the best

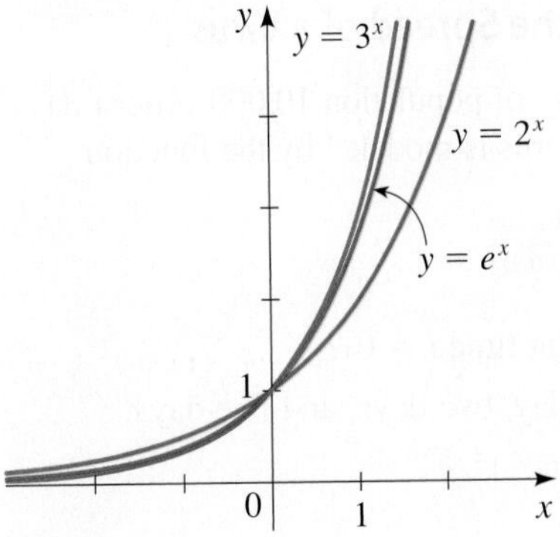

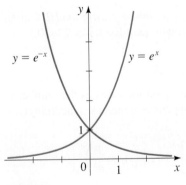

FIGURE 1 Graph of the natural exponential function

possible base. In this section we study how e occurs in the description of compound interest.

THE NATURAL EXPONENTIAL FUNCTION

The **natural exponential function** is the exponential function

$$f(x) = e^x$$

with base e. It is often referred to as *the* exponential function.

Since $2 < e < 3$, the graph of the natural exponential function lies between the graphs of $y = 2^x$ and $y = 3^x$, as shown in Figure 1.

Scientific calculators have a special key for the function $f(x) = e^x$. We use this key in the next example.

EXAMPLE 1 ■ Evaluating the Exponential Function

Evaluate each expression rounded to five decimal places.

(a) e^3 **(b)** $2e^{-0.53}$ **(c)** $e^{4.8}$

SOLUTION We use the $\boxed{e^x}$ key on a calculator to evaluate the exponential function.

(a) $e^3 \approx 20.08554$ **(b)** $2e^{-0.53} \approx 1.17721$ **(c)** $e^{4.8} \approx 121.51042$

✎ Now Try Exercise 3

EXAMPLE 2 ■ Graphing the Exponential Functions

Sketch the graph of each function. State the domain, range, and asymptote.

(a) $f(x) = e^{-x}$ **(b)** $g(x) = 3e^{0.5x}$

SOLUTION

(a) We start with the graph of $y = e^x$ and reflect in the y-axis to obtain the graph of $y = e^{-x}$ as in Figure 2. From the graph we see that the domain of f is the set $\mathbb{R}$ of all real numbers, the range is the interval $(0, \infty)$, and the line $y = 0$ is a horizontal asymptote.

(b) We calculate several values, plot the resulting points, then connect the points with a smooth curve. The graph is shown in Figure 3. From the graph we see that the domain of g is the set $\mathbb{R}$ of all real numbers, the range is the interval $(0, \infty)$, and the line $y = 0$ is a horizontal asymptote.

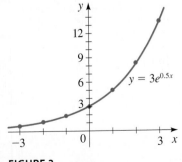

x	$f(x) = 3e^{0.5x}$
-3	0.67
-2	1.10
-1	1.82
0	3.00
1	4.95
2	8.15
3	13.45

FIGURE 2

FIGURE 3

✎ Now Try Exercises 5 and 7

EXAMPLE 3 ■ An Exponential Model for the Spread of a Virus

An infectious disease begins to spread in a small city of population 10,000. After t days, the number of people who have succumbed to the virus is modeled by the function

$$v(t) = \frac{10{,}000}{5 + 1245e^{-0.97t}}$$

(a) How many infected people are there initially (at time $t = 0$)?

(b) Find the number of infected people after one day, two days, and five days.

(c) Graph the function v, and describe its behavior.

SOLUTION

(a) Since $v(0) = 10{,}000/(5 + 1245e^0) = 10{,}000/1250 = 8$, we conclude that 8 people initially have the disease.

(b) Using a calculator, we evaluate $v(1)$, $v(2)$, and $v(5)$ and then round off to obtain the following values.

Days	Infected people
1	21
2	54
5	678

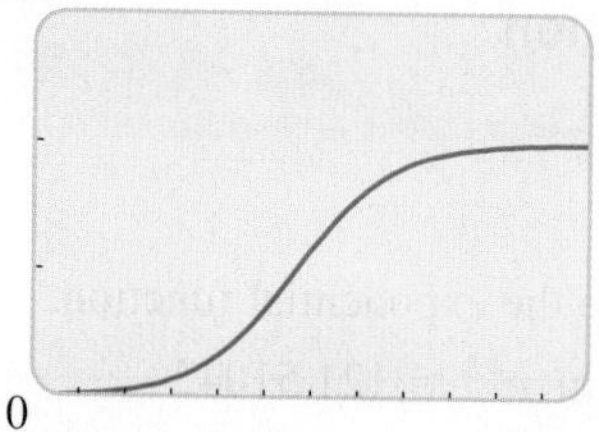

(c) From the graph in Figure 4 we see that the number of infected people first rises slowly, then rises quickly between day 3 and day 8, and then levels off when about 2000 people are infected.

✎ **Now Try Exercise 27**

FIGURE 4

$$v(t) = \frac{10{,}000}{5 + 1245e^{-0.97t}}$$

The graph in Figure 4 is called a *logistic curve* or a *logistic growth model*. Curves like it occur frequently in the study of population growth. (See Exercises 27–30.)

■ Continuously Compounded Interest

In Example 6 of Section 4.1 we saw that the interest paid increases as the number of compounding periods n increases. Let's see what happens as n increases indefinitely. If we let $m = n/r$, then

$$A(t) = P\left(1 + \frac{r}{n}\right)^{nt} = P\left[\left(1 + \frac{r}{n}\right)^{n/r}\right]^{rt} = P\left[\left(1 + \frac{1}{m}\right)^{m}\right]^{rt}$$

Recall that as m becomes large, the quantity $(1 + 1/m)^m$ approaches the number e. Thus the amount approaches $A = Pe^{rt}$. This expression gives the amount when the interest is compounded at "every instant."

CONTINUOUSLY COMPOUNDED INTEREST

Continuously compounded interest is calculated by the formula

$$A(t) = Pe^{rt}$$

where $\quad A(t) =$ amount after t years

$P =$ principal

$r =$ interest rate per year

$t =$ number of years

EXAMPLE 4 ■ Calculating Continuously Compounded Interest

Find the amount after 3 years if \$1000 is invested at an interest rate of 12% per year, compounded continuously.

SOLUTION   We use the formula for continuously compounded interest with $P = \$1000$, $r = 0.12$, and $t = 3$ to get

$$A(3) = 1000e^{(0.12)3} = 1000e^{0.36} = \$1433.33$$

Compare this amount with the amounts in Example 6 of Section 4.1.

■ Now Try Exercise 33

4.2 EXERCISES

CONCEPTS

1. The function $f(x) = e^x$ is called the _____ exponential function. The number e is approximately equal to _____.

2. In the formula $A(t) = Pe^{rt}$ for continuously compound interest, the letters P, r, and t stand for _____, _____, and _____, respectively, and $A(t)$ stands for _____. So if \$100 is invested at an interest rate of 6% compounded continuously, then the amount after 2 years is _____.

SKILLS

3–4 ■ Evaluating Exponential Functions   Use a calculator to evaluate the function at the indicated values. Round your answers to three decimals.

3. $h(x) = e^x$; $h(1), h(\pi), h(-3), h(\sqrt{2})$

4. $h(x) = e^{-3x}$; $h(\frac{1}{3}), h(1.5), h(-1), h(-\pi)$

5–6 ■ Graphing Exponential Functions   Complete the table of values, rounded to two decimal places, and sketch a graph of the function.

5.

x	$f(x) = 1.5e^x$
-2	
-1	
-0.5	
0	
0.5	
1	
2	

6.

x	$f(x) = 4e^{-x/3}$
-3	
-2	
-1	
0	
1	
2	
3	

7–16 ■ Graphing Exponential Functions   Graph the function, not by plotting points, but by starting from the graph of $y = e^x$ in Figure 1. State the domain, range, and asymptote.

7. $g(x) = 2 + e^x$

8. $h(x) = e^{-x} - 3$

9. $f(x) = -e^x$

10. $y = 1 - e^x$

11. $y = e^{-x} - 1$

12. $f(x) = -e^{-x}$

13. $f(x) = e^{x-2}$

14. $y = e^{x-3} + 4$

15. $h(x) = e^{x+1} - 3$

16. $g(x) = -e^{x-1} - 2$

SKILLS Plus

17. Hyperbolic Cosine Function   The *hyperbolic cosine function* is defined by

$$\cosh(x) = \frac{e^x + e^{-x}}{2}$$

(a) Sketch the graphs of the functions $y = \frac{1}{2}e^x$ and $y = \frac{1}{2}e^{-x}$ on the same axes, and use graphical addition (see Section 2.7) to sketch the graph of $y = \cosh(x)$.

(b) Use the definition to show that $\cosh(-x) = \cosh(x)$.

18. Hyperbolic Sine Function   The *hyperbolic sine function* is defined by

$$\sinh(x) = \frac{e^x - e^{-x}}{2}$$

(a) Sketch the graph of this function using graphical addition as in Exercise 17.

(b) Use the definition to show that $\sinh(-x) = -\sinh(x)$.

  19. Families of Functions

(a) Draw the graphs of the family of functions

$$f(x) = \frac{a}{2}(e^{x/a} + e^{-x/a})$$

for $a = 0.5, 1, 1.5$, and 2.

(b) How does a larger value of a affect the graph?

  20. The Definition of e   Illustrate the definition of the number e by graphing the curve $y = (1 + 1/x)^x$ and the line $y = e$ on the same screen, using the viewing rectangle $[0, 40]$ by $[0, 4]$.

  21–22 ■ Local Extrema   Find the local maximum and minimum values of the function and the value of x at which each occurs. State each answer rounded to two decimal places.

21. $g(x) = x^x$, $x > 0$

22. $g(x) = e^x + e^{-2x}$

APPLICATIONS

23. Medical Drugs When a certain medical drug is administered to a patient, the number of milligrams remaining in the patient's bloodstream after t hours is modeled by

$$D(t) = 50e^{-0.2t}$$

How many milligrams of the drug remain in the patient's bloodstream after 3 hours?

24. Radioactive Decay A radioactive substance decays in such a way that the amount of mass remaining after t days is given by the function

$$m(t) = 13e^{-0.015t}$$

where $m(t)$ is measured in kilograms.

(a) Find the mass at time $t = 0$.

(b) How much of the mass remains after 45 days?

 25. Sky Diving A sky diver jumps from a reasonable height above the ground. The air resistance she experiences is proportional to her velocity, and the constant of proportionality is 0.2. It can be shown that the downward velocity of the sky diver at time t is given by

$$v(t) = 180(1 - e^{-0.2t})$$

where t is measured in seconds (s) and $v(t)$ is measured in feet per second (ft/s).

(a) Find the initial velocity of the sky diver.

(b) Find the velocity after 5 s and after 10 s.

(c) Draw a graph of the velocity function $v(t)$.

(d) The maximum velocity of a falling object with wind resistance is called its *terminal velocity*. From the graph in part (c) find the terminal velocity of this sky diver.

$$v(t) = 180(1 - e^{-0.2t})$$

26. Mixtures and Concentrations A 50-gal barrel is filled completely with pure water. Salt water with a concentration of 0.3 lb/gal is then pumped into the barrel, and the resulting mixture overflows at the same rate. The amount of salt in the barrel at time t is given by

$$Q(t) = 15(1 - e^{-0.04t})$$

where t is measured in minutes and $Q(t)$ is measured in pounds.

(a) How much salt is in the barrel after 5 min?

(b) How much salt is in the barrel after 10 min?

 (c) Draw a graph of the function $Q(t)$.

 (d) Use the graph in part (c) to determine the value that the amount of salt in the barrel approaches as t becomes large. Is this what you would expect?

$$Q(t) = 15(1 - e^{-0.04t})$$

27. Logistic Growth Animal populations are not capable of unrestricted growth because of limited habitat and food supplies. Under such conditions the population follows a *logistic growth model*:

$$P(t) = \frac{d}{1 + ke^{-ct}}$$

where c, d, and k are positive constants. For a certain fish population in a small pond $d = 1200$, $k = 11$, $c = 0.2$, and t is measured in years. The fish were introduced into the pond at time $t = 0$.

(a) How many fish were originally put in the pond?

(b) Find the population after 10, 20, and 30 years.

(c) Evaluate $P(t)$ for large values of t. What value does the population approach as $t \to \infty$? Does the graph shown confirm your calculations?

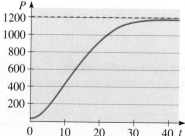

28. Bird Population The population of a certain species of bird is limited by the type of habitat required for nesting. The population behaves according to the logistic growth model

$$n(t) = \frac{5600}{0.5 + 27.5e^{-0.044t}}$$

where t is measured in years.

(a) Find the initial bird population.

(b) Draw a graph of the function $n(t)$.

(c) What size does the population approach as time goes on?

29. World Population   The relative growth rate of world population has been decreasing steadily in recent years. On the basis of this, some population models predict that world population will eventually stabilize at a level that the planet can support. One such logistic model is

$$P(t) = \frac{73.2}{6.1 + 5.9e^{-0.02t}}$$

where $t = 0$ is the year 2000 and population is measured in billions.

(a) What world population does this model predict for the year 2200? For 2300?

(b) Sketch a graph of the function P for the years 2000 to 2500.

(c) According to this model, what size does the world population seem to approach as time goes on?

30. Tree Diameter   For a certain type of tree the diameter D (in feet) depends on the tree's age t (in years) according to the logistic growth model

$$D(t) = \frac{5.4}{1 + 2.9e^{-0.01t}}$$

Find the diameter of a 20-year-old tree.

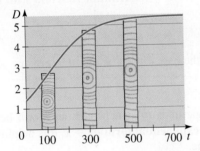

31–32 ■ Compound Interest   An investment of $7000 is deposited into an account in which interest is compounded continuously. Complete the table by filling in the amounts to which the investment grows at the indicated times or interest rates.

31. $r = 3\%$

Time (years)	Amount
1	
2	
3	
4	
5	
6	

32. $t = 10$ years

Rate per year	Amount
1%	
2%	
3%	
4%	
5%	
6%	

33. Compound Interest   If $2000 is invested at an interest rate of 3.5% per year, compounded continuously, find the value of the investment after the given number of years.

(a) 2 years

(b) 4 years

(c) 12 years

34. Compound Interest   If $3500 is invested at an interest rate of 6.25% per year, compounded continuously, find the value of the investment after the given number of years.

(a) 3 years

(b) 6 years

(c) 9 years

35. Compound Interest   If $600 is invested at an interest rate of 2.5% per year, find the amount of the investment at the end of 10 years for the following compounding methods.

(a) Annually

(b) Semiannually

(c) Quarterly

(d) Continuously

36. Compound Interest   If $8000 is invested in an account for which interest is compounded continuously, find the amount of the investment at the end of 12 years for the following interest rates.

(a) 2%

(b) 3%

(c) 4.5%

(d) 7%

37. Compound Interest   Which of the given interest rates and compounding periods would provide the best investment?

(a) $2\frac{1}{2}\%$ per year, compounded semiannually

(b) $2\frac{1}{4}\%$ per year, compounded monthly

(c) 2% per year, compounded continuously

38. Compound Interest   Which of the given interest rates and compounding periods would provide the better investment?

(a) $5\frac{1}{8}\%$ per year, compounded semiannually

(b) 5% per year, compounded continuously

39. Investment   A sum of $5000 is invested at an interest rate of 9% per year, compounded continuously.

(a) Find the value $A(t)$ of the investment after t years.

(b) Draw a graph of $A(t)$.

(c) Use the graph of $A(t)$ to determine when this investment will amount to $25,000.

4.3 LOGARITHMIC FUNCTIONS

■ Logarithmic Functions ■ Graphs of Logarithmic Functions ■ Common Logarithms
■ Natural Logarithms

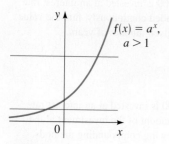

FIGURE 1 $f(x) = a^x$ is one-to-one.

In this section we study the inverses of exponential functions.

■ Logarithmic Functions

Every exponential function $f(x) = a^x$, with $a > 0$ and $a \neq 1$, is a one-to-one function by the Horizontal Line Test (see Figure 1 for the case $a > 1$) and therefore has an inverse function. The inverse function f^{-1} is called the *logarithmic function with base a* and is denoted by $\log_a$. Recall from Section 2.8 that f^{-1} is defined by

$$f^{-1}(x) = y \quad \Leftrightarrow \quad f(y) = x$$

This leads to the following definition of the logarithmic function.

DEFINITION OF THE LOGARITHMIC FUNCTION

Let a be a positive number with $a \neq 1$. The **logarithmic function with base a**, denoted by $\log_a$, is defined by

$$\log_a x = y \quad \Leftrightarrow \quad a^y = x$$

So $\log_a x$ is the *exponent* to which the base a must be raised to give x.

We read $\log_a x = y$ as "log base a of x is y."

By tradition the name of the logarithmic function is $\log_a$, not just a single letter. Also, we usually omit the parentheses in the function notation and write

$$\log_a(x) = \log_a x$$

When we use the definition of logarithms to switch back and forth between the **logarithmic form** $\log_a x = y$ and the **exponential form** $a^y = x$, it is helpful to notice that, in both forms, the base is the same.

Logarithmic form   **Exponential form**

Exponent   Exponent

$$\log_a x = y \qquad\qquad a^y = x$$

Base   Base

EXAMPLE 1 ■ Logarithmic and Exponential Forms

The logarithmic and exponential forms are equivalent equations: If one is true, then so is the other. So we can switch from one form to the other as in the following illustrations.

Logarithmic form	Exponential form
$\log_{10} 100{,}000 = 5$	$10^5 = 100{,}000$
$\log_2 8 = 3$	$2^3 = 8$
$\log_2\left(\frac{1}{8}\right) = -3$	$2^{-3} = \frac{1}{8}$
$\log_5 s = r$	$5^r = s$

🔊 Now Try Exercise 7   ■

x	$\log_{10} x$
10^4	4
10^3	3
10^2	2
10	1
1	0
10^{-1}	-1
10^{-2}	-2
10^{-3}	-3
10^{-4}	-4

It is important to understand that $\log_a x$ is an *exponent*. For example, the numbers in the right-hand column of the table in the margin are the logarithms (base 10) of the numbers in the left-hand column. This is the case for all bases, as the following example illustrates.

EXAMPLE 2 ■ Evaluating Logarithms

(a) $\log_{10} 1000 = 3$ because $10^3 = 1000$

(b) $\log_2 32 = 5$ because $2^5 = 32$

(c) $\log_{10} 0.1 = -1$ because $10^{-1} = 0.1$

(d) $\log_{16} 4 = \frac{1}{2}$ because $16^{1/2} = 4$

◥ **Now Try Exercises 9 and 11** ■

Inverse Function Property:

$$f^{-1}(f(x)) = x$$

$$f(f^{-1}(x)) = x$$

When we apply the Inverse Function Property described on page 258 to $f(x) = a^x$ and $f^{-1}(x) = \log_a x$, we get

$$\log_a(a^x) = x \qquad x \in \mathbb{R}$$

$$a^{\log_a x} = x \qquad x > 0$$

We list these and other properties of logarithms discussed in this section.

PROPERTIES OF LOGARITHMS

Property	Reason
1. $\log_a 1 = 0$	We must raise a to the power 0 to get 1.
2. $\log_a a = 1$	We must raise a to the power 1 to get a.
3. $\log_a a^x = x$	We must raise a to the power x to get a^x.
4. $a^{\log_a x} = x$	$\log_a x$ is the power to which a must be raised to get x.

EXAMPLE 3 ■ Applying Properties of Logarithms

We illustrate the properties of logarithms when the base is 5.

$$\log_5 1 = 0 \qquad \text{Property 1} \qquad \log_5 5 = 1 \qquad \text{Property 2}$$

$$\log_5 5^8 = 8 \qquad \text{Property 3} \qquad 5^{\log_5 12} = 12 \qquad \text{Property 4}$$

◥ **Now Try Exercises 25 and 31** ■

■ Graphs of Logarithmic Functions

Recall that if a one-to-one function f has domain A and range B, then its inverse function f^{-1} has domain B and range A. Since the exponential function $f(x) = a^x$ with $a \neq 1$ has domain $\mathbb{R}$ and range $(0, \infty)$, we conclude that its inverse function, $f^{-1}(x) = \log_a x$, has domain $(0, \infty)$ and range $\mathbb{R}$.

The graph of $f^{-1}(x) = \log_a x$ is obtained by reflecting the graph of $f(x) = a^x$ in the line $y = x$. Figure 2 shows the case $a > 1$. The fact that $y = a^x$ (for $a > 1$) is a very rapidly increasing function for $x > 0$ implies that $y = \log_a x$ is a very slowly increasing function for $x > 1$ (see Exercise 102).

Since $\log_a 1 = 0$, the x-intercept of the function $y = \log_a x$ is 1. The y-axis is a vertical asymptote of $y = \log_a x$ because $\log_a x \to -\infty$ as $x \to 0^+$.

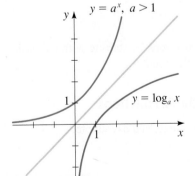

FIGURE 2 Graph of the logarithmic function $f(x) = \log_a x$

EXAMPLE 4 ■ Graphing a Logarithmic Function by Plotting Points

Sketch the graph of $f(x) = \log_2 x$.

SOLUTION   To make a table of values, we choose the x-values to be powers of 2 so that we can easily find their logarithms. We plot these points and connect them with a smooth curve as in Figure 3.

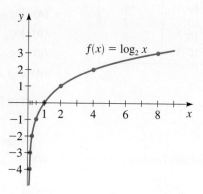

x	$\log_2 x$
2^3	3
2^2	2
2	1
1	0
2^{-1}	-1
2^{-2}	-2
2^{-3}	-3
2^{-4}	-4

FIGURE 3

Now Try Exercise 49

Figure 4 shows the graphs of the family of logarithmic functions with bases 2, 3, 5, and 10. These graphs are drawn by reflecting the graphs of $y = 2^x$, $y = 3^x$, $y = 5^x$, and $y = 10^x$ (see Figure 2 in Section 4.1) in the line $y = x$. We can also plot points as an aid to sketching these graphs, as illustrated in Example 4.

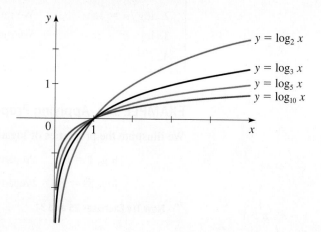

FIGURE 4 A family of logarithmic functions

In the next two examples we graph logarithmic functions by starting with the basic graphs in Figure 4 and using the transformations of Section 2.6.

EXAMPLE 5 ■ Reflecting Graphs of Logarithmic Functions

Sketch the graph of each function. State the domain, range, and asymptote.

(a) $g(x) = -\log_2 x$ **(b)** $h(x) = \log_2(-x)$

SOLUTION

(a) We start with the graph of $f(x) = \log_2 x$ and reflect in the x-axis to get the graph of $g(x) = -\log_2 x$ in Figure 5(a). From the graph we see that the domain of g is $(0, \infty)$, the range is the set $\mathbb{R}$ of all real numbers, and the line $x = 0$ is a vertical asymptote.

(b) We start with the graph of $f(x) = \log_2 x$ and reflect in the y-axis to get the graph of $h(x) = \log_2(-x)$ in Figure 5(b). From the graph we see that the domain of h is $(-\infty, 0)$, the range is the set $\mathbb{R}$ of all real numbers, and the line $x = 0$ is a vertical asymptote.

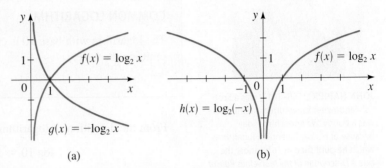

FIGURE 5   (a)   (b)

✎ Now Try Exercise 61

EXAMPLE 6 ■ Shifting Graphs of Logarithmic Functions

Sketch the graph of each function. State the domain, range, and asymptote.

(a) $g(x) = 2 + \log_5 x$ **(b)** $h(x) = \log_{10}(x - 3)$

SOLUTION

(a) The graph of g is obtained from the graph of $f(x) = \log_5 x$ (Figure 4) by shifting upward 2 units, as shown in Figure 6. From the graph we see that the domain of g is $(0, \infty)$, the range is the set $\mathbb{R}$ of all real numbers, and the line $x = 0$ is a vertical asymptote.

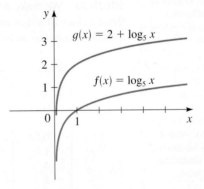

FIGURE 6

(b) The graph of h is obtained from the graph of $f(x) = \log_{10} x$ (Figure 4) by shifting to the right 3 units, as shown in Figure 7. From the graph we see that the domain of h is $(3, \infty)$, the range is the set $\mathbb{R}$ of all real numbers, and the line $x = 3$ is a vertical asymptote.

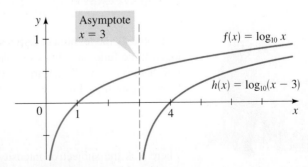

FIGURE 7

✎ Now Try Exercises 63 and 67

JOHN NAPIER (1550–1617) was a Scottish landowner for whom mathematics was a hobby. We know him today because of his key invention: logarithms, which he published in 1614 under the title *A Description of the Marvelous Rule of Logarithms*. In Napier's time, logarithms were used exclusively for simplifying complicated calculations. For example, to multiply two large numbers, we would write them as powers of 10. The exponents are simply the logarithms of the numbers. For instance,

$$4532 \times 57783$$
$$\approx 10^{3.65629} \times 10^{4.76180}$$
$$= 10^{8.41809}$$
$$\approx 261{,}872{,}564$$

The idea is that multiplying powers of 10 is easy (we simply add their exponents). Napier produced extensive tables giving the logarithms (or exponents) of numbers. Since the advent of calculators and computers, logarithms are no longer used for this purpose. The logarithmic functions, however, have found many applications, some of which are described in this chapter.

Napier wrote on many topics. One of his most colorful works is a book entitled *A Plaine Discovery of the Whole Revelation of Saint John*, in which he predicted that the world would end in the year 1700.

■ Common Logarithms

We now study logarithms with base 10.

> **COMMON LOGARITHM**
>
> The logarithm with base 10 is called the **common logarithm** and is denoted by omitting the base:
> $$\log x = \log_{10} x$$

From the definition of logarithms we can easily find that
$$\log 10 = 1 \quad \text{and} \quad \log 100 = 2$$

But how do we find log 50? We need to find the exponent y such that $10^y = 50$. Clearly, 1 is too small and 2 is too large. So
$$1 < \log 50 < 2$$

To get a better approximation, we can experiment to find a power of 10 closer to 50. Fortunately, scientific calculators are equipped with a $\boxed{\text{LOG}}$ key that directly gives values of common logarithms.

EXAMPLE 7 ■ Evaluating Common Logarithms

Use a calculator to find appropriate values of $f(x) = \log x$, and use the values to sketch the graph.

SOLUTION We make a table of values, using a calculator to evaluate the function at those values of x that are not powers of 10. We plot those points and connect them by a smooth curve as in Figure 8.

x	$\log x$
0.01	-2
0.1	-1
0.5	-0.301
1	0
4	0.602
5	0.699
10	1

FIGURE 8

✎ **Now Try Exercise 51**

Scientists model human response to stimuli (such as sound, light, or pressure) using logarithmic functions. For example, the intensity of a sound must be increased many-fold before we "feel" that the loudness has simply doubled. The psychologist Gustav Fechner formulated the law as

$$S = k \log\left(\frac{I}{I_0}\right)$$

where S is the subjective intensity of the stimulus, I is the physical intensity of the stimulus, I_0 stands for the threshold physical intensity, and k is a constant that is different for each sensory stimulus.

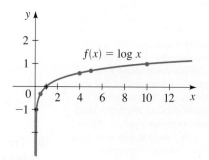

Human response to sound and light intensity is logarithmic.

We study the decibel scale in more detail in Section 4.7.

EXAMPLE 8 ▪ Common Logarithms and Sound

The perception of the loudness B (in decibels, dB) of a sound with physical intensity I (in W/m^2) is given by

$$B = 10 \log\left(\frac{I}{I_0}\right)$$

where I_0 is the physical intensity of a barely audible sound. Find the decibel level (loudness) of a sound whose physical intensity I is 100 times that of I_0.

SOLUTION   We find the decibel level B by using the fact that $I = 100I_0$.

$$
\begin{aligned}
B &= 10 \log\left(\frac{I}{I_0}\right) && \text{Definition of } B \\
&= 10 \log\left(\frac{100I_0}{I_0}\right) && I = 100I_0 \\
&= 10 \log 100 && \text{Cancel } I_0 \\
&= 10 \cdot 2 = 20 && \text{Definition of log}
\end{aligned}
$$

The loudness of the sound is 20 dB.

✎ **Now Try Exercise 97**

▪ Natural Logarithms

Of all possible bases a for logarithms, it turns out that the most convenient choice for the purposes of calculus is the number e, which we defined in Section 4.2.

The notation ln is an abbreviation for the Latin name *logarithmus naturalis*.

> ### NATURAL LOGARITHM
>
> The logarithm with base e is called the **natural logarithm** and is denoted by **ln**:
>
> $$\ln x = \log_e x$$

The natural logarithmic function $y = \ln x$ is the inverse function of the natural exponential function $y = e^x$. Both functions are graphed in Figure 9. By the definition of inverse functions we have

$$\ln x = y \quad \Leftrightarrow \quad e^y = x$$

If we substitute $a = e$ and write "ln" for "$\log_e$" in the properties of logarithms mentioned earlier, we obtain the following properties of natural logarithms.

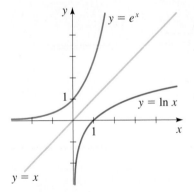

FIGURE 9 Graph of the natural logarithmic function

> ### PROPERTIES OF NATURAL LOGARITHMS
>
> | Property | Reason |
> |---|---|
> | 1. $\ln 1 = 0$ | We must raise e to the power 0 to get 1. |
> | 2. $\ln e = 1$ | We must raise e to the power 1 to get e. |
> | 3. $\ln e^x = x$ | We must raise e to the power x to get e^x. |
> | 4. $e^{\ln x} = x$ | $\ln x$ is the power to which e must be raised to get x. |

Calculators are equipped with an $\boxed{\text{LN}}$ key that directly gives the values of natural logarithms.

EXAMPLE 9 ■ Evaluating the Natural Logarithm Function

(a) $\ln e^8 = 8$ Definition of natural logarithm

(b) $\ln\left(\dfrac{1}{e^2}\right) = \ln e^{-2} = -2$ Definition of natural logarithm

(c) $\ln 5 \approx 1.609$ Use $\boxed{\text{LN}}$ key on calculator

✎ **Now Try Exercise 47**   ■

EXAMPLE 10 ■ Finding the Domain of a Logarithmic Function

Find the domain of the function $f(x) = \ln(4 - x^2)$.

SOLUTION   As with any logarithmic function, $\ln x$ is defined when $x > 0$. Thus the domain of f is

$$\{x \mid 4 - x^2 > 0\} = \{x \mid x^2 < 4\} = \{x \mid |x| < 2\}$$
$$= \{x \mid -2 < x < 2\} = (-2, 2)$$

✎ **Now Try Exercise 73**   ■

EXAMPLE 11 ■ Drawing the Graph of a Logarithmic Function

Draw the graph of the function $y = x \ln(4 - x^2)$, and use it to find the asymptotes and local maximum and minimum values.

SOLUTION   As in Example 10 the domain of this function is the interval $(-2, 2)$, so we choose the viewing rectangle $[-3, 3]$ by $[-3, 3]$. The graph is shown in Figure 10, and from it we see that the lines $x = -2$ and $x = 2$ are vertical asymptotes.

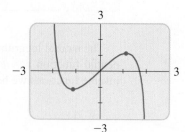

FIGURE 10
$y = x \ln(4 - x^2)$

DISCOVERY PROJECT

Orders of Magnitude

In this project we explore how to compare the sizes of real-world objects using logarithms. For example, how much bigger is an elephant than a flea? How much smaller is a man than a giant redwood? It is difficult to compare objects of such enormously varying sizes. In this project we learn how logarithms can be used to define the concept of "order of magnitude," which provides a simple and meaningful way of comparison. You can find the project at **www.stewartmath.com**.

The function has a local maximum point to the right of $x = 1$ and a local minimum point to the left of $x = -1$. By zooming in and tracing along the graph with the cursor, we find that the local maximum value is approximately 1.13 and this occurs when $x \approx 1.15$. Similarly (or by noticing that the function is odd), we find that the local minimum value is about -1.13, and it occurs when $x \approx -1.15$.

✎ **Now Try Exercise 79**

■

4.3 EXERCISES

CONCEPTS

1. $\log x$ is the exponent to which the base 10 must be raised to get _____. So we can complete the following table for $\log x$.

x	10^3	10^2	10^1	10^0	10^{-1}	10^{-2}	10^{-3}	$10^{1/2}$
$\log x$								

2. The function $f(x) = \log_9 x$ is the logarithm function with base _____. So $f(9) = $ _____, $f(1) = $ _____, $f(\frac{1}{9}) = $ _____, $f(81) = $ _____, and $f(3) = $ _____.

3. (a) $5^3 = 125$, so $\log_{\blacksquare} \blacksquare = \blacksquare$

(b) $\log_5 25 = 2$, so $\blacksquare^{\blacksquare} = \blacksquare$

4. Match the logarithmic function with its graph.

(a) $f(x) = \log_2 x$ (b) $f(x) = \log_2(-x)$

(c) $f(x) = -\log_2 x$ (d) $f(x) = -\log_2(-x)$

I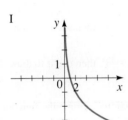

II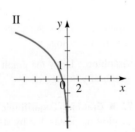

III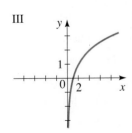

IV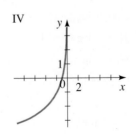

5. The natural logarithmic function $f(x) = \ln x$ has the _____ asymptote $x = $ _____.

6. The logarithmic function $f(x) = \ln(x - 1)$ has the _____ asymptote $x = $ _____.

SKILLS

7–8 ■ **Logarithmic and Exponential Forms** Complete the table by finding the appropriate logarithmic or exponential form of the equation, as in Example 1.

7.

Logarithmic form	Exponential form
$\log_8 8 = 1$	
$\log_8 64 = 2$	
	$8^{2/3} = 4$
	$8^3 = 512$
$\log_8(\frac{1}{8}) = -1$	
	$8^{-2} = \frac{1}{64}$

8.

Logarithmic form	Exponential form
	$4^3 = 64$
$\log_4 2 = \frac{1}{2}$	
	$4^{3/2} = 8$
$\log_4(\frac{1}{16}) = -2$	
$\log_4(\frac{1}{2}) = -\frac{1}{2}$	
	$4^{-5/2} = \frac{1}{32}$

9–16 ■ **Exponential Form** Express the equation in exponential form.

9. (a) $\log_3 81 = 4$ (b) $\log_3 1 = 0$

10. (a) $\log_5(\frac{1}{5}) = -1$ (b) $\log_4 64 = 3$

11. (a) $\log_8 2 = \frac{1}{3}$ (b) $\log_{10} 0.01 = -2$

12. (a) $\log_5(\frac{1}{125}) = -3$ (b) $\log_8 4 = \frac{2}{3}$

13. (a) $\log_3 5 = x$ (b) $\log_7(3y) = 2$

14. (a) $\log_6 z = 1$ (b) $\log_{10} 3 = 2t$

15. (a) $\ln 5 = 3y$ (b) $\ln(t + 1) = -1$

16. (a) $\ln(x + 1) = 2$ (b) $\ln(x - 1) = 4$

17–24 ■ **Logarithmic Form** Express the equation in logarithmic form.

17. (a) $10^4 = 10{,}000$ (b) $5^{-2} = \frac{1}{25}$

18. (a) $6^2 = 36$ (b) $10^{-1} = \frac{1}{10}$

19. (a) $8^{-1} = \frac{1}{8}$ (b) $2^{-3} = \frac{1}{8}$

20. (a) $4^{-3/2} = 0.125$ (b) $7^3 = 343$

21. (a) $4^x = 70$ (b) $3^5 = w$

22. (a) $3^{2x} = 10$ (b) $10^{-4x} = 0.1$

23. (a) $e^x = 2$ (b) $e^3 = y$

24. (a) $e^{x+1} = 0.5$ (b) $e^{0.5x} = t$

25–34 ■ Evaluating Logarithms Evaluate the expression.

25. (a) $\log_2 2$ (b) $\log_5 1$ (c) $\log_6 6^5$

26. (a) $\log_3 3^7$ (b) $\log_4 64$ (c) $\log_5 125$

27. (a) $\log_6 36$ (b) $\log_9 81$ (c) $\log_7 7^{10}$

28. (a) $\log_2 32$ (b) $\log_8 8^{17}$ (c) $\log_6 1$

29. (a) $\log_3\!\left(\frac{1}{27}\right)$ (b) $\log_{10} \sqrt{10}$ (c) $\log_5 0.2$

30. (a) $\log_5 125$ (b) $\log_{49} 7$ (c) $\log_9 \sqrt{3}$

31. (a) $3^{\log_3 5}$ (b) $5^{\log_5 27}$ (c) $e^{\ln 10}$

32. (a) $e^{\ln \sqrt{3}}$ (b) $e^{\ln(1/\pi)}$ (c) $10^{\log 13}$

33. (a) $\log_8 0.25$ (b) $\ln e^4$ (c) $\ln(1/e)$

34. (a) $\log_4 \sqrt{2}$ (b) $\log_4\!\left(\frac{1}{2}\right)$ (c) $\log_4 8$

35–44 ■ Logarithmic Equations Use the definition of the logarithmic function to find x.

35. (a) $\log_4 x = 3$ (b) $\log_{10} 0.01 = x$

36. (a) $\log_3 x = -2$ (b) $\log_5 125 = x$

37. (a) $\ln x = 3$ (b) $\ln e^2 = x$

38. (a) $\ln x = -1$ (b) $\ln(1/e) = x$

39. (a) $\log_7\!\left(\frac{1}{49}\right) = x$ (b) $\log_2 x = 5$

40. (a) $\log_4 2 = x$ (b) $\log_4 x = 2$

41. (a) $\log_2\!\left(\frac{1}{2}\right) = x$ (b) $\log_{10} x = -3$

42. (a) $\log_x 1000 = 3$ (b) $\log_x 25 = 2$

43. (a) $\log_x 16 = 4$ (b) $\log_x 8 = \frac{3}{2}$

44. (a) $\log_x 6 = \frac{1}{2}$ (b) $\log_x 3 = \frac{1}{3}$

45–48 ■ Evaluating Logarithms Use a calculator to evaluate the expression, correct to four decimal places.

45. (a) $\log 2$ (b) $\log 35.2$ (c) $\log\!\left(\frac{2}{3}\right)$

46. (a) $\log 50$ (b) $\log \sqrt{2}$ (c) $\log(3\sqrt{2})$

47. (a) $\ln 5$ (b) $\ln 25.3$ (c) $\ln(1 + \sqrt{3})$

48. (a) $\ln 27$ (b) $\ln 7.39$ (c) $\ln 54.6$

49–52 ■ Graphing Logarithmic Functions Sketch the graph of the function by plotting points.

49. $f(x) = \log_3 x$ **50.** $g(x) = \log_4 x$

51. $f(x) = 2 \log x$ **52.** $g(x) = 1 + \log x$

53–56 ■ Finding Logarithmic Functions Find the function of the form $y = \log_a x$ whose graph is given.

53.
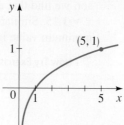

54.
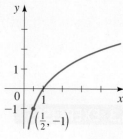

55.
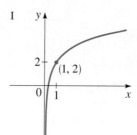

56.
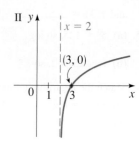

57–58 ■ Graphing Logarithmic Functions Match the logarithmic function with one of the graphs labeled I or II.

57. $f(x) = 2 + \ln x$ **58.** $f(x) = \ln(x - 2)$

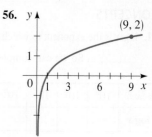

59. Graphing Draw the graph of $y = 4^x$, then use it to draw the graph of $y = \log_4 x$.

60. Graphing Draw the graph of $y = 3^x$, then use it to draw the graph of $y = \log_3 x$.

61–72 ■ Graphing Logarithmic Functions Graph the function, not by plotting points, but by starting from the graphs in Figures 4 and 9. State the domain, range, and asymptote.

61. $g(x) = \log_5(-x)$ **62.** $f(x) = -\log_{10} x$

63. $f(x) = \log_2(x - 4)$ **64.** $g(x) = \ln(x + 2)$

65. $h(x) = \ln(x + 5)$ **66.** $g(x) = \log_6(x - 3)$

67. $y = 2 + \log_3 x$ **68.** $y = 1 - \log_{10} x$

69. $y = \log_3(x - 1) - 2$ **70.** $y = 1 + \ln(-x)$

71. $y = |\ln x|$ **72.** $y = \ln|x|$

73–78 ■ Domain Find the domain of the function.

73. $f(x) = \log_{10}(x + 3)$ **74.** $f(x) = \log_5(8 - 2x)$

75. $g(x) = \log_3(x^2 - 1)$ **76.** $g(x) = \ln(x - x^2)$

77. $h(x) = \ln x + \ln(2 - x)$

78. $h(x) = \sqrt{x - 2} - \log_5(10 - x)$

 79–84 ■ Graphing Logarithmic Functions Draw the graph of the function in a suitable viewing rectangle, and use it to find the domain, the asymptotes, and the local maximum and minimum values.

79. $y = \log_{10}(1 - x^2)$ **80.** $y = \ln(x^2 - x)$

81. $y = x + \ln x$ **82.** $y = x(\ln x)^2$

83. $y = \dfrac{\ln x}{x}$ **84.** $y = x \log_{10}(x + 10)$

SKILLS Plus

85–88 ■ Domain of a Composition Find the functions $f \circ g$ and $g \circ f$ and their domains.

85. $f(x) = 2^x$, $g(x) = x + 1$

86. $f(x) = 3^x$, $g(x) = x^2 + 1$

87. $f(x) = \log_2 x$, $g(x) = x - 2$

88. $f(x) = \log x$, $g(x) = x^2$

 89. Rates of Growth Compare the rates of growth of the functions $f(x) = \ln x$ and $g(x) = \sqrt{x}$ by drawing their graphs on a common screen using the viewing rectangle $[-1, 30]$ by $[-1, 6]$.

 90. Rates of Growth

    (a) By drawing the graphs of the functions

$$f(x) = 1 + \ln(1 + x) \quad \text{and} \quad g(x) = \sqrt{x}$$

    in a suitable viewing rectangle, show that even when a logarithmic function starts out higher than a root function, it is ultimately overtaken by the root function.

    (b) Find, rounded to two decimal places, the solutions of the equation $\sqrt{x} = 1 + \ln(1 + x)$.

 91–92 ■ Family of Functions A family of functions is given. **(a)** Draw graphs of the family for $c = 1, 2, 3,$ and 4. **(b)** How are the graphs in part (a) related?

91. $f(x) = \log(cx)$ **92.** $f(x) = c \log x$

93–94 ■ Inverse Functions A function $f(x)$ is given. **(a)** Find the domain of the function f. **(b)** Find the inverse function of f.

93. $f(x) = \log_2(\log_{10} x)$ **94.** $f(x) = \ln(\ln(\ln x))$

95. Inverse Functions

    (a) Find the inverse of the function $f(x) = \dfrac{2^x}{1 + 2^x}$.

    (b) What is the domain of the inverse function?

APPLICATIONS

96. Absorption of Light A spectrophotometer measures the concentration of a sample dissolved in water by shining a light through it and recording the amount of light that emerges. In other words, if we know the amount of light that is absorbed, we can calculate the concentration of the sample. For a certain substance the concentration (in moles per liter, mol/L) is found by using the formula

$$C = -2500 \ln\left(\frac{I}{I_0}\right)$$

where I_0 is the intensity of the incident light and I is the intensity of light that emerges. Find the concentration of the substance if the intensity I is 70% of I_0.

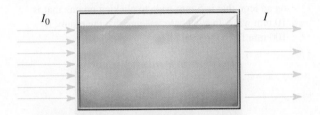

97. Carbon Dating The age of an ancient artifact can be determined by the amount of radioactive carbon-14 remaining in it. If D_0 is the original amount of carbon-14 and D is the amount remaining, then the artifact's age A (in years) is given by

$$A = -8267 \ln\left(\frac{D}{D_0}\right)$$

Find the age of an object if the amount D of carbon-14 that remains in the object is 73% of the original amount D_0.

98. Bacteria Colony A certain strain of bacteria divides every 3 hours. If a colony is started with 50 bacteria, then the time t (in hours) required for the colony to grow to N bacteria is given by

$$t = 3 \frac{\log(N/50)}{\log 2}$$

Find the time required for the colony to grow to a million bacteria.

99. Investment The time required to double the amount of an investment at an interest rate r compounded continuously is given by

$$t = \frac{\ln 2}{r}$$

Find the time required to double an investment at 6%, 7%, and 8%.

100. Charging a Battery The rate at which a battery charges is slower the closer the battery is to its maximum charge C_0. The time (in hours) required to charge a fully discharged battery to a charge C is given by

$$t = -k \ln\left(1 - \frac{C}{C_0}\right)$$

where k is a positive constant that depends on the battery. For a certain battery, $k = 0.25$. If this battery is fully discharged, how long will it take to charge to 90% of its maximum charge C_0?

101. Difficulty of a Task The difficulty in "acquiring a target" (such as using your mouse to click on an icon on your computer screen) depends on the distance to the target and the size of the target. According to Fitts's Law, the index of difficulty (ID) is given by

$$ID = \frac{\log(2A/W)}{\log 2}$$

where W is the width of the target and A is the distance to the center of the target. Compare the difficulty of clicking on an icon that is 5 mm wide to clicking on one that is 10 mm wide. In each case, assume that the mouse is 100 mm from the icon.

DISCUSS ■ **DISCOVER** ■ **PROVE** ■ **WRITE**

102. DISCUSS: The Height of the Graph of a Logarithmic Function Suppose that the graph of $y = 2^x$ is drawn on a coordinate plane where the unit of measurement is an inch.

   (a) Show that at a distance 2 ft to the right of the origin the height of the graph is about 265 mi.

   (b) If the graph of $y = \log_2 x$ is drawn on the same set of axes, how far to the right of the origin do we have to go before the height of the curve reaches 2 ft?

103. DISCUSS: The Googolplex A **googol** is 10^{100}, and a **googolplex** is 10^{googol}. Find

$$\log(\log(\text{googol})) \quad \text{and} \quad \log(\log(\log(\text{googolplex})))$$

104. DISCUSS: Comparing Logarithms Which is larger, $\log_4 17$ or $\log_5 24$? Explain your reasoning.

105. DISCUSS ■ **DISCOVER: The Number of Digits in an Integer** Compare log 1000 to the number of digits in 1000. Do the same for 10,000. How many digits does any number between 1000 and 10,000 have? Between what two values must the common logarithm of such a number lie? Use your observations to explain why the number of digits in any positive integer x is $[\![\log x]\!] + 1$. (The symbol $[\![n]\!]$ is the greatest integer function defined in Section 2.2.) How many digits does the number 2^{100} have?

4.4 LAWS OF LOGARITHMS

■ **Laws of Logarithms** ■ **Expanding and Combining Logarithmic Expressions**
■ **Change of Base Formula**

In this section we study properties of logarithms. These properties give logarithmic functions a wide range of applications, as we will see in Sections 4.6 and 4.7.

■ Laws of Logarithms

Since logarithms are exponents, the Laws of Exponents give rise to the Laws of Logarithms.

LAWS OF LOGARITHMS

Let a be a positive number, with $a \neq 1$. Let A, B, and C be any real numbers with $A > 0$ and $B > 0$.

Law	Description
1. $\log_a(AB) = \log_a A + \log_a B$	The logarithm of a product of numbers is the sum of the logarithms of the numbers.
2. $\log_a\left(\dfrac{A}{B}\right) = \log_a A - \log_a B$	The logarithm of a quotient of numbers is the difference of the logarithms of the numbers.
3. $\log_a(A^C) = C \log_a A$	The logarithm of a power of a number is the exponent times the logarithm of the number.

Proof   We make use of the property $\log_a a^x = x$ from Section 4.3.

Law 1   Let $\log_a A = u$ and $\log_a B = v$. When written in exponential form, these equations become

$$a^u = A \quad \text{and} \quad a^v = B$$

Thus
$$\log_a(AB) = \log_a(a^u a^v) = \log_a(a^{u+v})$$
$$= u + v = \log_a A + \log_a B$$

Law 2   Using Law 1, we have

$$\log_a A = \log_a\left[\left(\frac{A}{B}\right)B\right] = \log_a\left(\frac{A}{B}\right) + \log_a B$$

so
$$\log_a\left(\frac{A}{B}\right) = \log_a A - \log_a B$$

Law 3   Let $\log_a A = u$. Then $a^u = A$, so

$$\log_a(A^C) = \log_a(a^u)^C = \log_a(a^{uC}) = uC = C \log_a A \qquad \blacksquare$$

EXAMPLE 1 ■ Using the Laws of Logarithms to Evaluate Expressions

Evaluate each expression.
(a) $\log_4 2 + \log_4 32$
(b) $\log_2 80 - \log_2 5$
(c) $-\frac{1}{3} \log 8$

SOLUTION

(a) $\log_4 2 + \log_4 32 = \log_4(2 \cdot 32)$ Law 1
$\qquad\qquad\qquad\quad = \log_4 64 = 3$ Because $64 = 4^3$

(b) $\log_2 80 - \log_2 5 = \log_2\left(\frac{80}{5}\right)$ Law 2
$\qquad\qquad\qquad\quad = \log_2 16 = 4$ Because $16 = 2^4$

(c) $-\frac{1}{3} \log 8 = \log 8^{-1/3}$ Law 3
$\qquad\qquad\quad = \log\left(\frac{1}{2}\right)$ Property of negative exponents
$\qquad\qquad\quad \approx -0.301$ Calculator

✎ **Now Try Exercises 9, 11, and 13**   ■

■ Expanding and Combining Logarithmic Expressions

The Laws of Logarithms allow us to write the logarithm of a product or a quotient as the sum or difference of logarithms. This process, called *expanding* a logarithmic expression, is illustrated in the next example.

EXAMPLE 2 ■ Expanding Logarithmic Expressions

Use the Laws of Logarithms to expand each expression.

(a) $\log_2(6x)$ **(b)** $\log_5(x^3 y^6)$ **(c)** $\ln\left(\dfrac{ab}{\sqrt[3]{c}}\right)$

SOLUTION

(a) $\log_2(6x) = \log_2 6 + \log_2 x$ Law 1
(b) $\log_5(x^3 y^6) = \log_5 x^3 + \log_5 y^6$ Law 1
$\qquad\qquad\quad = 3 \log_5 x + 6 \log_5 y$ Law 3

(c) $\ln\left(\dfrac{ab}{\sqrt[3]{c}}\right) = \ln(ab) - \ln \sqrt[3]{c}$ Law 2

$\qquad\qquad\quad = \ln a + \ln b - \ln c^{1/3}$ Law 1

$\qquad\qquad\quad = \ln a + \ln b - \tfrac{1}{3}\ln c$ Law 3

■ **Now Try Exercises 23, 31, and 37**

The Laws of Logarithms also allow us to reverse the process of expanding that was done in Example 2. That is, we can write sums and differences of logarithms as a single logarithm. This process, called *combining* logarithmic expressions, is illustrated in the next example.

EXAMPLE 3 ■ Combining Logarithmic Expressions

Use the Laws of Logarithms to combine each expression into a single logarithm.

(a) $3 \log x + \tfrac{1}{2}\log(x + 1)$

(b) $3 \ln s + \tfrac{1}{2}\ln t - 4 \ln(t^2 + 1)$

SOLUTION

(a) $3 \log x + \tfrac{1}{2}\log(x + 1) = \log x^3 + \log(x + 1)^{1/2}$ Law 3

$\qquad\qquad\qquad\qquad\qquad = \log(x^3(x + 1)^{1/2})$ Law 1

(b) $3 \ln s + \tfrac{1}{2}\ln t - 4 \ln(t^2 + 1) = \ln s^3 + \ln t^{1/2} - \ln(t^2 + 1)^4$ Law 3

$\qquad\qquad\qquad\qquad\qquad\qquad = \ln(s^3 t^{1/2}) - \ln(t^2 + 1)^4$ Law 1

$\qquad\qquad\qquad\qquad\qquad\qquad = \ln\left(\dfrac{s^3 \sqrt{t}}{(t^2 + 1)^4}\right)$ Law 2

■ **Now Try Exercises 51 and 53**

Warning   Although the Laws of Logarithms tell us how to compute the logarithm of a product or a quotient, *there is no corresponding rule for the logarithm of a sum or a difference*. For instance,

$$\log_a(x + y) \ne \log_a x + \log_a y$$

In fact, we know that the right side is equal to $\log_a(xy)$. Also, don't improperly simplify quotients or powers of logarithms. For instance,

$$\frac{\log 6}{\log 2} \ne \log\left(\frac{6}{2}\right) \qquad \text{and} \qquad (\log_2 x)^3 \ne 3 \log_2 x$$

Logarithmic functions are used to model a variety of situations involving human behavior. One such behavior is how quickly we forget things we have learned. For example, if you learn algebra at a certain performance level (say, 90% on a test) and then don't use algebra for a while, how much will you retain after a week, a month, or a year? Hermann Ebbinghaus (1850–1909) studied this phenomenon and formulated the law described in the next example.

EXAMPLE 4 ■ The Law of Forgetting

If a task is learned at a performance level P_0, then after a time interval t the performance level P satisfies

$$\log P = \log P_0 - c \log(t + 1)$$

where c is a constant that depends on the type of task and t is measured in months.

(a) Solve for P.

(b) If your score on a history test is 90, what score would you expect to get on a similar test after two months? After a year? (Assume that $c = 0.2$.)

Forgetting what we've learned depends on how long ago we learned it.

SOLUTION

(a) We first combine the right-hand side.

$$\log P = \log P_0 - c \log(t + 1) \qquad \text{Given equation}$$

$$\log P = \log P_0 - \log(t + 1)^c \qquad \text{Law 3}$$

$$\log P = \log \frac{P_0}{(t + 1)^c} \qquad \text{Law 2}$$

$$P = \frac{P_0}{(t + 1)^c} \qquad \text{Because log is one-to-one}$$

(b) Here $P_0 = 90$, $c = 0.2$, and t is measured in months.

$$\text{In 2 months:} \quad t = 2 \quad \text{and} \quad P = \frac{90}{(2 + 1)^{0.2}} \approx 72$$

$$\text{In 1 year:} \quad t = 12 \quad \text{and} \quad P = \frac{90}{(12 + 1)^{0.2}} \approx 54$$

Your expected scores after 2 months and after 1 year are 72 and 54, respectively.

Now Try Exercise 73 ■

■ Change of Base Formula

For some purposes we find it useful to change from logarithms in one base to logarithms in another base. Suppose we are given $\log_a x$ and want to find $\log_b x$. Let

$$y = \log_b x$$

We write this in exponential form and take the logarithm, with base a, of each side.

$$b^y = x \qquad \text{Exponential form}$$

$$\log_a(b^y) = \log_a x \qquad \text{Take } \log_a \text{ of each side}$$

$$y \log_a b = \log_a x \qquad \text{Law 3}$$

$$y = \frac{\log_a x}{\log_a b} \qquad \text{Divide by } \log_a b$$

This proves the following formula.

We may write the Change of Base Formula as

$$\log_b x = \left(\frac{1}{\log_a b} \right) \log_a x$$

So $\log_b x$ is just a constant multiple of $\log_a x$; the constant is $\dfrac{1}{\log_a b}$.

CHANGE OF BASE FORMULA

$$\log_b x = \frac{\log_a x}{\log_a b}$$

In particular, if we put $x = a$, then $\log_a a = 1$, and this formula becomes

$$\log_b a = \frac{1}{\log_a b}$$

We can now evaluate a logarithm to *any* base by using the Change of Base Formula to express the logarithm in terms of common logarithms or natural logarithms and then using a calculator.

EXAMPLE 5 ■ Evaluating Logarithms with the Change of Base Formula

Use the Change of Base Formula and common or natural logarithms to evaluate each logarithm, rounded to five decimal places.

(a) $\log_8 5$ (b) $\log_9 20$

SOLUTION

(a) We use the Change of Base Formula with $b = 8$ and $a = 10$:

$$\log_8 5 = \frac{\log_{10} 5}{\log_{10} 8} \approx 0.77398$$

(b) We use the Change of Base Formula with $b = 9$ and $a = e$:

$$\log_9 20 = \frac{\ln 20}{\ln 9} \approx 1.36342$$

✎ Now Try Exercises 59 and 61

EXAMPLE 6 ■ Using the Change of Base Formula to Graph a Logarithmic Function

Use a graphing calculator to graph $f(x) = \log_6 x$.

SOLUTION Calculators don't have a key for $\log_6$, so we use the Change of Base Formula to write

$$f(x) = \log_6 x = \frac{\ln x}{\ln 6}$$

Since calculators do have an $\boxed{\text{LN}}$ key, we can enter this new form of the function and graph it. The graph is shown in Figure 1.

✎ Now Try Exercise 67

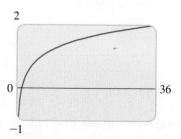

FIGURE 1
$f(x) = \log_6 x = \dfrac{\ln x}{\ln 6}$

4.4 EXERCISES

CONCEPTS

1. The logarithm of a product of two numbers is the same as the _____ of the logarithms of these numbers. So $\log_5(25 \cdot 125) = $ _____ + _____.

2. The logarithm of a quotient of two numbers is the same as the _____ of the logarithms of these numbers. So $\log_5\left(\frac{25}{125}\right) = $ _____ − _____.

3. The logarithm of a number raised to a power is the same as the _____ times the logarithm of the number. So $\log_5(25^{10}) = $ _____ · _____.

4. We can expand $\log\left(\dfrac{x^2 y}{z}\right)$ to get _____.

5. We can combine $2 \log x + \log y - \log z$ to get _____.

6. (a) Most calculators can find logarithms with base _____ and base _____. To find logarithms with different bases, we use the _____ Formula. To find $\log_7 12$, we write

$$\log_7 12 = \frac{\log \,\square}{\log \,\square} \approx \underline{\quad\quad}$$

(b) Do we get the same answer if we perform the calculation in part (a) using ln in place of log?

7–8 ■ *True or False?*

7. (a) $\log(A + B)$ is the same as $\log A + \log B$.

(b) $\log AB$ is the same as $\log A + \log B$.

8. (a) $\log \dfrac{A}{B}$ is the same as $\log A - \log B$.

(b) $\dfrac{\log A}{\log B}$ is the same as $\log A - \log B$.

SKILLS

9–22 ■ Evaluating Logarithms Use the Laws of Logarithms to evaluate the expression.

9. $\log 50 + \log 200$

10. $\log_6 9 + \log_6 24$

11. $\log_2 60 - \log_2 15$

12. $\log_3 135 - \log_3 45$

13. $\frac{1}{4} \log_3 81$

14. $-\frac{1}{3} \log_3 27$

15. $\log_5 \sqrt{5}$

16. $\log_5 \dfrac{1}{\sqrt{125}}$

17. $\log_2 6 - \log_2 15 + \log_2 20$

18. $\log_3 100 - \log_3 18 - \log_3 50$

19. $\log_4 16^{100}$

20. $\log_2 8^{33}$

21. $\log(\log 10^{10,000})$

22. $\ln(\ln e^{e^{200}})$

23–48 ■ Expanding Logarithmic Expressions Use the Laws of Logarithms to expand the expression.

23. $\log_3 8x$

24. $\log_6 7r$

25. $\log_3 2xy$

26. $\log_5 4st$

27. $\ln a^3$

28. $\log \sqrt{t^5}$

29. $\log_2(xy)^{10}$

30. $\ln \sqrt{ab}$

31. $\log_2(AB^2)$

32. $\log_3(x\sqrt{y})$

33. $\log_3 \dfrac{2x}{y}$

34. $\ln \dfrac{r}{3s}$

35. $\log_5\left(\dfrac{3x^2}{y^3}\right)$

36. $\log_2\left(\dfrac{s^5}{7t^2}\right)$

37. $\log_3 \dfrac{\sqrt{3x^5}}{y}$

38. $\log \dfrac{y^3}{\sqrt{2x}}$

39. $\log\left(\dfrac{x^3y^4}{z^6}\right)$

40. $\log_a\left(\dfrac{x^2}{yz^3}\right)$

41. $\ln \sqrt{x^4 + 2}$

42. $\log \sqrt[3]{x^2 + 4}$

43. $\ln\left(x\sqrt{\dfrac{y}{z}}\right)$

44. $\ln \dfrac{3x^2}{(x+1)^{10}}$

45. $\log \sqrt[4]{x^2 + y^2}$

46. $\log\left(\dfrac{x}{\sqrt[3]{1-x}}\right)$

47. $\log \sqrt{\dfrac{x^2 + 4}{(x^2 + 1)(x^3 - 7)^2}}$

48. $\log \sqrt{x\sqrt{y}\sqrt{z}}$

49–58 ■ Combining Logarithmic Expressions Use the Laws of Logarithms to combine the expression.

49. $\log_4 6 + 2 \log_4 7$

50. $\frac{1}{2} \log_2 5 - 2 \log_2 7$

51. $2 \log x - 3 \log(x + 1)$

52. $3 \ln 2 + 2 \ln x - \frac{1}{2} \ln(x + 4)$

53. $4 \log x - \frac{1}{3} \log(x^2 + 1) + 2 \log(x - 1)$

54. $\log_5(x^2 - 1) - \log_5(x - 1)$

55. $\ln(a + b) + \ln(a - b) - 2 \ln c$

56. $2(\log_5 x + 2 \log_5 y - 3 \log_5 z)$

57. $\frac{1}{3} \log(x + 2)^3 + \frac{1}{2}[\log x^4 - \log(x^2 - x - 6)^2]$

58. $\log_a b + c \log_a d - r \log_a s$

59–66 ■ Change of Base Formula Use the Change of Base Formula and a calculator to evaluate the logarithm, rounded to six decimal places. Use either natural or common logarithms.

59. $\log_2 5$

60. $\log_5 2$

61. $\log_3 16$

62. $\log_6 92$

63. $\log_7 2.61$

64. $\log_6 532$

65. $\log_4 125$

66. $\log_{12} 2.5$

67. Change of Base Formula Use the Change of Base Formula to show that

$$\log_3 x = \frac{\ln x}{\ln 3}$$

Then use this fact to draw the graph of the function $f(x) = \log_3 x$.

SKILLS Plus

68. Families of Functions Draw graphs of the family of functions $y = \log_a x$ for $a = 2, e, 5,$ and 10 on the same screen, using the viewing rectangle $[0, 5]$ by $[-3, 3]$. How are these graphs related?

69. Change of Base Formula Use the Change of Base Formula to show that

$$\log e = \frac{1}{\ln 10}$$

70. Change of Base Formula Simplify: $(\log_2 5)(\log_5 7)$

71. A Logarithmic Identity Show that
$$-\ln(x - \sqrt{x^2 - 1}) = \ln(x + \sqrt{x^2 - 1})$$

APPLICATIONS

72. Forgetting Use the Law of Forgetting (Example 4) to estimate a student's score on a biology test two years after he got a score of 80 on a test covering the same material. Assume that $c = 0.3$ and t is measured in months.

73. Wealth Distribution Vilfredo Pareto (1848–1923) observed that most of the wealth of a country is owned by a few members of the population. **Pareto's Principle** is

$$\log P = \log c - k \log W$$

where W is the wealth level (how much money a person has) and P is the number of people in the population having that much money.

(a) Solve the equation for P.

(b) Assume that $k = 2.1$ and $c = 8000$, and that W is measured in millions of dollars. Use part (a) to find the number of people who have \$2 million or more. How many people have \$10 million or more?

74. Biodiversity Some biologists model the number of species S in a fixed area A (such as an island) by the species-area relationship

$$\log S = \log c + k \log A$$

where c and k are positive constants that depend on the type of species and habitat.

(a) Solve the equation for S.

(b) Use part (a) to show that if $k = 3$, then doubling the area increases the number of species eightfold.

75. Magnitude of Stars The magnitude M of a star is a measure of how bright a star appears to the human eye. It is defined by

$$M = -2.5 \log\left(\frac{B}{B_0}\right)$$

where B is the actual brightness of the star and B_0 is a constant.

(a) Expand the right-hand side of the equation.

(b) Use part (a) to show that the brighter a star, the less its magnitude.

(c) Betelgeuse is about 100 times brighter than Albiero. Use part (a) to show that Betelgeuse is 5 magnitudes less bright than Albiero.

DISCUSS ■ **DISCOVER** ■ **PROVE** ■ **WRITE**

76. DISCUSS: True or False? Discuss each equation, and determine whether it is true for all possible values of the variables. (Ignore values of the variables for which any term is undefined.)

(a) $\log\left(\dfrac{x}{y}\right) = \dfrac{\log x}{\log y}$

(b) $\log_2(x - y) = \log_2 x - \log_2 y$

(c) $\log_5\left(\dfrac{a}{b^2}\right) = \log_5 a - 2 \log_5 b$

(d) $\log 2^z = z \log 2$

(e) $(\log P)(\log Q) = \log P + \log Q$

(f) $\dfrac{\log a}{\log b} = \log a - \log b$

(g) $(\log_2 7)^x = x \log_2 7$

(h) $\log_a a^a = a$

(i) $\log(x - y) = \dfrac{\log x}{\log y}$

(j) $-\ln\left(\dfrac{1}{A}\right) = \ln A$

77. DISCUSS: Find the Error What is wrong with the following argument?

$$\log 0.1 < 2 \log 0.1$$
$$= \log(0.1)^2$$
$$= \log 0.01$$
$$\log 0.1 < \log 0.01$$
$$0.1 < 0.01$$

78. PROVE: Shifting, Shrinking, and Stretching Graphs of Functions Let $f(x) = x^2$. Show that $f(2x) = 4f(x)$, and explain how this shows that shrinking the graph of f horizontally has the same effect as stretching it vertically. Then use the identities $e^{2+x} = e^2 e^x$ and $\ln(2x) = \ln 2 + \ln x$ to show that for $g(x) = e^x$ a horizontal shift is the same as a vertical stretch and for $h(x) = \ln x$ a horizontal shrinking is the same as a vertical shift.

4.5 EXPONENTIAL AND LOGARITHMIC EQUATIONS

■ **Exponential Equations** ■ **Logarithmic Equations** ■ **Compound Interest**

In this section we solve equations that involve exponential or logarithmic functions. The techniques that we develop here will be used in the next section for solving applied problems.

■ Exponential Equations

An *exponential equation* is one in which the variable occurs in the exponent. Some exponential equations can be solved by using the fact that exponential functions are one-to-one. This means that

$$a^x = a^y \quad \Rightarrow \quad x = y$$

We use this property in the next example.

EXAMPLE 1 ■ Exponential Equations

Solve the exponential equation.

(a) $5^x = 125$ **(b)** $5^{2x} = 5^{x+1}$

SOLUTION

(a) We first express 125 as a power of 5 and then use the fact that the exponential function $f(x) = 5^x$ is one-to-one.

$$
\begin{array}{lll}
5^x = 125 & \text{Given equation} \\
5^x = 5^3 & \text{Because } 125 = 5^3 \\
x = 3 & \text{One-to-one property}
\end{array}
$$

The solution is $x = 3$.

(b) We first use the fact that the function $f(x) = 5^x$ is one-to-one.

$$
\begin{array}{lll}
5^{2x} = 5^{x+1} & \text{Given equation} \\
2x = x + 1 & \text{One-to-one property} \\
x = 1 & \text{Solve for } x
\end{array}
$$

The solution is $x = 1$.

✎ **Now Try Exercises 3 and 7**   ■

The equations in Example 1 were solved by comparing exponents. This method is not suitable for solving an equation like $5^x = 160$ because 160 is not easily expressed as a power of the base 5. To solve such equations, we take the logarithm of each side and use Law 3 of logarithms to "bring down the exponent." The following guidelines describe the process.

Law 3: $\log_a A^C = C \log_a A$

GUIDELINES FOR SOLVING EXPONENTIAL EQUATIONS

1. Isolate the exponential expression on one side of the equation.

2. Take the logarithm of each side, then use the Laws of Logarithms to "bring down the exponent."

3. Solve for the variable.

EXAMPLE 2 ■ Solving an Exponential Equation

Consider the exponential equation $3^{x+2} = 7$.

(a) Find the exact solution of the equation expressed in terms of logarithms.

(b) Use a calculator to find an approximation to the solution rounded to six decimal places.

DISCOVERY PROJECT

Super Origami

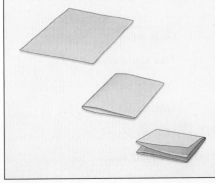

Origami is the traditional Japanese art of folding paper to create illustrations. In this project we explore some thought experiments about folding paper. Suppose that you fold a sheet of paper in half, then fold it in half again, and continue to fold the paper in half. How many folds are needed to obtain a mile-high stack of paper? To answer this question, we need to solve an exponential equation. In this project we use logarithms to answer this and other thought questions about folding paper. You can find the project at **www.stewartmath.com**.

SOLUTION

(a) We take the common logarithm of each side and use Law 3.

$$3^{x+2} = 7 \qquad \text{Given equation}$$

$$\log(3^{x+2}) = \log 7 \qquad \text{Take log of each side}$$

$$(x+2)\log 3 = \log 7 \qquad \text{Law 3 (bring down exponent)}$$

$$x + 2 = \frac{\log 7}{\log 3} \qquad \text{Divide by log 3}$$

$$x = \frac{\log 7}{\log 3} - 2 \qquad \text{Subtract 2}$$

We could have used natural logarithms instead of common logarithms. In fact, using the same steps, we get

$$x = \frac{\ln 7}{\ln 3} - 2 \approx -0.228756$$

The exact solution is $x = \dfrac{\log 7}{\log 3} - 2$.

(b) Using a calculator, we find the decimal approximation $x \approx -0.228756$.

✎ **Now Try Exercise 15**

■

Substituting $x = -0.228756$ into the original equation and using a calculator, we get

$$3^{(-0.228756)+2} \approx 7 \quad ✓$$

EXAMPLE 3 ■ Solving an Exponential Equation

Solve the equation $8e^{2x} = 20$.

SOLUTION We first divide by 8 to isolate the exponential term on one side of the equation.

$$8e^{2x} = 20 \qquad \text{Given equation}$$

$$e^{2x} = \tfrac{20}{8} \qquad \text{Divide by 8}$$

$$\ln e^{2x} = \ln 2.5 \qquad \text{Take ln of each side}$$

$$2x = \ln 2.5 \qquad \text{Property of ln}$$

$$x = \frac{\ln 2.5}{2} \qquad \text{Divide by 2 (exact solution)}$$

$$\approx 0.458 \qquad \text{Calculator (approximate solution)}$$

✎ **Now Try Exercise 17**

■

Substituting $x = 0.458$ into the original equation and using a calculator, we get

$$8e^{2(0.458)} \approx 20 \quad ✓$$

EXAMPLE 4 ■ Solving an Exponential Equation Algebraically and Graphically

Solve the equation $e^{3-2x} = 4$ algebraically and graphically.

SOLUTION 1: Algebraic

Since the base of the exponential term is e, we use natural logarithms to solve this equation.

$$e^{3-2x} = 4 \qquad \text{Given equation}$$

$$\ln(e^{3-2x}) = \ln 4 \qquad \text{Take ln of each side}$$

$$3 - 2x = \ln 4 \qquad \text{Property of ln}$$

$$-2x = -3 + \ln 4 \qquad \text{Subtract 3}$$

$$x = \tfrac{1}{2}(3 - \ln 4) \approx 0.807 \qquad \text{Multiply by } -\tfrac{1}{2}$$

You should check that this answer satisfies the original equation.

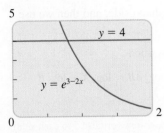

FIGURE 1

If we let $w = e^x$, we get the quadratic equation

$$w^2 - w - 6 = 0$$

which factors as

$$(w - 3)(w + 2) = 0$$

$x = 0$:

$$3(0)e^0 + 0^2 e^0 = 0 \quad \checkmark$$

$x = -3$:

$$3(-3)e^{-3} + (-3)^2 e^{-3}$$
$$= -9e^{-3} + 9e^{-3} = 0 \quad \checkmark$$

SOLUTION 2: Graphical

We graph the equations $y = e^{3-2x}$ and $y = 4$ in the same viewing rectangle as in Figure 1. The solutions occur where the graphs intersect. Zooming in on the point of intersection of the two graphs, we see that $x \approx 0.81$.

✎ Now Try Exercise 21   ■

EXAMPLE 5 ■ An Exponential Equation of Quadratic Type

Solve the equation $e^{2x} - e^x - 6 = 0$.

SOLUTION   To isolate the exponential term, we factor.

$$
\begin{array}{lll}
e^{2x} - e^x - 6 = 0 & & \text{Given equation} \\
(e^x)^2 - e^x - 6 = 0 & & \text{Law of Exponents} \\
(e^x - 3)(e^x + 2) = 0 & & \text{Factor (a quadratic in } e^x) \\
e^x - 3 = 0 \quad \text{or} \quad e^x + 2 = 0 & & \text{Zero-Product Property} \\
e^x = 3 \qquad\qquad e^x = -2 & &
\end{array}
$$

The equation $e^x = 3$ leads to $x = \ln 3$. But the equation $e^x = -2$ has no solution because $e^x > 0$ for all x. Thus $x = \ln 3 \approx 1.0986$ is the only solution. You should check that this answer satisfies the original equation.

✎ Now Try Exercise 39   ■

EXAMPLE 6 ■ An Equation Involving Exponential Functions

Solve the equation $3xe^x + x^2 e^x = 0$.

SOLUTION   First we factor the left side of the equation.

$$
\begin{array}{lll}
3xe^x + x^2 e^x = 0 & & \text{Given equation} \\
x(3 + x)e^x = 0 & & \text{Factor out common factors} \\
x(3 + x) = 0 & & \text{Divide by } e^x \text{ (because } e^x \neq 0) \\
x = 0 \quad \text{or} \quad 3 + x = 0 & & \text{Zero-Product Property}
\end{array}
$$

Thus the solutions are $x = 0$ and $x = -3$.

✎ Now Try Exercise 45   ■

■ Logarithmic Equations

A *logarithmic equation* is one in which a logarithm of the variable occurs. Some logarithmic equations can be solved by using the fact that logarithmic functions are one-to-one. This means that

$$\log_a x = \log_a y \quad \Rightarrow \quad x = y$$

We use this property in the next example.

EXAMPLE 7 ■ Solving a Logarithmic Equation

Solve the equation $\log(x^2 + 1) = \log(x - 2) + \log(x + 3)$.

SOLUTION   First we combine the logarithms on the right-hand side, and then we use the one-to-one property of logarithms.

$$\log_5(x^2 + 1) = \log_5(x - 2) + \log_5(x + 3) \qquad \text{Given equation}$$

$$\log_5(x^2 + 1) = \log_5[(x - 2)(x + 3)] \qquad \text{Law 1: } \log_a AB = \log_a A + \log_a B$$

$$\log_5(x^2 + 1) = \log_5(x^2 + x - 6) \qquad \text{Expand}$$

$$x^2 + 1 = x^2 + x - 6 \qquad \text{log is one-to-one (or raise 5 to each side)}$$

$$x = 7 \qquad \text{Solve for } x$$

The solution is $x = 7$. (You can check that $x = 7$ satisfies the original equation.)

✎ **Now Try Exercise 49** ▪

The method of Example 7 is not suitable for solving an equation like $\log_5 x = 13$ because the right-hand side is not expressed as a logarithm (base 5). To solve such equations, we use the following guidelines.

GUIDELINES FOR SOLVING LOGARITHMIC EQUATIONS

1. Isolate the logarithmic term on one side of the equation; you might first need to combine the logarithmic terms.
2. Write the equation in exponential form (or raise the base to each side of the equation).
3. Solve for the variable.

EXAMPLE 8 ▪ Solving Logarithmic Equations

Solve each equation for x.

(a) $\ln x = 8$

(b) $\log_2(25 - x) = 3$

SOLUTION

(a)
$$\ln x = 8 \qquad \text{Given equation}$$
$$x = e^8 \qquad \text{Exponential form}$$

Therefore $x = e^8 \approx 2981$.

We can also solve this problem another way.

$$\ln x = 8 \qquad \text{Given equation}$$
$$e^{\ln x} = e^8 \qquad \text{Raise } e \text{ to each side}$$
$$x = e^8 \qquad \text{Property of ln}$$

(b) The first step is to rewrite the equation in exponential form.

$$\log_2(25 - x) = 3 \qquad \text{Given equation}$$
$$25 - x = 2^3 \qquad \text{Exponential form (or raise 2 to each side)}$$
$$25 - x = 8$$
$$x = 25 - 8 = 17$$

CHECK YOUR ANSWER

If $x = 17$, we get

$$\log_2(25 - 17) = \log_2 8 = 3 \quad ✓$$

✎ **Now Try Exercises 55 and 59** ▪

EXAMPLE 9 ■ Solving a Logarithmic Equation

Solve the equation $4 + 3 \log(2x) = 16$.

SOLUTION   We first isolate the logarithmic term. This allows us to write the equation in exponential form.

$$
\begin{aligned}
4 + 3 \log(2x) &= 16 &&\text{Given equation} \\
3 \log(2x) &= 12 &&\text{Subtract 4} \\
\log(2x) &= 4 &&\text{Divide by 3} \\
2x &= 10^4 &&\text{Exponential form (or raise 10 to each side)} \\
x &= 5000 &&\text{Divide by 2}
\end{aligned}
$$

✎ Now Try Exercise 61

CHECK YOUR ANSWER

If $x = 5000$, we get

$$
\begin{aligned}
4 + 3 \log 2(5000) &= 4 + 3 \log 10{,}000 \\
&= 4 + 3(4) \\
&= 16 \quad \checkmark
\end{aligned}
$$

EXAMPLE 10 ■ Solving a Logarithmic Equation Algebraically and Graphically

Solve the equation $\log(x + 2) + \log(x - 1) = 1$ algebraically and graphically.

SOLUTION 1: Algebraic
We first combine the logarithmic terms, using the Laws of Logarithms.

$$
\begin{aligned}
\log[(x + 2)(x - 1)] &= 1 &&\text{Law 1} \\
(x + 2)(x - 1) &= 10 &&\text{Exponential form (or raise 10 to each side)} \\
x^2 + x - 2 &= 10 &&\text{Expand left side} \\
x^2 + x - 12 &= 0 &&\text{Subtract 10} \\
(x + 4)(x - 3) &= 0 &&\text{Factor} \\
x = -4 \quad &\text{or} \quad x = 3
\end{aligned}
$$

We check these potential solutions in the original equation and find that $x = -4$ is not a solution (because logarithms of negative numbers are undefined), but $x = 3$ is a solution. (See *Check Your Answers*.)

SOLUTION 2: Graphical
We first move all terms to one side of the equation:

$$
\log(x + 2) + \log(x - 1) - 1 = 0
$$

Then we graph

$$
y = \log(x + 2) + \log(x - 1) - 1
$$

as in Figure 2. The solutions are the x-intercepts of the graph. Thus the only solution is $x \approx 3$.

✎ Now Try Exercise 63

CHECK YOUR ANSWERS

$x = -4$:

$$
\begin{aligned}
\log(-4 + 2) + \log(-4 - 1) \\
= \log(-2) + \log(-5) \\
\text{undefined} \quad \textsf{X}
\end{aligned}
$$

$x = 3$:

$$
\begin{aligned}
\log(3 + 2) + \log(3 - 1) \\
= \log 5 + \log 2 = \log(5 \cdot 2) \\
= \log 10 = 1 \quad \checkmark
\end{aligned}
$$

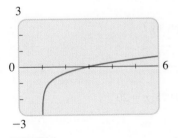

FIGURE 2

EXAMPLE 11 ■ Solving a Logarithmic Equation Graphically

Solve the equation $x^2 = 2 \ln(x + 2)$.

SOLUTION   We first move all terms to one side of the equation.

$$
x^2 - 2 \ln(x + 2) = 0
$$

Then we graph

$$
y = x^2 - 2 \ln(x + 2)
$$

In Example 11 it's not possible to isolate x algebraically, so we must solve the equation graphically.

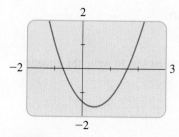

FIGURE 3

as in Figure 3. The solutions are the x-intercepts of the graph. Zooming in on the x-intercepts, we see that there are two solutions:

$$x \approx -0.71 \quad \text{and} \quad x \approx 1.60$$

✎ **Now Try Exercise 69** ∎

Logarithmic equations are used in determining the amount of light that reaches various depths in a lake. (This information helps biologists to determine the types of life a lake can support.) As light passes through water (or other transparent materials such as glass or plastic), some of the light is absorbed. It's easy to see that the murkier the water, the more light is absorbed. The exact relationship between light absorption and the distance light travels in a material is described in the next example.

EXAMPLE 12 ■ Transparency of a Lake

If I_0 and I denote the intensity of light before and after going through a material and x is the distance (in feet) the light travels in the material, then according to the **Beer-Lambert Law**,

$$-\frac{1}{k}\ln\left(\frac{I}{I_0}\right) = x$$

where k is a constant depending on the type of material.

(a) Solve the equation for I.

(b) For a certain lake $k = 0.025$, and the light intensity is $I_0 = 14$ lumens (lm). Find the light intensity at a depth of 20 ft.

SOLUTION

(a) We first isolate the logarithmic term.

$$-\frac{1}{k}\ln\left(\frac{I}{I_0}\right) = x \qquad \text{Given equation}$$

$$\ln\left(\frac{I}{I_0}\right) = -kx \qquad \text{Multiply by } -k$$

$$\frac{I}{I_0} = e^{-kx} \qquad \text{Exponential form}$$

$$I = I_0 e^{-kx} \qquad \text{Multiply by } I_0$$

(b) We find I using the formula from part (a).

$$I = I_0 e^{-kx} \qquad \text{From part (a)}$$
$$= 14e^{(-0.025)(20)} \qquad I_0 = 14,\ k = 0.025,\ x = 20$$
$$\approx 8.49 \qquad \text{Calculator}$$

The light intensity at a depth of 20 ft is about 8.5 lm.

✎ **Now Try Exercise 99** ∎

The intensity of light in a lake diminishes with depth.

▮ Compound Interest

Recall the formulas for interest that we found in Section 4.1. If a principal P is invested at an interest rate r for a period of t years, then the amount A of the investment is given by

$$A = P(1 + r) \qquad \text{Simple interest (for one year)}$$

$$A(t) = P\left(1 + \frac{r}{n}\right)^{nt} \qquad \text{Interest compounded } n \text{ times per year}$$

$$A(t) = Pe^{rt} \qquad \text{Interest compounded continuously}$$

We can use logarithms to determine the time it takes for the principal to increase to a given amount.

EXAMPLE 13 ■ Finding the Term for an Investment to Double

A sum of $5000 is invested at an interest rate of 5% per year. Find the time required for the money to double if the interest is compounded according to the following methods.

(a) Semiannually   (b) Continuously

SOLUTION

(a) We use the formula for compound interest with $P = \$5000$, $A(t) = \$10,000$, $r = 0.05$, and $n = 2$, and solve the resulting exponential equation for t.

$$5000\left(1 + \frac{0.05}{2}\right)^{2t} = 10,000 \qquad P\left(1 + \frac{r}{n}\right)^{nt} = A$$

$$(1.025)^{2t} = 2 \qquad \text{Divide by 5000}$$

$$\log 1.025^{2t} = \log 2 \qquad \text{Take log of each side}$$

$$2t \log 1.025 = \log 2 \qquad \text{Law 3 (bring down the exponent)}$$

$$t = \frac{\log 2}{2 \log 1.025} \qquad \text{Divide by 2 log 1.025}$$

$$t \approx 14.04 \qquad \text{Calculator}$$

The money will double in 14.04 years.

(b) We use the formula for continuously compounded interest with $P = \$5000$, $A(t) = \$10,000$, and $r = 0.05$ and solve the resulting exponential equation for t.

$$5000e^{0.05t} = 10,000 \qquad Pe^{rt} = A$$

$$e^{0.05t} = 2 \qquad \text{Divide by 5000}$$

$$\ln e^{0.05t} = \ln 2 \qquad \text{Take ln of each side}$$

$$0.05t = \ln 2 \qquad \text{Property of ln}$$

$$t = \frac{\ln 2}{0.05} \qquad \text{Divide by 0.05}$$

$$t \approx 13.86 \qquad \text{Calculator}$$

The money will double in 13.86 years.

◆ Now Try Exercise 89

EXAMPLE 14 ■ Time Required to Grow an Investment

A sum of $1000 is invested at an interest rate of 4% per year. Find the time required for the amount to grow to $4000 if interest is compounded continuously.

SOLUTION   We use the formula for continuously compounded interest with $P = \$1000$, $A(t) = \$4000$, and $r = 0.04$ and solve the resulting exponential equation for t.

$$1000e^{0.04t} = 4000 \qquad Pe^{rt} = A$$

$$e^{0.04t} = 4 \qquad \text{Divide by 1000}$$

$$0.04t = \ln 4 \qquad \text{Take ln of each side}$$

$$t = \frac{\ln 4}{0.04} \qquad \text{Divide by 0.04}$$

$$t \approx 34.66 \qquad \text{Calculator}$$

The amount will be $4000 in about 34 years and 8 months.

◆ Now Try Exercise 91

Radiocarbon Dating is a method that archeologists use to determine the age of ancient objects. The carbon dioxide in the atmosphere always contains a fixed fraction of radioactive carbon, carbon-14 (^{14}C), with a half-life of about 5730 years. Plants absorb carbon dioxide from the atmosphere, which then makes its way to animals through the food chain. Thus, all living creatures contain the same fixed proportions of ^{14}C to nonradioactive ^{12}C as the atmosphere.

After an organism dies, it stops assimilating ^{14}C, and the amount of ^{14}C in it begins to decay exponentially. We can then determine the time that has elapsed since the death of the organism by measuring the amount of ^{14}C left in it.

For example, if a donkey bone contains 73% as much ^{14}C as a living donkey and it died t years ago, then by the formula for radioactive decay (Section 4.6),

$$0.73 = (1.00)e^{-(t \ln 2)/5730}$$

We solve this exponential equation to find $t \approx 2600$, so the bone is about 2600 years old.

4.5 EXERCISES

CONCEPTS

1. Let's solve the exponential equation $2e^x = 50$.

   (a) First, we isolate e^x to get the equivalent equation

     _____.

   (b) Next, we take ln of each side to get the equivalent

     equation _____.

   (c) Now we use a calculator to find $x \approx$ _____.

2. Let's solve the logarithmic equation

$$\log 3 + \log(x - 2) = \log x$$

   (a) First, we combine the logarithms on the LHS to get the

     equivalent equation _____.

   (b) Next, we use the fact that log is one-to-one to get the

     equivalent equation _____.

   (c) Now we find $x =$ _____.

SKILLS

3–10 ■ **Exponential Equations** Find the solution of the exponential equation, as in Example 1.

3. $5^{x-1} = 125$ **4.** $e^{x^2} = e^9$

5. $5^{2x-3} = 1$ **6.** $10^{2x-3} = \frac{1}{10}$

7. $7^{2x-3} = 7^{6+5x}$ **8.** $e^{1-2x} = e^{3x-5}$

9. $6^{x^2-1} = 6^{1-x^2}$ **10.** $10^{2x^2-3} = 10^{9-x^2}$

11–38 ■ **Exponential Equations** **(a)** Find the exact solution of the exponential equation in terms of logarithms. **(b)** Use a calculator to find an approximation to the solution rounded to six decimal places.

11. $10^x = 25$ **12.** $10^{-x} = 4$

13. $e^{-5x} = 10$ **14.** $e^{0.4x} = 8$

15. $2^{1-x} = 3$ **16.** $3^{2x-1} = 5$

17. $3e^x = 10$ **18.** $2e^{12x} = 17$

19. $300(1.025)^{12t} = 1000$ **20.** $10(1.375)^{10t} = 50$

21. $e^{1-4x} = 2$ **22.** $e^{3-5x} = 16$

23. $2^{5-7x} = 15$ **24.** $2^{3x} = 34$

25. $3^{x/14} = 0.1$ **26.** $5^{-x/100} = 2$

27. $4(1 + 10^{5x}) = 9$ **28.** $2(5 + 3^{x+1}) = 100$

29. $8 + e^{1-4x} = 20$ **30.** $1 + e^{4x+1} = 20$

31. $4^x + 2^{1+2x} = 50$ **32.** $125^x + 5^{3x+1} = 200$

33. $5^x = 4^{x+1}$ **34.** $10^{1-x} = 6^x$

35. $2^{3x+1} = 3^{x-2}$ **36.** $7^{x/2} = 5^{1-x}$

37. $\dfrac{50}{1 + e^{-x}} = 4$ **38.** $\dfrac{10}{1 + e^{-x}} = 2$

39–44 ■ **Exponential Equations of Quadratic Type** Solve the equation.

39. $e^{2x} - 3e^x + 2 = 0$ **40.** $e^{2x} - e^x - 6 = 0$

41. $e^{4x} + 4e^{2x} - 21 = 0$ **42.** $3^{4x} - 3^{2x} - 6 = 0$

43. $2^x - 10(2^{-x}) + 3 = 0$ **44.** $e^x + 15e^{-x} - 8 = 0$

45–48 ■ **Equations Involving Exponential Functions** Solve the equation.

45. $x^2 2^x - 2^x = 0$ **46.** $x^2 10^x - x10^x = 2(10^x)$

47. $4x^3 e^{-3x} - 3x^4 e^{-3x} = 0$ **48.** $x^2 e^x + xe^x - e^x = 0$

49–54 ■ **Logarithmic Equations** Solve the logarithmic equation for x, as in Example 7.

49. $\log x + \log(x - 1) = \log(4x)$

50. $\log_5 x + \log_5(x + 1) = \log_5 20$

51. $2 \log x = \log 2 + \log(3x - 4)$

52. $\ln\left(x - \frac{1}{2}\right) + \ln 2 = 2 \ln x$

53. $\log_2 3 + \log_2 x = \log_2 5 + \log_2(x - 2)$

54. $\log_4(x + 2) + \log_4 3 = \log_4 5 + \log_4(2x - 3)$

55–68 ■ **Logarithmic Equations** Solve the logarithmic equation for x.

55. $\ln x = 10$ **56.** $\ln(2 + x) = 1$

57. $\log x = -2$ **58.** $\log(x - 4) = 3$

59. $\log(3x + 5) = 2$ **60.** $\log_3(2 - x) = 3$

61. $4 - \log(3 - x) = 3$

62. $\log_2(x^2 - x - 2) = 2$

63. $\log_2 x + \log_2(x - 3) = 2$

64. $\log x + \log(x - 3) = 1$

65. $\log_9(x - 5) + \log_9(x + 3) = 1$

66. $\ln(x - 1) + \ln(x + 2) = 1$

67. $\log_5(x + 1) - \log_5(x - 1) = 2$

68. $\log_3(x + 15) - \log_3(x - 1) = 2$

69–76 ■ **Solving Equations Graphically** Use a graphing device to find all solutions of the equation, rounded to two decimal places.

69. $\ln x = 3 - x$ **70.** $\log x = x^2 - 2$

71. $x^3 - x = \log(x + 1)$ **72.** $x = \ln(4 - x^2)$

73. $e^x = -x$ **74.** $2^{-x} = x - 1$

75. $4^{-x} = \sqrt{x}$ **76.** $e^{x^2} - 2 = x^3 - x$

77–78 ■ **More Exponential and Logarithmic Equations** Solve the equation for x.

77. $2^{2/\log_5 x} = \frac{1}{16}$ **78.** $\log_2(\log_3 x) = 4$

SKILLS Plus

79–82 ■ Solving Inequalities   Solve the inequality.

79. $\log(x - 2) + \log(9 - x) < 1$

80. $3 \le \log_2 x \le 4$

81. $2 < 10^x < 5$

82. $x^2 e^x - 2e^x < 0$

83–86 ■ Inverse Functions   Find the inverse function of f.

83. $f(x) = 2^{2x}$

84. $f(x) = 3^{x+1}$

85. $f(x) = \log_2(x - 1)$

86. $f(x) = \log 3x$

87–88 ■ Special Logarithmic Equations   Find the value(s) of x for which the equation is true.

87. $\log(x + 3) = \log x + \log 3$

88. $(\log x)^3 = 3 \log x$

APPLICATIONS

89. Compound Interest   A man invests $5000 in an account that pays 8.5% interest per year, compounded quarterly.
 (a) Find the amount after 3 years.
 (b) How long will it take for the investment to double?

90. Compound Interest   A woman invests $6500 in an account that pays 6% interest per year, compounded continuously.
 (a) What is the amount after 2 years?
 (b) How long will it take for the amount to be $8000?

91. Compound Interest   Find the time required for an investment of $5000 to grow to $8000 at an interest rate of 7.5% per year, compounded quarterly.

92. Compound Interest   Nancy wants to invest $4000 in saving certificates that bear an interest rate of 9.75% per year, compounded semiannually. How long a time period should she choose to save an amount of $5000?

93. Doubling an Investment   How long will it take for an investment of $1000 to double in value if the interest rate is 8.5% per year, compounded continuously?

94. Interest Rate   A sum of $1000 was invested for 4 years, and the interest was compounded semiannually. If this sum amounted to $1435.77 in the given time, what was the interest rate?

95. Radioactive Decay   A 15-g sample of radioactive iodine decays in such a way that the mass remaining after t days is given by $m(t) = 15e^{-0.087t}$, where $m(t)$ is measured in grams. After how many days are there only 5 g remaining?

96. Sky Diving   The velocity of a sky diver t seconds after jumping is given by $v(t) = 80(1 - e^{-0.2t})$. After how many seconds is the velocity 70 ft/s?

97. Fish Population   A small lake is stocked with a certain species of fish. The fish population is modeled by the function

$$P = \frac{10}{1 + 4e^{-0.8t}}$$

where P is the number of fish in thousands and t is measured in years since the lake was stocked.
 (a) Find the fish population after 3 years.
 (b) After how many years will the fish population reach 5000 fish?

98. Transparency of a Lake   Environmental scientists measure the intensity of light at various depths in a lake to find the "transparency" of the water. Certain levels of transparency are required for the biodiversity of the submerged macrophyte population. In a certain lake the intensity of light at depth x is given by

$$I = 10e^{-0.008x}$$

where I is measured in lumens and x in feet.
 (a) Find the intensity I at a depth of 30 ft.
 (b) At what depth has the light intensity dropped to $I = 5$?

99. Atmospheric Pressure   Atmospheric pressure P (in kilopascals, kPa) at altitude h (in kilometers, km) is governed by the formula

$$\ln\left(\frac{P}{P_0}\right) = -\frac{h}{k}$$

where $k = 7$ and $P_0 = 100$ kPa are constants.
 (a) Solve the equation for P.
 (b) Use part (a) to find the pressure P at an altitude of 4 km.

100. Cooling an Engine   Suppose you're driving your car on a cold winter day (20°F outside) and the engine overheats (at about 220°F). When you park, the engine begins to cool down. The temperature T of the engine t minutes after you park satisfies the equation

$$\ln\left(\frac{T - 20}{200}\right) = -0.11t$$

 (a) Solve the equation for T.
 (b) Use part (a) to find the temperature of the engine after 20 min ($t = 20$).

101. Electric Circuits   An electric circuit contains a battery that produces a voltage of 60 volts (V), a resistor with a resistance of 13 ohms (Ω), and an inductor with an inductance of 5 henrys (H), as shown in the figure on the following page. Using calculus, it can be shown that the current

$I = I(t)$ (in amperes, A) t seconds after the switch is closed is $I = \frac{60}{13}(1 - e^{-13t/5})$.

(a) Use this equation to express the time t as a function of the current I.

(b) After how many seconds is the current $2\,\text{A}$?

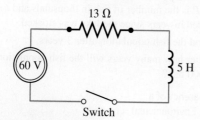

102. Learning Curve A *learning curve* is a graph of a function $P(t)$ that measures the performance of someone learning a skill as a function of the training time t. At first, the rate of learning is rapid. Then, as performance increases and approaches a maximal value M, the rate of learning decreases. It has been found that the function

$$P(t) = M - Ce^{-kt}$$

where k and C are positive constants and $C < M$ is a reasonable model for learning.

(a) Express the learning time t as a function of the performance level P.

(b) For a pole-vaulter in training, the learning curve is given by

$$P(t) = 20 - 14e^{-0.024t}$$

where $P(t)$ is the height he is able to pole-vault after t months. After how many months of training is he able to vault 12 ft?

 (c) Draw a graph of the learning curve in part (b).

DISCUSS ■ **DISCOVER** ■ **PROVE** ■ **WRITE**

103. DISCUSS: Estimating a Solution Without actually solving the equation, find two whole numbers between which the solution of $9^x = 20$ must lie. Do the same for $9^x = 100$. Explain how you reached your conclusions.

104. DISCUSS ■ DISCOVER: A Surprising Equation Take logarithms to show that the equation

$$x^{1/\log x} = 5$$

has no solution. For what values of k does the equation

$$x^{1/\log x} = k$$

have a solution? What does this tell us about the graph of the function $f(x) = x^{1/\log x}$? Confirm your answer using a graphing device.

105. DISCUSS: Disguised Equations Each of these equations can be transformed into an equation of linear or quadratic type by applying the hint. Solve each equation.

(a) $(x - 1)^{\log(x-1)} = 100(x - 1)$
[*Hint:* Take log of each side.]

(b) $\log_2 x + \log_4 x + \log_8 x = 11$
[*Hint:* Change all logs to base 2.]

(c) $4^x - 2^{x+1} = 3$
[*Hint:* Write as a quadratic in 2^x.]

4.6 MODELING WITH EXPONENTIAL FUNCTIONS

■ **Exponential Growth (Doubling Time)** ■ **Exponential Growth (Relative Growth Rate)**
■ **Radioactive Decay** ■ **Newton's Law of Cooling**

Many processes that occur in nature, such as population growth, radioactive decay, heat diffusion, and numerous others, can be modeled by using exponential functions. In this section we study exponential models.

■ Exponential Growth (Doubling Time)

Suppose we start with a single bacterium, which divides every hour. After one hour we have 2 bacteria, after two hours we have 2^2 or 4 bacteria, after three hours we have 2^3

or 8 bacteria, and so on (see Figure 1). We see that we can model the bacteria population after t hours by $f(t) = 2^t$.

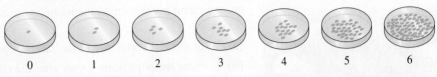

FIGURE 1 Bacteria population

If we start with 10 of these bacteria, then the population is modeled by $f(t) = 10 \cdot 2^t$. A slower-growing strain of bacteria doubles every 3 hours; in this case the population is modeled by $f(t) = 10 \cdot 2^{t/3}$. In general, we have the following.

EXPONENTIAL GROWTH (DOUBLING TIME)

If the initial size of a population is n_0 and the doubling time is a, then the size of the population at time t is

$$n(t) = n_0 2^{t/a}$$

where a and t are measured in the same time units (minutes, hours, days, years, and so on).

EXAMPLE 1 ■ Bacteria Population

Under ideal conditions a certain bacteria population doubles every three hours. Initially, there are 1000 bacteria in a colony.

(a) Find a model for the bacteria population after t hours.

(b) How many bacteria are in the colony after 15 hours?

(c) After how many hours will the bacteria count reach 100,000?

SOLUTION

(a) The population at time t is modeled by

$$n(t) = 1000 \cdot 2^{t/3}$$

where t is measured in hours.

(b) After 15 hours the number of bacteria is

$$n(15) = 1000 \cdot 2^{15/3} = 32{,}000$$

(c) We set $n(t) = 100{,}000$ in the model that we found in part (a) and solve the resulting exponential equation for t.

$100{,}000 = 1000 \cdot 2^{t/3}$	$n(t) = 1000 \cdot 2^{t/3}$
$100 = 2^{t/3}$	Divide by 1000
$\log 100 = \log 2^{t/3}$	Take log of each side
$2 = \dfrac{t}{3} \log 2$	Properties of log
$t = \dfrac{6}{\log 2} \approx 19.93$	Solve for t

The bacteria level reaches 100,000 in about 20 hours.

■

✎ **Now Try Exercise 1**

EXAMPLE 2 ■ Rabbit Population

A certain breed of rabbit was introduced onto a small island 8 months ago. The current rabbit population on the island is estimated to be 4100 and doubling every 3 months.

(a) What was the initial size of the rabbit population?

(b) Estimate the population 1 year after the rabbits were introduced to the island.

(c) Sketch a graph of the rabbit population.

SOLUTION

(a) The doubling time is $a = 3$, so the population at time t is

$$n(t) = n_0 2^{t/3} \qquad \text{Model}$$

where n_0 is the initial population. Since the population is 4100 when t is 8 months, we have

$$n(8) = n_0 2^{8/3} \qquad \text{From model}$$

$$4100 = n_0 2^{8/3} \qquad \text{Because } n(8) = 4100$$

$$n_0 = \frac{4100}{2^{8/3}} \qquad \text{Divide by } 2^{8/3} \text{ and switch sides}$$

$$n_0 \approx 645 \qquad \text{Calculator}$$

Thus we estimate that 645 rabbits were introduced onto the island.

(b) From part (a) we know that the initial population is $n_0 = 645$, so we can model the population after t months by

$$n(t) = 645 \cdot 2^{t/3} \qquad \text{Model}$$

After 1 year $t = 12$, so

$$n(12) = 645 \cdot 2^{12/3} = 10{,}320$$

So after 1 year there would be about 10,000 rabbits.

(c) We first note that the domain is $t \geq 0$. The graph is shown in Figure 2.

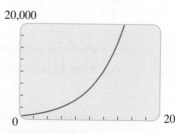

FIGURE 2 $n(t) = 645 \cdot 2^{t/3}$

✎ **Now Try Exercise 3**

■ Exponential Growth (Relative Growth Rate)

We have used an exponential function with base 2 to model population growth (in terms of the doubling time). We could also model the same population with an exponential function with base 3 (in terms of the tripling time). In fact, we can find an exponential model with any base. If we use the base e, we get a population model in terms of the **relative growth rate** r: the rate of population growth expressed as a proportion of the population at any time. In this case r is the "instantaneous" growth rate. (In calculus the concept of instantaneous rate is given a precise meaning.) For instance, if $r = 0.02$, then at any time t the growth rate is 2% of the population at time t.

The growth of a population with relative growth rate r is analogous to the growth of an investment with continuously compounded interest rate r.

EXPONENTIAL GROWTH (RELATIVE GROWTH RATE)

A population that experiences **exponential growth** increases according to the model

$$n(t) = n_0 e^{rt}$$

where $\quad n(t) =$ population at time t

$\qquad n_0 =$ initial size of the population

$\qquad r =$ relative rate of growth (expressed as a proportion of the population)

$\qquad t =$ time

Notice that the formula for population growth is the same as that for continuously compounded interest. In fact, the same principle is at work in both cases: The growth of a population (or an investment) per time period is proportional to the size of the population (or the amount of the investment). A population of 1,000,000 will increase more in one year than a population of 1000; in exactly the same way, an investment of $1,000,000 will increase more in one year than an investment of $1000.

In the following examples we assume that the populations grow exponentially.

EXAMPLE 3 ■ Predicting the Size of a Population

The initial bacterium count in a culture is 500. A biologist later makes a sample count of bacteria in the culture and finds that the relative rate of growth is 40% per hour.

(a) Find a function that models the number of bacteria after t hours.

(b) What is the estimated count after 10 hours?

(c) After how many hours will the bacteria count reach 80,000?

(d) Sketch a graph of the function $n(t)$.

SOLUTION

(a) We use the exponential growth model with $n_0 = 500$ and $r = 0.4$ to get

$$n(t) = 500e^{0.4t}$$

where t is measured in hours.

(b) Using the function in part (a), we find that the bacterium count after 10 hours is

$$n(10) = 500e^{0.4(10)} = 500e^4 \approx 27{,}300$$

(c) We set $n(t) = 80{,}000$ and solve the resulting exponential equation for t.

$$80{,}000 = 500 \cdot e^{0.4t} \qquad n(t) = 500 \cdot e^{0.4t}$$

$$160 = e^{0.4t} \qquad \text{Divide by 500}$$

$$\ln 160 = 0.4t \qquad \text{Take ln of each side}$$

$$t = \frac{\ln 160}{0.4} \approx 12.68 \qquad \text{Solve for } t$$

The bacteria level reaches 80,000 in about 12.7 hours.

(d) The graph is shown in Figure 3.

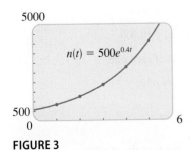

FIGURE 3

✎ Now Try Exercise 5

The relative growth of world population has been declining over the past few decades—from 2% in 1995 to 1.1% in 2013.

Standing Room Only

The population of the world was about 6.1 billion in 2000 and was increasing at 1.4% per year. Assuming that each person occupies an average of 4 ft^2 of the surface of the earth, the exponential model for population growth projects that by the year 2801 there will be standing room only! (The total land surface area of the world is about 1.8×10^{15} ft^2.)

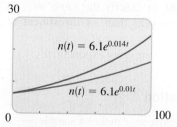

FIGURE 4

EXAMPLE 4 ■ Comparing Different Rates of Population Growth

In 2000 the population of the world was 6.1 billion, and the relative rate of growth was 1.4% per year. It is claimed that a rate of 1.0% per year would make a significant difference in the total population in just a few decades. Test this claim by estimating the population of the world in the year 2050 using a relative rate of growth of (a) 1.4% per year and (b) 1.0% per year.

Graph the population functions for the next 100 years for the two relative growth rates in the same viewing rectangle.

SOLUTION

(a) By the exponential growth model we have

$$n(t) = 6.1 e^{0.014t}$$

where $n(t)$ is measured in billions and t is measured in years since 2000. Because the year 2050 is 50 years after 2000, we find

$$n(50) = 6.1 e^{0.014(50)} = 6.1 e^{0.7} \approx 12.3$$

The estimated population in the year 2050 is about 12.3 billion.

(b) We use the function

$$n(t) = 6.1 e^{0.010t}$$

and find

$$n(50) = 6.1 e^{0.010(50)} = 6.1 e^{0.50} \approx 10.1$$

The estimated population in the year 2050 is about 10.1 billion.

The graphs in Figure 4 show that a small change in the relative rate of growth will, over time, make a large difference in population size.

✎ **Now Try Exercise 7**

EXAMPLE 5 ■ Expressing a Model in Terms of e

A culture starts with 10,000 bacteria, and the number doubles every 40 minutes.

(a) Find a function $n(t) = n_0 2^{t/a}$ that models the number of bacteria after t hours.

(b) Find a function $n(t) = n_0 e^{rt}$ that models the number of bacteria after t hours.

(c) Sketch a graph of the number of bacteria at time t.

SOLUTION

(a) The initial population is $n_0 = 10{,}000$. The doubling time is $a = 40$ min $= 2/3$ h. Since $1/a = 3/2 = 1.5$, the model is

$$n(t) = 10{,}000 \cdot 2^{1.5t}$$

(b) The initial population is $n_0 = 10{,}000$. We need to find the relative growth rate r. Since there are 20,000 bacteria when $t = 2/3$ h, we have

$$20{,}000 = 10{,}000 e^{r(2/3)} \qquad n(t) = 10{,}000 e^{rt}$$

$$2 = e^{r(2/3)} \qquad \text{Divide by 10,000}$$

$$\ln 2 = \ln e^{r(2/3)} \qquad \text{Take ln of each side}$$

$$\ln 2 = r(2/3) \qquad \text{Property of ln}$$

$$r = \frac{3 \ln 2}{2} \approx 1.0397 \qquad \text{Solve for } r$$

Now that we know the relative growth rate r, we can find the model:

$$n(t) = 10{,}000 e^{1.0397t}$$

(c) We can graph the model in part (a) or the one in part (b). The graphs are identical. See Figure 5.

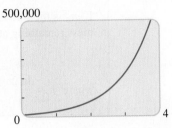

FIGURE 5 Graphs of $y = 10{,}000 \cdot 2^{1.5t}$ and $y = 10{,}000e^{1.0397t}$

✎ **Now Try Exercise 9** ∎

Radioactive Decay

The half-lives of **radioactive elements** vary from very long to very short. Here are some examples.

Element	Half-life
Thorium-232	14.5 billion years
Uranium-235	4.5 billion years
Thorium-230	80,000 years
Plutonium-239	24,360 years
Carbon-14	5,730 years
Radium-226	1,600 years
Cesium-137	30 years
Strontium-90	28 years
Polonium-210	140 days
Thorium-234	25 days
Iodine-135	8 days
Radon-222	3.8 days
Lead-211	3.6 minutes
Krypton-91	10 seconds

Radioactive substances decay by spontaneously emitting radiation. The rate of decay is proportional to the mass of the substance. This is analogous to population growth except that the mass *decreases*. Physicists express the rate of decay in terms of **half-life**, the time it takes for a sample of the substance to decay to half its original mass. For example, the half-life of radium-226 is 1600 years, so a 100-g sample decays to 50 g $\left(\text{or } \frac{1}{2} \times 100 \text{ g}\right)$ in 1600 years, then to 25 g $\left(\text{or } \frac{1}{2} \times \frac{1}{2} \times 100 \text{ g}\right)$ in 3200 years, and so on. In general, for a radioactive substance with mass m_0 and half-life h, the amount remaining at time t is modeled by

$$m(t) = m_0 2^{-t/h}$$

where h and t are measured in the same time units (minutes, hours, days, years, and so on).

To express this model in the form $m(t) = m_0 e^{rt}$, we need to find the relative decay rate r. Since h is the half-life, we have

$$m(t) = m_0 e^{-rt} \qquad \text{Model}$$

$$\frac{m_0}{2} = m_0 e^{-rh} \qquad h \text{ is the half-life}$$

$$\frac{1}{2} = e^{-rh} \qquad \text{Divide by } m_0$$

$$\ln \frac{1}{2} = -rh \qquad \text{Take ln of each side}$$

$$r = \frac{\ln 2}{h} \qquad \text{Solve for } r$$

This last equation allows us to find the relative decay rate r from the half-life h.

DISCOVERY PROJECT

Modeling Radiation with Coins and Dice

Radioactive elements decay when their atoms spontaneously emit radiation and change into smaller, stable atoms. But if atoms decay randomly, how is it possible to find a function that models their behavior? We'll try to answer this question by experimenting with randomly tossing coins and rolling dice. The experiments allow us to experience how a very large number of random events can result in predictable exponential results. You can find the project at **www.stewartmath.com**.

RADIOACTIVE DECAY MODEL

If m_0 is the initial mass of a radioactive substance with half-life h, then the mass remaining at time t is modeled by the function

$$m(t) = m_0 e^{-rt}$$

where $r = \dfrac{\ln 2}{h}$ is the **relative decay rate**.

EXAMPLE 6 ■ Radioactive Decay

Polonium-210 (^{210}Po) has a half-life of 140 days. Suppose a sample of this substance has a mass of 300 mg.

(a) Find a function $m(t) = m_0 2^{-t/h}$ that models the mass remaining after t days.

(b) Find a function $m(t) = m_0 e^{-rt}$ that models the mass remaining after t days.

(c) Find the mass remaining after one year.

(d) How long will it take for the sample to decay to a mass of 200 mg?

(e) Draw a graph of the sample mass as a function of time.

SOLUTION

(a) We have $m_0 = 300$ and $h = 140$, so the amount remaining after t days is

$$m(t) = 300 \cdot 2^{-t/140}$$

(b) We have $m_0 = 300$ and $r = \ln 2/140 \approx -0.00495$, so the amount remaining after t days is

$$m(t) = 300 \cdot e^{-0.00495t}$$

In parts (c) and (d) we can also use the model found in part (a). Check that the result is the same using either model.

(c) We use the function we found in part (a) with $t = 365$ (1 year):

$$m(365) = 300e^{-0.00495(365)} \approx 49.256$$

Thus approximately 49 mg of ^{210}Po remains after 1 year.

(d) We use the function that we found in part (b) with $m(t) = 200$ and solve the resulting exponential equation for t:

$$300e^{-0.00495t} = 200 \qquad m(t) = m_0 e^{-rt}$$
$$e^{-0.00495t} = \tfrac{2}{3} \qquad \text{Divide by 300}$$
$$\ln e^{-0.00495t} = \ln \tfrac{2}{3} \qquad \text{Take ln of each side}$$
$$-0.00495t = \ln \tfrac{2}{3} \qquad \text{Property of ln}$$
$$t = -\frac{\ln \tfrac{2}{3}}{0.00495} \qquad \text{Solve for } t$$
$$t \approx 81.9 \qquad \text{Calculator}$$

The time required for the sample to decay to 200 mg is about 82 days.

(e) We can graph the model in part (a) or the one in part (b). The graphs are identical. See Figure 6.

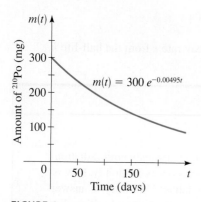

$m(t) = 300\, e^{-0.00495t}$

FIGURE 6

✎ **Now Try Exercise 17**

Newton's Law of Cooling

Newton's Law of Cooling states that the rate at which an object cools is proportional to the temperature difference between the object and its surroundings, provided that the temperature difference is not too large. By using calculus, the following model can be deduced from this law.

NEWTON'S LAW OF COOLING

If D_0 is the initial temperature difference between an object and its surroundings, and if its surroundings have temperature T_s, then the temperature of the object at time t is modeled by the function

$$T(t) = T_s + D_0 e^{-kt}$$

where k is a positive constant that depends on the type of object.

EXAMPLE 7 ■ Newton's Law of Cooling

A cup of coffee has a temperature of 200°F and is placed in a room that has a temperature of 70°F. After 10 min the temperature of the coffee is 150°F.

(a) Find a function that models the temperature of the coffee at time t.

(b) Find the temperature of the coffee after 15 min.

(c) After how long will the coffee have cooled to 100°F?

(d) Illustrate by drawing a graph of the temperature function.

SOLUTION

(a) The temperature of the room is $T_s = 70°F$, and the initial temperature difference is

$$D_0 = 200 - 70 = 130°F$$

So by Newton's Law of Cooling, the temperature after t minutes is modeled by the function

$$T(t) = 70 + 130e^{-kt}$$

We need to find the constant k associated with this cup of coffee. To do this, we use the fact that when $t = 10$, the temperature is $T(10) = 150$. So we have

$$70 + 130e^{-10k} = 150 \qquad \text{\small $T_s + D_0 e^{-kt} = T(t)$}$$

$$130e^{-10k} = 80 \qquad \text{\small Subtract 70}$$

$$e^{-10k} = \tfrac{8}{13} \qquad \text{\small Divide by 130}$$

$$-10k = \ln \tfrac{8}{13} \qquad \text{\small Take ln of each side}$$

$$k = -\tfrac{1}{10} \ln \tfrac{8}{13} \qquad \text{\small Solve for k}$$

$$k \approx 0.04855 \qquad \text{\small Calculator}$$

Substituting this value of k into the expression for $T(t)$, we get

$$T(t) = 70 + 130e^{-0.04855t}$$

(b) We use the function that we found in part (a) with $t = 15$.

$$T(15) = 70 + 130e^{-0.04855(15)} \approx 133°F$$

Radioactive Waste

Harmful radioactive isotopes are produced whenever a nuclear reaction occurs, whether as the result of an atomic bomb test, a nuclear accident such as the one at Fukushima Daiichi in 2011, or the uneventful production of electricity at a nuclear power plant.

One radioactive material that is produced in atomic bombs is the isotope strontium-90 (^{90}Sr), with a half-life of 28 years. This is deposited like calcium in human bone tissue, where it can cause leukemia and other cancers. However, in the decades since atmospheric testing of nuclear weapons was halted, ^{90}Sr levels in the environment have fallen to a level that no longer poses a threat to health.

Nuclear power plants produce radioactive plutonium-239 (^{239}Pu), which has a half-life of 24,360 years. Because of its long half-life, ^{239}Pu could pose a threat to the environment for thousands of years. So great care must be taken to dispose of it properly. The difficulty of ensuring the safety of the disposed radioactive waste is one reason that nuclear power plants remain controversial.

T (°F)

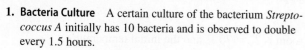

$$T = 70 + 130e^{-0.04855t}$$

$$T = 70$$

0   10   20   30   40   *t* (min)

FIGURE 7 Temperature of coffee after *t* minutes

(c) We use the function that we found in part (a) with $T(t) = 100$ and solve the resulting exponential equation for *t*.

$$70 + 130e^{-0.04855t} = 100 \qquad \qquad T_s + D_0 e^{-kt} = T(t)$$

$$130e^{-0.04855t} = 30 \qquad \qquad \text{Subtract 70}$$

$$e^{-0.04855t} = \tfrac{3}{13} \qquad \qquad \text{Divide by 130}$$

$$-0.04855t = \ln \tfrac{3}{13} \qquad \qquad \text{Take ln of each side}$$

$$t = \frac{\ln \tfrac{3}{13}}{-0.04855} \qquad \qquad \text{Solve for } t$$

$$t \approx 30.2 \qquad \qquad \text{Calculator}$$

The coffee will have cooled to 100°F after about half an hour.

(d) The graph of the temperature function is sketched in Figure 7. Notice that the line $t = 70$ is a horizontal asymptote. (Why?)

◣ **Now Try Exercise 25**

4.6 EXERCISES

APPLICATIONS

1–16 ■ Population Growth   These exercises use the population growth model.

1. Bacteria Culture   A certain culture of the bacterium *Strepto-coccus A* initially has 10 bacteria and is observed to double every 1.5 hours.

   (a) Find an exponential model $n(t) = n_0 2^{t/a}$ for the number of bacteria in the culture after *t* hours.

   (b) Estimate the number of bacteria after 35 hours.

   (c) After how many hours will the bacteria count reach 10,000?

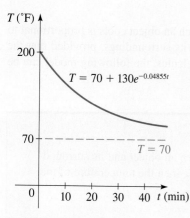

Streptococcus A
(12,000 × magnification)

2. Bacteria Culture   A certain culture of the bacterium *Rhodo-bacter sphaeroides* initially has 25 bacteria and is observed to double every 5 hours.

   (a) Find an exponential model $n(t) = n_0 2^{t/a}$ for the number of bacteria in the culture after *t* hours.

   (b) Estimate the number of bacteria after 18 hours.

   (c) After how many hours will the bacteria count reach 1 million?

3. Squirrel Population   A grey squirrel population was introduced in a certain county of Great Britain 30 years ago. Biologists observe that the population doubles every 6 years, and now the population is 100,000.

   (a) What was the initial size of the squirrel population?

   (b) Estimate the squirrel population 10 years from now.

   (c) Sketch a graph of the squirrel population.

4. Bird Population   A certain species of bird was introduced in a certain county 25 years ago. Biologists observe that the population doubles every 10 years, and now the population is 13,000.

   (a) What was the initial size of the bird population?

   (b) Estimate the bird population 5 years from now.

   (c) Sketch a graph of the bird population.

5. Fox Population   The fox population in a certain region has a relative growth rate of 8% per year. It is estimated that the population in 2013 was 18,000.

   (a) Find a function $n(t) = n_0 e^{rt}$ that models the population *t* years after 2013.

   (b) Use the function from part (a) to estimate the fox population in the year 2021.

   (c) After how many years will the fox population reach 25,000?

   (d) Sketch a graph of the fox population function for the years 2013–2021.

6. Fish Population The population of a certain species of fish has a relative growth rate of 1.2% per year. It is estimated that the population in 2010 was 12 million.

(a) Find an exponential model $n(t) = n_0 e^{rt}$ for the population t years after 2010.

(b) Estimate the fish population in the year 2015.

(c) After how many years will the fish population reach 14 million?

(d) Sketch a graph of the fish population.

7. Population of a Country The population of a country has a relative growth rate of 3% per year. The government is trying to reduce the growth rate to 2%. The population in 2011 was approximately 110 million. Find the projected population for the year 2036 for the following conditions.

(a) The relative growth rate remains at 3% per year.

(b) The relative growth rate is reduced to 2% per year.

8. Bacteria Culture It is observed that a certain bacteria culture has a relative growth rate of 12% per hour, but in the presence of an antibiotic the relative growth rate is reduced to 5% per hour. The initial number of bacteria in the culture is 22. Find the projected population after 24 hours for the following conditions.

(a) No antibiotic is present, so the relative growth rate is 12%.

(b) An antibiotic is present in the culture, so the relative growth rate is reduced to 5%.

9. Population of a City The population of a certain city was 112,000 in 2014, and the observed doubling time for the population is 18 years.

(a) Find an exponential model $n(t) = n_0 2^{t/a}$ for the population t years after 2014.

(b) Find an exponential model $n(t) = n_0 e^{rt}$ for the population t years after 2014.

(c) Sketch a graph of the population at time t.

(d) Estimate how long it takes the population to reach 500,000.

10. Bat Population The bat population in a certain Midwestern county was 350,000 in 2012, and the observed doubling time for the population is 25 years.

(a) Find an exponential model $n(t) = n_0 2^{t/a}$ for the population t years after 2012.

(b) Find an exponential model $n(t) = n_0 e^{rt}$ for the population t years after 2012.

(c) Sketch a graph of the population at time t.

(d) Estimate how long it takes the population to reach 2 million.

11. Deer Population The graph shows the deer population in a Pennsylvania county between 2010 and 2014. Assume that the population grows exponentially.

(a) What was the deer population in 2010?

(b) Find a function that models the deer population t years after 2010.

(c) What is the projected deer population in 2018?

(d) Estimate how long it takes the population to reach 100,000.

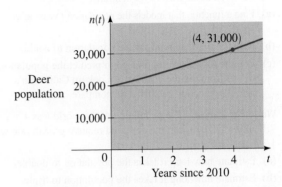

12. Frog Population Some bullfrogs were introduced into a small pond. The graph shows the bullfrog population for the next few years. Assume that the population grows exponentially.

(a) What was the initial bullfrog population?

(b) Find a function that models the bullfrog population t years since the bullfrogs were put into the pond.

(c) What is the projected bullfrog population after 15 years?

(d) Estimate how long it takes the population to reach 75,000.

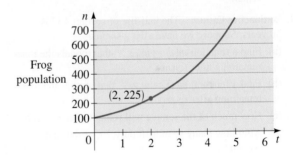

13. Bacteria Culture A culture starts with 8600 bacteria. After 1 hour the count is 10,000.

(a) Find a function that models the number of bacteria $n(t)$ after t hours.

(b) Find the number of bacteria after 2 hours.

(c) After how many hours will the number of bacteria double?

14. Bacteria Culture The count in a culture of bacteria was 400 after 2 hours and 25,600 after 6 hours.

(a) What is the relative rate of growth of the bacteria population? Express your answer as a percentage.

(b) What was the initial size of the culture?

(c) Find a function that models the number of bacteria $n(t)$ after t hours.

(d) Find the number of bacteria after 4.5 hours.

(e) After how many hours will the number of bacteria reach 50,000?

15. Population of California The population of California was 29.76 million in 1990 and 33.87 million in 2000. Assume that the population grows exponentially.

(a) Find a function that models the population t years after 1990.

(b) Find the time required for the population to double.

(c) Use the function from part (a) to predict the population of California in the year 2010. Look up California's actual population in 2010, and compare.

16. World Population The population of the world was 7.1 billion in 2013, and the observed relative growth rate was 1.1% per year.

(a) Estimate how long it takes the population to double.

(b) Estimate how long it takes the population to triple.

17–24 ■ Radioactive Decay These exercises use the radioactive decay model.

17. Radioactive Radium The half-life of radium-226 is 1600 years. Suppose we have a 22-mg sample.

(a) Find a function $m(t) = m_0 2^{-t/h}$ that models the mass remaining after t years.

(b) Find a function $m(t) = m_0 e^{-rt}$ that models the mass remaining after t years.

(c) How much of the sample will remain after 4000 years?

(d) After how many years will only 18 mg of the sample remain?

18. Radioactive Cesium The half-life of cesium-137 is 30 years. Suppose we have a 10-g sample.

(a) Find a function $m(t) = m_0 2^{-t/h}$ that models the mass remaining after t years.

(b) Find a function $m(t) = m_0 e^{-rt}$ that models the mass remaining after t years.

(c) How much of the sample will remain after 80 years?

(d) After how many years will only 2 g of the sample remain?

19. Radioactive Strontium The half-life of strontium-90 is 28 years. How long will it take a 50-mg sample to decay to a mass of 32 mg?

20. Radioactive Radium Radium-221 has a half-life of 30 s. How long will it take for 95% of a sample to decay?

21. Finding Half-Life If 250 mg of a radioactive element decays to 200 mg in 48 hours, find the half-life of the element.

22. Radioactive Radon After 3 days a sample of radon-222 has decayed to 58% of its original amount.

(a) What is the half-life of radon-222?

(b) How long will it take the sample to decay to 20% of its original amount?

23. Carbon-14 Dating A wooden artifact from an ancient tomb contains 65% of the carbon-14 that is present in living trees. How long ago was the artifact made? (The half-life of carbon-14 is 5730 years.)

24. Carbon-14 Dating The burial cloth of an Egyptian mummy is estimated to contain 59% of the carbon-14 it contained originally. How long ago was the mummy buried? (The half-life of carbon-14 is 5730 years.)

25–28 ■ Law of Cooling These exercises use Newton's Law of Cooling.

25. Cooling Soup A hot bowl of soup is served at a dinner party. It starts to cool according to Newton's Law of Cooling, so its temperature at time t is given by

$$T(t) = 65 + 145e^{-0.05t}$$

where t is measured in minutes and T is measured in °F.

(a) What is the initial temperature of the soup?

(b) What is the temperature after 10 min?

(c) After how long will the temperature be 100°F?

26. Time of Death Newton's Law of Cooling is used in homicide investigations to determine the time of death. The normal body temperature is 98.6 °F. Immediately following death, the body begins to cool. It has been determined experimentally that the constant in Newton's Law of Cooling is approximately $k = 0.1947$, assuming that time is measured in hours. Suppose that the temperature of the surroundings is 60°F.

(a) Find a function $T(t)$ that models the temperature t hours after death.

(b) If the temperature of the body is now 72°F, how long ago was the time of death?

27. Cooling Turkey A roasted turkey is taken from an oven when its temperature has reached 185°F and is placed on a table in a room where the temperature is 75°F.

(a) If the temperature of the turkey is 150°F after half an hour, what is its temperature after 45 min?

(b) After how many hours will the turkey cool to 100°F?

28. Boiling Water A kettle full of water is brought to a boil in a room with temperature 20°C. After 15 min the temperature of the water has decreased from 100°C to 75°C. Find the temperature after another 10 min. Illustrate by graphing the temperature function.

4.7 LOGARITHMIC SCALES

■ The pH Scale   ■ The Richter Scale   ■ The Decibel Scale

Animal	W (kg)	log W
Ant	0.000003	−5.5
Elephant	4000	3.6
Whale	170,000	5.2

When a physical quantity varies over a very large range, it is often convenient to take its logarithm in order to work with more manageable numbers. On a **logarithmic scale**, numbers are represented by their logarithms. For example, the table in the margin gives the weights W of some animals (in kilograms) and their logarithms ($\log W$).

The weights (W) vary enormously, but on a logarithmic scale, the weights are represented by more manageable numbers ($\log W$). Figure 1 shows that it is difficult to compare the weights W graphically but easy to compare them on a logarithmic scale.

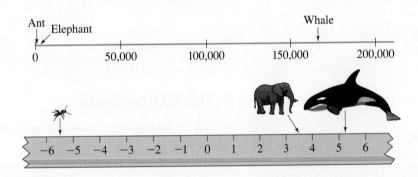

FIGURE 1 Weight graphed on the real line (top) and on a logarithmic scale (bottom)

We discuss three commonly used logarithmic scales: the pH scale, which measures acidity; the Richter scale, which measures the intensity of earthquakes; and the decibel scale, which measures the loudness of sounds. Other quantities that are measured on logarithmic scales are light intensity, information capacity, and radiation.

■ The pH Scale

pH for Some Common Substances

Substance	pH
Milk of magnesia	10.5
Seawater	8.0–8.4
Human blood	7.3–7.5
Crackers	7.0–8.5
Hominy	6.9–7.9
Cow's milk	6.4–6.8
Spinach	5.1–5.7
Tomatoes	4.1–4.4
Oranges	3.0–4.0
Apples	2.9–3.3
Limes	1.3–2.0
Battery acid	1.0

Chemists measured the acidity of a solution by giving its hydrogen ion concentration until Søren Peter Lauritz Sørensen, in 1909, proposed a more convenient measure. He defined

$$\text{pH} = -\log[\text{H}^+]$$

where $[\text{H}^+]$ is the concentration of hydrogen ions measured in moles per liter (M). He did this to avoid very small numbers and negative exponents. For instance,

$$\text{if} \quad [\text{H}^+] = 10^{-4}\text{ M}, \quad \text{then} \quad \text{pH} = -\log_{10}(10^{-4}) = -(-4) = 4$$

Solutions with a pH of 7 are defined as *neutral*, those with pH < 7 are *acidic*, and those with pH > 7 are *basic*. Notice that when the pH increases by one unit, $[\text{H}^+]$ decreases by a factor of 10.

EXAMPLE 1 ■ pH Scale and Hydrogen Ion Concentration

(a) The hydrogen ion concentration of a sample of human blood was measured to be $[\text{H}^+] = 3.16 \times 10^{-8}$ M. Find the pH, and classify the blood as acidic or basic.

(b) The most acidic rainfall ever measured occurred in Scotland in 1974; its pH was 2.4. Find the hydrogen ion concentration.

SOLUTION

(a) A calculator gives

$$pH = -\log[H^+] = -\log(3.16 \times 10^{-8}) \approx 7.5$$

Since this is greater than 7, the blood is basic.

(b) To find the hydrogen ion concentration, we need to solve for $[H^+]$ in the logarithmic equation

$$\log[H^+] = -pH$$

So we write it in exponential form:

$$[H^+] = 10^{-pH}$$

In this case pH = 2.4, so

$$[H^+] = 10^{-2.4} \approx 4.0 \times 10^{-3} \text{ M}$$

✎ Now Try Exercises 1 and 3

The Richter Scale

Largest Earthquakes		
Location	Date	Magnitude
Chile	1960	9.5
Alaska	1964	9.2
Japan	2011	9.1
Sumatra	2004	9.1
Kamchatka	1952	9.0
Chile	2010	8.8
Ecuador	1906	8.8
Alaska	1965	8.7
Alaska	1957	8.6
Sumatra	2005	8.6
Sumatra	2012	8.6
Tibet	1950	8.6
Indonesia	1938	8.5
Kamchatka	1923	8.5

Source: U.S. Geological Society

In 1935 the American geologist Charles Richter (1900–1984) defined the magnitude M of an earthquake to be

$$M = \log \frac{I}{S}$$

where I is the intensity of the earthquake (measured by the amplitude of a seismograph reading taken 100 km from the epicenter of the earthquake) and S is the intensity of a "standard" earthquake (whose amplitude is 1 micron $= 10^{-4}$ cm). (In practice, seismograph stations may not be exactly 100 km from the epicenter, so appropriate adjustments are made in calculating the magnitude of an earthquake.) The magnitude of a standard earthquake is

$$M = \log \frac{S}{S} = \log 1 = 0$$

Richter studied many earthquakes that occurred between 1900 and 1950. The largest had magnitude 8.9 on the Richter scale, and the smallest had magnitude 0. This corresponds to a ratio of intensities of 800,000,000, so the Richter scale provides more

---

Robert Vos/AFP/Getty Images

DISCOVERY PROJECT

The Even-Tempered Clavier

Poets, writers, philosophers, and even politicians have extolled the virtues of music—its beauty and its power to communicate emotion. But at the heart of music is a logarithmic scale. The tones that we are familiar with from our everyday listening can all be reproduced by the keys of a piano. The keys of a piano, in turn, are "evenly tempered" using a logarithmic scale. In this project we explore how exponential and logarithmic functions are used in properly tuning a piano. You can find the project at **www.stewartmath.com**.

manageable numbers to work with. For instance, an earthquake of magnitude 6 is ten times stronger than an earthquake of magnitude 5.

EXAMPLE 2 ■ Magnitude and Intensity

(a) Find the magnitude of an earthquake that has an intensity of 3.75 (that is, the amplitude of the seismograph reading is 3.75 cm).

(b) An earthquake was measured to have a magnitude of 5.1 on the Richter scale. Find the intensity of the earthquake.

SOLUTION

(a) From the definition of magnitude we see that

$$M = \log \frac{I}{S} = \log \frac{3.75}{10^{-4}} = \log 37500 \approx 4.6$$

Thus the magnitude is 4.6 on the Richter scale.

(b) To find the intensity, we need to solve for I in the logarithmic equation

$$M = \log \frac{I}{S}$$

So we write it in exponential form:

$$10^M = \frac{I}{S}$$

In this case $S = 10^{-4}$ and $M = 5.1$, so

$$10^{5.1} = \frac{I}{10^{-4}} \qquad M = 5.1, S = 10^{-4}$$

$$(10^{-4})(10^{5.1}) = I \qquad \text{Multiply by } 10^{-4}$$

$$I = 10^{1.1} \approx 12.6 \qquad \text{Add exponents}$$

Thus the intensity of the earthquake is about 12.6, which means that the amplitude of the seismograph reading is about 12.6 cm.

✎. **Now Try Exercise 9** ■

EXAMPLE 3 ■ Magnitude of Earthquakes

There are several other logarithmic scales used to calculate the magnitude of earthquakes. For instance, the U.S. Geological Survey uses the *moment magnitude scale*.

The 1906 earthquake in San Francisco had an estimated magnitude of 8.3 on the Richter scale. In the same year a powerful earthquake occurred on the Colombia-Ecuador border that was four times as intense. What was the magnitude of the Colombia-Ecuador earthquake on the Richter scale?

SOLUTION   If I is the intensity of the San Francisco earthquake, then from the definition of magnitude we have

$$M = \log \frac{I}{S} = 8.3$$

The intensity of the Colombia-Ecuador earthquake was $4I$, so its magnitude was

$$M = \log \frac{4I}{S} = \log 4 + \log \frac{I}{S} = \log 4 + 8.3 \approx 8.9$$

✎. **Now Try Exercise 11** ■

EXAMPLE 4 ■ Intensity of Earthquakes

The 1989 Loma Prieta earthquake that shook San Francisco had a magnitude of 7.1 on the Richter scale. How many times more intense was the 1906 earthquake (see Example 3) than the 1989 event?

SOLUTION If I_1 and I_2 are the intensities of the 1906 and 1989 earthquakes, then we are required to find I_1/I_2. To relate this to the definition of magnitude, we divide the numerator and denominator by S.

$$\log \frac{I_1}{I_2} = \log \frac{I_1/S}{I_2/S} \qquad \text{Divide numerator and denominator by } S$$

$$= \log \frac{I_1}{S} - \log \frac{I_2}{S} \qquad \text{Law 2 of logarithms}$$

$$= 8.3 - 7.1 = 1.2 \qquad \text{Definition of earthquake magnitude}$$

Therefore

$$\frac{I_1}{I_2} = 10^{\log(I_1/I_2)} = 10^{1.2} \approx 16$$

The 1906 earthquake was about 16 times as intense as the 1989 earthquake.

✏. **Now Try Exercise 13** ∎

■ The Decibel Scale

The ear is sensitive to an extremely wide range of sound intensities. We take as a reference intensity $I_0 = 10^{-12}$ W/m² (watts per square meter) at a frequency of 1000 hertz, which measures a sound that is just barely audible (the threshold of hearing). The psychological sensation of loudness varies with the logarithm of the intensity (the Weber-Fechner Law), so the **decibel level** B, measured in decibels (dB), is defined as

$$B = 10 \log \frac{I}{I_0}$$

The decibel level of the barely audible reference sound is

$$B = 10 \log \frac{I_0}{I_0} = 10 \log 1 = 0 \text{ dB}$$

EXAMPLE 5 ■ Decibel Level and Intensity

(a) Find the decibel level of a jet engine at takeoff if the intensity was measured at 100 W/m².

(b) Find the intensity level of a motorcycle engine at full throttle if the decibel level was measured at 90 dB.

SOLUTION

(a) From the definition of decibel level we see that

$$B = 10 \log \frac{I}{I_0} = 10 \log \frac{10^2}{10^{-12}} = 10 \log 10^{14} = 140 \text{ dB}$$

Thus the decibel level is 140 dB.

(b) To find the intensity, we need to solve for I in the logarithmic equation

$$B = 10 \log \frac{I}{I_0} \qquad \text{Definition of decibel level}$$

$$\frac{B}{10} = \log I - \log 10^{-12} \qquad \text{Divide by 10, } I_0 = 10^{-12}$$

$$\frac{B}{10} = \log I + 12 \qquad \text{Definition of logarithm}$$

$$\frac{B}{10} - 12 = \log I \qquad \text{Subtract 12}$$

$$\log I = \frac{90}{10} - 12 = -3 \qquad B = 90$$

$$I = 10^{-3} \qquad \text{Exponential form}$$

Thus the intensity is 10^{-3} W/m^2.

▶ **Now Try Exercises 15 and 17**

The table in the margin lists decibel levels for some common sounds ranging from the threshold of human hearing to the jet takeoff of Example 5. The threshold of pain is about 120 dB.

The **decibel levels of sounds** that we can hear vary from very loud to very soft. Here are some examples of the decibel levels of commonly heard sounds.

Source of sound	B (dB)
Jet takeoff	140
Jackhammer	130
Rock concert	120
Subway	100
Heavy traffic	80
Ordinary traffic	70
Normal conversation	50
Whisper	30
Rustling leaves	10–20
Threshold of hearing	0

4.7 EXERCISES

APPLICATIONS

1. **Finding pH** The hydrogen ion concentration of a sample of each substance is given. Calculate the pH of the substance.
   (a) Lemon juice: $[\text{H}^+] = 5.0 \times 10^{-3}$ M
   (b) Tomato juice: $[\text{H}^+] = 3.2 \times 10^{-4}$ M
   (c) Seawater: $[\text{H}^+] = 5.0 \times 10^{-9}$ M

2. **Finding pH** An unknown substance has a hydrogen ion concentration of $[\text{H}^+] = 3.1 \times 10^{-8}$ M. Find the pH and classify the substance as acidic or basic.

3. **Ion Concentration** The pH reading of a sample of each substance is given. Calculate the hydrogen ion concentration of the substance.
   (a) Vinegar: pH = 3.0   (b) Milk: pH = 6.5

4. **Ion Concentration** The pH reading of a glass of liquid is given. Find the hydrogen ion concentration of the liquid.
   (a) Beer: pH = 4.6   (b) Water: pH = 7.3

5. **Finding pH** The hydrogen ion concentrations in cheeses range from 4.0×10^{-7} M to 1.6×10^{-5} M. Find the corresponding range of pH readings.

6. **Ion Concentration in Wine** The pH readings for wines vary from 2.8 to 3.8. Find the corresponding range of hydrogen ion concentrations.

7. **pH of Wine** If the pH of a wine is too high, say, 4.0 or above, the wine becomes unstable and has a flat taste.
   (a) A certain California red wine has a pH of 3.2, and a certain Italian white wine has a pH of 2.9. Find the corresponding hydrogen ion concentrations of the two wines.
   (b) Which wine has the lower hydrogen ion concentration?

8. **pH of Saliva** The pH of saliva is normally in the range of 6.4 to 7.0. However, when a person is ill, the person's saliva becomes more acidic.
   (a) When Marco is sick, he tests the pH of his saliva and finds that it is 5.5. What is the hydrogen ion concentration of his saliva?
   (b) Will the hydrogen ion concentration in Marco's saliva increase or decrease as he gets better?
   (c) After Marco recovers, he tests the pH of his saliva, and it is 6.5. Was the saliva more acidic or less acidic when he was sick?

9. **Earthquake Magnitude and Intensity**
   (a) Find the magnitude of an earthquake that has an intensity that is 31.25 (that is, the amplitude of the seismograph reading is 31.25 cm).
   (b) An earthquake was measured to have a magnitude of 4.8 on the Richter scale. Find the intensity of the earthquake.

10. **Earthquake Magnitude and Intensity**
    (a) Find the magnitude of an earthquake that has an intensity that is 72.1 (that is, the amplitude of the seismograph reading is 72.1 cm).
    (b) An earthquake was measured to have a magnitude of 5.8 on the Richter scale. Find the intensity of the earthquake.

11. **Earthquake Magnitudes** If one earthquake is 20 times as intense as another, how much larger is its magnitude on the Richter scale?

12. **Earthquake Magnitudes** The 1906 earthquake in San Francisco had a magnitude of 8.3 on the Richter scale. At the same time in Japan an earthquake with magnitude 4.9 caused only minor damage. How many times more intense was the San Francisco earthquake than the Japan earthquake?

13. **Earthquake Magnitudes** The Japan earthquake of 2011 had a magnitude of 9.1 on the Richter scale. How many times more intense was this than the 1906 San Francisco earthquake? (See Exercise 12.)

14. **Earthquake Magnitudes** The Northridge, California, earthquake of 1994 had a magnitude of 6.8 on the Richter scale. A year later, a 7.2-magnitude earthquake struck Kobe, Japan. How many times more intense was the Kobe earthquake than the Northridge earthquake?

15. **Traffic Noise** The intensity of the sound of traffic at a busy intersection was measured at 2.0×10^{-5} W/m². Find the decibel level.

16. **Leaf Blower** The intensity of the sound from a certain leaf blower is measured at 3.2×10^{-2} W/m². Find the decibel level.

17. **Hair Dryer** The decibel level of the sound from a certain hair dryer is measured at 70 dB. Find the intensity of the sound.

18. **Subway Noise** The decibel level of the sound of a subway train was measured at 98 dB. Find the intensity in watts per square meter (W/m²).

19. **Hearing Loss from MP3 Players** Recent research has shown that the use of earbud-style headphones packaged with MP3 players can cause permanent hearing loss.
    (a) The intensity of the sound from the speakers of a certain MP3 player (without earbuds) is measured at 3.1×10^{-5} W/m². Find the decibel level.
    (b) If earbuds are used with the MP3 player in part (a), the decibel level is 95 dB. Find the intensity.
    (c) Find the ratio of the intensity of the sound from the MP3 player with earbuds to that of the sound without earbuds.

20. **Comparing Decibel Levels** The noise from a power mower was measured at 106 dB. The noise level at a rock concert was measured at 120 dB. Find the ratio of the intensity of the rock music to that of the power mower.

DISCUSS ■ DISCOVER ■ PROVE ■ WRITE

21. **PROVE: Inverse Square Law for Sound** A law of physics states that the intensity of sound is inversely proportional to the square of the distance d from the source: $I = k/d^2$.
    (a) Use this model and the equation

    $$B = 10 \log \frac{I}{I_0}$$

    (described in this section) to show that the decibel levels B_1 and B_2 at distances d_1 and d_2 from a sound source are related by the equation

    $$B_2 = B_1 + 20 \log \frac{d_1}{d_2}$$

    (b) The intensity level at a rock concert is 120 dB at a distance 2 m from the speakers. Find the intensity level at a distance of 10 m.

CHAPTER 4 ■ REVIEW

■ PROPERTIES AND FORMULAS

Exponential Functions (pp. 366–368)

The **exponential function** f with base a (where $a > 0$, $a \neq 1$) is defined for all real numbers x by

$$f(x) = a^x$$

The domain of f is $\mathbb{R}$, and the range of f is $(0, \infty)$ The graph of f has one of the following shapes, depending on the value of a:

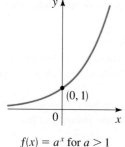

$f(x) = a^x$ for $a > 1$ $f(x) = a^x$ for $0 < a < 1$

The Natural Exponential Function (p. 375)

The **natural exponential function** is the exponential function with base e:

$$f(x) = e^x$$

The number e is defined to be the number that the expression $(1 + 1/n)^n$ approaches as $n \to \infty$. An approximate value for the irrational number e is

$$e \approx 2.7182818284590\ldots$$

Compound Interest (pp. 370, 376)

If a principal P is invested in an account paying an annual interest rate r, compounded n times a year, then after t years the **amount** $A(t)$ in the account is

$$A(t) = P\left(1 + \frac{r}{n}\right)^{nt}$$

If the interest is compounded **continuously**, then the amount is

$$A(t) = Pe^{rt}$$

Logarithmic Functions (pp. 380–381)

The **logarithmic function** $\log_a$ with base a (where $a > 0, a \neq 1$) is defined for $x > 0$ by

$$\log_a x = y \quad \Leftrightarrow \quad a^y = x$$

So $\log_a x$ is the exponent to which the base a must be raised to give y.

The domain of $\log_a$ is $(0, \infty)$, and the range is $\mathbb{R}$. For $a > 1$, the graph of the function $\log_a$ has the following shape:

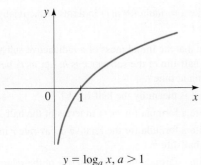

$$y = \log_a x,\ a > 1$$

Common and Natural Logarithms (pp. 384–385)

The logarithm function with base 10 is called the **common logarithm** and is denoted **log**. So

$$\log x = \log_{10} x$$

The logarithm function with base e is called the **natural logarithm** and is denoted **ln**. So

$$\ln x = \log_e x$$

Properties of Logarithms (pp. 381, 385)

1. $\log_a 1 = 0$ 2. $\log_a a = 1$

3. $\log_a a^x = x$ 4. $a^{\log_a x} = x$

Laws of Logarithms (p. 390)

Let a be a logarithm base ($a > 0, a \neq 1$), and let A, B, and C be any real numbers or algebraic expressions that represent real numbers, with $A > 0$ and $B > 0$. Then:

1. $\log_a(AB) = \log_a A + \log_a B$

2. $\log_a(A/B) = \log_a A - \log_a B$

3. $\log_a(A^C) = C \log_a A$

Change of Base Formula (p. 393)

$$\log_b x = \frac{\log_a x}{\log_a b}$$

Guidelines for Solving Exponential Equations (p. 397)

1. Isolate the exponential term on one side of the equation.

2. Take the logarithm of each side, and use the Laws of Logarithms to "bring down the exponent."

3. Solve for the variable.

Guidelines for Solving Logarithmic Equations (p. 400)

1. Isolate the logarithmic term(s) on one side of the equation, and use the Laws of Logarithms to combine logarithmic terms if necessary.

2. Rewrite the equation in exponential form.

3. Solve for the variable.

Exponential Growth Model (p. 409)

A population experiences **exponential growth** if it can be modeled by the exponential function

$$n(t) = n_0 e^{rt}$$

where $n(t)$ is the population at time t, n_0 is the initial population (at time $t = 0$), and r is the relative growth rate (expressed as a proportion of the population).

Radioactive Decay Model (pp. 411–412)

If a **radioactive substance** with half-life h has initial mass m_0, then at time t the mass $m(t)$ of the substance that remains is modeled by the exponential function

$$m(t) = m_0 e^{-rt}$$

where $r = \dfrac{\ln 2}{h}$.

Newton's Law of Cooling (p. 413)

If an object has an initial temperature that is D_0 degrees warmer than the surrounding temperature T_s, then at time t the temperature $T(t)$ of the object is modeled by the function

$$T(t) = T_s + D_0 e^{-kt}$$

where the constant $k > 0$ depends on the size and type of the object.

Logarithmic Scales (pp. 417–421)

The **pH scale** measures the acidity of a solution:

$$\text{pH} = -\log[\text{H}^+]$$

The **Richter scale** measures the intensity of earthquakes:

$$M = \log \frac{I}{S}$$

The **decibel scale** measures the intensity of sound:

$$B = 10 \log \frac{I}{I_0}$$

▪ CONCEPT CHECK

1. Let f be the exponential function with base a.
  (a) Write an equation that defines f.
  (b) Write an equation for the exponential function f with base 3.

2. Let f be the exponential function $f(x) = a^x$, where $a > 0$.
  (a) What is the domain of f?
  (b) What is the range of f?
  (c) Sketch graphs of f for the following cases.
    (i) $a > 1$ (ii) $0 < a < 1$

3. If x is large, which function grows faster, $f(x) = 2^x$ or $g(x) = x^2$?

4. (a) How is the number e defined?
  (b) Give an approximate value of e, rounded to five decimal places.
  (c) What is the natural exponential function?

5. (a) How is $\log_a x$ defined?
  (b) Find $\log_3 9$.
  (c) What is the natural logarithm?
  (d) What is the common logarithm?
  (e) Write the exponential form of the equation $\log_7 49 = 2$.

6. Let f be the logarithmic function $f(x) = \log_a x$.
  (a) What is the domain of f?
  (b) What is the range of f?
  (c) Sketch a graph of the logarithmic function for the case that $a > 1$.

7. State the three Laws of Logarithms.

8. (a) State the Change of Base Formula.
  (b) Find $\log_7 30$.

9. (a) What is an exponential equation?
  (b) How do you solve an exponential equation?
  (c) Solve for x: $2^x = 19$

10. (a) What is a logarithmic equation?
  (b) How do you solve a logarithmic equation?
  (c) Solve for x: $4 \log_3 x = 7$

11. Suppose that an amount P is invested at an interest rate r and $A(t)$ is the amount of the investment after t years. Write a formula for $A(t)$ in the following cases.
  (a) Interest is compounded n times per year.
  (b) Interest is compounded continuously.

12. Suppose that the initial size of a population is n_0 and the population grows exponentially. Let $n(t)$ be the size of the population at time t.
  (a) Write a formula for $n(t)$ in terms of the doubling time a.
  (b) Write a formula for $n(t)$ in terms of the relative growth rate r.

13. Suppose that the initial mass of a radioactive substance is m_0 and the half-life of the substance is h. Let $m(t)$ be the mass remaining at time t.
  (a) What is meant by the half-life h?
  (b) Write a formula for $m(t)$ in terms of the half-life h.
  (c) Write a formula for the relative decay rate r in terms of the half-life h.
  (d) Write a formula for $m(t)$ in terms of the relative decay rate r.

14. Suppose that the initial temperature difference between an object and its surroundings is D_0 and the surroundings have temperature T_s. Let $T(t)$ be the temperature at time t. State Newton's Law of Cooling for $T(t)$.

15. What is a logarithmic scale? If we use a logarithmic scale with base 10, what do the following numbers correspond to on the logarithmic scale?
  (i) 100   (ii) 100,000   (iii) 0.0001

16. (a) What does the pH scale measure?
  (b) Define the pH of a substance with hydrogen ion concentration of $[H^+]$.

17. (a) What does the Richter scale measure?
  (b) Define the magnitude M of an earthquake in terms of the intensity I of the earthquake and the intensity S of a standard earthquake.

18. (a) What does the decibel scale measure?
  (b) Define the decibel level B of a sound in terms of the intensity I of the sound and the intensity I_0 of a barely audible sound.

ANSWERS TO THE CONCEPT CHECK CAN BE FOUND AT THE BACK OF THE BOOK.

▪ EXERCISES

1–4 ▪ Evaluating Exponential Functions   Use a calculator to find the indicated values of the exponential function, rounded to three decimal places.

1. $f(x) = 5^x$; $f(-1.5), f(\sqrt{2}), f(2.5)$

2. $f(x) = 3 \cdot 2^x$; $f(-2.2), f(\sqrt{7}), f(5.5)$

3. $g(x) = 4e^{x-2}$; $g(-0.7), g(1), g(\pi)$

4. $g(x) = \frac{7}{4}e^{x+1}$; $g(-2), g(\sqrt{3}), g(3.6)$

5–16 ▪ Graphing Exponential and Logarithmic Functions
Sketch the graph of the function. State the domain, range, and asymptote.

5. $f(x) = 3^{x-2}$

6. $f(x) = 2^{-x+1}$

7. $g(x) = 3 + 2^x$

8. $g(x) = 5^{-x} - 5$

9. $F(x) = e^{x-1} + 1$

10. $G(x) = -e^{x+1} - 2$

11. $f(x) = \log_3(x - 1)$ **12.** $g(x) = \log(-x)$

13. $f(x) = 2 - \log_2 x$ **14.** $f(x) = 3 + \log_5(x + 4)$

15. $g(x) = 2 \ln x$ **16.** $g(x) = \ln(x^2)$

17–20 ■ Domain Find the domain of the function.

17. $f(x) = 10^{x^2} + \log(1 - 2x)$

18. $g(x) = \log(2 + x - x^2)$

19. $h(x) = \ln(x^2 - 4)$

20. $k(x) = \ln|x|$

21–24 ■ Exponential Form Write the equation in exponential form.

21. $\log_2 1024 = 10$ **22.** $\log_6 37 = x$

23. $\log x = y$ **24.** $\ln c = 17$

25–28 ■ Logarithmic Form Write the equation in logarithmic form.

25. $2^6 = 64$ **26.** $49^{-1/2} = \frac{1}{7}$

27. $10^x = 74$ **28.** $e^k = m$

29–44 ■ Evaluating Logarithmic Expressions Evaluate the expression without using a calculator.

29. $\log_2 128$ **30.** $\log_8 1$

31. $10^{\log 45}$ **32.** $\log 0.000001$

33. $\ln(e^6)$ **34.** $\log_4 8$

35. $\log_3\left(\frac{1}{27}\right)$ **36.** $2^{\log_2 13}$

37. $\log_5 \sqrt{5}$ **38.** $e^{2 \ln 7}$

39. $\log 25 + \log 4$ **40.** $\log_3 \sqrt{243}$

41. $\log_2 16^{23}$ **42.** $\log_5 250 - \log_5 2$

43. $\log_8 6 - \log_8 3 + \log_8 2$ **44.** $\log \log 10^{100}$

45–50 ■ Expanding Logarithmic Expressions Expand the logarithmic expression.

45. $\log(AB^2C^3)$ **46.** $\log_2(x\sqrt{x^2 + 1})$

47. $\ln\sqrt{\dfrac{x^2 - 1}{x^2 + 1}}$ **48.** $\log\left(\dfrac{4x^3}{y^2(x - 1)^5}\right)$

49. $\log_5\left(\dfrac{x^2(1 - 5x)^{3/2}}{\sqrt{x^3 - x}}\right)$ **50.** $\ln\left(\dfrac{\sqrt[3]{x^4 + 12}}{(x + 16)\sqrt{x - 3}}\right)$

51–56 ■ Combining Logarithmic Expressions Combine into a single logarithm.

51. $\log 6 + 4 \log 2$

52. $\log x + \log(x^2y) + 3 \log y$

53. $\frac{3}{2} \log_2(x - y) - 2 \log_2(x^2 + y^2)$

54. $\log_5 2 + \log_5(x + 1) - \frac{1}{3} \log_5(3x + 7)$

55. $\log(x - 2) + \log(x + 2) - \frac{1}{2} \log(x^2 + 4)$

56. $\frac{1}{2}[\ln(x - 4) + 5 \ln(x^2 + 4x)]$

57–70 ■ Exponential and Logarithmic Equations Solve the equation. Find the exact solution if possible; otherwise, use a calculator to approximate to two decimals.

57. $3^{2x-7} = 27$ **58.** $5^{4-x} = \frac{1}{125}$

59. $2^{3x-5} = 7$ **60.** $10^{6-3x} = 18$

61. $4^{1-x} = 3^{2x+5}$ **62.** $e^{3x/4} = 10$

63. $x^2e^{2x} + 2xe^{2x} = 8e^{2x}$ **64.** $3^{2x} - 3^x - 6 = 0$

65. $\log x + \log(x + 1) = \log 12$

66. $\ln(x - 2) + \ln 3 = \ln(5x - 7)$

67. $\log_2(1 - x) = 4$

68. $\ln(2x - 3) + 1 = 0$

69. $\log_3(x - 8) + \log_3 x = 2$

70. $\log_8(x + 5) - \log_8(x - 2) = 1$

71–74 ■ Exponential Equations Use a calculator to find the solution of the equation, rounded to six decimal places.

71. $5^{-2x/3} = 0.63$ **72.** $2^{3x-5} = 7$

73. $5^{2x+1} = 3^{4x-1}$ **74.** $e^{-15k} = 10,000$

 75–78 ■ Local Extrema and Asymptotes Draw a graph of the function and use it to determine the asymptotes and the local maximum and minimum values.

75. $y = e^{x/(x+2)}$ **76.** $y = 10^x - 5^x$

77. $y = \log(x^3 - x)$ **78.** $y = 2x^2 - \ln x$

 79–80 ■ Solving Equations Find the solutions of the equation, rounded to two decimal places.

79. $3 \log x = 6 - 2x$ **80.** $4 - x^2 = e^{-2x}$

 81–82 ■ Solving Inequalities Solve the inequality graphically.

81. $\ln x > x - 2$ **82.** $e^x < 4x^2$

 83. Increasing and Decreasing Use a graph of $f(x) = e^x - 3e^{-x} - 4x$ to find, approximately, the intervals on which f is increasing and on which f is decreasing.

84. Equation of a Line Find an equation of the line shown in the figure.

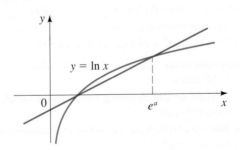

85–88 ■ Change of Base Use the Change of Base Formula to evaluate the logarithm, rounded to six decimal places.

85. $\log_4 15$ **86.** $\log_7\left(\frac{3}{4}\right)$

87. $\log_9 0.28$ **88.** $\log_{100} 250$

89. Comparing Logarithms Which is larger, $\log_4 258$ or $\log_5 620$?

90. Inverse Function Find the inverse of the function $f(x) = 2^{3^x}$, and state its domain and range.

91. Compound Interest If $12,000 is invested at an interest rate of 10% per year, find the amount of the investment at the end of 3 years for each compounding method.

(a) Semiannually   (b) Monthly

(c) Daily   (d) Continuously

92. Compound Interest A sum of $5000 is invested at an interest rate of $8\frac{1}{2}\%$ per year, compounded semiannually.

(a) Find the amount of the investment after $1\frac{1}{2}$ years.

(b) After what period of time will the investment amount to $7000?

(c) If interest were compounded continously instead of semiannually, how long would it take for the amount to grow to $7000?

93. Compound Interest A money market account pays 5.2% annual interest, compounded daily. If $100,000 is invested in this account, how long will it take for the account to accumulate $10,000 in interest?

94. Compound Interest A retirement savings plan pays 4.5% interest, compounded continuously. How long will it take for an investment in this plan to double?

95–96 ■ APY Determine the annual percentage yield (APY) for the given nominal annual interest rate and compounding frequency.

95. 4.25%;   daily

96. 3.2%;   monthly

97. Cat Population The stray-cat population in a small town grows exponentially. In 1999 the town had 30 stray cats, and the relative growth rate was 15% per year.

(a) Find a function that models the stray-cat population $n(t)$ after t years.

(b) Find the projected population after 4 years.

(c) Find the number of years required for the stray-cat population to reach 500.

98. Bacterial Growth A culture contains 10,000 bacteria initially. After 1 hour the bacteria count is 25,000.

(a) Find the doubling period.

(b) Find the number of bacteria after 3 hours.

99. Radioactive Decay Uranium-234 has a half-life of 2.7×10^5 years.

(a) Find the amount remaining from a 10-mg sample after a thousand years.

(b) How long will it take this sample to decompose until its mass is 7 mg?

100. Radioactive Decay A sample of bismuth-210 decayed to 33% of its original mass after 8 days.

(a) Find the half-life of this element.

(b) Find the mass remaining after 12 days.

101. Radioactive Decay The half-life of radium-226 is 1590 years.

(a) If a sample has a mass of 150 mg, find a function that models the mass that remains after t years.

(b) Find the mass that will remain after 1000 years.

(c) After how many years will only 50 mg remain?

102. Radioactive Decay The half-life of palladium-100 is 4 days. After 20 days a sample has been reduced to a mass of 0.375 g.

(a) What was the initial mass of the sample?

(b) Find a function that models the mass remaining after t days.

(c) What is the mass after 3 days?

(d) After how many days will only 0.15 g remain?

103. Bird Population The graph shows the population of a rare species of bird, where t represents years since 2009 and $n(t)$ is measured in thousands.

(a) Find a function that models the bird population at time t in the form $n(t) = n_0 e^{rt}$.

(b) What is the bird population expected to be in the year 2020?

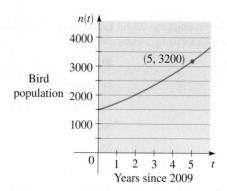

104. Law of Cooling A car engine runs at a temperature of 190°F. When the engine is turned off, it cools according to Newton's Law of Cooling with constant $k = 0.0341$, where the time is measured in minutes. Find the time needed for the engine to cool to 90°F if the surrounding temperature is 60°F.

105. pH The hydrogen ion concentration of fresh egg whites was measured as

$$[H^+] = 1.3 \times 10^{-8}\,M$$

Find the pH, and classify the substance as acidic or basic.

106. pH The pH of lime juice is 1.9. Find the hydrogen ion concentration.

107. Richter Scale If one earthquake has magnitude 6.5 on the Richter scale, what is the magnitude of another quake that is 35 times as intense?

108. Decibel Scale The drilling of a jackhammer was measured at 132 dB. The sound of whispering was measured at 28 dB. Find the ratio of the intensity of the drilling to that of the whispering.

1. Sketch the graph of each function, and state its domain, range, and asymptote. Show the
   x- and y-intercepts on the graph.

   (a) $f(x) = 2^{-x} + 4$ (b) $g(x) = \log_3(x + 3)$

2. Find the domain of the function.

   (a) $f(t) = \ln(2t - 3)$ (b) $g(x) = \log(x^2 - 1)$

3. (a) Write the equation $6^{2x} = 25$ in logarithmic form.

   (b) Write the equation $\ln A = 3$ in exponential form.

4. Find the exact value of the expression.

   (a) $10^{\log 36}$ (b) $\ln e^3$ (c) $\log_3 \sqrt{27}$

   (d) $\log_2 80 - \log_2 10$ (e) $\log_8 4$ (f) $\log_6 4 + \log_6 9$

5. Use the Laws of Logarithms to expand the expression.

   (a) $\log\left(\dfrac{xy^3}{z^2}\right)$ (b) $\ln\sqrt{\dfrac{x}{y}}$ (c) $\log\sqrt[3]{\dfrac{x + 2}{x^4(x^2 + 4)}}$

6. Use the Laws of Logarithms to combine the expression into a single logarithm.

   (a) $\log a + 2 \log b$ (b) $\ln(x^2 - 25) - \ln(x + 5)$ (c) $\log_2 3 - 3 \log_2 x + \frac{1}{2} \log_2(x + 1)$

7. Find the solution of the exponential equation, rounded to two decimal places.

   (a) $3^{4x} = 3^{100}$ (b) $e^{3x-2} = e^{x^2}$ (c) $5^{x/10} + 1 = 7$ (d) $10^{x+3} = 6^{2x}$

8. Solve the logarithmic equation for x.

   (a) $\log(2x) = 3$ (b) $\log(x + 1) + \log 2 = \log(5x)$

   (c) $5 \ln(3 - x) = 4$ (d) $\log_2(x + 2) + \log_2(x - 1) = 2$

9. Use the Change of Base Formula to evaluate $\log_{12} 27$.

10. The initial size of a culture of bacteria is 1000. After 1 hour the bacteria count is 8000.

    (a) Find a function $n(t) = n_0 e^{rt}$ that models the population after t hours.

    (b) Find the population after 1.5 hours.

    (c) After how many hours will the number of bacteria reach 15,000?

    (d) Sketch the graph of the population function.

11. Suppose that $12,000 is invested in a savings account paying 5.6% interest per year.

    (a) Write the formula for the amount in the account after t years if interest is compounded
        monthly.

    (b) Find the amount in the account after 3 years if interest is compounded daily.

    (c) How long will it take for the amount in the account to grow to $20,000 if interest is
        compounded continuously?

12. The half-life of krypton-91 (^{91}Kr) is 10 s. At time $t = 0$ a heavy canister contains 3 g of
    this radioactive gas.

    (a) Find a function $m(t) = m_0 2^{-t/h}$ that models the amount of ^{91}Kr remaining in the
        canister after t seconds.

    (b) Find a function $m(t) = m_0 e^{-rt}$ that models the amount of ^{91}Kr remaining in the
        canister after t seconds.

    (c) How much ^{91}Kr remains after 1 min?

    (d) After how long will the amount of ^{91}Kr remaining be reduced to 1 μg (1 microgram,
        or 10^{-6} g)?

13. An earthquake measuring 6.4 on the Richter scale struck Japan in July 2007, causing
    extensive damage. Earlier that year, a minor earthquake measuring 3.1 on the Richter scale
    was felt in parts of Pennsylvania. How many times more intense was the Japanese earth-
    quake than the Pennsylvania earthquake?

Fitting Exponential and Power Curves to Data

In a previous *Focus on Modeling* (page 361) we learned that the shape of a scatter plot helps us to choose the type of curve to use in modeling data. The first plot in Figure 1 strongly suggests that a line be fitted through it, and the second one points to a cubic polynomial. For the third plot it is tempting to fit a second-degree polynomial. But what if an exponential curve fits better? How do we decide this? In this section we learn how to fit exponential and power curves to data and how to decide which type of curve fits the data better. We also learn that for scatter plots like those in the last two plots in Figure 1, the data can be modeled by logarithmic or logistic functions.

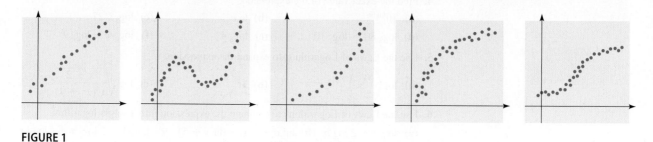

FIGURE 1

■ Modeling with Exponential Functions

If a scatter plot shows that the data increase rapidly, we might want to model the data using an *exponential model*, that is, a function of the form

$$f(x) = Ce^{kx}$$

where C and k are constants. In the first example we model world population by an exponential model. Recall from Section 4.6 that population tends to increase exponentially.

EXAMPLE 1 ■ An Exponential Model for World Population

Table 1 gives the population of the world in the 20th century.

(a) Draw a scatter plot, and note that a linear model is not appropriate.

(b) Find an exponential function that models population growth.

(c) Draw a graph of the function that you found together with the scatter plot. How well does the model fit the data?

(d) Use the model that you found to predict world population in the year 2020.

SOLUTION

(a) The scatter plot is shown in Figure 2. The plotted points do not appear to lie along a straight line, so a linear model is not appropriate.

TABLE 1
World population

Year (t)	World population $(P \text{ in millions})$
1900	1650
1910	1750
1920	1860
1930	2070
1940	2300
1950	2520
1960	3020
1970	3700
1980	4450
1990	5300
2000	6060

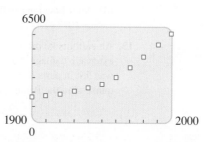

FIGURE 2 Scatter plot of world population

The population of the world increases exponentially.

(b) Using a graphing calculator and the `ExpReg` command (see Figure 3(a)), we get the exponential model

$$P(t) = (0.0082543) \cdot (1.0137186)^t$$

This is a model of the form $y = Cb^t$. To convert this to the form $y = Ce^{kt}$, we use the properties of exponentials and logarithms as follows.

$$1.0137186^t = e^{\ln 1.0137186^t} \qquad A = e^{\ln A}$$
$$= e^{t \ln 1.0137186} \qquad \ln A^B = B \ln A$$
$$= e^{0.013625t} \qquad \ln 1.0137186 \approx 0.013625$$

Thus we can write the model as

$$P(t) = 0.0082543e^{0.013625t}$$

(c) From the graph in Figure 3(b) we see that the model appears to fit the data fairly well. The period of relatively slow population growth is explained by the depression of the 1930s and the two world wars.

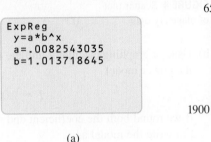

```
ExpReg
 y=a*b^x
 a=.0082543035
 b=1.013718645
```

(a)

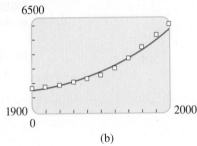

(b)

FIGURE 3 Exponential model for world population

(d) The model predicts that the world population in 2020 will be

$$P(2020) = 0.0082543e^{(0.013625)(2020)}$$
$$\approx 7,405,400,000 \qquad \blacksquare$$

■ Modeling with Power Functions

If the scatter plot of the data we are studying resembles the graph of $y = ax^2$, $y = ax^{1.32}$, or some other power function, then we seek a *power model*, that is, a function of the form

$$\boxed{f(x) = ax^n}$$

where a is a positive constant and n is any real number.

In the next example we seek a power model for some astronomical data. In astronomy, distance in the solar system is often measured in astronomical units. An *astronomical unit* (AU) is the mean distance from the earth to the sun. The *period* of a planet is the time it takes the planet to make a complete revolution around the sun (measured in earth years). In this example we derive the remarkable relationship, first discovered by Johannes Kepler (see page 852), between the mean distance of a planet from the sun and its period.

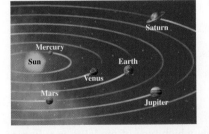

EXAMPLE 2 ■ A Power Model for Planetary Periods

Table 2 (see next page) gives the mean distance d of each planet from the sun in astronomical units and its period T in years.

TABLE 2
Distances and periods of the planets

Planet	d	T
Mercury	0.387	0.241
Venus	0.723	0.615
Earth	1.000	1.000
Mars	1.523	1.881
Jupiter	5.203	11.861
Saturn	9.541	29.457
Uranus	19.190	84.008
Neptune	30.086	164.784
Pluto*	39.507	248.350

*Pluto is a "dwarf planet."

(a) Sketch a scatter plot. Is a linear model appropriate?

(b) Find a power function that models the data.

(c) Draw a graph of the function you found and the scatter plot on the same graph. How well does the model fit the data?

(d) Use the model that you found to calculate the period of an asteroid whose mean distance from the sun is 5 AU.

SOLUTION

(a) The scatter plot shown in Figure 4 indicates that the plotted points do not lie along a straight line, so a linear model is not appropriate.

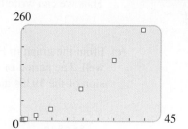

FIGURE 4 Scatter plot of planetary data

(b) Using a graphing calculator and the `PwrReg` command (see Figure 5(a)), we get the power model

$$T = 1.000396d^{1.49966}$$

If we round both the coefficient and the exponent to three significant figures, we can write the model as

$$T = d^{1.5}$$

This is the relationship discovered by Kepler (see page 852). Sir Isaac Newton (page 927) later used his Law of Gravity to derive this relationship theoretically, thereby providing strong scientific evidence that the Law of Gravity must be true.

(c) The graph is shown in Figure 5(b). The model appears to fit the data very well.

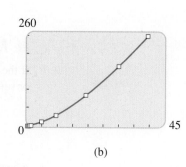

FIGURE 5 Power model for planetary data

(a)   (b)

(d) In this case $d = 5$ AU, so our model gives

$$T = 1.00039 \cdot 5^{1.49966} \approx 11.22$$

The period of the asteroid is about 11.2 years. ∎

▪ Linearizing Data

We have used the shape of a scatter plot to decide which type of model to use: linear, exponential, or power. This works well if the data points lie on a straight line. But it's difficult to distinguish a scatter plot that is exponential from one that requires a power model. So to help decide which model to use, we can *linearize* the data, that is, apply a function that "straightens" the scatter plot. The inverse of the linearizing function is then an appropriate model. We now describe how to linearize data that can be modeled by exponential or power functions.

■ Linearizing Exponential Data

If we suspect that the data points (x, y) lie on an exponential curve $y = Ce^{kx}$, then the points

$$(x, \ln y)$$

should lie on a straight line. We can see this from the following calculations.

$$\ln y = \ln Ce^{kx} \qquad \text{Assume that } y = Ce^{kx} \text{ and take ln}$$
$$= \ln e^{kx} + \ln C \qquad \text{Property of ln}$$
$$= kx + \ln C \qquad \text{Property of ln}$$

To see that $\ln y$ is a linear function of x, let $Y = \ln y$ and $A = \ln C$; then

$$Y = kx + A$$

We apply this technique to the world population data (t, P) to obtain the points $(t, \ln P)$ in Table 3. The scatter plot of $(t, \ln P)$ in Figure 6, called a **semi-log plot**, shows that the linearized data lie approximately on a straight line, so an exponential model should be appropriate.

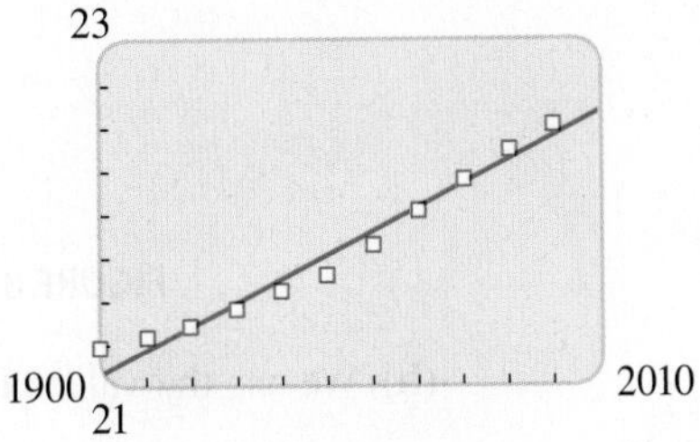

TABLE 3
World population data

t	Population P (in millions)	$\ln P$
1900	1650	21.224
1910	1750	21.283
1920	1860	21.344
1930	2070	21.451
1940	2300	21.556
1950	2520	21.648
1960	3020	21.829
1970	3700	22.032
1980	4450	22.216
1990	5300	22.391
2000	6060	22.525

FIGURE 6 Semi-log plot of data in Table 3

■ Linearizing Power Data

If we suspect that the data points (x, y) lie on a power curve $y = ax^n$, then the points

$$(\ln x, \ln y)$$

should be on a straight line. We can see this from the following calculations.

$$\ln y = \ln ax^n \qquad \text{Assume that } y = ax^n \text{ and take ln}$$
$$= \ln a + \ln x^n \qquad \text{Property of ln}$$
$$= \ln a + n \ln x \qquad \text{Property of ln}$$

To see that $\ln y$ is a linear function of $\ln x$, let $Y = \ln y$, $X = \ln x$, and $A = \ln a$; then

$$Y = nX + A$$

TABLE 4
Log-log table

$\ln d$	$\ln T$
-0.94933	-1.4230
-0.32435	-0.48613
0	0
0.42068	0.6318
1.6492	2.4733
2.2556	3.3829
2.9544	4.4309
3.4041	5.1046
3.6765	5.5148

We apply this technique to the planetary data (d, T) in Table 2 to obtain the points $(\ln d, \ln T)$ in Table 4. The scatter plot of $(\ln d, \ln T)$ in Figure 7, called a **log-log plot**, shows that the data lie on a straight line, so a power model seems appropriate.

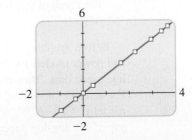

FIGURE 7 Log-log plot of data in Table 4

An Exponential or Power Model?

Suppose that a scatter plot of the data points (x, y) shows a rapid increase. Should we use an exponential function or a power function to model the data? To help us decide, we draw two scatter plots: one for the points $(x, \ln y)$ and the other for the points $(\ln x, \ln y)$. If the first scatter plot appears to lie along a line, then an exponential model is appropriate. If the second plot appears to lie along a line, then a power model is appropriate.

EXAMPLE 3 ■ An Exponential or Power Model?

Data points (x, y) are shown in Table 5.

(a) Draw a scatter plot of the data.

(b) Draw scatter plots of $(x, \ln y)$ and $(\ln x, \ln y)$.

(c) Is an exponential function or a power function appropriate for modeling this data?

(d) Find an appropriate function to model the data.

SOLUTION

(a) The scatter plot of the data is shown in Figure 8.

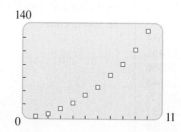

FIGURE 8

(b) We use the values from Table 6 to graph the scatter plots in Figures 9 and 10.

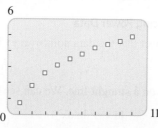

FIGURE 9 Semi-log plot

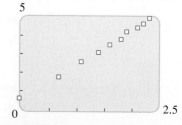

FIGURE 10 Log-log plot

(c) The scatter plot of $(x, \ln y)$ in Figure 9 does not appear to be linear, so an exponential model is not appropriate. On the other hand, the scatter plot of $(\ln x, \ln y)$ in Figure 10 is very nearly linear, so a power model is appropriate.

(d) Using the `PwrReg` command on a graphing calculator, we find that the power function that best fits the data point is

$$y = 1.85x^{1.82}$$

The graph of this function and the original data points are shown in Figure 11. ■

Before graphing calculators and statistical software became common, exponential and power models for data were often constructed by first finding a linear model for the linearized data. Then the model for the actual data was found by taking exponentials. For instance, if we find that $\ln y = A \ln x + B$, then by taking exponentials we get the model $y = e^B \cdot e^{A \ln x}$, or $y = Cx^A$ (where $C = e^B$). Special graphing paper called "log paper" or "log-log paper" was used to facilitate this process.

TABLE 5

x	y
1	2
2	6
3	14
4	22
5	34
6	46
7	64
8	80
9	102
10	130

TABLE 6

x	ln x	ln y
1	0	0.7
2	0.7	1.8
3	1.1	2.6
4	1.4	3.1
5	1.6	3.5
6	1.8	3.8
7	1.9	4.2
8	2.1	4.4
9	2.2	4.6
10	2.3	4.9

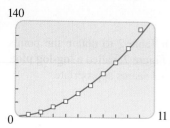

FIGURE 11

Modeling with Logistic Functions

A logistic growth model is a function of the form

$$f(t) = \frac{c}{1 + ae^{-bt}}$$

where a, b, and c are positive constants. Logistic functions are used to model populations where the growth is constrained by available resources. (See Exercises 27–30 of Section 4.2.)

EXAMPLE 4 ■ Stocking a Pond with Catfish

TABLE 7

Week	Catfish
0	1000
15	1500
30	3300
45	4400
60	6100
75	6900
90	7100
105	7800
120	7900

Much of the fish that is sold in supermarkets today is raised on commercial fish farms, not caught in the wild. A pond on one such farm is initially stocked with 1000 catfish, and the fish population is then sampled at 15-week intervals to estimate its size. The population data are given in Table 7.

(a) Find an appropriate model for the data.

(b) Make a scatter plot of the data and graph the model that you found in part (a) on the scatter plot.

(c) How does the model predict that the fish population will change with time?

SOLUTION

(a) Since the catfish population is restricted by its habitat (the pond), a logistic model is appropriate. Using the `Logistic` command on a calculator (see Figure 12(a)), we find the following model for the catfish population $P(t)$:

$$P(t) = \frac{7925}{1 + 7.7e^{-0.052t}}$$

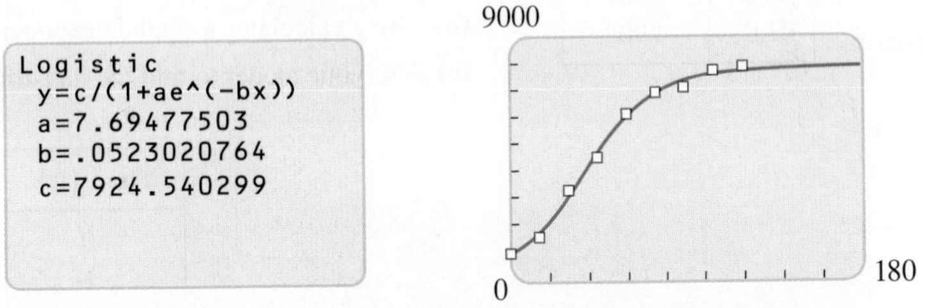

```
Logistic
y=c/(1+ae^(-bx))
a=7.69477503
b=.0523020764
c=7924.540299
```

FIGURE 12   (a)   (b) Catfish population $y = P(t)$

(b) The scatter plot and the logistic curve are shown in Figure 12(b).

(c) From the graph of P in Figure 12(b) we see that the catfish population increases rapidly until about $t = 80$ weeks. Then growth slows down, and at about $t = 120$ weeks the population levels off and remains more or less constant at slightly over 7900. ■

The behavior that is exhibited by the catfish population in Example 4 is typical of logistic growth. After a rapid growth phase, the population approaches a constant level called the **carrying capacity** of the environment. This occurs because as $t \to \infty$, we have $e^{-bt} \to 0$ (see Section 4.2), and so

$$P(t) = \frac{c}{1 + ae^{-bt}} \quad \longrightarrow \quad \frac{c}{1 + 0} = c$$

Thus the carrying capacity is c.

PROBLEMS

1. U.S. Population   The U.S. Constitution requires a census every 10 years. The census data for 1790–2010 are given in the table.

(a) Make a scatter plot of the data.

(b) Use a calculator to find an exponential model for the data.

(c) Use your model to predict the population at the 2020 census.

(d) Use your model to estimate the population in 1965.

Year	Population (in millions)	Year	Population (in millions)	Year	Population (in millions)
1790	3.9	1870	38.6	1950	151.3
1800	5.3	1880	50.2	1960	179.3
1810	7.2	1890	63.0	1970	203.3
1820	9.6	1900	76.2	1980	226.5
1830	12.9	1910	92.2	1990	248.7
1840	17.1	1920	106.0	2000	281.4
1850	23.2	1930	123.2	2010	308.7
1860	31.4	1940	132.2		

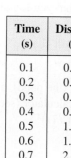

Time (s)	Distance (m)
0.1	0.048
0.2	0.197
0.3	0.441
0.4	0.882
0.5	1.227
0.6	1.765
0.7	2.401
0.8	3.136
0.9	3.969
1.0	4.902

2. A Falling Ball   In a physics experiment a lead ball is dropped from a height of 5 m. The students record the distance the ball has fallen every one-tenth of a second. (This can be done by using a camera and a strobe light.) Their data are shown in the margin.

(a) Make a scatter plot of the data.

(b) Use a calculator to find a power model.

(c) Use your model to predict how far a dropped ball would fall in 3 s.

3. Half-Life of Radioactive Iodine   A student is trying to determine the half-life of radioactive iodine-131. He measures the amount of iodine-131 in a sample solution every 8 hours. His data are shown in the table below.

(a) Make a scatter plot of the data.

(b) Use a calculator to find an exponential model.

(c) Use your model to find the half-life of iodine-131.

Time (h)	Amount of ^{131}I (g)
0	4.80
8	4.66
16	4.51
24	4.39
32	4.29
40	4.14
48	4.04

Light intensity decreases exponentially with depth.

4. The Beer-Lambert Law   As sunlight passes through the waters of lakes and oceans, the light is absorbed, and the deeper it penetrates, the more its intensity diminishes. The light intensity I at depth x is given by the Beer-Lambert Law:

$$I = I_0 e^{-kx}$$

where I_0 is the light intensity at the surface and k is a constant that depends on the murkiness of the water (see page 402). A biologist uses a photometer to investigate light penetration in a northern lake, obtaining the data in the table.

(a) Use a graphing calculator to find an exponential function of the form given by the Beer-Lambert Law to model these data. What is the light intensity I_0 at the surface on this day, and what is the "murkiness" constant k for this lake?   [*Hint:* If your calculator gives you a function of the form $I = ab^x$, convert this to the form you want using the identities $b^x = e^{\ln(b^x)} = e^{x \ln b}$. See Example 1(b).]

(b) Make a scatter plot of the data, and graph the function that you found in part (a) on your scatter plot.

(c) If the light intensity drops below 0.15 lumen (lm), a certain species of algae can't survive because photosynthesis is impossible. Use your model from part (a) to determine the depth below which there is insufficient light to support this algae.

Depth (ft)	Light intensity (lm)	Depth (ft)	Light intensity (lm)
5	13.0	25	1.8
10	7.6	30	1.1
15	4.5	35	0.5
20	2.7	40	0.3

5. Experimenting with "Forgetting" Curves   Every one of us is all too familiar with the phenomenon of forgetting. Facts that we clearly understood at the time we first learned them sometimes fade from our memory by the time the final exam rolls around. Psychologists have proposed several ways to model this process. One such model is Ebbinghaus' Law of Forgetting, described on page 392. Other models use exponential or logarithmic functions. To develop her own model, a psychologist performs an experiment on a group of volunteers by asking them to memorize a list of 100 related words. She then tests how many of these words they can recall after various periods of time. The average results for the group are shown in the table.

Time	Words recalled
15 min	64.3
1 h	45.1
8 h	37.3
1 day	32.8
2 days	26.9
3 days	25.6
5 days	22.9

(a) Use a graphing calculator to find a *power* function of the form $y = at^b$ that models the average number of words y that the volunteers remember after t hours. Then find an *exponential* function of the form $y = ab^t$ to model the data.

(b) Make a scatter plot of the data, and graph both the functions that you found in part (a) on your scatter plot.

(c) Which of the two functions seems to provide the better model?

6. Modeling the Species-Area Relation   The table gives the areas of several caves in central Mexico and the number of bat species that live in each cave.*

(a) Find a power function that models the data.

(b) Draw a graph of the function you found in part (a) and a scatter plot of the data on the same graph. Does the model fit the data well?

(c) The cave called El Sapo near Puebla, Mexico, has a surface area of $A = 205$ m². Use the model to estimate the number of bat species you would expect to find in that cave.

The number of different bat species in a cave is related to the size of the cave by a power function.

Cave	Area (m²)	Number of species
La Escondida	18	1
El Escorpion	19	1
El Tigre	58	1
Mision Imposible	60	2
San Martin	128	5
El Arenal	187	4
La Ciudad	344	6
Virgen	511	7

*A. K. Brunet and R. A. Medallin, "The Species-Area Relationship in Bat Assemblages of Tropical Caves." *Journal of Mammalogy,* 82(4):1114–1122, 2001.

7. Auto Exhaust Emissions A study by the U.S. Office of Science and Technology in 1972 estimated the cost of reducing automobile emissions by certain percentages. Find an exponential model that captures the "diminishing returns" trend of these data shown in the table below.

Reduction in emissions (%)	Cost per car ($)
50	45
55	55
60	62
65	70
70	80
75	90
80	100
85	200
90	375
95	600

8. Exponential or Power Model? Data points (x, y) are shown in the table.

(a) Draw a scatter plot of the data.

(b) Draw scatter plots of $(x, \ln y)$ and $(\ln x, \ln y)$.

(c) Which is more appropriate for modeling this data: an exponential function or a power function?

(d) Find an appropriate function to model the data.

x	2	4	6	8	10	12	14	16
y	0.08	0.12	0.18	0.25	0.36	0.52	0.73	1.06

9. Exponential or Power Model? Data points (x, y) are shown in the table in the margin.

(a) Draw a scatter plot of the data.

(b) Draw scatter plots of $(x, \ln y)$ and $(\ln x, \ln y)$.

(c) Which is more appropriate for modeling this data: an exponential function or a power function?

(d) Find an appropriate function to model the data.

x	10	20	30	40	50	60	70	80	90
y	29	82	151	235	330	430	546	669	797

10. Logistic Population Growth The table and scatter plot give the population of black flies in a closed laboratory container over an 18-day period.

(a) Use the `Logistic` command on your calculator to find a logistic model for these data.

(b) Use the model to estimate the time when there were 400 flies in the container.

Time (days)	Number of flies
0	10
2	25
4	66
6	144
8	262
10	374
12	446
16	492
18	498

10 Systems of Equations and Inequalities

Throughout the preceding chapters we modeled real-world situations by equations. But many real-world situations involve too many variables to be modeled by a single equation. For example, weather depends on the relationships among many variables, including temperature, wind speed, air pressure, and humidity. So to model the weather (and forecast a snowstorm like the one pictured above), scientists use many equations, each having many variables. Such collections of equations, called systems of equations, *work together* to describe the weather. Systems of equations with hundreds of variables are used by airlines to establish consistent flight schedules and by telecommunications companies to find efficient routings for telephone calls. In this chapter we learn how to solve systems of equations that consist of several equations in several variables.

715

10.1 SYSTEMS OF LINEAR EQUATIONS IN TWO VARIABLES

▪ Systems of Linear Equations and Their Solutions ▪ Substitution Method ▪ Elimination Method ▪ Graphical Method ▪ The Number of Solutions of a Linear System in Two Variables ▪ Modeling with Linear Systems

▪ Systems of Linear Equations and Their Solutions

A linear equation in two variables is an equation of the form

$$ax + by = c$$

The graph of a linear equation is a line (see Section 1.3).

A **system of equations** is a set of equations that involve the same variables. A **system of linear equations** is a system of equations in which each equation is linear. A **solution** of a system is an assignment of values for the variables that makes *each* equation in the system true. To **solve** a system means to find all solutions of the system.

Here is an example of a system of linear equations in two variables:

$$\begin{cases} 2x - y = 5 & \text{Equation 1} \\ x + 4y = 7 & \text{Equation 2} \end{cases}$$

We can check that $x = 3$ and $y = 1$ is a solution of this system.

Equation 1	**Equation 2**
$2x - y = 5$	$x + 4y = 7$
$2(3) - 1 = 5$ ✓	$3 + 4(1) = 7$ ✓

The solution can also be written as the ordered pair $(3, 1)$.

Note that the graphs of Equations 1 and 2 are lines (see Figure 1). Since the solution $(3,1)$ satisfies each equation, the point $(3,1)$ lies on each line. So it is the point of intersection of the two lines.

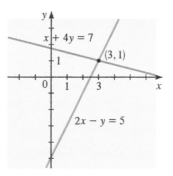

FIGURE 1

▪ Substitution Method

To solve a system using the **substitution method**, we start with one equation in the system and solve for one variable in terms of the other variable.

SUBSTITUTION METHOD

1. **Solve for One Variable.** Choose one equation, and solve for one variable in terms of the other variable.

2. **Substitute.** Substitute the expression you found in Step 1 into the other equation to get an equation in one variable, then solve for that variable.

3. **Back-Substitute.** Substitute the value you found in Step 2 back into the expression found in Step 1 to solve for the remaining variable.

EXAMPLE 1 ■ Substitution Method

Find all solutions of the system.

$$\begin{cases} 2x + y = 1 & \text{Equation 1} \\ 3x + 4y = 14 & \text{Equation 2} \end{cases}$$

SOLUTION **Solve for one variable.** We solve for y in the first equation.

$$y = 1 - 2x \qquad \text{Solve for } y \text{ in Equation 1}$$

Substitute. Now we substitute for y in the second equation and solve for x.

$$\begin{aligned} 3x + 4(1 - 2x) &= 14 & \text{Substitute } y = 1 - 2x \text{ into Equation 2} \\ 3x + 4 - 8x &= 14 & \text{Expand} \\ -5x + 4 &= 14 & \text{Simplify} \\ -5x &= 10 & \text{Subtract 4} \\ x &= -2 & \text{Solve for } x \end{aligned}$$

Back-substitute. Next we back-substitute $x = -2$ into the equation $y = 1 - 2x$.

$$y = 1 - 2(-2) = 5 \qquad \text{Back-substitute}$$

Thus $x = -2$ and $y = 5$, so the solution is the ordered pair $(-2, 5)$. Figure 2 shows that the graphs of the two equations intersect at the point $(-2, 5)$.

$x = -2, y = 5$:

$$\begin{cases} 2(-2) + 5 = 1 \\ 3(-2) + 4(5) = 14 \end{cases} \checkmark$$

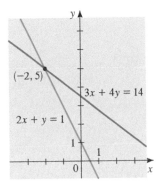

FIGURE 2

✎ Now Try Exercise 5

■ Elimination Method

To solve a system using the **elimination method**, we try to combine the equations using sums or differences so as to eliminate one of the variables.

ELIMINATION METHOD

1. **Adjust the Coefficients.** Multiply one or more of the equations by appropriate numbers so that the coefficient of one variable in one equation is the negative of its coefficient in the other equation.

2. **Add the Equations.** Add the two equations to eliminate one variable, then solve for the remaining variable.

3. **Back-Substitute.** Substitute the value that you found in Step 2 back into one of the original equations, and solve for the remaining variable.

EXAMPLE 2 ▪ Elimination Method

Find all solutions of the system.

$$\begin{cases} 3x + 2y = 14 & \text{Equation 1} \\ x - 2y = 2 & \text{Equation 2} \end{cases}$$

SOLUTION   Since the coefficients of the y-terms are negatives of each other, we can add the equations to eliminate y.

$$\begin{cases} 3x + 2y = 14 \\ \underline{\;\;x - 2y = \;\;2\;} \end{cases} \quad \text{System}$$

$$4x \qquad = 16 \qquad \text{Add}$$

$$x = 4 \qquad \text{Solve for } x$$

Now we back-substitute $x = 4$ into one of the original equations and solve for y. Let's choose the second equation because it looks simpler.

$$x - 2y = 2 \qquad \text{Equation 2}$$

$$4 - 2y = 2 \qquad \text{Back-substitute } x = 4 \text{ into Equation 2}$$

$$-2y = -2 \qquad \text{Subtract 4}$$

$$y = 1 \qquad \text{Solve for } y$$

The solution is $(4, 1)$. Figure 3 shows that the graphs of the equations in the system intersect at the point $(4, 1)$.

✎ Now Try Exercise 9

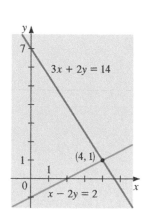

FIGURE 3

▪ Graphical Method

In the **graphical method** we use a graphing device to solve the system of equations.

GRAPHICAL METHOD

1. **Graph Each Equation.**   Express each equation in a form suitable for the graphing calculator by solving for y as a function of x. Graph the equations on the same screen.

2. **Find the Intersection Point(s).**   The solutions are the x- and y-coordinates of the point(s) of intersection.

EXAMPLE 3 ▪ Graphical Method

See Appendix C, *Graphing with a Graphing Calculator*, for guidelines on using a graphing calculator. See Appendix D, *Using the TI-83/84 Graphing Calculator*, for specific graphing instructions.

Find all solutions of the system

$$\begin{cases} 1.35x - 2.13y = -2.36 \\ 2.16x + 0.32y = \;\;\;1.06 \end{cases}$$

SOLUTION   Solving for y in terms of x, we get the equivalent system

$$\begin{cases} y = \;\;\;0.63x + 1.11 \\ y = -6.75x + 3.31 \end{cases}$$

where we have rounded the coefficients to two decimals. Figure 4 shows that the two lines intersect. Zooming in, we see that the solution is approximately $(0.30, 1.30)$.

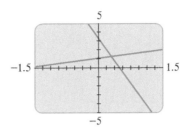

FIGURE 4

✎. Now Try Exercises 13 and 51

The Number of Solutions of a Linear System in Two Variables

The graph of a linear system in two variables is a pair of lines, so to solve the system graphically, we must find the intersection point(s) of the lines. Two lines may intersect in a single point, they may be parallel, or they may coincide, as shown in Figure 5. So there are three possible outcomes in solving such a system.

NUMBER OF SOLUTIONS OF A LINEAR SYSTEM IN TWO VARIABLES

For a system of linear equations in two variables, exactly one of the following is true. (See Figure 5.)

1. The system has exactly one solution.
2. The system has no solution.
3. The system has infinitely many solutions.

A system that has no solution is said to be **inconsistent**. A system with infinitely many solutions is called **dependent**.

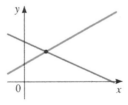

(a) Lines intersect at a single point. The system has one solution.

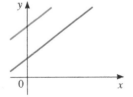

(b) Lines are parallel and do not intersect. The system has no solution.

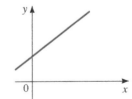

(c) Lines coincide—equations are for the same line. The system has infinitely many solutions.

FIGURE 5

EXAMPLE 4 ■ A Linear System with One Solution

Solve the system and graph the lines.

$$\begin{cases} 3x - y = 0 & \text{Equation 1} \\ 5x + 2y = 22 & \text{Equation 2} \end{cases}$$

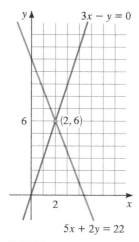

FIGURE 6

$x = 2, y = 6$:

$$\begin{cases} 3(2) - (6) = 0 \\ 5(2) + 2(6) = 22 \end{cases} \checkmark$$

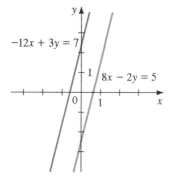

FIGURE 7

SOLUTION   We eliminate y from the equations and solve for x.

$$\begin{cases} 6x - 2y = 0 \\ 5x + 2y = 22 \end{cases} \qquad 2 \times \text{Equation 1}$$

$$\overline{11x = 22} \qquad \text{Add}$$

$$x = 2 \qquad \text{Solve for } x$$

Now we back-substitute into the first equation and solve for y:

$$6(2) - 2y = 0 \qquad \text{Back-substitute } x = 2$$

$$-2y = -12 \qquad \text{Subtract 12}$$

$$y = 6 \qquad \text{Solve for } y$$

The solution of the system is the ordered pair $(2, 6)$, that is,

$$x = 2 \qquad y = 6$$

The graph in Figure 6 shows that the lines in the system intersect at the point $(2, 6)$.

✎ Now Try Exercise 23

EXAMPLE 5   A Linear System with No Solution

Solve the system.

$$\begin{cases} 8x - 2y = 5 & \text{Equation 1} \\ -12x + 3y = 7 & \text{Equation 2} \end{cases}$$

SOLUTION   This time we try to find a suitable combination of the two equations to eliminate the variable y. Multiplying the first equation by 3 and the second equation by 2 gives

$$\begin{cases} 24x - 6y = 15 & 3 \times \text{Equation 1} \\ -24x + 6y = 14 & 2 \times \text{Equation 2} \end{cases}$$

$$\overline{ 0 = 29} \qquad \text{Add}$$

Adding the two equations eliminates *both x and y* in this case, and we end up with $0 = 29$, which is obviously false. No matter what values we assign to x and y, we cannot make this statement true, so the system has *no solution*. Figure 7 shows that the lines in the system are parallel so do not intersect. The system is inconsistent.

✎ Now Try Exercise 37

EXAMPLE 6 ■ A Linear System with Infinitely Many Solutions

Solve the system.

$$\begin{cases} 3x - 6y = 12 & \text{Equation 1} \\ 4x - 8y = 16 & \text{Equation 2} \end{cases}$$

SOLUTION   We multiply the first equation by 4 and the second equation by 3 to prepare for subtracting the equations to eliminate x. The new equations are

$$\begin{cases} 12x - 24y = 48 & 4 \times \text{Equation 1} \\ 12x - 24y = 48 & 3 \times \text{Equation 2} \end{cases}$$

We see that the two equations in the original system are simply different ways of expressing the equation of one single line. The coordinates of any point on this line

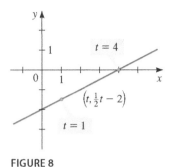

FIGURE 8

give a solution of the system. Writing the equation in slope-intercept form, we have $y = \frac{1}{2}x - 2$. So if we let t represent any real number, we can write the solution as

$$x = t$$
$$y = \frac{1}{2}t - 2$$

We can also write the solution in ordered-pair form as

$$\left(t, \tfrac{1}{2}t - 2\right)$$

where t is any real number. The system has infinitely many solutions (see Figure 8).

✎ Now Try Exercise 39

In Example 3, to get specific solutions we have to assign values to t. For instance, if $t = 1$, we get the solution $\left(1, -\frac{3}{2}\right)$. If $t = 4$, we get the solution $(4, 0)$. For every value of t we get a different solution. (See Figure 8.)

■ Modeling with Linear Systems

Frequently, when we use equations to solve problems in the sciences or in other areas, we obtain systems like the ones we've been considering. When modeling with systems of equations, we use the following guidelines, which are similar to those in Section P.9.

GUIDELINES FOR MODELING WITH SYSTEMS OF EQUATIONS

1. **Identify the Variables.** Identify the quantities that the problem asks you to find. These are usually determined by a careful reading of the question posed at the end of the problem. Introduce notation for the variables (call them x and y or some other letters).

2. **Express All Unknown Quantities in Terms of the Variables.** Read the problem again, and express all the quantities mentioned in the problem in terms of the variables you defined in Step 1.

3. **Set Up a System of Equations.** Find the crucial facts in the problem that give the relationships between the expressions you found in Step 2. Set up a system of equations (or a model) that expresses these relationships.

4. **Solve the System and Interpret the Results.** Solve the system you found in Step 3, check your solutions, and state your final answer as a sentence that answers the question posed in the problem.

The next two examples illustrate how to model with systems of equations.

EXAMPLE 7 ■ A Distance-Speed-Time Problem

A woman rows a boat upstream from one point on a river to another point 4 mi away in $1\frac{1}{2}$ hours. The return trip, traveling with the current, takes only 45 min. How fast does she row relative to the water, and at what speed is the current flowing?

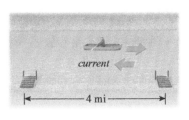

SOLUTION **Identify the variables.** We are asked to find the rowing speed and the speed of the current, so we let

$$x = \text{rowing speed (mi/h)}$$
$$y = \text{current speed (mi/h)}$$

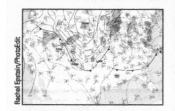

Rachel Epstein/PhotoEdit

Weather Prediction
Modern meteorologists do much more than predict tomorrow's weather. They research long-term weather patterns, depletion of the ozone layer, global warming, and other effects of human activity on the weather. But daily weather prediction is still a major part of meteorology; its value is measured by the innumerable human lives that are saved each year through accurate prediction of hurricanes, blizzards, and other catastrophic weather phenomena. Early in the 20th century mathematicians proposed to model weather with equations that used the current values of hundreds of atmospheric variables. Although this model worked in principle, it was impossible to predict future weather patterns with it because of the difficulty of measuring all the variables accurately and solving all the equations. Today, new mathematical models combined with high-speed computer simulations and better data have vastly improved weather prediction. As a result, many human as well as economic disasters have been averted. Mathematicians at the National Oceanographic and Atmospheric Administration (NOAA) are continually researching better methods of weather prediction.

Express unknown quantities in terms of the variable. The woman's speed when she rows upstream is her rowing speed minus the speed of the current; her speed downstream is her rowing speed plus the speed of the current. Now we translate this information into the language of algebra.

In Words	In Algebra
Rowing speed	x
Current speed	y
Speed upstream	$x - y$
Speed downstream	$x + y$

Set up a system of equations. The distance upstream and downstream is 4 mi, so using the fact that speed × time = distance for both legs of the trip, we get

speed upstream × time upstream = distance traveled

speed downstream × time downstream = distance traveled

In algebraic notation this translates into the following equations.

$$(x - y)\tfrac{3}{2} = 4 \qquad \text{Equation 1}$$
$$(x + y)\tfrac{3}{4} = 4 \qquad \text{Equation 2}$$

(The times have been converted to hours, since we are expressing the speeds in miles per *hour*.)

Solve the system. We multiply the equations by 2 and 4, respectively, to clear the denominators.

$$\begin{cases} 3x - 3y = 8 & 2 \times \text{Equation 1} \\ 3x + 3y = 16 & 4 \times \text{Equation 2} \end{cases}$$
$$6x \qquad\ = 24 \qquad \text{Add}$$
$$x \qquad = 4 \qquad \text{Solve for } x$$

Back-substituting this value of x into the first equation (the second works just as well) and solving for y, we get

$$3(4) - 3y = 8 \qquad \text{Back-substitute } x = 4$$
$$-3y = 8 - 12 \qquad \text{Subtract 12}$$
$$y = \tfrac{4}{3} \qquad \text{Solve for } y$$

The woman rows at 4 mi/h, and the current flows at $1\tfrac{1}{3}$ mi/h.

CHECK YOUR ANSWER

Speed upstream is

$$\frac{\text{distance}}{\text{time}} = \frac{4 \text{ mi}}{1\tfrac{1}{2} \text{ h}} = 2\tfrac{2}{3} \text{ mi/h}$$

and this should equal

rowing speed − current flow

$$= 4 \text{ mi/h} - \tfrac{4}{3} \text{ mi/h} = 2\tfrac{2}{3} \text{ mi/h}$$

Speed downstream is

$$\frac{\text{distance}}{\text{time}} = \frac{4 \text{ mi}}{\tfrac{3}{4} \text{ h}} = 5\tfrac{1}{3} \text{ mi/h}$$

and this should equal

rowing speed + current flow

$$= 4 \text{ mi/h} + \tfrac{4}{3} \text{ mi/h} = 5\tfrac{1}{3} \text{ mi/h} \quad \checkmark$$

✎ ▪ Now Try Exercise 65

EXAMPLE 8   A Mixture Problem

A vintner fortifies wine that contains 10% alcohol by adding a 70% alcohol solution to it. The resulting mixture has an alcoholic strength of 16% and fills 1000 one-liter bottles. How many liters (L) of the wine and of the alcohol solution does the vintner use?

SOLUTION Identify the variables.   Since we are asked for the amounts of wine and alcohol, we let

$$x = \text{amount of wine used (L)}$$

$$y = \text{amount of alcohol solution used (L)}$$

Express all unknown quantities in terms of the variable.   From the fact that the wine contains 10% alcohol and the solution contains 70% alcohol, we get the following.

In Words	In Algebra
Amount of wine used (L)	x
Amount of alcohol solution used (L)	y
Amount of alcohol in wine (L)	$0.10x$
Amount of alcohol in solution (L)	$0.70y$

Set up a system of equations.   The volume of the mixture must be the total of the two volumes the vintner is adding together, so

$$x + y = 1000$$

Also, the amount of alcohol in the mixture must be the total of the alcohol contributed by the wine and by the alcohol solution, that is,

$$0.10x + 0.70y = (0.16)1000$$

$$0.10x + 0.70y = 160 \qquad \text{Simplify}$$

$$x + 7y = 1600 \qquad \text{Multiply by 10 to clear decimals}$$

Thus we get the system

$$\begin{cases} x + \ y = 1000 & \text{Equation 1} \\ x + 7y = 1600 & \text{Equation 2} \end{cases}$$

Solve the system.   Subtracting the first equation from the second eliminates the variable x, and we get

$$6y = 600 \qquad \text{Subtract Equation 1 from Equation 2}$$

$$y = 100 \qquad \text{Solve for } y$$

We now back-substitute $y = 100$ into the first equation and solve for x.

$$x + 100 = 1000 \qquad \text{Back-substitute } y = 100$$

$$x = 900 \qquad \text{Solve for } x$$

The vintner uses 900 L of wine and 100 L of the alcohol solution.

✎ Now Try Exercise 67

10.1 EXERCISES

CONCEPTS

1. The system of equations

$$\begin{cases} 2x + 3y = 7 \\ 5x - y = 9 \end{cases}$$

is a system of two equations in the two variables _____

and _____. To determine whether $(5, -1)$ is a solution of
this system, we check whether $x = 5$ and $y = -1$ satisfy

each _____ in the system. Which of the following are
solutions of this system?

$$(5, -1), \quad (-1, 3), \quad (2, 1)$$

2. A system of equations in two variables can be solved by the

_____ method, the _____ method,

or the _____ method.

3. A system of two linear equations in two variables can have

one solution, _____ solution, or _____

_____ solutions.

4. The following is a system of two linear equations in two
variables.

$$\begin{cases} x + y = 1 \\ 2x + 2y = 2 \end{cases}$$

The graph of the first equation is the same as the graph of the

second equation, so the system has _____ _____
solutions. We express these solutions by writing

$$x = t$$
$$y = \underline{\quad\quad}$$

where t is any real number. Some of the solutions of this

system are $(1, \underline{\quad})$, $(-3, \underline{\quad})$, and $(5, \underline{\quad})$.

SKILLS

5–8 ■ Substitution Method   Use the substitution method to find
all solutions of the system of equations.

5. $\begin{cases} x - y = 1 \\ 4x + 3y = 18 \end{cases}$ **6.** $\begin{cases} 3x + y = 1 \\ 5x + 2y = 1 \end{cases}$

7. $\begin{cases} x - y = 2 \\ 2x + 3y = 9 \end{cases}$ **8.** $\begin{cases} 2x + y = 7 \\ x + 2y = 2 \end{cases}$

9–12 ■ Elimination Method   Use the elimination method to find
all solutions of the system of equations.

9. $\begin{cases} 3x + 4y = 10 \\ x - 4y = -2 \end{cases}$ **10.** $\begin{cases} 2x + 5y = 15 \\ 4x + y = 21 \end{cases}$

11. $\begin{cases} 3x - 2y = -13 \\ -6x + 5y = 28 \end{cases}$ **12.** $\begin{cases} 2x - 5y = -18 \\ 3x + 4y = 19 \end{cases}$

13–14 ■ Graphical Method   Two equations and their graphs are
given. Find the intersection point(s) of the graphs by solving the
system.

13. $\begin{cases} 2x + y = -1 \\ x - 2y = -8 \end{cases}$ **14.** $\begin{cases} x + y = 2 \\ 2x + y = 5 \end{cases}$

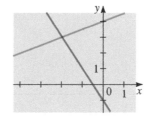   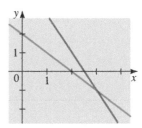

15–20 ■ Number of Solutions Determined Graphically   Graph
each linear system, either by hand or using a graphing device.
Use the graph to determine whether the system has one solution,
no solution, or infinitely many solutions. If there is exactly one
solution, use the graph to find it.

15. $\begin{cases} x - y = 4 \\ 2x + y = 2 \end{cases}$ **16.** $\begin{cases} 2x - y = 4 \\ 3x + y = 6 \end{cases}$

17. $\begin{cases} 2x - 3y = 12 \\ -x + \frac{3}{2}y = 4 \end{cases}$ **18.** $\begin{cases} 2x + 6y = 0 \\ -3x - 9y = 18 \end{cases}$

19. $\begin{cases} -x + \frac{1}{2}y = -5 \\ 2x - y = 10 \end{cases}$ **20.** $\begin{cases} 12x + 15y = -18 \\ 2x + \frac{5}{2}y = -3 \end{cases}$

21–50 ■ Solving a System of Equations   Solve the system, or
show that it has no solution. If the system has infinitely many solutions, express them in the ordered-pair form given in Example 6.

21. $\begin{cases} x + y = 4 \\ -x + y = 0 \end{cases}$ **22.** $\begin{cases} x - y = 3 \\ x + 3y = 7 \end{cases}$

23. $\begin{cases} 2x - 3y = 9 \\ 4x + 3y = 9 \end{cases}$ **24.** $\begin{cases} 3x + 2y = 0 \\ -x - 2y = 8 \end{cases}$

25. $\begin{cases} x + 3y = 5 \\ 2x - y = 3 \end{cases}$ **26.** $\begin{cases} x + y = 7 \\ 2x - 3y = -1 \end{cases}$

27. $\begin{cases} -x + y = 2 \\ 4x - 3y = -3 \end{cases}$ **28.** $\begin{cases} 4x - 3y = 28 \\ 9x - y = -6 \end{cases}$

29. $\begin{cases} x + 2y = 7 \\ 5x - y = 2 \end{cases}$ **30.** $\begin{cases} -4x + 12y = 0 \\ 12x + 4y = 160 \end{cases}$

31. $\begin{cases} -\frac{1}{3}x - \frac{1}{6}y = -1 \\ \frac{2}{3}x + \frac{1}{6}y = 3 \end{cases}$ **32.** $\begin{cases} \frac{3}{4}x + \frac{1}{2}y = 5 \\ -\frac{1}{4}x - \frac{3}{2}y = 1 \end{cases}$

33. $\begin{cases} \frac{1}{2}x + \frac{1}{3}y = 2 \\ \frac{1}{5}x - \frac{2}{3}y = 8 \end{cases}$ **34.** $\begin{cases} 0.2x - 0.2y = -1.8 \\ -0.3x + 0.5y = 3.3 \end{cases}$

35. $\begin{cases} 3x + 2y = 8 \\ x - 2y = 0 \end{cases}$ **36.** $\begin{cases} 4x + 2y = 16 \\ x - 5y = 70 \end{cases}$

37. $\begin{cases} x + 4y = 8 \\ 3x + 12y = 2 \end{cases}$ **38.** $\begin{cases} -3x + 5y = 2 \\ 9x - 15y = 6 \end{cases}$

39. $\begin{cases} 2x - 6y = 10 \\ -3x + 9y = -15 \end{cases}$ **40.** $\begin{cases} 2x - 3y = -8 \\ 14x - 21y = 3 \end{cases}$

41. $\begin{cases} 6x + 4y = 12 \\ 9x + 6y = 18 \end{cases}$ **42.** $\begin{cases} 25x - 75y = 100 \\ -10x + 30y = -40 \end{cases}$

43. $\begin{cases} 8s - 3t = -3 \\ 5s - 2t = -1 \end{cases}$ **44.** $\begin{cases} u - 30v = -5 \\ -3u + 80v = 5 \end{cases}$

45. $\begin{cases} \frac{1}{2}x + \frac{3}{5}y = 3 \\ \frac{5}{3}x + 2y = 10 \end{cases}$ **46.** $\begin{cases} \frac{3}{2}x - \frac{1}{3}y = \frac{1}{2} \\ 2x - \frac{1}{2}y = -\frac{1}{2} \end{cases}$

47. $\begin{cases} 0.4x + 1.2y = 14 \\ 12x - 5y = 10 \end{cases}$ **48.** $\begin{cases} 26x - 10y = -4 \\ -0.6x + 1.2y = 3 \end{cases}$

49. $\begin{cases} \frac{1}{3}x - \frac{1}{4}y = 2 \\ -8x + 6y = 10 \end{cases}$ **50.** $\begin{cases} -\frac{1}{10}x + \frac{1}{2}y = 4 \\ 2x - 10y = -80 \end{cases}$

51–54 ▪ Solving a System of Equations Graphically   Use a graphing device to graph both lines in the same viewing rectangle. (Note that you must solve for y in terms of x before graphing if you are using a graphing calculator.) Solve the system either by zooming in and using $\boxed{\text{TRACE}}$ or by using $\texttt{Intersect}$. Round your answers to two decimals.

51. $\begin{cases} 0.21x + 3.17y = 9.51 \\ 2.35x - 1.17y = 5.89 \end{cases}$

52. $\begin{cases} 18.72x - 14.91y = 12.33 \\ 6.21x - 12.92y = 17.82 \end{cases}$

53. $\begin{cases} 2371x - 6552y = 13,591 \\ 9815x + 992y = 618,555 \end{cases}$

54. $\begin{cases} -435x + 912y = 0 \\ 132x + 455y = 994 \end{cases}$

SKILLS Plus

55–58 ▪ Solving a General System of Equations   Find x and y in terms of a and b.

55. $\begin{cases} x + y = 0 \\ x + ay = 1 \end{cases}$ $(a \neq 1)$

56. $\begin{cases} ax + by = 0 \\ x + y = 1 \end{cases}$ $(a \neq b)$

57. $\begin{cases} ax + by = 1 \\ bx + ay = 1 \end{cases}$ $(a^2 - b^2 \neq 0)$

58. $\begin{cases} ax + by = 0 \\ a^2x + b^2y = 1 \end{cases}$ $(a \neq 0, b \neq 0, a \neq b)$

APPLICATIONS

59. Number Problem   Find two numbers whose sum is 34 and whose difference is 10.

60. Number Problem   The sum of two numbers is twice their difference. The larger number is 6 more than twice the smaller. Find the numbers.

61. Value of Coins   A man has 14 coins in his pocket, all of which are dimes and quarters. If the total value of his change is $2.75, how many dimes and how many quarters does he have?

62. Admission Fees   The admission fee at an amusement park is $1.50 for children and $4.00 for adults. On a certain day, 2200 people entered the park, and the admission fees that were collected totaled $5050. How many children and how many adults were admitted?

63. Gas Station   A gas station sells regular gas for $2.20 per gallon and premium gas for $3.00 a gallon. At the end of a business day 280 gallons of gas had been sold, and receipts totaled $680. How many gallons of each type of gas had been sold?

64. Fruit Stand   A fruit stand sells two varieties of strawberries: standard and deluxe. A box of standard strawberries sells for $7, and a box of deluxe strawberries sells for $10. In one day the stand sold 135 boxes of strawberries for a total of $1110. How many boxes of each type were sold?

65. Airplane Speed   A man flies a small airplane from Fargo to Bismarck, North Dakota—a distance of 180 mi. Because he is flying into a headwind, the trip takes him 2 h. On the way back, the wind is still blowing at the same speed, so the return trip takes only 1 h 12 min. What is his speed in still air, and how fast is the wind blowing?

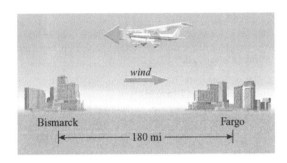

66. Boat Speed   A boat on a river travels downstream between two points, 20 mi apart, in 1 h. The return trip against the current takes $2\frac{1}{2}$ h. What is the boat's speed, and how fast does the current in the river flow?

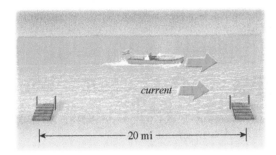

67. Nutrition   A researcher performs an experiment to test a hypothesis that involves the nutrients niacin and retinol. She feeds one group of laboratory rats a daily diet of precisely 32 units of niacin and 22,000 units of retinol. She uses two types of commercial pellet foods. Food A contains 0.12 unit of niacin and 100 units of retinol per gram. Food B contains 0.20 unit of niacin and 50 units of retinol per gram. How many grams of each food does she feed this group of rats each day?

68. Coffee Blends A customer in a coffee shop purchases a blend of two coffees: Kenyan, costing $3.50 a pound, and Sri Lankan, costing $5.60 a pound. He buys 3 lb of the blend, which costs him $11.55. How many pounds of each kind went into the mixture?

69. Mixture Problem A chemist has two large containers of sulfuric acid solution, with different concentrations of acid in each container. Blending 300 mL of the first solution and 600 mL of the second gives a mixture that is 15% acid, whereas blending 100 mL of the first with 500 mL of the second gives a $12\frac{1}{2}\%$ acid mixture. What are the concentrations of sulfuric acid in the original containers?

70. Mixture Problem A biologist has two brine solutions, one containing 5% salt and another containing 20% salt. How many milliliters of each solution should she mix to obtain 1 L of a solution that contains 14% salt?

71. Investments A woman invests a total of $20,000 in two accounts, one paying 5% and the other paying 8% simple interest per year. Her annual interest is $1180. How much did she invest at each rate?

72. Investments A man invests his savings in two accounts, one paying 6% and the other paying 10% simple interest per year. He puts twice as much in the lower-yielding account because it is less risky. His annual interest is $3520. How much did he invest at each rate?

73. Distance, Speed, and Time John and Mary leave their house at the same time and drive in opposite directions. John drives at 60 mi/h and travels 35 mi farther than Mary, who drives at 40 mi/h. Mary's trip takes 15 min longer than John's. For what length of time does each of them drive?

74. Aerobic Exercise A woman keeps fit by bicycling and running every day. On Monday she spends $\frac{1}{2}$ h at each activity, covering a total of $12\frac{1}{2}$ mi. On Tuesday she runs for 12 min and cycles for 45 min, covering a total of 16 mi. Assuming that her running and cycling speeds don't change from day to day, find these speeds.

75. Number Problem The sum of the digits of a two-digit number is 7. When the digits are reversed, the number is increased by 27. Find the number.

76. Area of a Triangle Find the area of the triangle that lies in the first quadrant (with its base on the x-axis) and that is bounded by the lines $y = 2x - 4$ and $y = -4x + 20$.

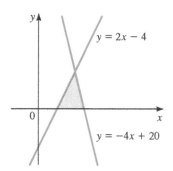

DISCUSS ■ DISCOVER ■ PROVE ■ WRITE

77. DISCUSS: The Least Squares Line The *least squares* line or *regression* line is the line that best fits a set of points in the plane. We studied this line in the *Focus on Modeling* that follows Chapter 1 (see page 174). By using calculus, it can be shown that the line that best fits the n data points $(x_1, y_1), (x_2, y_2), \ldots, (x_n, y_n)$ is the line $y = ax + b$, where the coefficients a and b satisfy the following pair of linear equations. (The notation $\sum_{k=1}^{n} x_k$ stands for the sum of all the x's. See Section 13.1 for a complete description of sigma (Σ) notation.)

$$\left(\sum_{k=1}^{n} x_k \right) a + nb = \sum_{k=1}^{n} y_k$$

$$\left(\sum_{k=1}^{n} x_k^2 \right) a + \left(\sum_{k=1}^{n} x_k \right) b = \sum_{k=1}^{n} x_k y_k$$

Use these equations to find the least squares line for the following data points.

$$(1, 3), \quad (2, 5), \quad (3, 6), \quad (5, 6), \quad (7, 9)$$

Sketch the points and your line to confirm that the line fits these points well. If your calculator computes regression lines, see whether it gives you the same line as the formulas.

10.2 SYSTEMS OF LINEAR EQUATIONS IN SEVERAL VARIABLES

■ Solving a Linear System ■ The Number of Solutions of a Linear System ■ Modeling Using Linear Systems

A **linear equation in n variables** is an equation that can be put in the form

$$a_1 x_1 + a_2 x_2 + \cdots + a_n x_n = c$$

where $a_1, a_2, \ldots, a_n$ and c are real numbers, and $x_1, x_2, \ldots, x_n$ are the variables. If we have only three or four variables, we generally use x, y, z, and w instead of x_1, x_2, x_3, and x_4. Such equations are called *linear* because if we have just two variables, the equation is $a_1 x + a_2 y = c$, which is the equation of a line. Here are some examples of equations in three variables that illustrate the difference between linear and nonlinear equations.

Linear equations	Nonlinear equations	
$6x_1 - 3x_2 + \sqrt{5}x_3 = 10$	$x^2 + 3y - \sqrt{z} = 5$	Not linear because it contains the square and the square root of a variable
$x + y + z = 2w - \frac{1}{2}$	$x_1x_2 + 6x_3 = -6$	Not linear because it contains a product of variables

In this section we study systems of linear equations in three or more variables.

■ Solving a Linear System

The following are two examples of systems of linear equations in three variables. The second system is in **triangular form**; that is, the variable x doesn't appear in the second equation, and the variables x and y do not appear in the third equation.

A system of linear equations

$$\begin{cases} x - 2y - z = 1 \\ -x + 3y + 3z = 4 \\ 2x - 3y + z = 10 \end{cases}$$

A system in triangular form

$$\begin{cases} x - 2y - z = 1 \\ y + 2z = 5 \\ z = 3 \end{cases}$$

It's easy to solve a system that is in triangular form by using back-substitution. So our goal in this section is to start with a system of linear equations and change it to a system in triangular form that has the same solutions as the original system. We begin by showing how to use back-substitution to solve a system that is already in triangular form.

EXAMPLE 1 ■ Solving a Triangular System Using Back-Substitution

Solve the following system using back-substitution:

$$\begin{cases} x - 2y - z = 1 & \text{Equation 1} \\ y + 2z = 5 & \text{Equation 2} \\ z = 3 & \text{Equation 3} \end{cases}$$

SOLUTION From the last equation we know that $z = 3$. We back-substitute this into the second equation and solve for y.

$$y + 2(3) = 5 \qquad \text{Back-substitute } z = 3 \text{ into Equation 2}$$
$$y = -1 \qquad \text{Solve for } y$$

Then we back-substitute $y = -1$ and $z = 3$ into the first equation and solve for x.

$$x - 2(-1) - (3) = 1 \qquad \text{Back-substitute } y = -1 \text{ and } z = 3 \text{ into Equation 1}$$
$$x = 2 \qquad \text{Solve for } x$$

The solution of the system is $x = 2$, $y = -1$, $z = 3$. We can also write the solution as the ordered triple $(2, -1, 3)$.

✎. Now Try Exercise 7

To change a system of linear equations to an **equivalent system** (that is, a system with the same solutions as the original system), we use the elimination method. This means that we can use the following operations.

OPERATIONS THAT YIELD AN EQUIVALENT SYSTEM

1. Add a nonzero multiple of one equation to another.
2. Multiply an equation by a nonzero constant.
3. Interchange the positions of two equations.

To solve a linear system, we use these operations to change the system to an equivalent triangular system. Then we use back-substitution as in Example 1. This process is called **Gaussian elimination**.

EXAMPLE 2 ■ Solving a System of Three Equations in Three Variables

Solve the following system using Gaussian elimination:

$$\begin{cases} x - 2y + 3z = 1 & \text{Equation 1} \\ x + 2y - z = 13 & \text{Equation 2} \\ 3x + 2y - 5z = 3 & \text{Equation 3} \end{cases}$$

SOLUTION We need to change this to a triangular system, so we begin by eliminating the x-term from the second equation.

$$\begin{aligned} x + 2y - z &= 13 \quad \text{Equation 2} \\ \underline{x - 2y + 3z = 1} \quad &\text{Equation 1} \\ 4y - 4z &= 12 \quad \text{Equation 2} + (-1) \times \text{Equation 1} = \text{new Equation 2} \end{aligned}$$

This gives us a new, equivalent system that is one step closer to triangular form.

$$\begin{cases} x - 2y + 3z = 1 & \text{Equation 1} \\ 4y - 4z = 12 & \text{Equation 2} \\ 3x + 2y - 5z = 3 & \text{Equation 3} \end{cases}$$

Now we eliminate the x-term from the third equation.

$$\begin{cases} x - 2y + 3z = 1 \\ 4y - 4z = 12 \\ 8y - 14z = 0 \quad \text{Equation 3} + (-3) \times \text{Equation 1} = \text{new Equation 3} \end{cases}$$

Then we eliminate the y-term from the third equation.

$$\begin{cases} x - 2y + 3z = 1 \\ 4y - 4z = 12 \\ -6z = -24 \quad \text{Equation 3} + (-2) \times \text{Equation 2} = \text{new Equation 3} \end{cases}$$

The system is now in triangular form, but it will be easier to work with if we divide the second and third equations by the common factors of each term.

$$\begin{cases} x - 2y + 3z = 1 \\ y - z = 3 \quad \frac{1}{4} \times \text{Equation 2} = \text{new Equation 2} \\ z = 4 \quad -\frac{1}{6} \times \text{Equation 3} = \text{new Equation 3} \end{cases}$$

Now we use back-substitution to solve the system. From the third equation we get $z = 4$. We back-substitute this into the second equation and solve for y.

$$y - (4) = 3 \quad \text{Back-substitute } z = 4 \text{ into Equation 2}$$
$$y = 7 \quad \text{Solve for } y$$

Now we back-substitute $y = 7$ and $z = 4$ into the first equation and solve for x.

$$x - 2(7) + 3(4) = 1 \quad \text{Back-substitute } y = 7 \text{ and } z = 4 \text{ into Equation 1}$$
$$x = 3 \quad \text{Solve for } x$$

The solution of the system is $x = 3$, $y = 7$, $z = 4$, which we can write as the ordered triple $(3, 7, 4)$.

🪶 Now Try Exercise 17

Sidebar:

$$\begin{aligned} 3x + 2y - 5z &= 3 \\ \underline{-3x + 6y - 9z = -3} \\ 8y - 14z &= 0 \end{aligned}$$

$$\begin{aligned} 8y - 14z &= 0 \\ \underline{-8y + 8z = -24} \\ -6z &= -24 \end{aligned}$$

CHECK YOUR ANSWER

$x = 3, y = 7, z = 4$:

$$\begin{aligned} (3) - 2(7) + 3(4) &= 1 \\ (3) + 2(7) - (4) &= 13 \\ 3(3) + 2(7) - 5(4) &= 3 \ \checkmark \end{aligned}$$

■ The Number of Solutions of a Linear System

The graph of a linear equation in three variables is a plane in three-dimensional space. A system of three equations in three variables represents three planes in space. The solutions of the system are the points where all three planes intersect. Three planes may intersect in a point, in a line, or not at all, or all three planes may coincide. Figure 1 illustrates some of these possibilities. Checking these possibilities we see that there are three possible outcomes when solving such a system.

NUMBER OF SOLUTIONS OF A LINEAR SYSTEM

For a system of linear equations, exactly one of the following is true.

1. The system has exactly one solution.
2. The system has no solution.
3. The system has infinitely many solutions.

A system with no solution is said to be **inconsistent**, and a system with infinitely many solutions is said to be **dependent**. As we see in the next example, a linear system has no solution if we end up with a *false equation* after applying Gaussian elimination to the system.

(a) The three planes intersect at a single point. The system has one solution.

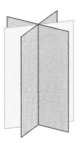

(b) The three planes intersect at more than one point. The system has infinitely many solutions.

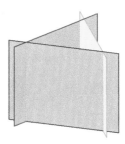

(c) The three planes have no point in common. The system has no solution.

FIGURE 1

EXAMPLE 3 ■ A System with No Solution

Solve the following system:

$$\begin{cases} x + 2y - 2z = 1 & \text{Equation 1} \\ 2x + 2y - z = 6 & \text{Equation 2} \\ 3x + 4y - 3z = 5 & \text{Equation 3} \end{cases}$$

SOLUTION To put this in triangular form, we begin by eliminating the x-terms from the second equation and the third equation.

$$\begin{cases} x + 2y - 2z = 1 \\ -2y + 3z = 4 & \text{Equation 2} + (-2) \times \text{Equation 1} = \text{new Equation 2} \\ 3x + 4y + 3z = 5 \end{cases}$$

$$\begin{cases} x + 2y - 2z = 1 \\ -2y + 3z = 4 \\ -2y + 3z = 2 & \text{Equation 3} + (-3) \times \text{Equation 1} = \text{new Equation 3} \end{cases}$$

Now we eliminate the y-term from the third equation.

$$\begin{cases} x + 2y - 2z = 1 \\ \quad\ -2y + 3z = 4 \\ \qquad\qquad\ 0 = -2 \qquad \text{Equation 3} + (-1) \times \text{Equation 2} = \text{new Equation 3} \end{cases}$$

The system is now in triangular form, but the third equation says $0 = -2$, which is false. No matter what values we assign to x, y, and z, the third equation will never be true. This means that the system has *no solution*.

✎. Now Try Exercise 29

EXAMPLE 4 ■ A System with Infinitely Many Solutions

Solve the following system:

$$\begin{cases} x - \ y + 5z = -2 & \text{Equation 1} \\ 2x + \ y + 4z = \ \ 2 & \text{Equation 2} \\ 2x + 4y - 2z = \ \ 8 & \text{Equation 3} \end{cases}$$

SOLUTION To put this in triangular form, we begin by eliminating the x-terms from the second equation and the third equation.

$$\begin{cases} x - \ y + 5z = -2 \\ \qquad 3y - 6z = \ \ 6 \qquad \text{Equation 2} + (-2) \times \text{Equation 1} = \text{new Equation 2} \\ 2x + 4y - 2z = \ \ 8 \end{cases}$$

$$\begin{cases} x - y + \ 5z = -2 \\ \quad 3y - \ 6z = \ \ 6 \\ \quad 6y - 12z = \ 12 \qquad \text{Equation 3} + (-2) \times \text{Equation 1} = \text{new Equation 3} \end{cases}$$

Now we eliminate the y-term from the third equation.

$$\begin{cases} x - y + 5z = -2 \\ \quad 3y - 6z = \ \ 6 \\ \qquad\qquad 0 = \ \ 0 \qquad \text{Equation 3} + (-2) \times \text{Equation 2} = \text{new Equation 3} \end{cases}$$

The new third equation is true, but it gives us no new information, so we can drop it from the system. Only two equations are left. We can use them to solve for x and y in terms of z, but z can take on any value, so there are infinitely many solutions.

DISCOVERY PROJECT

Best Fit Versus Exact Fit

The law of gravity is precise. But when we obtain data on the distance an object falls in a given time, our measurements are not exact. We can, however, find the line (or parabola) that *best* fits our data. Not all of the data points will lie on the line (or parabola). But if we are given just two points, we can find a line of *exact* fit—that is, a line that passes through the two points. Similarly, we can find a parabola through three points. In this project we compare exact data with models of real-world data. You can find the project at **www.stewartmath.com**.

To find the complete solution of the system, we begin by solving for y in terms of z, using the new second equation.

$$3y - 6z = 6 \qquad \text{Equation 2}$$
$$y - 2z = 2 \qquad \text{Multiply by } \tfrac{1}{3}$$
$$y = 2z + 2 \qquad \text{Solve for } y$$

Then we solve for x in terms of z, using the first equation.

$$x - (2z + 2) + 5z = -2 \qquad \text{Substitute } y = 2z + 2 \text{ into Equation 1}$$
$$x + 3z - 2 = -2 \qquad \text{Simplify}$$
$$x = -3z \qquad \text{Solve for } x$$

To describe the complete solution, we let z be any real number t. The solution is

$$x = -3t$$
$$y = 2t + 2$$
$$z = t$$

We can also write this as the ordered triple $(-3t, 2t + 2, t)$.

 Now Try Exercise 33

In the solution of Example 4 the variable t is called a **parameter**. To get a specific solution, we give a specific value to the parameter t. For instance, if we set $t = 2$, we get

$$x = -3(2) = -6$$
$$y = 2(2) + 2 = 6$$
$$z = 2$$

Thus $(-6, 6, 2)$ is a solution of the system. Here are some other solutions of the system obtained by substituting other values for the parameter t.

Parameter t	Solution $(-3t, 2t + 2, t)$
-1	$(3, 0, -1)$
0	$(0, 2, 0)$
3	$(-9, 8, 3)$
10	$(-30, 22, 10)$

You should check that these points satisfy the original equations. There are infinitely many choices for the parameter t, so the system has infinitely many solutions.

■ Modeling Using Linear Systems

Linear systems are used to model situations that involve several varying quantities. In the next example we consider an application of linear systems to finance.

EXAMPLE 5 ■ Modeling a Financial Problem Using a Linear System

Jason receives an inheritance of $50,000. His financial advisor suggests that he invest this in three mutual funds: a money-market fund, a blue-chip stock fund, and a high-tech stock fund. The advisor estimates that the money-market fund will return 5% over the next year, the blue-chip fund 9%, and the high-tech fund 16%. Jason wants a total first-year return of $4000. To avoid excessive risk, he decides to invest three times as much in the money-market fund as in the high-tech stock fund. How much should he invest in each fund?

SOLUTION

Let $x =$ amount invested in the money-market fund

   $y =$ amount invested in the blue-chip stock fund

   $z =$ amount invested in the high-tech stock fund

We convert each fact given in the problem into an equation.

$$x + y + z = 50{,}000 \qquad \text{Total amount invested is \$50,000}$$
$$0.05x + 0.09y + 0.16z = 4000 \qquad \text{Total investment return is \$4000}$$
$$x = 3z \qquad \text{Money-market amount is } 3 \times \text{high-tech amount}$$

Multiplying the second equation by 100 and rewriting the third, we get the following system, which we solve using Gaussian elimination.

$$\begin{cases} x + y + z = 50{,}000 \\ 5x + 9y + 16z = 400{,}000 \qquad \text{100} \times \text{Equation 2} \\ x \qquad - 3z = \qquad 0 \qquad \text{Subtract } 3z \end{cases}$$

$$\begin{cases} x + y + z = 50{,}000 \\ 4y + 11z = 150{,}000 \qquad \text{Equation 2} + (-5) \times \text{Equation 1} = \text{new Equation 2} \\ -y - 4z = -50{,}000 \qquad \text{Equation 3} + (-1) \times \text{Equation 1} = \text{new Equation 3} \end{cases}$$

$$\begin{cases} x + y + z = 50{,}000 \\ -5z = -50{,}000 \qquad \text{Equation 2} + 4 \times \text{Equation 3} = \text{new Equation 2} \\ -y - 4z = -50{,}000 \end{cases}$$

$$\begin{cases} x + y + z = 50{,}000 \\ z = 10{,}000 \qquad \left(-\tfrac{1}{5}\right) \times \text{Equation 2} \\ y + 4z = 50{,}000 \qquad (-1) \times \text{Equation 3} \end{cases}$$

$$\begin{cases} x + y + z = 50{,}000 \\ y + 4z = 50{,}000 \qquad \text{Interchange Equations 2 and 3} \\ z = 10{,}000 \end{cases}$$

Now that the system is in triangular form, we use back-substitution to find that $x = 30{,}000$, $y = 10{,}000$, and $z = 10{,}000$. This means that Jason should invest

$30,000 in the money-market fund

$10,000 in the blue-chip stock fund

$10,000 in the high-tech stock fund

✎ Now Try Exercise 39

10.2 EXERCISES

CONCEPTS

1–2 ■ These exercises refer to the following system:

$$\begin{cases} x - y + z = 2 \\ -x + 2y + z = -3 \\ 3x + y - 2z = 2 \end{cases}$$

1. If we add 2 times the first equation to the second equation, the second equation becomes _____ = ____.

2. To eliminate x from the third equation, we add _____ times the first equation to the third equation. The third equation becomes _____ = ____.

SKILLS

3–6 ■ Is the System of Equations Linear? State whether the equation or system of equations is linear.

3. $6x - \sqrt{3}y + \frac{1}{2}z = 0$

4. $x^2 + y^2 + z^2 = 4$

5. $\begin{cases} xy - 3y + z = 5 \\ x - y^2 + 5z = 0 \\ 2x + yz = 3 \end{cases}$

6. $\begin{cases} x - 2y + 3z = 10 \\ 2x + 5y = 2 \\ y + 2z = 4 \end{cases}$

7–12 ■ Triangular Systems Use back-substitution to solve the triangular system.

7. $\begin{cases} x - 3y + z = 0 \\ y - z = 3 \\ z = -2 \end{cases}$

8. $\begin{cases} 3x - 3y + z = 0 \\ y + 4z = 10 \\ z = 3 \end{cases}$

9. $\begin{cases} x + 2y + z = 7 \\ -y + 3z = 9 \\ 2z = 6 \end{cases}$

10. $\begin{cases} x - 2y + 3z = 10 \\ 2y - z = 2 \\ 3z = 12 \end{cases}$

11. $\begin{cases} 2x - y + 6z = 5 \\ y + 4z = 0 \\ -2z = 1 \end{cases}$

12. $\begin{cases} 4x + 3z = 10 \\ 2y - z = -6 \\ \frac{1}{2}z = 4 \end{cases}$

13–16 ■ Eliminating a Variable Perform an operation on the given system that eliminates the indicated variable. Write the new equivalent system.

13. $\begin{cases} 3x + y + z = 4 \\ -x + y + 2z = 0 \\ x - 2y - z = -1 \end{cases}$

Eliminate the x-term from the second equation.

14. $\begin{cases} -5x + 2y - 3z = 3 \\ 10x - 3y + z = -20 \\ -x + 3y + z = 8 \end{cases}$

Eliminate the x-term from the second equation.

15. $\begin{cases} 2x + y - 3z = 5 \\ 2x + 3y + z = 13 \\ 6x - 5y - z = 7 \end{cases}$

Eliminate the x-term from the third equation.

16. $\begin{cases} x - 3y + 2z = -1 \\ y + z = -1 \\ 2y - z = 1 \end{cases}$

Eliminate the y-term from the third equation.

17–38 ■ Solving a System of Equations in Three Variables Find the complete solution of the linear system, or show that it is inconsistent.

17. $\begin{cases} x - y - z = 4 \\ 2y + z = -1 \\ -x + y - 2z = 5 \end{cases}$

18. $\begin{cases} x - y + z = 0 \\ y + 2z = -2 \\ x + y - z = 2 \end{cases}$

19. $\begin{cases} x + 2y - z = -6 \\ y - 3z = -16 \\ x - 3y + 2z = 14 \end{cases}$

20. $\begin{cases} x - 2y + 3z = -10 \\ 3y + z = 7 \\ x + y - z = 7 \end{cases}$

21. $\begin{cases} x + y + z = 4 \\ x + 3y + 3z = 10 \\ 2x + y - z = 3 \end{cases}$

22. $\begin{cases} x + y + z = 0 \\ -x + 2y + 5z = 3 \\ 3x - y = 6 \end{cases}$

23. $\begin{cases} x - 4z = 1 \\ 2x - y - 6z = 4 \\ 2x + 3y - 2z = 8 \end{cases}$

24. $\begin{cases} x - y + 2z = 2 \\ 3x + y + 5z = 8 \\ 2x - y - 2z = -7 \end{cases}$

25. $\begin{cases} 2x + 4y - z = 2 \\ x + 2y - 3z = -4 \\ 3x - y + z = 1 \end{cases}$

26. $\begin{cases} 2x + y - z = -8 \\ -x + y + z = 3 \\ -2x + 4z = 18 \end{cases}$

27. $\begin{cases} 2y + 4z = -1 \\ -2x + y + 2z = -1 \\ 4x - 2y = 0 \end{cases}$

28. $\begin{cases} y - z = -1 \\ 6x + 2y + z = 2 \\ -x - y - 3z = -2 \end{cases}$

29. $\begin{cases} x + 2y - z = 1 \\ 2x + 3y - 4z = -3 \\ 3x + 6y - 3z = 4 \end{cases}$

30. $\begin{cases} -x + 2y + 5z = 4 \\ x - 2z = 0 \\ 4x - 2y - 11z = 2 \end{cases}$

31. $\begin{cases} 2x + 3y - z = 1 \\ x + 2y = 3 \\ x + 3y + z = 4 \end{cases}$

32. $\begin{cases} x - 2y - 3z = 5 \\ 2x + y - z = 5 \\ 4x - 3y - 7z = 5 \end{cases}$

33. $\begin{cases} x + y - z = 0 \\ x + 2y - 3z = -3 \\ 2x + 3y - 4z = -3 \end{cases}$

34. $\begin{cases} x - 2y + z = 3 \\ 2x - 5y + 6z = 7 \\ 2x - 3y - 2z = 5 \end{cases}$

35. $\begin{cases} x + 3y - 2z = 0 \\ 2x + 4z = 4 \\ 4x + 6y = 4 \end{cases}$

36. $\begin{cases} 2x + 4y - z = 3 \\ x + 2y + 4z = 6 \\ x + 2y - 2z = 0 \end{cases}$

37. $\begin{cases} x + z + 2w = 6 \\ y - 2z = -3 \\ x + 2y - z = -2 \\ 2x + y + 3z - 2w = 0 \end{cases}$

38. $\begin{cases} x + y + z + w = 0 \\ x + y + 2z + 2w = 0 \\ 2x + 2y + 3z + 4w = 1 \\ 2x + 3y + 4z + 5w = 2 \end{cases}$

APPLICATIONS

39. Financial Planning Mark has $100,000 to invest. His financial consultant advises him to diversify his investment in three types of bonds: short-term, intermediate-term, and long-term. The short-term bonds pay 4%, the intermediate-term bonds pay 5%, and the long-term bonds pay 6% simple interest per year. Mark wishes to realize a total annual income of 5.1%, with equal amounts invested in short- and intermediate-term bonds. How much should he invest in each type of bond?

40. Financial Planning Cyndee wants to invest $50,000. Her financial planner advises her to invest in three types of accounts: one paying 3%, one paying $5\frac{1}{2}$%, and one paying 9% simple interest per year. Cyndee wants to put twice as much in the lowest-yielding, least-risky account as in the highest-yielding account. How much should she invest in each account to achieve a total annual return of $2540?

41. Agriculture A farmer has 1200 acres of land on which he grows corn, wheat, and soybeans. It costs $45 per acre to grow corn, $60 to grow wheat, and $50 to grow soybeans. Because of market demand, the farmer will grow twice as many acres of wheat as of corn. He has allocated $63,750 for the cost of growing his crops. How many acres of each crop should he plant?

42. Gas Station A gas station sells three types of gas: Regular for $3.00 a gallon, Performance Plus for $3.20 a gallon, and Premium for $3.30 a gallon. On a particular day 6500 gallons of gas were sold for a total of $20,050. Three times as many gallons of Regular as Premium gas were sold. How many gallons of each type of gas were sold that day?

43. Nutrition A biologist is performing an experiment on the effects of various combinations of vitamins. She wishes to feed each of her laboratory rabbits a diet that contains exactly 9 mg of niacin, 14 mg of thiamin, and 32 mg of riboflavin. She has available three different types of commercial rabbit pellets; their vitamin content (per ounce) is given in the table. How many ounces of each type of food should each rabbit be given daily to satisfy the experiment requirements?

	Type A	Type B	Type C
Niacin (mg/oz)	2	3	1
Thiamin (mg/oz)	3	1	3
Riboflavin (mg/oz)	8	5	7

44. Diet Program Nicole started a new diet that requires each meal to have 460 calories, 6 g of fiber, and 11 g of fat. The table shows the fiber, fat, and calorie content of one serving of each of three breakfast foods. How many servings of each food should Nicole eat to follow her diet?

Food	Fiber (g)	Fat (g)	Calories
Toast	2	1	100
Cottage cheese	0	5	120
Fruit	2	0	60

45. Juice Blends The Juice Company offers three kinds of smoothies: Midnight Mango, Tropical Torrent, and Pineapple Power. Each smoothie contains the amounts of juices shown in the table.

Smoothie	Mango juice (oz)	Pineapple juice (oz)	Orange juice (oz)
Midnight Mango	8	3	3
Tropical Torrent	6	5	3
Pineapple Power	2	8	4

On a particular day the Juice Company used 820 oz of mango juice, 690 oz of pineapple juice, and 450 oz of orange juice. How many smoothies of each kind were sold that day?

46. Appliance Manufacturing Kitchen Korner produces refrigerators, dishwashers, and stoves at three different factories. The table gives the number of each product produced at each factory per day. Kitchen Korner receives an order for 110 refrigerators, 150 dishwashers, and 114 ovens. How many days should each plant be scheduled to fill this order?

Appliance	Factory A	Factory B	Factory C
Refrigerators	8	10	14
Dishwashers	16	12	10
Stoves	10	18	6

47. Stock Portfolio An investor owns three stocks: A, B, and C. The closing prices of the stocks on three successive trading days are given in the table.

	Stock A	Stock B	Stock C
Monday	$10	$25	$29
Tuesday	$12	$20	$32
Wednesday	$16	$15	$32

Despite the volatility in the stock prices, the total value of the investor's stocks remained unchanged at $74,000 at the end of each of these three days. How many shares of each stock does the investor own?

48. Electricity By using Kirchhoff's Laws, it can be shown that the currents I_1, I_2, and I_3 that pass through the three branches of the circuit in the figure satisfy the given linear system. Solve the system to find I_1, I_2, and I_3.

$$\begin{cases} I_1 + I_2 - I_3 = 0 \\ 16I_1 - 8I_2 \quad\quad = 4 \\ \quad\quad 8I_2 + 4I_3 = 5 \end{cases}$$

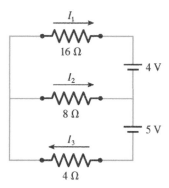

49. PROVE: Can a Linear System Have Exactly Two Solutions?

(a) Suppose that (x_0, y_0, z_0) and (x_1, y_1, z_1) are solutions of the system

$$\begin{cases} a_1x + b_1y + c_1z = d_1 \\ a_2x + b_2y + c_2z = d_2 \\ a_3x + b_3y + c_3z = d_3 \end{cases}$$

Show that $\left(\dfrac{x_0 + x_1}{2}, \dfrac{y_0 + y_1}{2}, \dfrac{z_0 + z_1}{2}\right)$ is also a solution.

(b) Use the result of part (a) to prove that if the system has two different solutions, then it has infinitely many solutions.

10.3 PARTIAL FRACTIONS

■ Distinct Linear Factors ■ Repeated Linear Factors ■ Irreducible Quadratic Factors
■ Repeated Irreducible Quadratic Factors

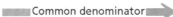

Common denominator ➡

$$\frac{1}{x-1} + \frac{1}{2x+1} = \frac{3x}{2x^2 - x - 1}$$

⬅ Partial fractions

To write a sum or difference of fractional expressions as a single fraction, we bring them to a common denominator. For example,

$$\frac{1}{x-1} + \frac{1}{2x+1} = \frac{(2x+1)+(x-1)}{(x-1)(2x+1)} = \frac{3x}{2x^2 - x - 1}$$

But for some applications of algebra to calculus we must reverse this process—that is, we must express a fraction such as $3x/(2x^2 - x - 1)$ as the sum of the simpler fractions $1/(x-1)$ and $1/(2x+1)$. These simpler fractions are called *partial fractions*; we learn how to find them in this section.

Let r be the rational function

$$r(x) = \frac{P(x)}{Q(x)}$$

where the degree of P is less than the degree of Q. By the Linear and Quadratic Factors Theorem in Section 3.5, every polynomial with real coefficients can be factored completely into linear and irreducible quadratic factors, that is, factors of the form $ax + b$ and $ax^2 + bx + c$, where a, b, and c are real numbers. For instance,

$$x^4 - 1 = (x^2 - 1)(x^2 + 1) = (x - 1)(x + 1)(x^2 + 1)$$

After we have completely factored the denominator Q of r, we can express $r(x)$ as a sum of **partial fractions** of the form

$$\frac{A}{(ax+b)^i} \quad \text{and} \quad \frac{Ax+B}{(ax^2+bx+c)^j}$$

This sum is called the **partial fraction decomposition** of r. Let's examine the details of the four possible cases.

■ Distinct Linear Factors

We first consider the case in which the denominator factors into distinct linear factors.

**CASE 1: THE DENOMINATOR IS A PRODUCT OF DISTINCT
LINEAR FACTORS**

Suppose that we can factor $Q(x)$ as

$$Q(x) = (a_1x + b_1)(a_2x + b_2) \cdots (a_nx + b_n)$$

with no factor repeated. In this case the partial fraction decomposition of $P(x)/Q(x)$ takes the form

$$\frac{P(x)}{Q(x)} = \frac{A_1}{a_1x + b_1} + \frac{A_2}{a_2x + b_2} + \cdots + \frac{A_n}{a_nx + b_n}$$

The constants $A_1, A_2, \ldots, A_n$ are determined as in the following example.

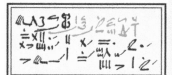

EXAMPLE 1 ▪ Distinct Linear Factors

Find the partial fraction decomposition of $\dfrac{5x + 7}{x^3 + 2x^2 - x - 2}$.

SOLUTION The denominator factors as follows.

$$x^3 + 2x^2 - x - 2 = x^2(x + 2) - (x + 2) = (x^2 - 1)(x + 2)$$
$$= (x - 1)(x + 1)(x + 2)$$

This gives us the partial fraction decomposition

$$\frac{5x + 7}{x^3 + 2x^2 - x - 2} = \frac{A}{x - 1} + \frac{B}{x + 1} + \frac{C}{x + 2}$$

Multiplying each side by the common denominator, $(x - 1)(x + 1)(x + 2)$, we get

$$5x + 7 = A(x + 1)(x + 2) + B(x - 1)(x + 2) + C(x - 1)(x + 1)$$
$$= A(x^2 + 3x + 2) + B(x^2 + x - 2) + C(x^2 - 1) \qquad \text{Expand}$$
$$= (A + B + C)x^2 + (3A + B)x + (2A - 2B - C) \qquad \text{Combine like terms}$$

If two polynomials are equal, then their coefficients are equal. Thus since $5x + 7$ has no x^2-term, we have $A + B + C = 0$. Similarly, by comparing the coefficients of x, we see that $3A + B = 5$, and by comparing constant terms, we get $2A - 2B - C = 7$. This leads to the following system of linear equations for A, B, and C.

$$\begin{cases} A + B + C = 0 & \text{Equation 1: Coefficients of } x^2 \\ 3A + B = 5 & \text{Equation 2: Coefficients of } x \\ 2A - 2B - C = 7 & \text{Equation 3: Constant coefficients} \end{cases}$$

We use Gaussian elimination to solve this system.

$$\begin{cases} A + B + C = 0 \\ -2B - 3C = 5 & \text{Equation 2} + (-3) \times \text{Equation 1} \\ -4B - 3C = 7 & \text{Equation 3} + (-2) \times \text{Equation 1} \end{cases}$$

$$\begin{cases} A + B + C = 0 \\ -2B - 3C = 5 \\ 3C = -3 & \text{Equation 3} + (-2) \times \text{Equation 2} \end{cases}$$

From the third equation we get $C = -1$. Back-substituting, we find that $B = -1$ and $A = 2$. So the partial fraction decomposition is

$$\frac{5x + 7}{x^3 + 2x^2 - x - 2} = \frac{2}{x - 1} + \frac{-1}{x + 1} + \frac{-1}{x + 2}$$

✎ ▸ Now Try Exercises 3 and 13

The same approach works in the remaining cases. We set up the partial fraction decomposition with the unknown constants A, B, C, ... Then we multiply each side of the resulting equation by the common denominator, combine like terms on the right-hand side of the equation, and equate coefficients. This gives a set of linear equations that will always have a unique solution (provided that the partial fraction decomposition has been set up correctly).

▪ Repeated Linear Factors

We now consider the case in which the denominator factors into linear factors, some of which are repeated.

CASE 2: THE DENOMINATOR IS A PRODUCT OF LINEAR FACTORS, SOME OF WHICH ARE REPEATED

Suppose the complete factorization of $Q(x)$ contains the linear factor $ax + b$ repeated k times; that is, $(ax + b)^k$ is a factor of $Q(x)$. Then, corresponding to each such factor, the partial fraction decomposition for $P(x)/Q(x)$ contains

$$\frac{A_1}{ax + b} + \frac{A_2}{(ax + b)^2} + \cdots + \frac{A_k}{(ax + b)^k}$$

EXAMPLE 2   Repeated Linear Factors

Find the partial fraction decomposition of $\dfrac{x^2 + 1}{x(x - 1)^3}$.

SOLUTION   Because the factor $x - 1$ is repeated three times in the denominator, the partial fraction decomposition has the form

$$\frac{x^2 + 1}{x(x - 1)^3} = \frac{A}{x} + \frac{B}{x - 1} + \frac{C}{(x - 1)^2} + \frac{D}{(x - 1)^3}$$

Multiplying each side by the common denominator, $x(x - 1)^3$, gives

$$
\begin{aligned}
x^2 + 1 &= A(x - 1)^3 + Bx(x - 1)^2 + Cx(x - 1) + Dx \\
&= A(x^3 - 3x^2 + 3x - 1) + B(x^3 - 2x^2 + x) + C(x^2 - x) + Dx &&\text{Expand} \\
&= (A + B)x^3 + (-3A - 2B + C)x^2 + (3A + B - C + D)x - A &&\text{Combine like terms}
\end{aligned}
$$

Equating coefficients, we get the following equations.

$$
\begin{cases}
A + B && = 0 &&\text{Coefficients of } x^3 \\
-3A - 2B + C && = 1 &&\text{Coefficients of } x^2 \\
3A + B - C + D && = 0 &&\text{Coefficients of } x \\
-A && = 1 &&\text{Constant coefficients}
\end{cases}
$$

If we rearrange these equations by putting the last one in the first position, we can easily see (using substitution) that the solution to the system is $A = -1, B = 1$, $C = 0, D = 2$, so the partial fraction decomposition is

$$\frac{x^2 + 1}{x(x - 1)^3} = \frac{-1}{x} + \frac{1}{x - 1} + \frac{2}{(x - 1)^3}$$

✎ Now Try Exercises 5 and 29

■ Irreducible Quadratic Factors

We now consider the case in which the denominator has distinct irreducible quadratic factors.

CASE 3: THE DENOMINATOR HAS IRREDUCIBLE QUADRATIC FACTORS, NONE OF WHICH IS REPEATED

Suppose the complete factorization of $Q(x)$ contains the quadratic factor $ax^2 + bx + c$ (which can't be factored further). Then, corresponding to this, the partial fraction decomposition of $P(x)/Q(x)$ will have a term of the form

$$\frac{Ax + B}{ax^2 + bx + c}$$

EXAMPLE 3 ■ Distinct Quadratic Factors

Find the partial fraction decomposition of $\dfrac{2x^2 - x + 4}{x^3 + 4x}$.

SOLUTION Since $x^3 + 4x = x(x^2 + 4)$, which can't be factored further, we write

$$\frac{2x^2 - x + 4}{x^3 + 4x} = \frac{A}{x} + \frac{Bx + C}{x^2 + 4}$$

Multiplying by $x(x^2 + 4)$, we get

$$2x^2 - x + 4 = A(x^2 + 4) + (Bx + C)x$$
$$= (A + B)x^2 + Cx + 4A$$

Equating coefficients gives us the equations

$$\begin{cases} A + B = 2 & \text{Coefficients of } x^2 \\ C = -1 & \text{Coefficients of } x \\ 4A = 4 & \text{Constant coefficients} \end{cases}$$

so $A = 1$, $B = 1$, and $C = -1$. The required partial fraction decomposition is

$$\frac{2x^2 - x + 4}{x^3 + 4x} = \frac{1}{x} + \frac{x - 1}{x^2 + 4}$$

✎ Now Try Exercises 7 and 37

■ Repeated Irreducible Quadratic Factors

We now consider the case in which the denominator has irreducible quadratic factors, some of which are repeated.

CASE 4: THE DENOMINATOR HAS A REPEATED IRREDUCIBLE QUADRATIC FACTOR

Suppose the complete factorization of $Q(x)$ contains the factor $(ax^2 + bx + c)^k$, where $ax^2 + bx + c$ can't be factored further. Then the partial fraction decomposition of $P(x)/Q(x)$ will have the terms

$$\frac{A_1 x + B_1}{ax^2 + bx + c} + \frac{A_2 x + B_2}{(ax^2 + bx + c)^2} + \cdots + \frac{A_k x + B_k}{(ax^2 + bx + c)^k}$$

EXAMPLE 4 ■ Repeated Quadratic Factors

Write the form of the partial fraction decomposition of

$$\frac{x^5 - 3x^2 + 12x - 1}{x^3(x^2 + x + 1)(x^2 + 2)^3}$$

SOLUTION

$$\frac{x^5 - 3x^2 + 12x - 1}{x^3(x^2 + x + 1)(x^2 + 2)^3}$$

$$= \frac{A}{x} + \frac{B}{x^2} + \frac{C}{x^3} + \frac{Dx + E}{x^2 + x + 1} + \frac{Fx + G}{x^2 + 2} + \frac{Hx + I}{(x^2 + 2)^2} + \frac{Jx + K}{(x^2 + 2)^3}$$

✎ Now Try Exercises 11 and 41

To find the values of $A, B, C, D, E, F, G, H, I, J,$ and K in Example 4, we would have to solve a system of 11 linear equations. Although possible, this would certainly involve a great deal of work!

The techniques that we have described in this section apply only to rational functions $P(x)/Q(x)$ in which the degree of P is less than the degree of Q. If this isn't the case, we must first use long division to divide Q into P.

EXAMPLE 5 ■ Using Long Division to Prepare for Partial Fractions

Find the partial fraction decomposition of

$$\frac{2x^4 + 4x^3 - 2x^2 + x + 7}{x^3 + 2x^2 - x - 2}$$

SOLUTION Since the degree of the numerator is larger than the degree of the denominator, we use long division to obtain

$$x^3 + 2x^2 - x - 2\overline{)\begin{array}{l} 2x \\ 2x^4 + 4x^3 - 2x^2 + x + 7 \\ \underline{2x^4 + 4x^3 - 2x^2 - 4x} \\ 5x + 7 \end{array}}$$

$$\frac{2x^4 + 4x^3 - 2x^2 + x + 7}{x^3 + 2x^2 - x - 2} = 2x + \frac{5x + 7}{x^3 + 2x^2 - x - 2}$$

The remainder term now satisfies the requirement that the degree of the numerator is less than the degree of the denominator. At this point we proceed as in Example 1 to obtain the decomposition

$$\frac{2x^4 + 4x^3 - 2x^2 + x + 7}{x^3 + 2x^2 - x - 2} = 2x + \frac{2}{x - 1} + \frac{-1}{x + 1} + \frac{-1}{x + 2}$$

✎ Now Try Exercise 43

10.3 EXERCISES

CONCEPTS

1–2 ■ For each rational function r, choose from (i)–(iv) the appropriate form for its partial fraction decomposition.

1. $r(x) = \dfrac{4}{x(x - 2)^2}$

(i) $\dfrac{A}{x} + \dfrac{B}{x - 2}$ (ii) $\dfrac{A}{x} + \dfrac{B}{(x - 2)^2}$

(iii) $\dfrac{A}{x} + \dfrac{B}{x - 2} + \dfrac{C}{(x - 2)^2}$ (iv) $\dfrac{A}{x} + \dfrac{B}{x - 2} + \dfrac{Cx + D}{(x - 2)^2}$

2. $r(x) = \dfrac{2x + 8}{(x - 1)(x^2 + 4)}$

(i) $\dfrac{A}{x - 1} + \dfrac{B}{x^2 + 4}$

(ii) $\dfrac{A}{x - 1} + \dfrac{Bx + C}{x^2 + 4}$

(iii) $\dfrac{A}{x - 1} + \dfrac{B}{x + 2} + \dfrac{C}{x^2 + 4}$

(iv) $\dfrac{Ax + B}{x - 1} + \dfrac{Cx + D}{x^2 + 4}$

SKILLS

3–12 ■ **Form of the Partial Fraction Decomposition** Write the form of the partial fraction decomposition of the function (as in Example 4). Do not determine the numerical values of the coefficients.

3. $\dfrac{1}{(x - 1)(x + 2)}$ **4.** $\dfrac{x}{x^2 + 3x - 4}$

5. $\dfrac{x^2 - 3x + 5}{(x - 2)^2(x + 4)}$ **6.** $\dfrac{1}{x^4 - x^3}$

7. $\dfrac{x^2}{(x - 3)(x^2 + 4)}$ **8.** $\dfrac{1}{x^4 - 1}$

9. $\dfrac{x^3 - 4x^2 + 2}{(x^2 + 1)(x^2 + 2)}$ **10.** $\dfrac{x^4 + x^2 + 1}{x^2(x^2 + 4)^2}$

11. $\dfrac{x^3 + x + 1}{x(2x - 5)^3(x^2 + 2x + 5)^2}$ **12.** $\dfrac{1}{(x^3 - 1)(x^2 - 1)}$

13–44 ■ **Partial Fraction Decomposition** Find the partial fraction decomposition of the rational function.

13. $\dfrac{2}{(x - 1)(x + 1)}$ **14.** $\dfrac{2x}{(x - 1)(x + 1)}$

15. $\dfrac{5}{(x-1)(x+4)}$

16. $\dfrac{x+6}{x(x+3)}$

17. $\dfrac{12}{x^2-9}$

18. $\dfrac{x-12}{x^2-4x}$

19. $\dfrac{4}{x^2-4}$

20. $\dfrac{2x+1}{x^2+x-2}$

21. $\dfrac{x+14}{x^2-2x-8}$

22. $\dfrac{8x-3}{2x^2-x}$

23. $\dfrac{x}{8x^2-10x+3}$

24. $\dfrac{7x-3}{x^3+2x^2-3x}$

25. $\dfrac{9x^2-9x+6}{2x^3-x^2-8x+4}$

26. $\dfrac{-3x^2-3x+27}{(x+2)(2x^2+3x-9)}$

27. $\dfrac{x^2+1}{x^3+x^2}$

28. $\dfrac{3x^2+5x-13}{(3x+2)(x^2-4x+4)}$

29. $\dfrac{2x}{4x^2+12x+9}$

30. $\dfrac{x-4}{(2x-5)^2}$

31. $\dfrac{4x^2-x-2}{x^4+2x^3}$

32. $\dfrac{x^3-2x^2-4x+3}{x^4}$

33. $\dfrac{-10x^2+27x-14}{(x-1)^3(x+2)}$

34. $\dfrac{-2x^2+5x-1}{x^4-2x^3+2x-1}$

35. $\dfrac{3x^3+22x^2+53x+41}{(x+2)^2(x+3)^2}$

36. $\dfrac{3x^2+12x-20}{x^4-8x^2+16}$

37. $\dfrac{x-3}{x^3+3x}$

38. $\dfrac{3x^2-2x+8}{x^3-x^2+2x-2}$

39. $\dfrac{2x^3+7x+5}{(x^2+x+2)(x^2+1)}$

40. $\dfrac{x^2+x+1}{2x^4+3x^2+1}$

41. $\dfrac{x^4+x^3+x^2-x+1}{x(x^2+1)^2}$

42. $\dfrac{2x^2-x+8}{(x^2+4)^2}$

43. $\dfrac{x^5-2x^4+x^3+x+5}{x^3-2x^2+x-2}$

44. $\dfrac{x^5-3x^4+3x^3-4x^2+4x+12}{(x-2)^2(x^2+2)}$

SKILLS Plus

45. Partial Fractions Determine A and B in terms of a and b.

$$\frac{ax+b}{x^2-1}=\frac{A}{x-1}+\frac{B}{x+1}$$

46. Partial Fractions Determine A, B, C, and D in terms of a and b.

$$\frac{ax^3+bx^2}{(x^2+1)^2}=\frac{Ax+B}{x^2+1}+\frac{Cx+D}{(x^2+1)^2}$$

DISCUSS ▪ DISCOVER ▪ PROVE ▪ WRITE

47. DISCUSS: Recognizing Partial Fraction Decompositions
For each expression, determine whether it is already a partial fraction decomposition or whether it can be decomposed further.

(a) $\dfrac{x}{x^2+1}+\dfrac{1}{x+1}$

(b) $\dfrac{x}{(x+1)^2}$

(c) $\dfrac{1}{x+1}+\dfrac{2}{(x+1)^2}$

(d) $\dfrac{x+2}{(x^2+1)^2}$

48. DISCUSS: Assembling and Disassembling Partial Fractions
The following expression is a partial fraction decomposition.

$$\frac{2}{x-1}+\frac{1}{(x-1)^2}+\frac{1}{x+1}$$

Use a common denominator to combine the terms into one fraction. Then use the techniques of this section to find its partial fraction decomposition. Did you get back the original expression?

10.4 SYSTEMS OF NONLINEAR EQUATIONS

▪ Substitution and Elimination Methods ▪ Graphical Method

In this section we solve systems of equations in which the equations are not all linear. The methods we learned in Section 10.1 can also be used to solve nonlinear systems.

▪ Substitution and Elimination Methods

To solve a system of nonlinear equations, we can use the substitution or elimination method, as illustrated in the next examples.

EXAMPLE 1 ▪ Substitution Method

Find all solutions of the system.

$$\begin{cases} x^2+y^2=100 & \text{Equation 1} \\ 3x-y=10 & \text{Equation 2} \end{cases}$$

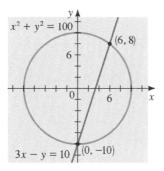

FIGURE 1

$x = 0, y = -10$:

$$\begin{cases} (0)^2 + (-10)^2 = 100 \\ 3(0) - (-10) = 10 \end{cases} \checkmark$$

$x = 6, y = 8$:

$$\begin{cases} (6)^2 + (8)^2 = 36 + 64 = 100 \\ 3(6) - (8) = 18 - 8 = 10 \end{cases} \checkmark$$

SOLUTION **Solve for one variable.**   We start by solving for y in the second equation.

$$y = 3x - 10 \qquad \text{Solve for } y \text{ in Equation 2}$$

Substitute.   Next we substitute for y in the first equation and solve for x.

$$x^2 + (3x - 10)^2 = 100 \qquad \text{Substitute } y = 3x - 10 \text{ into Equation 1}$$
$$x^2 + (9x^2 - 60x + 100) = 100 \qquad \text{Expand}$$
$$10x^2 - 60x = 0 \qquad \text{Simplify}$$
$$10x(x - 6) = 0 \qquad \text{Factor}$$
$$x = 0 \quad \text{or} \quad x = 6 \qquad \text{Solve for } x$$

Back-substitute.   Now we back-substitute these values of x into the equation $y = 3x - 10$.

$$\text{For} \quad x = 0: \quad y = 3(0) - 10 = -10 \qquad \text{Back-substitute}$$
$$\text{For} \quad x = 6: \quad y = 3(6) - 10 = \quad 8 \qquad \text{Back-substitute}$$

So we have two solutions: $(0, -10)$ and $(6, 8)$.

The graph of the first equation is a circle, and the graph of the second equation is a line. Figure 1 shows that the graphs intersect at the two points $(0, -10)$ and $(6, 8)$.

✎. Now Try Exercise 5

EXAMPLE 2   Elimination Method

Find all solutions of the system.

$$\begin{cases} 3x^2 + 2y = 26 & \text{Equation 1} \\ 5x^2 + 7y = 3 & \text{Equation 2} \end{cases}$$

SOLUTION   We choose to eliminate the x-term, so we multiply the first equation by 5 and the second equation by -3. Then we add the two equations and solve for y.

$$\begin{cases} 15x^2 + 10y = \quad 130 & 5 \times \text{Equation 1} \\ -15x^2 - 21y = \quad -9 & (-3) \times \text{Equation 2} \end{cases}$$
$$-11y = \quad 121 \qquad \text{Add}$$
$$y = -11 \qquad \text{Solve for } y$$

Now we back-substitute $y = -11$ into one of the original equations, say $3x^2 + 2y = 26$, and solve for x.

$$3x^2 + 2(-11) = 26 \qquad \text{Back-substitute } y = -11 \text{ into Equation 1}$$
$$3x^2 = 48 \qquad \text{Add 22}$$
$$x^2 = 16 \qquad \text{Divide by 3}$$
$$x = -4 \quad \text{or} \quad x = 4 \qquad \text{Solve for } x$$

So we have two solutions: $(-4, -11)$ and $(4, -11)$.

The graphs of both equations are parabolas (see Section 3.1). Figure 2 shows that the graphs intersect at the two points $(-4, -11)$ and $(4, -11)$.

✎. Now Try Exercise 11

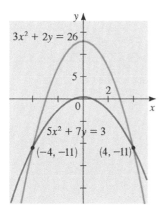

FIGURE 2

$x = -4, y = -11$:

$$\begin{cases} 3(-4)^2 + 2(-11) = 26 \\ 5(-4)^2 + 7(-11) = 3 \end{cases} \checkmark$$

$x = 4, y = -11$:

$$\begin{cases} 3(4)^2 + 2(-11) = 26 \\ 5(4)^2 + 7(-11) = 3 \end{cases} \checkmark$$

▪ Graphical Method

The graphical method is particularly useful in solving systems of nonlinear equations.

EXAMPLE 3 ■ Graphical Method

Find all solutions of the system

$$\begin{cases} x^2 - y = 2 \\ 2x - y = -1 \end{cases}$$

SOLUTION **Graph each equation.** To graph, we solve for y in each equation.

$$\begin{cases} y = x^2 - 2 \\ y = 2x + 1 \end{cases}$$

Find intersection points. Figure 3 shows that the graphs of these equations intersect at two points. Zooming in, we see that the solutions are

$$(-1, -1) \quad \text{and} \quad (3, 7)$$

See Appendix C, *Graphing with a Graphing Calculator*, for guidelines on using a graphing calculator. See Appendix D, *Using the TI-83/84 Graphing Calculator*, for specific graphing instructions.

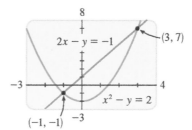

FIGURE 3

CHECK YOUR ANSWERS

$x = -1, y = -1$:

$$\begin{cases} (-1)^2 - (-1) = 2 \\ 2(-1) - (-1) = -1 \quad \checkmark \end{cases}$$

$x = 3, y = 7$:

$$\begin{cases} 3^2 - 7 = 2 \\ 2(3) - 7 = -1 \quad \checkmark \end{cases}$$

✎ ■ Now Try Exercise 33

EXAMPLE 4 ■ Solving a System of Equations Graphically

Find all solutions of the system, rounded to one decimal place.

$$\begin{cases} x^2 + y^2 = 12 & \text{Equation 1} \\ y = 2x^2 - 5x & \text{Equation 2} \end{cases}$$

Mathematics in the Modern World

Courtesy of NASA

Global Positioning System (GPS)

On a cold, foggy day in 1707 a British naval fleet was sailing home at a fast clip. The fleet's navigators didn't know it, but the fleet was only a few yards from the rocky shores of England. In the ensuing disaster the fleet was totally destroyed. This tragedy could have been avoided had the navigators known their positions. In those days latitude was determined by the position of the North Star (and this could be done only at night in good weather), and

longitude was determined by the position of the sun relative to where it would be in England *at that same time*. So navigation required an accurate method of telling time on ships. (The invention of the spring-loaded clock brought about the eventual solution.)

Since then, several different methods have been developed to determine position, and all rely heavily on mathematics (see LORAN, page 848). The latest method, called the Global Positioning System (GPS), uses triangulation. In this system, 24 satellites are strategically located above the surface of the earth. A handheld GPS device measures distance from a satellite, using the travel time of radio signals emitted from the satellite. Knowing the distances to three different satellites tells us that we are at the point of intersection of three different spheres. This uniquely determines our position (see Exercise 51, page 745).

SOLUTION   The graph of the first equation is a circle, and the graph of the second is a parabola. To graph the circle on a graphing calculator, we must first solve for y in terms of x.

$$x^2 + y^2 = 12$$

$$y^2 = 12 - x^2 \qquad \text{Isolate } y^2 \text{ on LHS}$$

$$y = \pm\sqrt{12 - x^2} \qquad \text{Take square roots}$$

To graph the circle, we must graph both functions.

$$y = \sqrt{12 - x^2} \qquad \text{and} \qquad y = -\sqrt{12 - x^2}$$

In Figure 4 the graph of the circle is shown in red, and the parabola is shown in blue. The graphs intersect in Quadrants I and II. Zooming in, or using the `Intersect` command, we see that the intersection points are $(-0.559, 3.419)$ and $(2.847, 1.974)$. There also appears to be an intersection point in Quadrant IV. However, when we zoom in, we see that the curves come close to each other but don't intersect (see Figure 5). Thus the system has two solutions; rounded to the nearest tenth, they are

$$(-0.6, 3.4) \quad \text{and} \quad (2.8, 2.0)$$

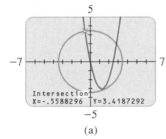
(a)

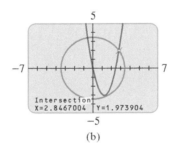
(b)

FIGURE 4 $x^2 + y^2 = 12$, $y = 2x^2 - 5x$

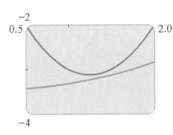

FIGURE 5 Zooming in

✎ Now Try Exercise 37

10.4 EXERCISES

CONCEPTS

1–2 ■ The system of equations

$$\begin{cases} 2y - x^2 = 0 \\ y - x = 4 \end{cases}$$

is graphed below.

1. Use the graph to find the solution(s) of the system.

2. Check that the solutions you found in Exercise 1 satisfy the system.

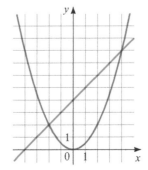

SKILLS

3–8 ■ **Substitution Method**   Use the substitution method to find all solutions of the system of equations.

3. $\begin{cases} y = x^2 \\ y = x + 12 \end{cases}$

4. $\begin{cases} x^2 + y^2 = 25 \\ y = 2x \end{cases}$

5. $\begin{cases} x^2 + y^2 = 8 \\ x + y = 0 \end{cases}$

6. $\begin{cases} x^2 + y = 9 \\ x - y + 3 = 0 \end{cases}$

7. $\begin{cases} x + y^2 = 0 \\ 2x + 5y^2 = 75 \end{cases}$

8. $\begin{cases} x^2 - y = 1 \\ 2x^2 + 3y = 17 \end{cases}$

9–14 ■ **Elimination Method**   Use the elimination method to find all solutions of the system of equations.

9. $\begin{cases} x^2 - 2y = 1 \\ x^2 + 5y = 29 \end{cases}$

10. $\begin{cases} 3x^2 + 4y = 17 \\ 2x^2 + 5y = 2 \end{cases}$

11. $\begin{cases} 3x^2 - y^2 = 11 \\ x^2 + 4y^2 = 8 \end{cases}$

12. $\begin{cases} 2x^2 + 4y = 13 \\ x^2 - y^2 = \frac{7}{2} \end{cases}$

13. $\begin{cases} x - y^2 + 3 = 0 \\ 2x^2 + y^2 - 4 = 0 \end{cases}$

14. $\begin{cases} x^2 - y^2 = 1 \\ 2x^2 - y^2 = x + 3 \end{cases}$

15–18 ■ Finding Intersection Points Graphically Two equations and their graphs are given. Find the intersection point(s) of the graphs by solving the system.

15. $\begin{cases} x^2 + y = 8 \\ x - 2y = -6 \end{cases}$

16. $\begin{cases} x - y^2 = -4 \\ x - y = 2 \end{cases}$

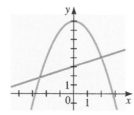

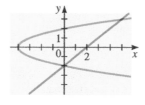

17. $\begin{cases} x^2 + y = 0 \\ x^3 - 2x - y = 0 \end{cases}$

18. $\begin{cases} x^2 + y^2 = 4x \\ x = y^2 \end{cases}$

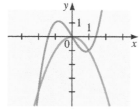

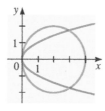

19–32 ■ Solving Nonlinear Systems Find all solutions of the system of equations.

19. $\begin{cases} y + x^2 = 4x \\ y + 4x = 16 \end{cases}$

20. $\begin{cases} x - y^2 = 0 \\ y - x^2 = 0 \end{cases}$

21. $\begin{cases} x - 2y = 2 \\ y^2 - x^2 = 2x + 4 \end{cases}$

22. $\begin{cases} y = 4 - x^2 \\ y = x^2 - 4 \end{cases}$

23. $\begin{cases} x - y = 4 \\ xy = 12 \end{cases}$

24. $\begin{cases} xy = 24 \\ 2x^2 - y^2 + 4 = 0 \end{cases}$

25. $\begin{cases} x^2y = 16 \\ x^2 + 4y + 16 = 0 \end{cases}$

26. $\begin{cases} x + \sqrt{y} = 0 \\ y^2 - 4x^2 = 12 \end{cases}$

27. $\begin{cases} x^2 + y^2 = 9 \\ x^2 - y^2 = 1 \end{cases}$

28. $\begin{cases} x^2 + 2y^2 = 2 \\ 2x^2 - 3y = 15 \end{cases}$

29. $\begin{cases} 2x^2 - 8y^3 = 19 \\ 4x^2 + 16y^3 = 34 \end{cases}$

30. $\begin{cases} x^4 + y^3 = 17 \\ 3x^4 + 5y^3 = 53 \end{cases}$

31. $\begin{cases} \dfrac{2}{x} - \dfrac{3}{y} = 1 \\ -\dfrac{4}{x} + \dfrac{7}{y} = 1 \end{cases}$

32. $\begin{cases} \dfrac{4}{x^2} + \dfrac{6}{y^4} = \dfrac{7}{2} \\ \dfrac{1}{x^2} - \dfrac{2}{y^4} = 0 \end{cases}$

33–40 ■ Graphical Method Use the graphical method to find all solutions of the system of equations, rounded to two decimal places.

33. $\begin{cases} y = x^2 + 8x \\ y = 2x + 16 \end{cases}$

34. $\begin{cases} y = x^2 - 4x \\ 2x - y = 2 \end{cases}$

35. $\begin{cases} x^2 + y^2 = 25 \\ x + 3y = 2 \end{cases}$

36. $\begin{cases} x^2 + y^2 = 17 \\ x^2 - 2x + y^2 = 13 \end{cases}$

37. $\begin{cases} \dfrac{x^2}{9} + \dfrac{y^2}{18} = 1 \\ y = -x^2 + 6x - 2 \end{cases}$

38. $\begin{cases} x^2 - y^2 = 3 \\ y = x^2 - 2x - 8 \end{cases}$

39. $\begin{cases} x^4 + 16y^4 = 32 \\ x^2 + 2x + y = 0 \end{cases}$

40. $\begin{cases} y = e^x + e^{-x} \\ y = 5 - x^2 \end{cases}$

SKILLS Plus

41–44 ■ Some Trickier Systems Follow the hints and solve the systems.

41. $\begin{cases} \log x + \log y = \frac{3}{2} \\ 2 \log x - \log y = 0 \end{cases}$ [*Hint:* Add the equations.]

42. $\begin{cases} 2^x + 2^y = 10 \\ 4^x + 4^y = 68 \end{cases}$ [*Hint:* Note that $4^x = 2^{2x} = (2^x)^2$.]

43. $\begin{cases} x - y = 3 \\ x^3 - y^3 = 387 \end{cases}$ [*Hint:* Factor the left-hand side of the second equation.]

44. $\begin{cases} x^2 + xy = 1 \\ xy + y^2 = 3 \end{cases}$ [*Hint:* Add the equations, and factor the result.]

APPLICATIONS

45. Dimensions of a Rectangle A rectangle has an area of 180 cm^2 and a perimeter of 54 cm. What are its dimensions?

46. Legs of a Right Triangle A right triangle has an area of 84 ft^2 and a hypotenuse 25 ft long. What are the lengths of its other two sides?

47. Dimensions of a Rectangle The perimeter of a rectangle is 70, and its diagonal is 25. Find its length and width.

48. Dimensions of a Rectangle A circular piece of sheet metal has a diameter of 20 in. The edges are to be cut off to form a rectangle of area 160 in^2 (see the figure). What are the dimensions of the rectangle?

49. Flight of a Rocket A hill is inclined so that its "slope" is $\frac{1}{2}$, as shown in the figure. We introduce a coordinate system with the origin at the base of the hill and with the scales on the axes measured in meters. A rocket is fired from the base of the hill in such a way that its trajectory is the parabola $y = -x^2 + 401x$. At what point does the rocket strike the hillside? How far is this point from the base of the hill (to the nearest centimeter)?

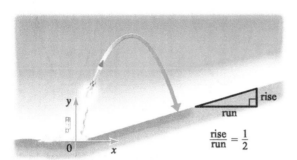

50. Making a Stovepipe A rectangular piece of sheet metal with an area of $1200\ \text{in}^2$ is to be bent into a cylindrical length of stovepipe having a volume of $600\ \text{in}^3$. What are the dimensions of the sheet metal?

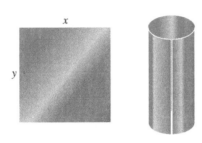

51. Global Positioning System (GPS) The Global Positioning System determines the location of an object from its

distances to satellites in orbit around the earth. In the simplified, two-dimensional situation shown in the following figure, determine the coordinates of P from the fact that P is 26 units from satellite A and 20 units from satellite B.

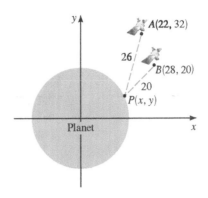

DISCUSS ■ DISCOVER ■ PROVE ■ WRITE

52. DISCOVER ■ PROVE: Intersection of a Parabola and a Line On a sheet of graph paper or using a graphing calculator, draw the parabola $y = x^2$. Then draw the graphs of the linear equation $y = x + k$ on the same coordinate plane for various values of k. Try to choose values of k so that the line and the parabola intersect at two points for some of your k's and not for others. For what value of k is there exactly one intersection point? Use the results of your experiment to make a conjecture about the values of k for which the following system has two solutions, one solution, and no solution. Prove your conjecture.

$$\begin{cases} y = x^2 \\ y = x + k \end{cases}$$

10.5 SYSTEMS OF INEQUALITIES

■ Graphing an Inequality ■ Systems of Inequalities ■ Systems of Linear Inequalities
■ Application: Feasible Regions

In this section we study systems of inequalities in two variables from a graphical point of view.

■ Graphing an Inequality

We begin by considering the graph of a single inequality. We already know that the graph of $y = x^2$, for example, is the *parabola* in Figure 1. If we replace the equal sign by the symbol $\geq$, we obtain the *inequality*

$$y \geq x^2$$

Its graph consists of not just the parabola in Figure 1, but also every point whose y-coordinate is *larger* than x^2. We indicate the solution in Figure 2(a) by shading the points *above* the parabola.

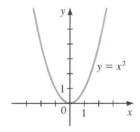

FIGURE 1

Similarly, the graph of $y \le x^2$ in Figure 2(b) consists of all points on and *below* the parabola. However, the graphs of $y > x^2$ and $y < x^2$ do not include the points on the parabola itself, as indicated by the dashed curves in Figures 2(c) and 2(d).

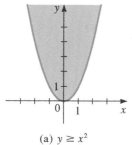

(a) $y \ge x^2$

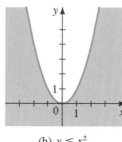

(b) $y \le x^2$

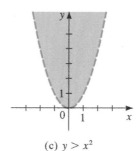

(c) $y > x^2$

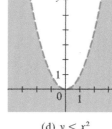

(d) $y < x^2$

FIGURE 2

The graph of an inequality, in general, consists of a region in the plane whose boundary is the graph of the equation obtained by replacing the inequality sign ($\ge$, $\le$, $>$, or $<$) with an equal sign. To determine which side of the graph gives the solution set of the inequality, we need only check **test points**.

GRAPHING AN INEQUALITY

To graph an inequality, we carry out the following steps.

1. **Graph the Equation.**   Graph the equation that corresponds to the inequality. Use a dashed curve for $>$ or $<$ and a solid curve for $\le$ or $\ge$.

2. **Graph the Inequality.**   The graph of the inequality consists of all the points on one side of the curve that we graphed in Step 1. We use **test points** on either side of the curve to determine whether the points on that side satisfy the inequality. If the point satisfies the inequality, then all the points on that side of the curve satisfy the inequality. In that case, **shade that side of the curve** to indicate that it is part of the graph. If the test point does not satisfy the inequality, then the region isn't part of the graph.

EXAMPLE 1 ■ **Graphs of Inequalities**

Graph each inequality.

(a) $x^2 + y^2 < 25$ **(b)** $x + 2y \ge 5$

SOLUTION   We follow the guidelines given above.

(a) Graph the equation.   The graph of the equation $x^2 + y^2 = 25$ is a circle of radius 5 centered at the origin. The points on the circle itself do not satisfy the inequality because it is of the form $<$, so we graph the circle with a dashed curve, as shown in Figure 3.

Graph the inequality.   To determine whether the inside or the outside of the circle satisfies the inequality, we use the test points $(0, 0)$ on the inside and $(6, 0)$ on the outside. To do this, we substitute the coordinates of each point into the inequality and check whether the result satisfies the inequality.

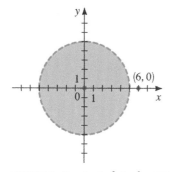

FIGURE 3 Graph of $x^2 + y^2 < 25$

Note that *any* point inside or outside the circle can serve as a test point. We have chosen these points for simplicity.

Test point	Inequality $x^2 + y^2 < 25$	Conclusion
$(0, 0)$	$0^2 + 0^2 \overset{?}{<} 25$ ✓	Part of graph
$(6, 0)$	$6^2 + 0^2 \overset{?}{<} 25$ ✗	Not part of graph

Our check shows that the points *inside* the circle satisfy the inequality. A graph of the inequality is shown in Figure 3.

(b) **Graph the equation.**   We first graph the equation $x + 2y = 5$. The graph is the line shown in Figure 4.

Graph the inequality.   Let's use the test points $(0, 0)$ and $(5, 5)$ on either side of the line.

Test point	Inequality $x + 2y \geq 5$	Conclusion
$(0, 0)$	$0 + 2(0) \overset{?}{\geq} 5$ ✗	Not part of graph
$(5, 5)$	$5 + 2(5) \overset{?}{\geq} 5$ ✓	Part of graph

We can write the inequality in Example 1 as

$$y \geq -\tfrac{1}{2}x + \tfrac{5}{2}$$

From this form of the inequality we see that the solution consists of the points with y-values *on* or *above* the line $y = -\tfrac{1}{2}x + \tfrac{5}{2}$. So the graph of the inequality is the region *above* the line.

Our check shows that the points *above* the line satisfy the inequality. A graph of the inequality is shown in Figure 4.

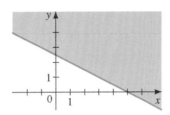

FIGURE 4 Graph of $x + 2y \geq 5$

✎ Now Try Exercises 15 and 21

■ Systems of Inequalities

We now consider *systems* of inequalities. The **solution set of a system of inequalities** in two variables is the set of all points in the coordinate plane that satisfy every inequality in the system. The **graph of a system of inequalities** is the graph of the solution set.

To find the solution of a system of inequalities, we first graph each inequality in the system. The solution of the system consists of those points in the coordinate plane that belong to the solution of each inequality in the system. In other words, the solution of the system is the intersection of the solutions of the individual inequalities in the system. So to solve a system of inequalities, we use the following guidelines.

THE SOLUTION OF A SYSTEM OF INEQUALITIES

To graph the solution of a system of inequalities, we carry out the following steps.

1. **Graph Each Inequality.**   Graph each inequality in the system on the same graph.
2. **Graph the Solution of the System.**   Shade the region where the graphs of all the inequalities intersect. All the points in this region satisfy each inequality, so they belong to the solution of the system.
3. **Find the Vertices.**   Label the vertices of the region that you shaded in Step 2.

EXAMPLE 2   A System of Two Inequalities

Graph the solution of the system of inequalities, and label its vertices.

$$\begin{cases} x^2 + y^2 < 25 \\ x + 2y \geq 5 \end{cases}$$

SOLUTION   These are the two inequalities of Example 1. Here we want to graph only those points that simultaneously satisfy both inequalities.

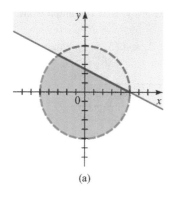

(a)

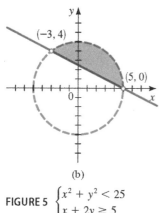

(b)

FIGURE 5 $\begin{cases} x^2 + y^2 < 25 \\ x + 2y \geq 5 \end{cases}$

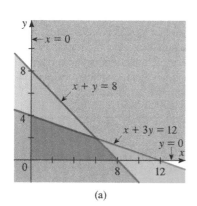

(a)

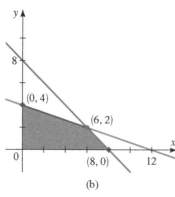

(b)

FIGURE 6

Graph each inequality. In Figure 5(a) we graph the solutions of the two inequalities on the same axes (in different colors).

Graph the solution of the system. The solution of the system of inequalities is the intersection of the two graphs. This is the region where the two regions overlap, which is the purple region graphed in Figure 5(b).

Find the vertices. The points $(-3, 4)$ and $(5, 0)$ in Figure 5(b) are the **vertices** of the solution set. They are obtained by solving the system of *equations*

$$\begin{cases} x^2 + y^2 = 25 \\ x + 2y = 5 \end{cases}$$

We solve this system of equations by substitution. Solving for x in the second equation gives $x = 5 - 2y$, and substituting this into the first equation gives

$$(5 - 2y)^2 + y^2 = 25 \qquad \text{Substitute } x = 5 - 2y$$
$$(25 - 20y + 4y^2) + y^2 = 25 \qquad \text{Expand}$$
$$-20y + 5y^2 = 0 \qquad \text{Simplify}$$
$$-5y(4 - y) = 0 \qquad \text{Factor}$$

Thus $y = 0$ or $y = 4$. When $y = 0$, we have $x = 5 - 2(0) = 5$, and when $y = 4$, we have $x = 5 - 2(4) = -3$. So the points of intersection of these curves are $(5, 0)$ and $(-3, 4)$.

Note that in this case the vertices are not part of the solution set, since they don't satisfy the inequality $x^2 + y^2 < 25$ (so they are graphed as open circles in the figure). They simply show where the "corners" of the solution set lie.

✎ Now Try Exercise 43

■ Systems of Linear Inequalities

An inequality is **linear** if it can be put into one of the following forms:

$$ax + by \geq c \qquad ax + by \leq c \qquad ax + by > c \qquad ax + by < c$$

In the next example we graph the solution set of a system of linear inequalities.

EXAMPLE 3 ◈ A System of Four Linear Inequalities

Graph the solution set of the system, and label its vertices.

$$\begin{cases} x + 3y \leq 12 \\ x + y \leq 8 \\ x \geq 0 \\ y \geq 0 \end{cases}$$

SOLUTION **Graph each inequality.** In Figure 6 we first graph the lines given by the equations that correspond to each inequality. To determine the graphs of the first two inequalities, we need to check only one test point. For simplicity let's use the point $(0, 0)$.

Inequality	Test point $(0, 0)$	Conclusion
$x + 3y \leq 12$	$0 + 3(0) \overset{?}{\leq} 12$ ✓	Satisfies inequality
$x + y \leq 8$	$0 + 0 \overset{?}{\leq} 8$ ✓	Satisfies inequality

Since $(0, 0)$ is below the line $x + 3y = 12$, our check shows that the region on or below the line must satisfy the inequality. Likewise, since $(0, 0)$ is below the line $x + y = 8$, our check shows that the region on or below this line must satisfy the inequality. The inequalities $x \geq 0$ and $y \geq 0$ say that x and y are nonnegative. These regions are sketched in Figure 6(a).

Graph the solution of the system.   The solution of the system of inequalities is the intersection of the graphs. This is the purple region graphed in Figure 6(b).

Find the vertices.   The coordinates of each vertex are obtained by simultaneously solving the equations of the lines that intersect at that vertex. From the system

$$\begin{cases} x + 3y = 12 \\ x + y = 8 \end{cases}$$

we get the vertex $(6, 2)$. The origin $(0, 0)$ is also clearly a vertex. The other two vertices are at the x- and y-intercepts of the corresponding lines: $(8, 0)$ and $(0, 4)$. In this case all the vertices *are* part of the solution set.

✎ Now Try Exercise 51

EXAMPLE 4 ■ A System of Linear Inequalities

Graph the solution set of the system of inequalities, and label the vertices.

(a) $$\begin{cases} 10x + 20y \geq 60 \\ 30x + 20y \geq 100 \\ 10x + 40y \geq 80 \\ x \geq 0, \quad y \geq 0 \end{cases}$$ (b) $$\begin{cases} 10x + 20y \leq 60 \\ 30x + 20y \geq 100 \\ 10x + 40y \geq 80 \\ x \geq 0, \quad y \geq 0 \end{cases}$$

SOLUTION

(a) **Graph each inequality.**   We must graph the lines that correspond to these inequalities and then shade the appropriate regions. The graph of $10x + 20y \geq 60$ is the region above the line $y = 3 - \frac{1}{2}x$. The graph of $30x + 20y \geq 100$ is the region above the line $y = 5 - \frac{3}{2}x$, and the graph of $10x + 40y \geq 80$ is the region above the line $y = 2 - \frac{1}{4}x$.

Graph the solution of the system.   The inequalities $x \geq 0$ and $y \geq 0$ indicate that the region is in the first quadrant. With this information we graph the system of inequalities in Figure 7.

Find the vertices.   We determine the vertices of the region by finding the points of intersection of the appropriate lines. You can check that the vertices of the region are the ones indicated in Figure 7.

(b) The graph of the first inequality $10x + 20y \leq 60$ is the region below the line $y = 3 - \frac{1}{2}x$, and all the other inequalities are the same as those in part (a), so the solution to the system is the region (colored purple) shown in Figure 8.

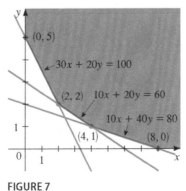

FIGURE 7

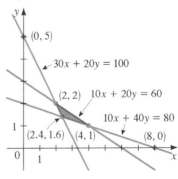

FIGURE 8

✎ Now Try Exercises 59 and 63

EXAMPLE 5 ■ A System of Linear Inequalities

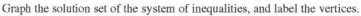

Graph the solution set of the system of inequalities, and label the vertices.

$$\begin{cases} x + 2y \ge 8 \\ -x + 2y \le 4 \\ 3x - 2y \le 8 \end{cases}$$

SOLUTION Graph each inequality. We must graph the lines that correspond to these inequalities and then shade the appropriate regions, as in Example 2. We will use a graphing calculator, so we must first isolate y on the left-hand side of each inequality.

$$\begin{cases} y \ge -\frac{1}{2}x + 4 \\ y \le \frac{1}{2}x + 2 \\ y \ge \frac{3}{2}x - 4 \end{cases}$$

Using the shading feature of the calculator, we obtain the graph in Figure 9(a). Note that the calculator shades each region in a different pattern.

Graph the solution of the system. The solution set is the triangular region that is shaded in all three patterns. The solution set is graphed in Figure 9(b).

Find the vertices. We use the $\boxed{\text{TRACE}}$ or the Intersect command to find the vertices of the region. The vertices are labeled in Figure 9(b).

See Appendix D, *Using the TI-83/84 Graphing Calculator*, for specific instructions on graphing inequalities.

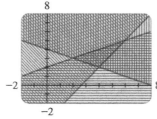

(a) Graphing calculator output

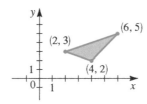

(b) Graph of solution set

FIGURE 9

✎. Now Try Exercise 65

A region in the plane is called **bounded** if it can be enclosed in a (sufficiently large) circle. A region that is not bounded is called **unbounded**. For example, the regions graphed in Figures 3, 5(b), 6(b), 8, and 9 are bounded because they can be enclosed in a circle, as illustrated in Figure 10(a). But the regions graphed in Figures 2, 4, and 7 are unbounded, because we cannot enclose them in a circle as illustrated in Figure 10(b).

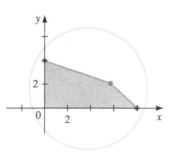

(a) A bounded region can be enclosed in a circle.

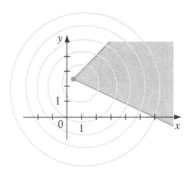

(b) An unbounded region cannot be enclosed in a circle.

FIGURE 10

■ Application: Feasible Regions

Many applied problems involve **constraints** on the variables. For instance, a factory manager has only a certain number of workers who can be assigned to perform jobs on the factory floor. A farmer deciding what crops to cultivate has only a certain amount of land that can be seeded. Such constraints or limitations can usually be expressed as systems of inequalities. When dealing with applied inequalities, we usually refer to the solution set of a system as a **feasible region**, because the points in the solution set represent feasible (or possible) values for the quantities being studied.

EXAMPLE 6 ■ Restricting Pollutant Outputs

A factory produces two agricultural pesticides, A and B. For every barrel of pesticide A, the factory emits 0.25 kg of carbon monoxide (CO) and 0.60 kg of sulfur dioxide (SO_2); and for every barrel of pesticide B, it emits 0.50 kg of CO and 0.20 kg of SO_2. Pollution laws restrict the factory's output of CO to a maximum of 75 kg per day and its output of SO_2 to a maximum of 90 kg per day.

(a) Find a system of inequalities that describes the number of barrels of each pesticide the factory can produce per day and still satisfy the pollution laws. Graph the feasible region.

(b) Would it be legal for the factory to produce 100 barrels of pesticide A and 80 barrels of pesticide B per day?

(c) Would it be legal for the factory to produce 60 barrels of pesticide A and 160 barrels of pesticide B per day?

SOLUTION

(a) We state the constraints as a system of inequalities and then graph the solution of the system.

Set up the inequalities.   We first identify and name the variables, and we then express each statement in the problem in terms of the variables. We let the variable x represent the number of barrels of A produced per day and let y be the number of barrels of B produced per day. We can organize the information in the problem as follows.

In Words	In Algebra
Barrels of A produced	x
Barrels of B produced	y
Total CO produced	$0.25x + 0.50y$
Total SO_2 produced	$0.60x + 0.20y$

From the information in the problem and the fact that x and y can't be negative we obtain the following inequalities.

$$\begin{cases} 0.25x + 0.50y \le 75 & \text{At most 75 kg of CO can be produced} \\ 0.60x + 0.20y \le 90 & \text{At most 90 kg of } SO_2 \text{ can be produced} \\ x \ge 0, \quad y \ge 0 \end{cases}$$

Multiplying the first inequality by 4 and the second by 5 simplifies the system to the following:

$$\begin{cases} x + 2y \le 300 \\ 3x + \ y \le 450 \\ x \ge 0, \quad y \ge 0 \end{cases}$$

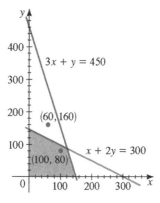

FIGURE 11

Graph the solution set.   We first graph the equations

$$x + 2y = 300$$
$$3x + y = 450$$

The graphs are the two lines shown in Figure 11. Using the test point $(0, 0)$, we see that the solution set of each of these inequalities is the region below the corresponding line. So the solution to the system is the intersection of these sets as shown in Figure 11.

(b) Since the point $(100, 80)$ lies inside the feasible region, this production plan is legal (see Figure 11).

(c) Since the point $(60, 160)$ lies outside the feasible region, this production plan is not legal. It violates the CO restriction, although it does not violate the SO_2 restriction (see Figure 11).

✎. Now Try Exercise 69

10.5 EXERCISES

CONCEPTS

1. If the point $(2, 3)$ is a solution of an inequality in x and y, then the inequality is satisfied when we replace x by

_____ and y by _____. Is the point $(2, 3)$ a solution of the inequality $4x - 2y \geq 1$?

2. To graph an inequality, we first graph the corresponding

_____. So to graph the inequality $y \leq x + 1$, we

first graph the equation _____. To decide which side of the graph of the equation is the graph of the

inequality, we use _____ points. Complete the table, and sketch a graph of the inequality by shading the appropriate region.

Test point	Inequality $y \leq x + 1$	Conclusion
$(0, 0)$		
$(0, 2)$		

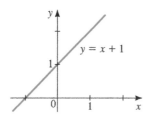

3. If the point $(2, 3)$ is a solution of a *system* of inequalities in x and y, then *each* inequality is satisfied when we replace x by

_____ and y by _____. Is the point $(2, 3)$ a solution of the following system?

$$\begin{cases} 2x + 4y \leq 17 \\ 6x + 5y \leq 29 \end{cases}$$

4. Shade the solution of each system of inequalities on the given graph.

(a) $\begin{cases} x - y \geq 0 \\ x + y \geq 2 \end{cases}$ **(b)** $\begin{cases} x - y \leq 0 \\ x + y \leq 2 \end{cases}$

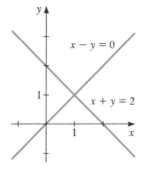 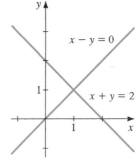

(c) $\begin{cases} x - y \geq 0 \\ x + y \leq 2 \end{cases}$ **(d)** $\begin{cases} x - y \leq 0 \\ x + y \geq 2 \end{cases}$

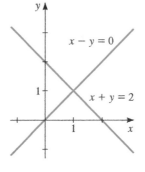 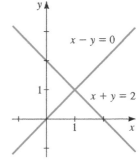

SKILLS

5–6 ■ Solutions of Inequalities An inequality and several points are given. For each point determine whether it is a solution of the inequality.

5. $x - 5y > 3$; $(-1, -2), (1, -2), (1, 2), (8, 1)$

6. $3x + 2y \le 2$; $(-2, 1), (1, 3), (1, -3), (0, 1)$

7–8 ■ Solutions of Systems of Inequalities A system of inequalities and several points are given. Determine which points are solutions of the system.

7. $\begin{cases} 3x - 2y \le 5 \\ 2x + y \ge 3 \end{cases}$; $(0, 0), (1, 2), (1, 1), (3, 1)$

8. $\begin{cases} x + 2y \ge 4 \\ 4x + 3y \ge 11 \end{cases}$; $(0, 0), (1, 3), (3, 0), (1, 2)$

9–22 ■ Graphing Inequalities Graph the inequality.

9. $y < -2x$ **10.** $y \ge 3x$

11. $y \ge 2$ **12.** $x \le -1$

13. $x < 2$ **14.** $y > 1$

15. $y > x - 3$ **16.** $y \le 1 - x$

17. $2x - y \ge -4$ **18.** $3x - y - 9 < 0$

19. $-x^2 + y \ge 5$ **20.** $y > x^2 + 1$

21. $x^2 + y^2 > 9$ **22.** $x^2 + (y - 2)^2 \le 4$

23–26 ■ Graphing Inequalities Use a graphing calculator to graph the linear inequality.

23. $3x - 2y \ge 18$ **24.** $4x + 3y \le 9$

25. $5x + 2y > 8$ **26.** $5x - 3y \ge 15$

27–30 ■ Finding Inequalities from a Graph An equation and its graph are given. Find an inequality whose solution is the shaded region.

27. $y = \frac{1}{2}x - 1$

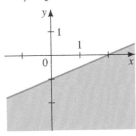

28. $y = x^2 + 2$

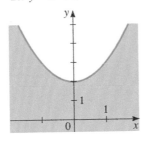

29. $x^2 + y^2 = 4$

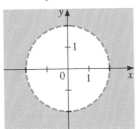

30. $y = x^3 - 4x$

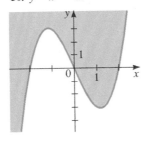

31–58 ■ Systems of Inequalities Graph the solution set of the system of inequalities. Find the coordinates of all vertices, and determine whether the solution set is bounded.

31. $\begin{cases} x + y \le 4 \\ y \ge x \end{cases}$ **32.** $\begin{cases} 2x + 3y > 12 \\ 3x - y < 21 \end{cases}$

33. $\begin{cases} y < \frac{1}{4}x + 2 \\ y \ge 2x - 5 \end{cases}$ **34.** $\begin{cases} x - y > 0 \\ 4 + y \le 2x \end{cases}$

35. $\begin{cases} y \le -2x + 8 \\ y \le -\frac{1}{2}x + 5 \\ x \ge 0, \quad y \ge 0 \end{cases}$ **36.** $\begin{cases} 4x + 3y \le 18 \\ 2x + y \le 8 \\ x \ge 0, \quad y \ge 0 \end{cases}$

37. $\begin{cases} x \ge 0 \\ y \ge 0 \\ 3x + 5y \le 15 \\ 3x + 2y \le 9 \end{cases}$ **38.** $\begin{cases} x > 2 \\ y < 12 \\ 2x - 4y > 8 \end{cases}$

39. $\begin{cases} y \le 9 - x^2 \\ x \ge 0, \quad y \ge 0 \end{cases}$ **40.** $\begin{cases} y \ge x^2 \\ y \le 4 \\ x \ge 0 \end{cases}$

41. $\begin{cases} y < 9 - x^2 \\ y \ge x + 3 \end{cases}$ **42.** $\begin{cases} y \ge x^2 \\ x + y \ge 6 \end{cases}$

43. $\begin{cases} x^2 + y^2 \le 4 \\ x - y > 0 \end{cases}$ **44.** $\begin{cases} x > 0 \\ y > 0 \\ x + y < 10 \\ x^2 + y^2 > 9 \end{cases}$

45. $\begin{cases} x^2 - y \le 0 \\ 2x^2 + y \le 12 \end{cases}$ **46.** $\begin{cases} 2x^2 + y > 4 \\ x^2 - y \le 8 \end{cases}$

47. $\begin{cases} x^2 + y^2 \le 9 \\ 2x + y^2 \le 1 \end{cases}$ **48.** $\begin{cases} x^2 + y^2 \le 4 \\ x^2 - 2y > 1 \end{cases}$

49. $\begin{cases} x + 2y \le 14 \\ 3x - y \ge 0 \\ x - y \ge 2 \end{cases}$ **50.** $\begin{cases} y < x + 6 \\ 3x + 2y \ge 12 \\ x - 2y \le 2 \end{cases}$

51. $\begin{cases} x \ge 0 \\ y \ge 0 \\ x \le 5 \\ x + y \le 7 \end{cases}$ **52.** $\begin{cases} x \ge 0 \\ y \ge 0 \\ y \le 4 \\ 2x + y \le 8 \end{cases}$

53. $\begin{cases} y > x + 1 \\ x + 2y \le 12 \\ x + 1 > 0 \end{cases}$ **54.** $\begin{cases} x + y > 12 \\ y < \frac{1}{2}x - 6 \\ 3x + y < 6 \end{cases}$

55. $\begin{cases} x^2 + y^2 \le 8 \\ x \ge 2 \\ y \ge 0 \end{cases}$ **56.** $\begin{cases} x^2 - y \ge 0 \\ x + y < 6 \\ x - y < 6 \end{cases}$

57. $\begin{cases} x^2 + y^2 < 9 \\ x + y > 0 \\ x \le 0 \end{cases}$ **58.** $\begin{cases} y \ge x^3 \\ y \le 2x + 4 \\ x + y \ge 0 \end{cases}$

59–64 ■ Systems of Inequalities Graph the system of inequalities, label the vertices, and determine whether the region is bounded or unbounded.

59. $\begin{cases} x + 2y \le 14 \\ 3x - y \ge 0 \\ x - y \le 2 \end{cases}$ **60.** $\begin{cases} x + 2y \le 14 \\ 3x - y \ge 0 \\ x - y \ge 2 \end{cases}$

61. $\begin{cases} x + y \le 12 \\ y \le \frac{1}{2}x - 6 \\ y \le 2x + 6 \end{cases}$

62. $\begin{cases} y \ge x + 1 \\ x + 2y \le 12 \\ x + 1 \ge 0 \end{cases}$

63. $\begin{cases} 30x + 10y \ge 50 \\ 10x + 20y \ge 50 \\ 10x + 60y \ge 90 \\ x \ge 0, \quad y \ge 0 \end{cases}$

64. $\begin{cases} x + y \ge 6 \\ 4x + 7y \le 39 \\ x + 5y \ge 13 \\ x \ge 0, \quad y \ge 0 \end{cases}$

65–68 ■ **Graphing Systems of Inequalities** Use a graphing calculator to graph the solution of the system of inequalities. Find the coordinates of all vertices, rounded to one decimal place.

65. $\begin{cases} y \ge x - 3 \\ y \ge -2x + 6 \\ y \le 8 \end{cases}$

66. $\begin{cases} x + y \ge 12 \\ 2x + y \le 24 \\ x - y \ge -6 \end{cases}$

67. $\begin{cases} y \le 6x - x^2 \\ x + y \ge 4 \end{cases}$

68. $\begin{cases} y \ge x^3 \\ 2x + y \ge 0 \\ y \le 2x + 6 \end{cases}$

APPLICATIONS

69. Planting Crops A farmer has 500 acres of arable land on which he wants to plant potatoes and corn. The farmer has $40,000 available for planting and $30,000 for fertilizer. Planting 1 acre of potatoes costs $90, and planting 1 acre of corn costs $50. Fertilizer costs $30 for 1 acre of potatoes and $80 for 1 acre of corn.

(a) Find a system of inequalities that describes the number of acres of each crop that the farmer can plant with the available resources. Graph the feasible region.

(b) Can the farmer plant 300 acres of potatoes and 180 acres of corn?

(c) Can the farmer plant 150 acres of potatoes and 325 acres of corn?

70. Planting Crops A farmer has 300 acres of arable land on which she wants to plant cauliflower and cabbage. The farmer has $17,500 available for planting and $12,000 for fertilizer. Planting 1 acre of cauliflower costs $70, and planting 1 acre of cabbage costs $35. Fertilizer costs $25 for 1 acre of cauliflower and $55 for 1 acre of cabbage.

(a) Find a system of inequalities that describes the number of acres of each crop that the farmer can plant with the available resources. Graph the feasible region.

(b) Can the farmer plant 155 acres of cauliflower and 115 acres of cabbage?

(c) Can the farmer plant 115 acres of cauliflower and 175 acres of cabbage?

71. Publishing Books A publishing company publishes a total of no more than 100 books every year. At least 20 of these are nonfiction, but the company always publishes at least as much fiction as nonfiction. Find a system of inequalities that describes the possible numbers of fiction and nonfiction books that the company can produce each year consistent with these policies. Graph the solution set.

72. Furniture Manufacturing A man and his daughter manufacture unfinished tables and chairs. Each table requires 3 h of sawing and 1 h of assembly. Each chair requires 2 h of sawing and 2 h of assembly. Between the two of them, they can put in up to 12 h of sawing and 8 h of assembly work each day. Find a system of inequalities that describes all possible combinations of tables and chairs that they can make daily. Graph the solution set.

73. Coffee Blends A coffee merchant sells two different coffee blends. The Standard blend uses 4 oz of arabica and 12 oz of robusta beans per package; the Deluxe blend uses 10 oz of arabica and 6 oz of robusta beans per package. The merchant has 80 lb of arabica and 90 lb of robusta beans available. Find a system of inequalities that describes the possible number of Standard and Deluxe packages the merchant can make. Graph the solution set.

74. Nutrition A cat food manufacturer uses fish and beef by-products. The fish contains 12 g of protein and 3 g of fat per ounce. The beef contains 6 g of protein and 9 g of fat per ounce. Each can of cat food must contain at least 60 g of protein and 45 g of fat. Find a system of inequalities that describes the possible number of ounces of fish and beef by-products that can be used in each can to satisfy these minimum requirements. Graph the solution set.

DISCUSS ■ **DISCOVER** ■ **PROVE** ■ **WRITE**

75. DISCUSS: Shading Unwanted Regions To graph the solution of a system of inequalities, we have shaded the solution of each inequality in a different color; the solution of the system is the region where all the shaded parts overlap. Here is a different method: For each inequality, shade the region that does *not* satisfy the inequality. Explain why the part of the plane that is left unshaded is the solution of the system. Solve the following system by both methods. Which do you prefer? Why?

$$\begin{cases} x + 2y > 4 \\ -x + y < 1 \\ x + 3y < 9 \\ x < 3 \end{cases}$$

CHAPTER 10 ■ REVIEW

■ PROPERTIES AND FORMULAS

Systems of Equations (p. 716)

A **system of equations** is a set of equations that involve the same variables. A **system of linear equations** is a system of equations in which each equation is linear. Systems of of linear equations in two variables (x and y) and three variables (x, y, and z) have the following forms:

**Linear system
2 variables**

$$a_{11}x + a_{12}y = b_1$$
$$a_{21}x + a_{22}y = b_2$$

**Linear system
3 variables**

$$a_{11}x + a_{12}y + a_{13}z = b_1$$
$$a_{21}x + a_{22}y + a_{23}z = b_2$$
$$a_{31}x + a_{32}y + a_{33}z = b_3$$

A **solution** of a system of equations is an assignment of values for the variables that makes *each* equation in the system true. To **solve** a system means to find all solutions of the system.

Substitution Method (p. 716)

To solve a pair of equations in two variables by substitution:

1. **Solve for one variable** in terms of the other variable in one equation.

2. **Substitute** into the other equation to get an equation in one variable, and solve for this variable.

3. **Back-substitute** the value(s) of the variable you have found into either original equation, and solve for the remaining variable.

Elimination Method (p. 717)

To solve a pair of equations in two variables by elimination:

1. **Adjust the coefficients** by multiplying the equations by appropriate constants so that the term(s) involving one of the variables are of opposite sign in the equations.

2. **Add the equations** to eliminate that one variable; this gives an equation in the other variable. Solve for this variable.

3. **Back-substitute** the value(s) of the variable that you have found into either original equation, and solve for the remaining variable.

Graphical Method (p. 718)

To solve a pair of equations in two variables graphically, first put each equation in function form, $y = f(x)$.

1. **Graph the equations** on a common screen.

2. **Find the points of intersection** of the graphs. The solutions are the x- and y-coordinates of the points of intersection.

Gaussian Elimination (p. 727)

When we use **Gaussian elimination** to solve a system of linear equations, we use the following operations to change the system to an **equivalent** simpler system:

1. Add a nonzero multiple of one equation to another.

2. Multiply an equation by a nonzero constant.

3. Interchange the position of two equations in the system.

Number of Solutions of a Linear System (p. 729)

A system of linear equations can have:

1. A unique solution for each variable.

2. No solution, in which case the system is **inconsistent**.

3. Infinitely many solutions, in which case the system is **dependent**.

How to Determine the Number of Solutions of a Linear System (p. 729)

When we use **Gaussian elimination** to solve a system of linear equations, then we can tell that the system has:

1. **No solution** (is *inconsistent*) if we arrive at a false equation of the form $0 = c$, where c is nonzero.

2. **Infinitely many solutions** (is *dependent*) if the system is consistent but we end up with fewer equations than variables (after discarding redundant equations of the form $0 = 0$).

Partial Fractions (pp. 735–739)

The *partial fraction decomposition* of a rational function

$$r(x) = \frac{P(x)}{Q(x)}$$

(where the degree of P is less than the degree of Q) is a sum of simpler fractional expressions that equal $r(x)$ when brought to a common denominator. The denominator of each simpler fraction is either a linear or quadratic factor of $Q(x)$ or a power of such a linear or quadratic factor. So to find the terms of the partial fraction decomposition, we first factor $Q(x)$ into linear and irreducible quadratic factors. The terms then have the following forms, depending on the factors of $Q(x)$.

1. For every **distinct linear factor** $ax + b$ there is a term of the form

$$\frac{A}{ax + b}$$

2. For every **repeated linear factor** $(ax + b)^m$ there are terms of the form

$$\frac{A_1}{ax + b} + \frac{A_2}{(ax + b)^2} + \cdots + \frac{A_m}{(ax + b)^m}$$

3. For every **distinct quadratic factor** $ax^2 + bx + c$ there is a term of the form

$$\frac{Ax + B}{ax^2 + bx + c}$$

4. For every **repeated quadratic factor** $(ax^2 + bx + c)^m$ there are terms of the form

$$\frac{A_1x + B_1}{ax^2 + bx + c} + \frac{A_2x + B_2}{(ax^2 + bx + c)^2} + \cdots + \frac{A_mx + B_m}{(ax^2 + bx + c)^m}$$

Graphing Inequalities (pp. 745–746)

To graph an inequality:

1. Graph the equation that corresponds to the inequality. This "boundary curve" divides the coordinate plane into separate regions.

2. Use **test points** to determine which region(s) satisfy the inequality.

3. Shade the region(s) that satisfy the inequality, and use a solid line for the boundary curve if it satisfies the inequality ($\leq$ or $\geq$) and a dashed line if it does not ($<$ or $>$).

Graphing Systems of Inequalities (p. 747)

To graph the solution of a system of inequalities (or **feasible region** determined by the inequalities):

1. Graph all the inequalities on the same coordinate plane.

2. The solution is the intersection of the solutions of all the inequalities, so shade the region that satisfies all the inequalities.

3. Determine the coordinates of the intersection points of all the boundary curves that touch the solution set of the system. These points are the **vertices** of the solution.

▪ CONCEPT CHECK

1. (a) What is a system of equations in the variables x, y, and z?

   (b) What are the three methods we use to solve a system of equations?

2. Consider the following system of equations:

$$\begin{cases} x + y = 3 \\ 3x - y = 1 \end{cases}$$

   (a) Describe the steps you would use to solve a system by the substitution method. Use the substitution method to solve the given system.

   (b) Describe the steps you would use to solve a system by the elimination method. Use the elimination method to solve the given system.

   (c) Describe the steps you would use to solve a system by the graphical method. Use the graph shown below to solve the system.

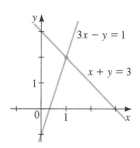

3. What is a system of linear equations in the variables x, y, and z?

4. For a system of two linear equations in two variables,

   (a) How many solutions are possible?

   (b) What is meant by an inconsistent system? ●

   (c) What is meant by a dependent system?

5. What operations can be performed on a linear system to arrive at an equivalent system?

6. (a) Explain how Gaussian elimination works.

   (b) Use Gaussian elimination to put the following system in triangular form, and then solve the system.

System	Triangular form
$\begin{cases} x + y - 2z = 3 \\ x + 2y + z = 5 \\ 3x - y + 5z = 1 \end{cases}$	

7. (a) How do we express a rational function r as a partial fraction decomposition?

   (b) Give the form of the partial fraction decomposition.

   (i) $\dfrac{2x}{(x - 5)(x - 1)^2}$

   (ii) $\dfrac{2x}{(x - 5)(x^2 + 1)}$

   (iii) $\dfrac{3x + 1}{x(x^2 + 1)^2}$

8. (a) How do we graph an inequality in two variables?

   (b) Graphs of equations in two variables are shown. On each graph, shade the solution set of the indicated inequality.

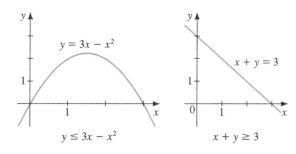

$y \leq 3x - x^2$ 　　　　　 $x + y \geq 3$

9. (a) How do we graph the solution set of a system of inequalities?

   (b) Graphs of the equations in the following system of inequalities are given. Graph the solution set of the system of inequalities.

$$\begin{cases} x + y \geq 3 \\ 3x - y \geq 1 \end{cases}$$

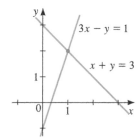

(c) Graphs of the equations in the following system of inequalities are given. Graph the solution set of the system of inequalities.

$$\begin{cases} x + y \geq 3 \\ y \leq 3x - x^2 \end{cases}$$

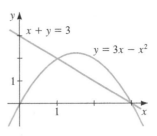

ANSWERS TO THE CONCEPT CHECK CAN BE FOUND AT THE BACK OF THE BOOK.

■ EXERCISES

1–6 ■ Systems of Linear Equations in Two Variables   Solve the system of equations, and graph the lines.

1. $\begin{cases} 3x - y = 5 \\ 2x + y = 5 \end{cases}$

2. $\begin{cases} y = 2x + 6 \\ y = -x + 3 \end{cases}$

3. $\begin{cases} 2x - 7y = 28 \\ y = \frac{2}{7}x - 4 \end{cases}$

4. $\begin{cases} 6x - 8y = 15 \\ -\frac{3}{2}x + 2y = -4 \end{cases}$

5. $\begin{cases} 2x - y = 1 \\ x + 3y = 10 \\ 3x + 4y = 15 \end{cases}$

6. $\begin{cases} 2x + 5y = 9 \\ -x + 3y = 1 \\ 7x - 2y = 14 \end{cases}$

7–10 ■ Systems of Nonlinear Equations   Solve the system of equations.

7. $\begin{cases} y = x^2 + 2x \\ y = 6 + x \end{cases}$

8. $\begin{cases} x^2 + y^2 = 8 \\ y = x + 2 \end{cases}$

9. $\begin{cases} 3x + \dfrac{4}{y} = 6 \\ x - \dfrac{8}{y} = 4 \end{cases}$

10. $\begin{cases} x^2 + y^2 = 10 \\ x^2 + 2y^2 - 7y = 0 \end{cases}$

 11–14 ■ Systems of Nonlinear Equations   Use a graphing device to solve the system. Round answers to the nearest hundredth.

11. $\begin{cases} 0.32x + 0.43y = 0 \\ 7x - 12y = 341 \end{cases}$

12. $\begin{cases} \sqrt{12}x - 3\sqrt{2}y = 660 \\ 7137x + 3931y = 20{,}000 \end{cases}$

13. $\begin{cases} x - y^2 = 10 \\ x = \frac{1}{22}y + 12 \end{cases}$

14. $\begin{cases} y = 5^x + x \\ y = x^5 + 5 \end{cases}$

15–24 ■ Systems of Linear Equations in Several Variables   Solve the system of equations.

15. $\begin{cases} x - 2y + z = 8 \\ 4x + z = 9 \\ -2x + y - z = -8 \end{cases}$

16. $\begin{cases} x - y + 3z = -4 \\ 4x + 2y - z = 11 \\ -5x - y + z = -16 \end{cases}$

17. $\begin{cases} x + y + 2z = 6 \\ 2x + 5z = 12 \\ x + 2y + 3z = 9 \end{cases}$

18. $\begin{cases} x - 2y + 3z = 1 \\ x - 3y - z = 0 \\ 2x - 6z = 6 \end{cases}$

19. $\begin{cases} x - 2y + 3z = 1 \\ 2x - y + z = 3 \\ 2x - 7y + 11z = 2 \end{cases}$

20. $\begin{cases} x + y + z + w = 2 \\ 2x - 3z = 5 \\ x - 2y + 4w = 9 \\ x + y + 2z + 3w = 5 \end{cases}$

21. $\begin{cases} x - 3y + z = 4 \\ 4x - y + 15z = 5 \end{cases}$

22. $\begin{cases} 2x - 3y + 4z = 3 \\ 4x - 5y + 9z = 13 \\ 2x + 7z = 0 \end{cases}$

23. $\begin{cases} x - z + w = 2 \\ 2x + y - 2w = 12 \\ 3y + z + w = 4 \\ x + y - z = 10 \end{cases}$

24. $\begin{cases} -x + 4y + z = 8 \\ 2x - 6y + z = -9 \\ x - 6y - 4z = -15 \end{cases}$

25. Finding Ages of Children   Eleanor has two children, Kieran and Siobhan. Kieran is 4 years older than Siobhan, and the sum of their ages is 22. How old are the children?

26. Investments   A man invests his savings in two accounts, one paying 6% interest per year and the other paying 7%. He has twice as much invested in the 7% account as in the 6% account, and his annual interest income is $600. How much is invested in each account?

27. Number of Coins   A piggy bank contains 50 coins, all of them nickels, dimes, or quarters. The total value of the coins is $5.60, and the value of the dimes is five times the value of the nickels. How many coins of each type are there?

28. Number of Fish Caught   Tornie is a commercial fisherman who trolls for salmon on the British Columbia coast. One day he catches a total of 25 fish of three salmon species: coho, sockeye, and pink. He catches three more coho than the other two species combined; moreover, he catches twice as many coho as sockeye. How many fish of each species has he caught?

29–36 ■ Partial Fraction Decomposition   Find the partial fraction decomposition of the rational expression.

29. $\dfrac{3x + 1}{x^2 - 2x - 15}$

30. $\dfrac{8}{x^3 - 4x}$

31. $\dfrac{2x - 4}{x(x - 1)^2}$

32. $\dfrac{x + 6}{x^3 - 2x^2 + 4x - 8}$

33. $\dfrac{2x - 1}{x^3 + x}$

34. $\dfrac{5x^2 - 3x + 10}{x^4 + x^2 - 2}$

35. $\dfrac{3x^2 - x + 6}{(x^2 + 2)^2}$

36. $\dfrac{x^2 + x + 1}{x(x^2 + 1)^2}$

37–40 ▪ Intersection Points Two equations and their graphs are given. Find the intersection point(s) of the graphs by solving the system.

37. $\begin{cases} 2x + 3y = 7 \\ x - 2y = 0 \end{cases}$

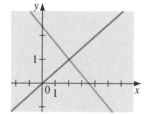

38. $\begin{cases} 3x + y = 8 \\ y = x^2 - 5x \end{cases}$

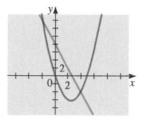

39. $\begin{cases} x^2 + y = 2 \\ x^2 - 3x - y = 0 \end{cases}$

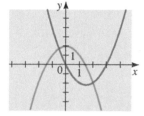

40. $\begin{cases} x - y = -2 \\ x^2 + y^2 - 4y = 4 \end{cases}$

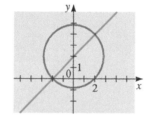

41–42 ▪ Finding an Inequality from a Graph An equation and its graph are given. Find an inequality whose solution is the shaded region.

41. $x + y^2 = 4$

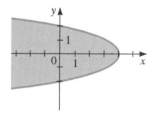

42. $x^2 + y^2 = 8$

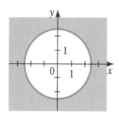

43–46 ▪ Graphing Inequalities Graph the inequality.

43. $3x + y \le 6$

44. $y \ge x^2 - 3$

45. $x^2 + y^2 > 9$

46. $x - y^2 < 4$

47–50 ▪ Solution Set of a System of Inequalities The figure shows the graphs of the equations corresponding to the given inequalities. Shade the solution set of the system of inequalities.

47. $\begin{cases} y \ge x^2 - 3x \\ y \le \frac{1}{3}x - 1 \end{cases}$

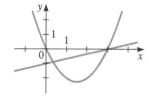

48. $\begin{cases} y \ge x - 1 \\ x^2 + y^2 \le 1 \end{cases}$

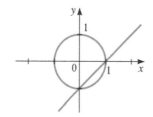

49. $\begin{cases} x + y \ge 2 \\ y - x \le 2 \\ x \le 3 \end{cases}$

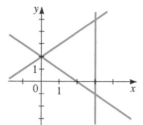

50. $\begin{cases} y \ge -2x \\ y \le 2x \\ y \le -\frac{1}{2}x + 2 \end{cases}$

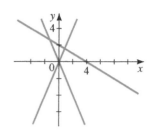

51–54 ▪ Systems of Inequalities Graph the solution set of the system of inequalities. Find the coordinates of all vertices, and determine whether the solution set is bounded or unbounded.

51. $\begin{cases} x^2 + y^2 < 9 \\ x + y < 0 \end{cases}$

52. $\begin{cases} y - x^2 \ge 4 \\ y < 20 \end{cases}$

53. $\begin{cases} x \ge 0, \quad y \ge 0 \\ x + 2y \le 12 \\ y \le x + 4 \end{cases}$

54. $\begin{cases} x \ge 4 \\ x + y \ge 24 \\ x \le 2y + 12 \end{cases}$

55–56 ▪ General Systems of Equations Solve for x, y, and z in terms of a, b, and c.

55. $\begin{cases} -x + y + z = a \\ x - y + z = b \\ x + y - z = c \end{cases}$

56. $\begin{cases} ax + by + cz = a - b + c \\ bx + by + cz = c \\ cx + cy + cz = c \end{cases}$ $\qquad (a \ne b, b \ne c, c \ne 0)$

57. General Systems of Equations For what values of k do the following three lines have a common point of intersection?

$$x + y = 12$$
$$kx - y = 0$$
$$y - x = 2k$$

58. General Systems of Equations For what value of k does the following system have infinitely many solutions?

$$\begin{cases} kx + y + z = 0 \\ x + 2y + kz = 0 \\ -x \qquad + 3z = 0 \end{cases}$$

1–3 ■ A system of equations is given. **(a)** Determine whether the system is linear or nonlinear. **(b)** Find all solutions of the system.

1. $\begin{cases} x + 3y = 7 \\ 5x + 2y = -4 \end{cases}$

2. $\begin{cases} 6x + y^2 = 10 \\ 3x - y = 5 \end{cases}$

3. $\begin{cases} x^2 + y^2 = 100 \\ y = 3x \end{cases}$

4. Use a graphing device to find all solutions of the system rounded to two decimal places.

$$\begin{cases} x - 2y = 1 \\ y = x^3 - 2x^2 \end{cases}$$

5–8 ■ A system of linear equations is given. **(a)** Find the complete solution of the system, or show that there is no solution. **(b)** State whether the system is inconsistent, dependent, or neither.

5. $\begin{cases} x + 2y + z = 3 \\ x + 3y + 2z = 3 \\ 2x + 3y - z = 8 \end{cases}$

6. $\begin{cases} x - y + 9z = -8 \\ -4z = 7 \\ 3x - y + z = 5 \end{cases}$

7. $\begin{cases} 2x - y + z = 0 \\ 3x + 2y - 3z = 1 \\ x - 4y + 5z = -1 \end{cases}$

8. $\begin{cases} x + y - 2z = 8 \\ 2x - y = 20 \\ 2x + 2y - 5z = 15 \end{cases}$

9. In $2\frac{1}{2}$ h an airplane travels 600 km against the wind. It takes 50 min to travel 300 km with the wind. Find the speed of the wind and the speed of the airplane in still air.

10. Anne, Barry, and Cathy enter a coffee shop. Anne orders two coffees, one juice, and two doughnuts and pays $6.25. Barry orders one coffee and three doughnuts and pays $3.75. Cathy orders three coffees, one juice, and four doughnuts and pays $9.25. Find the price of coffee, juice, and doughnuts at this coffee shop.

11–12 ■ Graph the inequality.

11. $3x + 4y < 6$

12. $-x^2 + y \geq 3$

13–14 ■ Graph the solution set of the system of inequalities. Label the vertices with their coordinates.

13. $\begin{cases} 2x + y \leq 8 \\ x - y \geq -2 \\ x + 2y \geq 4 \end{cases}$

14. $\begin{cases} x^2 + y \leq 5 \\ y \leq 2x + 5 \end{cases}$

15–16 ■ Find the partial fraction decomposition of the rational expression.

15. $\dfrac{4x - 1}{(x - 1)^2(x + 2)}$

16. $\dfrac{2x - 3}{x^3 + 3x}$

Linear programming is a modeling technique that is used to determine the optimal allocation of resources in business, the military, and other areas of human endeavor. For example, a manufacturer who makes several different products from the same raw materials can use linear programming to determine how much of each product should be produced to maximize the profit. This modeling technique is probably the most important practical application of systems of linear inequalities. In 1975 Leonid Kantorovich and T. C. Koopmans won the Nobel Prize in economics for their work in the development of this technique.

Although linear programming can be applied to very complex problems with hundreds or even thousands of variables, we consider only a few simple examples to which the graphical methods of Section 10.5 can be applied. (For large numbers of variables a linear programming method based on matrices is used.) Let's examine a typical problem.

EXAMPLE 1 Manufacturing for Maximum Profit

A small shoe manufacturer makes two styles of shoes: oxfords and loafers. Two machines are used in the process: a cutting machine and a sewing machine. Each type of shoe requires 15 min per pair on the cutting machine. Oxfords require 10 min of sewing per pair, and loafers require 20 min of sewing per pair. Because the manufacturer can hire only one operator for each machine, each process is available for just 8 h per day. If the profit is $15 on each pair of oxfords and $20 on each pair of loafers, how many pairs of each type should be produced per day for maximum profit?

Because loafers produce more profit, it would seem best to manufacture only loafers. Surprisingly, this does not turn out to be the most profitable solution.

SOLUTION   First we organize the given information into a table. To be consistent, let's convert all times to hours.

	Oxfords	Loafers	Time available
Time on cutting machine (h)	$\frac{1}{4}$	$\frac{1}{4}$	8
Time on sewing machine (h)	$\frac{1}{6}$	$\frac{1}{3}$	8
Profit	$15	$20	

We describe the model and solve the problem in four steps.

■ Choose the Variables

To make a mathematical model, we first give names to the variable quantities. For this problem we let

$$x = \text{number of pairs of oxfords made daily}$$

$$y = \text{number of pairs of loafers made daily}$$

■ Find the Objective Function

Our goal is to determine which values for x and y give maximum profit. Since each pair of oxfords provides $15 profit and each pair of loafers provides $20, the total profit is given by

$$P = 15x + 20y$$

This function is called the *objective function*.

Graph the Feasible Region

The larger x and y are, the greater is the profit. But we cannot choose arbitrarily large values for these variables because of the restrictions, or *constraints*, in the problem. Each restriction is an inequality in the variables.

In this problem the total number of cutting hours needed is $\frac{1}{4}x + \frac{1}{4}y$. Since only 8 h are available on the cutting machine, we have

$$\tfrac{1}{4}x + \tfrac{1}{4}y \le 8$$

Similarly, by considering the amount of time needed and available on the sewing machine, we get

$$\tfrac{1}{6}x + \tfrac{1}{3}y \le 8$$

We cannot produce a negative number of shoes, so we also have

$$x \ge 0 \qquad \text{and} \qquad y \ge 0$$

Thus x and y must satisfy the constraints

$$\begin{cases} \tfrac{1}{4}x + \tfrac{1}{4}y \le 8 \\ \tfrac{1}{6}x + \tfrac{1}{3}y \le 8 \\ x \ge 0, \quad y \ge 0 \end{cases}$$

If we multiply the first inequality by 4 and the second by 6, we obtain the simplified system

$$\begin{cases} x + y \le 32 \\ x + 2y \le 48 \\ x \ge 0, \quad y \ge 0 \end{cases}$$

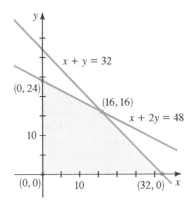

$x + y = 32$

$(0, 24)$

$(16, 16)$

$x + 2y = 48$

10

$(0, 0)$ 10 $(32, 0)$ x

FIGURE 1

The solution of this system (with vertices labeled) is sketched in Figure 1. The only values that satisfy the restrictions of the problem are the ones that correspond to points of the shaded region in Figure 1. This is called the *feasible region* for the problem.

Find the Maximum Profit

As x or y increases, profit increases as well. Thus it seems reasonable that the maximum profit will occur at a point on one of the outside edges of the feasible region, where it is impossible to increase x or y without going outside the region. In fact, it can be shown that the maximum value occurs at a vertex. This means that we need to check the profit only at the vertices. The largest value of P occurs at the point $(16, 16)$, where $P = \$560$. Thus the manufacturer should make 16 pairs of oxfords and 16 pairs of loafers, for a maximum daily profit of $560.

Vertex	$P = 15x + 20y$	
$(0, 0)$	0	
$(0, 24)$	$15(0) + 20(24) = \$480$	
$(16, 16)$	$15(16) + 20(16) = \$560$	Maximum profit
$(32, 0)$	$15(32) + 20(0) = \$480$	

Linear Programming helps the telephone industry to determine the most efficient way to route telephone calls. The computerized routing decisions must be made very rapidly so that callers are not kept waiting for connections. Since the database of customers and routes is huge, an extremely fast method for solving linear programming problems is essential. In 1984 the 28-year-old mathematician **Narendra Karmarkar**, working at Bell Labs in Murray Hill, New Jersey, discovered just such a method. His idea is so ingenious and his method so fast that the discovery caused a sensation in the mathematical world. Although mathematical discoveries rarely make the news, this one was reported in *Time*, on December 3, 1984. Today airlines routinely use Karmarkar's technique to minimize costs in scheduling passengers, flight personnel, fuel, baggage, and maintenance workers.

The linear programming problems that we consider all follow the pattern of Example 1. Each problem involves two variables. The problem describes restrictions, called **constraints**, that lead to a system of linear inequalities whose solution is called the **feasible region**. The function that we wish to maximize or minimize is called the **objective function**. This function always attains its largest and smallest values at the **vertices** of the feasible region. This modeling technique involves four steps, summarized in the following box.

GUIDELINES FOR LINEAR PROGRAMMING

1. **Choose the Variables.** Decide what variable quantities in the problem should be named x and y.

2. **Find the Objective Function.** Write an expression for the function we want to maximize or minimize.

3. **Graph the Feasible Region.** Express the constraints as a system of inequalities, and graph the solution of this system (the feasible region).

4. **Find the Maximum or Minimum.** Evaluate the objective function at the vertices of the feasible region to determine its maximum or minimum value.

EXAMPLE 2 ▸ A Shipping Problem

A car dealer has warehouses in Millville and Trenton and dealerships in Camden and Atlantic City. Every car that is sold at the dealerships must be delivered from one of the warehouses. On a certain day the Camden dealers sell 10 cars, and the Atlantic City dealers sell 12. The Millville warehouse has 15 cars available, and the Trenton warehouse has 10. The cost of shipping one car is $50 from Millville to Camden, $40 from Millville to Atlantic City, $60 from Trenton to Camden, and $55 from Trenton to Atlantic City. How many cars should be moved from each warehouse to each dealership to fill the orders at minimum cost?

SOLUTION   Our first step is to organize the given information. Rather than construct a table, we draw a diagram to show the flow of cars from the warehouses to the dealerships (see Figure 2 below). The diagram shows the number of cars available at each warehouse or required at each dealership and the cost of shipping between these locations.

■ **Choose the Variables**

The arrows in Figure 2 indicate four possible routes, so the problem seems to involve four variables. But we let

$$x = \text{number of cars to be shipped from Millville to Camden}$$

$$y = \text{number of cars to be shipped from Millville to Atlantic City}$$

To fill the orders, we must have

$$10 - x = \text{number of cars shipped from Trenton to Camden}$$

$$12 - y = \text{number of cars shipped from Trenton to Atlantic City}$$

So the only variables in the problem are x and y.

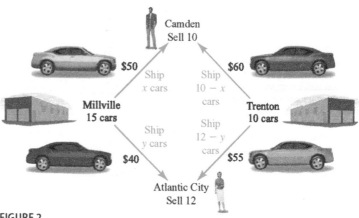

FIGURE 2

■ Find the Objective Function

The objective of this problem is to minimize cost. From Figure 2 we see that the total cost C of shipping the cars is

$$C = 50x + 40y + 60(10 - x) + 55(12 - y)$$
$$= 50x + 40y + 600 - 60x + 660 - 55y$$
$$= 1260 - 10x - 15y$$

This is the objective function.

■ Graph the Feasible Region

Now we derive the constraint inequalities that define the feasible region. First, the number of cars shipped on each route can't be negative, so we have

$$x \geq 0 \qquad\qquad y \geq 0$$
$$10 - x \geq 0 \qquad 12 - y \geq 0$$

Second, the total number of cars shipped from each warehouse can't exceed the number of cars available there, so

$$x + y \leq 15$$
$$(10 - x) + (12 - y) \leq 10$$

Simplifying the latter inequality, we get

$$22 - x - y \leq 10$$
$$-x - y \leq -12$$
$$x + y \geq 12$$

The inequalities $10 - x \geq 0$ and $12 - y \geq 0$ can be rewritten as $x \leq 10$ and $y \leq 12$. Thus the feasible region is described by the constraints

$$\begin{cases} x + y \leq 15 \\ x + y \geq 12 \\ 0 \leq x \leq 10 \\ 0 \leq y \leq 12 \end{cases}$$

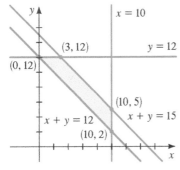

FIGURE 3

The feasible region is graphed in Figure 3.

■ Find the Minimum Cost

We check the value of the objective function at each vertex of the feasible region.

Vertex	$C = 1260 - 10x - 15y$	
$(0, 12)$	$1260 - 10(0)\ \ - 15(12) = \$1080$	
$(3, 12)$	$1260 - 10(3)\ \ - 15(12) = \$1050$	Minimum cost
$(10, 5)$	$1260 - 10(10) - 15(5)\ \ = \$1085$	
$(10, 2)$	$1260 - 10(10) - 15(2)\ \ = \$1130$	

The lowest cost is incurred at the point $(3, 12)$. Thus the dealer should ship

3 cars from Millville to Camden
12 cars from Millville to Atlantic City
7 cars from Trenton to Camden
0 cars from Trenton to Atlantic City ■

In the 1940s mathematicians developed matrix methods for solving linear programming problems that involve more than two variables. These methods were first used by the Allies in World War II to solve supply problems similar to (but, of course, much more complicated than) Example 2. Improving such matrix methods is an active and exciting area of current mathematical research.

PROBLEMS

1–4 ■ Find the maximum and minimum values of the given objective function on the indicated feasible region.

1. $M = 200 - x - y$

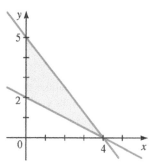

2. $N = \frac{1}{2}x + \frac{1}{4}y + 40$

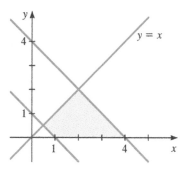

3. $P = 140 - x + 3y$

$$\begin{cases} x \geq 0, y \geq 0 \\ 2x + y \leq 10 \\ 2x + 4y \leq 28 \end{cases}$$

4. $Q = 70x + 82y$

$$\begin{cases} x \geq 0, y \geq 0 \\ x \leq 10, y \leq 20 \\ x + y \geq 5 \\ x + 2y \leq 18 \end{cases}$$

5. Making Furniture A furniture manufacturer makes wooden tables and chairs. The production process involves two basic types of labor: carpentry and finishing. A table requires 2 h of carpentry and 1 h of finishing, and a chair requires 3 h of carpentry and $\frac{1}{2}$ h of finishing. The profit is $35 per table and $20 per chair. The manufacturer's employees can supply a maximum of 108 h of carpentry work and 20 h of finishing work per day. How many tables and chairs should be made each day to maximize profit?

6. A Housing Development A housing contractor has subdivided a farm into 100 building lots. She has designed two types of homes for these lots: colonial and ranch style. A colonial requires $30,000 of capital and produces a profit of $4000 when sold. A ranch-style house requires $40,000 of capital and provides an $8000 profit. If the contractor has $3.6 million of capital on hand, how many houses of each type should she build for maximum profit? Will any of the lots be left vacant?

7. Hauling Fruit A trucker hauls citrus fruit from Florida to Montreal. Each crate of oranges is 4 ft³ in volume and weighs 80 lb. Each crate of grapefruit has a volume of 6 ft³ and weighs 100 lb. His truck has a maximum capacity of 300 ft³ and can carry no more than 5600 lb. Moreover, he is not permitted to carry more crates of grapefruit than crates of oranges. If his profit is $2.50 on each crate of oranges and $4 on each crate of grapefruit, how many crates of each fruit should he carry for maximum profit?

8. Manufacturing Calculators A manufacturer of calculators produces two models: standard and scientific. Long-term demand for the two models mandates that the company manufacture at least 100 standard and 80 scientific calculators each day. However, because of limitations on production capacity, no more than 200 standard and 170 scientific calculators can be made daily. To satisfy a shipping contract, a total of at least 200 calculators must be shipped every day.

(a) If the production cost is $5 for a standard calculator and $7 for a scientific one, how many of each model should be produced daily to minimize this cost?

(b) If each standard calculator results in a $2 loss but each scientific one produces a $5 profit, how many of each model should be made daily to maximize profit?

9. Shipping Televisions An electronics discount chain has a sale on a certain brand of 60-in. high-definition television set. The chain has stores in Santa Monica and El Toro and warehouses in Long Beach and Pasadena. To satisfy rush orders, 15 sets must be shipped from the warehouses to the Santa Monica store, and 19 must be shipped to the El Toro store. The cost of shipping a set is $5 from Long Beach to Santa Monica, $6 from Long

Beach to El Toro, $4 from Pasadena to Santa Monica, and $5.50 from Pasadena to El Toro. If the Long Beach warehouse has 24 sets and the Pasadena warehouse has 18 sets in stock, how many sets should be shipped from each warehouse to each store to fill the orders at a minimum shipping cost?

10. **Delivering Plywood** A man owns two building supply stores, one on the east side and one on the west side of a city. Two customers order some $\frac{1}{2}$-inch plywood. Customer A needs 50 sheets, and customer B needs 70 sheets. The east-side store has 80 sheets, and the west-side store has 45 sheets of this plywood in stock. The east-side store's delivery costs per sheet are $0.50 to customer A and $0.60 to customer B. The west-side store's delivery costs per sheet are $0.40 to customer A and $0.55 to customer B. How many sheets should be shipped from each store to each customer to minimize delivery costs?

11. **Packaging Nuts** A confectioner sells two types of nut mixtures. The standard-mixture package contains 100 g of cashews and 200 g of peanuts and sells for $1.95. The deluxe-mixture package contains 150 g of cashews and 50 g of peanuts and sells for $2.25. The confectioner has 15 kg of cashews and 20 kg of peanuts available. On the basis of past sales, the confectioner needs to have at least as many standard as deluxe packages available. How many bags of each mixture should he package to maximize his revenue?

12. **Feeding Lab Rabbits** A biologist wishes to feed laboratory rabbits a mixture of two types of foods. Type I contains 8 g of fat, 12 g of carbohydrate, and 2 g of protein per ounce. Type II contains 12 g of fat, 12 g of carbohydrate, and 1 g of protein per ounce. Type I costs $0.20 per ounce and type II costs $0.30 per ounce. Each rabbit receives a daily minimum of 24 g of fat, 36 g of carbohydrate, and 4 g of protein, but get no more than 5 oz of food per day. How many ounces of each food type should be fed to each rabbit daily to satisfy the dietary requirements at minimum cost?

13. **Investing in Bonds** A woman wishes to invest $12,000 in three types of bonds: municipal bonds paying 7% interest per year, bank certificates paying 8%, and high-risk bonds paying 12%. For tax reasons she wants the amount invested in municipal bonds to be at least three times the amount invested in bank certificates. To keep her level of risk manageable, she will invest no more than $2000 in high-risk bonds. How much should she invest in each type of bond to maximize her annual interest yield? [*Hint:* Let x = amount in municipal bonds and y = amount in bank certificates. Then the amount in high-risk bonds will be $12,000 - x - y$.]

14. **Annual Interest Yield** Refer to Problem 13. Suppose the investor decides to increase the maximum invested in high-risk bonds to $3000 but leaves the other conditions unchanged. By how much will her maximum possible interest yield increase?

15. **Business Strategy** A small software company publishes computer games, educational software, and utility software. Their business strategy is to market a total of 36 new programs each year, at least four of these being games. The number of utility programs published is never more than twice the number of educational programs. On average, the company makes an annual profit of $5000 on each computer game, $8000 on each educational program, and $6000 on each utility program. How many of each type of software should the company publish annually for maximum profit?

16. **Feasible Region** All parts of this problem refer to the following feasible region and objective function.

$$\begin{cases} x \geq 0 \\ x \geq y \\ x + 2y \geq 12 \\ x + y \leq 10 \end{cases}$$
$$P = x + 4y$$

(a) Graph the feasible region.

(b) On your graph from part (a), sketch the graphs of the linear equations obtained by setting P equal to 40, 36, 32, and 28.

(c) If you continue to decrease the value of P, at which vertex of the feasible region will these lines first touch the feasible region?

(d) Verify that the maximum value of P on the feasible region occurs at the vertex you chose in part (c).

In this appendix we review the concepts of similarity and congruence as well as the Pythagorean Theorem.

■ Congruent Triangles

In general, two geometric figures are congruent if they have the same shape and size. In particular, two line segments are congruent if they have the same length, and two angles are congruent if they have the same measure. For triangles we have the following definition.

CONGRUENT TRIANGLES

Two triangles are **congruent** if their vertices can be matched up so that corresponding sides and angles are congruent.

We write $\triangle ABC \cong \triangle PQR$ to mean that triangle ABC is congruent to triangle PQR and that the sides and angles correspond as follows.

$AB = PQ \qquad \angle A = \angle P$

$BC = QR \qquad \angle B = \angle Q$

$AC = PR \qquad \angle C = \angle R$

To prove that two triangles are congruent, we don't need to show that all six corresponding parts (side and angles) are congruent. For instance, if all three sides are congruent, then all three angles must also be congruent. You can easily see why the following properties lead to congruent triangles.

- **Side-Side-Side (SSS).** If each side of one triangle is congruent to the corresponding side of another triangle, then the two triangles are congruent. See Figure 1(a).

- **Side-Angle-Side (SAS).** If two sides and the included angle in one triangle are congruent to the corresponding sides and angle in another triangle, then the two triangles are congruent. See Figure 1(b).

- **Angle-Side-Angle (ASA).** If two angles and the included side in one triangle are congruent to the corresponding angles and side in another triangle, then the triangles are congruent. See Figure 1(c).

(a) SSS

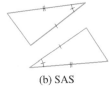

(b) SAS

(c) ASA

FIGURE 1

EXAMPLE 1 ■ Congruent Triangles

(a) $\triangle ADB \cong \triangle CBD$ by SSS.

(b) $\triangle ABE \cong \triangle CBD$ by SAS.

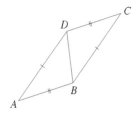

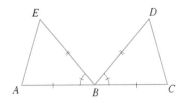

985

(c) $\triangle ABD \cong \triangle CBD$ by ASA.

(d) These triangles are not necessarily congruent. "Side-side-angle" does *not* determine congruence.

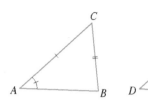

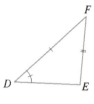

▪ Similar Triangles

Two geometric figures are similar if they have the same shape, but not necessarily the same size. (See *Discovery Project: Similarity* referenced on page 450.) In the case of triangles we can define similarity as follows.

SIMILAR TRIANGLES

Two triangles are **similar** if their vertices can be matched up so that corresponding angles are congruent. In this case corresponding sides are proportional.

We write $\triangle ABC \sim \triangle PQR$ to mean that triangle ABC is similar to triangle PQR and that the following conditions hold.

The angles correspond as follows:

$$\angle A = \angle P, \quad \angle B = \angle Q, \quad \angle C = \angle R$$

The sides are proportional as follows:

$$\frac{AB}{PQ} = \frac{BC}{QR} = \frac{AC}{PR}$$

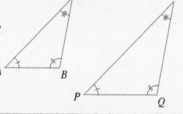

The sum of the angles in any triangle is $180°$. So if we know two angles in a triangle, the third is determined. Thus to prove that two triangles are similar, we need only show that two angles in one are congruent to two angles in the other.

EXAMPLE 2 ▪ Similar Triangles

Find all pairs of similar triangles in the figures.

(a)

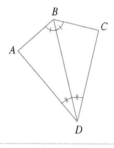

(b)

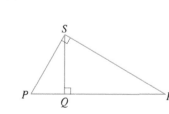

SOLUTION

(a) Since $\angle AEB$ and $\angle CED$ are opposite angles, they are equal. Thus

$$\triangle AEB \sim \triangle CED$$

(b) Since all triangles in the figure are right triangles, we have

$$\angle QSR + \angle QRS = 90°$$

$$\angle QSR + \angle QSP = 90°$$

Subtracting these equations we find that $\angle QSP = \angle QRS$. Thus

$$\triangle PQS \sim \triangle SQR \sim \triangle PSR$$

EXAMPLE 3 ▪ Proportional Sides in Similar Triangles

Given that the triangles in the figure are similar, find the lengths x and y.

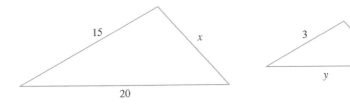

SOLUTION By similarity, we know that the lengths of corresponding sides in the triangles are proportional. First we find x.

$$\frac{x}{2} = \frac{15}{3} \qquad \text{Corresponding sides are proportional}$$

$$x = \frac{2 \cdot 15}{3} = 10 \qquad \text{Solve for } x$$

Now we find y.

$$\frac{15}{3} = \frac{20}{y} \qquad \text{Corresponding sides are proportional}$$

$$y = \frac{20 \cdot 3}{15} = 4 \qquad \text{Solve for } y$$

▪ The Pythagorean Theorem

In a right triangle the side opposite the right angle is called the **hypotenuse**, and the other two sides are called the **legs**.

THE PYTHAGOREAN THEOREM

In a right triangle the square of the hypotenuse is equal to the sum of the squares of the legs. That is, in triangle ABC in the figure

$$a^2 + b^2 = c^2$$

EXAMPLE 4   Using the Pythagorean Theorem

Find the lengths x and y in the right triangles shown.

(a)

(b)

SOLUTION

(a) We use the Pythagorean Theorem with $a = 20$, and $b = 21$, and $c = x$. Then $x^2 = 20^2 + 21^2 = 841$. So $x = \sqrt{841} = 29$.

(b) We use the Pythagorean Theorem with $c = 25$, $a = 7$, and $b = y$. Then $25^2 = 7^2 + y^2$, so $y^2 = 25^2 - 7^2 = 576$. Thus $y = \sqrt{576} = 24$.

The converse of the Pythagorean Theorem is also true.

CONVERSE OF THE PYTHAGOREAN THEOREM

If the square of one side of a triangle is equal to the sum of the squares of the other two sides, then the triangle is a right triangle.

EXAMPLE 5   Proving That a Triangle Is a Right Triangle

Prove that the triangle with sides of length 8, 15, and 17 is a right triangle.

SOLUTION   You can check that $8^2 + 15^2 = 17^2$. So the triangle must be a right triangle by the converse of the Pythagorean Theorem.

A EXERCISES

1–4 ■ Congruent Triangles?   Determine whether the pair of triangles is congruent. If so, state the congruence principle you are using.

1.

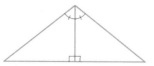

2.   **3.**

4.

5–8 ■ Similar Triangles?   Determine whether the pair of triangles is similar.

5.

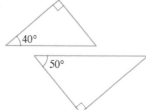

6.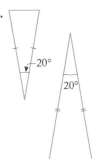

7.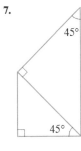

8.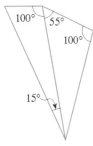

9–12 ■ Similar Triangles Given that the pair of triangles is similar, find the length(s) x and/or y.

9.

10.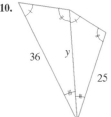

11. 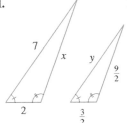   **12.**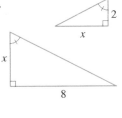

13–14 ■ Using Similarity Express x in terms of a, b, and c.

13.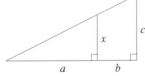

14.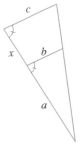

15. Proving Similarity In the figure CDEF is a rectangle. Prove that $\triangle ABC \sim \triangle AED \sim \triangle EBF$.

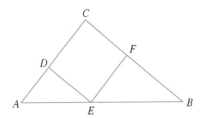

16. Proving Similarity In the figure *DEFG* is a square. Prove the following:

(a) $\triangle ADG \sim \triangle GCF$
(b) $\triangle ADG \sim \triangle FEB$
(c) $AD \cdot EB = DG \cdot FE$
(d) $DE = \sqrt{AD \cdot EB}$

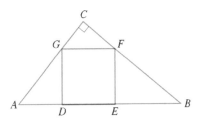

17–22 ■ Pythagorean Theorem In the given right triangle, find the side labeled x.

17. 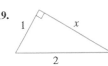   **18.**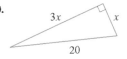

19. 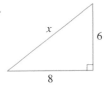   **20.**

21.

22.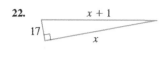

23–28 ▪ Right Triangle? The lengths of the sides of a triangle are given. Determine whether the triangle is a right triangle.

23. 5, 12, 13

24. 15, 20, 25

25. 8, 10, 12

26. 6, 17, 18

27. 48, 55, 73

28. 13, 84, 85

29–32 ▪ Pythagorean Theorem These exercises require the use of the Pythagorean Theorem.

29. One leg of a right triangle measures 11 cm. The hypotenuse is 1 cm longer than the other leg. Find the length of the hypotenuse.

30. The length of a rectangle is 1 ft greater than its width. Each diagonal is 169 ft long. Find the dimensions of the rectangle.

31. Each of the diagonals of a quadrilateral is 27 cm long. Two adjacent sides measure 17 cm and 21 cm. Is the quadrilateral a rectangle?

32. Find the height h of the right triangle ABC shown in the figure. [*Hint:* Find the area of triangle ABC in two different ways.]

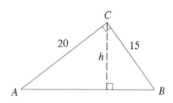

33. Diagonal of a Box Find the length of the diagonal of the rectangular box shown in the figure.

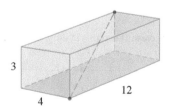

34. Pythagorean Triples If a, b, c are positive integers such that $a^2 + b^2 = c^2$, then (a, b, c) is called a **Pythagorean triple**.

(a) Let m and n be positive integers with $m > n$. Let $a = m^2 - n^2$, $b = 2mn$, and $c = m^2 + n^2$. Show that (a, b, c) is a Pythagorean triple.

(b) Use part (a) to find the rest of the Pythagorean triples in the table.

m	n	(a, b, c)
2	1	$(3, 4, 5)$
3	1	$(8, 6, 10)$
3	2	
4	1	
4	2	
4	3	
5	1	
5	2	
5	3	
5	4	

35. Finding a Length Two vertical poles, one 8 ft tall and the other 24 ft tall, have ropes stretched from the top of each to the base of the other (see the figure). How high above the ground is the point where the ropes cross? [*Hint:* Use similarity.]

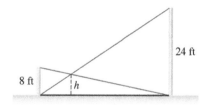

Most of the applied examples and exercises in this book involve approximate values. For example, one exercise states that the moon has a radius of 1074 miles. This does not mean that the moon's radius is exactly 1074 miles; it simply means that this is the radius rounded to the nearest mile.

One simple method for specifying the accuracy of a number is to state how many **significant digits** it has. The significant digits in a number are the ones from the first nonzero digit to the last nonzero digit (reading from left to right). Thus 1074 has four significant digits, 1070 has three, 1100 has two, and 1000 has one significant digit. This rule may sometimes lead to ambiguities. For example, if a distance is 200 km to the nearest kilometer, then the number 200 really has three significant digits, not just one. This ambiguity is avoided if we use scientific notation—that is, if we express the number as a multiple of a power of 10:

$$2.00 \times 10^2$$

When working with approximate values, students often make the mistake of giving a final answer with *more* significant digits than the original data. This is incorrect because you cannot "create" precision by using a calculator. The final result can be no more accurate than the measurements given in the problem. For example, suppose we are told that the two shorter sides of a right triangle are measured to be 1.25 in. and 2.33 in. long. By the Pythagorean Theorem we find, using a calculator, that the hypotenuse has length

$$\sqrt{1.25^2 + 2.33^2} \approx 2.644125564 \text{ in.}$$

But since the given lengths were expressed to three significant digits, the answer cannot be any more accurate. We can therefore say only that the hypotenuse is 2.64 in. long, rounding to the nearest hundredth.

In general, the final answer should be expressed with the same accuracy as the *least-accurate* measurement given in the statement of the problem. The following rules make this principle more precise.

RULES FOR WORKING WITH APPROXIMATE DATA

1. When multiplying or dividing, round off the final result so that it has as many *significant digits* as the given value with the fewest number of significant digits.

2. When adding or subtracting, round off the final result so that it has its last significant digit in the *decimal place* in which the least-accurate given value has its last significant digit.

3. When taking powers or roots, round off the final result so that it has the same number of *significant digits* as the given value.

EXAMPLE 1   Working with Approximate Data

A rectangular table top is measured to be 122.64 in. by 37.3 in. Find the area and perimeter.

SOLUTION   Using the formulas for area and perimeter, we get the following.

Area = length $\times$ width = $122.64 \times 37.3 \approx 4570$ in^2 Three significant digits

Perimeter = 2(length + width) = $2(122.54 + 37.3) \approx 319.9$ in.   Tenths digit

So the area is approximately 4570 in^2, and the perimeter is approximately 319.9 in.

⊘ Note that in the formula for the perimeter the value 2 is an exact value, not an approximate measurement. It therefore does not affect the accuracy of the final result. In general, if a problem involves only exact values, we may express the final answer with as many significant digits as we wish.

Note also that to make the final result as accurate as possible, *you should wait until the last step to round off your answer*. If necessary, use the memory feature of your calculator to retain the results of intermediate calculations.

B EXERCISES

1–10 ▪ Significant Figures   Evaluate the expression. Round your final answer to the appropriate number of decimal places or significant figures.

1. $3.27 - 0.1834$

2. $102.68 + 26.7$

3. 28.36×501.375

4. $\dfrac{201{,}186}{5238}$

5. $(1.36)^3$

6. $\sqrt{427.3}$

7. $3.3(642.75 + 66.787)$

8. $\dfrac{701}{1.27 - 10.5}$

9. $(5.10 \times 10^{-3})(12.4 \times 10^7)(6.007 \times 10^{-6})$

10. $\dfrac{(1.361 \times 10^7)(4.7717 \times 10^{-5})}{1.281876}$

11–12 ▪ Significant Figures in Geometry   Use the geometric formulas on the inside front cover of the book to solve these problems.

11. Find the circumference and area of a circle whose radius is 5.27 ft.

12. Find the volume of a cone whose height is 52.3 cm and whose radius is 4.267 cm.

13–14 ▪ Newton's Law of Gravity   The gravitational force F (in newtons) between two objects with masses m_1 and m_2 (in kg), separated by a distance r (in meters), is given by Newton's Law of Gravity:

$$F = G \frac{m_1 m_2}{r^2}$$

where $G \approx 6.67428 \times 10^{-11} \, \text{Nm}^2/\text{kg}^2$.

13. Find the gravitational force between two satellites in stationary earth orbit, 57.2 km apart, each with a mass of 11,426 kg.

14. The sun and the earth are 1.50×10^{11} m apart, with masses 1.9891×10^{30} kg and 5.972×10^{24} kg, respectively.

   (a) Find the gravitational force between the sun and the earth.

   (b) Convert your answer in part (a) from newtons to pounds, using the fact that $1 \, \text{N} \approx 0.225 \, \text{lb}$.

Graphing with a Graphing Calculator

A graphing calculator is a powerful tool for graphing equations and functions. In this appendix we give general guidelines to follow and common pitfalls to avoid when graphing with a graphing calculator. See Appendix D for specific guidelines on graphing with the TI-83/84 graphing calculators.

■ Selecting the Viewing Rectangle

A graphing calculator or computer displays a rectangular portion of the graph of an equation in a display window or viewing screen, which we call a **viewing rectangle**. The default screen often gives an incomplete or misleading picture, so it is important to choose the viewing rectangle with care. If we choose the x-values to range from a minimum value of $\text{Xmin} = a$ to a maximum value of $\text{Xmax} = b$ and the y-values to range from a minimum value of $\text{Ymin} = c$ to a maximum value of $\text{Ymax} = d$, then the displayed portion of the graph lies in the rectangle

$$[a, b] \times [c, d] = \{(x, y) \mid a \le x \le b, c \le y \le d\}$$

as shown in Figure 1. We refer to this as the $[a, b]$ by $[c, d]$ viewing rectangle.

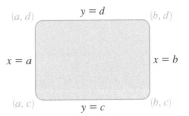

FIGURE 1 The viewing rectangle $[a, b]$ by $[c, d]$

The graphing device draws the graph of an equation much as you would. It plots points of the form (x, y) for a certain number of values of x, equally spaced between a and b. If the equation is not defined for an x-value or if the corresponding y-value lies outside the viewing rectangle, the device ignores this value and moves on to the next x-value. The machine connects each point to the preceding plotted point to form a representation of the graph of the equation.

EXAMPLE 1 Choosing an Appropriate Viewing Rectangle

Graph the equation $y = x^2 + 3$ in an appropriate viewing rectangle.

SOLUTION Let's experiment with different viewing rectangles. We start with the viewing rectangle $[-2, 2]$ by $[-2, 2]$, so we set

$$\text{Xmin} = -2 \qquad \text{Ymin} = -2$$
$$\text{Xmax} = 2 \qquad \text{Ymax} = 2$$

The resulting graph in Figure 2(a) (on the next page) is blank! This is because $x^2 \ge 0$, so $x^2 + 3 \ge 3$ for all x. Thus the graph lies entirely above the viewing rectangle, so this viewing rectangle is not appropriate. If we enlarge the viewing rectangle to $[-4, 4]$ by $[-4, 4]$, as in Figure 2(b), we begin to see a portion of the graph.

Now let's try the viewing rectangle $[-10, 10]$ by $[-5, 30]$. The graph in Figure 2(c) seems to give a more complete view of the graph. If we enlarge the viewing rectangle even further, as in Figure 2(d), the graph doesn't show clearly that the y-intercept is 3.

So the viewing rectangle $[-10, 10]$ by $[-5, 30]$ gives an appropriate representation of the graph.

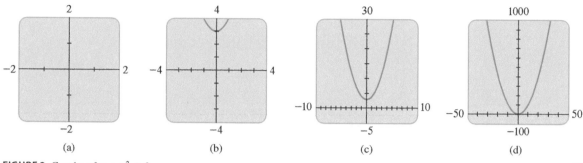

(a) (b) (c) (d)

FIGURE 2 Graphs of $y = x^2 + 3$

EXAMPLE 2 ▪ Graphing a Cubic Equation

Graph the equation $y = x^3 - 49x$.

SOLUTION Let's experiment with different viewing rectangles. If we start with the viewing rectangle

$$[-5, 5] \text{ by } [-5, 5]$$

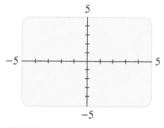

FIGURE 3

we get the graph in Figure 3. On most graphing calculators the screen appears to be blank, but it is not quite blank because the point $(0, 0)$ has been plotted. It turns out that for all other x-values that the calculator chooses, the corresponding y-value is greater than 5 or less than -5, so the resulting point on the graph lies outside the viewing rectangle.

Let's use the zoom-out feature of a graphing calculator to change the viewing rectangle to the larger rectangle

$$[-10, 10] \text{ by } [-10, 10]$$

In this case we get the graph shown in Figure 4(a), which appears to consist of vertical lines, but we know that cannot be true. If we look carefully while the graph is being drawn, we see that the graph leaves the screen and reappears during the graphing process. That indicates that we need to see more of the graph in the vertical direction, so we change the viewing rectangle to

$$[-10, 10] \text{ by } [-100, 100]$$

The resulting graph is shown in Figure 4(b). It still doesn't reveal all the main features of the equation. It appears that we need to see still more in the vertical direction. So we try the viewing rectangle

$$[-10, 10] \text{ by } [-200, 200]$$

The resulting graph is shown in Figure 4(c). Now we are more confident that we have arrived at an appropriate viewing rectangle. In Chapter 3, where third-degree polynomials are discussed, we learn that the graph shown in Figure 4(c) does indeed reveal all the main features of the equation.

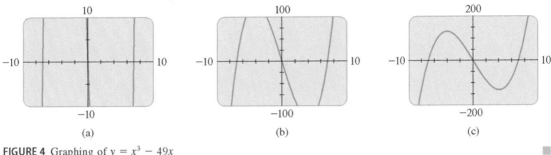

(a) (b) (c)

FIGURE 4 Graphing of $y = x^3 - 49x$

▪ Interpreting the Screen Image

Once a graph of an equation has been obtained by using a graphing calculator, we sometimes need to interpret what the graph means in terms of the equation. Certain limitations of the calculator can cause it to produce graphs that are inaccurate or need further modifications. Here are two examples.

EXAMPLE 3 ▪ Two Graphs on the Same Screen

Graph the equations $y = 3x^2 - 6x + 1$ and $y = 0.23x - 2.25$ together in the viewing rectangle $[-1, 3]$ by $[-2.5, 1.5]$. Do the graphs intersect in this viewing rectangle?

SOLUTION   Figure 5(a) shows the essential features of both graphs. One is a parabola, and the other is a line. It looks as if the graphs intersect near the point $(1, -2)$. However, if we zoom in on the area around this point as shown in Figure 5(b), we see that although the graphs almost touch, they do not actually intersect.

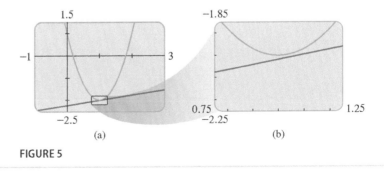

(a) (b)

FIGURE 5

You can see from Examples 1, 2, and 3 that the choice of a viewing rectangle makes a big difference in the appearance of a graph. If you want an overview of the essential features of a graph, you must choose a relatively large viewing rectangle to obtain a global view of the graph. If you want to investigate the details of a graph, you must zoom in to a small viewing rectangle that shows just the feature of interest.

EXAMPLE 4 ▪ Avoiding Extraneous Lines in Graphs

Graph the equation $y = \dfrac{1}{1 - x}$.

SOLUTION   Figure 6(a) shows the graph produced by a graphing calculator with viewing rectangle

$$[-5, 5] \text{ by } [-5, 5]$$

In connecting successive points on the graph, the calculator produced a steep line segment from the top to the bottom of the screen. That line segment should not be part of the graph. The right side of the equation is not defined for $x = 1$, so the calculator connects points on the graph to the left and right of $x = 1$, and this produces the extraneous line segment. We can get rid of the extraneous near-vertical line by changing the graphing mode on the calculator. If we choose the Dot mode, in which points on the graph are not connected, we get the better graph in Figure 6(b). The graph in Figure 6(b) has gaps, so we have to interpret it as having the points connected but without creating the extraneous line segment.

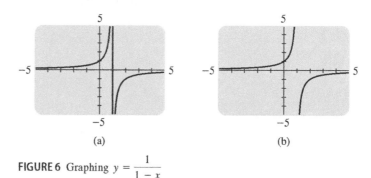

(a)   (b)

FIGURE 6 Graphing $y = \dfrac{1}{1 - x}$

▪ Graphing Equations That Are Not Functions

Most graphing calculators can only graph equations in which y is isolated on one side of the equal sign. Such equations are ones that represent functions (see page 200). The next example shows how to graph equations that don't have this property.

EXAMPLE 5 ▪ Graphing a Circle

Graph the circle $x^2 + y^2 = 1$.

SOLUTION   We first solve for y, to isolate it on one side of the equal sign.

$$y^2 = 1 - x^2 \qquad \text{Subtract } x^2$$

$$y = \pm\sqrt{1 - x^2} \qquad \text{Take square roots}$$

Therefore the circle is described by the graphs of *two* equations:

$$y = \sqrt{1 - x^2} \quad \text{and} \quad y = -\sqrt{1 - x^2}$$

The first equation represents the top half of the circle (because $y \geq 0$), and the second represents the bottom half of the circle (because $y \leq 0$). If we graph the first equation in the viewing rectangle $[-2, 2]$ by $[-2, 2]$, we get the semicircle shown in Figure 7(a). The graph of the second equation is the semicircle in Figure 7(b).

The graph in Figure 7(c) looks somewhat flattened. Most graphing calculators allow you to set the scales on the axes so that circles really look like circles. On the TI-83/84, from the ZOOM menu, choose ZSquare to set the scales appropriately.

Graphing these semicircles together on the same viewing screen, we get the full circle in Figure 7(c).

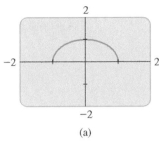

(a)

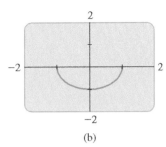

(b)

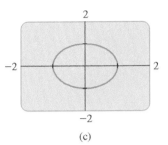

(c)

FIGURE 7 Graphing the equation $x^2 + y^2 = 1$

C EXERCISES

1–6 ▪ Choosing a Window Use a graphing calculator or computer to decide which viewing rectangle (a)–(d) produces the most appropriate graph of the equation.

1. $y = x^4 + 2$
   (a) $[-2, 2]$ by $[-2, 2]$
   (b) $[0, 4]$ by $[0, 4]$
   (c) $[-8, 8]$ by $[-4, 40]$
   (d) $[-40, 40]$ by $[-80, 800]$

2. $y = x^2 + 7x + 6$
   (a) $[-5, 5]$ by $[-5, 5]$
   (b) $[0, 10]$ by $[-20, 100]$
   (c) $[-15, 8]$ by $[-20, 100]$
   (d) $[-10, 3]$ by $[-100, 20]$

3. $y = 100 - x^2$
   (a) $[-4, 4]$ by $[-4, 4]$
   (b) $[-10, 10]$ by $[-10, 10]$
   (c) $[-15, 15]$ by $[-30, 110]$
   (d) $[-4, 4]$ by $[-30, 110]$

4. $y = 2x^2 - 1000$
   (a) $[-10, 10]$ by $[-10, 10]$
   (b) $[-10, 10]$ by $[-100, 100]$
   (c) $[-10, 10]$ by $[-1000, 1000]$
   (d) $[-25, 25]$ by $[-1200, 200]$

5. $y = 10 + 25x - x^3$
   (a) $[-4, 4]$ by $[-4, 4]$
   (b) $[-10, 10]$ by $[-10, 10]$
   (c) $[-20, 20]$ by $[-100, 100]$
   (d) $[-100, 100]$ by $[-200, 200]$

6. $y = \sqrt{8x - x^2}$
   (a) $[-4, 4]$ by $[-4, 4]$
   (b) $[-5, 5]$ by $[0, 100]$
   (c) $[-10, 10]$ by $[-10, 40]$
   (d) $[-2, 10]$ by $[-2, 6]$

7–18 ▪ Graphing with a Graphing Calculator Determine an appropriate viewing rectangle for the equation, and use it to draw the graph.

7. $y = 100x^2$ **8.** $y = -100x^2$

9. $y = 4 + 6x - x^2$ **10.** $y = 0.3x^2 + 1.7x - 3$

11. $y = \sqrt[4]{256 - x^2}$ **12.** $y = \sqrt{12x - 17}$

13. $y = 0.01x^3 - x^2 + 5$ **14.** $y = x(x + 6)(x - 9)$

15. $y = \dfrac{1}{x^2 - 2x}$ **16.** $y = \dfrac{x}{x^2 + 25}$

17. $y = 1 + |x - 1|$ **18.** $y = 2x - |x^2 - 5|$

19–26 ▪ Intersection Points Do the graphs intersect in the given viewing rectangle? If they do, how many points of intersection are there?

19. $y = -3x^2 + 6x - \frac{1}{2}$, $y = \sqrt{7 - \frac{7}{12}x^2}$; $[-4, 4]$ by $[-1, 3]$

20. $y = \sqrt{49 - x^2}$, $y = \frac{1}{5}(41 - 3x)$; $[-8, 8]$ by $[-1, 8]$

21. $y = 6 - 4x - x^2$, $y = 3x + 18$; $[-6, 2]$ by $[-5, 20]$

22. $y = x^3 - 4x$, $y = x + 5$; $[-4, 4]$ by $[-15, 15]$

23. Graph the circle $x^2 + y^2 = 9$ by solving for y and graphing two equations as in Example 3.

24. Graph the circle $(y - 1)^2 + x^2 = 1$ by solving for y and graphing two equations as in Example 3.

25. Graph the equation $4x^2 + 2y^2 = 1$ by solving for y and graphing two equations corresponding to the negative and positive square roots. (This graph is called an *ellipse*.)

26. Graph the equation $y^2 - 9x^2 = 1$ by solving for y and graphing the two equations corresponding to the positive and negative square roots. (This graph is called a *hyperbola*.)

APPENDIX D Using the TI-83/84 Graphing Calculator

A TI-83 or TI-84 graphing calculator is a powerful tool that can draw graphs as well as do many of the other calculations that we study in this book. Here we give some of the basic calculator operations. When you master these, you'll be able to easily use the calculator to do many other tasks.

1. Set the Mode

Make sure the calculator is in the "mode" that you want.

STEP 1 Find the Mode Menu To get the mode menu, press the `MODE` key.

STEP 2 Make the Appropriate Selections Use the cursor to highlight a selection, then press `ENTER` to make the selection. For example, choose `Normal` for decimal notation, `Sci` for scientific notation, `Func` to graph functions in rectangular coordinates, `Real` to work with real numbers, or `a+bi` to work with complex numbers. The standard choices are shown here.

NOTE: Press `2nd` `QUIT` to exit this menu (or to exit any other menu).

2. Graph an Equation

To graph one or more equations on the same screen, first express each equation in function form, with y on one side of the equation. Let's graph $y = x^3 + 1$ and $y = -x + 2$.

STEP 1 Enter the Equation Press the `Y=` key, and then enter the equations as shown.

STEP 2 Choose the Window Press the `WINDOW` key, and then enter the values for `Xmin`, `Xmax`, `Ymin`, and `Ymax` that you want.

STEP 3 Get the Graph To get the graph, press the `GRAPH` key.

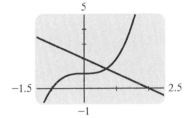

3. Zoom in on a Graph

To zoom in on a portion of a graph, first draw the graph(s) by following the steps in Part 2. With the graph(s) on the screen, follow these steps.

STEP 1 Choose the Zoom Menu Press the `ZOOM` key to obtain the zoom menu. Choose `ZBox`, and press `ENTER`. (You can experiment with other choices also.)

STEP 2 Draw the Zoom Box Move the cursor to the location of the bottom left corner of the rectangle (or box) that you want to zoom in on, then press `ENTER`. Then move the cursor to the location of the top right corner of the zoom box.

STEP 3 Zoom In   Press [ENTER] to zoom in on the portion of the graph that is in the zoom box.

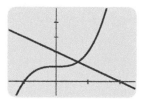
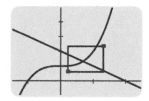

▪ 4. Trace a Graph

Once a graph has been drawn on the calculator screen, you can find the coordinates of any point on the graph.

STEP 1 Graph an Equation   Graph an equation (or several equations) as in Part 2. Keep the graph(s) on the calculator screen.

STEP 2 Choose the Command   Go to the trace command by pressing the [TRACE] key. A cursor (⊠) appears on the screen.

STEP 3 Trace the Graph   Move the cursor along the curve by using the left or right arrow keys. You can jump from one curve to another by using the up or down arrow keys. The numbers at the bottom of the screen give the coordinates of the location of the cursor.

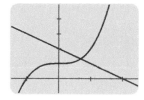
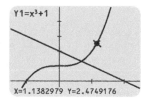
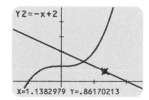

▪ 5. Find Points of Intersection of Two Graphs

To find the point of intersection of the graphs of two equations, first graph the two equations on the same screen, as in Part 2.

STEP 1 Choose the Calc Menu   Press [2nd] [CALC] to obtain the menu. Choose the intersect command, and press [ENTER]. (You can also experiment with the other commands on this menu.)

STEP 2 Choose the Two Curves   Use the up and down keys to display the equations you have entered (they appear at the top of the screen). Select the first equation you want by pressing [ENTER]. Use the up and down keys again, and select the second equation. A cursor appears on one of the graphs. The numbers at the bottom of the screen give the coordinates of the cursor.

STEP 3 Get the Intersection Point   Now Guess? appears on the screen. Move the cursor to a point near the point of intersection that you want to find (this is your guess). Press [ENTER]. The point of intersection is displayed at the bottom of the screen.

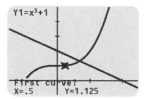
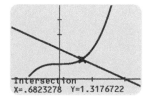

■ 6. Find Zeros of a Function

To find the zeros (or *x*-intercepts) of a function, we first graph the function, as in Part 2. Suppose we've graphed $y = x^3 - 2x^2 - 5x + 6$.

STEP 1 Choose the Calc Menu   Press $\boxed{\text{2nd}}$ $\boxed{\text{CALC}}$ to obtain the menu, as shown in Part 5 above. Choose the `zero` command, and press $\boxed{\text{ENTER}}$.

STEP 2 Choose Left and Right Bounds   The question `Left Bound?` appears at the bottom of the screen. Use the arrow keys to move the cursor to a point on the graph to the left of the zero you want, and then press $\boxed{\text{ENTER}}$. The question `Right Bound?` appears. Move the cursor to a point to the right of the zero you want, and then press $\boxed{\text{ENTER}}$.

STEP 3 Get the Zero   Now `Guess?` appears on the screen. Press $\boxed{\text{ENTER}}$. The coordinates of the zero appear at the bottom of the screen.

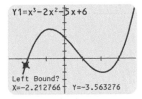 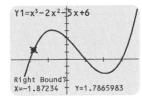 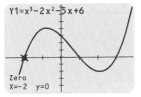

■ 7. Find Maximum and Minimum Values of a Function

To find local maximum or minimum values of a function, we first graph the function, as in Part 2. Let's find the local maximum of the function in $y = x^3 - 2x^2 - 5x + 6$, graphed in Part 6 above.

STEP 1 Choose the Calc Menu   Press $\boxed{\text{2nd}}$ $\boxed{\text{CALC}}$ to obtain the menu, as shown in Part 5 above. Choose the `maximum` command, and press $\boxed{\text{ENTER}}$.

STEP 2 Choose Left and Right Bounds   The question `Left Bound?` appears at the bottom of the screen. Use the arrow keys to move the cursor to a point on the graph to the left of the local maximum that you want, and then press $\boxed{\text{ENTER}}$. The question `Right Bound?` appears. Move the cursor to a point to the right of the local maximum that you want, and then press $\boxed{\text{ENTER}}$.

STEP 3 Get the Maximum or Minimum   Now `Guess?` appears on the screen. Press $\boxed{\text{ENTER}}$. The coordinates of the maximum between the selected bounds appear at the bottom of the screen.

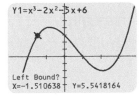 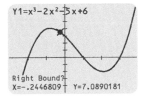 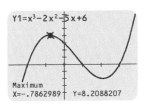

■ 8. Make a Table of Values of a Function

To make a table of values of a function, first enter the function. Let's work with the function $y = x^2$.

STEP 1 Enter the Function   Press the $\boxed{\text{Y=}}$ key, and then enter the definition of the function as shown on the next page.

STEP 2 Set the Table Properties   Press $\boxed{\text{2nd}}$ $\boxed{\text{TBLSET}}$, and then select the value at which you want the table to start (`TblStart`) and the step size (Δ`Tbl`).

STEP 3 Get the Table Press 2nd TABLE to obtain the table. Scroll up or down to see more of the table.

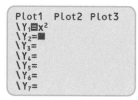
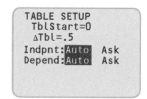
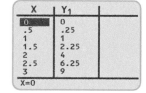

▪ 9. Graph a Piecewise Defined Function

To graph a piecewise defined function, we use the TEST menu, which includes the inequality symbols $<$, $\leq$, $>$, $\geq$ and the logical symbol and. Let's graph

$$f(x) = \begin{cases} x + 2 & \text{if } x < -1 \\ x^2 & \text{if } -1 \leq x \leq 1 \\ 2 & \text{if } 1 < x \end{cases}$$

STEP 1 Enter the Equation Press the Y= key, and enter the equation as shown. Put each part of the function in parentheses followed by the corresponding condition in parentheses. To obtain inequality symbols, press 2nd TEST, and select the required symbol. A double inequality such as $-1 \leq x \leq 1$ is entered as $-1 \leq x$ and $x \leq 1$. To get the logical symbol and, press 2nd TEST and select LOGIC, and then choose and.

STEP 2 Choose the Window Press the WINDOW key, and then enter the values for Xmin, Xmax, Ymin, and Ymax that you want.

STEP 3 Get the Graph To get the graph, press the GRAPH key.

NOTE: To avoid extraneous vertical lines between the different parts of the graph, put the calculator in Dot mode (see Part 1).

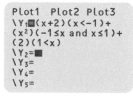
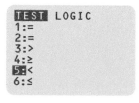
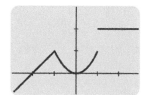

▪ 10. Graph an Inequality

To graph an inequality in two variables, first enter the corresponding equation, as in Part 2. We illustrate the process with the inequalities $y \geq x^3 + 1$ and $y \leq -x + 2$.

STEP 1 Enter the Equation(s) Enter the equation(s) as in Part 2, and set the window.

STEP 2 Choose the Inequalities For each equation, use the left arrow key to move the cursor to the very left of the equation. Press ENTER repeatedly to cycle through the inequality options (◥ and ◣). When the desired inequality appears, move on to the next equation.

STEP 3 Get the Graph   To get the graph, press the $\boxed{\text{GRAPH}}$ key.

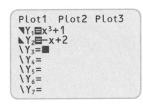 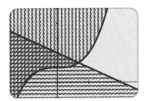

▪ 11. Enter Data

To enter data such as a list of one-variable data or a list of two-variable data into the calculator, we use the $\boxed{\text{STAT}}$ menu.

STEP 1 Go to the Statistics Menu   Press the $\boxed{\text{STAT}}$ key. From the top menu choose EDIT, then 1:Edit, and then press $\boxed{\text{ENTER}}$.

STEP 2 Enter the Data   Enter the data in one or more of the columns labeled L1, L2, L3, ... For example, for two-variable data enter the x-coordinates of the data points in L1 and the y-coordinates in L2. To clear a list from an entire column, place the cursor at the title of the column (L1, for example) and press $\boxed{\text{CLEAR}}$.

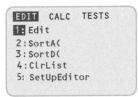

▪ 12. Find the Curve of Best Fit

To find the curve that best fits a given set of two-variable data, we first enter the data.

STEP 1 Enter the Data   Enter the two-variable data in two columns, say L1 and L2, as in Part 11.

STEP 2 Choose the Regression Command   Press the $\boxed{\text{STAT}}$ key again. From the top menu choose CALC, then select the type of curve you want (LinReg(ax+b), QuadReg, ExpReg, PwrReg, . . .) and press $\boxed{\text{ENTER}}$.

STEP 3 Obtain the Regression Line   Now select the columns in which you stored the data. For example, for Xlist select L1, and for Ylist select L2, as in the middle graph. Note that the column names are located at $\boxed{\text{2ND}}$ $\boxed{\text{ENTER}}$ and $\boxed{\text{2nd}}$ $\boxed{\text{L2}}$. Scroll down to Calculate, and press $\boxed{\text{ENTER}}$. The regression equation with the values of the coefficients appears on the screen.

NOTE: To get r^2 and r, go to $\boxed{\text{2nd}}$ $\boxed{\text{CATALOG}}$ (above 0) and select DiagnosticOn.

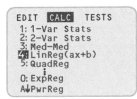 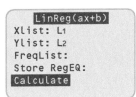 

■ 13. Enter a Matrix

To enter a matrix into the calculator, we start with the $\boxed{\texttt{MATRIX}}$ menu.

STEP 1 Go to the Matrix Menu   Press the $\boxed{\texttt{2nd}}$ $\boxed{\texttt{MATRIX}}$ key to obtain the matrix menu. From the top menu choose ED IT, then select a matrix name (ᴄ A ᴅ, for example), and press $\boxed{\texttt{ENTER}}$.

STEP 2 Enter the Matrix   Now enter the dimension of the matrix you want, (3×4, for example), and press $\boxed{\texttt{ENTER}}$. A matrix with the desired dimension appears. Key in the entries of the matrix, pressing $\boxed{\texttt{ENTER}}$ after inputting each entry. Press $\boxed{\texttt{2nd}}$ $\boxed{\texttt{QUIT}}$ when you have completed entering the matrix.

STEP 3 Enter Another Matrix   Press the $\boxed{\texttt{2nd}}$ $\boxed{\texttt{MATRIX}}$ key again, and repeat the process in Step 2 to enter another matrix ᴄ B ᴅ.

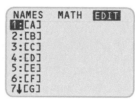
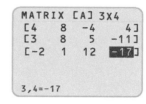
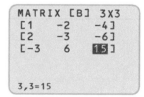

■ 14. Find the (Reduced) Row-Echelon Form of a Matrix

To find the row-echelon form or the reduced row-echelon form of a matrix, we first enter the matrix.

STEP 1 Enter the Matrix   Enter a matrix as in Part 13.

STEP 2 Choose the Form   Press the $\boxed{\texttt{2nd}}$ $\boxed{\texttt{MATRIX}}$ key again. From the top menu choose MA TH, then select r r e f (or r e f) and press $\boxed{\texttt{ENTER}}$. (You can also experiment with the other commands on this menu.) Press the $\boxed{\texttt{2nd}}$ $\boxed{\texttt{MATRIX}}$ key yet again. From the top menu choose NA ME S, then select the name of the matrix you want (ᴄ A ᴅ, for example).

STEP 3 Obtain the (Reduced) Row-Echelon Form   You now have r r e f (ᴄ A ᴅ) on the screen. Press $\boxed{\texttt{ENTER}}$ to obtain the reduced row-echelon form of the matrix you stored in ᴄ A ᴅ.

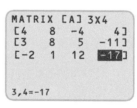
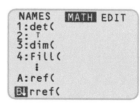

■ 15. Perform Algebraic Operations on Matrices

Before performing operations on matrices, store the matrices in the memory of the calculator with the names ᴄ A ᴅ, ᴄ B ᴅ, . . . as in Part 13.

STEP 1 Select a Matrix by Name   To enter the name of a matrix on the screen, go to $\boxed{\texttt{2nd}}$ $\boxed{\texttt{MATRIX}}$. From the top menu choose NA ME S, then select the name of the matrix you want (ᴄ A ᴅ, ᴄ B ᴅ, . . .) and press $\boxed{\texttt{ENTER}}$.

STEP 2 Choose the Operation   To do algebraic operations on matrices, use the ordinary arithmetic operation keys $\boxed{\texttt{+}}$, $\boxed{\texttt{x}}$, or $\boxed{\texttt{x}^{-1}}$. To multiply or add matrices, enter ᴄ A ᴅ * ᴄ B ᴅ or ᴄ A ᴅ + ᴄ B ᴅ. For the inverse use the $\boxed{\texttt{x}^{-1}}$ key to enter ᴄ B ᴅ$^{-1}$.

STEP 3 Obtain the Result   On the screen you now have ᴄ A ᴅ * ᴄ B ᴅ, ᴄ A ᴅ + ᴄ B ᴅ, or ᴄ B ᴅ$^{-1}$. Press $\boxed{\texttt{ENTER}}$ to obtain the result. The error message DIM

MISMATCH indicates that the dimensions of the matrices are incompatible for the requested operation. When you are attempting to find the inverse of a matrix, the error messages `SINGULAR MAT` or `INVALID DIM` indicate that the matrix is not invertible or is not a square matrix, respectively.

NOTE: To obtain the result of any calculation as a fraction (as opposed to a decimal), go to `MATH` and select ▶ `Frac` (see the second screen below).

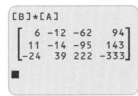
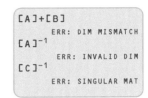

16. Find the Determinant of a Matrix

To find the determinant of a matrix, we must first store the matrix in the memory of the calculator with a name `[A]`, `[B]`, ... as in Part 13.

STEP 1 Select the Determinant Command   Press `2nd` `MATRIX` to go to the matrix menu. From the top menu select `MATH`, then choose `det(`, and then press `ENTER`. The symbol `det(` appears on the screen.

STEP 2 Choose the Name of a Matrix   To find the determinant of the matrix B, press `2nd` `MATRIX`. From the top menu choose `NAMES`, and then select `[B]`.

STEP 3 Obtain the Result   On the screen you now have `det([B])`. Press `ENTER` to obtain the value of the determinant.

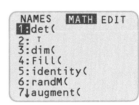
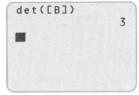

17. Find a Term of a Sequence

We can work with sequences on the calculator, but we must first put the calculator in the proper mode by following the instructions in Part 1.

STEP 1 Select the Sequence Mode   Press `MODE`, then select `seq` and press `ENTER`. This puts the calculator in sequence mode. Press `2nd` `QUIT` to exit the mode menu.

STEP 2 Enter the Sequence   Press the `Y=` key, and then enter the definition of the sequence. For the sequence $a_n = 2n + 1$, enter `u(n)=2n+1`, as shown. You must also enter the minimum value of n (in this case `nMin=1`) and the first term of the sequence (in this case `u(nMin)={3}`).

STEP 3 Obtain Results   To find a term of the sequence, say a_{10}, use the keypad to enter `u(10)`. Note that `u` is located at `2nd` `u` on the keypad.

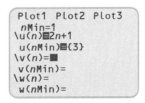
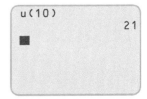

▦ 18. Find a Term of a Recursive Sequence

To find a term of a recursively defined sequence, first put the calculator in sequence mode. We find the 20th term of the Fibonacci sequence.

STEP 1 Select the Sequence Mode   Put the calculator in sequence mode as in Part 17. Press `2nd` `QUIT` to exit the mode menu.

STEP 2 Enter the Sequence   Press the `Y=` key, and then enter the definition of the sequence. For the Fibonacci sequence, enter u(n)=u(n−1)+u(n−2), as shown. You must also enter the minimum value of n (in this case nMin=1) and the first two terms of the sequence (in this case u(nMin)={1,1}).

STEP 3 Obtain Results   To find a term of the sequence, say, F_{20}, use the keypad to enter u(20). Note that u is located at `2nd` `u` on the keypad.

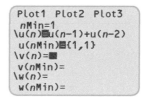
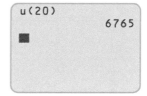

▦ 19. List Terms of a Sequence

To list the terms of a sequence, first put the calculator in sequence mode, as in Part 17. We illustrate the process with the sequence $a_n = 1/n$ from $n = 1$ to $n = 5$.

STEP 1 Get the Sequence Command   Press `2nd` `LIST`. From the top menu choose OPS, select seq(, and then press `ENTER`.

STEP 2 Define the Sequence   Define the sequence by completing the commands on the screen. In this case enter $1/n$ for Expr, n for Variable, 1 for start, 5 for end, and 1 for step. Scroll down to Paste, and press `ENTER`. We get the following: seq(1/n,n,1,5,1). The entries have the following meaning: The expression is $1/n$, the variable is n, the starting point is 1, the ending point is 5, and the step size is 1.

STEP 3 Obtain the List of Terms of the Sequence   Press `ENTER` to obtain a list of the terms of the sequence.

NOTE: Use the ▶ Frac command to obtain the result in fractions. (See the note in Part 12.)

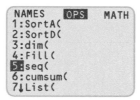
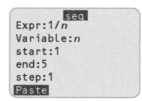
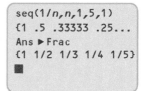

▦ 20. Make a Table of Values of a Sequence

To make a table of values of a sequence, first put the calculator in sequence mode (see Part 1). Let's work with the sequence $u(n) = n^2$.

STEP 1 Enter the Sequence   Press the `Y=` key, and then enter the definition of the sequence as shown.

STEP 2 Set the Table Properties   Press [2nd] [TBLSET], and then select the value of n at which you want the table to start (TblStart) and the step size (ΔTbl) to be 1.

STEP 3 Get the Table   Press [2nd] [TABLE] to obtain the table. Scroll up or down to see more of the table.

```
Plot1 Plot2 Plot3
 nMin=1
\u(n)⊟n²
 u(nMin)⊟{1}
\v(n)=▪
 v(nMin)=
\w(n)=
 w(nMin)=
```

```
TABLE SETUP
 TblStart=1
 ∆Tbl=1
Indpnt: Auto  Ask
Depend: Auto  Ask
```

n	u(n)
1	1
2	4
3	9
4	16
5	25
6	36
7	49
n=1	

21. Graph a Sequence

To graph a sequence, first put the calculator in sequence mode (see Part 1). Let's work with the sequence $u(n) = n/(n + 1)$.

STEP 1 Enter the Sequence   Press the [Y=] key, and then enter the definition of the sequence. To obtain a sequence graph where the dots are not connected, use the left arrow key to move the cursor to the very left of the equation. Press [ENTER] repeatedly to obtain the dots ($\cdot\cdot$) to the left of the equation, as shown.

STEP 2 Choose the Window   Press the [WINDOW] key, and then enter the required values. Make sure you scroll down far enough to enter the values for Xmin, Xmax, Ymin, and Ymax that you want.

STEP 3 Get the Graph   Press [GRAPH] to obtain the graph.

```
Plot1 Plot2 Plot3
 nMin=1
∴u(n)⊟n/(n+1)
 u(nMin)⊟{.5}
\v(n)=▪
 v(nMin)=
\w(n)=
 w(nMin)=
```

```
WINDOW
 nMin=1
 nMax=10
 PlotStart=1
 PlotStep=1
 Xmin=1
 Xmax=10
 Xscl=1
↓Ymin=0▪
```

22. Find a Partial Sum of a Sequence

To find a partial sum of a sequence, we use the LIST menu. We work with the sequence of odd numbers $a_n = 2n - 1$ from $n = 1$ to $n = 5$.

STEP 1 Find a Sum of a Sequence   Press [2nd] [LIST]. From the top menu choose MATH, select sum(, and then press [ENTER]. Key in the sequence as in Part 19: sum(seq(2n-1,n,1,5,1)). Press [ENTER] to get the sum.

STEP 2 Find the Partial Sums   Press [2nd] [LIST]. From the top menu choose OPS, select cumsum(, and then press [ENTER]. Key in the sequence as in Part 19: cumsum(seq(2n-1,n,1,5,1)). Press [ENTER] to get the sequence of partial sums.

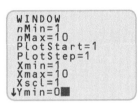

```
NAMES  OPS  MATH
1:min(
2:max(
3:mean(
4:median(
5:sum(
6:prod(
7↓stdDev(
```

```
NAMES  OPS  MATH
1:SortA(
2:SortD(
3:dim(
4:Fill(
5:seq(
6:cumsum(
7↓List(
```

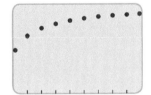

```
sum(seq(2n-1,n,1,5,1))
                    25
cumsum(seq(2n-1,n,1,
5,1))
      {1  4  9  16  25}
▪
```

▨ 23. Perform Operations with Complex Numbers

We can work with complex numbers on the calculator, but we must first put the calculator in the proper mode (see Part 1).

STEP 1 Select the Complex Number Mode Press $\boxed{\text{MODE}}$, then select a+bi and press $\boxed{\text{ENTER}}$. This puts the calculator in complex number mode. Press $\boxed{\text{2nd}}$ $\boxed{\text{QUIT}}$ to exit the mode menu.

STEP 2 Enter the Operation The imaginary unit i is located above the decimal point. To get it, press $\boxed{\text{2nd}}$ $\boxed{\text{.}}$. Enter complex number operations as shown.

STEP 3 Obtain Results Press $\boxed{\text{ENTER}}$ to obtain the requested answer.

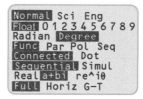
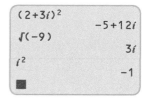

▨ 24. Graph Parametric Equations

Let's graph the parametric equations $x = t^3 - 9t$, $y = t^2$.

STEP 1 Select Parametric Mode Press $\boxed{\text{MODE}}$, select Par, then press $\boxed{\text{ENTER}}$. This puts the calculator in parametric mode. Press $\boxed{\text{2nd}}$ $\boxed{\text{QUIT}}$ to exit the mode menu.

STEP 2 Enter the Equation Press the $\boxed{\text{Y=}}$ key, and enter the pair of parametric equations as X_{1T} and Y_{1T}, as shown. Press the $\boxed{\text{WINDOW}}$ key, and select appropriate values for the parameter t as well as for the dimensions of the window.

STEP 3 Get the Graph To get the graph, press the $\boxed{\text{GRAPH}}$ key.

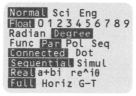
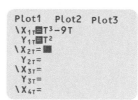
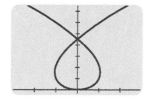

▨ 25. Graph a Polar Equation

Let's graph the polar equation $r = \theta - \sin 3\theta$.

STEP 1 Select Polar Mode Press $\boxed{\text{MODE}}$, select Pol, and then press $\boxed{\text{ENTER}}$. This puts the calculator in polar mode. Press $\boxed{\text{2nd}}$ $\boxed{\text{QUIT}}$ to exit the mode menu.

STEP 2 Enter the Equation Press the $\boxed{\text{Y=}}$ key, and enter the equation as r1, as shown. Press the $\boxed{\text{WINDOW}}$ key, and select appropriate values for θ min and θ max as well as for the dimensions of the window.

STEP 3 Get the Graph To get the graph, press the $\boxed{\text{GRAPH}}$ key.

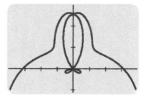

CHAPTER 1
SECTION 1.1 ■ PAGE 91

1. $(-2, 4)$ **2.** IV **3.** $\sqrt{(c-a)^2 + (d-b)^2}$; 10

4. $\left(\dfrac{a+c}{2}, \dfrac{b+d}{2}\right)$; $(4, 6)$

5. $A(5, 1)$, $B(1, 2)$, $C(-2, 6)$, $D(-6, 2)$, $E(-4, -1)$, $F(-2, 0)$, $G(-1, -3)$, $H(2, -2)$

7.

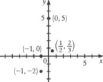

9.

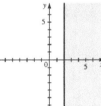

11.

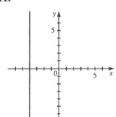

13.

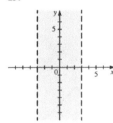

15.

17.

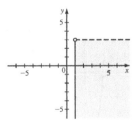

19.

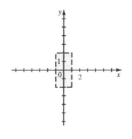

21. (a) $\sqrt{13}$ (b) $\left(\frac{3}{2}, 1\right)$ **23.** (a) 10 (b) $(1, 0)$
25. (a) (b) 10 (c) $(3, 12)$

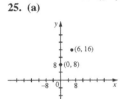

27. (a) (b) $7\sqrt{2}$ (c) $\left(-\frac{1}{2}, \frac{3}{2}\right)$

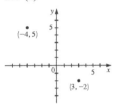

29. (a) (b) $4\sqrt{10}$ (c) $(0, 0)$

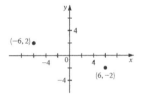

31. 24 **33.** Trapezoid, area $= 9$

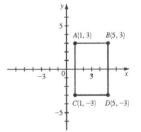 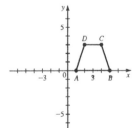

A1

35. $A(6, 7)$ **37.** $Q(-1, 3)$ **41. (b)** 10   **45.** $(0, -4)$
47. $(2, -3)$

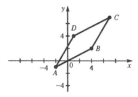

49. (a) 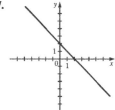   **(b)** $\left(\frac{5}{2}, 3\right)$, $\left(\frac{5}{2}, 3\right)$

51. (a) $(8, 5)$ **(b)** $(a + 3, b + 2)$ **(c)** $(0, 2)$
(d) $A'(-2, 1)$, $B'(0, 4)$, $C'(5, 3)$
53. (a) 5   **(b)** 31; 25   **(c)** Points P and Q must be on either the
same street or the same avenue.   **55.** $(66, 45)$; the y-value of the
midpoint is the pressure experienced by the diver at a depth of
66 ft.

SECTION 1.2 ▪ PAGE 101

1. 2; 3; No

x	y	(x, y)
-2	$-\frac{1}{2}$	$\left(-2, -\frac{1}{2}\right)$
-1	0	$(-1, 0)$
0	$\frac{1}{2}$	$\left(0, \frac{1}{2}\right)$
1	1	$(1, 1)$
2	$\frac{3}{2}$	$\left(2, \frac{3}{2}\right)$

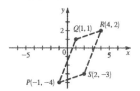

2. y; x; -1 **3.** x; y; $\frac{1}{2}$ **4.** $(1, 2)$; 3
5. (a) $(a, -b)$ **(b)** $(-a, b)$ **(c)** $(-a, -b)$
6. (a) -3 and 3; -1 and 2   **(b)** y-axis   **7.** Yes   **8.** No
9. Yes, no, yes   **11.** No, yes, yes   **13.** Yes, yes, yes

15. 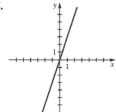   **17.**

19. 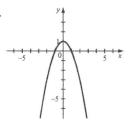   **21.**

23. 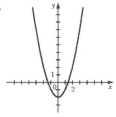   **25.**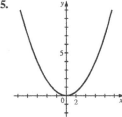

27. 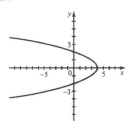   **29.**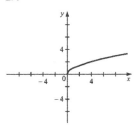

31. 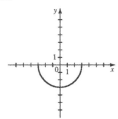   **33.**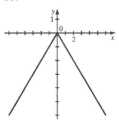

35. 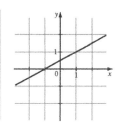   **37.**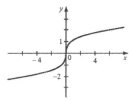

39. 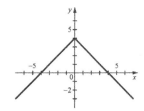   **41.**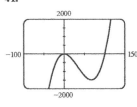

43. 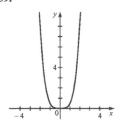   **45.**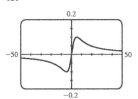

47. x-intercept -6; y-intercept 6

49. (a)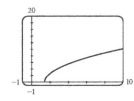

49. x-intercepts $\pm\sqrt{5}$; y-intercept -5
51. x-intercept $\frac{1}{2}$; y-intercept 1
53. x-intercept -1; y-intercept 1
55. x-intercepts ±5; y-intercepts ±2
57. x-intercepts 0, 4; y-intercept 0
59. x-intercepts ±2; y-intercepts ±4
61. (a)

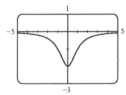

(b) x-intercepts 0, 1; y-intercept 0
63. (a)

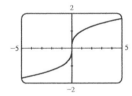

(b) No x-intercept; y-intercept -2
65. (a)

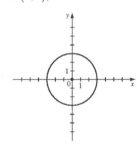

(b) x-intercept 0; y-intercept 0
67. $(0,0), 3$ **69.** $(3,0), 4$

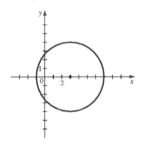

71. $(-3,4), 5$

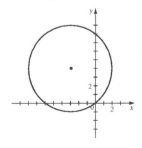

73. $(x+3)^2 + (y-2)^2 = 25$
75. $x^2 + y^2 = 65$ **77.** $(x-2)^2 + (y-5)^2 = 25$
79. $(x-7)^2 + (y+3)^2 = 9$ **81.** $(x+2)^2 + (y-2)^2 = 4$
83. $(1,-2), 2$ **85.** $(2,-5), 4$ **87.** $\left(-\frac{1}{2},0\right), \frac{1}{2}$ **89.** $\left(\frac{1}{4},-\frac{1}{4}\right), \frac{1}{2}$
91.   **93.**

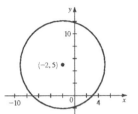   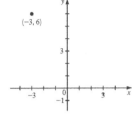

95. Symmetry about y-axis
97. Symmetry about the origin
99. Symmetry about x-axis, y-axis, and the origin
101.   **103.**

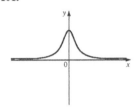   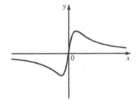

105.   **107.** 12π

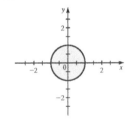

109. (a) $(8,5)$ **(b)** $(a+3, b+2)$ **(c)** $(0,2)$
(d) $A'(-2,1), B'(0,4), C'(5,3)$
111. (a) $14\%, 6\%, 2\%$ **(b)** 1975–1976, 1978–1982
(c) Decrease, increase   **(d)** $14\%, 1\%$

SECTION 1.3 ■ PAGE 112

1. $y; x; 2$ **2. (a)** 3   **(b)** 3   **(c)** $-\frac{1}{3}$ **3.** $y-2 = 3(x-1)$
4. $6, 4; -\frac{2}{3}x + 4; -\frac{2}{3}$ **5.** $0; y = 3$ **6.** Undefined; $x = 2$
7. (a) Yes   **(b)** Yes   **(c)** No   **(d)** Yes
8.   Yes

9. -2 **11.** $\frac{1}{5}$ **13.** 0   **15.** $\frac{3}{4}$ **17.** $-2, \frac{1}{2}, 3, -\frac{1}{4}$

19. $x + y - 4 = 0$ **21.** $3x - 2y - 6 = 0$
23. $3x - y - 2 = 0$ **25.** $5x - y - 7 = 0$
27. $2x - 3y + 19 = 0$ **29.** $5x + y - 11 = 0$
31. $8x + y + 11 = 0$ **33.** $3x - y - 3 = 0$
35. $y = 3$ **37.** $x = 2$ **39.** $3x - y - 1 = 0$
41. $y = 5$ **43.** $x + 2y + 11 = 0$ **45.** $x = -1$
47. $5x - 2y + 1 = 0$ **49.** $x - y + 6 = 0$
51. (a)

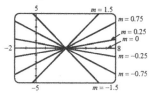

(b) $3x - 2y + 8 = 0$
53. They all have the same slope.

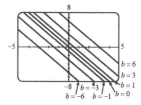

55. They all have the same x-intercept.

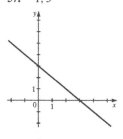

57. $-1, 3$ **59.** $2, 7$

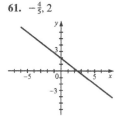

61. $-\frac{4}{5}, 2$ **63.** $0, 4$

65. Undefined, none **67.** $2, 5$

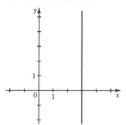 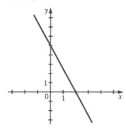

69. $-2, 3$ **71.** $-\frac{2}{3}, 4$

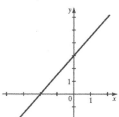 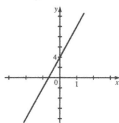

73. Parallel **75.** Perpendicular **77.** Neither
83. $x - y - 3 = 0$ **85. (b)** $4x - 3y - 24 = 0$
87. (a) The slope represents an increase of 0.02°C every year, and the T-intercept is the average surface temperature in 1950.
(b) 17.0°C

89. (a)

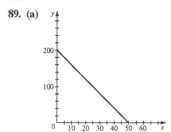

(b) The slope represents a decrease of 4 spaces rented for each one dollar increase in rental price, the y-intercept indicates that 200 spaces are rented if there is no increase in price, and the x-intercept indicates that no spaces are rented with an increase of \$50 in rental price.

91. (a)

C	$-30°$	$-20°$	$-10°$	$0°$	$10°$	$20°$	$30°$
F	$-22°$	$-4°$	$14°$	$32°$	$50°$	$68°$	$86°$

(b) $-40°$
93. (a) $V = -950t + 4000$

(b)

(c) The slope represents a decrease of \$950 each year in the value of the computer, and the V-intercept is the original price of the computer. **(d)** \$1150

SECTION 1.4 ■ PAGE 122

1. (a) $\dfrac{-b \pm \sqrt{b^2 - 4ac}}{2a}$ **(b)** $\frac{1}{2}, -1, -4; 4, -2$

2. (a) Factor into $(x + 1)(x - 5)$ and use the Zero-Product Property. **(b)** Add 5 to each side, then complete the square by adding 4 to both sides. **(c)** Insert coefficients into the Quadratic Formula. **3.** $b^2 - 4ac$; two distinct real; exactly one real; no real

5. $3, 5$ **7.** $-2, 3$ **9.** $-\frac{1}{3}, 2$ **11.** $-\frac{1}{2}, 3$ **13.** $-\frac{5}{6}, \frac{9}{2}$
15. $-20, 25$ **17.** $4 \pm \sqrt{15}$ **19.** $3 \pm 2\sqrt{5}$ **21.** $\frac{1}{2}, -\frac{3}{2}$

23. $-21, -1$ **25.** $-1 \pm \dfrac{2\sqrt{15}}{5}$ **27.** $-\dfrac{7}{4} \pm \dfrac{\sqrt{17}}{4}$

29. $2, 6$ **31.** $-10, 2$ **33.** $-\frac{3}{2}, 1$ **35.** $\dfrac{-3 \pm 2\sqrt{6}}{3}$ **37.** $\frac{2}{3}$

39. $-\frac{9}{2}, \frac{1}{2}$ **41.** No real solution **43.** $\dfrac{8 \pm \sqrt{14}}{10}$

45. No real solution **47.** $-0.248, 0.259$ **49.** No real solution

51. $t = \dfrac{-v_0 \pm \sqrt{v_0^2 + 2gh}}{g}$ **53.** $x = \dfrac{-2h \pm \sqrt{4h^2 + 2A}}{2}$

55. $s = \dfrac{-(a + b - 2c) \pm \sqrt{a^2 + b^2 + 4c^2 - 2ab}}{2}$

57. 2 **59.** 1 **61.** No real solution **63.** $\dfrac{-1}{a}$ **65.** $k = \pm 20$

67. 19 and 36 **69.** 25 ft by 35 ft **71.** 60 ft by 40 ft
73. 48 cm **75.** 13 in. by 13 in. **77.** 120 ft by 126 ft
79. 50 mi/h (or 240 mi/h) **81.** 6 km/h **83.** 4.24 s
85. (a) After 1 s and $1\frac{1}{2}$ s **(b)** Never **(c)** 25 ft
(d) After $1\frac{1}{4}$ s **(e)** After $2\frac{1}{2}$ s
87. (a) After 17 years, on Jan. 1, 2019
(b) After 18.612 years, on Aug. 12, 2020
89. 30 ft; 120 ft by 180 ft **91.** Irene 3 h, Henry $4\frac{1}{2}$ h
93. 215,000 mi

SECTION 1.5 ■ PAGE 130

1. -1 **2.** $3, 4$ **3. (a)** $3 - 4i$ **(b)** $9 + 16 = 25$
4. $3 - 4i$ **5.** Yes **6.** Yes **7.** Real part 5, imaginary part -7
9. Real part $-\frac{2}{3}$, imaginary part $-\frac{5}{3}$ **11.** Real part 3, imaginary part 0 **13.** Real part 0, imaginary part $-\frac{2}{3}$
15. Real part $\sqrt{3}$, imaginary part 2 **17.** $3 + 7i$ **19.** $1 - 10i$
21. $3 + 5i$ **23.** $2 - 2i$ **25.** $-19 + 4i$ **27.** $-4 + 8i$
29. $30 + 10i$ **31.** $27 - 8i$ **33.** 29 **35.** $-21 + 20i$ **37.** $-i$
39. $\frac{8}{5} + \frac{1}{5}i$ **41.** $-4 + 2i$ **43.** $2 - \frac{4}{3}i$ **45.** $-i$ **47.** $-i$
49. $243i$ **51.** 1 **53.** $7i$ **55.** -6
57. $(3 + \sqrt{5}) + (3 - \sqrt{5})i$ **59.** 2 **61.** $\pm 7i$
63. $\dfrac{1}{2} \pm \dfrac{\sqrt{7}}{2}i$ **65.** $-\dfrac{3}{2} \pm \dfrac{\sqrt{19}}{2}i$ **67.** $-\dfrac{1}{2} \pm \dfrac{\sqrt{3}}{2}i$

69. $\frac{1}{2} \pm \frac{1}{2}i$ **71.** $-1 \pm \dfrac{\sqrt{6}}{6}i$ **73.** $8 + 2i$ **75.** 25

SECTION 1.6 ■ PAGE 138

1. (a) factor **(b)** $0, 4$ **2. (a)** $\sqrt{2x} = -x$ **(b)** $2x = x^2$
(c) $0, 2$ **(d)** 0 **3.** quadratic; $x + 1$; $W^2 - 5W + 6 = 0$
4. quadratic; x^3; $W^2 + 7W - 8 = 0$ **5.** $0, 1$ **7.** $-5, 0, 5$
9. $0, \sqrt[3]{3}$ **11.** $0, \sqrt[3]{\frac{5}{2}}$ **13.** $-2, 0$ **15.** $0, 2, 3$

17. $0, -2 \pm \sqrt{2}$ **19.** $-\frac{5}{3}, -\frac{4}{3}$ **21.** $\pm\sqrt{2}, 5$ **23.** 2 **25.** 1
27. $-\frac{7}{5}, 2$ **29.** $-50, 100$ **31.** $\pm\sqrt{2}$ **33.** $-4, -\frac{7}{3}$
35. $\dfrac{-5 \pm 4\sqrt{2}}{7}$ **37.** 7 **39.** 4 **41.** 2 **43.** 4 **45.** 5
47. 8 **49.** $\pm 1, \pm\sqrt{3}$ **51.** No real solution **53.** $-1, 3$
55. $-7, 0$ **57.** $-\frac{3}{2}, -\frac{3}{4}$ **59.** $\pm 3\sqrt{3}, \pm 2\sqrt{2}$ **61.** $-1, 0, 3$
63. 5 **65.** $27, 729$ **67.** $-\frac{1}{2}$ **69.** 20 **71.** $-3, \dfrac{1 \pm \sqrt{13}}{2}$
73. 2 **75.** $\pm\sqrt{a}, \pm 2\sqrt{a}$ **77.** $\sqrt{a^2 + 36}$ **79.** 50
81. 89 days **83.** 7.52 ft **85.** 4.63 mm **87.** 16 mi; No
89. 49 ft, 168 ft, and 175 ft **91.** 132.6 ft

SECTION 1.7 ■ PAGE 148

1. (a) $<$ **(b)** $\leq$ **(c)** $\leq$ **(d)** $>$
2. $-1, 2$

Interval	$(-\infty, -1)$	$(-1, 2)$	$(2, \infty)$
Sign of $x + 1$	$-$	$+$	$+$
Sign of $x - 2$	$-$	$-$	$+$
Sign of $(x + 1)/(x - 2)$	$+$	$-$	$+$

Yes, 2; $[-1, 2)$
3. (a) No **(b)** No **4. (a)** Divide both sides by 3.
(b) Add 2 to both sides. **5.** $\left\{\frac{5}{6}, 1, \sqrt{5}, 3, 5\right\}$ **7.** $\{3, 5\}$
9. $\{-5, -1, \sqrt{5}, 3, 5\}$

11. $\left(-\infty, \frac{6}{5}\right]$

13. $(4, \infty)$

15. $(-\infty, -2)$

17. $\left(-\infty, -\frac{1}{2}\right)$

19. $\left(-\infty, \frac{2}{3}\right]$

21. $\left(\frac{16}{3}, \infty\right)$

23. $(-\infty, -1]$

25. $[-3, -1]$

27. $\left[\frac{1}{3}, 5\right]$

29. $\left[\frac{9}{2}, 5\right)$

31. $\left(\frac{5}{2}, \frac{11}{2}\right]$

33. $(-2, 3)$

35. $\left(-\infty, -\frac{7}{2}\right] \cup [0, \infty)$

37. $[-3, 6]$

39. $(-\infty, -1] \cup \left[\frac{1}{2}, \infty\right)$

41. $(-1, 4)$

43. $(-\infty, -3) \cup (6, \infty)$

45. $(-2, 2)$

47. $(-\infty, -2] \cup [1, 3]$

49. $(-\infty, -2) \cup (-2, 4)$

51. $[-1, 3]$

53. $(-2, 0) \cup (2, \infty)$

55. $(-\infty, -3] \cup (\frac{1}{2}, \infty)$

57. $(-\infty, -\frac{3}{2})$

59. $(-\infty, 5) \cup [16, \infty)$

61. $(-2, 0) \cup (2, \infty)$

63. $[-2, -1) \cup (0, 1]$

65. $[-2, 0) \cup (1, 3]$

67. $(-3, -\frac{1}{2}) \cup (2, \infty)$

69. $(-\infty, -2] \cup [1, 2) \cup (2, \infty)$

71. $(-\infty, -1) \cup (1, \infty)$

73. $-\frac{4}{3} \le x \le \frac{4}{3}$ **75.** $x < -2$ or $x > 7$ **77.** $x \ge \dfrac{c}{a} + \dfrac{c}{b}$

79. $68 \le F \le 86$ **81.** More than 200 mi
83. Between 12,000 mi and 14,000 mi
85. (a) $-\frac{1}{3}P + \frac{560}{3}$ (b) From \$215 to \$290
87. Distances between 20,000 km and 100,000 km
89. From 0 s to 3 s **91.** Between 0 and 60 mi/h
93. Between 20 and 40 ft

SECTION 1.8 ▪ PAGE 152

1. $3, -3$ **2.** (a) $[-3, 3]$ (b) $(-\infty, -3], [3, \infty)$ **3.** (a) < 3
(b) > 3 **4.** (a) Rewrite as two separate equations: $2x - 1 = 5$
and $2x - 1 = -5$. (b) Rewrite as: $-8 \le 3x - 2 \le 8$.
5. ± 4 **7.** ± 5 **9.** $1, 5$ **11.** $-4.5, -3.5$ **13.** $-4, 7$
15. $-3, -1$ **17.** $-8, -2$ **19.** $-\frac{25}{2}, \frac{35}{2}$ **21.** $-\frac{3}{2}, -\frac{1}{4}$
23. $[-5, 5]$ **25.** $(-\infty, -\frac{7}{2}) \cup (\frac{7}{2}, \infty)$ **27.** $[-6, 14]$
29. $(-\infty, -2] \cup [0, \infty)$ **31.** $(-\infty, -2] \cup [1, \infty)$
33. $[1.3, 1.7]$ **35.** $(-4, 8)$ **37.** $(-6.001, -5.999)$
39. $(-6, 2)$ **41.** $[-\frac{1}{2}, \frac{3}{2}]$ **43.** $(-\infty, -\frac{1}{2}) \cup (\frac{1}{3}, \infty)$
45. $[-4, -1] \cup [1, 4]$ **47.** $(-\frac{15}{2}, -7) \cup (-7, -\frac{13}{2})$
49. $|x| < 3$ **51.** $|x - 7| \ge 5$ **53.** $|x| \le 2$
55. $|x| > 3$ **57.** (a) $|x - 0.020| \le 0.003$
(b) $0.017 \le x \le 0.023$

SECTION 1.9 ▪ PAGE 158

1. x **2.** above **3.** (a) $x = -1, 0, 1, 3$ (b) $[-1, 0] \cup [1, 3]$
4. (a) $x = 1, 4$ (b) $(1, 4)$ **5.** -4 **7.** $\frac{5}{14}$
9. $\pm 4\sqrt{2} \approx \pm 5.7$ **11.** No solution **13.** $2.5, -2.5$
15. $5 + 2\sqrt[3]{5} \approx 7.99, 5 - 2\sqrt[3]{5} \approx 2.01$ **17.** $3.00, 4.00$
19. $1.00, 2.00, 3.00$ **21.** 1.62 **23.** $-1.00, 0.00, 1.00$ **25.** 4

27. No solution **29.** 2.55 **31.** $-2.05, 0, 1.05$
33. $[-2.00, 5.00]$ **35.** $(-\infty, 1.00] \cup [2.00, 3.00]$
37. $(-1.00, 0) \cup (1.00, \infty)$ **39.** $(-\infty, 0)$ **41.** $(-1, 4)$
43. $[-1, 3]$ **45.** 2.27

47. (a) 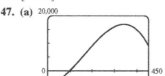 (b) 101 cooktops
(c) $279 < x < 400$

SECTION 1.10 ▪ PAGE 164

1. directly proportional; proportionality **2.** inversely
proportional; proportionality **3.** directly proportional;
inversely proportional **4.** $\frac{1}{2}xy$
5. (a) Directly proportional (b) Not proportional
6. (a) Not proportional (b) Inversely proportional
7. $T = kx$ **9.** $v = k/z$ **11.** $y = ks/t$ **13.** $z = k\sqrt{y}$
15. $V = klwh$ **17.** $R = \dfrac{kP^2 t^2}{b^3}$ **19.** $y = 7x$ **21.** $A = \dfrac{21}{r}$
23. $A = \dfrac{18x}{t}$ **25.** $W = 360/r^2$ **27.** $C = 16lwh$
29. $R = \dfrac{27.5}{\sqrt{x}}$ **31.** (a) $z = k\dfrac{x^3}{y^2}$ (b) $\frac{27}{4}$
33. (a) $z = kx^3 y^5$ (b) 864
35. (a) $F = kx$ (b) 7.5 (c) 45 N
37. (a) $P = ks^3$ (b) 0.012 (c) 324
39. 46 mi/h **41.** 5.3 mi/h
43. (a) $P = kT/V$ (b) 8.3 (c) 51.9 kPa
45. (a) $L = k/d^2$ (b) 7000 (c) $\frac{1}{4}$ (d) 4
47. (a) $R = kL/d^2$ (b) $0.002916\overline{\ }$ (c) $R \approx 137\,\Omega$ (d) $\frac{3}{4}$
49. (a) $160,000$ (b) $1,930,670,340$
51. (a) $T = k\sqrt{l}$ (b) quadruple the length l
53. (a) $f = k/L$ (b) Halves it **55.** 3.47×10^{-14} W/m²

CHAPTER 1 REVIEW ▪ PAGE 169

1. (a) 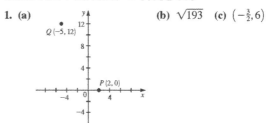 (b) $\sqrt{193}$ (c) $(-\frac{3}{2}, 6)$

(d) $y = -\frac{12}{7}x + \frac{24}{7}$ (e) $(x - 2)^2 + y^2 = 193$

3. (a)

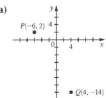

(b) $2\sqrt{89}$ **(c)** $(-1, -6)$

(d) $y = -\frac{8}{5}x - \frac{38}{5}$

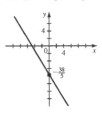

(e) $(x + 6)^2 + (y - 2)^2 = 356$

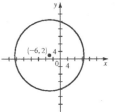

5.

7. B **9.** $(x + 5)^2 + (y + 1)^2 = 26$

11. (a) Circle

(b) Center $(-1, 3)$, radius 1

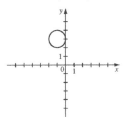

13. (a) No graph

15.

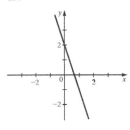

17.

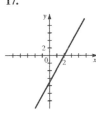

19.

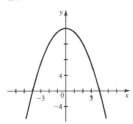

21.

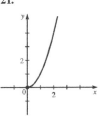

23. (a) Symmetry about y-axis
(b) x-intercepts $-3, 3$; y-intercept 9
25. (a) Symmetry about y-axis
(b) x-intercept 0; y-intercepts 0, 2
27. (a) Symmetry about x- and y-axes and the origin
(b) x-intercepts $-4, 4$; no y-intercept
29. (a) Symmetry about the origin
(b) x-intercepts $-1, 1$; y-intercepts $-1, 1$

31. (a)

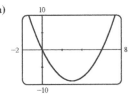

(b) x-intercepts 0, 6; y-intercept 0

33. (a)

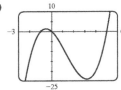

(b) x-intercepts $-1, 0, 5$; y-intercept 0

35. (a) $y = 2x + 6$ **(b)** $2x - y + 6 = 0$
(c)

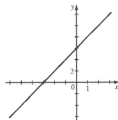

37. (a) $y = \frac{2}{3}x - \frac{16}{3}$ **(b)** $2x - 3y - 16 = 0$
(c)

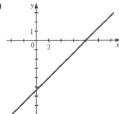

39. (a) $x = 3$ **(b)** $x - 3 = 0$
(c)

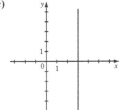

41. (a) $y = \frac{2}{5}x + \frac{3}{5}$ **43. (a)** $y = -2x$
(b) $2x - 5y + 3 = 0$ **(b)** $2x + y = 0$
(c) 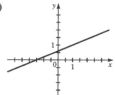   **(c)**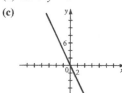

45. Parallel
47. (a) The slope represents a stretch of 0.3 in. for each one-pound increase in weight. The S-intercept represents the unstretched length of the spring.   **(b)** 4 in.

49. $2, 7$ **51.** $-1, \frac{1}{2}$ **53.** $0, \pm\frac{5}{2}$ **55.** $\dfrac{-2 \pm \sqrt{7}}{3}$

57. $\dfrac{3 \pm \sqrt{6}}{3}$ **59.** ± 3 **61.** 1 **63.** $3, 11$

65. (a) $3 + i$ **(b)** $8 - i$ **67. (a)** $\frac{6}{5} + \frac{8}{5}i$ **(b)** 2
69. $\pm 4i$ **71.** $-3 \pm i$ **73.** $\pm 4, \pm 4i$
75. $\frac{1}{4}(\sqrt{329} - 3) \approx 3.78$ mi/h
77. 12 cm, 16 cm

79. $(-3, \infty)$ **81.** $\left[\frac{10}{3}, \infty\right)$

83. $(-\infty, -6) \cup (2, \infty)$ **85.** $[-4, -1)$

87. $(-\infty, -2) \cup (2, 4]$ **89.** $[2, 8]$

91. $(-\infty, -1] \cup [0, \infty)$

93. (a) $\left[-3, \frac{8}{3}\right]$ **(b)** $(0, 1)$

95. $-1, 6$ **97.** $[-1, 6]$ **99.** $(-\infty, 0] \cup [4, \infty)$
101. $-1, 7$ **103.** $-2.72, -1.15, 1.00, 2.87$ **105.** $[1, 3]$
107. $(-1.85, -0.60) \cup (0.45, 2.00)$
109. $x^2 + y^2 = 169, 5x - 12y + 169 = 0$
111. $M = 8z$ **113. (a)** $I = k/d^2$ **(b)** 64,000 **(c)** 160 candles
115. 11.0 mi/h

CHAPTER 1 TEST ■ PAGE 172

1. (a) $S(3, 6)$ **(b)** 18
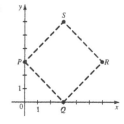

2. (a)
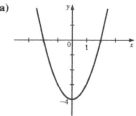

(b) x-intercepts $-2, 2$; y-intercept -4
(c) Symmetric about y-axis
3. (a)
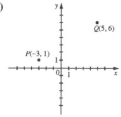

(b) $\sqrt{89}$ **(c)** $\left(1, \frac{7}{2}\right)$ **(d)** $\frac{5}{8}$ **(e)** $y = -\frac{8}{5}x + \frac{51}{10}$
(f) $(x - 1)^2 + \left(y - \frac{7}{2}\right)^2 = \frac{89}{4}$

4. (a) $(0, 0), 5$ **(b)** $(2, -1), 3$
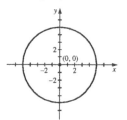   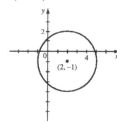

(c) $(-3, 1), 2$
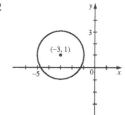

5. (a) Symmetry about   **(b)** No symmetry;
x-axis; x-intercept 4; x-intercept 2; y-intercept 2
y-intercepts -2 and 2

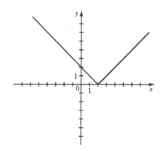

6. (a) x-intercept 5, y-intercept -3

(b) 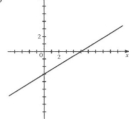 **(c)** $y = \frac{3}{5}x - 3$ **(d)** $\frac{3}{5}$ **(e)** $-\frac{5}{3}$

7. (a) $3x + y - 3 = 0$ **(b)** $2x + 3y - 12 = 0$

8. (a) 4°C **(b)**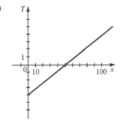

(c) The slope represents an increase of 0.08°C for each one-centimeter increase in depth, the x-intercept is the depth at which the temperature is 0°C, and the T-intercept is the temperature at ground level.

9. (a) $-3, 4$ **(b)** $-1 \pm \dfrac{\sqrt{2}}{2}$ **(c)** 3 **(d)** 1, 16

(e) $\pm 1, \pm\sqrt{2}$ **(f)** $\frac{2}{3}, \frac{22}{3}$

10. (a) $7 + i$ **(b)** $-1 - 5i$ **(c)** $18 + i$ **(d)** $\frac{6}{25} - \frac{17}{25}i$

(e) 1 **(f)** $6 - 2i$

11. $-1 \pm \dfrac{\sqrt{2}}{2}i$ **12.** 50 ft by 120 ft

13. (a) $[-4, 3)$

(b) $(-2, 0) \cup (1, \infty)$

(c) $(1, 7)$

(d) $(-1, 4]$

14. Between 41°F and 50°F

15. $0 \le x \le 6$

16. (a) $-2.94, -0.11, 3.05$ **(b)** $[-1, 2]$

17. (a) $M = kwh^2/L$ **(b)** 400 **(c)** 12,000 lb

FOCUS ON MODELING ■ PAGE 179

1. (a)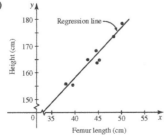

(b) $y = 1.8807x + 82.65$ **(c)** 191.7 cm

3. (a)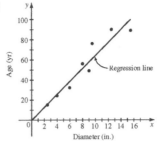

(b) $y = 6.451x - 0.1523$ **(c)** 116 years

5. (a)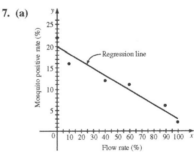

(b) $y = 4.857x - 220.97$ **(c)** 265 chirps/min

7. (a)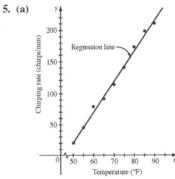

(b) $y = -0.168x + 19.89$ **(c)** 8.13%

9. (a)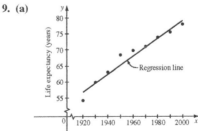

(b) $y = 0.2708x - 462.9$ **(c)** 80.4 years

CHAPTER 2
SECTION 2.1 ■ PAGE 191

1. (a) $f(-1) = 0$ **(b)** $f(2) = 9$ **(c)** $f(2) - f(-1) = 9$

2. domain, range **3. (a)** f and g **(b)** $f(5) = 10, g(5) = 0$

4. (a) square, add 3

(b)

x	0	2	4	6
$f(x)$	19	7	3	7

5. one; (i) **6. (a)** Yes **(b)** No **7.** $f(x) = 3x - 5$
9. $f(x) = (x - 1)^2$ **11.** Multiply by 2, then add 3
13. Add 1, then multiply by 5

15.

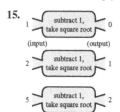

17.

x	$f(x)$
-1	8
0	2
1	0
2	2
3	8

19. $3, 3, -6, -\frac{23}{4}$ **21.** $-1, \frac{5}{3}, 0, \frac{1-2a}{3}, \frac{1+2a}{3}, \frac{3-2a}{3}$

23. $0, 15, 3, a^2 + 2a, x^2 - 2x, \frac{1}{a^2} + \frac{2}{a}$

25. $-\frac{1}{3}$, undefined, $\frac{1}{3}, \frac{1-a}{1+a}, \frac{2-a}{a}, \frac{2-x^2}{x^2}$

27. $3, -5, 3, 1 - 2\sqrt{2}, -a^2 - 6a - 5, -x^2 + 2x + 3,$
$-x^4 - 2x^2 + 3$

29. $6, 2, 1, 2, 2|x|, 2(x^2 + 1)$ **31.** $4, 1, 1, 2, 3$
33. $8, -\frac{3}{4}, -1, 0, -1$ **35.** $x^2 + 4x + 5, x^2 + 6$
37. $x^2 + 4, x^2 + 8x + 16$ **39.** 12 **41.** -21
43. $5 - 2a, 5 - 2a - 2h, -2$ **45.** $5, 5, 0$

47. $\dfrac{a}{a+1}, \dfrac{a+h}{a+h+1}, \dfrac{1}{(a+h+1)(a+1)}$

49. $3 - 5a + 4a^2, 3 - 5a - 5h + 4a^2 + 8ah + 4h^2,$
$-5 + 8a + 4h$ **51.** $(-\infty, \infty), (-\infty, \infty)$
53. $[-2, 6], [-6, 18]$ **55.** $\{x \mid x \neq 3\}$ **57.** $\{x \mid x \neq \pm 1\}$
59. $[-1, \infty)$ **61.** $(-\infty, \infty)$ **63.** $(-\infty, \frac{1}{2}]$ **65.** $[-2, 3) \cup (3, \infty)$
67. $(-\infty, 0] \cup [6, \infty)$ **69.** $(4, \infty)$ **71.** $(\frac{1}{2}, \infty)$

73. (a) $f(x) = \dfrac{x}{3} + \dfrac{2}{3}$

(b)

x	$f(x)$
2	$\frac{4}{3}$
4	2
6	$\frac{8}{3}$
8	$\frac{10}{3}$

(c)

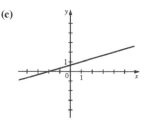

75. (a) $T(x) = 0.08x$

(b)

x	$T(x)$
2	0.16
4	0.32
6	0.48
8	0.64

(c)

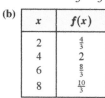

77. $(-\infty, \infty), \{1, 5\}$
79. (a) $50, 0$ **(b)** $V(0)$ is the volume of the full tank, and
$V(20)$ is the volume of the empty tank, 20 min later.

(c)

x	$V(x)$
0	50
5	28.125
10	12.5
15	3.125
20	0

(d) -50 gal
81. (a) 8.66 m, 6.61 m, 4.36 m
(b) It will appear to get shorter.
83. (a) $v(0.1) = 4440, v(0.4) = 1665$
(b) Flow is faster near central axis.

(c)

r	$v(r)$
0	4625
0.1	4440
0.2	3885
0.3	2960
0.4	1665
0.5	0

(d) -4440 cm/s
85. (a) $T(5000) = 0, T(12,000) = 960, T(25,000) = 5350$
(b) The amount of tax paid on incomes of 5000, 12,000,
and 25,000

87. (a) $T(x) = \begin{cases} 75x & \text{if } 0 \le x \le 2 \\ 150 + 50(x - 2) & \text{if } x > 2 \end{cases}$

(b) $\$150, \$200, \$300$ **(c)** Total cost of staying at the hotel
89.

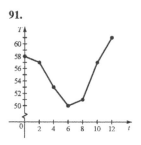

91.

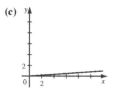

SECTION 2.2 ▪ PAGE 202

1. $f(x)$, $x^2 - 2$, 7, 7

x	$f(x)$	(x,y)
-2	2	$(-2, 2)$
-1	-1	$(-1, -1)$
0	-2	$(0, -2)$
1	-1	$(1, -1)$
2	2	$(2, 2)$

2. 10   **3.** 7   **4. (a)** IV   **(b)** II   **(c)** I   **(d)** III

5.

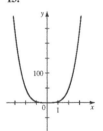

7.

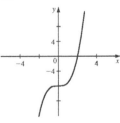

9.

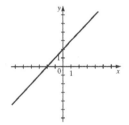

11.

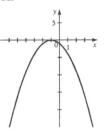

13.

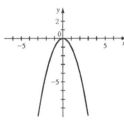

15.

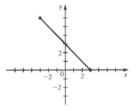

17.

19.

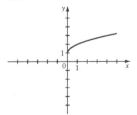

21.

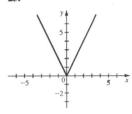

23.

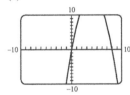

25.

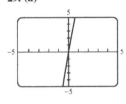

27.

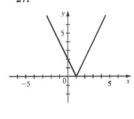

29. (a)

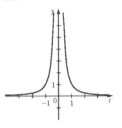

(b)

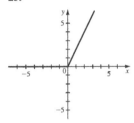

(c)

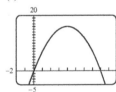

(d)

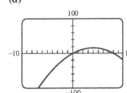

Graph (c) is the most appropriate.

31. (a)

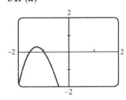

(b)

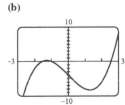

(c)

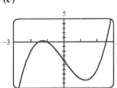

(d)

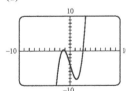

Graph (c) is the most appropriate.

33.

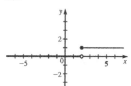

35.

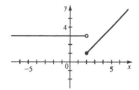

71. (a)

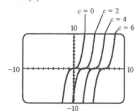

(b)

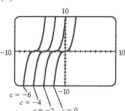

37.

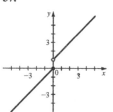

39.

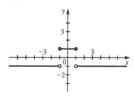

(c) If $c > 0$, then the graph of $f(x) = (x - c)^3$ is the same as the graph of $y = x^3$ shifted to the right c units. If $c < 0$, then the graph of $f(x) = (x - c)^3$ is the same as the graph of $y = x^3$ shifted to the left $|c|$ units.

73. (a)

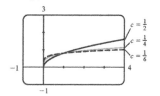

(b)

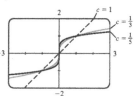

41.

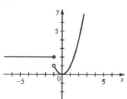

43.

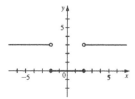

(c) Graphs of even roots are similar to $\sqrt{x}$; graphs of odd roots are similar to $\sqrt[3]{x}$. As c increases, the graph of $y = \sqrt[c]{x}$ becomes steeper near 0 and flatter when $x > 1$.

75. $f(x) = -\frac{7}{6}x - \frac{4}{3}, -2 \le x \le 4$

77. $f(x) = \sqrt{9 - x^2}, -3 \le x \le 3$

45.

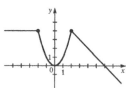

47.

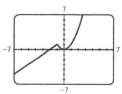

79.

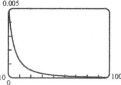

49. $f(x) = \begin{cases} -2 & \text{if } x < -2 \\ x & \text{if } -2 \le x \le 2 \\ 2 & \text{if } x > 2 \end{cases}$

51. (a) Yes **(b)** No **(c)** Yes **(d)** No

53. Function, domain $[-3, 2]$, range $[-2, 2]$ **55.** Not a function

57. Yes **59.** No **61.** No **63.** No **65.** Yes **67.** Yes

69. (a)

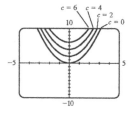

(b)

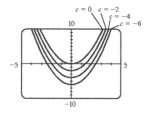

(c) If $c > 0$, then the graph of $f(x) = x^2 + c$ is the same as the graph of $y = x^2$ shifted upward c units. If $c < 0$, then the graph of $f(x) = x^2 + c$ is the same as the graph of $y = x^2$ shifted downward c units.

81. (a) $E(x) = \begin{cases} 6 + 0.10x & \text{if } 0 \le x \le 300 \\ 36 + 0.06(x - 300) & \text{if } x > 300 \end{cases}$

(b)

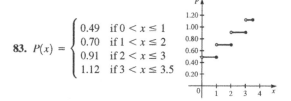

83. $P(x) = \begin{cases} 0.49 & \text{if } 0 < x \le 1 \\ 0.70 & \text{if } 1 < x \le 2 \\ 0.91 & \text{if } 2 < x \le 3 \\ 1.12 & \text{if } 3 < x \le 3.5 \end{cases}$

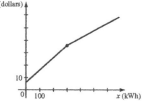

SECTION 2.3 ■ PAGE 214

1. $a, 4, 0, f(3) - f(1) = 4$ **2.** $x, y, (-\infty, \infty)(-\infty, 7]$
3. **(a)** increase, $(-\infty, 2), (4, 5)$ **(b)** decrease, $(2, 4), (5, \infty)$
4. **(a)** largest, $7, 6, 5$ **(b)** smallest, $2, 4$ **5.** $x; x; 1, 7, [1, 7]$
6. **(a)** $2x + 1, -x + 4; 1$ **(b)** $2x + 1, -x + 4$, higher;
$(-\infty, 1)$ **7.** **(a)** $1, -1, 3, 4$ **(b)** Domain $[-3, 4]$, range
$[-1, 4]$ **(c)** $-3, 2, 4$ **(d)** $-3 \le x \le 2$ and $x = 4$ **(e)** 1
9. **(a)** $f(0)$ **(b)** $g(-3)$ **(c)** $-2, 2$
(d) $\{x \mid -4 \le x \le -2$ or $2 \le x \le 3\}$ **(e)** $\{x \mid -2 < x < 2\}$
11. **(a)**

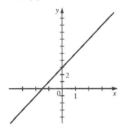

(b) $(-\infty, \infty), (-\infty, \infty)$

13. **(a)**

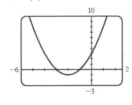

(b) $[-2, 5], [-4, 3]$

15. **(a)**

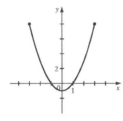

(b) $[-3, 3], [-1, 8]$

17. **(a)**

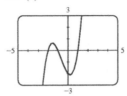

(b) Domain $(-\infty, \infty)$,
range $[-1, \infty)$

19. **(a)**

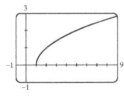

(b) Domain $[1, \infty)$,
range $[0, \infty)$

21. **(a)**

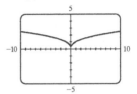

(b) Domain $[-4, 4]$,
range $[0, 4]$

23. **(a)** $x = 3$ **(b)** $x > 3$
25. **(a)** $x = -2, 1$ **(b)** $-2 \le x \le 1$
27. **(a)** $x \approx -4.32, -1.12, 1.44$
(b) $-4.32 \le x \le -1.12$ or $x \ge 1.44$
29. **(a)** $x = -1, -0.25, 0.25$
(b) $-1 \le x \le -0.25$ or $x \ge 0.25$
31. **(a)** Domain $[-1, 4]$, range $[-1, 3]$ **(b)** Increasing on
$(-1, 1)$ and $(2, 4)$, decreasing on $(1, 2)$
33. **(a)** Domain $[-3, 3]$, range $[-2, 2]$ **(b)** Increasing on
$(-2, -1)$ and $(1, 2)$, decreasing on $(-3, -2), (-1, 1)$, and
$(2, 3)$

35. **(a)**

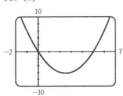

(b) Domain $(-\infty, \infty)$,
range $[-6.25, \infty)$
(c) Increasing on $(2.5, \infty)$;
decreasing on $(-\infty, 2.5)$

37. **(a)**

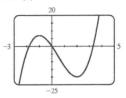

(b) Domain $(-\infty, \infty)$,
range $(-\infty, \infty)$
(c) Increasing on $(-\infty, -1)$,
$(2, \infty)$; decreasing on $(-1, 2)$

39. **(a)**

(b) Domain $(-\infty, \infty)$,
range $(-\infty, \infty)$
(c) Increasing on
$(-\infty, -1.55), (0.22, \infty)$;
decreasing on $(-1.55, 0.22)$

41. **(a)**

(b) Domain $(-\infty, \infty)$,
range $[0, \infty)$
(c) Increasing on $(0, \infty)$;
decreasing on $(-\infty, 0)$

43. **(a)** Local maximum 2 when $x = 0$; local minimum -1 when
$x = -2$, local minimum 0 when $x = 2$ **(b)** Increasing on
$(-2, 0) \cup (2, \infty)$; decreasing on $(-\infty, -2) \cup (0, 2)$
45. **(a)** Local maximum 0 when $x = 0$; local maximum 1 when
$x = 3$, local minimum -2 when $x = -2$, local minimum -1
when $x = 1$ **(b)** Increasing on $(-2, 0) \cup (1, 3)$; decreasing on
$(-\infty, -2) \cup (0, 1) \cup (3, \infty)$
47. **(a)** Local maximum ≈ 0.38 when $x \approx -0.58$; local minimum ≈ -0.38 when $x \approx 0.58$ **(b)** Increasing on
$(-\infty, -0.58) \cup (0.58, \infty)$; decreasing on $(-0.58, 0.58)$
49. **(a)** Local maximum ≈ 0 when $x = 0$;
local minimum ≈ -13.61 when $x \approx -1.71$, local
minimum ≈ -73.32 when $x \approx 3.21$
(b) Increasing on $(-1.71, 0) \cup (3.21, \infty)$; decreasing on
$(-\infty, -1.71) \cup (0, 3.21)$
51. **(a)** Local maximum ≈ 5.66 when $x \approx 4.00$ **(b)** Increasing
on $(-\infty, 4.00)$; decreasing on $(4.00, 6.00)$
53. **(a)** Local maximum ≈ 0.38 when $x \approx -1.73$; local minimum ≈ -0.38 when $x \approx 1.73$ **(b)** Increasing on
$(-\infty, -1.73) \cup (1.73, \infty)$; decreasing on $(-1.73, 0) \cup (0, 1.73)$
55. **(a)** 500 MW, 725 MW   **(b)** Between 3:00 A.M. and
4:00 A.M.   **(c)** Just before noon   **(d)** -100 MW
57. **(a)** Increasing on $(0, 30) \cup (32, 68)$; decreasing on
$(30, 32)$ **(b)** He went on a crash diet and lost weight, only to
regain it again later.   **(c)** 100 lb
59. **(a)** Increasing on $(0, 150) \cup (300, \infty)$; decreasing on
$(150, 300)$ **(b)** Local maximum when $x = 150$; local minimum
when $x = 300$ **(c)** -50 ft
61. Runner A won the race. All runners finished. Runner B fell
but got up again to finish second.

63. (a)

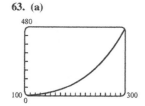

(b) Increases **65.** 7.5 mi/h

SECTION 2.4 ■ PAGE 223

1. $\dfrac{100 \text{ miles}}{2 \text{ hours}} = 50$ mi/h **2.** $\dfrac{f(b) - f(a)}{b - a}$ **3.** $\dfrac{25 - 1}{5 - 1} = 6$

4. (a) secant **(b)** 3 **5. (a)** Yes **(b)** Yes **6. (a)** No
(b) No **7. (a)** 2 **(b)** $\frac{2}{3}$ **9. (a)** -4 **(b)** $-\frac{4}{3}$ **11. (a)** 3
(b) 3 **13. (a)** -5 **(b)** -1 **15. (a)** 51 **(b)** 17
17. (a) 600 **(b)** 60 **19. (a)** $5h^2 + 30h$ **(b)** $5h + 30$

21. (a) $\dfrac{1 - a}{a}$ **(b)** $-\dfrac{1}{a}$ **23. (a)** $\dfrac{-2h}{a(a + h)}$ **(b)** $\dfrac{-2}{a(a + h)}$

25. (a) $\frac{1}{2}$ **27.** $f; g; 0, 1.5$ **29.** -0.25 ft/day
31. (a) 245 persons/year **(b)** -328.5 persons/year
(c) 1997–2001 **(d)** 2001–2006 **33. (a)** 14 players/year
(b) 18 players/year **(c)** -103 players/year **(d)** 2006–2007,
2004–2005 **35.** First 20 minutes: $-4.05°$F/min, next 20 minutes:
$-1.5°$F/min; first interval **37. (a)** All 10 m/s **(b)** Skier A
started quickly and slowed down, skier B maintained a constant
speed, and skier C started slowly and sped up.

SECTION 2.5 ■ PAGE 231

1. (a) linear, a, b **(b)** line **2. (a)** -5 **(b)** line, $-5, 7$
3. 15 **4.** 15 gal/min **5.** Upward **6.** Yes, 0, 0 **7.** Yes,
$f(x) = \frac{1}{3}x + 3$ **9.** No **11.** Yes, $f(x) = \frac{1}{5}x + \frac{1}{5}$ **13.** No
15. 2 **17.** $-\frac{2}{3}$

19. (a)

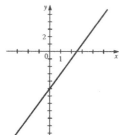

21. (a)

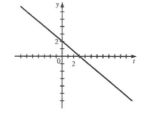

(b) 2 **(c)** 2 **(b)** -0.5 **(c)** -0.5

23. (a)

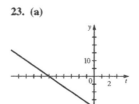

25. (a)

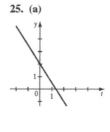

(b) $-\frac{10}{3}$ **(c)** $-\frac{10}{3}$ **(b)** $-\frac{3}{2}$ **(c)** $-\frac{3}{2}$
27. $f(x) = 3x - 1$ **29.** $h(x) = \frac{1}{2}x + 3$
31. (a) $\frac{3}{2}$ **(b)** $f(x) = \frac{3}{2}x + 7$
33. (a) 1 **(b)** $f(x) = x + 3$
35. (a) $-\frac{1}{2}$ **(b)** $f(x) = -\frac{1}{2}x + 2$
37.

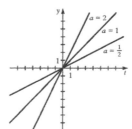

39. (a)

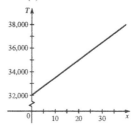

As a increases, the graph of **(b)** 150
f becomes steeper and the **(c)** 150,000 tons/year
rate of change increases.
41. (a) $V(t) = 0.5t + 2$ **(b)** 26 s
43. (a) $\frac{1}{12}, H(x) = \frac{1}{12}x$ **(b)** 12.5 in.
45. (a) Jari **(b)** Jade: 60 mi/h; Jari: 70 mi/h
(c) Jade: $f(t) = t + 10$; Jari $g(t) = \frac{7}{6}t$ **47.** 3.16 mi
49. (a) $C(x) = \frac{1}{4}x + 260$
(b) $\frac{1}{4}$ **(c)** \$0.25/mi

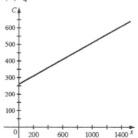

SECTION 2.6 ■ PAGE 242

1. (a) up **(b)** left **2. (a)** down **(b)** right **3. (a)** x-axis
(b) y-axis **4. (a)** II **(b)** I **(c)** III **(d)** IV **5.** Symmetric
about the y-axis **6.** Symmetric about the origin **7. (a)** Shift
downward 1 unit **(b)** Shift to the right 2 units **9. (a)** Reflect
about the y-axis **(b)** Stretch vertically by a factor of 3
11. (a) Shift to the right 5 units, then upward 2 units
(b) Shift to the left 1 unit, then downward 1 unit
13. (a) Reflect in the x-axis, then shift upward 5 units
(b) Stretch vertically by a factor of 3, then shift downward
5 units **15. (a)** Shift to the left 5 units, stretch vertically by a
factor of 2, then shift downward 1 unit **(b)** Shift to the right
3 units, shrink vertically by a factor of $\frac{1}{4}$, then shift upward
5 units

17. (a) Shrink horizontally by a factor of $\frac{1}{4}$
(b) Stretch horizontally by a factor of 4   **19.** (a) Shift to the
left 2 units   (b) Shift upward 2 units   **21.** (a) Shift to the left
2 units, then shift downward 2 units   (b) Shift to the right
2 units, then shift upward 2 units

23. (a)

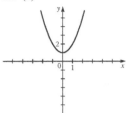

(b)

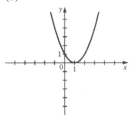

(c)

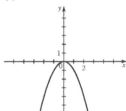

(d)

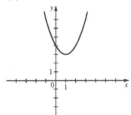

25. II   **27.** I

29.

 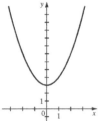

31.

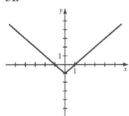

33.

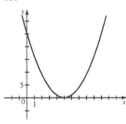

35.

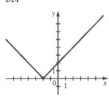

37.

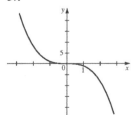

39.

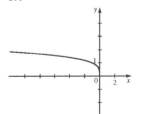

41.

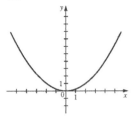

43.

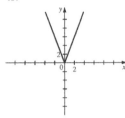

45.

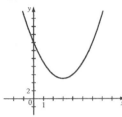

47.

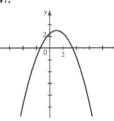

49.

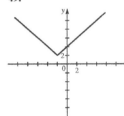

51.

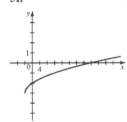

53. $y = x^2 - 3$ **55.** $y = \sqrt{x + 2}$ **57.** $y = |x + 2| - 5$
59. $y = \sqrt[4]{-x} + 1$ **61.** $y = 2(x - 3)^2 - 2$
63. $g(x) = (x - 2)^2$ **65.** $g(x) = |x + 1| + 2$
67. $g(x) = -\sqrt{x + 2}$ **69.** (a) 3   (b) 1   (c) 2   (d) 4
71. (a)

(b)

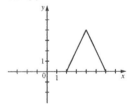

(c)

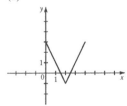

(d)

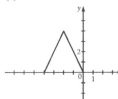

(e)

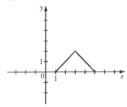

(f)

73. (a)   **(b)**

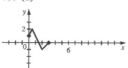   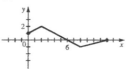

75.

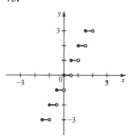

77.

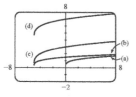

For part (b) shift the graph in (a) to the left
5 units; for part (c) shift the graph in (a) to
the left 5 units and stretch vertically by a
factor of 2; for part (d) shift the graph in (a)
to the left 5 units, stretch vertically by a factor of 2, and then shift upward 4 units.

79.

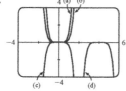

For part (b) shrink the graph in (a) vertically
by a factor of $\frac{1}{3}$; for part (c) shrink the graph
in (a) vertically by a factor of $\frac{1}{3}$ and reflect in
the x-axis; for part (d) shift the graph in (a) to
the right 4 units, shrink vertically by a factor
of $\frac{1}{3}$, and then reflect in the x-axis.

81.

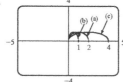

The graph in part (b) is shrunk horizontally
by a factor of $\frac{1}{2}$ and the graph in part (c) is
stretched by a factor of 2.

83. Even

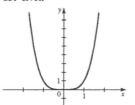

85. Neither
87. Odd

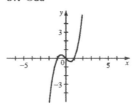

89. Neither
91. (a)   **(b)**

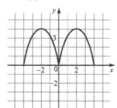   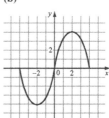

93. To obtain the graph of g, reflect in the x-axis the part of the
graph of f that is below the x-axis.
95. (a)   **(b)**

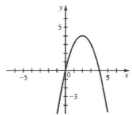   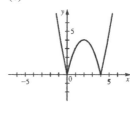

97. (a) She drops to 200 ft, bounces up and down, then settles at
350 ft.

(b)

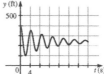

(c) Shift downward 100 ft; $H(t) = h(t) - 100$

99. (a) 80 ft/min; 20 min; 800 ft

(b)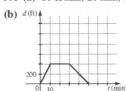

Shrunk vertically by a factor of 0.50; 40 ft/min; 400 ft

(c)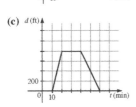

Shifted to the right 10 min; the class left 10 min later

SECTION 2.7 ▪ PAGE 252

1. $8, -2, 15, \frac{3}{5}$ **2.** $f(g(x)), 12$ **3.** Multiply by 2, then add 1; Add 1, then multiply by 2 **4.** $x + 1, 2x, 2x + 1, 2(x + 1)$

5. (a) f, g **(b)** f, g **(c)** $f, g, 0$ **6.** g, f

7. $(f + g)(x) = 3x, (-\infty, \infty); (f - g)(x) = -x, (-\infty, \infty);$

$(fg)(x) = 2x^2, (-\infty, \infty); \left(\dfrac{f}{g}\right)(x) = \dfrac{1}{2}, (-\infty, 0) \cup (0, \infty)$

9. $(f + g)(x) = 2x^2 + x, (-\infty, \infty); (f - g)(x) = x, (-\infty, \infty);$

$(fg)(x) = x^4 + x^3, (-\infty, \infty); \left(\dfrac{f}{g}\right)(x) = 1 + \dfrac{1}{x},$

$(-\infty, 0) \cup (0, \infty)$

11. $(f + g)(x) = x^2 - 4x + 5, (-\infty, \infty);$

$(f - g)(x) = -x^2 + 2x + 5, (-\infty, \infty);$

$(fg)(x) = -x^3 + 8x^2 - 15x, (-\infty, \infty);$

$\left(\dfrac{f}{g}\right)(x) = \dfrac{5 - x}{x^2 - 3x}, (-\infty, 0) \cup (0, 3) \cup (3, \infty)$

13. $(f + g)(x) = \sqrt{25 - x^2} + \sqrt{x + 3}, [-3, 5];$

$(f - g)(x) = \sqrt{25 - x^2} - \sqrt{x + 3}, [-3, 5];$

$(fg)(x) = \sqrt{(25 - x^2)(x + 3)}, [-3, 5];$

$\left(\dfrac{f}{g}\right)(x) = \sqrt{\dfrac{25 - x^2}{x + 3}}, (-3, 5]$

15. $(f + g)(x) = \dfrac{6x + 8}{x^2 + 4x}, x \neq -4, x \neq 0;$

$(f - g)(x) = \dfrac{-2x + 8}{x^2 + 4x}, x \neq -4, x \neq 0;$

$(fg)(x) = \dfrac{8}{x^2 + 4x}, x \neq -4, x \neq 0;$

$\left(\dfrac{f}{g}\right)(x) = \dfrac{x + 4}{2x}, x \neq -4, x \neq 0$

17. $[0, 3]$ **19.** $(3, \infty)$

21.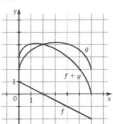

23.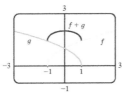

25.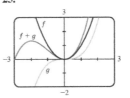

27. (a) 5 **(b)** −5 **29. (a)** −3 **(b)** −45

31. (a) $-2x^2 + 5$ **(b)** $-4x^2 + 12x - 5$ **33.** 4

35. 5 **37.** 4 **39.** 6 **41.** 3 **43.** 1 **45.** 3

47. $(f \circ g)(x) = 8x + 1, (-\infty, \infty);$

$(g \circ f)(x) = 8x + 11, (-\infty, \infty); (f \circ f)(x) = 4x + 9, (-\infty, \infty);$

$(g \circ g)(x) = 16x - 5, (-\infty, \infty)$

49. $(f \circ g)(x) = (x + 1)^2, (-\infty, \infty);$

$(g \circ f)(x) = x^2 + 1, (-\infty, \infty); (f \circ f)(x) = x^4, (-\infty, \infty);$

$(g \circ g)(x) = x + 2, (-\infty, \infty)$

51. $(f \circ g)(x) = \dfrac{1}{2x + 4}, x \neq -2; (g \circ f)(x) = \dfrac{2}{x} + 4, x \neq 0;$

$(f \circ f)(x) = x, x \neq 0, (g \circ g)(x) = 4x + 12, (-\infty, \infty)$

53. $(f \circ g)(x) = |2x + 3|, (-\infty, \infty);$

$(g \circ f)(x) = 2|x| + 3, (-\infty, \infty); (f \circ f)(x) = |x|, (-\infty, \infty);$

$(g \circ g)(x) = 4x + 9, (-\infty, \infty)$

55. $(f \circ g)(x) = \dfrac{2x - 1}{2x}, x \neq 0;$

$(g \circ f)(x) = \dfrac{2x}{x + 1} - 1, x \neq -1;$

$(f \circ f)(x) = \dfrac{x}{2x + 1}, x \neq -1, x \neq -\frac{1}{2};$

$(g \circ g)(x) = 4x - 3, (-\infty, \infty)$

57. $(f \circ g)(x) = \dfrac{1}{x + 1}, x \neq -1, x \neq 0; (g \circ f)(x) = \dfrac{x + 1}{x},$

$x \neq -1, x \neq 0; (f \circ f)(x) = \dfrac{x}{2x + 1}, x \neq -1, x \neq -\frac{1}{2};$

$(g \circ g)(x) = x, x \neq 0$

59. $(f \circ g \circ h)(x) = \sqrt{x - 1} - 1$

61. $(f \circ g \circ h)(x) = (\sqrt{x} - 5)^4 + 1$

63. $g(x) = x - 9, f(x) = x^5$ **65.** $g(x) = x^2, f(x) = x/(x + 4)$

67. $g(x) = 1 - x^3, f(x) = |x|$

69. $h(x) = x^2, g(x) = x + 1, f(x) = 1/x$

71. $h(x) = \sqrt[3]{x}, g(x) = 4 + x, f(x) = x^9$

73. Yes; m_1m_2 **75.** $R(x) = 0.15x - 0.000002x^2$

77. (a) $g(t) = 60t$ **(b)** $f(r) = \pi r^2$ **(c)** $(f \circ g)(t) = 3600\pi t^2$

79. $A(t) = 16\pi t^2$ **81. (a)** $f(x) = 0.9x$

(b) $g(x) = x - 100$ **(c)** $(f \circ g)(x) = 0.9x - 90,$

$(g \circ f)(x) = 0.9x - 100, (f \circ g)$: first rebate, then discount,

$(g \circ f)$: first discount, then rebate, $g \circ f$ is the better deal

SECTION 2.8 ▪ PAGE 261

1. different, Horizontal Line **2. (a)** one-to-one, $g(x) = x^3$

(b) $g^{-1}(x) = x^{1/3}$ **3. (a)** Take the cube root, subtract 5, then

divide the result by 3. **(b)** $f(x) = (3x + 5)^3, f^{-1}(x) = \dfrac{x^{1/3} - 5}{3}$

4. Yes, 4, 5 **5.** $(4, 3)$ **6. (a)** False **(b)** True **7.** No

9. Yes **11.** No **13.** Yes **15.** Yes **17.** No **19.** No **21.** Yes

23. No **25. (a)** 2 **(b)** 3 **27.** 1 **29. (a)** 6 **(b)** 2 **(c)** 0

31. 4 **33.** 1 **35.** 2 **49.** $f^{-1}(x) = \frac{1}{3}x - \frac{5}{3}$

51. $f^{-1}(x) = \sqrt[3]{\frac{1}{4}(5 - x)}$ **53.** $f^{-1}(x) = (1/x) - 2$

55. $f^{-1}(x) = \dfrac{4x}{1 - x}$ **57.** $f^{-1}(x) = \dfrac{7x + 5}{x - 2}$

59. $f^{-1}(x) = \dfrac{x - 3}{5x + 2}$ **61.** $f^{-1}(x) = \sqrt{4 - x}, x \le 4$

63. $f^{-1}(x) = \sqrt[6]{x}, x \ge 0$ **65.** $f^{-1}(x) = \sqrt[3]{2 - 5x}$

67. $f^{-1}(x) = \dfrac{x^2 - 5}{8}, x \ge 0$ **69.** $f^{-1}(x) = (x - 2)^3$

71. (a)   **(b)**

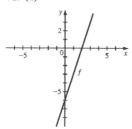
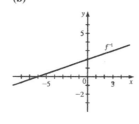

(c) $f^{-1}(x) = \frac{1}{3}(x + 6)$

73. (a)   **(b)**

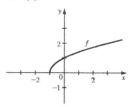
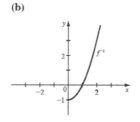

(c) $f^{-1}(x) = x^2 - 1, x \ge 0$

75. Not one-to-one   **77.** One-to-one

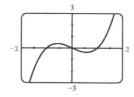
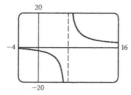

79. Not one-to-one

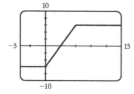

81. (a) $f^{-1}(x) = x - 2$
(b)

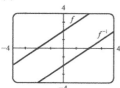

83. (a) $g^{-1}(x) = x^2 - 3, x \ge 0$
(b)

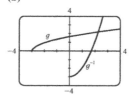

85. $x \ge 0, f^{-1}(x) = \sqrt{4 - x}$ **87.** $x \ge -2, h^{-1}(x) = \sqrt{x} - 2$
89.   **91. (a)**

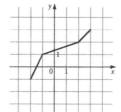
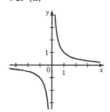

(b) Yes   **(c)** $f^{-1}(x) = \dfrac{1}{x}$

93. (a) $f(n) = 16 + 1.5n$ **(b)** $f^{-1}(x) = \frac{2}{3}(x - 16)$; the number of toppings on a pizza that costs x dollars   **(c)** 6
95. (a) $f^{-1}(V) = 40 - 4\sqrt{V}$, time elapsed when V gal of water remain   **(b)** 24.5 min; in 24.5 min the tank has 15 gal of water remaining   **97. (a)** $f^{-1}(D) = 50 - \frac{1}{3}D$; the price associated with the demand D **(b)** \$40; when the demand is 30 units, the price is \$40   **99. (a)** $f(x) = 0.9766x$ **(b)** $f^{-1}(x) = 1.02396x$; the exchange rate from U.S. dollars to Canadian dollars
(c) \$12,543.52   **101. (a)** $f(x) = 0.85x$ **(b)** $g(x) = x - 1000$
(c) $H = 0.85x - 850$ **(d)** $H^{-1}(x) = 1.176x + 1000$, the original sticker price for a given discounted price   **(e)** \$16,288, the original price of the car when the discounted price (\$1000 rebate, then 15% off) is \$13,000

CHAPTER 2 REVIEW ▪ PAGE 267

1. $f(x) = x^2 - 5$ **3.** Add 10, then multiply the result by 3.

5.

x	$g(x)$
-1	5
0	0
1	-3
2	-4
3	-3

7. (a) $C(1000) = 34,000$, $C(10,000) = 205,000$
(b) The costs of printing 1000 and 10,000 copies of the book
(c) $C(0) = 5000$; fixed costs   **(d)** \$171,000; \$19/copy
9. $6, 2, 18, a^2 - 4a + 6, a^2 + 4a + 6, x^2 - 2x + 3, 4x^2 - 8x + 6$
11. (a) Not a function   **(b)** Function   **(c)** Function, one-to-one   **(d)** Not a function   **13.** Domain $[-3, \infty)$, range $[0, \infty)$
15. $(-\infty, \infty)$ **17.** $[-4, \infty)$ **19.** $\{x \mid x \ne -2, -1, 0\}$
21. $(-\infty, -1] \cup [1, 4]$

23.

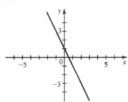

25.

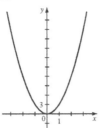

27.

29.

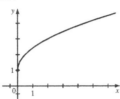

31.

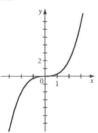

33.

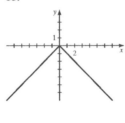

35.

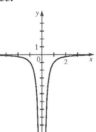

37.

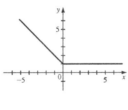

39. No   **41.** Yes   **43.** (iii)

45. (a)

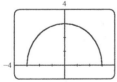

(b) Domain $[-3, 3]$, range $[0, 3]$

47. (a)

(b) Domain $[-2.11, 0.25] \cup [1.86, \infty)$, range $[0, \infty)$

49.

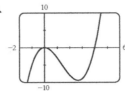

Increasing on $(-\infty, 0)$, $(2.67, \infty)$; decreasing on $(0, 2.67)$

51. $-4, -1$ **53.** $4, \frac{4}{3}$ **55.** $9, 3$ **57.** No

59. (a)

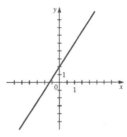

(b) 3   **(c)** 3

61. $f(x) = -2x + 3$ **63.** $f(x) = 2x + 3$

65. $f(x) = -\frac{1}{2}x + 4$ **67. (a)** $P(10) = 5010$, $P(20) = 7040$; the populations in 1995 and 2005   **(b)** 203 people/year; average annual population increase   **69. (a)** $\frac{1}{2}, \frac{1}{2}$ **(b)** Yes   **(c)** Yes, $\frac{1}{2}$

71. (a) Shift upward 8 units   **(b)** Shift to the left 8 units
(c) Stretch vertically by a factor of 2, then shift upward 1 unit
(d) Shift to the right 2 units and downward 2 units   **(e)** Reflect in
y-axis   **(f)** Reflect in y-axis, then in x-axis   **(g)** Reflect in x-axis
(h) Reflect in line $y = x$

73. (a) Neither   **(b)** Odd   **(c)** Even   **(d)** Neither

75. Local minimum $= -7$ when $x = -1$

77. Local maximum ≈ 3.79 when $x \approx 0.46$; local
minimum ≈ 2.81 when $x \approx -0.46$ **79.** 68 ft

81.

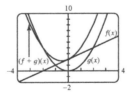

83. (a) $(f + g)(x) = x^2 - 6x + 6$ **(b)** $(f - g)(x) = x^2 - 2$
(c) $(fg)(x) = -3x^3 + 13x^2 - 18x + 8$
(d) $(f/g)(x) = (x^2 - 3x + 2)/(4 - 3x)$
(e) $(f \circ g)(x) = 9x^2 - 15x + 6$
(f) $(g \circ f)(x) = -3x^2 + 9x - 2$

85. $(f \circ g)(x) = -3x^2 + 6x - 1, (-\infty, \infty)$;
$(g \circ f)(x) = -9x^2 + 12x - 3, (-\infty, \infty)$; $(f \circ f)(x) = 9x - 4$,
$(-\infty, \infty)$; $(g \circ g)(x) = -x^4 + 4x^3 - 6x^2 + 4x, (-\infty, \infty)$

87. $(f \circ g \circ h)(x) = 1 + \sqrt{x}$ **89.** Yes   **91.** No

93. No   **95.** $f^{-1}(x) = \dfrac{x + 2}{3}$ **97.** $f^{-1}(x) = \sqrt[3]{x} - 1$

99. Yes, 1, 3

101. (a), (b)

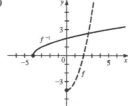

(c) $f^{-1}(x) = \sqrt{x+4}$

CHAPTER 2 TEST ▪ PAGE 271

1. (a) and **(b)** are graphs of functions, **(a)** is one-to-one

2. (a) $0, \dfrac{\sqrt{2}}{3}, \dfrac{\sqrt{a+2}}{a+3}$ **(b)** $[0, \infty)$

(c) $\dfrac{3\sqrt{10} - 11\sqrt{2}}{264} \approx -0.023$

3. (a) $f(x) = (x-2)^3$

(b)

x	$f(x)$
-1	-27
0	-8
1	-1
2	0
3	1
4	8

(c)

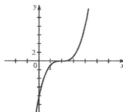

(d) By the Horizontal Line Test; take the cube root, then add 2
(e) $f^{-1}(x) = x^{1/3} + 2$ **4. (a)** Local minimum $f(-1) = -4$, local maxima $f(-4) = -1$ and $f(3) = 4$ **(b)** Increasing on $(-\infty, -4)$ and $(-1, 3)$, decreasing on $(-4, -1)$ and $(3, \infty)$
5. (a) $R(2) = 4000$, $R(4) = 4000$; total sales revenue with prices of $2 and $4

(b)

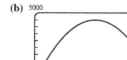

Revenue increases until price reaches $3, then decreases

(c) $4500; $3 **6.** $2h + h^2, 2 + h$
7. (a) g; f is not linear because it has a square term

(b)

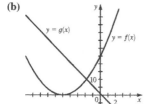

(c) -5

8. (a)

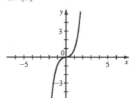

(b)

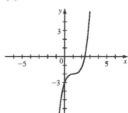

9. (a) Shift to the right 3 units, then shift upward 2 units
(b) Reflect in y-axis
10. (a) $3, 0$
(b)

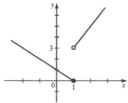

11. (a) $x^2 + 2x - 2$ **(b)** $x^2 + 4$ **(c)** $x^2 - 5x + 7$
(d) $x^2 + x - 2$ **(e)** 1 **(f)** 4 **(g)** $x - 9$

12. (a) Yes **(b)** No **14.** $f^{-1}(x) = -\dfrac{5x + 3}{2x - 1}$

15. (a) $f^{-1}(x) = 3 - x^2, x \geq 0$
(b)

16. Domain $[0, 6]$, range $[1, 7]$ **17.** $1, 3$

18.

19. $5, \dfrac{5}{4}$ **20.** $0, 4$

21.

22. (a)   **(b)** No

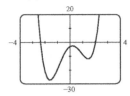

(c) Local minimum ≈ -27.18 when $x \approx -1.61$;
local maximum ≈ -2.55 when $x \approx 0.18$;
local minimum ≈ -11.93 when $x \approx 1.43$
(d) $[-27.18, \infty)$ **(e)** Increasing on $(-1.61, 0.18) \cup (1.43, \infty)$;
decreasing on $(-\infty, -1.61) \cup (0.18, 1.43)$

FOCUS ON MODELING ▪ PAGE 276

1. $A(w) = 3w^2, w > 0$ **3.** $V(w) = \frac{1}{2}w^3, w > 0$
5. $A(x) = 10x - x^2, 0 < x < 10$
7. $A(x) = (\sqrt{3}/4)x^2, x > 0$

9. $r(A) = \sqrt{A/\pi}, A > 0$ **11.** $S(x) = 2x^2 + \dfrac{240}{x}, x > 0$

13. $D(t) = 25t, t \geq 0$ **15.** $A(b) = b\sqrt{4 - b}, 0 < b < 4$
17. $A(h) = 2h\sqrt{100 - h^2}, 0 < h < 10$
19. (b) $p(x) = x(19 - x)$ **(c)** $9.5, 9.5$
21. (b) $A(x) = x(2400 - 2x)$ **(c)** 600 ft by 1200 ft
23. (a) $f(w) = 8w + (7200/w)$ **(b)** Width along road is
30 ft, length is 40 ft   **(c)** 15 ft to 60 ft

25. (a) $A(x) = 15x - \left(\dfrac{\pi + 4}{8}\right)x^2$

(b) Width ≈ 8.40 ft, height of rectangular part ≈ 4.20 ft

27. (a) $A(x) = x^2 + \dfrac{48}{x}$ **(b)** Height ≈ 1.44 ft, width ≈ 2.88 ft

29. (a) $A(x) = 2x + \dfrac{200}{x}$ **(b)** 10 m by 10 m

31. (b) To point C, 5.1 mi from B

CHAPTER 3
SECTION 3.1 ▪ PAGE 287

1. square   **2. (a)** (h, k) **(b)** upward, minimum
(c) downward, maximum   **3.** upward, $(2, -6)$, -6, minimum
4. downward, $(2, -6)$, -6, maximum
5. (a) $(3, 4)$; x-intercepts 1, 5; y-intercept -5
(b) maximum 4   **(c)** $\mathbb{R}, (-\infty, 4]$

7. (a) $(1, -3)$; x-intercepts $\dfrac{2 \pm \sqrt{6}}{2}$; y-intercept -1

(b) minimum -3 **(c)** $\mathbb{R}, [-3, \infty)$
9. (a) $f(x) = (x - 1)^2 + 2$
(b) Vertex $(1, 2)$; no x-intercepts; y-intercept 3
(c)   **(d)** $\mathbb{R}, [2, \infty)$

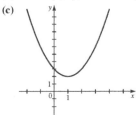

11. (a) $f(x) = (x - 3)^2 - 9$
(b) Vertex $(3, -9)$; x-intercepts 0, 6; y-intercept 0
(c)   **(d)** $\mathbb{R}, [-9, \infty)$

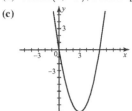

13. (a) $f(x) = 3(x + 1)^2 - 3$ **15. (a)** $f(x) = (x + 2)^2 - 1$
(b) Vertex $(-1, -3)$ **(b)** Vertex $(-2, -1)$
x-intercepts $-2, 0$ x-intercepts $-1, -3$
y-intercept 0 y-intercept 3
(c)   **(c)**

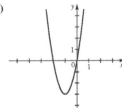   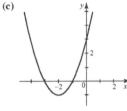

(d) $\mathbb{R}, [-3, \infty)$ **(d)** $\mathbb{R}, [-1, \infty)$
17. (a) $f(x) = -(x - 3)^2 + 13$
(b) Vertex $(3, 13)$; x-intercepts $3 \pm \sqrt{13}$; y-intercept 4
(c)   **(d)** $\mathbb{R}, (-\infty, 13]$

19. (a) $f(x) = 2(x + 1)^2 + 1$
(b) Vertex $(-1, 1)$; no x-intercept; y-intercept 3
(c)   **(d)** $\mathbb{R}, [1, \infty)$

21. (a) $f(x) = 2(x - 5)^2 + 7$
(b) Vertex $(5, 7)$; no x-intercept; y-intercept 57
(c)   **(d)** $\mathbb{R}, [7, \infty)$

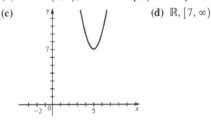

23. (a) $f(x) = -4\left(x + \frac{3}{2}\right)^2 + 10$
(b) Vertex $\left(-\frac{3}{2}, 10\right)$; x-intercepts $-\frac{3}{2} - \frac{\sqrt{10}}{2}, -\frac{3}{2} + \frac{\sqrt{10}}{2}$;
y-intercept 1

(c)    (d) $\mathbb{R}, (-\infty, 10]$

25. (a) $f(x) = (x + 1)^2 - 2$ **27.** (a) $f(x) = 3(x - 1)^2 - 2$
(b) 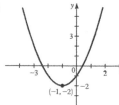   (b)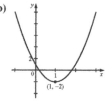

(c) Minimum $f(-1) = -2$ (c) Minimum $f(1) = -2$
29. (a) $f(x) = -\left(x + \frac{3}{2}\right)^2 + \frac{21}{4}$ **31.** (a) $g(x) = 3(x - 2)^2 + 1$
(b) 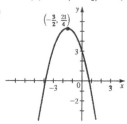   (b)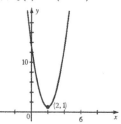

(c) Maximum $f\left(-\frac{3}{2}\right) = \frac{21}{4}$ (c) Minimum $g(2) = 1$
33. (a) $h(x) = -\left(x + \frac{1}{2}\right)^2 + \frac{5}{4}$
(b)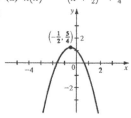

(c) Maximum $h\left(-\frac{1}{2}\right) = \frac{5}{4}$
35. Minimum $f(-1) = -3$
37. Maximum $f(2) = 77$
39. Minimum $f(0.6) = 15.64$
41. Minimum $h(-2) = -8$
43. Maximum $f(-1) = \frac{7}{2}$
45. (a) -4.01 (b) -4.011025
47. $f(x) = 4(x - 2)^2 - 3$
49. 7 **51.** 25 ft **53.** \$4000, 100 units **55.** 30 times
57. 50 trees/acre **59.** 600 ft by 1200 ft
61. Width 8.40 ft, height of rectangular part 4.20 ft
63. (a) $f(x) = x(1200 - x)$ (b) 600 ft by 600 ft
65. (a) $R(x) = x(57{,}000 - 3000x)$ (b) \$9.50 (c) \$19.00

SECTION 3.2 ■ PAGE 301

1. II **2.** (a) $\infty, -\infty$ (b) $-\infty, -\infty$
3. (a) 0 (b) factor (c) x **4.** (a)
5. (a) 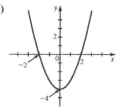   (b)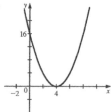

(c) 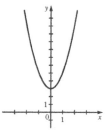   (d)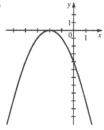

7. (a) 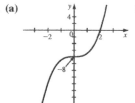   (b)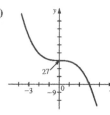

(c) 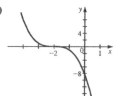   (d)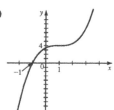

9. (a) $y \to \infty$ as $x \to \infty$, $y \to -\infty$ as $x \to -\infty$ (b) III
11. (a) $y \to -\infty$ as $x \to \infty$, $y \to \infty$ as $x \to -\infty$ (b) V
13. (a) $y \to \infty$ as $x \to \infty$, $y \to \infty$ as $x \to -\infty$ (b) VI
15. 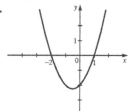   **17.**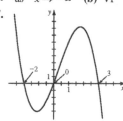

19. 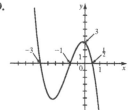   **21.**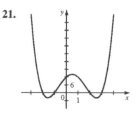

23.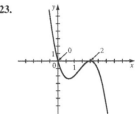

25.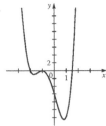

43. $P(x) = (x^2 + 1)(x + 2)(x - 2)$

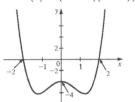

45. $y \to \infty$ as $x \to \infty$, $y \to -\infty$ as $x \to -\infty$
47. $y \to \infty$ as $x \to \pm\infty$
49. $y \to \infty$ as $x \to \infty$,
$y \to -\infty$ as $x \to -\infty$
51. (a) x-intercepts $0, 4$; y-intercept 0 **(b)** Maximum $(2, 4)$
53. (a) x-intercepts $-2, 1$; y-intercept -1
(b) Minimum $(-1, -2)$, maximum $(1, 0)$

27.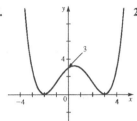

29.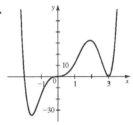

55. 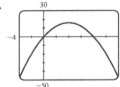   local maximum $(4, 16)$,
domain $(-\infty, \infty)$,
range $(-\infty, 16]$

31. $P(x) = x(x + 2)(x - 3)$ **33.** $P(x) = -x(x + 3)(x - 4)$

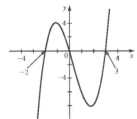   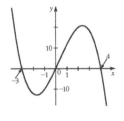

57. 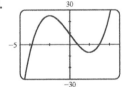   **59.**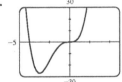

local maximum $(-2, 25)$,
local minimum $(2, -7)$,
domain $(-\infty, \infty)$,
range $(-\infty, \infty)$

local minimum $(-3, -27)$,
domain $(-\infty, \infty)$,
range $[-27, \infty)$

35. $P(x) = x^2(x - 1)(x - 2)$ **37.** $P(x) = (x + 1)^2(x - 1)$

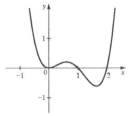   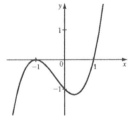

61. 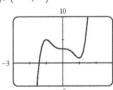   local maximum $(-1, 5)$,
local minimum $(1, 1)$,
domain $(-\infty, \infty)$,
range $(-\infty, \infty)$

39. $P(x) = (2x - 1)(x + 3)(x - 3)$

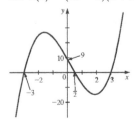

63. One local maximum, no local minimum   **65.** One local
maximum, one local minimum   **67.** One local maximum, two
local minima   **69.** No local extrema   **71.** One local maximum,
two local minima

73.   **75.**

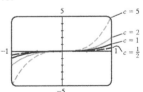   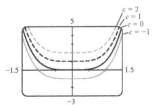

Increasing the value of c
stretches the graph vertically.

Increasing the value of c
moves the graph up.

41. $P(x) = (x - 2)^2(x^2 + 2x + 4)$

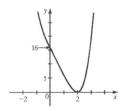

77.

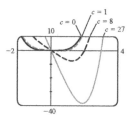

Increasing the value of c causes a deeper dip in the graph in the fourth quadrant and moves the positive x-intercept to the right.

79. (a)

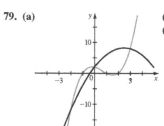

(b) Three
(c) $(0, 2), (3, 8), (-2, -12)$

81. (d) $P(x) = P_O(x) + P_E(x)$, where $P_O(x) = x^5 + 6x^3 - 2x$ and $P_E(x) = -x^2 + 5$

83. (a)

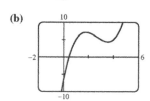

local maximum $(1.8, 2.1)$
local minimum $(3.6, -0.6)$

(b)

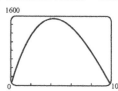

local maximum $(1.8, 7.1)$
local minimum
$(3.5, 4.4)$

85. 5; there are four local extrema
87. (a) 26 blenders   **(b)** No; $3276.22
89. (a) $V(x) = 4x^3 - 120x^2 + 800x$ **(b)** $0 < x < 10$
(c) Maximum volume ≈ 1539.6 cm^3

SECTION 3.3 ▪ PAGE 309

1. quotient, remainder   **2. (a)** factor   **(b)** k

3. $2x - 1 + \dfrac{-9}{x - 2}$ **5.** $2x - \dfrac{1}{2} + \dfrac{-\frac{15}{2}}{2x - 1}$

7. $2x^2 - x + 1 + \dfrac{4x - 4}{x^2 + 4}$ **9.** $(x + 1)(-x^2 + x - 3) + 9$

11. $(2x - 3)(x^2 - 1) - 3$
13. $(2x^2 + 1)(4x^2 + 2x + 1) + (-2x - 1)$

In answers 15–37 the first polynomial given is the quotient, and the second is the remainder.
15. $x - 1, 5$ **17.** $2x^2 - 1, -2$ **19.** $x + 1, -2$
21. $3x + 1, 7x - 5$ **23.** $x^4 + 1, 0$ **25.** $2x + 1, 6$
27. $3x - 2, 2$ **29.** $x^2 + 2, -3$ **31.** $x^2 - 3x + 1, -1$
33. $x^4 + x^3 + 4x^2 + 4x + 4, -2$ **35.** $2x^2 + 4x, 1$
37. $x^2 + 3x + 9, 0$ **39.** -3 **41.** 12   **43.** -7
45. -483 **47.** 2159   **49.** $\frac{7}{3}$ **51.** -8.279 **57.** $-3, 3$

59. $-1 \pm \sqrt{6}$ **61.** $\dfrac{5 \pm \sqrt{37}}{6}$ **63.** $x^3 - 3x^2 - x + 3$

65. $x^4 - 8x^3 + 14x^2 + 8x - 15$
67. $-2x^4 + 4x^3 + 10x^2 - 12x$ **69.** $3x^4 - 9x^2 + 6$
71. $(x + 1)(x - 1)(x - 2)$ **73.** $(x + 2)^2(x - 1)^2$

SECTION 3.4 ▪ PAGE 319

1. $a_0, a_n, \pm 1, \pm\frac{1}{2}, \pm\frac{1}{3}, \pm\frac{1}{6}, \pm 2, \pm\frac{2}{3}, \pm 5, \pm\frac{5}{2}, \pm\frac{5}{3}, \pm\frac{5}{6}, \pm 10, \pm\frac{10}{3}$
2. $1, 3, 5; 0$ **3.** True   **4.** False   **5.** $\pm 1, \pm 3$
7. $\pm 1, \pm 2, \pm 4, \pm 8, \pm\frac{1}{2}$ **9.** $\pm 1, \pm 7, \pm\frac{1}{2}, \pm\frac{7}{2}, \pm\frac{1}{4}, \pm\frac{7}{4}$
11. (a) $\pm 1, \pm\frac{1}{5}$ **(b)** $-1, 1, \frac{1}{5}$ **13. (a)** $\pm 1, \pm 3, \pm\frac{1}{2}, \pm\frac{3}{2}$
(b) $-\frac{1}{2}, 1, 3$ **15.** $-5, 1, 2; P(x) = (x + 5)(x - 1)(x - 2)$
17. $-2, 1; P(x) = (x + 2)^2(x - 1)$
19. $2; P(x) = (x - 2)^3$
21. $-3, -2, 5; P(x) = (x + 3)(x + 2)(x - 5)$
23. $-3, -1, 1; P(x) = (x + 3)(x + 1)(x - 1)$
25. $\pm 1, \pm 2; P(x) = (x - 2)(x + 2)(x - 1)(x + 1)$
27. $-4, -2, -1, 1; P(x) = (x + 4)(x + 2)(x - 1)(x + 1)$
29. $-3, -\frac{1}{2}, \frac{1}{2}, 3; P(x) = (x + 3)(2x + 1)(2x - 1)(x - 3)$
31. $\pm 2, \frac{1}{3}, 3; P(x) = (x - 2)(x + 2)(x - 3)(3x - 1)$
33. $-1, \pm\frac{1}{2}; P(x) = (x + 1)(2x - 1)(2x + 1)$
35. $-\frac{3}{2}, \frac{1}{2}, 1; P(x) = (x - 1)(2x + 3)(2x - 1)$
37. $-\frac{2}{3}, -\frac{1}{2}, \frac{3}{4}; P(x) = (3x + 2)(2x + 1)(4x - 3)$
39. $-1, \frac{1}{2}, 2; P(x) = (x + 1)(x - 2)^2(2x - 1)$
41. $-3, -2, 1, 3; P(x) = (x + 3)(x + 2)^2(x - 1)(x - 3)$
43. $-1, -\frac{1}{3}, 2, 5; P(x) = (x + 1)^2(x - 2)(x - 5)(3x + 1)$

45. $-1, -\dfrac{1 \pm \sqrt{13}}{3}$ **47.** $-1, 4, \dfrac{3 \pm \sqrt{13}}{2}$

49. $3, \dfrac{1 \pm \sqrt{5}}{2}$ **51.** $\frac{1}{2}, \dfrac{1 \pm \sqrt{3}}{2}$ **53.** $-1, -\frac{1}{2}, -3 \pm \sqrt{10}$

55. (a) $-2, 2, 3$ **(b)**

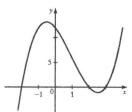

57. (a) $-\frac{1}{2}, 2$ **(b)**

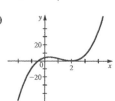

59. **(a)** $-1, 2$ **(b)**

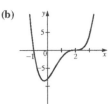

61. **(a)** $-1, 2$ **(b)**

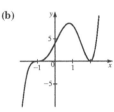

63. 1 positive, 2 or 0 negative; 3 or 1 real **65.** 1 positive,
1 negative; 2 real **67.** 2 or 0 positive, 0 negative; 3 or 1 real
(since 0 is a zero but is neither positive nor negative) **77.** 3, -2
79. 3, -1 **81.** $-2, \frac{1}{2}, \pm 1$ **83.** $\pm \frac{1}{2}, \pm \sqrt{5}$ **85.** $-2, 1, 3, 4$
91. $-2, 2, 3$ **93.** $-\frac{3}{2}, -1, 1, 4$ **95.** $-1.28, 1.53$ **97.** -1.50
99. 11.3 ft **101.** **(a)** It began to snow again. **(b)** No
(c) Just before midnight on Saturday night **103.** 2.76 m
105. 88 in. (or 3.21 in.)

SECTION 3.5 ▪ PAGE 329

1. 6; -7; 2, 3 **2.** **(a)** $x - a$ **(b)** $(x - a)^m$ **3.** n **4.** $a - bi$;
$3 - i$ **5.** **(a)** True **(b)** True **(c)** False, $x^4 + 1 > 0$ for all
real x **6.** **(a)** False, $x^2 + 1$ has no real zeros
(b) True **(c)** False, $x^2 + 1$ factors into linear factors with
complex coefficients **7.** **(a)** $0, \pm 2i$ **(b)** $x^2(x - 2i)(x + 2i)$
9. **(a)** $0, 1 \pm i$ **(b)** $x(x - 1 - i)(x - 1 + i)$
11. **(a)** $\pm i$ **(b)** $(x - i)^2(x + i)^2$
13. **(a)** $\pm 2, \pm 2i$ **(b)** $(x - 2)(x + 2)(x - 2i)(x + 2i)$
15. **(a)** $-2, 1 \pm i\sqrt{3}$
(b) $(x + 2)(x - 1 - i\sqrt{3})(x - 1 + i\sqrt{3})$
17. **(a)** $\pm 1, \frac{1}{2} \pm \frac{1}{2}i\sqrt{3}, -\frac{1}{2} \pm \frac{1}{2}i\sqrt{3}$
(b) $(x - 1)(x + 1)(x - \frac{1}{2} - \frac{1}{2}i\sqrt{3})(x - \frac{1}{2} + \frac{1}{2}i\sqrt{3}) \times$
$(x + \frac{1}{2} - \frac{1}{2}i\sqrt{3})(x + \frac{1}{2} + \frac{1}{2}i\sqrt{3})$

*In answers 19–35 the factored form is given first, then the zeros
are listed with the multiplicity of each in parentheses.*
19. $(x - 5i)(x + 5i)$; $\pm 5i\,(1)$
21. $[x - (-1 + i)][x - (-1 - i)]$; $-1 + i\,(1), -1 - i\,(1)$
23. $x(x - 2i)(x + 2i)$; $0\,(1), 2i\,(1), -2i\,(1)$
25. $(x - 1)(x + 1)(x - i)(x + i)$; $1\,(1), -1\,(1), i\,(1), -i\,(1)$
27. $16(x - \frac{3}{2})(x + \frac{3}{2})(x - \frac{3}{2}i)(x + \frac{3}{2}i)$; $\frac{3}{2}\,(1), -\frac{3}{2}\,(1), \frac{3}{2}i\,(1),$
$-\frac{3}{2}i\,(1)$ **29.** $(x + 1)(x - 3i)(x + 3i)$; $-1\,(1), 3i\,(1), -3i\,(1)$
31. $(x - i)^2(x + i)^2$; $i\,(2), -i\,(2)$
33. $(x - 1)(x + 1)(x - 2i)(x + 2i)$; $1\,(1), -1\,(1),$
$2i(1), -2i(1)$
35. $x(x - i\sqrt{3})^2(x + i\sqrt{3})^2$; $0\,(1), i\sqrt{3}\,(2), -i\sqrt{3}\,(2)$
37. $P(x) = x^2 - 2x + 2$ **39.** $Q(x) = x^3 - 3x^2 + 4x - 12$
41. $P(x) = x^3 - 2x^2 + x - 2$
43. $R(x) = x^4 - 4x^3 + 10x^2 - 12x + 5$

45. $T(x) = 6x^4 - 12x^3 + 18x^2 - 12x + 12$ **47.** $-2, \pm 2i$
49. $1, \dfrac{1 \pm i\sqrt{3}}{2}$ **51.** $2, \dfrac{1 \pm i\sqrt{3}}{2}$ **53.** $-\frac{3}{2}, -1 \pm i\sqrt{2}$
55. $-2, 1, \pm 3i$ **57.** $1, \pm 2i, \pm i\sqrt{3}$ **59.** 3 (multiplicity 2), $\pm 2i$
61. $-\frac{1}{2}$ (multiplicity 2), $\pm i$ **63.** 1 (multiplicity 3), $\pm 3i$
65. **(a)** $(x - 5)(x^2 + 4)$ **(b)** $(x - 5)(x - 2i)(x + 2i)$
67. **(a)** $(x - 1)(x + 1)(x^2 + 9)$
(b) $(x - 1)(x + 1)(x - 3i)(x + 3i)$
69. **(a)** $(x - 2)(x + 2)(x^2 - 2x + 4)(x^2 + 2x + 4)$
(b) $(x - 2)(x + 2)[x - (1 + i\sqrt{3})][x - (1 - i\sqrt{3})] \times$
$[x + (1 + i\sqrt{3})][x + (1 - i\sqrt{3})]$
71. **(a)** 4 real **(b)** 2 real, 2 non-real **(c)** 4 non-real

SECTION 3.6 ▪ PAGE 344

1. $-\infty, \infty$ **2.** 2 **3.** $-1, 2$ **4.** $\frac{1}{3}$ **5.** $-2, 3$ **6.** 1
7. **(a)** False **(b)** True **(c)** False **(d)** True **8.** True
9. **(a)** $-3, -19, -199, -1999; 5, 21, 201, 2001$;
$1.2500, 1.0417, 1.0204, 1.0020; 0.8333, 0.9615, 0.9804, 0.9980$
(b) $r(x) \to -\infty$ as $x \to 2^-$; $r(x) \to \infty$ as $x \to 2^+$
(c) Horizontal asymptote $y = 1$
11. **(a)** $-22, -430, -40,300, -4,003,000; -10, -370,$
$-39,700, -3,997,000; 0.3125, 0.0608, 0.0302, 0.0030$;
$-0.2778, -0.0592, -0.0298, -0.0030$
(b) $r(x) \to -\infty$ as $x \to 2^-$; $r(x) \to -\infty$ as $x \to 2^+$
(c) Horizontal asymptote $y = 0$

13. 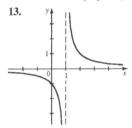 **15.**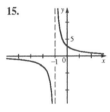

domain $\{x \mid x \neq 1\}$ domain $\{x \mid x \neq -1\}$
range $\{y \mid y \neq 0\}$ range $\{y \mid y \neq 0\}$

17. **19.**

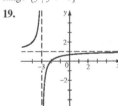

domain $\{x \mid x \neq 2\}$ domain $\{x \mid x \neq -3\}$
range $\{y \mid y \neq 2\}$ range $\{y \mid y \neq 1\}$

21. x-intercept 1, y-intercept $-\frac{1}{4}$ **23.** x-intercepts $-1, 2$;
y-intercept $\frac{1}{3}$ **25.** x-intercepts $-3, 3$; no y-intercept
27. x-intercept 3, y-intercept 3, vertical $x = 2$; horizontal $y = 2$
29. x-intercepts $-1, 1$; y-intercept $\frac{1}{4}$; vertical $x = -2, x = 2$;
horizontal $y = 1$ **31.** Vertical $x = 2$; horizontal $y = 0$
33. Horizontal $y = 0$ **35.** Vertical $x = \frac{1}{2}, x = -1$;
horizontal $y = 3$ **37.** Vertical $x = -\frac{7}{4}, x = 2$; horizontal $y = \frac{1}{2}$
39. Vertical $x = 0$; horizontal $y = 3$ **41.** Vertical $x = 1$

43.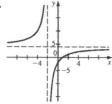

x-intercept 1
y-intercept −2
vertical *x* = −2
horizontal *y* = 4
domain $\{x \mid x \neq -2\}$
range $\{y \mid y \neq 4\}$

55.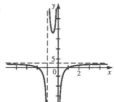

x-intercepts 1, −2
vertical *x* = −1, *x* = 0
horizontal *y* = 2
domain $\{x \mid x \neq -1, 0\}$
range $\{y \mid y < 2 \text{ or } y \geq 18.4\}$

45.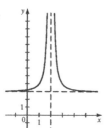

no *x*-intercept
y-intercept $\frac{13}{4}$
vertical *x* = 2
horizontal *y* = 3
domain $\{x \mid x \neq 2\}$
range $\{y \mid y > 3\}$

57.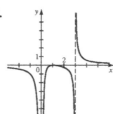

x-intercept 1
vertical *x* = 0, *x* = 3
horizontal *y* = 0
domain $\{x \mid x \neq 0, 3\}$
range $\mathbb{R}$

47.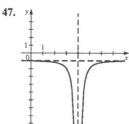

no *x*-intercept
y-intercept $-\frac{9}{8}$
vertical *x* = 4
horizontal *y* = −1
domain $\{x \mid x \neq 4\}$
range $\{y \mid y < -1\}$

59.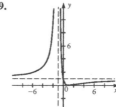

x-intercept 1
y-intercept 1
vertical *x* = −1
horizontal *y* = 1
domain $\{x \mid x \neq -1\}$
range $\{y \mid y \geq 0\}$

49.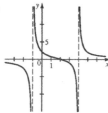

x-intercept 2
y-intercept 2
vertical *x* = −1, *x* = 4
horizontal *y* = 0
domain $\{x \mid x \neq -1, 4\}$
range $\mathbb{R}$

61.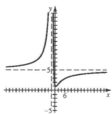

y-intercept $\frac{5}{4}$
vertical *x* = −2
horizontal *y* = 5
domain $\{x \mid x \neq -2\}$
range $\{y \mid y \geq 1.0\}$

51.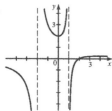

x-intercept 2
y-intercept 2
vertical *x* = −2, *x* = 1
horizontal *y* = 0
domain $\{x \mid x \neq -2, 1\}$
range $\{y \mid y \leq 0.2 \text{ or } y \geq 2\}$

63.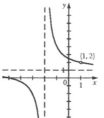

x-intercept −5
y-intercept $\frac{5}{2}$
vertical *x* = −2
horizontal *y* = 1
domain $\{x \mid x \neq -2, 1\}$
range $\{y \mid y \neq 1, 2\}$

53.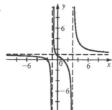

x-intercepts −2, 1
y-intercept $\frac{2}{3}$
vertical *x* = −1, *x* = 3
horizontal *y* = 1
domain $\{x \mid x \neq -1, 3\}$
range $\mathbb{R}$

65.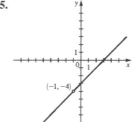

x-intercept 3
y-intercept −3
no asymptote
domain $\{x \mid x \neq -1\}$
range $\{y \mid y \neq -4\}$

67.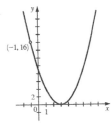

x-intercept 3
y-intercept 9
no asymptote
domain $\{x \mid x \neq -1\}$
range $\{y \mid y \geq 0\}$

69.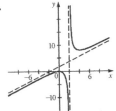

slant $y = x + 2$
vertical $x = 2$

71.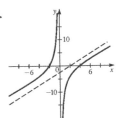

slant $y = x - 2$
vertical $x = 0$

73.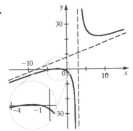

slant $y = x + 8$
vertical $x = 3$

75.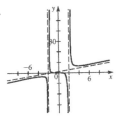

slant $y = x + 1$
vertical $x = 2, x = -2$

77.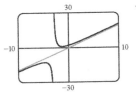

vertical $x = -3$

79.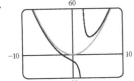

vertical $x = 2$

81.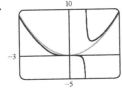

vertical $x = -1.5$
x-intercepts 0, 2.5
y-intercept 0, local
maximum $(-3.9, -10.4)$
local minimum $(0.9, -0.6)$
end behavior $y = x - 4$

83.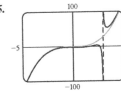

vertical $x = 1$
x-intercept 0
y-intercept 0
local minimum $(1.4, 3.1)$
end behavior $y = x^2$

85.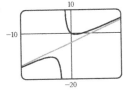

vertical $x = 3$
x-intercepts 1.6, 2.7
y-intercept -2
local maxima $(-0.4, -1.8)$,
$(2.4, 3.8)$,
local minima $(0.6, -2.3)$,
$(3.4, 54.3)$
end behavior $y = x^3$

87. (a) 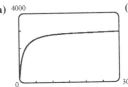   **(b)** It levels off at 3000.

89. (a) 2.50 mg/L   **(b)** It decreases to 0.   **(c)** 16.61 h

91.

If the speed of the train
approaches the speed of sound,
then the pitch increases
indefinitely (a sonic boom).

SECTION 3.7 ■ PAGE 352

1. zeros; zeros; $[-2, 0], [1, \infty)$

Sign of	-2		0		1	
x	$-$	$-$		$+$		$+$
$x + 2$	$-$	$+$		$+$		$+$
$x - 1$	$-$	$-$		$-$		$+$
$x(x + 2)(x - 1)$	$-$	$+$		$-$		$+$

2. zeros; zeros; cut points; $(-\infty, -4,), [-2, 1], (3, \infty)$

Sign of		-4		-2		1		3	
$x + 2$	$-$		$-$		$+$		$+$		$+$
$x - 1$	$-$		$-$		$-$		$+$		$+$
$x - 3$	$-$		$-$		$-$		$-$		$+$
$x + 4$	$-$		$+$		$+$		$+$		$+$
$\dfrac{(x+2)(x-1)}{(x-3)(x+4)}$	$+$		$-$		$+$		$-$		$+$

3. $(-\infty, -5) \cup \left(-\frac{5}{2}, 3\right)$ **5.** $(-\infty, -5) \cup (-5, -3) \cup (1, \infty)$
7. $[-4, -2] \cup [2, \infty)$ **9.** $\left(-\infty, \frac{1}{2}\right)$ **11.** $(-3, 3)$
13. $[-5, 1] \cup [3, \infty)$ **15.** $(-\infty, -1) \cup (1, 7)$ **17.** $(1, 10)$
19. $\left(-7, -\frac{5}{2}\right] \cup (5, \infty)$ **21.** $(-\infty, -1 - \sqrt{3}) \cup [0, \sqrt{3} - 1)$
23. $(-\infty, -3) \cup \left(-\frac{2}{3}, 1\right) \cup (3, \infty)$ **25.** $(-4, 3]$
27. $\left[-8, -\frac{5}{2}\right)$ **29.** $\left(0, \frac{3-\sqrt{3}}{2}\right] \cup \left(1, \frac{3+\sqrt{3}}{2}\right]$
31. $(-\infty, -2) \cup (-1, 1) \cup (1, \infty)$ **33.** $[-2, 0) \cup (1, 3]$
35. $\left(-3, -\frac{1}{2}\right) \cup (2, \infty)$ **37.** $(-\infty, -2) \cup (5, \infty)$
39. $\left(-\frac{1}{2}, 0\right) \cup \left(\frac{1}{2}, \infty\right)$ **41.** $[-2, 3]$ **43.** $(-\infty, -1] \cup [1, \infty)$
45. $[-2, 1] \cup [3, \infty)$ **47.** $(-\infty, -1.37) \cup (0.37, 1)$
49. $(0, 1.60)$ **51.** $(0, 1]$ **53.** $(-\infty, a] \cup [b, c] \cup [d, \infty)$
55. More than 35.6 m
57.

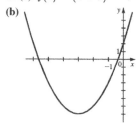

Between 9.5 and 42.3 mi/h

CHAPTER 3 REVIEW ▪ PAGE 356

1. (a) $f(x) = (x + 3)^2 - 7$ **3. (a)** $f(x) = -(x + 5)^2 + 26$
(b)

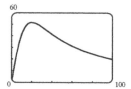

(b)

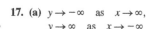

5. Maximum $f\left(\frac{3}{2}\right) = \frac{5}{4}$ **7.** 68 ft
9.

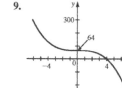

11.

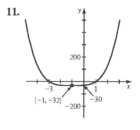

13.

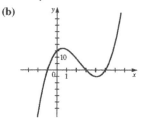

15. (a) $y \to \infty$ as $x \to \infty$,
$y \to -\infty$ as $x \to -\infty$

17. (a) $y \to -\infty$ as $x \to \infty$,
$y \to \infty$ as $x \to -\infty$

(b)

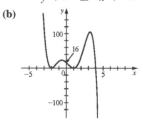

(b)

19. (a) 0 (multiplicity 3), 2 (multiplicity 2)
(b)

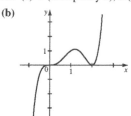

21.

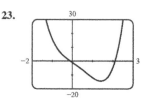

x-intercepts $-2.1, 0.3, 1.9$
y-intercept 1
local maximum $(-1.2, 4.1)$
local minimum $(1.2, -2.1)$
$y \to \infty$ as $x \to \infty$ and
$y \to -\infty$ as $x \to -\infty$

23.

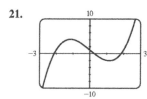

x-intercepts $-0.1, 2.1$
y-intercept -1
local minimum $(1.4, -14.5)$
$y \to \infty$ as $x \to \infty$ and
$y \to \infty$ as $x \to -\infty$

25. (a) $S = 13.8x(100 - x^2)$ **(b)** $0 \le x \le 10$
(c)

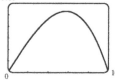

(d) 5.8 in.

In answers 27–33 the first polynomial given is the quotient, and the second is the remainder.
27. $x - 2, -4$ **29.** $2x^2 - 11x + 58, -294$
31. $x^3 - 5x^2 + 17x - 83, 422$ **33.** $2x - 3, 12$ **35.** 3   **37.** 8

41. (a) $\pm 1, \pm 2, \pm 3, \pm 6, \pm 9, \pm 18$
(b) 2 or 0 positive, 3 or 1 negative
43. (a) $\pm 1, \pm 2, \pm 4, \pm 8, \pm \frac{1}{3}, \pm \frac{2}{3}, \pm \frac{4}{3}, \pm \frac{8}{3}$
(b) 0 or 2 positive, 1 or 3 negative
45. (a) $-4, 0, 4$ **(b)**

47. (a) $-2, 0$ (multiplicity 2), 1 **(b)**

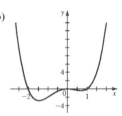

49. (a) $-2, -1, 2, 3$ **51. (a)** $-\frac{1}{2}, 1$
(b) **(b)**

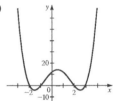 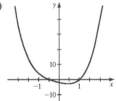

53. $4x^3 - 18x^2 + 14x + 12$
55. No; since the complex conjugates of imaginary zeros will also be zeros, the polynomial would have 8 zeros, contradicting the requirement that it have degree 4.
57. $1, \pm i$ **59.** $-3, 1, 5$
61. $-1 \pm 2i, -2$ (multiplicity 2)
63. $\pm 2, 1$ (multiplicity 3)
65. $\pm 2, \pm 1 \pm i\sqrt{3}$ **67.** $1, 3, \dfrac{-1 \pm i\sqrt{7}}{2}$
69. $x = -0.5, 3$ **71.** $x \approx -0.24, 4.24$
73. $2, P(x) = (x - 2)(x^2 + 2x + 2)$
75. (a) Vertical asymptote $x = -4$, horizontal asymptote $y = 0$, no x-intercept, y-intercept $\frac{3}{4}$, domain $\{x \mid x \neq -4\}$ range $\{y \mid y \neq 0\}$
(b)

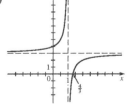

77. (a) Vertical asymptote $x = 1$, horizontal asymptote $y = 3$, x-intercept $\frac{4}{3}$, y-intercept 4, domain $\{x \mid x \neq 1\}$ range $\{y \mid y \neq 3\}$
(b)

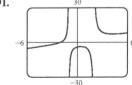

79.

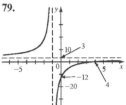

Domain $\{x \mid x \neq -1\}$, range $\{y \mid y \neq 3\}$

81.

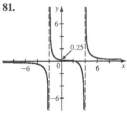

Domain $\{x \mid x \neq -2, 4\}$, range $(-\infty, \infty)$

83.

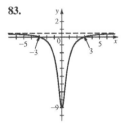

Domain $(-\infty, \infty)$, range $\{y \mid -9 \leq y < \frac{1}{2}\}$

85.

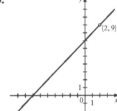

x-intercept -7
y-intercept 7
no asymptote
domain $\{x \mid x \neq 2\}$
range $\{y \mid y \neq 9\}$

87.

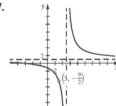

x-intercept -6
y-intercept $-\frac{6}{5}$
vertical $x = 5$
horizontal $y = 1$
domain $\{x \mid x \neq 3, 5\}$
range $\{y \mid y \neq 1, -\frac{9}{2}\}$

89.

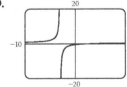

x-intercept 3
y-intercept -0.5
vertical $x = -3$
horizontal $y = 0.5$
no local extrema

91.

x-intercept -2
y-intercept -4
vertical $x = -1, x = 2$
slant $y = x + 1$
local maximum $(0.425, -3.599)$
local minimum $(4.216, 7.175)$

93. $(-\infty, -1] \cup \left[\frac{3}{2}, \infty\right)$ **95.** $(-3, 3)$
97. $(-\infty, -2) \cup (1, 2)$ **99.** $(-3, 0) \cup \left(2, \frac{9}{2}\right]$
101. $\left[-3, \frac{8}{3}\right]$ **103.** $[0.74, 1.95]$

CHAPTER 3 TEST ■ PAGE 359

1. $f(x) = \left(x - \frac{1}{2}\right)^2 - \frac{25}{4}$

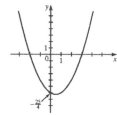

2. Minimum $g\left(-\frac{3}{2}\right) = -\frac{3}{2}$ **3. (a)** 2500 ft   **(b)** 1000 ft

4.

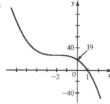

5. (a) $x^3 + 2x^2 + 2, 9$ **(b)** $x^3 + 2x^2 + \frac{1}{2}, \frac{15}{2}$
6. (a) $\pm 1, \pm 3, \pm\frac{1}{2}, \pm\frac{3}{2}$ **(b)** $2(x - 3)\left(x - \frac{1}{2}\right)(x + 1)$
(c) $-1, \frac{1}{2}, 3$ **(d)**

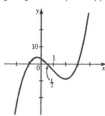

7. $3, -1 \pm i$ **8.** $(x - 1)^2(x - 2i)(x + 2i)$
9. $x^4 + 2x^3 + 10x^2 + 18x + 9$
10. (a) 4, 2, or 0 positive; 0 negative
(c) 0.17, 3.93

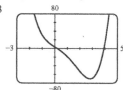

(d) Local minimum $(2.82, -70.31)$
11. (a) r, u **(b)** s **(c)** s, w **(d)** w
(e) Vertical $x = -1, x = 2$; horizontal $y = 0$
(f)

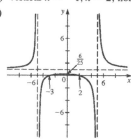

(g) $x^2 - 2x - 5$

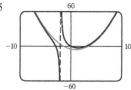

12. $\left\{x \mid x \le -1 \text{ or } \frac{5}{2} < x \le 3\right\}$
13. $\left\{x \mid -1 - \sqrt{5} < x < -1 + \sqrt{5}\right\}$
14. (a)

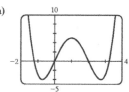

x-intercepts $-1.24, 0, 2, 3.24$, local maximum $P(1) = 5$,
local minima $P(-0.73) = P(2.73) = -4$
(b) $(-\infty, -1.24] \cup [0, 2] \cup [3.24, \infty)$

FOCUS ON MODELING ■ PAGE 363

1. (a) $y = -0.275428x^2 + 19.7485x - 273.5523$
(b)

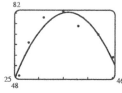

(c) 35.85 lb/in^2
3. (a) $y = 0.00203708x^3 - 0.104521x^2 + 1.966206x + 1.45576$
(b)

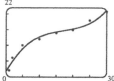

(c) 43 vegetables   **(d)** 2.0 s
5. (a) $y = 0.0120536x^2 - 0.490357x + 4.96571$
(b)

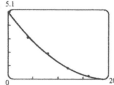

(c) 19.0 min

CHAPTER 4

SECTION 4.1 ■ PAGE 372

1. $5; \frac{1}{25}; 1; 25; 15,625$ **2. (a)** III   **(b)** I   **(c)** II   **(d)** IV
3. (a) downward   **(b)** right   **4.** principal, interest rate per year, number of times interest is compounded per year, number of years, amount after t years; $112.65   **5.** horizontal, 0; 0

6. horizontal, 3; 3   **7.** 2.000, 22.195, 0.063, 1.516
9. 0.192, 0.070, 15.588, 1.552

11.

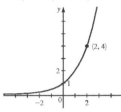

13.

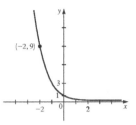

15.

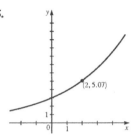

17.

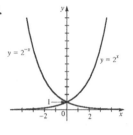

19.

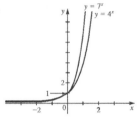

21. $f(x) = 3^x$ **23.** $f(x) = \left(\frac{1}{4}\right)^x$ **25.** ll
27. $\mathbb{R}, (-3, \infty), y = -3$ **29.** $\mathbb{R}, (-\infty, 0), y = 0$

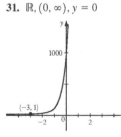

31. $\mathbb{R}, (0, \infty), y = 0$ **33.** $\mathbb{R}, (1, \infty), y = 1$

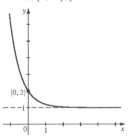

35. $\mathbb{R}, (-\infty, 2), y = 2$

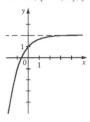

37. $\mathbb{R}, (1, \infty), y = 1$

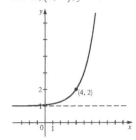

39. $\mathbb{R}, (-\infty, 1), y = 1$

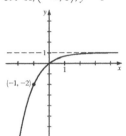

41. (a)

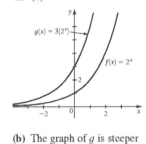

(b) The graph of g is steeper than that of f.

43.

x	0	1	2	3	4	6	8	10
$f(x)$	0	1	8	27	64	216	512	1000
$g(x)$	1	3	9	27	81	729	6561	59,049

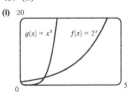

45. (a)

(i) 20

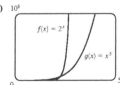

(ii) 10^7

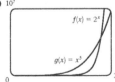

(iii) 10^8

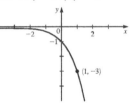

The graph of f ultimately increases much more quickly than that of g.

(b) 1.2, 22.4

47.

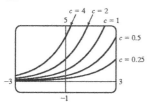

The larger the value of c, the more rapidly the graph increases.

49. (a) Increasing on $(-\infty, 0.50)$; decreasing on $(0.50, \infty)$
(b) $(0, 1.78)$
53. (a) $N(t) = 1500 \cdot 2^t$ **(b)** 25,165,824,000
55. \$5203.71, \$5415.71, \$5636.36, \$5865.99, \$6104.98, \$6353.71
57. (a) \$11,605.41 **(b)** \$13,468.55 **(c)** \$15,630.80
59. (a) \$519.02 **(b)** \$538.75 **(c)** \$726.23
61. \$7678.96 **63.** 8.30%

SECTION 4.2 ■ PAGE 377

1. natural; 2.71828
2. principal, interest rate per year, number of years; amount after t years; \$112.75
3. 2.718, 23.141, 0.050, 4.113

5.

x	y
-2	0.20
-1	0.55
-0.5	0.91
0	1.5
0.5	2.47
1	4.08
2	11.08

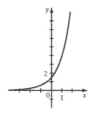

7. $\mathbb{R}, (2, \infty), y = 2$

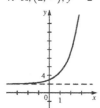

9. $\mathbb{R}, (-\infty, 0), y = 0$

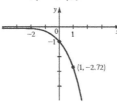

11. $\mathbb{R}, (-1, \infty), y = -1$

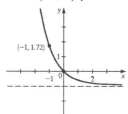

13. $\mathbb{R}, (0, \infty), y = 0$

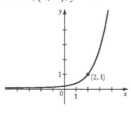

15. $\mathbb{R}, (-3, \infty), y = -3$

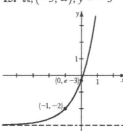

17. (a)

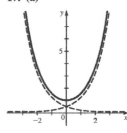

19. (a)

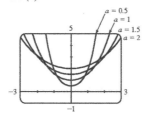

(b) The larger the value of a, the wider the graph.
21. Local minimum $(0.37, 0.69)$ **23.** 27.4 mg
25. (a) 0 **(b)** 113.8 ft/s, 155.6 ft/s
(c)

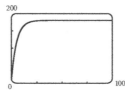

(d) 180 ft/s
27. (a) 100 **(b)** 482, 999, 1168 **(c)** 1200
29. (a) 11.79 billion, 11.97 billion
(b)

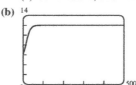

(c) 12 billion

31. \$7213.18, \$7432.86, \$7659.22, \$7892.48, \$8132.84, \$8380.52
33. (a) \$2145.02 **(b)** \$2300.55 **(c)** \$3043.92
35. (a) \$768.05 **(b)** \$769.22 **(c)** \$769.82 **(d)** \$770.42
37. (a) is best.
39. (a) $A(t) = 5000e^{0.09t}$ **(b)**

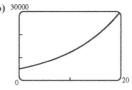

(c) After 17.88 years

SECTION 4.3 ▪ PAGE 387

1. x

x	10^3	10^2	10^1	10^0	10^{-1}	10^{-2}	10^{-3}	$10^{1/2}$
$\log x$	3	2	1	0	-1	-2	-3	$\frac{1}{2}$

2. $9; 1, 0, -1, 2, \frac{1}{2}$ **3.** (a) $\log_5 125 = 3$ (b) $5^2 = 25$
4. (a) III   (b) II   (c) I   (d) IV
5. vertical, 0   **6.** vertical, 1

7.

Logarithmic form	Exponential form
$\log_8 8 = 1$	$8^1 = 8$
$\log_8 64 = 2$	$8^2 = 64$
$\log_8 4 = \frac{2}{3}$	$8^{2/3} = 4$
$\log_8 512 = 3$	$8^3 = 512$
$\log_8\left(\frac{1}{8}\right) = -1$	$8^{-1} = \frac{1}{8}$
$\log_8\left(\frac{1}{64}\right) = -2$	$8^{-2} = \frac{1}{64}$

9. (a) $3^4 = 81$ (b) $3^0 = 1$
11. (a) $8^{1/3} = 2$ (b) $10^{-2} = 0.01$
13. (a) $3^x = 5$ (b) $7^2 = 3y$
15. (a) $e^{3y} = 5$ (b) $e^{-1} = t + 1$
17. (a) $\log_{10} 10{,}000 = 4$ (b) $\log_5\left(\frac{1}{25}\right) = -2$
19. (a) $\log_8\left(\frac{1}{8}\right) = -1$ (b) $\log_2\left(\frac{1}{8}\right) = -3$
21. (a) $\log_4 70 = x$ (b) $\log_3 w = 5$
23. (a) $\ln 2 = x$ (b) $\ln y = 3$
25. (a) 1   (b) 0   (c) 5   **27.** (a) 2   (b) 2   (c) 10
29. (a) -3 (b) $\frac{1}{2}$ (c) -1 **31.** (a) 5   (b) 27   (c) 10
33. (a) $-\frac{2}{3}$ (b) 4   (c) -1 **35.** (a) 64   (b) -2
37. (a) e^3 (b) 2   **39.** (a) -2 (b) 32
41. (a) -1 (b) $\frac{1}{1000}$ **43.** (a) 2   (b) 4
45. (a) 0.3010   (b) 1.5465   (c) -0.1761
47. (a) 1.6094   (b) 3.2308   (c) 1.0051
49.

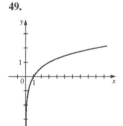

51.

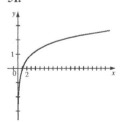

53. $y = \log_5 x$ **55.** $y = \log_9 x$ **57.** I
59.

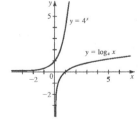

61. $(-\infty, 0), \mathbb{R}, x = 0$

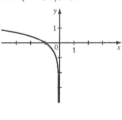

63. $(4, \infty), \mathbb{R}, x = 4$

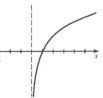

65. $(-5, \infty), \mathbb{R}, x = -5$

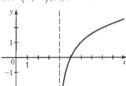

67. $(0, \infty), \mathbb{R}, x = 0$

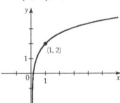

69. $(1, \infty), \mathbb{R}, x = 1$

71. $(0, \infty), [0, \infty), x = 0$

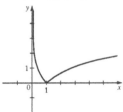

73. $(-3, \infty)$ **75.** $(-\infty, -1) \cup (1, \infty)$ **77.** $(0, 2)$
79.

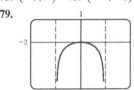

domain $(-1, 1)$
vertical asymptotes $x = 1$,
$x = -1$
local maximum $(0, 0)$

81.

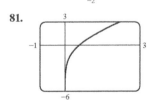

domain $(0, \infty)$
vertical asymptote $x = 0$
no maximum or minimum

83.

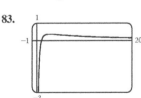

domain $(0, \infty)$
vertical asymptote $x = 0$
horizontal asymptote $y = 0$
local maximum
$\approx (2.72, 0.37)$

85. $(f \circ g)(x) = 2^{x+1}, (-\infty, \infty); (g \circ f)(x) = 2^x + 1, (-\infty, \infty)$
87. $(f \circ g)(x) = \log_2(x - 2), (2, \infty);$
$(g \circ f)(x) = \log_2 x - 2, (0, \infty)$
89. The graph of f grows more slowly than g.

91. (a)

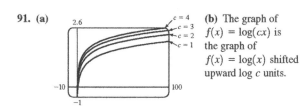

(b) The graph of $f(x) = \log(cx)$ is the graph of $f(x) = \log(x)$ shifted upward $\log c$ units.

93. (a) $(1, \infty)$ **(b)** $f^{-1}(x) = 10^{2^x}$

95. (a) $f^{-1}(x) = \log_2\left(\dfrac{x}{1-x}\right)$ **(b)** $(0, 1)$ **97.** 2602 years

99. 11.6 years, 9.9 years, 8.7 years **101.** 5.32, 4.32

SECTION 4.4 ▪ PAGE 394

1. sum; $\log_5 25 + \log_5 125 = 2 + 3$
2. difference; $\log_5 25 - \log_5 125 = 2 - 3$
3. power; $10 \cdot \log_5 25 = 10 \cdot 2$ **4.** $2 \log x + \log y - \log z$
5. $\log\left(\dfrac{x^2 y}{z}\right)$ **6. (a)** 10, e; Change of Base;

$\log_7 12 = \dfrac{\log 12}{\log 7} \approx 1.277$ **(b)** Yes **7. (a)** False

(b) True **8. (a)** True **(b)** False **9.** 4 **11.** 2 **13.** 1
15. $\frac{1}{2}$ **17.** 3 **19.** 200 **21.** 4 **23.** $\log_3 8 + \log_3 x$
25. $\log_3 2 + \log_3 x + \log_3 y$ **27.** $3 \ln a$
29. $10(\log_2 x + \log_2 y)$ **31.** $\log_2 A + 2 \log_2 B$
33. $\log_3 2 + \log_3 x - \log_3 y$ **35.** $\log_5 3 + 2 \log_5 x - 3 \log_5 y$
37. $\frac{1}{2} + \frac{5}{2}\log_3 x - \log_3 y$ **39.** $3 \log x + 4 \log y - 6 \log z$
41. $\frac{1}{2}\ln(x^4 + 2)$ **43.** $\ln x + \frac{1}{2}(\ln y - \ln z)$ **45.** $\frac{1}{4}\log(x^2 + y^2)$
47. $\frac{1}{2}[\log(x^2 + 4) - \log(x^2 + 1) - 2\log(x^3 - 7)]$
49. $\log_4 294$ **51.** $\log\dfrac{x^2}{(x+1)^3}$ **53.** $\log\left(\dfrac{x^4(x-1)^2}{\sqrt[3]{x^2+1}}\right)$
55. $\ln\dfrac{a^2 - b^2}{c^2}$ **57.** $\log\left(\dfrac{x^2}{x-3}\right)$ **59.** 2.321928
61. 2.523719 **63.** 0.493008 **65.** 3.482892
67.

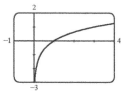

73. (a) $P = c/W^k$ **(b)** 1866, 64
75. (a) $M = -2.5 \log B + 2.5 \log B_0$

SECTION 4.5 ▪ PAGE 404

1. (a) $e^x = 25$ **(b)** $x = \ln 25$ **(c)** 3.219
2. (a) $\log 3(x - 2) = \log x$ **(b)** $3(x - 2) = x$ **(c)** 3 **3.** 4
5. $\frac{3}{2}$ **7.** -3 **9.** $-1, 1$ **11. (a)** $2 \log 5$ **(b)** 1.397940
13. (a) $-\frac{1}{5}\ln 10$ **(b)** -0.460517 **15. (a)** $1 - \dfrac{\log 3}{\log 2}$
(b) -0.584963 **17. (a)** $\ln\left(\frac{10}{3}\right)$ **(b)** 1.203973
19. (a) $\dfrac{\ln(10/3)}{12 \ln(41/40)}$ **(b)** 4.063202 **21. (a)** $\dfrac{1 - \ln 2}{4}$
(b) 0.076713 **23. (a)** $\dfrac{5}{7} - \dfrac{\ln 15}{7 \ln 2}$ **(b)** 0.156158

25. (a) $\dfrac{14 \log 0.1}{\log 3}$ **(b)** -29.342646
27. (a) $\frac{1}{5}\log\left(\frac{5}{4}\right)$ **(b)** 0.019382
29. (a) $\dfrac{1 - \ln 12}{4}$ **(b)** -0.371227
31. (a) $\dfrac{\ln(50/3)}{2 \ln 2}$ **(b)** 2.029447
33. (a) $\dfrac{\log 4}{\log(5/4)}$ **(b)** 6.212567
35. (a) $-\dfrac{\log 18}{\log(8/3)}$ **(b)** -2.946865
37. (a) $-\ln 11.5$ **(b)** -2.442347 **39.** $\ln 2 \approx 0.6931, 0$
41. $\frac{1}{2}\ln 3 \approx 0.5493$ **43.** 1 **45.** ± 1 **47.** $0, \frac{4}{3}$ **49.** 5
51. 2, 4 **53.** 5 **55.** $e^{10} \approx 22{,}026$ **57.** 0.01 **59.** $\frac{95}{3}$
61. -7 **63.** 4 **65.** 6 **67.** $\frac{13}{12}$ **69.** 2.21 **71.** 0.00, 1.14
73. -0.57 **75.** 0.36 **77.** $1/\sqrt{5} \approx 0.4472$
79. $2 < x < 4$ or $7 < x < 9$ **81.** $\log 2 < x < \log 5$

83. $f^{-1}(x) = \dfrac{\ln x}{2 \ln 2}$ **85.** $f^{-1}(x) = 2^x + 1$ **87.** $\frac{3}{2}$

89. (a) $\$6435.09$ **(b)** 8.24 years
91. 6.33 years **93.** 8.15 years **95.** 13 days
97. (a) 7337 **(b)** 1.73 years
99. (a) $P = P_0 e^{-h/k}$ **(b)** 56.47 kPa
101. (a) $t = -\frac{5}{13}\ln\left(1 - \frac{13}{60}I\right)$ **(b)** 0.218 s

SECTION 4.6 ▪ PAGE 414

1. (a) $n(t) = 10 \cdot 2^{2t/3}$ **(b)** 1.06×10^8 **(c)** 14.9
3. (a) 3125 **(b)** 317,480
(c)

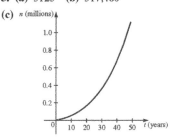

5. (a) $n(t) = 18{,}000e^{0.08t}$ **(b)** 34,100 **(c)** 4.1
(d)

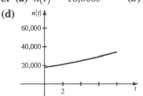

7. (a) 233 million **(b)** 181 million
9. (a) $n(t) = 112{,}000 \cdot 2^{t/18}$ **(b)** $n(t) = 112{,}000e^{0.0385t}$
(c) **(d)** 38.9 years

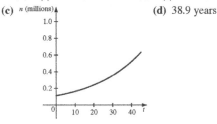

11. (a) 20,000 (b) $n(t) = 20,000e^{0.1096t}$
(c) About 48,000 (d) 14.7 years
13. (a) $n(t) = 8600e^{0.1508t}$ (b) About 11,600 (c) 4.6 h
15. (a) $n(t) = 29.76e^{0.012936t}$ million (b) 53.6 years
(c) 38.55 million **17.** (a) $m(t) = 22 \cdot 2^{-t/1600}$
(b) $m(t) = 22e^{-0.000433t}$ (c) 3.9 mg (d) 463.4
19. 18 years **21.** 149 h **23.** 3560 years **25.** (a) 210°F
(b) 153°F (c) 28 min **27.** (a) 137°F (b) About 2 h

SECTION 4.7 ■ PAGE 421

1. (a) 2.3 (b) 3.5 (c) 8.3 **3.** (a) 10^{-3} M (b) 3.2×10^{-7} M
5. $4.8 \leq$ pH ≤ 6.4 **7.** (a) 6.31×10^{-4} M, 1.26×10^{-3} M
(b) California **9.** (a) 5.49 (b) 6.3 cm **11.** $\log 20 \approx 1.3$
13. Six times as intense **15.** 73 dB **17.** 10^{-5} W/m²
19. (a) 75 dB (b) 10^{-3} W/m² (c) 32.3

CHAPTER 4 REVIEW ■ PAGE 424

1. 0.089, 9.739, 55.902 **3.** 0.269, 1.472, 12.527
5. $\mathbb{R}, (0, \infty), y = 0$ **7.** $\mathbb{R}, (3, \infty), y = 3$

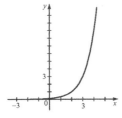   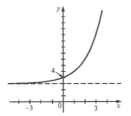

9. $\mathbb{R}, (1, \infty), y = 1$ **11.** $(1, \infty), \mathbb{R}, x = 1$

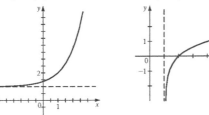

13. $(0, \infty), \mathbb{R}, x = 0$ **15.** $(0, \infty), \mathbb{R}, x = 0$

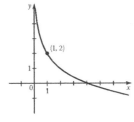   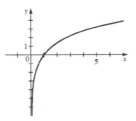

17. $\left(-\infty, \frac{1}{2}\right)$ **19.** $(-\infty, -2) \cup (2, \infty)$ **21.** $2^{10} = 1024$
23. $10^y = x$ **25.** $\log_2 64 = 6$ **27.** $\log 74 = x$ **29.** 7 **31.** 45
33. 6 **35.** -3 **37.** $\frac{1}{2}$ **39.** 2 **41.** 92 **43.** $\frac{2}{3}$
45. $\log A + 2 \log B + 3 \log C$
47. $\frac{1}{2}[\ln(x - 1) + \ln(x + 1) - \ln(x^2 + 1)]$
49. $2 \log_5 x + \frac{3}{2} \log_5(1 - 5x) -$
$\quad \frac{1}{2}[\log_5 x + \log_5(x - 1) + \log_5(x + 1)]$
51. $\log 96$ **53.** $\log_2\left(\dfrac{(x - y)^{3/2}}{(x^2 + y^2)^2}\right)$ **55.** $\log\left(\dfrac{x^2 - 4}{\sqrt{x^2 + 4}}\right)$

57. 5 **59.** $\dfrac{1}{3}\left[\dfrac{\log 7}{\log 2} + 5\right] \approx 2.60$ **61.** $\dfrac{\log(4/243)}{\log 36} \approx -1.15$
63. $-4, 2$ **65.** 3 **67.** -15 **69.** 9 **71.** 0.430618
73. 2.303600
75.

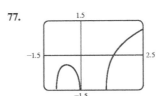

vertical asymptote
$x = -2$
horizontal asymptote
$y \approx 2.72$
no maximum or minimum

77.

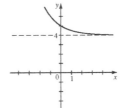

vertical asymptotes
$x = -1, x = 0, x = 1$
local maximum
$\approx (-0.58, -0.41)$

79. 2.42 **81.** $0.16 < x < 3.15$
83. Increasing on $(-\infty, 0)$ and $(1.10, \infty)$, decreasing on $(0, 1.10)$
85. 1.953445 **87.** -0.579352 **89.** $\log_4 258$
91. (a) \$16,081.15 (b) \$16,178.18 (c) \$16,197.64
(d) \$16,198.31 **93.** 1.83 years **95.** 4.341%
97. (a) $n(t) = 30e^{0.15t}$ (b) 55 (c) 19 years
99. (a) 9.97 mg (b) 1.39×10^5 years
101. (a) $n(t) = 150e^{-0.0004359t}$ (b) 97.0 mg (c) 2520 years
103. (a) $n(t) = 1500e^{0.1515t}$ (b) 7940 **105.** 7.9, basic
107. 8.0

CHAPTER 4 TEST ■ PAGE 427

1. (a) $\mathbb{R}, (4, \infty), y = 4$ (b) $(-3, \infty), \mathbb{R}, x = -3$

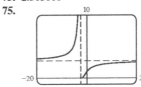   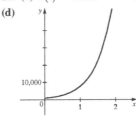

2. (a) $\left(\frac{3}{2}, \infty\right)$ (b) $(-\infty, -1) \cup (1, \infty)$
3. (a) $\log_6 25 = 2x$ (b) $e^3 = A$
4. (a) 36 (b) 3 (c) $\frac{3}{2}$ (d) 3 (e) $\frac{2}{3}$ (f) 2
5. (a) $\log x + 3 \log y - 2 \log z$ (b) $\frac{1}{2} \ln x - \frac{1}{2} \ln y$
(c) $\frac{1}{3}[\log(x + 2) - 4 \log x - \log(x^2 + 4)]$
6. (a) $\log(ab^2)$ (b) $\ln(x - 5)$ (c) $\log_2 \dfrac{3\sqrt{x + 1}}{x^3}$

7. (a) 25 (b) 1, 2 (c) 11.13 (d) 5.39
8. (a) 500 (b) $\frac{2}{3}$ (c) $3 - e^{4/5} \approx 0.774$ (d) 2 **9.** 1.326
10. (a) $n(t) = 1000e^{2.07944t}$ (b) 22,600 (c) 1.3
(d)

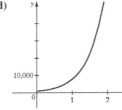

11. (a) $A(t) = 12,000\left(1 + \dfrac{0.056}{12}\right)^{12t}$ **(b)** $14,195.06

(c) 9.12 years   **12. (a)** $m(t) = 3 \cdot 2^{-t/10}$ **(b)** $m(t) = 3e^{-0.0693t}$
(c) 0.047 g   **(d)** after 3.6 min   **13.** 1995 times more intense

FOCUS ON MODELING ▪ PAGE 434

1. (a)

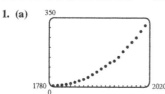

(b) $y = ab^t$, where $a = 3.334926 \times 10^{-15}$, $b = 1.019844$, and
y is the population in millions in the year t **(c)** 577 million
(d) 196 million

3. (a)

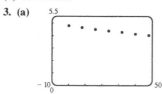

(b) $y = ab^t$, where $a = 4.79246$ and $b = 0.99642$ **(c)** 192.8 h
5. (a) $y = at^b$, where $a = 49.70030$ and $b = -0.15437$;
$y = ab^t$, where $a = 44.82418$ and $b = 0.99317$

(b)

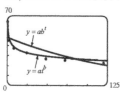

(c) The power function
7. $y = ab^x$, where $a = 2.414$ and $b = 1.05452$
9. (a)

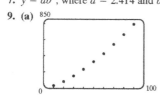

(b)

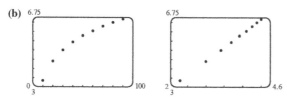

(c) The power function
(d) $y = ax^b$, where $a = 0.893421326$ and $b = 1.50983$

CHAPTER 10
SECTION 10.1 ▪ PAGE 724

1. x, y; equation; $(2, 1)$
2. substitution, elimination, graphical
3. no, infinitely many
4. infinitely many; $1 - t$; $(1, 0)$, $(-3, 4)$, $(5, -4)$
5. $(3, 2)$ **7.** $(3, 1)$ **9.** $(2, 1)$ **11.** $(-3, 2)$ **13.** $(-2, 3)$
15. $(2, -2)$ **17.** No solution

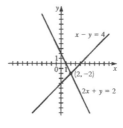   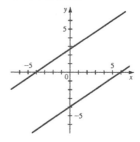

19. Infinitely many solutions

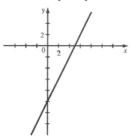

21. $(2, 2)$ **23.** $(3, -1)$ **25.** $(2, 1)$ **27.** $(3, 5)$
29. $(1, 3)$ **31.** $(6, -6)$ **33.** $(10, -9)$ **35.** $(2, 1)$
37. No solution   **39.** $\left(x, \frac{1}{3}x - \frac{5}{3}\right)$ **41.** $\left(x, 3 - \frac{3}{2}x\right)$
43. $(-3, -7)$ **45.** $\left(x, 5 - \frac{5}{6}x\right)$ **47.** $(5, 10)$
49. No solution   **51.** $(3.87, 2.74)$ **53.** $(61.00, 20.00)$
55. $\left(-\dfrac{1}{a - 1}, \dfrac{1}{a - 1}\right)$ **57.** $\left(\dfrac{1}{a + b}, \dfrac{1}{a + b}\right)$ **59.** 22, 12

61. 5 dimes, 9 quarters   **63.** 200 gallons of regular gas,
80 gallons of premium gas   **65.** Plane's speed 120 mi/h,
wind speed 30 mi/h   **67.** 200 g of A, 40 g of B
69. 25%, 10%   **71.** $14,000 at 5%, $6,000 at 8%
73. John $2\frac{1}{4}$ h, Mary $2\frac{1}{2}$ h   **75.** 25

SECTION 10.2 ▪ PAGE 732

1. $x + 3z = 1$ **2.** -3; $4y - 5z = -4$ **3.** Linear
5. Nonlinear   **7.** $(5, 1, -2)$ **9.** $(4, 0, 3)$ **11.** $\left(5, 2, -\frac{1}{2}\right)$
13. $\begin{cases} 3x + y + z = 4 \\ \quad\;\; -y + z = -1 \\ x - 2y - z = -1 \end{cases}$ **15.** $\begin{cases} 2x + y - 3z = 5 \\ 2x + 3y + z = 13 \\ \quad\quad -8y + 8z = -8 \end{cases}$
17. $(2, 1, -3)$ **19.** $(1, -1, 5)$ **21.** $(1, 2, 1)$ **23.** $(5, 0, 1)$
25. $(0, 1, 2)$ **27.** $\left(\frac{1}{4}, \frac{1}{2}, -\frac{1}{2}\right)$ **29.** No solution

31. No solution **33.** $(3 - t, -3 + 2t, t)$

35. $\left(2 - 2t, -\frac{2}{3} + \frac{4}{3}t, t\right)$ **37.** $(1, -1, 1, 2)$

39. \$30,000 in short-term, \$30,000 in intermediate-term, \$40,000 in long-term

41. 250 acres corn, 500 acres wheat, 450 acres soybeans

43. Impossible

45. 50 Midnight Mango, 60 Tropical Torrent, 30 Pineapple Power

47. 1500 shares of A, 1200 shares of B, 1000 shares of C

SECTION 10.3 ▪ PAGE 739

1. (iii) **2.** (ii) **3.** $\dfrac{A}{x - 1} + \dfrac{B}{x + 2}$

5. $\dfrac{A}{x - 2} + \dfrac{B}{(x - 2)^2} + \dfrac{C}{x + 4}$

7. $\dfrac{A}{x - 3} + \dfrac{Bx + C}{x^2 + 4}$ **9.** $\dfrac{Ax + B}{x^2 + 1} + \dfrac{Cx + D}{x^2 + 2}$

11. $\dfrac{A}{x} + \dfrac{B}{2x - 5} + \dfrac{C}{(2x - 5)^2} + \dfrac{D}{(2x - 5)^3} +$

$\dfrac{Ex + F}{x^2 + 2x + 5} + \dfrac{Gx + H}{(x^2 + 2x + 5)^2}$

13. $\dfrac{1}{x - 1} - \dfrac{1}{x + 1}$ **15.** $\dfrac{1}{x - 1} - \dfrac{1}{x + 4}$

17. $\dfrac{2}{x - 3} - \dfrac{2}{x + 3}$ **19.** $\dfrac{1}{x - 2} - \dfrac{1}{x + 2}$

21. $\dfrac{3}{x - 4} - \dfrac{2}{x + 2}$ **23.** $\dfrac{-\frac{1}{2}}{2x - 1} + \dfrac{\frac{3}{2}}{4x - 3}$

25. $\dfrac{2}{x - 2} + \dfrac{3}{x + 2} - \dfrac{1}{2x - 1}$

27. $\dfrac{2}{x + 1} - \dfrac{1}{x} + \dfrac{1}{x^2}$ **29.** $\dfrac{1}{2x + 3} - \dfrac{3}{(2x + 3)^2}$

31. $\dfrac{2}{x} - \dfrac{1}{x^3} - \dfrac{2}{x + 2}$

33. $\dfrac{4}{x + 2} - \dfrac{4}{x - 1} + \dfrac{2}{(x - 1)^2} + \dfrac{1}{(x - 1)^3}$

35. $\dfrac{3}{x + 2} - \dfrac{1}{(x + 2)^2} - \dfrac{1}{(x + 3)^2}$

37. $\dfrac{x + 1}{x^2 + 3} - \dfrac{1}{x}$ **39.** $\dfrac{2x - 5}{x^2 + x + 2} + \dfrac{5}{x^2 + 1}$

41. $\dfrac{1}{x^2 + 1} - \dfrac{x + 2}{(x^2 + 1)^2} + \dfrac{1}{x}$

43. $x^2 + \dfrac{3}{x - 2} - \dfrac{x + 1}{x^2 + 1}$

45. $A = \dfrac{a + b}{2}, B = \dfrac{a - b}{2}$

SECTION 10.4 ▪ PAGE 743

1. $(4, 8), (-2, 2)$ **3.** $(4, 16), (-3, 9)$ **5.** $(2, -2), (-2, 2)$

7. $(-25, 5), (-25, -5)$ **9.** $(-3, 4) (3, 4)$

11. $(-2, -1), (-2, 1), (2, -1), (2, 1)$

13. $(-1, \sqrt{2}), (-1, -\sqrt{2}), \left(\frac{1}{2}, \sqrt{\frac{7}{2}}\right), \left(\frac{1}{2}, -\sqrt{\frac{7}{2}}\right)$

15. $(2, 4), \left(-\frac{5}{2}, \frac{7}{4}\right)$ **17.** $(0, 0), (1, -1), (-2, -4)$

19. $(4, 0)$ **21.** $(-2, -2)$ **23.** $(6, 2), (-2, -6)$

25. No solution

27. $(\sqrt{5}, 2), (\sqrt{5}, -2), (-\sqrt{5}, 2), (-\sqrt{5}, -2)$

29. $\left(3, -\frac{1}{2}\right), \left(-3, -\frac{1}{2}\right)$ **31.** $\left(\frac{1}{5}, \frac{1}{3}\right)$ **33.** $(2.00, 20.00),$

$(-8.00, 0)$ **35.** $(-4.51, 2.17), (4.91, -0.97)$

37. $(1.23, 3.87), (-0.35, -4.21)$ **39.** $(-2.30, -0.70),$

$(0.48, -1.19)$ **41.** $(\sqrt{10}, 10)$ **43.** $(-5, -8), (8, 5)$

45. 12 cm by 15 cm **47.** 15, 20

49. $(400.50, 200.25), 447.77$ m **51.** $(12, 8)$

SECTION 10.5 ▪ PAGE 752

1. 2, 3; yes

2. equation; $y = x + 1$; test

Test point	Inequality $y \leq x + 1$	Conclusion
$(0, 0)$	$0 \overset{?}{\leq} 0 + 1$ ✓	Part of graph
$(0, 2)$	$2 \overset{?}{\leq} 0 + 1$ ✗	Not part of graph

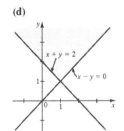

3. 2, 3; yes

4. (a)

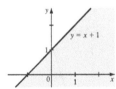

(b)

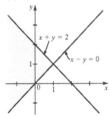

(c)

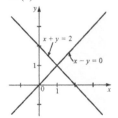

(d)

5. $(-1, -2), (1, -2)$ **7.** $(1, 2), (1, 1)$

9.

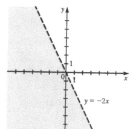

11.

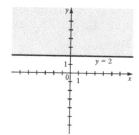

13.

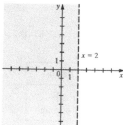

15.

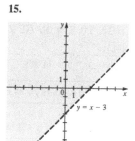

17.

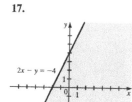

19.

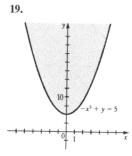

21.

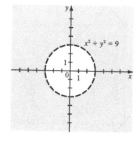

23.

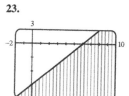

25.

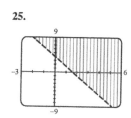

27. $y \le \frac{1}{2}x - 1$ **29.** $x^2 + y^2 > 4$

31.

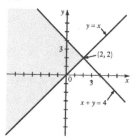

Not bounded

33.

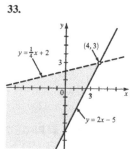

Not bounded

35.

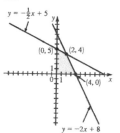

Bounded

37.

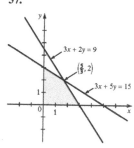

Bounded

39.

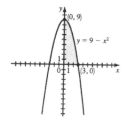

Bounded

41.

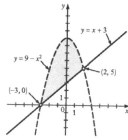

Bounded

43.

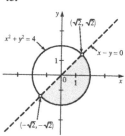

Bounded

45.

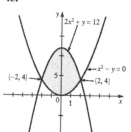

Bounded

47.

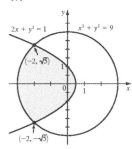

Bounded

49.

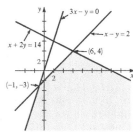

Not bounded

65.

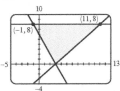

67.

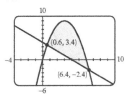

69. (a) $\begin{cases} x + \quad y \le 500 \\ 90x + 50y \le 40{,}000 \\ 30x + 80y \le 30{,}000 \\ x \ge 0, \quad y \ge 0 \end{cases}$

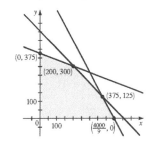

(b) Yes **(c)** No

51.

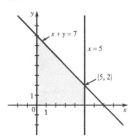

Bounded

53.

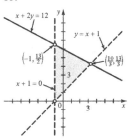

Bounded

55.

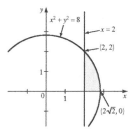

Bounded

57.

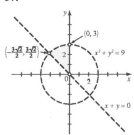

Bounded

71. x = number of fiction books
y = number of nonfiction books

$\begin{cases} x + y \le 100 \\ 20 \le y, \quad x \ge y \\ x \ge 0, \quad y \ge 0 \end{cases}$

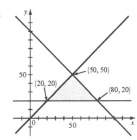

59.

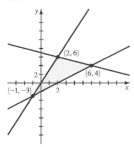

Bounded

63.

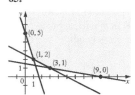

Not bounded

61.

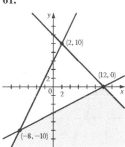

Not bounded

73. x = number of standard packages
y = number of deluxe packages

$\begin{cases} \frac{1}{4}x + \frac{5}{8}y \le 80 \\ \frac{3}{4}x + \frac{3}{8}y \le 90 \\ x \ge 0, \quad y \ge 0 \end{cases}$

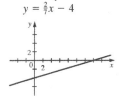

CHAPTER 10 REVIEW ■ PAGE 757

1. $(2, 1)$

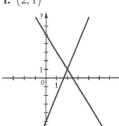

3. x = any number
$y = \frac{2}{7}x - 4$

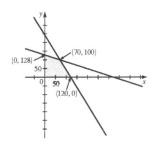

5. No solution

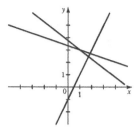

7. $(-3, 3), (2, 8)$ **9.** $\left(\frac{16}{7}, -\frac{14}{3}\right)$ **11.** $(21.41, -15.93)$
13. $(11.94, -1.39), (12.07, 1.44)$ **15.** $(1, -1, 5)$
17. $(1, 1, 2)$ **19.** No solution   **21.** $(-4t + 1, -t - 1, t)$
23. $\left(\frac{2}{11}, \frac{48}{11}, -\frac{60}{11}, -\frac{40}{11}\right)$
25. Siobhan is 9 years old; Kieran is 13 years old.
27. 12 nickels, 30 dimes, 8 quarters

29. $\dfrac{2}{x - 5} + \dfrac{1}{x + 3}$ **31.** $\dfrac{-4}{x} + \dfrac{4}{x - 1} + \dfrac{-2}{(x - 1)^2}$

33. $\dfrac{-1}{x} + \dfrac{x + 2}{x^2 + 1}$ **35.** $\dfrac{3}{x^2 + 2} - \dfrac{x}{(x^2 + 2)^2}$

37. $(2, 1)$ **39.** $\left(-\frac{1}{2}, \frac{7}{4}\right), (2, -2)$ **41.** $x + y^2 \le 4$
43.   **45.**

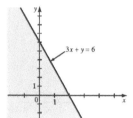   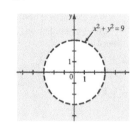

47.   **49.**

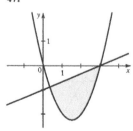   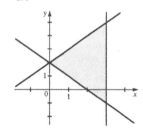

51.   **53.**

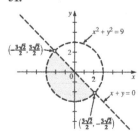   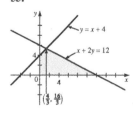

Bounded   Bounded

55. $x = \dfrac{b + c}{2}, y = \dfrac{a + c}{2}, z = \dfrac{a + b}{2}$ **57.** 2, 3

CHAPTER 10 TEST ▪ PAGE 759

1. **(a)** Linear   **(b)** $(-2, 3)$
2. **(a)** Nonlinear   **(b)** $(1, -2), \left(\frac{5}{3}, 0\right)$
3. **(a)** Nonlinear   **(b)** $\left(-\sqrt{10}, -3\sqrt{10}\right), \left(\sqrt{10}, 3\sqrt{10}\right)$
4. $(-0.55, -0.78), (0.43, -0.29), (2.12, 0.56)$
5. **(a)** $(2, 1, -1)$ **(b)** Neither
6. **(a)** No solution   **(b)** Inconsistent
7. **(a)** $\left(\frac{1}{7}(t + 1), \frac{1}{7}(9t + 2), t\right)$ **(b)** Dependent
8. **(a)** $(10, 0, 1)$ **(b)** Neither
9. Wind 60 km/h, airplane 300 km/h
10. Coffee $1.50, juice $1.75, doughnut $0.75
11.   **12.**

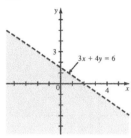   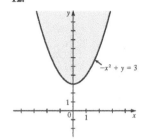

13.   **14.**

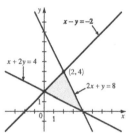   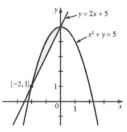

15. $\dfrac{1}{x - 1} + \dfrac{1}{(x - 1)^2} - \dfrac{1}{x + 2}$ **16.** $-\dfrac{1}{x} + \dfrac{x + 2}{x^2 + 3}$

FOCUS ON MODELING ▪ PAGE 764

1. 198, 195
3.   maximum 161
                         minimum 135

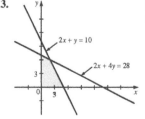

5. 3 tables, 34 chairs   **7.** 30 grapefruit crates, 30 orange crates
9. 15 Pasadena to Santa Monica, 3 Pasadena to El Toro,
0 Long Beach to Santa Monica, 16 Long Beach to El Toro
11. 90 standard, 40 deluxe   **13.** $7500 in municipal bonds,
$2500 in bank certificates, $2000 in high-risk bonds
15. 4 games, 32 educational, 0 utility

1. What is an algebra model for a real-world situation? If Shellie's wages are $12 an hour, find a model for the amount W that Shellie earns after working x hours.

   A model is a mathematical representation of a real-world situation. A model for the amount W that Shellie earns after working x hours is $W = 12x$.

2. (a) What does the set of natural numbers consist of? What does the set of integers consist of? Give an example of an integer that is not a natural number.

   The set of natural numbers consists of the counting numbers $1, 2, 3, \ldots$. The set of integers consists of the natural numbers together with their negatives and 0. The number -1 is an integer that is not a natural number.

   (b) What does the set of rational numbers consist of? Give an example of a rational number that is not an integer.

   The set of rational numbers is constructed by taking all ratios of nonzero integers, and then adding the number 0. The number $2/3$ is a rational number that is not an integer.

   (c) What does the set of irrational numbers consist of? Give an example of an irrational number.

   The set of irrational numbers consists of all those numbers that cannot be expressed as a ratio of integers. The number $\sqrt{5}$ is an irrational number.

   (d) What does the set of real numbers consist of?

   The set of real numbers consists of all the rational numbers along with all the irrational numbers.

3. A property of real numbers is given. State the property and give an example in which the property is used.

   (i) Commutative Property:

   $a + b = b + a$ and $ab = ba$. For example, $5 + 8 = 8 + 5$ and $5 \cdot 8 = 8 \cdot 5$.

   (ii) Associative Property:

   $(a + b) + c = a + (b + c)$ and $(ab)c = a(bc)$. For example, $(2 + 5) + 3 = 2 + (5 + 3)$ and $(2 \cdot 5)3 = 2(5 \cdot 3)$.

   (iii) Distributive Property:

   $a(b + c) = ab + ac$ and $(b + c)a = ab + ac$. For example, $7(1 + 4) = 7 \cdot 1 + 7 \cdot 4$ and $(2 + 5)9 = 9 \cdot 2 + 9 \cdot 5$.

4. Explain the difference between the open interval (a, b) and the closed interval $[a, b]$. Give an example of an interval that is neither open nor closed.

   The open interval excludes the endpoints a and b, and the closed interval includes the endpoints a and b. The interval $(0, 1]$ is neither open nor closed.

5. Give the formula for finding the distance between two real numbers a and b. Use the formula to find the distance between 103 and -52.

   The distance between a and b is $|b - a|$. The distance between 103 and -52 is $|(-52) - 103| = 155$.

6. Suppose $a \neq 0$ is any real number.

   (a) In the expression a^n, which is the base and which is the exponent?

   The base is a and the exponent is n.

   (b) What does a^n mean if n is a positive integer? What does 6^5 mean?

   The expression a^n means to multiply a by itself n times. For example, $6^5 = 6 \cdot 6 \cdot 6 \cdot 6 \cdot 6$.

   (c) What does a^{-n} mean if n is a positive integer? What does 3^{-2} mean?

   The expression a^{-n} means the reciprocal of a^n, that is, $a^{-n} = \dfrac{1}{a^n}$. For example, $3^{-2} = \dfrac{1}{3^2}$.

   (d) What does a^n mean if n is zero?

   Any number raised to the 0 power is always equal to 1.

   (e) If m and n are positive integers, what does $a^{m/n}$ mean? What does $4^{3/2}$ mean?

   The expression $a^{m/n}$ means the nth root of the mth power of a. So $4^{3/2}$ means that you take the square root of 4 and then raise it to the third power: $4^{3/2} = 8$.

7. State the first five Laws of Exponents. Give examples in which you would use each law.

   Law 1: $a^m a^n = a^{m+n}$; $5^2 \cdot 5^6 = 5^8$

   Law 2: $\dfrac{a^m}{a^n} = a^{m-n}$; $\dfrac{3^4}{3^2} = 3^{4-2} = 3^2$

   Law 3: $(a^m)^n = a^{mn}$; $(3^2)^4 = 3^{2 \cdot 4} = 3^8$

   Law 4: $(ab)^n = a^n b^n$; $(3 \cdot 5)^4 = 3^4 \cdot 5^4$

   Law 5: $\left(\dfrac{a}{b}\right)^n = \dfrac{a^n}{b^n}$; $\left(\dfrac{3}{5}\right)^2 = \dfrac{3^2}{5^2}$

8. When you multiply two powers of the same number, what should you do with the exponents? When you raise a power to a new power, what should you do with the exponents?

   When you multiply two powers of the same number, you add the exponents. When you raise a power to a new power, you multiply the two exponents.

9. (a) What does $\sqrt[n]{a} = b$ mean?

   The number b is the nth root of a.

   (b) Is it true that $\sqrt{a^2}$ is equal to $|a|$? Try values for a that are positive and negative.

   Yes, $\sqrt{a^2} = |a|$.

   (c) How many real nth roots does a positive real number have if n is even? If n is odd?

   There are two real nth roots if n is even and one real nth root if n is odd.

   (d) Is $\sqrt[4]{-2}$ a real number? Is $\sqrt[3]{-2}$ a real number? Explain why or why not.

   The expression $\sqrt[4]{-2}$ does not represent a real number because the fourth root of a negative number is undefined. The expression $\sqrt[3]{-2}$ does represent a real number because the third root of a negative number is defined.

   (continued)

10. Explain the steps involved in rationalizing a denominator. What is the logical first step in rationalizing the denominator of the expression $\dfrac{5}{\sqrt{3}}$?

The logical first step in rationalizing $\dfrac{5}{\sqrt{3}}$ is to multiply the numerator and denominator by $\sqrt{3}$:

$$\frac{5}{\sqrt{3}} \cdot \frac{\sqrt{3}}{\sqrt{3}} = \frac{5\sqrt{3}}{3}$$

11. Explain the difference between expanding an expression and factoring an expression.

We use the Distributive Property to expand algebraic expressions, and we reverse this process by factoring an expression as a product of simpler ones.

12. State the Special Product Formulas used for expanding the given expression. Use the appropriate formula to expand $(x + 5)^2$ and $(x + 5)(x - 5)$.

(i) $(a + b)^2 = a^2 + 2ab + b^2$

(ii) $(a - b)^2 = a^2 - 2ab + b^2$

(iii) $(a + b)^3 = a^3 + 3a^2b + 3ab^2 + b^3$

(iv) $(a - b)^3 = a^3 - 3a^2b + 3ab^2 - b^3$

(v) $(a + b)(a - b) = a^2 - b^2$

By (i) we have $(x + 5)^2 = x^2 + 10x + 25$, and by (v) we have $(x + 5)(x - 5) = x^2 - 25$.

13. State the following Special Factoring Formulas. Use the appropriate formula to factor $x^2 - 9$.

(i) Difference of Squares:
$$a^2 - b^2 = (a + b)(a - b)$$

(ii) Perfect Square:
$$a^2 + 2ab + b^2 = (a + b)^2$$

(iii) Sum of Cubes:
$$a^3 + b^3 = (a + b)(a^2 - ab + b^2)$$

By (i) we have $x^2 - 9 = (x + 3)(x - 3)$.

14. If the numerator and the denominator of a rational expression have a common factor, how would you simplify the expression? Simplify the expression $\dfrac{x^2 + x}{x + 1}$.

You would simplify the expression by canceling the common factors in the numerator and the denominator. We simplify the expression as follows:

$$\frac{x^2 + x}{x + 1} = \frac{x(\cancel{x + 1})}{\cancel{x + 1}} = x$$

15. Explain the following.

(a) How to multiply and divide rational expressions.

To multiply two rational expressions, we multiply their numerators and multiply their denominators. To divide a rational expression by another rational expression, we invert the divisor and multiply.

(b) How to add and subtract rational expressions.

To add or subtract two rational expressions, we first find the least common denominator (LCD), then rewrite the expressions using the LCD, and then add the fractions and combine the terms in the numerator.

(c) What LCD do we use to perform the addition in the expression $\dfrac{3}{x - 1} + \dfrac{5}{x + 2}$?

We use $(x - 1)(x + 2)$.

16. What is the logical first step in rationalizing the denominator of $\dfrac{3}{1 + \sqrt{x}}$?

Multiply both the numerator and the denominator by $(1 - \sqrt{x})$: $\dfrac{3}{1 + \sqrt{x}} \cdot \dfrac{1 - \sqrt{x}}{1 - \sqrt{x}} = \dfrac{3(1 - \sqrt{x})}{1 - x}$

17. What is the difference between an algebraic expression and an equation? Give examples.

An algebraic expression is a combination of variables; for example, $2x^2 + xy + 6$. An equation is a statement that two mathematical expressions are equal; for example, $3x - 2y = 9x - 1$.

18. Consider the equation $5x + 7 = 10 - 3x$.

(a) Determine whether $x = -1$ is a solution to the equation.

We replace the variable x in the equation with the value -1 and get $5(-1) + 7 = 10 - 3(-1)$, which is not a true equation, so $x = -1$ is not a solution.

(b) Show how to use the rules of algebra to solve the equation.

$5x + 7 = 10 - 3x$	Given equation
$5x = 3 - 3x$	Subtract 7
$8x = 3$	Add $3x$
$x = \frac{3}{8}$	Divide by 8

19. (a) Give some examples of power equations.

$$x^2 = 2, \quad 3x^3 = 15, \quad x^{3/2} = 27, \quad (x + 1)^4 = 16$$

(b) Find all real solutions to the power equation $x^2 = 15$.

$$x = \pm\sqrt{15}$$

(c) Find all real solutions to the power equation $x^3 = 15$.

$$x = \sqrt[3]{15}$$

1. (a) In the coordinate plane, what is the horizontal axis called and what is the vertical axis called?

The horizontal axis is called the x-axis and the vertical axis is called the y-axis.

(b) To graph an ordered pair of numbers (x, y), you need the coordinate plane. For the point $(2, 3)$, which is the x-coordinate and which is the y-coordinate?

The x-coordinate is 2, and the y-coordinate is 3.

(c) For an equation in the variables x and y, how do you determine whether a given point is on the graph? Is the point $(5, 3)$ on the graph of the equation $y = 2x - 1$?

Any point (x, y) on the graph must satisfy the equation. Since $3 \neq 2(5) - 1$, the point $(5, 3)$ is *not* on the graph of the equation $y = 2x - 1$.

2. (a) What is the formula for finding the distance between the points (x_1, y_1) and (x_2, y_2)?

$$d = \sqrt{(x_2 - x_1)^2 + (y_2 - y_1)^2}$$

(b) What is the formula for finding the midpoint between (x_1, y_1) and (x_2, y_2)?

$$\left(\frac{x_1 + x_2}{2}, \frac{y_1 + y_2}{2} \right)$$

3. How do you find x-intercepts and y-intercepts of a graph of an equation?

To find the x-intercepts, you set $y = 0$ and solve for x. To find the y-intercepts, you set $x = 0$ and solve for y.

4. (a) Write an equation of the circle with center (h, k) and radius r.

$$(x - h)^2 + (y - k)^2 = r^2$$

(b) Find the equation of the circle with center $(2, -1)$ and radius 3.

$$(x - 2)^2 + (y + 1)^2 = 9$$

5. (a) How do you test whether the graph of an equation is symmetric with respect to the (i) x-axis, (ii) y-axis, and (iii) origin?

(i) When you replace y by $-y$, the resulting equation is equivalent to the original one.

(ii) When you replace x by $-x$, the resulting equation is equivalent to the original one.

(iii) When you replace x by $-x$ and y by $-y$, the resulting equation is equivalent to the original one.

(b) What type of symmetry does the graph of the equation $xy^2 + y^2x^2 = 3x$ have?

The graph is symmetric with respect to the x-axis.

6. (a) What is the slope of a line? How do you compute the slope of the line through the points $(-1, 4)$ and $(1, -2)$?

The slope of a line is a measure of "steepness." The slope of the line through the points $(-1, 4)$ and $(1, -2)$ is

$$m = \frac{\text{rise}}{\text{run}} = \frac{-2 - 4}{1 - (-1)} = -3$$

(b) How do you find the slope and y-intercept of the line $6x + 3y = 12$?

You write the equation in slope-intercept form $y = mx + b$. The slope is m, and the y-intercept is b. The slope-intercept form of this line is $y = -2x + 4$, so the slope is -2 and the intercept is 4.

(c) How do you write the equation for a line that has slope 3 and passes through the point $(1, 2)$?

Use the point-slope form of the equation of a line. So the equation is $y - 2 = 3(x - 1)$.

7. Give an equation of a vertical line and of a horizontal line that passes through the point $(2, 3)$.

An equation of a vertical line that passes through $(2, 3)$ is $x = 2$. An equation of a horizontal line that passes through $(2, 3)$ is $y = 3$.

8. State the general equation of a line.

$Ax + By = C$, where A and B are not both zero

9. Given lines with slopes m_1 and m_2, explain how you can tell whether the lines are (i) parallel, (ii) perpendicular.

(i) The lines are parallel if $m_1 = m_2$.

(ii) The lines are perpendicular if $m_2 = -\dfrac{1}{m_1}$.

10. Write the general form of each type of equation.

(i) Linear equation: $ax + b = 0$

(ii) Quadratic equation: $ax^2 + bx + c = 0$

11. What are the three ways to solve a quadratic equation?

(i) Factor the equation and use the Zero-Product property.

(ii) Complete the square and solve.

(iii) Use the Quadratic Formula.

12. State the Zero-Product Property. Use the property to solve the equation $x(x - 1) = 0$.

The Zero-Product Property states that $AB = 0$ if and only if $A = 0$ or $B = 0$.

To solve the equation $x(x - 1) = 0$, the Zero-Product Property shows that either $x = 0$ or $x = 1$.

(continued)

13. What do you need to add to $ax^2 + bx$ to complete the square? Complete the square for the expression $x^2 + 6x$.

To complete the square, add $\left(\dfrac{b}{2}\right)^2$. To make $x^2 + 6x$ a

perfect square, add $\left(\dfrac{6}{2}\right)^2 = 9$, and this gives the perfect

square $x^2 + 6x + 9 = (x + 3)^2$.

14. State the Quadratic Formula for the quadratic equation $ax^2 + bx + c = 0$, and use it to solve the equation $x^2 + 6x - 1 = 0$.

The Quadratic Formula is $x = \dfrac{-b \pm \sqrt{b^2 - 4ac}}{2a}$.

Using the Quadratic Formula we get

$$x = \frac{-6 \pm \sqrt{36 - 4(1)(-1)}}{2(1)} = -3 \pm \sqrt{10}$$

15. What is the discriminant of the quadratic equation $ax^2 + bx + c = 0$? Find the discriminant of $2x^2 - 3x + 5 = 0$. How many real solutions does this equation have?

The discriminant is $b^2 - 4ac$. The discriminant of $2x^2 - 3x + 5 = 0$ is negative, so there are no real solutions.

16. What is a complex number? Give an example of a complex number, and identify the real and imaginary parts.

A complex number is an expression of the form $a + bi$, where a and b are real numbers and $i^2 = -1$. The complex number $2 + 3i$ has real part 2 and imaginary part 3.

17. What is the complex conjugate of a complex number $a + bi$?

The complex conjugate of $a + bi$ is $a - bi$.

18. (a) How do you add complex numbers?

To add complex numbers, add the real parts and the imaginary parts.

(b) How do you multiply $(3 + 5i)(2 - i)$?

Multiply complex numbers like binomials:
$(3 + 5i)(2 - i) = 6 + 10i - 3i - 5i^2 = 11 + 7i$

(c) Is $(3 - i)(3 + i)$ a real number?

Yes, $(3 - i)(3 + i) = 9 - i^2 = 10$

(d) How do you simplify the quotient $(3 + 5i)/(3 - i)$?

Multiply the numerator and the denominator by $3 + i$, the complex conjugate of the denominator.

19. What is the logical first step in solving the equation $\sqrt{x - 1} = x - 3$? Why is it important to check your answers when solving equations of this type?

The logical first step in solving this equation is to square both sides. It is important to check your answers because the operation of squaring both sides can turn a false equation into a true one. In this case $x = 5$ and $x = 2$ are potential solutions, but after checking, we see that $x = 5$ is the only solution.

20. Explain how to solve the given type of problem.

(a) Linear inequality: $2x \geq 1$

Divide both sides by 2; the solution set is $\left[\frac{1}{2}, \infty\right)$.

(b) Nonlinear inequality: $(x - 1)(x - 4) < 0$

Find the intervals and make a table or diagram; the solution set is $(1, 4)$.

(c) Absolute value equation: $|2x - 5| = 7$

Solve the two equations $2x - 5 = 7$ and $2x - 5 = -7$; the solutions are $x = 6$ and $x = -1$.

(d) Absolute value inequality: $|2x - 5| \leq 7$

Solve the equivalent inequality $-7 \leq 2x - 5 \leq 7$; the solution set is $[-1, 6]$.

21. How do you solve an equation (i) algebraically? (ii) graphically?

(i) Use the rules of algebra to isolate the unknown on one side of the equation.

(ii) Move all terms to one side and set that side equal to y. Sketch a graph of the resulting equation to find the values of x at which $y = 0$.

22. How do you solve an inequality (i) algebraically? (ii) graphically?

(i) Use the rules of algebra to isolate the unknown on one side of the inequality.

(ii) Move all terms to one side, and set that side equal to y. Sketch a graph to find the values x where the graph is above (or below) the x-axis.

23. Write an equation that expresses each relationship.

(a) y is directly proportional to x: $y = kx$

(b) y is inversely proportional to x: $y = \dfrac{k}{x}$

(c) z is jointly proportional to x and y: $z = kxy$

1. Define each concept.

(a) Function

A function f is a rule that assigns to each input x in a set A exactly one output $f(x)$ in a set B.

(b) Domain and range of a function

The domain of a function is the set of all the possible input values, and the range is the set of all possible output values.

(c) Graph of a function

The graph of a function f is the set of all ordered pairs $(x, f(x))$ plotted in a coordinate plane for x in the domain of f.

(d) Independent and dependent variables

The symbol that represents any value in the domain of a function f is called an independent variable, and the symbol that represents any value in the range of f is called a dependent variable.

2. Describe the four ways of representing a function.

A function can be represented verbally (using words), algebraically (using a formula), visually (using a graph), and numerically (using a table of values).

3. Sketch graphs of the following functions by hand.

(a) $f(x) = x^2$

(b) $g(x) = x^3$

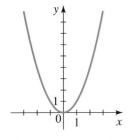

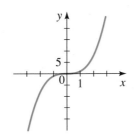

(c) $h(x) = |x|$

(d) $k(x) = \sqrt{x}$

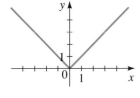
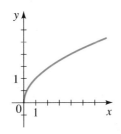

4. What is a piecewise defined function? Give an example.

A piecewise defined function is defined by different formulas on different parts of its domain. An example is

$$f(x) = \begin{cases} x^2 & \text{if } x > 0 \\ 2 & \text{if } x \le 0 \end{cases}$$

5. **(a)** What is the Vertical Line Test, and what is it used for?

The Vertical Line Test states that a curve in the coordinate plane represents a function if and only if no vertical line intersects the curve more than once. It is used to determine when a given curve represents a function.

(b) What is the Horizontal Line Test, and what is it used for?

The Horizontal Line Test states that a function is one-to-one if and only if no horizontal line intersects its graph more than once. It is used to determine when a function is one-to-one.

6. Define each concept, and give an example of each.

(a) Increasing function

A function is increasing when its graph rises. More precisely, a function is increasing on an interval I if $f(x_1) < f(x_2)$ whenever $x_1 < x_2$ in I. For example, the function $f(x) = x^2$ is an increasing function on the interval $(0, \infty)$.

(b) Decreasing function

A function is decreasing when its graph falls. More precisely, a function is decreasing on an interval I if $f(x_1) > f(x_2)$ whenever $x_1 < x_2$ in I. For example, the function $f(x) = x^2$ is a decreasing function on the interval $(-\infty, 0)$.

(c) Constant function

A function f is constant if $f(x) = c$. For example, the function $f(x) = 3$ is constant.

7. Suppose we know that the point $(3, 5)$ is a point on the graph of a function f. Explain how to find $f(3)$ and $f^{-1}(5)$.

Since $(3, 5)$ is on the graph of f, the value 3 is the input and the value 5 is the output, so $f(3) = 5$ and $f^{-1}(5) = 3$.

8. What does it mean to say that $f(4)$ is a local maximum value of f?

The value $f(4)$ is a local maximum if $f(4) \ge f(x)$ for all x near 4.

9. Explain how to find the average rate of change of a function f between $x = a$ and $x = b$.

The average rate of change of f is

$$\frac{\text{change in } y}{\text{change in } x} = \frac{f(b) - f(a)}{b - a}$$

10. **(a)** What is the slope of a linear function? How do you find it? What is the rate of change of a linear function?

The slope of the graph of a linear function $f(x) = ax + b$ is the same as the rate of change of f, and they are both equal to a, the coefficient of x.

(b) Is the rate of change of a linear function constant? Explain.

Yes, because it is equal to the slope, and the slope is the same between any two points.

(continued)

(c) Give an example of a linear function, and sketch its graph.

An example is $f(x) = 2x + 1$, and the graph is shown below.

$$f(x) = 2x + 1$$

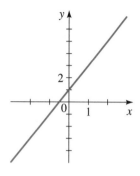

11. Suppose the graph of a function f is given. Write an equation for each of the graphs that are obtained from the graph of f as follows.

(a) Shift upward 3 units: $y = f(x) + 3$

(b) Shift downward 3 units: $y = f(x) - 3$

(c) Shift 3 units to the right: $y = f(x - 3)$

(d) Shift 3 units to the left: $y = f(x + 3)$

(e) Reflect in the x-axis: $y = -f(x)$

(f) Reflect in the y-axis: $y = f(-x)$

(g) Stretch vertically by a factor of 3: $y = 3f(x)$

(h) Shrink vertically by a factor of $\frac{1}{3}$: $y = \frac{1}{3}f(x)$

(i) Shrink horizontally by a factor of $\frac{1}{3}$: $y = f(3x)$

(j) Stretch horizontally by a factor of 3: $y = f(\frac{1}{3}x)$

12. (a) What is an even function? How can you tell that a function is even by looking at its graph? Give an example of an even function.

An even function f satisfies $f(-x) = f(x)$ for all x in its domain. If the graph of a function is symmetric with respect to the y-axis, then the function is even. Some examples are $f(x) = x^2$ and $f(x) = |x|$.

(b) What is an odd function? How can you tell that a function is odd by looking at its graph? Give an example of an odd function.

An odd function f satisfies $f(-x) = -f(x)$ for all x in its domain. If the graph of a function is symmetric with respect to the origin, then the function is odd. Some examples are $f(x) = x^3$ and $f(x) = \sqrt[3]{x}$.

13. Suppose that f has domain A and g has domain B. What are the domains of the following functions?

(a) Domain of $f + g$: $A \cap B$

(b) Domain of fg: $A \cap B$

(c) Domain of f/g: $\{x \in A \cap B \,|\, g(x) \neq 0\}$

14. (a) How is the composition function $f \circ g$ defined? What is its domain?

The function $f \circ g$ is defined by $f \circ g(x) = f(g(x))$. The domain is the set of all x in the domain of g such that $g(x)$ is in the domain of f.

(b) If $g(a) = b$ and $f(b) = c$, then explain how to find $(f \circ g)(a)$.

To find $f \circ g(a)$, we evaluate the following:

$$f \circ g(a) = f(g(a)) = f(b) = c$$

15. (a) What is a one-to-one function?

A function with domain A is called a one-to-one function if no two elements of A have the same image. More precisely, $f(x_1) \neq f(x_2)$ whenever $x_1 \neq x_2$.

(b) How can you tell from the graph of a function whether it is one-to-one?

We use the Horizontal Line Test, which states that a function is one-to-one if and only if no horizontal line intersects its graph more than once.

(c) Suppose that f is a one-to-one function with domain A and range B. How is the inverse function f^{-1} defined? What are the domain and range of f^{-1}?

The inverse function of f has domain B and range A and is defined by

$$f^{-1}(y) = x \iff f(x) = y$$

(d) If you are given a formula for f, how do you find a formula for f^{-1}? Find the inverse of the function $f(x) = 2x$.

We write $y = f(x)$, solve the equation for x in terms of y, and interchange x and y. The resulting equation is $y = f^{-1}(x)$. If $f(x) = 2x$, we write $y = 2x$, solve for x to get $x = \frac{1}{2}y$, interchange x and y to get $f^{-1}(x) = \frac{1}{2}x$.

(e) If you are given a graph of f, how do you find a graph of the inverse function f^{-1}?

The graph of the inverse function f^{-1} is obtained by reflecting the graph of f in the line $y = x$.

1. (a) What is the degree of a quadratic function f? What is the standard form of a quadratic function? How do you put a quadratic function into standard form?

A quadratic function f is a polynomial of degree 2. The standard form of a quadratic function f is $f(x) = a(x - h)^2 + k$. Complete the square to put a quadratic function into standard form.

(b) The quadratic function $f(x) = a(x - h)^2 + k$ is in standard form. The graph of f is a parabola. What is the vertex of the graph of f? How do you determine whether $f(h) = k$ is a minimum or a maximum value?

The vertex of the graph of f is (h, k). If the coefficient a is positive, then the graph of f opens upward and $f(h) = k$ is a minimum value. If a is negative, then the graph of f opens downward and $f(h) = k$ is a maximum value.

(c) Express $f(x) = x^2 + 4x + 1$ in standard form. Find the vertex of the graph and the maximum or minimum value of f.

We complete the square to get $f(x) = (x + 2)^2 - 3$. The graph is a parabola that opens upward with vertex $(-2, -3)$. The minimum value is $f(-2) = -3$.

2. (a) Give the general form of polynomial function P of degree n.

$$P(x) = a_n x^n + a_{n-1}x^{n-1} + \cdots + a_1 x + a_0 \qquad a_n \neq 0$$

(b) What does it mean to say that c is a zero of P? Give two equivalent conditions that tell us that c is a zero of P.

The value c is a zero of P if $P(c) = 0$. Equivalently, c is a zero of P if $x - c$ is a factor of P or if c is an x-intercept of the graph of P.

3. Sketch graphs showing the possible end behaviors of polynomials of odd degree and of even degree.

Odd degree

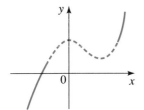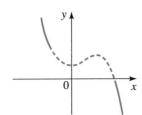

Even degree

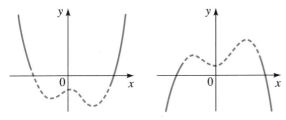

4. What steps do you follow to graph a polynomial function P?

We first find the zeros of P and then make a table using test points between successive zeros. We then determine the end behavior and use all this information to graph P.

5. (a) What is a local maximum point or local minimum point of a polynomial P?

The point $(a, P(a))$ is a local maximum if it is the highest point on the graph of P within some viewing rectangle. The point $(b, P(b))$ is a local minimum if it is the lowest point on the graph of P within some viewing rectangle.

(b) How many local extrema can a polynomial P of degree n have?

The graph of P has at most $n - 1$ local extrema.

6. When we divide a polynomial $P(x)$ by a divisor $D(x)$, the Division Algorithm tells us that we can always obtain a quotient $Q(x)$ and a remainder $R(x)$. State the two forms in which the result of this division can be written.

$$\frac{P(x)}{D(x)} = Q(x) + \frac{R(x)}{D(x)}$$

$$P(x) = D(x)Q(x) + R(x)$$

7. (a) State the Remainder Theorem.

If a polynomial $P(x)$ is divided by $x - c$, then the remainder is the value $P(c)$.

(b) State the Factor Theorem.

The number c is a zero of P if and only if $x - c$ is a factor of $P(x)$.

(c) State the Rational Zeros Theorem.

If the polynomial

$$P(x) = a_n x^n + a_{n-1}x^{n-1} + \cdots + a_1 x + a_0$$

has integer coefficients, then every rational zero of P is of the form p/q, where p is a factor of the constant coefficient a_0 and q is a factor of the leading coefficient a_n.

8. What steps would you take to find the rational zeros of a polynomial P?

First list all possible rational zeros of P given by the Rational Zeros Theorem. Evaluate P at a possible zero (using synthetic division), and note the quotient if the remainder is 0. Repeat this process on the quotient until you reach a quotient that is quadratic. Then use the quadratic formula to find the remaining zeros.

(continued)

9. Let $P(x) = 2x^4 - 3x^3 + x - 15$.

(a) Explain how Descartes' Rule of Signs is used to determine the possible number of positive and negative real roots of P.

Since there are three variations in sign in $P(x)$, by Descartes' Rule of Signs there are either three or one positive real zeros. Since there is one variation in sign in $P(-x)$, by Descartes' Rule of Signs there is exactly one negative real zero.

(b) What does it mean to say that a is a lower bound and b is an upper bound for the zeros of a polynomial?

We say that a is a lower bound and b is an upper bound for the zeros of a polynomial if every real zero c of the polynomial satisfies $a \le c \le b$.

(c) Explain how the Upper and Lower Bounds Theorem is used to show that all the real zeros of P lie between -3 and 3.

When we divide P by $x - 3$, the row that contains the quotient and the remainder has only nonnegative entries, so 3 is an upper bound. When we divide P by $x - (-3) = x + 3$, the row that contains the quotient and the remainder has entries that alternate in sign, so -3 is a lower bound.

10. (a) State the Fundamental Theorem of Algebra.

Every polynomial has at least one complex zero.

(b) State the Complete Factorization Theorem.

Every polynomial of degree $n \ge 1$ can be factored completely into linear factors (with complex coefficients).

(c) State the Zeros Theorem.

Every polynomial of degree $n \ge 1$ has exactly n zeros, provided that a zero of multiplicity k is counted k times.

(d) State the Conjugate Zeros Theorem.

If a polynomial has real coefficients and if the complex number z is a zero of the polynomial, then its complex conjugate $\bar{z}$ is also a zero of the polynomial.

11. (a) What is a rational function?

A rational function is a function of the form $r(x) = \dfrac{P(x)}{Q(x)}$, where P and Q are polynomials.

(b) What does it mean to say that $x = a$ is a vertical asymptote of $y = f(x)$?

The line $x = a$ is a vertical asymptote if

$$y \to \pm\infty \quad \text{as} \quad x \to a^+ \quad \text{or} \quad x \to a^-$$

(c) What does it mean to say that $y = b$ is a horizontal asymptote of $y = f(x)$?

The line $y = b$ is a horizontal asymptote if

$$y \to b \quad \text{as} \quad x \to \infty \quad \text{or} \quad x \to -\infty$$

12. (a) How do you find vertical asymptotes of rational functions?

Vertical asymptotes of a rational function are the line $x = a$, where a is a zero of the denominator.

(b) Let s be the rational function

$$s(x) = \frac{a_n x^n + a_{n-1}x^{n-1} + \cdots + a_1 x + a_0}{b_m x^m + b_{m-1}x^{m-1} + \cdots + b_1 x + b_0}$$

How do you find the horizontal asymptote of s?

If $n < m$, then the horizontal asymptote is

$$y = 0$$

If $n = m$, then the horizontal asymptote is

$$y = \frac{a_n}{b_m}$$

If $n > m$, then there is no horizontal asymptote.

(c) Find the vertical and horizontal asymptotes of

$$f(x) = \frac{5x^2 + 3}{x^2 - 4}$$

The denominator factors as $(x - 2)(x + 2)$, so the vertical asymptotes are $x = 2$ and $x = -2$. The horizontal asymptote is $y = 5$.

13. (a) Under what circumstances does a rational function have a slant asymptote?

If $r(x) = P(x)/Q(x)$ and the degree of P is one greater than the degree of Q, then r has a slant asymptote.

(b) How do you determine the end behavior of a rational function?

Divide the numerator by the denominator; the quotient determines the end behavior of the function.

14. (a) Explain how to solve a polynomial inequality.

Move all terms to one side, factor the polynomial, find the zeros of the polynomial, use the zeros and test points to make a sign diagram, and use the diagram to solve the inequality.

(b) What are the cut points of a rational function? Explain how to solve a rational inequality.

The cut points are the zeros of the numerator and zeros of the denominator. To solve a rational inequality, move all terms to one side, factor the numerator and denominator to find all the cut points, use the cut points and test points to make a sign diagram, and use the diagram to solve the inequality.

(c) Solve the inequality $x^2 - 9 \le 8x$.

Move all terms to one side and then factor: $(x + 1)(x - 9) \le 0$. We make a sign diagram as shown.

	-1		9	
Sign of $x + 1$	$-$	$+$		$+$
Sign of $x - 9$	$-$	$-$		$+$
Sign of $(x + 1)(x - 9)$	$+$	$-$		$+$

The solution is the interval $[-1, 9]$.

1. Let f be the exponential function with base a.

(a) Write an equation that defines f.

$$f(x) = a^x$$

(b) Write an equation for the exponential function f with base 3.

$$f(x) = 3^x$$

2. Let f be the exponential function $f(x) = a^x$, where $a > 0$.

(a) What is the domain of f?

All real numbers $(-\infty, \infty)$

(b) What is the range of f?

All positive real numbers $(0, \infty)$

(c) Sketch graphs of f for the following cases.

(i) $a > 1$ (ii) $0 < a < 1$

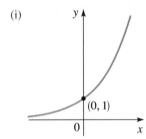

(i) $(0, 1)$

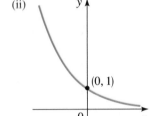

(ii) $(0, 1)$

3. If x is large, which function grows faster, $f(x) = 2^x$ or $g(x) = x^2$?

The function $f(x) = 2^x$ grows faster. We can see this by graphing both functions in a sufficiently large viewing rectangle.

4. (a) How is the number e defined?

The number e is the value that $\left(1 + \dfrac{1}{n}\right)^n$ approaches as n becomes large.

(b) Give an approximate value of e, rounded to five decimal places.

$$e \approx 2.71828$$

(c) What is the natural exponential function?

It is the exponential function with base e:

$$f(x) = e^x$$

5. (a) How is $\log_a x$ defined?

$$\log_a x = y \quad \Leftrightarrow \quad a^y = x$$

(b) Find $\log_3 9$.

$$\log_3 9 = 2 \quad \text{because} \quad 3^2 = 9$$

(c) What is the natural logarithm?

It is the logarithm with base e: $\ln x = \log_e x$

(d) What is the common logarithm?

It is the logarithm with base 10: $\log x = \log_{10} x$

(e) Write the exponential form of the equation $\log_7 49 = 2$.

$$7^2 = 49$$

6. Let f be the logarithmic function $f(x) = \log_a x$.

(a) What is the domain of f?

All positive real numbers $(0, \infty)$

(b) What is the range of f?

All real numbers $(-\infty, \infty)$

(c) Sketch a graph of the logarithmic function for the case that $a > 1$.

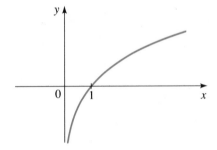

7. State the three Laws of Logarithms.

$$\log_a xy = \log_a x + \log_a y$$

$$\log_a\left(\frac{x}{y}\right) = \log_a x - \log_a y$$

$$\log_a x^N = N \log_a x$$

8. (a) State the Change of Base Formula.

$$\log_a x = \frac{\log_b x}{\log_b a}$$

(b) Find $\log_7 30$.

By the Change of Base Formula

$$\log_7 30 = \frac{\log 30}{\log 7} \approx 1.7479$$

9. (a) What is an exponential equation?

An exponential equation is one in which the unknown occurs in an exponent.

(b) How do you solve an exponential equation?

First isolate the exponential term on one side, take logarithms of each side, and then use the laws of logarithms to bring down the exponent. Then solve for the unknown.

(c) Solve for x: $2^x = 19$

$$\log 2^x = \log 19$$

$$x \log 2 = \log 19$$

$$x = \frac{\log 19}{\log 2} \approx 4.2479$$

(continued)

10. (a) What is a logarithmic equation?

A logarithmic equation is one in which a logarithm of the unknown occurs.

(b) How do you solve a logarithmic equation?

First combine the logarithmic terms on one side of the equation, write the resulting equation in exponential form, and then solve for the unknown.

(c) Solve for x: $4 \log_3 x = 7$

$$4 \log_3 x = 7$$

$$\log_3 x = 1.75$$

$$x = 3^{1.75} \approx 6.84$$

11. Suppose that an amount P is invested at an interest rate r and $A(t)$ is the amount of the investment after t years. Write a formula for $A(t)$ in the following cases.

(a) Interest is compounded n times per year.

$$A(t) = P\left(1 + \frac{r}{n}\right)^{nt}$$

(b) Interest is compounded continuously.

$$A(t) = Pe^{rt}$$

12. Suppose that the initial size of a population is n_0 and the population grows exponentially. Let $n(t)$ be the size of the population at time t.

(a) Write a formula for $n(t)$ in terms of the doubling time a.

$$n(t) = n_0 2^{t/a}$$

(b) Write a formula for $n(t)$ in terms of the relative growth rate r.

$$n(t) = n_0 e^{rt}$$

13. Suppose that the initial mass of a radioactive substance is m_0 and the half-life of the substance is h. Let $m(t)$ be the mass remaining at time t.

(a) What is meant by the half-life h?

The time it takes for a mass to decay to half its amount

(b) Write a formula for $m(t)$ in terms of the half-life h.

$$m(t) = m_0 2^{-t/h}$$

(c) Write a formula for the relative decay rate r in terms of the half-life h.

$$r = \frac{\ln 2}{h}$$

(d) Write a formula for $m(t)$ in terms of the relative decay rate r.

$$m(t) = m_0 e^{-rt}$$

14. Suppose that the initial temperature difference between an object and its surroundings is D_0 and the surroundings have temperature T_s. Let $T(t)$ be the temperature at time t. State Newton's Law of Cooling for $T(t)$.

$$T(t) = T_s + D_0 e^{-kt}$$

where k is a constant that depends on the type of object.

15. What is a logarithmic scale? If we use a logarithmic scale with base 10, what do the following numbers correspond to on the logarithmic scale?

(i) 100   (ii) 100,000   (iii) 0.0001

On a logarithmic scale, numbers are represented by their logarithms.

(i) 2   (ii) 5   (iii) -4

16. (a) What does the pH scale measure?

The acidity (or alkalinity) of a substance

(b) Define the pH of a substance with hydrogen ion concentration of $[H^+]$.

$$pH = -\log[H^+]$$

17. (a) What does the Richter scale measure?

The magnitude of earthquakes

(b) Define the magnitude M of an earthquake in terms of the intensity I of the earthquake and the intensity S of a standard earthquake.

$$M = -\log \frac{I}{S}$$

18. (a) What does the decibel scale measure?

The loudness of sound

(b) Define the decibel level B of a sound in terms of the intensity I of the sound and the intensity I_0 of a barely audible sound.

$$B = 10 \log \frac{I}{I_0}$$

1. **(a)** What is a system of equations in the variables x, y, and z?

   A system of equations in the variables x, y, and z is a set of equations in which each equation contains these variables.

   (b) What are the three methods we use to solve a system of equations?

   The three methods are the substitution method, the elimination method, and the graphical method.

2. Consider the following system of equations:

   $$\begin{cases} x + y = 3 \\ 3x - y = 1 \end{cases}$$

   (a) Describe the steps you would use to solve a system by the substitution method. Use the substitution method to solve the given system.

   We solve for one of the variables in one equation and then substitute the result into the other equation.

   Solving for y in the first equation, we get $y = 3 - x$.

   Substituting for y into the second equation, we get

   $$3x - (3 - x) = 1$$

   Solving for x we get $x = 1$. Substituting this value of x into the first equation, we get $y = 2$. So the solution is $(1, 2)$.

   (b) Describe the steps you would use to solve a system by the elimination method. Use the elimination method to solve the given system.

   We add a multiple of one equation to the other to eliminate one of the variables.

   To eliminate y, we add the two equations to get $4x = 4$, so $x = 1$. Substituting 1 for x in the first equation, we get $1 + y = 3$, so $y = 2$. The solution is $(1, 2)$.

   (c) Describe the steps you would use to solve a system by the graphical method. Use the graph shown below to solve the system.

   We graph the two equations; the solution is the point of intersection of the two graphs.

   From the graphs we see that the point of intersection is $(1, 2)$. So the solution of the system is $(1, 2)$.

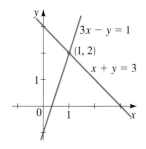

3. What is a system of linear equations in the variables x, y, and z?

   A system of equations in the variables x, y, and z is a linear system if each equation in the system is a linear equation. Recall that a linear equation in the variables x, y, and z is an equation of the form $ax + by + cz = d$, where the co-efficients a, b, c, and d are real numbers.

4. For a system of two linear equations in two variables,

   (a) How many solutions are possible?

   Such a system can have one solution, no solution, or infinitely many solutions.

   (b) What is meant by an inconsistent system?

   A system is inconsistent if it has no solution.

   (c) What is meant by a dependent system?

   A system is dependent if it has infinitely many solutions.

5. What operations can be performed on a linear system to arrive at an equivalent system?

   1. Add a nonzero multiple of one equation to another.
   2. Multiply an equation by a nonzero constant.
   3. Interchange the position of two equations.

6. **(a)** Explain how Gaussian elimination works.

   We use the operations in Question 5 above to obtain a system in triangular form and then use back-substitution to solve for the variables.

   (b) Use Gaussian elimination to put the following system in triangular form, and then solve the system.

System	Triangular form
$\begin{cases} x + y - 2z = 3 \\ x + 2y + z = 5 \\ 3x - y + 5z = 1 \end{cases}$	$\begin{cases} x + y - 2z = 3 \\ y + 3z = 2 \\ 23z = 0 \end{cases}$

   Using back-substitution, we get the solution $(1, 2, 0)$.

7. **(a)** How do we express a rational function r as a partial fraction decomposition?

   We express r as a sum of fractions whose denominators consist of linear or irreducible quadratic factors.

   (b) Give the form of the partial fraction decomposition.

   (i) $\dfrac{2x}{(x-5)(x-1)^2} = \dfrac{A}{x-5} + \dfrac{B}{x-1} + \dfrac{C}{(x-1)^2}$

   (ii) $\dfrac{2x}{(x-5)(x^2+1)} = \dfrac{A}{x-5} + \dfrac{Bx+C}{x^2+1}$

   (iii) $\dfrac{3x+1}{x(x^2+1)^2} = \dfrac{A}{x} + \dfrac{Bx+C}{x^2+1} + \dfrac{Dx+E}{(x^2+1)^2}$

(continued)

8. (a) How do we graph an inequality in two variables?

We first graph the corresponding equation and then use test points to determine the solution set.

(b) Graphs of equations in two variables are shown. On each graph, shade the solution set of the indicated inequality.

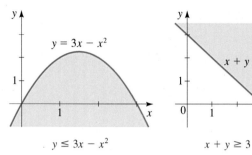

$y \le 3x - x^2$ $x + y \ge 3$

9. (a) How do we graph the solution set of a system of inequalities?

We first graph the corresponding equations and then use test points in each region formed by the graphs to determine whether the region is part of the solution set.

(b) Graphs of the equations in the following system of inequalities are given. Graph the solution set of the system of inequalities.

$$\begin{cases} x + y \ge 3 \\ 3x - y \ge 1 \end{cases}$$

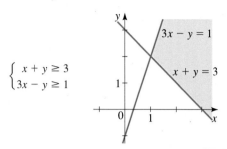

(c) Graphs of the equations in the following system of inequalities are given. Graph the solution set of the system of inequalities.

The inequalities in this system are graphed in 8(b). The solution of the system is graphed below.

$$\begin{cases} x + y \ge 3 \\ y \le 3x - x^2 \end{cases}$$

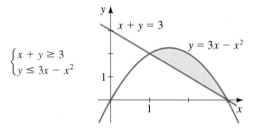

Web**Assign.**

- If your teacher wants you to **Self-Enroll** in the WebAssign course they will provide you with a **Class Key**. You will create your own username and password. It is important that you remember this information so you can log in for the remainder of the class. In this case, just click the **I have a Class Key** button. You don't need to enter any other information on this page.

  Then, enter the **Class Key** your instructor provided and click **Submit**. Verify you are enrolling in the correct class on the next page.

Class Key

Enter the Class Key that you received from your instructor. You will only need to complete this once. After you have created your account, you can log in on the main page.

Class Key

Class Keys generally start with an institution code, followed by two sets of four digits.

[Submit]

- Enter your preferred Login and Student information.

- Click the **Create My Account** button to complete the enrollment process.

- A review screen will display, showing your username, institution code, and password. **Retain a copy of this information.** You will need it to log into WebAssign.

Log In Information

Required fields are marked with an asterisk (*).

Preferred Username	*	[ ] [Check Availability]
		Your username may contain letters, numbers, and the following characters: underscore (_), hyphen (-), period (.)
Institution Code		**webassign**
Password	*	[ ]
Re-Enter Password	*	[ ]
		Passwords are case-sensitive.

Student Information

Required fields are marked with an asterisk (*).

First Name	*	[ ]
Last Name	*	[ ]
Email Address	*	[ ]
Student ID Number		[ ]

[Create My Account]

WebAssign.

Access Codes

Once you log in, you may see a WebAssign Notice about entering an access code for your class. You can get an Access Code from any of the following places if you need to use one:

- A new textbook you purchased for the class.
- Your bookstore, which may sell Access Code cards.
- Online, where you can purchase an access code with a credit card.

You have a 14 day grace period to use WebAssign, starting with the WebAssign class start date. During this time you can work on and view your WebAssign assignments without registering a code.

After the grace period is over you will only see the code registration message until you submit or purchase a code.

There are two types of WebAssign access code cards. The small card requires you to scratch off the silver surface in order to reveal the complete access code.

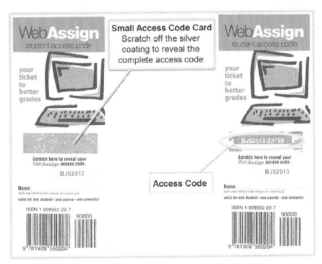

Web**Assign**.

The larger security envelope card requires you to open the card to reveal the access code number.

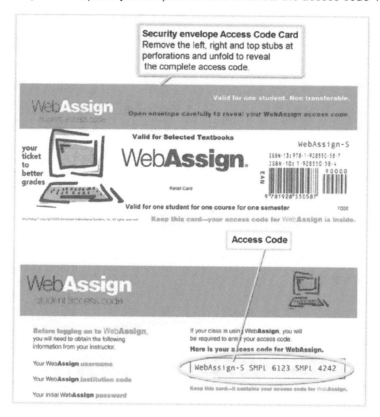

If you would like to purchase an access code directly from WebAssign online, you may do so with a credit card. Your code will be automatically registered to your WebAssign account as soon as the transaction is complete. You will receive an email confirmation. Please keep a copy for your records.

WebAssign.

Your WebAssign Home Page

Once you have successfully logged in you will see your WebAssign homepage. If you are taking more than one WebAssign class, you will need to select which class you wish to view first.

The upper right corner features links to a complete Student **Guide**, as well as a link to WebAssign Technical Support under **Help**. If you want to change your password or add or update your email address, simply click **My Options** in the upper right hand corner.

You will see your assignments and due dates listed, as well as any Communications, Grades, and Announcements posted by your teacher.

WebAssign
Wednesday, August 6, 2008 02:37 PM EDT

Home | My Assignments | Grades | Communication | Calendar

Demo Class, section 001, Fall 2009 ⌄

Home

My Assignments

Current Assignments (13)

Name	Due
Basic Question Types with Practice (all)	Aug 13 2008 03:31 PM EDT
Intro to WebAssign 2008	Aug 15 2008 10:00 PM EDT
General Questions	Oct 25 2008 10:00 PM EDT

Past Assignments (4)

Communication

Class Forums

Homework	12 topics

Grades

My Grade : 92.40 (A)

David Thomson
Instructor: John Smith
Demo school

Announcements

Welcome

I hope you are all ready to learn in our class. I look forward to any questions you might have.

Archived Announcements

My Calendar

Jump to...

About this Class

Class Started: Wednesday, January 1, 2003
Class Ends: Thursday, January 14, 2010

Answering Questions

WebAssign has a variety of different question types, ranging from multiple choice to fill-in-the-blank to symbolic questions. Here are some things to keep in mind as you work through your assignments:

- Some questions may include numbers or words that appear in red. This signifies that the number or word has been randomized, so that you receive a different version of the same basic question from your classmates.

- Some WebAssign questions check the number of significant figures in your answer. If you enter the correct value with the wrong number of significant figures, you will not receive credit, but you will receive a hint that your number does not have the correct number of significant figures.

- Some questions require entering symbolic notation. Answer symbolic questions by using calculator notation. You must use the exact variables specified in the questions. The order is not important as long as it is mathematically correct. Clicking on the eye button previews the expression you enter in proper mathematical notation. Clicking on the symbolic formatting help button provides tips for using the correct keystrokes.

WebAssign.

- When you click on some WebAssign chemistry or math questions an input palette will open. These palettes, called chemPad and mathPad, will help you enter your answer in proper notation.

- Some questions may require the use of an Active Figure simulation. Active Figures require the free Macromedia Flash Player plug-in, downloadable from www.macromedia.com.

- If your instructor allows it, you can save your work without grading by selecting the Save Work button at the end of the question. After you save your work, it will be available to you the next time you click the assignment.

- Please note that WebAssign will **not** automatically submit your answers for scoring if you only **Save** your work. Your teacher will not be able to see your submissions. Please be sure to **Submit** prior to the due date and time.

- If your instructor allows it, you can submit answers by question part or for the entire assignment. To submit an individual question answer for grading, click the **Submit New Answers to Question __** button at the bottom of each question. To submit the entire assignment for grading, click the **Submit All New Answers** button at the end of the assignment.

Technical Support

If you are having difficulty logging in, please be sure to check with your teacher and verify whether an account has been created for you or whether you need to self-enroll. In either case your teacher needs to provide the appropriate information (username, institution code and password OR Class Key).

To email WebAssign Support go to http://www.webassign.net/info/support/report.html. This page also lists answers to **Common Problems**, and provides links to the **Student Guide**.

August 7, 2008